Math 100: Connecting Concepts through Applications

D1370735

Custom Edition for Tarleton State University

Mark Clark | Cynthia Anfinson

CENGAGE
Learning·

Australia • Brazil • Japan • Korea • Mexico • Singapore • Spain • United Kingdom • United States

Math 100: Connecting Concepts through Applications, Custom Edition for Tarleton State University

Beginning and Intermediate Algebra: Connecting Concepts Through Applications, 1st Edition
Mark Clark | Cynthia Anfinson

© 2013 Brooks/Cole, Cengage Learning. All rights reserved.

Executive Editors:
 Maureen Staudt
 Michael Stranz

Senior Project Development Manager:
 Linda deStefano

Marketing Specialist:
 Courtney Sheldon

Senior Production/Manufacturing Manager:
 Donna M. Brown

Production Editorial Manager:
 Kim Fry

Sr. Rights Acquisition Account Manager:
 Todd Osborne

For product information and technology assistance, contact us at
Cengage Learning Customer & Sales Support, 1-800-354-9706

For permission to use material from this text or product,
submit all requests online at **cengage.com/permissions**
Further permissions questions can be emailed to
permissionrequest@cengage.com

This book contains select works from existing Cengage Learning resources and was produced by Cengage Learning Custom Solutions for collegiate use. As such, those adopting and/or contributing to this work are responsible for editorial content accuracy, continuity and completeness.

Compilation © 2012 Cengage Learning
ISBN-13: 978-1-285-10805-6

ISBN-10: 1-285-10805-1

Cengage Learning
5191 Natorp Boulevard
Mason, Ohio 45040
USA

Cengage Learning is a leading provider of customized learning solutions with office locations around the globe, including Singapore, the United Kingdom, Australia, Mexico, Brazil, and Japan. Locate your local office at:
international.cengage.com/region.
Cengage Learning products are represented in Canada by Nelson Education, Ltd.
For your lifelong learning solutions, visit **www.cengage.com/custom.**
Visit our corporate website at **www.cengage.com.**

Printed at CLDPC, USA, 05-18

Brief Contents

Contents

R — Review of Prealgebra

1 — Building Blocks of Algebra

2 Linear Equations and Inequalities with One Variable

3 Linear Equations with Two Variables

4 Systems of Linear Equations

5 Exponents and Polynomials

6 Factoring and Quadratic Equations

7 Rational Expressions and Equations

8 Modeling Data and Functions

9 Inequalities and Absolute Values

10 Radical Functions

11 Quadratic Functions

12 Exponential Functions

13 Logarithmic Functions

14 Conic Sections, Sequences, and Series

Applications Index

Preface

Our goal in writing this book is to help college students learn how to solve problems generated from realistic applications, while they build a strong mathematical basis in algebra. We think that focusing our book on concepts and applications makes the mathematics more useful and vivid to college students. By learning how to solve problems generated from realistic applications, instead of learning techniques without conceptual understanding, students develop sound mathematical skills.

We include applications throughout the text, rather than in a stand-alone chapter or section. Our goal is to tie applications to realistic situations, providing straightforward background explanations of the mathematics so that students have a down-to-earth rationale in their heads for how to set up a problem. At the same time, traditional algebra concepts and skills are presented throughout the book and the problem sets. The applications give students a chance to practice their skills as well as to see the importance of mathematics in the real world. We think that the combination of basic mathematical skills, concepts, and applications will allow students to think critically about mathematics and communicate their results better, too.

Discovery-Based Approach

Worked Examples with Practice Problems

Examples range from basic skills and techniques to realistic applications with manageable data sets to intriguing applications that call for critical thinking about phenomena and daily activities. In-text practice problems help students to gain a sense of a concept through an example and then to practice what was taught in the preceding discussion.

Worked examples and exercises require students to answer by explaining the meaning of concepts such as slope, the x-intercept, and the y-intercept in context. The benefit of requiring verbal explanations is that the student learns to communicate mathematical concepts and applications in a precise way that will carry over to other disciplines and coursework such as psychology, chemistry, and business.

Concept Investigations

Concept Investigations are directed-discovery activities. They are ideal as group work during class, as part of a lecture, or as individual assignments to investigate concepts further.

Example 1 Graphing lines using the slope and y-intercept

Graph the following linear equations using the slope and y-intercept. Graph at least three points.

a. $y = \frac{2}{3}x + 1$ **b.** $y = -2x + 3$

SOLUTION

a. From the equation $y = \frac{2}{3}x + 1$, we see that the slope is $m = \frac{2}{3} = \frac{\text{rise}}{\text{run}}$ and the y-intercept is the point $(0, 1)$. Start by plotting the y-intercept, $(0, 1)$, and then use the slope to rise 2 and run 3 from the y-intercept. Repeat the rise/run process twice to find two additional points on the line and then connect them with a straight line.

b. From the equation $y = -2x +$ the y-intercept is the point $(0, 3)$. Start by plotting the y-intercept, $(0, 3)$, and then use the slope to rise -2 and run 1 from the y-intercept. Since the rise is negative, we go down 2 instead of up. Repeating this process twice yields two more points on the graph.

Example 4 Purchasing school supplies

Siria buys two spiral notebooks and one USB drive at the campus bookstore for $25.60. Two days later, Siria buys three more spiral notebooks and two USB drives at the campus bookstore for $48.40. How much does each notebook and USB drive cost individually?

SOLUTION

First, define the variables. Let

$n = $ cost of each spiral notebook in dollars

$b = $ cost of each USB drive in dollars

Siria first purchased two spiral notebooks and one USB drive for $25.60. This purchase translates into the equation

$$2n + b = 25.60$$

On her second trip to the campus bookstore, Siria bought three more spiral notebooks and two more USB drives for $48.40. This translates into the equation

$$3n + 2b = 48.40$$

The system of equations to solve is

$$2n + b = 25.60$$
$$3n + 2b = 48.40$$

To eliminate b, multiply the first equation by -2 to get the coefficients of b to be opposites.

$-2(2n + b) = -2(25.60)$ $-4n - 2b = -51.20$
$3n + 2b = 48.40$ ⟶ $3n + 2b = 48.40$

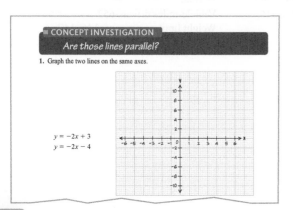

■ CONCEPT INVESTIGATION
Are those lines parallel?

1. Graph the two lines on the same axes.

$y = -2x + 3$
$y = -2x - 4$

Inserted at key points within the chapter, each Concept Investigation helps students explore patterns and relationships such as the graphical and algebraic representations of the concepts being studied. The goals are to have students understand WHY math rules are the way they are and then to be able to apply them.

Reinforcement of Visual Learning Through Graphs and Tables

Graphs and tables are used throughout the book to organize data, examine trends, and have students gain an understanding of how to graph linear and quadratic equations. The graphical and numeric approach helps support visual learners, incorporating realistic situations into the text and reinforcing the graphs and data that students see in their daily lives.

Hand-Drawn Graphs

A hand-drawn style graph is often used when illustrating graphing examples and answers to exercises. The hand-drawn style helps students visualize what their work should look like.

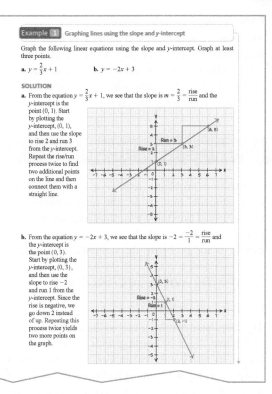

Example 1 Graphing lines using the slope and y-intercept

Graph the following linear equations using the slope and y-intercept. Graph at least three points.

a. $y = \frac{2}{3}x + 1$ **b.** $y = -2x + 3$

SOLUTION

a. From the equation $y = \frac{2}{3}x + 1$, we see that the slope is $m = \frac{2}{3} = \frac{\text{rise}}{\text{run}}$ and the y-intercept is the point $(0, 1)$. Start by plotting the y-intercept, $(0, 1)$, and then use the slope to rise 2 and run 3 from the y-intercept. Repeat the rise/run process twice to find two additional points on the line and then connect them with a straight line.

b. From the equation $y = -2x + 3$, we see that the slope is $-2 = \frac{-2}{1} = \frac{\text{rise}}{\text{run}}$ and the y-intercept is the point $(0, 3)$. Start by plotting the y-intercept, $(0, 3)$, and then use the slope to rise -2 and run 1 from the y-intercept. Since the rise is negative, we go down 2 instead of up. Repeating this process twice yields two more points on the graph.

46. $(5x^4)^3$

Kaila	Hannah
$15x^{12}$	$125x^{12}$

47. $(-3x)^2$

Yomaira	Steven
$-9x^2$	$9x^2$

48. $(-2x^3)^4$

Danaya	Sabrina
$16x^{12}$	$-16x^{12}$

49. $\frac{5^5}{5^2}$

Andrew	Joel
1	125

50. $\frac{6^3}{6}$

Lydia	Eleene
1	36

For Exercises 51 through 80, simplify each exponential expression. List the exponent rule or other rule that was used to simplify.

51. $\frac{x^2x^4y^5}{x^4y^2}$ 52. $\frac{a^6a^2b^5}{a^4a^3b}$

53. $\frac{m^7m^4n^2}{mn}$ 54. $\frac{c^4c^3d^3d^2}{c^3cd^4}$

55. $\frac{30x^5y^2}{14xy^2}$ 56. $\frac{-16a^3b^5}{6a^3b}$

57. $\frac{x^4}{25} \cdot \frac{5}{x^2}$ 58. $\frac{-12}{n} \cdot \frac{n^5}{3}$

59. $\frac{a^3b}{a^2b} \cdot \frac{b^3}{a}$ 60. $\frac{xy^5}{xy^2} \cdot \frac{x^4y^3}{xy}$

67. $\left(\frac{12x^3y^4}{2x^3y}\right)^2$ 68. $\left(\frac{24a^7b^5}{8a^3b^2}\right)^3$

69. $\left(\frac{-26x^3y^5}{6xy}\right)^2$ 70. $\left(\frac{-18m^9n^3}{4m^3n}\right)^2$

71. $(3xy^2)^2(5x^3y^7)$ 72. $(2a^3b^3)^4(5a^2b)^2$

73. $(4m^4n^3)^2(3mn^5)^3$ 74. $(7p^3r^2)^2(2p^4r^6)^3$

75. $(-3a^2)^4(2ab^3)^3$ 76. $(-5m^2)^3(4m^3n)^2$

77. $\frac{(2x^3y)^4}{(5xy^2)^2}$ 78. $\frac{(6a^3b^5)^2}{(3ab^2)^3}$

79. $\frac{(-4x^5y^3)^2}{(2x^3y)^3}$ 80. $\frac{(-2a^4h^3)^4}{(5g^3h^2)^3}$

For Exercises 81 through 88, examine the student's work, and find the mistake that the student made. Hint: Remember the order of operations.

81.
Elias
$-2^2 = 4$

82.
Reggie
$-3^2 = 9$

83.
Beverly
$3^2 \cdot 2 = 6^2$

84.
Eliseo
$4 \cdot 5^3 = 20^3$

85.
Alexis
$(2 + 3)^2 = 2^2 + 3^2 = 4 + 9 = 13$

86.
Oscar
$(7 - 5)^2 = 7^2 - 5^2 = 49 - 25 = 24$

87.
Victoria
$\frac{9^4}{3} = 3^4$

88.
Cooper
$\frac{4^3}{2} = 2^3$

89. a. Can th[...] be simplified

Integrated "Student Work"

Clearly identifiable examples of "student work" appear throughout the text in examples and exercises. These boxes present examples of correct and incorrect student work. Students are asked to identify and fix common student errors.

Margin Notes

The margin contains three kinds of notes written to help the student with specific types of information:

1. *Skill Connections* provide a just-in-time review of skills covered in previous sections of the text or courses, reinforcing student skill sets.

2. *Connecting the Concepts* reinforce a concept by showing relationships across sections and courses.

3. The specific vocabulary of mathematics and applications is helpfully defined and reinforced through margin notes called *What's That Mean?*

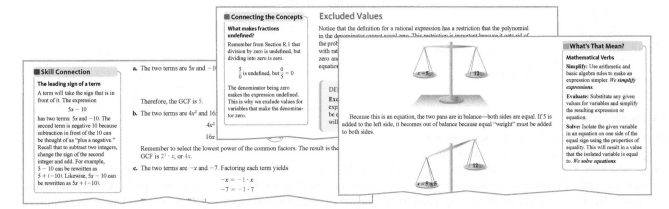

Skill Connection

The leading sign of a term

A term will take the sign that is in front of it. The expression

$$5x - 10$$

has two terms: $5x$ and -10. The second term is negative 10 because subtraction in front of the 10 can be thought of as "plus a negative." Recall that to subtract two integers, change the sign of the second integer and add. For example, $5 - 10$ can be rewritten as $5 + (-10)$. Likewise, $5x - 10$ can be rewritten as $5x + (-10)$.

a. The two terms are $5x$ and -10[...]

Therefore, the GCF is 5.

b. The two terms are $4x^2$ and $16x$[...]

$$4x^2$$
$$16x$$

Remember to select the lowest power of the common factors. The result is the[...] GCF is $2^2 \cdot x$, or $4x$.

c. The two terms are $-x$ and -7. Factoring each term yields

$$-x = -1 \cdot x$$
$$-7 = -1 \cdot 7$$

Connecting the Concepts

What makes fractions undefined?

Remember from Section R.1 that division by zero is undefined, but dividing into zero is zero.

$$\frac{5}{0} \text{ is undefined, but } \frac{0}{5} = 0$$

The denominator being zero makes the expression undefined. This is why we exclude values for variables that make the denominator zero.

Excluded Values

Notice that the definition for a rational expression has a restriction that the polynomial in the denominator cannot equal zero. This restriction is important because it gets rid of the prob[...] with rat[...] zero an[...] equation[...]

Because this is an equation, the two pans are in balance—both sides are equal. If 5 is added to the left side, it becomes out of balance because equal "weight" must be added to both sides.

What's That Mean?

Mathematical Verbs

Simplify: Use arithmetic and basic algebra rules to make an expression simpler. *We simplify expressions.*

Evaluate: Substitute any given values for variables and simplify the resulting expression or equation.

Solve: Isolate the given variable in an equation on one side of the equal sign using the properties of equality. This will result in a value that the isolated variable is equal to. *We solve equations.*

Exercise Sets

The exercise sets include a balance of both applications- and skill-based problems developed with a clear level of progression in terms of level of difficulty. Most exercise sets begin with a few warm-up problems before focusing on applications and additional skills practice. Graphical, numerical, and algebraic skill problems are balanced throughout the book to help students see mathematics from several different perspectives. End-of-book answers are written in full sentences to underscore the emphasis on student communication skills.

Making Connections

Application problems require a complete-sentence answer, encouraging students to consider the reasonableness of their solution. As a result, model breakdown is discussed and is used as a way of teaching critical thinking about the reasonableness of answers in some of the examples and problems throughout each chapter.

Learning with Technology

Flexible Use of the Calculator

The calculator emphasis across the beginning and intermediate portions of the text differ in keeping with the goals of each course. Calculator Details margin boxes will appear as necessary to instruct students on the correct use of a scientific calculator in the beginning portion of the text, though most exercises do not require its use. These boxes also appear in the intermediate portion of the text and include tips on graphing calculators. Modeling is introduced in Chapter 8 and though students are required to solve problems, graph, and do other algebraic skills by hand, graphing calculators are used to create scatterplots of real data and to check the reasonableness of algebraic models for the data. They are used to check solutions both graphically and numerically and to do some numerical calculations.

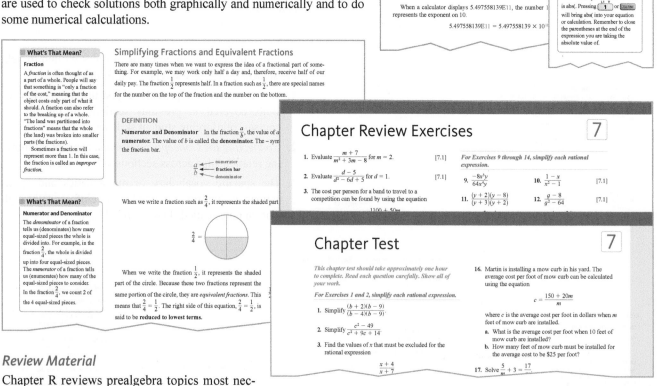

Review Material

Chapter R reviews prealgebra topics most necessary for beginning algebra. It includes operations with integers, operations with fractions, operations with decimals and percents, and the real number system.

Extensive end-of-chapter material includes Chapter Summaries, Review Exercises, Chapter Tests, Chapter Projects, Cumulative Reviews, and Equation Solving Toolboxes. Chapter Summaries revisit the big ideas of the chapter and reinforce them with *new* worked-out examples. Students can also review and practice what they have learned with the Chapter Review Exercises before taking the Chapter Test.

Cumulative Review Exercises

Cumulative reviews group together the major topics across chapters. Answers to all the exercises are available to students in the answer appendix. (Cumulative Reviews are included after Chapters 2, 4, 6, 7, 9, 11, 13, and 14.)

Chapter Projects

To enhance critical thinking, end-of-chapter projects can be assigned either individually or as group work. Instructors can choose which projects best suit the focus of their class and give their students the chance to show how well they can tie together the concepts they have learned in that chapter. Some of these projects include online research or activities that students must perform to analyze data and make conclusions.

Equation-Solving Toolbox

The equation-solving toolbox covers the processes for finding models as the models are introduced. (They appear in Chapters 2, 4, 6, 7, 8, 10, 11, and 13.)

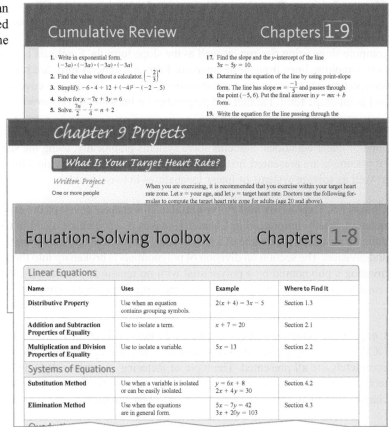

Chapter-by-Chapter Overview

Chapter R, Review of Prealgebra: The text begins in Chapter R by reviewing some prealgebra concepts. This chapter helps students to acquire a working knowledge of prealgebra and to review those topics most necessary for success in beginning algebra, such as arithmetic with signed numbers, fractions, absolute value, the idea of opposites, and the order-of-operations agreement. This chapter also reviews the traditional student weak spots—fractions, decimals, and percents. This chapter culminates in the real number system. The Rule of Four is covered implicitly throughout the book (numeric–symbolic–graphical–verbal), beginning with Chapter R.

Chapter 1, Building Blocks of Algebra: This chapter centers on order of operations, the properties of real numbers, variables, and graphing. Students will become aware that they are making an important transition with this chapter. Variables and variable expressions are introduced using a variety of approaches. For example, students will learn how to translate phrases into algebraic expressions, as well as how to set up an input-output table and look for underlying patterns to generate expressions. Students are also introduced to graphing, with a detailed explanation of scale and how that relates to graphing real-life data and reading real-life graphs. The importance of units and unit conversions is also covered, with the goal of helping students contend with units in real-life problems such as computing college tuition, purchasing school supplies, and event planning.

Chapter 2, Linear Equations and Inequalities with One Variable: Linear equations and inequalities with one variable are discussed from the perspective of the properties of equality. After students become familiar with these properties, solving linear equations in one variable where the variable appears on both sides is presented. The focus is on the underlying concepts of the properties of equality to help students understand the algebra, as well as develop a useful skill set. The chapter ends with solving linear inequalities with one variable and graphing the solution set on a number line. Interval notation is presented in conjunction with number lines. Types of applications covered in this chapter include production problems (see LEGO problems in Section 2.2), business problems (profit, cost, and revenue), commission problems, and budgeting problems.

Chapter 3, Linear Equations with Two Variables: Linear equations with two variables are the primary topic of this chapter. Students initially graph equations in two variables by generating a table of values. Some of these graphs are nonlinear, such as absolute value equations and simple quadratic equations. Slope is introduced as a rate of change. Students learn how to compute slope using rise/run, as well as the slope formula. Emphasis is given to interpreting slope in the context of an application. Graphing lines from slope-intercept form and general form are both presented. Finding intercepts is covered, as well as interpreting intercepts in the context of an application. The chapter covers finding equations of lines using slope-intercept form and point-slope form. Parallel and perpendicular lines are also covered.

Chapter 4, Systems of Linear Equations: Here, the theme of linear equations is continued and leads into a discussion of systems of linear equations. Students solve systems graphically, using the substitution method, and with the elimination method. Applications are presented, mixed in with all three methods. Solving a linear inequality in two variables graphically is covered, as well as solving systems of linear inequalities in two variables.

Chapter 5, Exponents and Polynomials: This chapter develops the exponent rules, including negative exponents. Scientific notation, briefly introduced in Chapter 1, makes its appearance again in Chapter 5 in a more complete form. Polynomials are defined, as well as the degree of a polynomial. Polynomial operations are then presented—addition, subtraction, multiplication, and division. The section on division of polynomials is broken up into three subsections (dividing a polynomial by a monomial, dividing a polynomial by a polynomial with no remainder, and finally, dividing a polynomial by a polynomial resulting in a remainder), so that instructors can select the topics they need to cover for their course. Applications in this chapter include total cost, average income and number of families in the United States, and area problems from geometry.

Chapter 6, Factoring and Quadratic Equations: This chapter introduces factoring and quadratic equations. Factoring out the GCF, factoring by grouping, factoring trinomials, factoring differences of squares and perfect square trinomials, and factoring completely are all presented. The topic of factoring is summarized with a "Factoring Tool Kit" to help students know which technique to use and when to use it. Applications from business, such as average profit, cost, and revenue are introduced in this chapter as well as area problems and falling object problems.

Chapter 7, Rational Expressions and Equations: This chapter introduces rational expressions and equations. Evaluating and simplifying rational expressions is presented, as well as the idea of excluded values. Next, operations on rational expressions are covered: multiplying, dividing, adding, and subtracting rational expressions. Adding and subtracting rational expressions is broken up into subsections on adding and subtracting with like denominators, finding a common denominator, and adding and subtracting with unlike denominators. Solving rational equations is then covered, with applications from shared work problems. Proportions, similar triangles, and direct and inverse variation end the chapter.

Chapter 8, Modeling Data and Functions: In Chapter 8, modeling is introduced in the context of linear equations. First, solving linear equations is reviewed, with a new emphasis on real-world "messy" data. Then, graphing real-world data in scatterplots and finding an "eyeball best-fit" line are introduced. Next, finding a linear model for the eyeball best-fit line is presented. The chapter ends with coverage of functions and function notation, domain and range, operations with functions, and composing functions. Excluded values for rational expressions are revisited, leading to the idea of the domain of a rational function. Radical expressions are introduced.

Chapter 9, Inequalities and Absolute Values: Absolute value equations and inequalities are discussed from both the algebraic and graphical perspectives. Non-linear inequalities, with an emphasis on polynomial and rational inequalities, are solved algebraically. The chapter ends with a look at systems of inequalities from the graphical perspective.

Chapter 10, Radical Functions: In Chapter 10, radical expressions and functions are introduced. Square roots are emphasized, but cube roots and higher-order roots, as well as rational exponents are presented. Simplifying radical expressions is covered, as well as adding and subtracting radical expressions. Multiplying and dividing radical expressions is presented, including an introduction to rationalizing the denominator. Radical functions are covered with their applications, as well as the domain and range of radical functions. Solving radical equations is covered, including equations with an extraneous solution. Now that students understand radicals, quadratic equations are revisited and solved using the square root property. The Pythagorean Theorem is covered. The chapter concludes with a section on complex numbers and their operations.

Chapter 11, Quadratic Functions: In this chapter, the concepts of quadratic functions are discussed. The chapter starts with the basic features of quadratics and then focuses on the vertex form of a quadratic. This gives many students a new way to look at quadratics and their graphs. Graphing is introduced early and carried throughout the chapter to help students build graphing skills. Quadratic models are presented in Section 11.3. Solving quadratics using the square root property, completing the square, factoring, and the quadratic formula are covered in Sections 11.4 through 11.6 of the chapter. Section 11.4 is on solving quadratic equations using the square root property and also revisits graphing from the vertex form to incorporate horizontal intercepts. Finally, graphing from standard form reinforces the characteristics of parabolas, and many of the connections between the vertex and standard form of a quadratic function.

Chapter 12, Exponential Functions: This chapter starts with an introduction to exponential functions by means of a pattern-finding approach. Section 12.1 helps students explore the characteristics of exponential growth and decay by building a table and looking for patterns. This pattern-finding approach may be different for many students, but it helps to reinforce the basic idea of repeated multiplication and exponents. Section 12.2 reviews the rules for exponents and uses rational exponents to solve power equations. Graphing exponential functions and finding their domain and range are covered in Section 12.3. Solving power equations and the characteristics of exponential graphs are then used in Section 12.4 when developing exponential models. This chapter is wrapped up with Section 12.5 covering exponential growth and decay rates as well as other applications of exponentials. Compounding interest and the number e are introduced in this final section, to be revisited again in the next chapter.

Chapter 13, Logarithmic Functions: This chapter begins with inverse functions and their applications. Section 13.2 introduces logarithms and looks at some of the basic rules for logarithms including the change of base formula. This section gives the students a chance to absorb the idea of this new function before doing too much work with logs. Section 13.3 looks at the graphs of logarithms and discusses their domain and range. The properties of logarithms are covered next to give the students the rules needed to expand and combine logarithms. Solving exponential functions is covered in Section 13.5. This section also includes the development of the change of base formula and continues work with compounding interest problems. Section 13.6 concludes the chapter with solving logarithmic equations, including applications of logarithms such as pH in chemistry and calculating the magnitude of earthquakes.

Chapter 14, Conic Sections, Sequences, and Series: Chapter 14 covers the topics of conic sections, sequences, and series. Section 14.1 looks at the basic characteristics of the common conic sections including circles and parabolas. Section 14.2 looks at the equations and graphs of ellipses and hyperbolas. Section 14.3 introduces arithmetic sequences and looks at their relationship with linear functions. Geometric sequences are introduced in Section 14.4. The final section of this chapter includes an introduction to arithmetic and geometric series.

Appendices:

Appendix A   Matrices covers matrices and systems of three equations and three variables for those schools that wish to extend the material covered in Chapters 2 and 4.

Appendix B   Using the Graphing Calculator appendix covers the basic steps of how to use a Texas Instruments 83/84 graphing calculator. Key-by-key instructions including screen shots are provided for each feature used in the book. Common error messages and how to fix them are also discussed. Additional features of the calculator not discussed in the main chapters are also provided for more advanced users.

Appendix C   Answers to Practice Problems

Appendix D   Answers to Selected Exercises

For the Instructor:

Annotated Instructor's Edition

The *Annotated Instructor's Edition* provides the complete student text with answers next to each respective exercise. As shown here, it includes **new classroom examples** with answers to use in the lecture that parallel each example in the text. These could also be used in class as additional practice problems for students and are also available in PowerPoint® on the PowerLecture CD-ROM. **Teaching tips** are also embedded to help with pacing as well as key ideas that instructors may want to point out to their students.

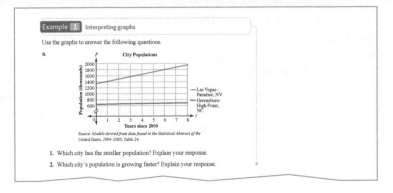

Complete Solutions Manual (978-1-133-36576-1)

Eve Nolan
Karen Mifflin, Palomar College
Gina Hayes, Palomar College

The *Complete Solutions Manual* provides worked-out solutions to all of the problems in the text.

Instructor's Resource Binder (978-0-538-73675-6)

Maria H. Andersen, *Muskegon Community College*

Each section of the main text is discussed in uniquely designed *Teaching Guides* containing instruction tips, examples, activities, worksheets, overheads, assessments, and solutions to all worksheets and activities.

PowerLecture with ExamView® (978-1-133-58794-1)

This CD-ROM provides the instructor with dynamic media tools for teaching. Create, deliver, and customize tests (both print and online) in minutes with ExamView® Computerized Testing featuring algorithmic equations. Microsoft® PowerPoint® lecture slides, figures, additional new examples from the annotated instructor's edition, and Concept Investigations for Graphing Calculator Users are also included on this CD-ROM.

Solution Builder

This online instructor database offers complete worked solutions to all exercises in the text, allowing you to create customized, secure solutions printouts (in PDF format) matched exactly to the problems you assign in class.
Visit **www.cengage.com/solutionbuilder**

Text-Specific Videos

Rena Petrello, *Moorpark College*

These text-specific instructional videos provide students with visual reinforcement of concepts and explanations given in easy-to-understand terms with detailed examples and sample problems. A flexible format offers versatility for quickly accessing topics or catering lectures to self-paced, online, or hybrid courses. Closed captioning is provided for the hearing impaired. The videos are available in WebAssign.

Enhanced WebAssign with eBook (978-0-538-73810-1)

Exclusively from Cengage Learning, Enhanced WebAssign® combines the exceptional mathematics content that you know and love with the most powerful online homework solution, WebAssign. Enhanced WebAssign engages students with immediate feedback, rich tutorial content, and interactive, fully customizable eBooks (YouBook) helping students to develop a deeper conceptual understanding of their subject matter. Online assignments can

be built by selecting from thousands of text-specific problems or supplemented with problems from any Cengage Learning textbook.

The authors worked very closely with their media team, writing problems with Enhanced WebAssign in mind and selecting exercises that offer a balance of applications and skill development. The "Master It" questions break exercises into multiple parts, forcing students to confirm their understanding as they work through each step of a problem. These problems support the conceptual applied approach of the textbook, and instructors can choose to assign these or use the tutorial version. The Master It problems focus on modeling in the intermediate section of the text.

For the Student:

Student Solutions Manual (978-1-133-36509-9)

Eve Nolan
Karen Mifflin, Palomar College
Gina Hayes, Palomar College

Contains fully worked-out solutions to all of the odd-numbered end-of-section exercises as well as the complete worked-out solutions to all of the exercises included at the end of each chapter in the text, giving students a way to check their answers and ensure that they took the correct steps to arrive at an answer.

Student Workbook (978-1-133-36518-1)

Maria H. Andersen, *Muskegon Community College*

Get a head-start. The *Student Workbook* contains all of the assessments, activities, and worksheets from the *Instructor's Resource Binder* for classroom discussions, in-class activities, and group work.

Enhanced WebAssign with eBook (978-0-538-73810-1)

Exclusively from Cengage Learning, Enhanced WebAssign® combines exceptional mathematics content with the most powerful online homework solution, WebAssign. Enhanced WebAssign gives you immediate feedback, rich tutorial content, and interactive eBooks (YouBook) helping you to develop a deeper conceptual understanding of the subject matter.

In addition, diagnostic quizzing for each chapter identifies concepts that you may still need to master, and directs you to the appropriate review material. All of this is available to you with Enhanced WebAssign.

Accuracy and Development Process

Periodically during the authoring process, there were several phases of development where our manuscript was sent out to be reviewed by fellow college mathematics instructors either via a traditional "paper" review and/or via in-person focus groups. The feedback we received, very often including very thoughtful markups of the manuscript, related to accuracy, pacing, ordering of topics, accessibility and reading level, integration of technology, and completeness of coverage. At each stage, we analyzed and incorporated this feedback into the manuscript.

The manuscript also benefited from student and instructor feedback from class tests. Bearing in mind the developmental math student and our applications-first approach, we took great pains to ensure the reading level was appropriate, working closely with a developmental reading and writing instructor to confirm this.

The final manuscript was delivered to Brooks/Cole-Cengage Learning considerably improved following this rigorous review, development, and revision process. Once in production, the manuscript was cycled through a process by specialized team members: production editor, copyeditor, accuracy reviewer, designer, proofreader, art editor, artists, and compositor. Each team member pays special attention to accuracy and completeness. As each phase of the cycle was completed, the manuscript was sent to us to verify any suggested changes or corrections. By the time this manuscript was published, it had been through the many phases of the production process and at least 10 pair of highly trained eyes verified its accuracy and completeness. Please be assured that accuracy was our primary goal and we take great pride in having partnered with many people to deliver an accurate, engaging, and meaningful teaching tool for your beginning algebra classes.

Reviewers

Authoring a textbook series is a huge undertaking and we are very grateful to so many colleagues who assisted us throughout the many stages of development. It was a painstaking process made possible by your willingness to collaborate with us and share your thoughtful feedback and comments. We thank you most sincerely for your many efforts on our behalf. You all gave of your time and expertise most generously: reviewing *multiple* rounds of manuscript, preparing for and attending our detailed development focus groups, class testing the manuscript in its many iterations, and class testing and reviewing the online homework problems we created. We couldn't have done this without you and your students, and the series and its accompanying ancillary program are a testimony to that.

Beginning Algebra and Intermediate Algebra
Advisory Board Members

Scott Barnett, *Henry Ford Community College*
Maryann Firpo, *Seattle Central Community College*
Kevin Fox, *Shasta College*
Brian Karasek, *South Mountain Community College*

Krystyna Karminska, *Thomas Nelson Community College*
Amy Keith, *University of Alaska, Fairbanks*
Brianne Lodholtz, *Grand Rapids Community College*
Marilyn Platt, *Gaston College*
Janice Roy, *Montcalm Community College*
James Vallade, *Monroe County Community College*

Reviewers

Katherine M. Adams, *Eastern Michigan University*

Kent Aeschliman, *Oakland Community College*

Tim Allen, *Delta College*

Alex Ambriosa, *Hillsborough Community College, Brandon Campus*

Ken Anderson, *Chemeketa Community College*

Frank Appiah, *Maysville Community & Technical College*

Sonia Avetisian, *Orange Coast College*

Margaret Balachowski, *Everett Community College*

Farshad Barman, *Portland Community College*

Scott Barnett, *Henry Ford Community College*

Mariah Beck, *Umpqua Community College*

Alison Becker Moses, *Mercer County Community College*

Michelle Beerman, *Pasco-Hernando Community College*

Nadia Benakli, *New York City College of Technology*

David Bendler, *Arkansas State University*

Joel Berman, *Valencia Community College East*

Rebecca Berthiaume, *Edison Community College*

Scott Berthiaume, *Edison Community College*

Nina Bohrod, *Anoka-Ramsey Community College*

Jennifer Borrello, *Grand Rapids Community College*

Ron Breitfelder, *Manatee Community College*

Mary Brown, *Eastern Oregon University*

Reynaldo Casiple, *Florida Community College*

James Chesla, *Grand Rapids Community College*

Shawn Chiappetta, *University of Sioux Falls*

Lisa Christman, *University of Central Arkansas*

Astrida Cirulis, *Concordia University Chicago*

Adam Cloutier, *Henry Ford Community College*

Elizabeth Cunningham, *Santa Barbara City College*

Amy Cupit, *Copiah-Lincoln Community College*

Robert Diaz, *Fullerton College*

William Dickinson, *Grand Valley State University*

Susan Dimick, *Spokane Community College*

Christopher Donnelly, *Macomb Community College*

Randall Dorman, *Cochise College*

Karen Edwards, *Diablo Valley College*

Janet Evert, *Erie Community College, South*

Maryann Faller, *Adirondack Community College*

Robert Farinelli, *Community College of Allegheny County*

Terran Felter, *California State University, Bakersfield*

Maryann Firpo, *Seattle Central Community College*

Thomas Fitzkee, *Francis Marion University*

Nancy Forrest, *Grand Rapids Community College*

Kevin Fox, *Shasta College*

Marcia Frobish, *Grand Valley State University*

John Golden, *Grand Valley State University*

Gail Gonyo, *Adirondack Community College*

Lori Grady, *University of Wisconsin, Whitewater*

James Gray, *Tacoma Community College*

John Greene, *Henderson State University*

Kathryn Gundersen, *Three Rivers College*

Joseph Haberfeld, *Columbia College Chicago*

Susan Hahn, *Kean University*

Julie Harland, *Mira Costa College*

Shelle Hartzel, *Lake Land College*

Mahshid Hassani, *Hillsborough Community College*

Stephanie Haynes, *Davis & Elkins College*

Julie Hess, *Grand Rapids Community College*

Elaine Hodz, *Florida Community College, Kent*

Kalynda Holton, *Tallahassee Community College*

Sharon Hudson, *Gulf Coast Community College*

Daniel Jordan, *Columbia College Chicago*

Laura Kalbaugh, *Wake Tech Community College*

Brian Karasek, *South Mountain Community College*

Krystyna Karminska, *Thomas Nelson Community College*

Ryan Kasha, *Valencia Community College*

Fred Katirae, *Montgomery College*

Amy Keith, *University of Alaska, Fairbanks*

Tom Kelley, *Henry Ford Community College*

Gary S. Kersting, *North Central Michigan College*

Dennis Kimzey, *Rogue Community College*

Mike Kirby, *Tidewater Community College*

Mark Krasij, *University of Texas at Arlington*

Theodore Lai, *Hudson County Community College*

Ivy Langford, *Collin County Community College*

Richard Leedy, *Polk State College*

Mary Legner, *Riverside City College*

Allyn Leon, *Imperial Valley Community College*

Andrea Levy, *Seattle Central Community College*

Brianne Lodholtz, *Grand Rapids Community College*

Tristan Londre, *Blue River Community College*

Daniel Lopez, *Brookdale Community College*

Cathy Lovingier, *Linn Benton Community College*

David Maina, *Columbia College Chicago*

Vivian Martinez, *Coastal Bend College*

Jane Mays, *Grand Valley State University*

Tim Mezernich, *Chemeketa Community College*

Pam Miller, *Phoenix College*

Christopher Milner, *Clark College*

Jeff Morford, *Henry Ford Community College*

Brian Moudry, *Davis & Elkins College*

Ellen Musen, *Brookdale Community College and Palm Beach State College*

Charlie Naffziger, *Central Oregon Community College*

Lisa Nanni, *Jackson Community College*

Douglas Nerig, *Ivy Tech Community College*

Coleen Neroda, *Austin Community College*

Ken Nickels, *Black Hawk College*

Marilyn Platt, *Gaston College*

Sandra Poinsett, *College of Southern Maryland*

Michael Price, *University of Oregon*

Jill Rafael, *Sierra College*

Linda Reist, *Macomb Community College*

David Reynolds, *Treasure Valley Community College*

Jolene Rhodes, *Valencia Community College*

Patricia Rhodes, *Treasure Valley Community College*

Janice Roy, *Montcalm Community College*

Sean Rule, *Central Oregon Community College*

Lily Sainsbury, *Brevard Community College, Cocoa*

Mark Schwartz, *Southern Maine Community College*

Cindy Scofield, *Polk Community College*

Lenora Shepherd, *Atlantic University*

Sailakshmi Srinivasan, *Grand Valley State University*
Barbara Tozzi, *Brookdale Community College*
Jeannette Tyson, *Valencia Community College*
James Vallade, *Monroe County Community College*
Andria Villines, *Bellevue College*
Xiaomin Wang, *Rochester Community and Technical College*
Kim Ward, *Eastern Connecticut University*
Matt Williamson, *Hillsborough Community College, South Shore*
Deborah Wolfson, *Suffolk County Community College*
Fred Worth, *Henderson State University*
Carol Zavarella, *Hillsborough Community College, Ybor*

Developmental Focus Group Participants

Khadija Ahmed, *Monroe Community College*
Elaine Alhand, *Ivy Tech Community College*
Katherine Jankoviak Anderson, *Schoolcraft College*
Ken Anderson, *Chemeketa Community College*
Margaret Balachowski, *Everett Community College*
Farshad Barman, *Portland Community College*
Lois Bearden, *Schoolcraft College*
Clairessa Bender, *Henry Ford Community College*
Kathy Burgis, *Lansing Community College*
Caroline Castel, *Delta College*
Mariana Coanda, *Broward College*
Kay Cornelius, *Sinclair Community College*
Lisa Crawford, *Piedmont Technical College*
Greg Cripe, *Spokane Falls Community College*
Alex Cushnier, *Henry Ford Community College*
Susan Dimick, *Spokane Community College*
Julie Fisher, *Austin Community College*
Will Freeman, *Portland Community College*
Deede Furman, *Austin Community College*
Irie Glajar, *Austin Community College*
James Gray, *Tacoma Community College*
Mahshid Hassani, *Hillsborough Community College*
Farah Hojjaty, *North Central Texas College*
Sherrie Holland, *Piedmont Technical College*
Catherine Holl-Cross, *Brookdale Community College*
Susan Hord, *Austin Community College*
Liz Hylton, *Clatsop Community College*
Eric Kean, *Western Washington University*
Jack Keating, *Massasoit Community College*
Beth Kelch, *Delta College*
Becca Kimzey
Dennis Kimzey, *Rogue Community College*
Mike Kirby, *Tidewater Community College*
Patricia Kopf, *Kellogg Community College*
Kay Kriewald, *Laredo Community College*
Riki Kucheck, *Orange Coast College*
Ivy Langford, *Collin County Community College*
Joanne Lauterbur, *Baker College*
Melanie Ledwig, *Victoria College*
Richard Leedy, *Polk State College*
Brianne Lodholtz, *Grand Rapids Community College*
Daniel Lopez, *Brookdale Community College*

Babette Lowe, *Victoria College*
Doug Mace, *Kirtland Community College*
Vinnie Maltese, *Monroe Community College*
Vivian Martinez, *Coastal State College*
Michael McCoy, *Schoolcraft College*
Carol McKilip, *Southwestern Oregon Community College*
Anna Maria Mendiola, *Laredo Community College*
Tim Mezernich, *Chemeketa Community College*
Karen Mifflin, *Palomar College*
Maria Miles, *Mount Hood Community College*
Pam Miller, *Phoenix College*
Christopher Milner, *Clark College*
Ellen Musen, *Brookdale Community College and Palm Beach State College*
Joyce Nemeth, *Broward College*
Charlotte Newsome, *Tidewater Community College*
Katrina Nichols, *Delta College*
Joanna Oberthur, *Ivy Tech Community College*
Ceci Oldmixon, *Victoria College*
Mary B. Oliver, *Baker College*
Diana Pagel, *Victoria College*
Joanne Peeples, *El Paso Community College*
Sandra Poinsett, *College of Southern Maryland*
Bob Quigley, *Austin Community College*
Jayanthy Ramakrishnan, *Lansing Community College*
Patricia Rhodes, *Treasure Valley Community College*
Fary Sami, *Harford Community College*
Billie Shannon, *Southwestern Oregon Community College*
Pam Tindel, *Tyler Junior College*
Barbara Tozzi, *Brookdale Community College*
James Vallade, *Monroe Community College*
Andy Villines, *Bellevue Community College*
Beverly Vredevelt, *Spokane Falls Community College*
Thomas Wells, *Delta College*
Charles Wickman, *Everett Community College*
Eric Wiesenauer, *Delta College*
Mary Young, *Brookdale Community College*

Class Testers

Tim Allen, *Delta College*
Scott Barnett, *Henry Ford Community College*
Jennifer Borrello, *Grand Rapids Community College*
Damon Ellingston, *Seattle Central Community College*
Maryann Firpo, *Seattle Central Community College*
Marcia Frobish, *Grand Valley State University*
Rathi Kanthimathi, *Seattle Central Community College*
Daniel Lopez, *Brookdale Community College*
Ellen Musen, *Brookdale Community College and Palm Beach State College*
Mary Stinnett, *Umpqua Community College*
Barbara Tozzi, *Brookdale Community College*
Randy Trip, *Jefferson Community College*
Thomas Wells, *Delta College*
Michael White, *Jefferson Community College*
Eric Wiesenauer, *Delta College*
Paul Yu, *Grand Valley State University*

Acknowledgments

We would like to thank Eve Nolan for her many helpful suggestions for improving the text. We are also grateful to Scott Barnett, Pam Miller, and Edythe Carter for their excellent work accuracy checking our text and ancillaries. We also thank the editorial, production, and marketing staffs of Brooks/Cole: Charlie Van Wagner, Carolyn Crockett, Rita Lombard, Stefanie Beeck, Carrie Jones, Jennifer Cordoba, Cheryll Linthicum, Gordon Lee, Mandee Eckersley, Heleny Wong, and Maryanne Payumo for all of their help and support during the development and production of this text. Thanks also to Vernon Boes, Leslie Lahr, and Lisa Torri for their work on the design and art program, and to Barbara Willette and Susan Reiland for their copyediting and proofreading expertise. We especially want to thank our developmental editors, Danielle Derbenti and Rita Lombard for all of their timely advice and support. Our gratitude also goes to Cheryll Linthicum and Jill Traut, who had an amazing amount of patience with us throughout production. We truly appreciate all the hard work and efforts of the entire team.

Mark Clark
Cynthia Anfinson

To the Student

Welcome to courses on beginning and intermediate algebra. This text was designed to help you learn the algebra skills and concepts you need in future math, science, and other courses. Critical algebra skills are presented to give you a solid foundation in mathematics. Concepts are presented so that you understand the "why" of what you are doing. The applications selected are based more in real-life situations, so you can learn how to interpret mathematical results.

We hope that you will find the real-life applications to be interesting and helpful in understanding the material. An emphasis is placed on thinking critically about the results you find throughout the book and communicating these results clearly. The *answers in the back* of the book will help demonstrate this level of thinking and communication. We believe improving these skills will benefit you in many of your classes and in life.

There are several features of the book that are meant to help you review and prepare for exams. Throughout the sections are *definition boxes* and *margin features* that point out key skills or vocabulary that will be important to your success in mastering the skills and concepts. We encourage you to use the *end-of-chapter reviews* and *chapter tests* as an opportunity to try a variety of problems from the chapter and test your understanding of the concepts and skills being covered. There is a review of prealgebra topics at the beginning of the text—see Chapter R if you find yourself in need of a refresher.

We hope these tools will be a good reference if you find yourself in need of a little more help. Remember that your instructor and fellow classmates are some of the best resources you have to help you be successful in this course and in using this text.

Good luck in your Beginning and Intermediate Algebra courses!

Sincerely,
Mark Clark
Cindy Anfinson

Review of Prealgebra

Mathematics has been used by humans throughout recorded history and even in prehistoric times. The Ishango bone was found in 1960 in Africa, in an area near the border between Uganda and the Congo. The bone is that of a baboon, and it is currently estimated to be more than 20,000 years old. The tally marks on the bone were originally thought to be counting marks, but some scientists now believe that the marks indicate knowledge of multiplication and division by two. This bone shows that prehistoric peoples had a firm understanding of counting.

R.1   Operations with Integers

LEARNING OBJECTIVES

- Distinguish natural numbers, whole numbers, and integers.
- Use number lines.
- Write inequalities.
- Find the absolute value of an integer.
- Find the opposite.
- Use the order-of-operations agreement for integers.

Natural Numbers, Whole Numbers, and Integers

People have been doing mathematics continuously throughout recorded history. There is strong evidence that in prehistory (before recorded history), people were using mathematics. First, they invented numbers and counting. Then people invented ways of combining numbers. Arithmetic is the study of combining numbers through the operations of addition, subtraction, multiplication, and division.

Humans like to classify objects into various sets. For example, in the animal kingdom, animals have been classified into sets such as the reptiles, amphibians, birds, mammals, and fish. In the plant world, some classifications are ferns, conifers, and flowering plants. Mathematicians also like to classify numbers into sets.

The first set of numbers that people used are the **natural** (or **counting**) **numbers.** Ancient peoples did not see numbers as ideas, as we do today. They used numbers to count things up. For example, "two sheep" is how ancient peoples would have used the value 2. It is a big step to make the mental shift from "two sheep" to "two things" and then to "2" as an idea with no "things" attached to it. Zero (0) is not in the set of counting numbers, as the ancients would have had no reason to count a set of no sheep.

Zero was a difficult concept for people to grasp, even though zero is taken for granted today. Zero seems to have developed from two different needs. One is the use of zero as a placeholder, and the other is a symbol to represent that no objects are present. As an example of zero as a placeholder, in our number system, 102 is a different number from 12. The value of zero holds the place of tens, and the zero is necessary to distinguish between the numbers 102 and 12. It appears that zero as a placeholder developed in both India and Mexico (in the Mayan civilization) independently.

Zero also represents the number 0 or, as the ancients would have seen it, no objects are present. This idea of zero as a symbol was published in three different Indian texts about 600 c.e. When we add zero to the set of natural numbers, we call this new set the **whole numbers.**

What's That Mean?

Sets

Mathematicians call a collection of objects a *set*.

The curly brace symbols, { }, in mathematics indicate a set.

The symbols, …, denote a pattern. These symbols mean that the set continues in this way indefinitely.

A set with no elements is called the empty set. It is written { } or $\varnothing$.

DEFINITIONS

Natural Numbers   The **natural numbers** consist of the set $\{1, 2, 3, \ldots\}$.

Whole Numbers   The **whole numbers** consist of the set $\{0, 1, 2, 3, \ldots\}$.

When we count the number of wheels on a wheeled vehicle (such as a bike or a car), it is clear that the vehicle can have 1, 2, 3, 4, or more wheels. Counting the number of wheels is an example of using values from the set of *natural* numbers.

Suppose we want to count up the number of people in a room. The room can contain 0, 1, 2, … people. The value of 0 needs to be included, since the room could be empty. The number of people in the room takes on values from the set of *whole* numbers.

The use of negative numbers first appeared in ancient China (200 B.C.E. to 220 C.E.) as answers to certain equations. Negative numbers also appeared when traders balanced their accounts and had to show a loss. As with the number 0, it took a while for the concept of negative numbers to be widely accepted. Today, we use negative numbers in different fields, such as the measurement of extremely cold temperatures, double-entry bookkeeping, and describing profit-loss situations. The set of positive and negative whole numbers is called the set of **integers.** In weather forecasts, the temperature of the day is often measured in integers. The temperature on a cold winter's day in Fargo, North Dakota, could be −30°F. The summer temperature in San Diego, California, could be 75°F. Pure oxygen freezes at about −361°F.

> ### DEFINITION
>
> **Integers**   The integers consist of the set $\{\ldots, -3, -2, -1, 0, 1, 2, 3, \ldots\}$.

The diagram at the right will help you to visualize the number systems. The set of natural numbers is contained in the set of whole numbers, and the set of whole numbers is contained in the set of integers. This diagram is a visual way to see that if a number is a natural number, then it is also a whole number and an integer.

CONCEPT INVESTIGATION

What kind of number is that?

1. Place each number in the *smallest* possible set it fits into.

   a. −16   **b.** 29   **c.** 0

   d. 5°F   **e.** 65 mph   **f.** −12°C

2. List all the natural numbers between −5 and 4, including the endpoints −5 and 4.

3. List all the whole numbers between −7 and 3, including the endpoints −7 and 3.

4. List all the integers between −3 and 5, including the endpoints −3 and 5.

Example 1   Classifying numbers

Determine the set(s), natural numbers, whole numbers, or integers, to which all possible numbers described by the statement could belong.

a. The number of dogs boarding at a kennel during a two-week period.

b. The average daily low temperature, in degrees Fahrenheit, in Fairbanks, Alaska, over the course of a year.

c. The number of tires on a truck used for long-haul trucking (long-distance transportation of goods) in the United States.

SOLUTION

a. This value (the number of dogs) is a whole number. The number of dogs boarding at a kennel could be 0, 1, 2, … . Since the kennel could be empty on any given day (0 dogs), the value 0 is included as a possibility. These values are also integers.

b. This is an example from the set of integers. The average daily low in Fairbanks was −13°F in January to 50°F in July. The temperatures range from negative numbers to positive numbers.

c. This is an example from the natural numbers, whole numbers, or integers. Trucks can have four or more tires, so the number of tires could be 4, 5, 6, … .

PRACTICE PROBLEM FOR EXAMPLE 1

Determine the set(s), natural numbers, whole numbers, or integers, to which all possible numbers described by the statement could belong.

a. The number of children attending kindergarten at Park View Elementary School.

b. The average daily low temperature, in degrees Fahrenheit, in Minneapolis, Minnesota, over the course of a year.

c. The number of people in the quiet study room in the library at Irvine Valley Community College.

What's That Mean?

Scale

The *scale* of a number line is the distance between the consistent and evenly spaced tick marks on the number line.

Number Lines

Number lines are a useful way to visualize numbers. A number line is like a ruler. It is straight with a *consistent scale*. This means the tick marks on the ruler are the same distance apart, and the number of units the marks are apart is called the **scale.** Numbers get larger (increase) as we move to the right on the number line. Numbers get smaller (decrease) as we move to the left on the number line. The positive numbers are to the right of 0, and the negative numbers are to the left of 0.

The number line below has scale of 1. This is because the tick marks on the line are 1 unit apart.

The number line below has scale of 10. The tick marks on the line are 10 units apart.

The number line below has scale of 0.5. The tick marks on the line are a half unit apart.

Example 2 Finding the scale

Determine the scale of the following number line.

SOLUTION

The tick marks on the number line are 5 units apart. The scale of this number line is 5.

PRACTICE PROBLEM FOR EXAMPLE 2

Determine the scale of the following number line.

Each number corresponds to one point on the number line. To graph a number on the number line, we locate its position and draw in a darkened circle.

Example 3 Graphing points

Graph the numbers -3, 0, 1, and 4 on the following number line.

SOLUTION

The numbers are graphed as darkened circles on the number line.

PRACTICE PROBLEM FOR EXAMPLE 3

Graph the numbers -6, 8, -3, and 7 on the following number line.

Relations Between Numbers

When we look at a number line, we can see that some numbers are larger than others. Mathematicians express this idea by saying that the integers are a number system that has *order*. Order means that we can organize a set of numbers from smallest to largest. The symbols given in the following table are mathematical notation used to express order in numbers.

Symbols	In Words	Example
$a < b$	a is less than b	$5 < 10$
$a > b$	a is greater than b	$2 > -2$
$a \leq b$	a is less than or equal to b	$-1 \leq 0$
$a \geq b$	a is greater than or equal to b	$-2 \geq -4$
$a < b < c$	b is between a and c, not including a or c	$3 < 5 < 7$
$a \leq b \leq c$	b is between a and c, including a and c	$1 \leq 1 \leq 3$
$a = b$	a is equal to b	$2 = 2$
$a \neq b$	a is not equal to b	$3 \neq 5$
$a \approx b$	a is approximately equal to b	$0.249 \approx 0.25$

The symbols $\leq$, $<$, $\geq$, $>$, and $\neq$ are called *inequality symbols*, and the first six rows in the table are called *inequalities*.

Example 4 Classifying inequalities

Fill in each blank column with $<$ or $>$. Draw a number line to visualize the correct relationship between the values. This is especially helpful in comparing two negative numbers.

a.	-2		-5
b.	-6		-1
c.	0		7

SOLUTION

Use the following number line to determine which number is larger. Remember that the numbers to the right are larger.

a.	-2	$>$	-5	-2 is to the right of -5 on the number line.
b.	-6	$<$	-1	-6 is to the left of -1 on the number line.
c.	0	$<$	7	0 is to the left of 7 on the number line.

PRACTICE PROBLEM FOR EXAMPLE 4

Fill in each blank with $<$ or $>$. If needed, draw a number line to visualize the correct relationship between the values.

a.	-5		-8
b.	3		-3
c.	-2		0

Absolute Value

■ CONCEPT INVESTIGATION

What is the distance between a number and zero?

Use the following number line to answer the questions.

1. What is the distance between -6 and 0?

2. What is the distance between 6 and 0?

3. What is the distance between 0 and 0?

4. Can a distance be positive?

5. Can a distance be negative?

6. Can a distance be zero?

■ What's That Mean?

Nonnegative

When a quantity takes on only values that are 0 or positive (that is, greater than or equal to 0), mathematicians say the quantity is *nonnegative*.

To discuss distance on a number line, we use the idea of **absolute value.** Absolute value is defined to be a distance measurement, so it must be a positive number or 0 (nonnegative). Distances cannot be negative. Therefore, absolute value can never result in a negative number.

DEFINITION

Absolute Value   The absolute value of a number is the distance between that number and 0.

Note   The $|\ |$ symbols are the notation for absolute value.

For example, $|-4| = 4$, since the distance between -4 and 0 is 4. See the number line below.

Example 5   Finding absolute value

Find the value of the absolute value expressions.

a. $|5|$ **b.** $|-7|$

SOLUTION

a. $|5| = 5$, since the distance between 5 and 0 is 5 units.

b. $|-7| = 7$, since the distance between -7 and 0 is 7 units.

PRACTICE PROBLEM FOR EXAMPLE 5

Find the value of the absolute value expressions.

a. $|10|$ **b.** $|-16|$

Example 6   Ordering numbers

Place the following numbers in increasing order (from smallest to largest):

$$|-2|, |0|, |3|, -5, |12|$$

SOLUTION

First, find any absolute values.

$$|-2| = 2$$
$$|0| = 0$$
$$|3| = 3$$
$$-5 = -5$$
$$|12| = 12$$

Order the numbers from smallest to largest.

$$-5, 0, 2, 3, 12$$

Convert back to the original notation.

$$-5, |0|, |-2|, |3|, |12|$$

PRACTICE PROBLEM FOR EXAMPLE 6

Place the following numbers in increasing order (from smallest to largest):

$$|6|, |-4|, -2, |0|, 8$$

Opposite of a Number

Look at the following number line. The numbers 7 and -7 are the same distance from 0, so they have the same absolute value.

Numbers that have the same absolute value but different signs are called **opposites.** Another way to read the number -7 (negative 7) is the opposite of 7.

> **DEFINITION**
>
> **Opposite of a Real Number** The opposite of any number has the same absolute value but differs in sign.
>
> **Note** Read $-a$ as the "opposite of a," not as "negative a."

Example 7 Rewriting an expression in phrase form

First, rewrite the math expression in phrase form. Then find the value of the expression.

a. $-(-7)$ **b.** $-(6)$

SOLUTION

a. The expression translates as "the opposite of negative seven."

$$-(-7) = 7$$

b. The expression translates as "the opposite of six."

$$-(6) = -6$$

PRACTICE PROBLEM FOR EXAMPLE 7

First, rewrite the math expression in phrase form. Then find the value of the expression.

a. $-(8)$ **b.** $-(-1)$ **c.** $-(0)$

Operations with Integers

We can use the number line to visualize adding and subtracting integers (signed numbers). Let's discuss addition first. To add signed numbers, we move to the right on the number line when adding a positive number. Suppose we want to add $-8 + 7$. We start on the number line at -8 and count over 7 units to the right (since 7 is a positive number). The solution is -1.

We move to the left on the number line when adding a negative number. Suppose we want to add $-2 + (-5)$. We start at -2 on the number line and move over 5 units to the left, because -5 is a negative number. The solution is -7.

Drawing a number line each time we want to add or subtract signed numbers can be time-consuming. We usually add and subtract signed numbers using the following steps.

What's That Mean?

Expression

In English, an *expression* can mean a word or a phrase. In mathematics, an *expression* is a mathematical phrase. It is a combination of numbers and symbols. An expression does not contain an equal sign.

What's That Mean?

Signed Numbers

In algebra, a *signed number* refers to a number with either a positive or negative sign. Positive numbers are written with no sign. Thus, $5 = +5$. Negative numbers are always written with the negative sign, such as -5.

Steps to Add or Subtract Integers

1. **To add integers with the same sign:** Add the absolute values of the numbers. Attach the same sign of the numbers to the sum.
2. **To add integers with different signs:** Take the absolute value of each number. Subtract the smaller absolute value from the larger. Attach the sign of the number that is larger in absolute value.
3. **To subtract integers:** Change the sign of the second integer (reading left to right) and add as explained above.

What's That Mean?

Sum

The *sum* is the result of performing an addition. In $5 + 7 = 12$, the sum is 12.

Example 8   Adding integers

Add the integers.

a. $-29 + 15$ **b.** $-13 + 18$

SOLUTION

a. These two integers have different signs. Take the absolute value of each number and subtract the smaller absolute value from the larger. Subtract 15 from 29.

$$29 - 15 = 14$$

The number that is larger in absolute value is -29, so the answer will be negative. Attach a negative sign to 14.

$$-29 + 15 = -14$$

The final answer is -14.

b. These two integers have different signs. Take the absolute value of each number and subtract the smaller absolute value from the larger. Subtract 13 from 18.

$$18 - 13 = 5$$

Since the number that is larger is $+18$, the answer is $+5$ or just 5.

PRACTICE PROBLEM FOR EXAMPLE 8

Add the integers.

a. $-42 + 8$ **b.** $-12 + 26$

Example 9   Subtracting integers

Subtract the integers.

a. $3 - 7$ **b.** $-5 - (-9)$

SOLUTION

a. The two integers are being subtracted. Change the sign of the second number (7 to -7). Add the two numbers using the rule for adding integers.

$$3 - 7 = 3 + (-7) = -4$$

The final answer is -4.

b. The two integers are being subtracted. Change the sign of the second integer (-9 to 9). Add the two numbers using the rule for adding integers.

$$-5 - (-9) = -5 + (9) = 4$$

The final answer is 4.

PRACTICE PROBLEM FOR EXAMPLE 9

Subtract the integers.

a. $8 - 15$ **b.** $7 - (-10)$

Example 10 Rising and falling temperatures

a. If the temperature is $-5°F$ and the temperature rises by $8°F$, then what is the new temperature?

b. If the temperature is $-12°F$ and the temperature drops by $2°F$, then what is the new temperature?

SOLUTION

a. The temperature can be found by adding $-5 + 8$. These integers have different signs. The number with the larger absolute value is 8.

$$8 - 5 = 3$$ Subtract 5 from 8, as the number with the larger absolute value is 8.

$$-5 + 8 = 3$$ The result is positive, as the number with the larger absolute value was positive 8.

The final temperature is $3°F$.

b. The temperature can be found by subtracting $-12 - 2$. To subtract two integers, change the sign of the second integer and add. Therefore, we compute

$$-12 + (-2) = -14$$

The final temperature is $-14°F$.

PRACTICE PROBLEM FOR EXAMPLE 10

The highest point in the state of California is Mount Whitney, which has an elevation of 14,494 feet, and the lowest point in California is Death Valley, which is 282 feet below sea level.

Source: www.netstate.com/states/geography.

a. Write the elevation of Mount Whitney as an integer. Note: A positive elevation will be above sea level.

b. Write the elevation of Death Valley as an integer. Note: A negative elevation will be below sea level.

c. Find the difference in elevation between the highest and lowest points in the state of California.

Absolute value can be used to find the distance between two points on a number line.

DEFINITION

Distance Between Two Points on the Number Line The distance between two points on a number line, a and b, can be found as $|b - a|$.

> **Example 11** Finding the distance between two points on a number line

Find the distance between -8 and -3.

SOLUTION

One way to find the distance between -8 and -3 is to graph the two points on a number line and count the spaces in between them.

Since there are five spaces in between -8 and -3, the distance between these two numbers is 5.

Another way to find the distance between these two points is to use the formula $|b - a|$. Let $a = -8$ and $b = -3$ and substitute into the formula.

$$\begin{aligned} |b - a| &= |-3 - (-8)| \\ &= |-3 + 8| \\ &= |5| \\ &= 5 \end{aligned}$$

Note that if we switch the order of the points, the formula still gives the correct answer. Let $a = -3$ and $b = -8$ and substitute into the formula.

$$\begin{aligned} |b - a| &= |-8 - (-3)| \\ &= |-8 + 3| \\ &= |-5| \\ &= 5 \end{aligned}$$

PRACTICE PROBLEM FOR EXAMPLE 11

Find the distance between -9 and -2.

The two other basic operations are multiplication and division. Recall that multiplication of natural numbers is shorthand for a repeated addition. So $3 \cdot 4 = 4 + 4 + 4 = 3 + 3 + 3 + 3$. So $3 \cdot 4$ is the same as adding 4 three times or adding 3 four times.

Likewise, division of natural numbers is a shortcut for a repeated subtraction. In $12 \div 3 = 4$, when we repeatedly subtract 3 from 12, we get

$$\begin{aligned} 12 - 3 &= 9 \\ 9 - 3 &= 6 \\ 6 - 3 &= 3 \\ 3 - 3 &= 0 \end{aligned}$$

The number of times we subtract 3 from 12 is 4. Therefore, $12 \div 3 = 4$.

Writing multiplication and division problems as repeated additions and/or subtractions can be time-consuming. That is why people memorize multiplication tables. The following Concept Investigation will review the rules for multiplying signed numbers.

CONCEPT INVESTIGATION

What pattern of signs do you see?

1. Complete the following table.

Calculation	Result
$4 \cdot 4$	16
$4 \cdot 3$	
$4 \cdot 2$	
$4 \cdot 1$	
$4 \cdot 0$	

2. What happens to the result as the number you multiply 4 by goes down by 1 in each row?

3. When you multiply two positive numbers together, is the result a positive or negative number?

4. Use the pattern from part 1 to complete the following table.

Calculation	Result
4 · 2	8
4 · 1	
4 · 0	
4 · (−1)	
4 · (−2)	
4 · (−3)	
4 · (−4)	

5. When a positive number and a negative number are multiplied together, is the result a positive or negative number?

6. Use a pattern to complete the following table.

Problem	Solution
−4 · 4	−16
−4 · 3	
−4 · 2	
−4 · 1	
−4 · 0	
−4 · (−1)	
−4 · (−2)	
−4 · (−3)	
−4 · (−4)	

7. When a negative number and a negative number are multiplied together, is the result a positive or negative number?

Steps to Multiply or Divide Signed Numbers

1. **To multiply or divide two integers with the same sign:** Multiply or divide the absolute values of the numbers. The solution is always positive.
2. **To multiply or divide two integers with different signs:** Multiply or divide the absolute values of the two numbers. The solution is always negative.

Example 12 Multiplying integers

Multiply the following integers.

a. $(-3)(7)$ **b.** $(-9)(-6)$

SOLUTION

a. $(-3)(7) = -21$

The answer is negative, since the two integers have different signs.

b. $(-9)(-6) = 54$

The answer is positive, since the two integers have the same sign.

PRACTICE PROBLEM FOR EXAMPLE 12

Multiply the following integers.

a. $(-2)(4)$ **b.** $(-5)(-3)$

Example 13 Dividing integers

Divide the following integers.

a. $15 \div (-5)$ **b.** $(-48) \div 12$ **c.** $\dfrac{-27}{-3}$

SOLUTION

a. $15 \div (-5) = -3$

The answer is negative, since the two integers have different signs.

b. $(-48) \div 12 = -4$

The answer is negative, since the two integers have different signs.

c. $\dfrac{-27}{-3} = 9$

The answer is positive, since the two integers have the same sign.

PRACTICE PROBLEM FOR EXAMPLE 13

Divide the following integers.

a. $20 \div (-4)$ **b.** $\dfrac{-16}{-8}$ **c.** $(-27) \div 3$

Keep in mind that division by 0 means that 0 is the divisor or is in the denominator. When 0 is the dividend, such as $0 \div 16$ or $\dfrac{0}{16}$, the answer is 0. It is important to note that division by zero is **undefined** (sometimes, mathematicians say the result of such an operation "does not exist" or "DNE"). We know that $16 \div 2 = 8$ or $\dfrac{16}{2} = 8$, since $8 \cdot 2 = 16$. Now suppose $16 \div 0 = c$ or $\dfrac{16}{0} = c$, where c is some real number. This would mean that $0 \cdot c = 16$, which is impossible. Any number multiplied by 0 is 0. Therefore, we say that division by zero is undefined mathematically.

DEFINITION

Division by 0 If a is a real number, then $a \div 0$ is undefined.

Order of Operations

In arithmetic, we have the following basic operations.

DEFINITIONS

Basic Operations The basic operations used in arithmetic are as follows.

1. **Addition** The two (or more) numbers being added are called **addends** or **terms.** The result of an addition is called a **sum.**
2. **Subtraction** The result of a subtraction is called a **difference.**
3. **Multiplication** The two (or more) numbers being multiplied are called **factors.** The result of a multiplication is called a **product.**
4. **Division** The result of a division is called a **quotient.**

■ Connecting the Concepts

Is there more than one way to write divide?

There are several ways to show division. One way is with the $\div$ sign, such as $8 \div (-4)$.

Another way is with a fraction bar:

$$8 \div (-4) = \dfrac{8}{-4}.$$

Another way is using long division:

$8 \div (-4)$ means $-4\overline{)8}$.

■ What's That Mean?

Dividend, Divisor, and Quotient

The parts of a division problem have special names.

dividend $\div$ divisor = quotient.

Written using a fraction bar, we have

$$\dfrac{dividend}{divisor} = quotient$$

Sometimes, when a fraction bar is used, the parts are called the numerator and denominator.

$$\dfrac{numerator}{denominator}$$

■ **What's That Mean?**

Evaluate

In mathematics, to *evaluate* something means to compute the numerical value.

■ **Connecting the Concepts**

Why does a subtraction symbol separate terms?

Recall that subtraction is the same as adding the opposite of the second number.

$$2 - 3 = 2 + (-3)$$

Therefore, 2 and -3 are the two terms being added.

There are many times in a problem when we are faced with calculating more than one operation. For example, suppose we want to find the value of $4 \cdot 3 + 8$.

Janelle says to evaluate the multiplication first and then do the addition. Thus, we would get $4 \cdot 3 = 12$ and then compute $12 + 8 = 20$. But Curtis says to do the addition first and then the multiplication (working right to left). This would give us $3 + 8 = 11$ and then $4 \cdot 11 = 44$. This is not the same result at all.

$$4 \cdot 3 + 8 = ?$$

Janelle	Curtis
$(4 \cdot 3) + 8 = 12 + 8 = 20$	$4 \cdot (3 + 8) = 4 \cdot 11 = 44$

In mathematics, there cannot be two different answers, 20 and 44, for the same problem, $4 \cdot 3 + 8$.

To see which answer is correct, let's think about this problem in context. Suppose we buy four items for $3.00 each and one item for $8.00. How much did we spend? The four items at $3.00 cost $12.00, and then we add on the $8.00 for a total of $20.00. Thus, we know that 20 is the correct answer.

Because of this potential for confusion, mathematicians have come up with an order-of-operations agreement. This agreement will tell us in what order we should perform operations. In arithmetic, terms are identified as the quantities that are being added or subtracted. To determine the number of terms in an expression, look for the quantities that are separated by addition or subtraction symbols.

Example 14 Identifying terms

Identify the terms in each expression below.

a. $6 - 4 \cdot 5 + 10 \div 2$ **b.** $8 \div 4 - 16 + 9 \cdot 3 - 5$ **c.** $50 \cdot 2 \div 10$

SOLUTION

a. This expression has three terms. Terms are things we add or subtract, so they will be separated by addition and subtraction symbols. The terms in the expressions above are circled.

$$6 - 4 \cdot 5 + 10 \div 2$$

b. This expression has four terms. Remember, the terms are things we add or subtract, so they will be separated by addition and subtraction symbols. The terms are circled.

$$8 \div 4 - 16 + 9 \cdot 3 - 5$$

c. This expression has one term. There are no additions or subtractions.

$$50 \cdot 2 \div 10$$

PRACTICE PROBLEM FOR EXAMPLE 14

Identify the terms in each expression.

a. $4 - 2 \cdot 6 + 8$ **b.** $3 \cdot 7 - 10 \div 2 \cdot 3 - 5 \cdot 4 + 1$ **c.** $-65 \div 5 \cdot 4$ ■

Now that we have learned to identify terms, we can use the order-of-operations agreement.

> **Steps to Use the Order-of-Operations Agreement**
> 1. Circle or underline the terms. (Remember: Terms are parts that are added or subtracted.)
> 2. Evaluate the operations (multiplications and divisions) inside of each term, working from left to right.
> 3. Add and subtract the simplified terms, working from left to right.

Example 15 Placing the operations in order

Simplify each expression.

a. $9 - 6 \cdot 3 + 2$

b. $48 \div 3 \cdot 4$

c. $7 \cdot 5 - 10 \div 2 + 5 \cdot 2$

d. $36 \div 9 \cdot 3 - 2 \cdot 4 + 7 \cdot 2 - 5$

SOLUTION

First, circle the terms. Then, working from left to right inside each term, do the multiplications and divisions. Do the additions and subtractions last, working from left to right.

a. This expression has three terms.

$$\text{(9)} - \text{(6} \cdot \text{3)} + \text{(2)} \qquad \text{Circle the terms.}$$
$$= 9 - 6 \cdot 3 + 2 \qquad \text{Do the operation in each term.}$$
$$= 9 - 18 + 2 \qquad \text{Add and subtract in order from left to right.}$$
$$= -9 + 2$$
$$= -7$$

What's That Mean?

Simplify

In mathematics, to *simplify* something means to use arithmetic or algebraic operations to express the answer in the simplest possible form. In this chapter, we will work with arithmetic. In later chapters, we will work with both arithmetic and algebraic operations.

b. There are no additions or subtractions, so this expression has one term.

$$\text{(48} \div \text{3} \cdot \text{4)} \qquad \text{Circle the term.}$$
$$= 48 \div 3 \cdot 4 \qquad \text{Inside the term, do the operations in order, working from left to right.}$$
$$= 16 \cdot 4$$
$$= 64$$

c. This expression has three terms.

$$\text{(7} \cdot \text{5)} - \text{(10} \div \text{2)} + \text{(5} \cdot \text{2)} \qquad \text{Circle the terms.}$$
$$= 35 - 5 + 10 \qquad \text{Do the operations inside each term.}$$
$$= 30 + 10 \qquad \text{Do additions and subtractions, working from left to right.}$$
$$= 40$$

d. This expression has four terms.

$$\text{(36} \div \text{9} \cdot \text{3)} - \text{(2} \cdot \text{4)} + \text{(7} \cdot \text{2)} - \text{(5)} \qquad \text{Circle the terms.}$$
$$= \text{(4} \cdot \text{3)} - 8 + 14 - 5 \qquad \text{Do the operations inside each term.}$$
$$= 12 - 8 + 14 - 5 \qquad \text{Do the additions and subtractions, working from left to right.}$$
$$= 4 + 14 - 5$$
$$= 18 - 5$$
$$= 13$$

PRACTICE PROBLEM FOR EXAMPLE 15

Simplify each of the following expressions.

a. $24 \div 2 \cdot 3$ **b.** $9 + 6 \cdot 5 - 8 \div 4$ **c.** $6 \div 3 + 4 \cdot 5 - 2 \cdot 2 + 24 \div 8$

R.1 Exercises

For Exercises 1 through 10, classify each number as a natural number, a whole number, or an integer. If a number belongs to more than one set, list all possible sets it belongs to.

1. 0
2. 6
3. −20
4. −7
5. 11
6. 0
7. −9
8. −3
9. 1
10. −1

For Exercises 11 through 20, determine the set(s), natural numbers, whole numbers, or integers, to which all possible numbers described by the statement could belong.

11. The population of Los Angeles, California, each year.

12. The number of people in a crowd at the beach.

13. The population of Norfolk, Virginia.

14. The number of children attending Sullivan Middle School graduation.

15. The number of kittens in a local animal shelter.

16. The number of puppies in a local animal shelter.

17. The number of hours worked weekly by a Home Depot employee.

18. The number of hours worked yearly by an auto worker.

19. The daily high temperature in Missoula, Montana.

20. The daily high temperature in Honolulu, Hawaii.

For Exercises 21 through 26, list all numbers in the given set.

21. All integers between −5 and 1, including −5 and 1.

22. All integers between −2 and 4, including −2 and 4.

23. All natural numbers between −5 and 5, not including −5 and 5.

24. All natural numbers between −6 and 4, not including −6 and 4.

25. All whole numbers between −4 and 0, including −4 and 0.

26. All whole numbers between −3 and 3, including −3 and 3.

For Exercises 27 through 30, determine the scale of the number line.

27.

28.

29.

30.

For Exercises 31 through 36, graph each number on a number line like the one below.

31. −5
32. −2
33. 1
34. 9
35. −4
36. −7

For Exercises 37 through 44, use an appropriate inequality symbol ($<$, $>$, $\leq$, or $\geq$) between the two numbers.

37. −5   −15
38. −6   0
39. −3   −3
40. 8   8
41. −4   −3
42. −9   −8
43. 0   −7
44. 0   −1

For Exercises 45 through 52, find the value of the absolute value expression. See Example 5.

45. $|-3|$
46. $|-11|$
47. $|8|$
48. $|0|$
49. $|16|$
50. $|9|$
51. $|-7|$
52. $|-15|$

For Exercises 53 through 58, place the list of numbers in increasing order (from smallest to largest).

53. $3 \quad \dfrac{-3}{2} \quad -1 \quad 2.95 \quad 0.5 \quad \dfrac{1}{3}$

54. $-2 \quad \dfrac{-1}{4} \quad 5 \quad -1.75 \quad 3.5 \quad -4.5$

55. $|-5| \quad -5 \quad |-2| \quad -2$

56. $|8| \quad -8 \quad |-0| \quad 0$

57. $|-4| \quad -3.5 \quad |-5| \quad \dfrac{2}{3} \quad 4.2$

58. $-7 \quad |-7| \quad \dfrac{5}{4} \quad |-1| \quad \dfrac{9}{3} \quad |-3|$

For Exercises 59 through 64, first rewrite the mathematical expression in phrase form and then find the value of the expression.

59. $-(5)$ **60.** $-(-5)$ **61.** $-|-2|$

62. $-|-4|$ **63.** $-(-6)$ **64.** $-(-(-5))$

For Exercises 65 through 76, add or subtract the integers without a calculator.

65. $-3 + (-5)$ **66.** $-4 + (-9)$

67. $16 + (-7)$ **68.** $-8 + 15$

69. $-13 + 6$ **70.** $-20 + 12$

71. $-7 - 9$ **72.** $-6 - 13$

73. $-4 - (-8)$ **74.** $-7 - (-1)$

75. $-12 - (-11)$ **76.** $-17 - (-18)$

For Exercises 77 through 80, use the information given in each exercise to answer the questions.

77. At noon, it was $-23°F$ outside. The temperature drops 3 degrees in an hour. What is the new temperature?

78. At 10:00 A.M., it was $-6°F$, and the temperature rose 20 degrees by 1:00 P.M. that afternoon. What was the temperature at 1:00 P.M.?

79. Assume that depths below the ocean's surface are represented by negative values and heights above the ocean's surface are represented by positive values. Ray and Karin are scuba diving in the Bahamas. They are at 30 feet below the surface of the ocean, and they dive another 20 feet. Now what is their depth?

80. The Badwater Ultramarathon is a 135-mile race that is run every year in California. The runners begin in Death Valley, at an elevation of 282 feet below sea level. They end up at the Mount Whitney Portal, which is 8360 feet above sea level. What is the total change in elevation that the runners experience in the race?

For Exercises 81 through 86, find the distance between the two points on the number line. See Example 11.

81. Find the distance between 7 and -2.

82. Find the distance between 5 and -6.

83. Find the distance between -1 and -9.

84. Find the distance between -8 and -22.

85. Find the distance between -16 and -35.

86. Find the distance between -26 and -5.

For Exercises 87 through 100, multiply or divide as indicated without a calculator.

87. $3(-2)$ **88.** $5(-6)$

89. $(-4)(5)$ **90.** $(-3)(15)$

91. $(-3)(-6)$ **92.** $(-5)(-9)$

93. $(-24) \div (-8)$ **94.** $(-12) \div (-3)$

95. $(30) \div (-5)$ **96.** $(27) \div (-9)$

97. $9 \div 0$ **98.** $-5 \div 0$

99. $0 \div 8$ **100.** $0 \div (-2)$

For Exercises 101 through 108, identify the terms in each expression.

101. $-3 + 5 \cdot 6$

102. $16 \cdot 3 + 9$

103. $-24 \div 3 \cdot 7$

104. $100 \cdot (-2) \div 5$

105. $3 + 22 \div 11 - 16 \div 4$

106. $42 \div 5 - (-6)7 + 12$

107. $92 \cdot (-8) + 26 \div 13 - 1 + 7(-3)$

108. $(-5) \cdot (-6) - 4 \div (-2) + 10 - 4(-2)$

For Exercises 109 through 118, identify the number of terms. Then simplify using the order-of-operations agreement.

109. $16 \div (-8) \cdot 3$ **110.** $(-25) \div 5 \cdot (-4)$

111. $-9 + 3 \cdot 5$ **112.** $6 \cdot (-2) + 18$

113. $9 + 24 \div 3 - 3 \cdot (-2)$

114. $56 \div (-8) + 3 \cdot 5 - (-7)$

115. $-14 \div 2 + 5 \cdot 4 \div 10 - (-1)$

116. $9 \cdot 4 \div (-6) - (-16) + 8 \cdot 2$

117. $100 \div 50 \cdot 3 - 2 \cdot (-7) + 4 \cdot 2 - (-2)$

118. $32 \div (-8) + 3 \cdot 7 - 9 - 48 \div 12 \cdot 5$

R.2 Operations with Fractions

LEARNING OBJECTIVES

▓ Find the prime factorization.

▓ Reduce a fraction to lowest terms.

▓ Find an equivalent fraction.

▓ Graph fractions on a number line.

▓ Add and subtract fractions.

▓ Multiply and divide fractions.

▓ Use the order-of-operations agreement with fractions.

Prime Numbers and Prime Factorization

Prime numbers are natural numbers greater than 1 that are evenly divisible only by themselves and 1. Natural numbers that are not prime are said to be **composite numbers.** Prime numbers are useful in several applications, including cryptography. Cryptography is the mathematics of encoding and decoding information. When you purchase an item over the Internet, your credit card information is most often encoded by using a procedure that uses prime numbers.

▓ What's That Mean?

Factor

A *factor* of a number divides the number evenly. For example, 3 is a factor of 6, since

$$6 \div 3 = 2$$

We say that 2 and 3 are factors of 6.

To *factor* a number means to write it as a product. For example, one factorization of 6 is $2 \cdot 3$, and another is $6 \cdot 1$.

DEFINITION

Prime Numbers Prime numbers are natural numbers greater than 1 that are divisible only by themselves and 1. The prime numbers are the infinite set $\{2, 3, 5, 7, 11, 13, 17, 19, \ldots\}$.

In this course, we will encounter prime numbers when we are "factoring" a number (or expression). We will use the following fact. Any natural number greater than 1 may be factored uniquely by using only prime numbers. This factorization is called the **prime factorization** of the number.

To find the prime factorization of a number means to write the number using only prime numbers as the factors. When we say that the factorization is unique, we mean that there is only one final answer.

Example 1 Writing a number with prime factors only

Write the prime factorization of each number.

a. 12   **b.** 30   **c.** 48

SOLUTION

a. 12   Think of any factorization of 12.

    $= 3 \cdot 4$ 4 is not prime, so we continue to factor.

    $= 3 \cdot 2 \cdot 2$ Factor 4 into prime factors.

Note that in the last step, 4 is not a prime number, and we factor 4 into its prime factors, that is, we write $4 = 2 \cdot 2$.

We could start the problem by rewriting $12 = 6 \cdot 2$. Then factor 6 as $6 = 3 \cdot 2$.

12
$= 6 \cdot 2$ *6 is not prime, so we continue to factor.*
$= 3 \cdot 2 \cdot 2$ *Factor 6 into prime factors.*

Notice that the final answer is the same.

b. 30 *Think of any factorization of 30.*
     $= 5 \cdot 6$ *Keep factoring until only prime factors remain.*
     $= 5 \cdot 2 \cdot 3$
     $= 2 \cdot 3 \cdot 5$

c. Another way to factor is by using a factor tree.

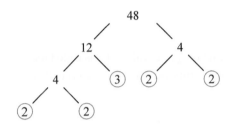

Only the factors at the bottom of each branch of the tree are part of the prime factorization.

$48 = 2 \cdot 2 \cdot 2 \cdot 2 \cdot 3$

PRACTICE PROBLEM FOR EXAMPLE 1

Write the prime factorization of each number.

a. 32   **b.** 10   **c.** 100

We use the idea of prime factorization to find the **greatest common factor (GCF)** for a list of numbers.

> **Steps to Find the Greatest Common Factor**
> **1.** Write the prime factorization of each number.
> **2.** The greatest common factor is the product of the common prime factors.

Example 2   Finding the greatest common factor

Find the GCF for each set of numbers.

a. 8 and 20   **b.** 12 and 18

SOLUTION

a. First, find the prime factorization of both 8 and 20.

$$8 = 2 \cdot 4 = 2 \cdot 2 \cdot 2$$
$$20 = 4 \cdot 5 = 2 \cdot 2 \cdot 5$$

The GCF is the product of the common factors. Therefore, the

$$\text{GCF is } 2 \cdot 2 = 4$$

b. Find the prime factorization of both 12 and 18.

$$12 = 4 \cdot 3 = 2 \cdot 2 \cdot 3$$
$$18 = 2 \cdot 9 = 2 \cdot 3 \cdot 3$$

The GCF is the product of the common factors. Therefore, the

$$\text{GCF is } 2 \cdot 3 = 6$$

PRACTICE PROBLEM FOR EXAMPLE 2
Find the GCF for each set of numbers.

a. 4 and 22   **b.** 64 and 32

Simplifying Fractions and Equivalent Fractions

There are many times when we want to express the idea of a fractional part of something. For example, we may work only half a day and, therefore, receive half of our daily pay. The fraction $\frac{1}{2}$ represents half. In a fraction such as $\frac{1}{2}$, there are special names for the number on the top of the fraction and the number on the bottom.

DEFINITION

Numerator and Denominator   In the fraction $\frac{a}{b}$, the value of a is called the **numerator.** The value of b is called the **denominator.** The – symbol is called the fraction bar.

When we write a fraction such as $\frac{2}{4}$, it represents the shaded part of the circle.

$$\frac{2}{4} =$$

When we write the fraction $\frac{1}{2}$, it represents the shaded part of the circle. Because these two fractions represent the same portion of the circle, they are *equivalent fractions*. This means that $\frac{2}{4} = \frac{1}{2}$. The right side of this equation, $\frac{2}{4} = \frac{1}{2}$, is said to be **reduced to lowest terms.**

$$\frac{1}{2} =$$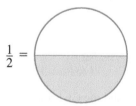

Steps to Reduce a Fraction to Lowest Terms

1. Find the GCF for the numerator and denominator.
2. Factor the numerator and denominator, using the GCF as one of the factors.
3. Divide out the GCF from the numerator and denominator. The remaining fraction will be the reduced or simplified form of the fraction.

Example 3   Reducing fractions to lowest terms

Reduce each fraction to lowest terms.

a. $\frac{9}{18}$ **b.** $\frac{16}{36}$ **c.** $\frac{25}{70}$

What's That Mean?

Fraction

A *fraction* is often thought of as a part of a whole. People will say that something is "only a fraction of the cost," meaning that the object costs only part of what it should. A fraction can also refer to the breaking up of a whole. "The land was partitioned into fractions" means that the whole (the land) was broken into smaller parts (the fractions).

Sometimes a fraction will represent more than 1. In this case, the fraction is called an *improper fraction*.

What's That Mean?

Numerator and Denominator

The *denominator* of a fraction tells us (denominates) how many equal-sized pieces the whole is divided into. For example, in the fraction $\frac{2}{4}$, the whole is divided up into four equal-sized pieces. The *numerator* of a fraction tells us (enumerates) how many of the equal-sized pieces to consider. In the fraction $\frac{2}{4}$, we count 2 of the 4 equal-sized pieces.

SOLUTION

a. The GCF for 9 and 18 is 9. Divide out 9 from the numerator and denominator of the fraction.

$$\frac{9}{18} = \frac{\cancel{9}}{\cancel{9} \cdot 2} = \frac{1}{2}$$

b. The GCF for 16 and 36 is 4. Divide out 4 from the numerator and denominator of the fraction.

$$\frac{16}{36} = \frac{4 \cdot \cancel{4}}{9 \cdot \cancel{4}} = \frac{4}{9}$$

c. The GCF for 25 and 70 is 5. Divide out 5 from the numerator and denominator of the fraction.

$$\frac{25}{70} = \frac{5 \cdot \cancel{5}}{14 \cdot \cancel{5}} = \frac{5}{14}$$

PRACTICE PROBLEM FOR EXAMPLE 3

Reduce each fraction to lowest terms.

a. $\dfrac{3}{27}$ 　　　　 b. $\dfrac{21}{30}$ 　　　　 c. $\dfrac{32}{48}$

To reduce a fraction to lowest terms, divide the numerator and denominator by the GCF. To rewrite a fraction as an equivalent fraction, multiply the numerator and denominator by the same factor. We often use equivalent fractions to make two or more fractions have a common denominator.

> **Steps to Write an Equivalent Fraction**
>
> 1. When given the problem $\dfrac{a}{b} = \dfrac{?}{d}$, find the missing factor c such that $b \cdot c = d$.
>
> 2. Multiply the numerator and denominator by the missing factor c: $\dfrac{a \cdot c}{b \cdot c}$. This will give the equivalent fraction with a denominator of d.

Example 4 Writing an equivalent fraction

Rewrite each fraction as an equivalent fraction with the given denominator.

a. $\dfrac{2}{3} = \dfrac{?}{12}$ 　　　　 b. $\dfrac{5}{7} = \dfrac{?}{42}$

SOLUTION

a. Comparing the denominators of 3 and 12, we have that $3 \cdot 4 = 12$. Therefore, we multiply the numerator and denominator by 4.

$$\frac{2 \cdot 4}{3 \cdot 4} = \frac{8}{12}$$

b. Comparing the denominators of 7 and 42, we have that $7 \cdot 6 = 42$. Therefore, we multiply the numerator and denominator by 6.

$$\frac{5 \cdot 6}{7 \cdot 6} = \frac{30}{42}$$

PRACTICE PROBLEM FOR EXAMPLE 4

Rewrite each fraction as an equivalent fraction with the given denominator.

a. $\dfrac{6}{11} = \dfrac{?}{33}$ 　　　　 b. $\dfrac{3}{8} = \dfrac{?}{56}$

Skill Connection

Scale

In Section R.1, we learned that the scale of a number line is the distance between the consistent and evenly spaced tick marks. Another way to find the scale is to count the spaces between integers. For example, if there are four spaces between 0 and 1, the scale is in fourths (or quarters).

What's That Mean?

Mixed Numbers and Improper Fractions

A *mixed number* has a whole number part and a fraction part, such as $1\frac{2}{3}$.

An *improper fraction* is a fraction in which the numerator is larger than the denominator, such as $\frac{10}{9}$.

Fractions on Number Lines

To graph fractions on a number line, we must first determine the scale of the number line.

CONCEPT INVESTIGATION
What is the scale of that ruler?

The ruler above has two measurement systems on it. The bottom side uses the metric system (in centimeters), and the top side uses the English system (in inches).

1. What is the scale for the metric (bottom) side of the ruler?

2. What is the scale for the English (top) side of the ruler?

3. Draw a point to show where $1\frac{5}{16}$ inches is located on the ruler.

4. Draw a point to show where $11\frac{7}{10}$ cm is located on the ruler.

Once the scale of a number line has been determined, fractions are graphed on number lines much as integers are. For example, the fraction $\frac{1}{2}$ is halfway between 0 and 1, so that is where the point is graphed on a number line.

Example 5 Graphing fractions on a number line

Answer each of the following questions.

a. What is the scale of this number line?

b. Graph the number $\frac{1}{2}$.

c. Graph the number $\frac{-3}{2}$.

d. Graph the number $\frac{3}{4}$.

e. Graph the number $\frac{-7}{2}$.

SOLUTION

a. The scale of the number line is 0.5 or $\frac{1}{2}$. This is because there are two even spaces between each whole number and the next whole number.

b. Graphing the point $\frac{1}{2}$ gives the number line below.

c. Graphing the point $\frac{-3}{2}$ gives the number line below.

d. Graphing the point $\frac{3}{4}$ gives the number line below.

e. Graphing the point $\frac{-7}{2}$ gives the number line below.

PRACTICE PROBLEM FOR EXAMPLE 5

Answer each of the following questions.

a. What is the scale of this number line?

b. Graph the point $\frac{1}{4}$.

c. Graph the point $\frac{-7}{4}$.

d. Graph the point $\frac{5}{4}$.

Addition and Subtraction of Fractions

To add or subtract fractions that have the same denominator, just add or subtract the numerators and then reduce the answer to lowest terms.

> **Steps to Add or Subtract Fractions with Like (Common) Denominators**
> 1. **Add or subtract** the fractions by adding (subtracting) the numerators.
> 2. **Reduce** the final answer to lowest terms (simplest form).

Example 6   Adding and subtracting fractions with like denominators

Add or subtract the fractions as shown. Reduce the answer to simplest form.

a. $\frac{5}{12} + \frac{7}{12}$ **b.** $2\frac{3}{8} - \frac{7}{8}$

SOLUTION

a. $\frac{5}{12} + \frac{7}{12}$ Add the numerators.

$= \frac{12}{12}$ Reduce to simplest form.

$= 1$

b. $2\frac{3}{8} - \frac{7}{8}$ Rewrite the mixed number as an improper fraction.

$= \frac{19}{8} - \frac{7}{8}$ Subtract the numerators.

$= \frac{12}{8}$ Reduce to lowest terms.

$= \frac{3}{2} = 1\frac{1}{2}$

Connecting the Concepts

Where does the negative sign go?

A negative sign in a fraction may go in one of three places:

$$\frac{-3}{2} = -\frac{3}{2} = \frac{3}{-2}$$

The first two forms are most commonly used: $\frac{-3}{2}$ or $-\frac{3}{2}$.

The last form, $\frac{3}{-2}$, is usually rewritten in one of the other two forms. Many people often do not "see" the negative sign in the denominator, and it gets lost.

Be careful to notice that $\frac{-3}{-2}$ is *not* the same as any of the above expressions.

PRACTICE PROBLEM FOR EXAMPLE 6

Add or subtract the fractions as indicated. Reduce the answer to simplest form.

a. $\dfrac{5}{6} + 2\dfrac{4}{6}$ **b.** $\dfrac{7}{15} - \dfrac{2}{15}$

Example 7   How much ribbon is left?

© 2010 oscarcwilliams. Image from BigStockPhoto.com.

Florencia has $1\dfrac{1}{3}$ yards of ribbon for trim, and she uses $\dfrac{2}{3}$ yard. How much ribbon does she have left over?

SOLUTION

First, convert the mixed number $1\dfrac{1}{3}$ to the equivalent improper fraction $\dfrac{4}{3}$. Then subtract the $\dfrac{2}{3}$ yard she used. Thus,

$$1\dfrac{1}{3} - \dfrac{2}{3} = \dfrac{4}{3} - \dfrac{2}{3}$$
$$= \dfrac{2}{3}$$

Florencia has $\dfrac{2}{3}$ yard of ribbon left over.

PRACTICE PROBLEM FOR EXAMPLE 7

Henry buys $\dfrac{1}{4}$ gallon of gas for his lawn mower and $\dfrac{1}{4}$ gallon of gas for his lawn trimmer. How much gas does he buy?

Adding and subtracting fractions with different denominators requires that each fraction be expressed with a common denominator.

> **DEFINITION**
>
> **Least Common Denominator**   The least common denominator is the smallest number that is a multiple of all the denominators. It is also known as the *least common multiple* of the denominators.

To find the least common denominator and then add or subtract fractions using the least common denominator, use the following steps.

> **Steps to Add or Subtract Fractions with Unlike Denominators**
>
> 1. **Factor** each denominator into its prime factorization.
> 2. **The least common denominator** will be the product of all the different factors from step 1. If a factor occurs repeatedly (more than once), include the maximum number of times that factor is repeated.
> 3. **Rewrite** each fraction as an equivalent fraction with the denominator equal to the least common denominator.
> 4. **Add or subtract** the fractions by adding (subtracting) the numerators.
> 5. **Reduce** the final answer to lowest terms.

■ Skill Connection

Convert a mixed number to an improper fraction

To convert a mixed number to an improper fraction, multiply the whole number part with the denominator and add on the numerator. Doing so gives the numerator of the improper fraction. The denominator will be the same.

$$1\dfrac{3}{4} = \dfrac{(4)(1) + 3}{4} = \dfrac{7}{4}$$

■ What's That Mean?

Multiple

A *multiple* of a given number is a value into which the given number divides evenly. Multiples can also be thought of as the numbers that appear on the "times tables" for a given number. The multiples of 3 are 3, 6, 9, 12, 15, 18,....

Example 8   Adding and subtracting with unlike denominators

Add or subtract the fractions. Reduce the answer to simplest form.

a. $\dfrac{5}{3} + \dfrac{5}{6}$ **b.** $\dfrac{11}{12} - \dfrac{3}{8}$

SOLUTION

a. 3 is prime, and $6 = 2 \cdot 3$. The LCD is $2 \cdot 3 = 6$. So

$$\dfrac{5}{3} + \dfrac{5}{6} \qquad\qquad \textit{Find a common denominator.}$$

$$= \dfrac{5 \cdot 2}{3 \cdot 2} + \dfrac{5}{6} \qquad\qquad \textit{Rewrite each fraction over the common denominator.}$$

$$= \dfrac{10}{6} + \dfrac{5}{6} \qquad\qquad \textit{Add the numerators.}$$

$$= \dfrac{15}{6}$$

$$= \dfrac{5}{2} \qquad\qquad \textit{Reduce to lowest terms.}$$

b. The factorization of 12 is $12 = 3 \cdot 2 \cdot 2$, and that of 8 is $8 = 2 \cdot 2 \cdot 2$. The LCD is $3 \cdot 2 \cdot 2 \cdot 2 = 24$. Since 2 is a repeated factor, be sure to include 2 the maximum number of times it occurs (which is 3).

$$\dfrac{11}{12} - \dfrac{3}{8} \qquad\qquad \textit{Find a common denominator.}$$

$$= \dfrac{11 \cdot 2}{12 \cdot 2} - \dfrac{3 \cdot 3}{8 \cdot 3} \qquad\qquad \textit{Rewrite each fraction over the common denominator.}$$

$$= \dfrac{22}{24} - \dfrac{9}{24} \qquad\qquad \textit{Subtract the numerators.}$$

$$= \dfrac{13}{24} \qquad\qquad \textit{Reduce to lowest terms if possible.}$$

Example 9   How much paint is needed?

Lisa buys $1\dfrac{1}{2}$ quarts of blue paint for a home painting project and then buys an additional $2\dfrac{3}{4}$ quarts of yellow paint. How many quarts of paint does she buy?

SOLUTION

To find the total amount of paint Lisa bought, add the two amounts.

$$1\dfrac{1}{2} + 2\dfrac{3}{4} = \qquad\qquad \textit{Change mixed numbers to improper fractions.}$$

$$\dfrac{3}{2} + \dfrac{11}{4} =$$

$$\dfrac{3 \cdot 2}{2 \cdot 2} + \dfrac{11}{4} = \qquad\qquad \textit{Rewrite fractions using common denominators.}$$

$$\dfrac{6}{4} + \dfrac{11}{4} =$$

$$\dfrac{17}{4} = 4\dfrac{1}{4} \text{ quarts} \qquad\qquad \textit{Add the numerators and reduce the final answer.}$$

Lisa bought a total of $4\dfrac{1}{4}$ quarts of paint.

The denominator of a whole number

The denominator of a whole number is 1. Therefore, $9 = \dfrac{9}{1}$.

PRACTICE PROBLEM FOR EXAMPLE 9

Don bought 20 feet of molding to install in his living room. He used $12\dfrac{7}{8}$ feet. How much molding did he have left over?

Multiplication and Division of Fractions

We will now review how to multiply or divide fractions. To do these operations, we need a definition of the **reciprocal** of a number.

> **DEFINITION**
>
> **Reciprocal**   If a is a nonzero number, then $\dfrac{1}{a}$ is the reciprocal of a.

Informally, to find the reciprocal of a number means to invert, or flip, the fraction form of the number, so the reciprocal of $\dfrac{2}{3}$ is $\dfrac{3}{2}$.

Example 10   Finding reciprocals

Find the reciprocal of the given number.

a. Find the reciprocal of -7.

b. Find the reciprocal of $\dfrac{1}{9}$.

c. Find the reciprocal of $\dfrac{-2}{3}$.

SOLUTION

To find a reciprocal, we invert the fraction.

a. To find the reciprocal of -7, recall that $-7 = \dfrac{-7}{1}$. Find the reciprocal, which is $\dfrac{-1}{7}$. Note that the reciprocal has the same sign as the original number.

b. The reciprocal of $\dfrac{1}{9}$ is $\dfrac{9}{1} = 9$.

c. The reciprocal of $\dfrac{-2}{3}$ is $\dfrac{-3}{2}$.

To multiply or divide fractions, we use the following steps.

■ **Connecting the Concepts**

What are the different symbols used?

Multiplication can be written in the following ways:

$$3 \times 5 = 15$$
$$3 \cdot 5 = 15$$
$$(3)(5) = 15$$
$$3(5) = 15$$

In algebra, we do not generally use the form $3 \times 5 = 15$, writing the $\times$ to mean multiplication. Letters will be used for variables, and x is frequently used as a variable. In this book, we will often use the small dot $3 \cdot 5$ or parentheses $3(5)$ to represent multiplication.

Symbols used for division:

The following symbols all represent division.

$$6/3$$
$$3\overline{)6}$$
$$6 \div 3$$
$$\dfrac{6}{3}$$

In this book, we will use the last two forms, $6 \div 3$ or $\dfrac{6}{3}$.

> **Steps to Multiply or Divide Fractions**
>
> **To multiply fractions:**
> 1. Multiply the numerators together.
> 2. Multiply the denominators together.
> 3. Reduce the final answer to lowest terms.
>
> **To divide fractions:**
> 1. Invert (or find the reciprocal) of the second fraction.
> 2. Multiply the two fractions as explained above.
> 3. Reduce the final answer to lowest terms.

Example 11   Multiplying and dividing fractions

Multiply or divide the fractions. Reduce the answer to simplest form.

a. $\dfrac{2}{3} \cdot \dfrac{6}{5}$ **b.** $\dfrac{4}{7} \div \dfrac{8}{35}$

SOLUTION

a. $\dfrac{2}{3} \cdot \dfrac{6}{5}$

$= \dfrac{2 \cdot 6}{3 \cdot 5}$ *Multiply numerators and denominators.*

$= \dfrac{2 \cdot 2 \cdot \cancel{3}}{\cancel{3} \cdot 5}$ *Factor. Divide out like factors.*

$= \dfrac{4}{5}$

b. $\dfrac{4}{7} \div \dfrac{8}{35}$ *Find the reciprocal of the second fraction and multiply.*

$= \dfrac{4}{7} \cdot \dfrac{35}{8}$

$= \dfrac{4 \cdot 35}{7 \cdot 8}$ *Factor the numerator and denominator.*

$= \dfrac{\cancel{4} \cdot \cancel{7} \cdot 5}{\cancel{7} \cdot \cancel{4} \cdot 2}$ *Divide out like factors.*

$= \dfrac{5}{2}$

PRACTICE PROBLEM FOR EXAMPLE 11

Multiply or divide as indicated. Reduce the answer to simplest form.

a. $\dfrac{2}{3} \cdot \dfrac{12}{17}$ **b.** $\dfrac{5}{27} \div \dfrac{20}{9}$

Order of Operations

The order-of-operations agreement works the same when fractions are involved. What is different is that the rules for adding, subtracting, multiplying, and dividing fractions must also be used.

Example 12   Following the order of operations with fractions

Identify the terms. Then simplify using the order-of-operations agreement.

a. $\dfrac{3}{2} + \dfrac{1}{2} \cdot \dfrac{6}{5}$ **b.** $\dfrac{4}{5} \div \dfrac{6}{5} - \dfrac{1}{4} + 2$

SOLUTION

a. There are two terms. $\left(\dfrac{3}{2}\right) + \left(\dfrac{1}{2} \cdot \dfrac{6}{5}\right)$. Start by simplifying inside each term.

$\left(\dfrac{3}{2}\right) + \left(\dfrac{1}{2} \cdot \dfrac{6}{5}\right)$ *Multiply the fractions in the second term.*

$= \dfrac{3}{2} + \dfrac{6}{10}$ *Find the LCD is 10.*

$= \dfrac{3 \cdot 5}{2 \cdot 5} + \dfrac{6}{10}$ *Rewrite each fraction over the LCD.*

$= \dfrac{15}{10} + \dfrac{6}{10}$ *Add the two fractions.*

$= \dfrac{21}{10}$ *This fraction is reduced.*

b. There are three terms. $\left(\dfrac{4}{5} \div \dfrac{6}{5}\right) - \left(\dfrac{1}{4}\right) + (2.)$

$$\left(\dfrac{4}{5} \div \dfrac{6}{5}\right) - \left(\dfrac{1}{4}\right) + (2)$$

Simplify inside each term.

$$= \left(\dfrac{4}{5} \cdot \dfrac{5}{6}\right) - \dfrac{1}{4} + 2$$

To divide fractions, invert the second fraction and multiply.

$$= \dfrac{4}{6} - \dfrac{1}{4} + 2$$

Reduce the first term.

$$= \dfrac{2}{3} - \dfrac{1}{4} + \dfrac{2}{1}$$

To add and subtract fractions, find the LCD is 12.

$$= \dfrac{2 \cdot 4}{3 \cdot 4} - \dfrac{1 \cdot 3}{4 \cdot 3} + \dfrac{2 \cdot 12}{1 \cdot 12}$$

Rewrite each fraction over the LCD.

$$= \dfrac{8}{12} - \dfrac{3}{12} + \dfrac{24}{12}$$

Do additions and subtractions in order from left to right.

$$= \dfrac{5}{12} + \dfrac{24}{12}$$

$$= \dfrac{29}{12}$$

This fraction is reduced to lowest terms.

PRACTICE PROBLEM FOR EXAMPLE 12

Identify the terms. Then simplify, using the order-of-operations agreement.

a. $\dfrac{1}{3} \div \dfrac{5}{6} + \dfrac{5}{2}$ **b.** $7 - \dfrac{2}{5} \cdot \dfrac{15}{4} + \dfrac{1}{3}$

R.2   Exercises

For Exercises 1 through 10, find the prime factorization of the given number.

1. 16   **2.** 15   **3.** 34   **4.** 75

5. 42   **6.** 18   **7.** 64   **8.** 60

9. 70   **10.** 96

For Exercises 11 through 20, find the GCF for each set of numbers.

11. 12 and 15   **12.** 12 and 20

13. 60 and 15   **14.** 20 and 36

15. 9, 27, and 18   **16.** 21, 49, and 14

17. 48, 36, and 60   **18.** 32, 64, and 16

19. 51 and 27   **20.** 72 and 18

For Exercises 21 through 30, reduce each fraction to lowest terms.

21. $\dfrac{6}{15}$ **22.** $\dfrac{20}{25}$ **23.** $\dfrac{8}{42}$ **24.** $\dfrac{9}{33}$

25. $\dfrac{16}{48}$ **26.** $\dfrac{12}{60}$ **27.** $\dfrac{-9}{108}$ **28.** $\dfrac{-22}{121}$

29. $-5\dfrac{6}{21}$ **30.** $-9\dfrac{20}{36}$

For Exercises 31 through 40, rewrite each fraction as an equivalent fraction with the given denominator.

31. $\dfrac{2}{3} = \dfrac{?}{15}$ **32.** $\dfrac{4}{5} = \dfrac{?}{30}$

33. $\dfrac{5}{7} = \dfrac{?}{56}$ **34.** $\dfrac{3}{8} = \dfrac{?}{32}$

35. $\dfrac{-5}{16} = \dfrac{?}{32}$ **36.** $\dfrac{-2}{15} = \dfrac{?}{45}$

37. $4\dfrac{2}{9} = 4\dfrac{?}{45}$ **38.** $6\dfrac{7}{8} = 6\dfrac{?}{40}$

39. $5 = \dfrac{?}{3}$ **40.** $7 = \dfrac{?}{4}$

For Exercises 41 through 50, graph each value on the following number line.

41. $\dfrac{3}{2}$ **42.** $\dfrac{5}{2}$

43. -3

44. -5

45. $\dfrac{-5}{2}$

46. $\dfrac{-7}{2}$

47. $\dfrac{1}{4}$

48. $\dfrac{5}{4}$

49. $\dfrac{-9}{4}$

50. $\dfrac{-7}{4}$

For Exercises 51 through 60, add or subtract the fractions with like denominators without a calculator. Reduce to simplest form.

51. $\dfrac{2}{3} + \dfrac{4}{3}$

52. $\dfrac{3}{8} + \dfrac{5}{8}$

53. $\dfrac{7}{5} - \dfrac{4}{5}$

54. $\dfrac{11}{14} - \dfrac{3}{14}$

55. $\dfrac{11}{15} - \dfrac{2}{15}$

56. $\dfrac{13}{24} + \dfrac{5}{24}$

57. $1\dfrac{1}{4} + 3\dfrac{3}{4}$

58. $4\dfrac{1}{5} + 7\dfrac{2}{5}$

59. $5\dfrac{2}{3} - 2\dfrac{1}{3}$

60. $8\dfrac{1}{6} - 3\dfrac{5}{6}$

For Exercises 61 through 70, add or subtract as indicated without a calculator. Reduce to simplest form.

61. $\dfrac{2}{3} + \dfrac{5}{6}$

62. $\dfrac{1}{4} + \dfrac{3}{8}$

63. $\dfrac{-4}{8} + \dfrac{1}{3}$

64. $\dfrac{-5}{6} + \dfrac{1}{4}$

65. $\dfrac{-2}{3} - \dfrac{3}{4}$

66. $\dfrac{-1}{5} - \dfrac{7}{10}$

67. $1\dfrac{1}{6} + 3\dfrac{2}{3}$

68. $2\dfrac{1}{3} + 1\dfrac{1}{2}$

69. $-2\dfrac{1}{4} - 3\dfrac{1}{2}$

70. $-1\dfrac{1}{5} - 3\dfrac{1}{2}$

For Exercises 71 through 76, add or subtract as indicated.

71. Sandy needs $2\dfrac{1}{4}$ gallons of ivory paint and $1\dfrac{1}{4}$ gallons of blue paint on a remodeling project. How many gallons of paint in total does she need?

72. James needs $\dfrac{2}{3}$ cup of milk for one recipe and an additional $1\dfrac{1}{2}$ cups of milk for another recipe. How much milk does James need in all?

73. Dominique uses $\dfrac{1}{4}$ teaspoon of salt in one dish and $\dfrac{1}{2}$ teaspoon of salt in another dish. How much salt does Dominique use in all?

74. A carpenter needs $7\dfrac{3}{4}$ feet of molding for each side of a doorway and $3\dfrac{1}{4}$ feet for the top of the doorway. How many feet of molding does he need in all?

75. Ted needs $10\dfrac{3}{8}$ feet of lumber for a project, and he has 20 feet of lumber. How much will he have left over after his project?

76. Hanna needs $2\dfrac{1}{2}$ pounds of onions for a stew and $\dfrac{3}{4}$ pound of onions for soup. If she bought a 5-pound bag of onions, how many pounds will she have left over?

For Exercises 77 through 86, find the reciprocal.

77. -3

78. -5

79. $\dfrac{5}{3}$

80. $\dfrac{2}{7}$

81. $\dfrac{1}{9}$

82. $\dfrac{1}{12}$

83. 8

84. -2

85. 0

86. 1

For Exercises 87 through 98, multiply or divide as indicated. Reduce to simplest form.

87. $\dfrac{1}{4} \cdot 8$

88. $\dfrac{2}{3} \cdot 6$

89. $\dfrac{-3}{4} \cdot \dfrac{-5}{9}$

90. $\dfrac{-1}{6} \cdot \dfrac{-12}{5}$

91. $\dfrac{2}{3} \div \dfrac{14}{27}$

92. $\dfrac{3}{4} \div \dfrac{9}{16}$

93. $-100 \div (-20)$

94. $(-36) \div (-12)$

95. $\dfrac{4}{15} \div \dfrac{-8}{45}$

96. $\dfrac{-2}{5} \div \dfrac{4}{9}$

97. $\dfrac{-2}{9} \div (-12)$

98. $\dfrac{-3}{5} \div (15)$

For Exercises 99 through 108, identify the number of terms. Then simplify using the order-of-operations agreement.

99. $24 \div (-3) \cdot 2 + \dfrac{3}{2}$

100. $32 \cdot 2 \div (-8) + \dfrac{1}{3}$

101. $3 - \dfrac{1}{3} \div \dfrac{5}{6}$

102. $\dfrac{2}{5} \div \dfrac{7}{10} - 4$

103. $\dfrac{3}{8} \cdot \dfrac{4}{5} + \dfrac{1}{2} - 1$

104. $\dfrac{4}{15} \cdot \dfrac{3}{2} - \dfrac{1}{10} + 6$

105. $\dfrac{5}{8} \cdot \dfrac{4}{15} + \dfrac{1}{2} \cdot \dfrac{3}{2} + 2$

106. $\dfrac{3}{4} \cdot \dfrac{5}{9} + \dfrac{2}{3} \cdot \dfrac{7}{8} - 3$

107. $\dfrac{4}{9} \div \dfrac{5}{18} \cdot \dfrac{3}{2}$

108. $\dfrac{4}{7} \div \dfrac{3}{14} \cdot \dfrac{9}{16}$

R.3 Operations with Decimals and Percents

LEARNING OBJECTIVES

- Find the place value.
- Show the relationship between fractions and decimals.
- Graph decimals on a number line.
- Add and subtract decimals.
- Multiply and divide decimals.
- Use the order-of-operations agreement with decimals.
- Round decimals to a given place value.
- Interpret a percent.
- Convert between percents, decimals, and fractions.
- Solve problems involving percents.

Place Value

The system that we use to write numbers is called the Hindu-Arabic number system. It was developed in the arc of countries starting with India to the Middle East to Egypt to North Africa. This number system is base 10. It is an efficient way to write numbers, because numbers are written using **place value.** This means that each place held by a number represents a multiple of ten. For example, the number 842 can be written as 8 hundreds, 4 tens, and 2 ones. The number 8 is in the hundreds place.

Many numbers involve decimals. For example, the average temperature of humans is 98.6°F. When a number is written with decimals, such as 345.1267, the part to the right of the decimal point also has place value. Some common place values are represented in the table at the right. Notice when the ending contains a "ths," it represents a place value to the right of the decimal point.

3	4	5	.	1	2	6	7
Hundreds place	Tens place	Ones place	Decimal point	Tenths place	Hundredths place	Thousandths place	Ten-thousandths place

Example 1 Identifying place value

Identify the digit in each number that has the given place value.

a. The hundredths place: 6.3257

b. The thousandths place: 1.9108

SOLUTION

a. The digit in the hundredths place is 2.   6.3257

b. The digit in the thousandths place is 0.   1.9108

PRACTICE PROBLEM FOR EXAMPLE 1

Identify the digit in each number that has the given place value.

a. The tenths place: 897.351

b. The ten-thousandths place: 0.0025

Relationships Between Fractions and Decimals

Finite and infinite repeating decimals may be written as fractions. To write a finite decimal as a fraction, identify the place value of the last nonzero digit. For example, the decimal 0.25 is read as "25 hundredths." To write 0.25 as a fraction, write it as $0.25 = \frac{25}{100} = \frac{1}{4}$. Recall that fractions should always be written in simplest form.

Example 2 Writing a decimal in fraction form

Write each decimal in fraction form. Reduce all fractions to simplest form.

a. 1.6 **b.** 0.042 **c.** 2.67

SOLUTION

a. The number 1.6 is written in words as one and six tenths. Writing 1.6 in fraction form gives

$$1.6 = 1\frac{6}{10} \qquad \text{Write the decimal part in fraction form.}$$

$$= 1\frac{3}{5} \qquad \text{Reduce to lowest terms.}$$

b. The number 0.042 is written in words as forty-two thousandths. Writing 0.042 in fraction form gives

$$0.042 = \frac{42}{1000} \qquad \text{Write the decimal part in fraction form.}$$

$$= \frac{42 \div 2}{1000 \div 2} \qquad \text{Reduce to lowest terms.}$$

$$= \frac{21}{500}$$

c. The number 2.67 is written in words as two and sixty-seven hundredths. Writing 2.67 in fraction form gives

$$2.67 = 2\frac{67}{100} \qquad \text{Write the decimal part in fraction form.}$$

$$= 2\frac{67}{100} \qquad \text{This fraction is reduced.}$$

PRACTICE PROBLEM FOR EXAMPLE 2

Write each decimal in fraction form. Reduce all fractions to simplest form.

a. 2.46 **b.** 1.025 **c.** 10.9

To write a fraction in decimal form, use long division. Remember that the fraction bar in $\frac{a}{b}$ indicates division. So $\frac{a}{b} = a \div b$. In a long division problem, all of the parts making up the problem have special names.

$$\frac{\text{dividend}}{\text{divisor}} = \text{quotient} + \frac{\text{remainder}}{\text{divisor}}$$

Connecting the Concepts

What kind of decimal?

Decimals are classified as *finite* or *infinite*. A finite decimal has a number of nonzero decimal digits that come to an end. An infinite decimal has an unlimited number of nonzero decimal digits. Infinite decimals may be either repeating or nonrepeating. An example of a repeating infinite decimal is 0.333.... Here, the three dots indicate the 3's continue on forever. In an infinite nonrepeating decimal, the decimal digits never settle into a pattern of repetition.

When setting up a long division problem, recall that

$$\frac{\text{dividend}}{\text{divisor}} = \text{dividend} \div \text{divisor}$$

$$= \text{divisor} \overline{)\text{dividend}}^{\text{quotient}}$$

Example 3 Writing a fraction as a decimal

Write each fraction in decimal form.

a. $\dfrac{4}{5}$ b. $\dfrac{3}{8}$ c. $\dfrac{1}{3}$

SOLUTION

a. To convert $\dfrac{4}{5}$ to decimal form, use long division. $\dfrac{4}{5}$ means $5\overline{)4}$. Since 4 is less than 5, add a decimal point and continue dividing.

$$
\begin{array}{r}
0.8 \\
5\overline{)4.0} \\
-40 \\
\hline
0
\end{array}
$$

Therefore, $\dfrac{4}{5} = 0.8$.

b. To convert $\dfrac{3}{8}$ to decimal form, use long division. $\dfrac{3}{8}$ means $8\overline{)3}$. Add a decimal point and continue dividing.

$$
\begin{array}{r}
0.375 \\
8\overline{)3.000} \\
-24 \\
\hline
60 \\
-56 \\
\hline
40 \\
-40 \\
\hline
0
\end{array}
$$

Therefore, $\dfrac{3}{8} = 0.375$.

c. To convert $\dfrac{1}{3}$ to decimal form, use long division. $\dfrac{1}{3}$ means $3\overline{)1}$.

$$
\begin{array}{r}
0.333\ldots \\
3\overline{)1.000} \\
-9 \\
\hline
10 \\
-9 \\
\hline
10 \\
-9 \\
\hline
10
\end{array}
$$

To show the decimal expansion continues in this repeating pattern, write $0.333\ldots = 0.\overline{3}$.

Therefore, $\dfrac{1}{3} = 0.\overline{3}$.

Connecting the Concepts

How is a repeating, infinite decimal written?

To show that a decimal repeats infinitely, we put a bar over the repeating part. Therefore, $0.333\ldots = 0.\overline{3}$, where the bar over the 3 indicates the 3s continue on forever. The infinite repeating decimal $0.125125125\ldots$ would be written as $0.\overline{125}$.

PRACTICE PROBLEM FOR EXAMPLE 3

Write each fraction in decimal form.

a. $\dfrac{2}{5}$ b. $\dfrac{3}{4}$ c. $\dfrac{1}{9}$

Graphing Decimals on a Number Line

To graph decimals on a number line, determine the scale of the number line. Then graph the number, using a dot to mark the location on the number line.

Example 4   Graphing the decimals on a number line

Answer each of the following questions.

a. What is the scale of this number line?

b. Graph the number 1.6.

c. Graph the number −0.4.

d. Graph the number 0.7.

e. Graph the number −1.5.

SOLUTION

a. The scale on this number line is 0.2 because that is how far the tick marks are apart.

b.

c.

d. 0.7 lies halfway between 0.6 and 0.8.

e. −1.5 lies halfway between −1.4 and −1.6.

PRACTICE PROBLEM FOR EXAMPLE 4

Answer each of the following questions.

a. What is the scale of this number line?

b. Graph the number 1.4.

c. Graph the number −2.25.

d. Graph the number −0.4.

e. Graph the number 1.9.

Rounding Decimals

Decimals are sometimes rounded to a given place value. Some people when grocery shopping will keep a running tally in their head to estimate how much money they are spending. Instead of remembering that an item costs $2.99, many people will round that amount to $3.00.

To round a decimal, use the following steps.

Steps to Round a Decimal to a Given Place Value

1. Underline the given place value in the number.
2. Look at the digit directly to the right of the underlined place.
   a. If that digit is 0, 1, 2, 3, or 4, then delete all digits to the right of the underlined place. This is often called *rounding down.*
   b. If that digit is 5, 6, 7, 8, or 9, then add 1 to the underlined place and delete all the digits to the right. This is often called *rounding up.*

Example 5 Rounding decimals

Round each decimal to the given place value.

a. 1.69 to the tenths place

b. 11.05 to the ones place

c. 0.3691 to the thousandths place

d. 16.895 to the hundredths place

SOLUTION

a. 1.6̲9   Underline the tenths place. The next digit to the right is 9.

   1.7   Round up. Add 1 to 6.

b. 1̲1.05   Underline the ones place. The next digit to the right is 0.

   11   Round down.

c. 0.369̲1   Underline the thousandths place. The next digit to the right is 1.

   0.369   Round down.

d. 16.89̲5   Underline the hundredths place. The next digit to the right is 5.

   16.90   Round up.

Addition and Subtraction of Decimals

To add or subtract decimals, line the decimals up vertically by matching place values. Starting with the rightmost digit, add or subtract vertically. Carry or borrow as needed.

Example 6 Adding and subtracting decimals

a. Add the decimals: $1.367 + 4.241$.

b. Subtract the decimals: $8.52 - 6.04$.

c. Esme buys 1 gallon of milk at \$4.99 and a dozen eggs for \$2.29. How much money did she spend?

SOLUTION

a. Write the problem vertically, carefully matching place values, and add.

$$\begin{array}{r} \overset{1}{1}.367 \\ +4.241 \\ \hline 5.608 \end{array}$$

b. Write the problem vertically, carefully matching place values, and subtract.

$$\begin{array}{r} 8.\overset{4}{\cancel{5}}\overset{1}{2} \\ -6.04 \\ \hline 2.48 \end{array}$$

c. Add the amounts Esme spent on milk and eggs to get the total.

$$\begin{array}{r} \overset{1}{4}.\overset{1}{9}9 \\ +2.29 \\ \hline 7.28 \end{array}$$

Esme spent $7.28 on milk and eggs.

PRACTICE PROBLEM FOR EXAMPLE 6

a. Add the decimals: $4.891 + 6.099$.

b. Subtract the decimals: $9.73 - 2.57$.

c. Laurence bought a bottle of water for $1.69 and a box of cheese-flavored crackers for $0.99. He paid with a $10.00 bill. How much change did he receive?

Multiplication and Division of Decimals

When two decimals are multiplied, ignore the decimal points and multiply as if they were two integers. After that step, count the number of digits after the decimal point in both factors (numbers). Starting at the far right of the result, move the decimal point left the same number of places as the number of digits in both decimals.

Example 7 Multiplying decimals

a. Multiply $2.35(1.2)$.

b. If you downloaded two albums for $8.99 apiece, how much money did you spend?

SOLUTION

a.
$$\begin{array}{r} \overset{1}{2.3}5 \\ \times 1.2 \\ \hline \overset{1}{4}70 \\ +235 \\ \hline 2820 \end{array}$$

Ignore the decimal places.
Multiply as if two integers.

The numbers **2.35** and **1.2** have a total of *three* digits after the decimal point. Move the decimal point from the right over three digits to get the solution.

2.820

b. You spent $2(8.99)$, or

$$\begin{array}{r} 8.99 \\ \times 2 \\ \hline 1798 \end{array}$$

Ignore the decimal places.
Multiply as if two integers.

The numbers 8.99 and 2 have a total of two digits after the decimal point. Move the decimal point from the right over two digits to get the solution.

17.98

You spent a total of $17.98 on the two albums.

PRACTICE PROBLEM FOR EXAMPLE 7

a. Multiply $4.21 \cdot 2.3$.

b. If you purchased three shirts for $7.99 each, how much money did you spend?

To divide decimals, use long division. Before starting long division, move the decimal point in the divisor (on the outside) all the way over to the right. Move the decimal point in the dividend (inside) the same number of places to the right. Then begin the long division process.

Example 8 Using long division of decimals

a. Divide: $4.25 \div 2.5$. Round to two decimal places if necessary.

b. Divide: $23.56 \div 2.4$. Round to two decimal places if necessary.

SOLUTION

a. $4.25 \div 2.5$ Write in long division form.

$$2.5)\overline{4.25}$$ Move the decimal point on 2.5 and 4.25 one place to the right.

$$
\begin{array}{r}
1.7 \\
25)\overline{42.5} \\
-25 \\
\hline
175 \\
-175 \\
\hline
0
\end{array}
$$
          Perform long division.

          The remainder is 0.

Since the remainder was 0, the numbers divided exactly. There is no need to round the answer. So $4.25 \div 2.5 = 1.7$.

b. $23.56 \div 2.4$ Write in long division form.

$$2.4)\overline{23.56}$$ Move the decimal point on 2.4 and 23.56 one place to the right.

$$
\begin{array}{r}
9.8166\ldots \\
24)\overline{235.600} \\
-216 \\
\hline
196 \\
-192 \\
\hline
40 \\
-24 \\
\hline
160 \\
-144 \\
\hline
160 \\
-144 \\
\hline
16
\end{array}
$$
          Perform long division.

          The pattern will continue to repeat.

The quotient is $9.8166\ldots$. Rounding to two decimal places gives the solution 9.82.

PRACTICE PROBLEM FOR EXAMPLE 8

a. Divide $6.24 \div 2.6$. Round to two decimal places if necessary.

b. Divide $30.65 \div 1.6$. Round to two decimal places if necessary.

Order of Operations with Decimals

The order-of-operations agreement is used the same way when decimals are involved. First, identify the terms. Then simplify inside each term. Finally, add and subtract in order, working from left to right.

Example 9   Applying the order-of-operations agreement to decimals

Identify the terms. Then simplify using the order-of-operations agreement.

a. $1.5 + 2.6 \cdot 8.4$ **b.** $7 \div 3.5 - 0.67 + 12$

SOLUTION

a. To simplify $1.5 + 2.6 \cdot 8.4$, first identify the terms. This expression has two terms.

$$\boxed{1.5} + \boxed{2.6 \cdot 8.4}$$

Then simplify the inside of each term and add.

$$\boxed{1.5} + \boxed{2.6 \cdot 8.4} \qquad \text{Do the multiplication in the second term.}$$
$$= 1.5 + 21.84 \qquad \text{Add the two terms.}$$
$$= 23.34$$

b. Identify the terms. This expression has three terms.

$$\boxed{7 \div 3.5} - \boxed{0.67} + \boxed{12}$$

Simplify the inside of each term and then add and subtract in order from left to right.

$$\boxed{7 \div 3.5} - \boxed{0.67} + \boxed{12} \qquad \text{Do the division in the first term.}$$
$$= 2 - 0.67 + 12 \qquad \text{Do the subtraction.}$$
$$= 1.33 + 12 \qquad \text{Do the addition.}$$
$$= 13.33$$

PRACTICE PROBLEM FOR EXAMPLE 9

Identify the terms. Then simplify using the order-of-operations agreement.

a. $3.2 + 4.1 \cdot 2.5$ **b.** $6 \div 1.5 - 3.1 + 4$

What Is a Percent?

Percent means "a part of hundred" or "per 100." *Per* in mathematics means to divide. So 1% means one part of 100, or $1\% = \dfrac{1}{100}$. The symbol % is the *percent sign*.

DEFINITION

Percent   Percent means "per 100."

$$1\% = \frac{1}{100}$$

Converting Between Percents, Decimals, and Fractions

In the definition for percent, we can see a relationship between percents and fractions. Because $1\% = \dfrac{1}{100}$, we have that $p\% = \dfrac{p}{100}$. So $19\% = \dfrac{19}{100}$. Likewise, $25\% = \dfrac{25}{100} = \dfrac{1}{4}$. Always reduce fractions to lowest terms.

Example 10 Converting between percents and fractions

Convert each quantity as indicated. Write all fractions in lowest terms.

a. Write as a fraction: 40%

b. Write as a percent: $\dfrac{9}{100}$

c. Write as a percent: $\dfrac{3}{20}$

SOLUTION

a.
$$40\% = \frac{40}{100} \qquad \text{Rewrite as a fraction.}$$
$$= \frac{40 \div 20}{100 \div 20} \qquad \text{Reduce fractions to lowest terms.}$$
$$= \frac{2}{5}$$

b. $\dfrac{9}{100} = 9\%$

c. This fraction is not written with a denominator of 100, so we cannot immediately write it as a percent. First, rewrite the fraction with a denominator of 100. Then write it as a percent.

$$\frac{3}{20} = \frac{?}{100} \qquad \text{Rewrite with a denominator of 100.}$$
$$\frac{3 \cdot 5}{20 \cdot 5} = \frac{15}{100}$$
$$\frac{3}{20} = 15\% \qquad \text{Write as a percent.}$$

PRACTICE PROBLEM FOR EXAMPLE 10

Convert each quantity as indicated. Write all fractions in lowest terms.

a. Write as a fraction: 55%

b. Write as a percent: $\dfrac{84}{100}$

c. Write as a percent: $\dfrac{1}{5}$

Steps to Convert Between Percents and Decimals

1. **To convert a percent to a decimal:** Move the decimal point two places to the left, and remove the % sign. This is the same as multiplying by $1\% = \dfrac{1}{100} = 0.01$ or dividing by 100.

2. **To convert a decimal to a percent:** Move the decimal point two places to the right, and add the % sign. This is the same as multiplying by 100.

Example 11 Converting between percents and decimals

Convert each quantity as indicated.

a. Write as a decimal: 18%

b. Write as a decimal: 0.5%

c. Write as a percent: 0.125

d. Write as a percent: 4.01

SOLUTION

a. Move the decimal point two places to the left. 18% = 0.18

b. Move the decimal point two places to the left. 0.5% = 0.005

a. Move the decimal point two places to the right, and add the percent sign.
$0.125 = 12.5\%$

b. Move the decimal point two places to the right, and add the percent sign.
$4.01 = 401\%$

PRACTICE PROBLEM FOR EXAMPLE 11

a. Write as a decimal: 8.25%

b. Write as a decimal: 0.36%

c. Write as a percent: 0.22

d. Write as a percent: 110

Example 12   Converting between percents, decimals, and fractions

Complete the table by filling in the missing values.

Percent	Decimal	Fraction
	0.35	

SOLUTION

To convert the decimal 0.35 to a percent, move the decimal point two places to the right and add the percent sign. $0.35 = 35\%$.

To convert 0.35 to a fraction, first figure out the place value of the last digit, 5. The place value of the last digit, 5, is the hundredths place. Rewrite 0.35 as a fraction with a denominator of 100.

$$0.35 = \frac{35}{100}$$ *Write the decimal part in fraction form.*

$$= \frac{35 \div 5}{100 \div 5}$$ *Reduce to lowest terms.*

$$= \frac{7}{20}$$

So the completed table is as follows:

Percent	Decimal	Fraction
35%	0.35	$\frac{7}{20}$

> **What's That Mean?**
>
> **Of**
>
> In a mathematics problem, what the word *of* means depends on what comes before it. When a percent or fraction comes before the word *of* it translates as multiplication.
>
> $$20\% \text{ of } 60 = 20\%(60)$$
>
> $$\frac{1}{3} \text{ of } 90 = \frac{1}{3}(90)$$
>
> If the word *of* follows another operation it means that same operation.
>
> The sum of ... = addition.
> The quotient of ... = division.
> The product of ... = multiplication.

Problem Solving with Percents

Many quantities in life are listed as percents, such as interest rates (APR of 5.25%) and discounts at sales (take 20 percent off). When calculating with percents in a problem, first convert the percents into decimals.

Example 13   Calculating with percents

a. Find 25% of 42.

b. 55% of the students in a math class are female. There are 40 students in the class. How many are female?

c. You purchase an iPad for $499. Find the tax you paid if the sales tax rate in your area is 8%.

SOLUTION

a. First, convert 25% to its decimal form. 25% = 0.25. A percent of means to multiply, so using the decimal form, calculate the answer.

$$25\% \cdot 42 = 0.25(42)$$
$$= 10.5$$

Therefore, 25% of 42 is 10.5.

b. This problem asks us to find 55% of 40.

$$55\% \cdot 40 = 0.55(40)$$
$$= 22$$

There are 22 female students in the class.

c. To find the tax, we multiply the price by the tax rate.

$$8\% \cdot 499 = 0.08(499)$$
$$= 39.92$$

The sales tax paid on the iPad was $39.92.

PRACTICE PROBLEM FOR EXAMPLE 13

a. Find 8% of 95.

b. 30% of the students in a woodworking class are female. There are 50 students in the class. How many are female?

c. You purchase a 55-inch LED flat panel HDTV for $2500. Find the tax paid if the sales tax rate in your area is 9%.

© Banana Stock/Photo Library

R.3 Exercises

For Exercises 1 through 10, identify the digit in each number that has the given place value.

1. The tenths place: 0.4732

2. The tenths place: 1.0943

3. The ten-thousandths place: 6.9154

4. The ten-thousandths place: 4.61507

5. The ones place: 7.25

6. The ones place: 8.91

7. The hundredths place: 6.2801

8. The hundredths place: 0.00541

9. The thousandths place: 8.9504

10. The thousandths place: 3.2974

For Exercises 11 through 20, write each decimal as a fraction.

11. 2.9   12. 3.7   13. 0.84   14. 0.42

15. 7.71   16. 5.23   17. 1.008   18. 2.014

19. 1.33   20. 2.67

For Exercises 21 through 30, write each fraction as a decimal. Write any repeating decimals with a bar over the repeating part.

21. $\dfrac{3}{5}$ 22. $\dfrac{1}{5}$ 23. $1\dfrac{1}{4}$ 24. $3\dfrac{3}{4}$ 25. $\dfrac{5}{12}$

26. $\dfrac{7}{12}$ 27. $3\dfrac{1}{6}$ 28. $4\dfrac{2}{3}$ 29. $\dfrac{7}{8}$ 30. $\dfrac{1}{8}$

For Exercises 31 through 40, graph each decimal on a number line like that below.

31. 0.2   32. 0.8   33. 1.7   34. 1.4   35. −0.9

36. −1.3   37. 1.3   38. 1.5   39. −1.6   40. −2.0

For Exercises 41 through 54, round each decimal to the given place value.

41. 8.25 to the tenths place

42. 6.27 to the tenths place

43. 9.207 to the hundredths place

44. 13.029 to the hundredths place

45. 205.69 to the tens place

46. 127.995 to the tens place

47. 0.12999 to the tenths place

48. 5.34997 to the tenths place

49. 0.99 to the ones place

50. 4.62 to the ones place

51. 4.32601 to the thousandths place

52. 9.99219 to the thousandths place

53. 6.51757 to the ten-thousandths place

54. 4.593217 to the ten-thousandths place

For Exercises 55 through 64, add or subtract the decimals as indicated without a calculator.

55. $2.75 + 3.01$

56. $6.14 + 9.73$

57. $8.68 - 1.39$

58. $10.701 - 3.334$

59. $0.2275 + 96.371$

60. $9.017 + 16.9027$

61. $9 - 3.67$

62. $16 - 2.994$

63. $9.75 - 3.001$

64. $16.2 - 5.447$

For Exercises 65 through 68, use the information in each exercise to answer the questions.

65. Michelle purchased textbooks for her two online courses. One book cost $149.95, and the other book cost $124.95. How much did the two books cost Michelle?

66. Jorge purchased textbooks for his math and reading courses. One book cost $120.95, and the other book cost $95.99. How much did the two books cost Jorge?

67. Rani purchased a soda for $4.00 and popcorn for $6.50. She paid with a $20 bill. How much change did she receive?

68. Ransi purchased a binder for $5.50 and a mechanical pencil for $2.50. He paid with a $20 bill. How much change did he receive?

For Exercises 69 through 74, multiply without a calculator.

69. $1.8 \cdot 3.01$

70. $2.01 \cdot 8.3$

71. $(3.5)(6.07)$

72. $(5.7)(1.24)$

73. $7(0.016)$

74. $(5.047)(8)$

For Exercises 75 through 78, use the information given in each exercise to answer the questions.

75. If you downloaded three songs for $0.99 apiece, how much money did you spend?

76. If you downloaded six songs for $0.99 apiece, how much money did you spend?

77. Sam bought three candy bars on sale for $0.65 apiece. How much money did she spend?

78. Brogan bought two blouses for $23.75 apiece. How much did she spend?

For Exercises 79 through 86, divide the decimals without a calculator.

79. $8.2 \div 0.01$

80. $6.95 \div 0.01$

81. $0.12 \div 2$

82. $0.81 \div 9$

83. $19.32 \div 2.3$

84. $57.34 \div 6.1$

85. $0.01073 \div 0.29$

86. $0.09144 \div 0.36$

For Exercises 87 through 96, identify the number of terms. Then use the order-of-operations agreement to simplify each expression.

87. $4.2 + 1.5 \cdot 6.1$

88. $9.7 \cdot 2.3 + 7.1$

89. $4(8.95) - 16.23$

90. $7(1.02) - 21.54$

91. $4.6 + 8 \div 2.5 - 22.1$

92. $-3.7 + 10 \div 1.6 + 8.1$

93. $-12.3 + 5 \div 0.1 + 9.72$

94. $18.7 + 28 \div 0.1 - 14.25$

95. $24 \div 1.5 \cdot 8.4$

96. $20 \div 0.25 \cdot 0.61$

For Exercises 97 through 100, use the information given in each exercise to answer the questions.

97. Luc purchased one soda for $1.25, a bag of crackers for $0.99, and two packages of gum that cost $0.59 each.

  a. Write an expression that gives the *total* cost of Luc's purchase. Do not simplify.
  b. What two operations (addition, subtraction, multiplication, or division) are there in the expression?
  c. How many terms are in the expression?
  d. Which operation should be done first? Which operation should be done second?
  e. Find the total amount of Luc's purchase.

98. At the movies, Van purchased two sodas for $4.00 each, a bag of candy for $5.25, and two small buttered popcorns that cost $5.00 each.

  a. Write an expression that gives the *total* cost of Van's purchase. Do not simplify.
  b. What two operations (addition, subtraction, multiplication, or division) are there in the expression?
  c. How many terms are in the expression?
  d. Which operation should be done first? Which should be done second?
  e. Find the total amount of Van's purchase.

99. At the local taco shop, Kym purchased two sodas for $1.59 each and two taco meal deals for $3.99 each.

   a. Write an expression that gives the *total* cost of Kym's purchase. Do not simplify.

   b. What two operations (addition, subtraction, multiplication, or division) are there in the expression?

   c. How many terms are in the expression?

   d. Which operation should be done first? Which operation should be done second?

   e. Find the total amount of Kym's purchase.

100. Kwan purchased 5 gallons of gas for $3.95 a gallon and two bottles of water for $2.75 each.

   a. Write an expression that gives the *total* cost of Kwan's purchase. Do not simplify.

   b. What two operations (addition, subtraction, multiplication, or division) do you see in your expression?

   c. How many terms are in your expression?

   d. Which operation should be done first? Which operation should be done second?

   e. Find the total amount of Kwan's purchase.

For Exercises 101 through 108, convert each value as indicated.

101. Convert 34% to a decimal.

102. Convert 5.1% to a decimal.

103. Convert $\frac{47}{100}$ to a percent.

104. Convert $\frac{9}{100}$ to a percent.

105. Convert 0.017 to a percent.

106. Convert 3.002 to a percent.

107. Convert $\frac{9}{25}$ to a percent.

108. Convert $\frac{3}{4}$ to a percent.

For Exercises 109 through 114, complete each table by filling in the missing values.

109.

Percent	Decimal	Fraction
	0.16	

110.

Percent	Decimal	Fraction
		$\frac{3}{5}$

111.

Percent	Decimal	Fraction
28.5%		

112.

Percent	Decimal	Fraction
		$\frac{7}{20}$

113.

Percent	Decimal	Fraction
0.12%		

114.

Percent	Decimal	Fraction
	0.067	

For Exercises 115 through 130, answer each problem as indicated.

115. Find 16% of 64.

116. Find 5% of 2.

117. Find 0.5% of 112.

118. Find 0.75% of 9.

119. 40% of the dogs in puppy class at an obedience school are Labrador retrievers. There are 25 dogs in the class. How many are Labrador retrievers?

120. 16% of the dogs in puppy class in an obedience school are American Eskimos. There are 25 dogs in the class. How many are American Eskimos?

121. 20% of the diners in a restaurant have a coupon. There are 30 diners in the restaurant. How many have a coupon?

122. 25% of the shoppers in a grocery store have coupons. There are 68 shoppers in the store. How many have coupons?

123. One serving of yellow split peas contains 48% of the recommended daily amount of 25 grams of dietary fiber. How many grams of dietary fiber are in one serving of yellow split peas?

124. One serving of lentils contains 6% of the recommended daily amount of 300 grams of total carbohydrates. How many grams of total carbohydrates are in one serving of lentils?

125. One serving of pasta sauce contains 25% of the recommended daily amount of 2400 milligrams of sodium. How many milligrams of sodium are in one serving of pasta sauce?

126. One serving of rice pilaf contains 27% of the recommended daily amount of 2400 milligrams of sodium. How many milligrams of sodium are in one serving of rice pilaf?

127. Brianna buys a purse for $25. Find the tax paid if the sales tax rate in her city is 6%.

128. Taria buys a cookware set for $270. Find the tax paid if the sales tax rate in her city is 7%.

129. Yerica buys a new set of tires for her car for $384. Find the sales tax if the tax rate in her city is 9.5%.

130. Jerrod needs $245 worth of supplies to fix up his bathroom at home. Find the tax Jerrod will pay if the sales tax rate in his city is 8.5%.

R.4 The Real Number System

LEARNING OBJECTIVES

- Define and categorize rational numbers.
- Define and categorize irrational numbers.
- Distinguish between rational and irrational numbers.
- Describe the sets that make up the real number system.
- Distinguish between exact and approximate answers.

Rational Numbers

In Section R.1, we studied natural numbers, whole numbers, and the integers. In Section R.2, we studied fractions. Fractions do not fit into the sets of numbers studied in Section R.1. After the set of integers, the number system expanded to include fractions. Some decimals may be represented as fractions.

Notice that all finite decimals may be expressed as fractions. For example, $0.25 = \frac{25}{100} = \frac{1}{4}$. Remember, to write a decimal as a fraction means to read the place value of the rightmost decimal digit and use this value for the denominator of the fraction. Infinite repeating decimals can also be represented as fractions. So $0.333333... = 0.\overline{3} = \frac{1}{3}$ is also a fraction.

When the set of integers is expanded to contain all fractions, the resulting set is called the **rational numbers.** Notice that the word *rational* has the word *ratio* in it. Because fractions are ratios of integers, the expanded set including fractions is called the rational numbers. Finite decimals and infinite repeating decimals are also fractions expressed in another form, so they are also rational numbers. It is also true that all integers can be written as fractions. Any whole number (or integer) can be written with a denominator of 1. For example, $5 = \frac{5}{1}$.

Consider your bank account balance. Suppose you have $158.92 in your bank account and you withdraw $20.00. You now have a total of $138.92 in your account. Your bank account balance is an example from the set of rational numbers, since it is a finite decimal. You can write $138.92 in fractional form by remembering that the name of the last decimal place in this number is the hundredths place. Therefore, $138.92 = \frac{13892}{100}$.

What's That Mean?

Ratio

A *ratio* is the quotient of one value divided by another, usually expressed as a fraction.

DEFINITION

Rational Numbers   The rational numbers consist of the set of numbers that are *ratios* of integers. This category includes all of the integers, finite decimals, and infinite repeating decimals.

Example 1 Is it an integer or a rational number?

Determine the set(s), integers or rational numbers, to which all possible numbers described by the statement could belong.

a. The average monthly charge for a cell phone.

b. The number of free minutes (included minutes) on a cell phone plan every month.

c. The elevation of any location in California. Note that the highest elevation in California is Mount Whitney at 14,494 feet above sea level, and the lowest elevation is in Death Valley, which is 282 feet below sea level.

SOLUTION

a. The average monthly balance will often be a decimal number with two decimal digits, such as $55.92. Therefore, these values belong to the set of rational numbers.

b. Suppose a plan gives the user 500 "free" minutes per month. The number 500 is an integer but can be considered both an integer and a rational number, since $500 = \frac{500}{1}$. Therefore, these values belong to both the integers and rational numbers.

c. The elevation of any location in California is a value between −282 feet and 14,494 feet. Elevations are typically measured to the nearest foot. Therefore, the elevations are integers and therefore also rational numbers.

PRACTICE PROBLEM FOR EXAMPLE 1

Determine the set(s), integers or rational numbers, to which all possible numbers described by the statement could belong.

a. The amount owed on a home electricity bill every month.

b. The number of people who attend a jazz concert.

c. The amount of time (in hours) that a college student exercises every week.

Irrational Numbers

■ CONCEPT INVESTIGATION

What number is that?

Use your calculator to fill in the third column of the following table. Divide the circumference by the diameter and put the result in the third column. Carry out all results to four decimal digits of accuracy. Measure two additional circular objects as accurately as you can and add two rows to the table.

What's That Mean?

Circles

The *circumference* is the measure of the distance around a circle.
The *diameter* is the measure of the distance from one side to the other of a circle through the center.

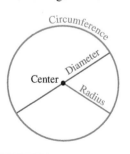

Circumference	Diameter	Circumference / Diameter
37.699	12	$\frac{37.699}{12} \approx 3.1416$
28"	8.91268"	
14 cm	4.45633 cm	
73.2200 m	23.3066 m	

What number does the last column always (approximately) come out to be? Can you think of another name for this number?

The number π is an example of an irrational number. You will encounter irrational numbers other than π in mathematics. A number like $\sqrt{5}$ is also irrational. The first irrational number discovered was $\sqrt{2}$. It was discovered by the Greek mathematician Hippasus, who used geometric methods to prove that it was irrational.

> **DEFINITION**
>
> **Irrational Numbers**   Irrational numbers can be expressed by infinite, nonrepeating decimals. These numbers cannot be written as a ratio of integers.

Because irrational numbers are infinite, nonrepeating decimals, we will approximate them using a calculator.

The Real Number System

Combining all rational numbers and all irrational numbers into one set results in what mathematicians call the **real number system.**

> **DEFINITION**
>
> **Real Number System**   The real number system consists of the set of all rational and irrational numbers.

The following diagram is to help visualize the real number system. Notice that the set of natural numbers is contained in the set of whole numbers, the set of whole numbers is contained in the set of integers, and the set of integers is contained in the set of rational numbers. The irrational numbers are separate from the rational numbers, but these two sets together make up the entire real number system.

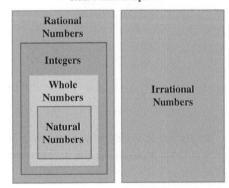

Real Number System

Example 2   Classifying numbers

Check all boxes that are appropriate for each number in the following table.

	Whole Number	Integer	Rational Number	Irrational Number	Real Number
-5					
$\dfrac{2}{5}$					
0					
$\sqrt{2}$					
0.29					

SOLUTION

−5 is an integer, a rational number, and a real number. So we will check all of those boxes.

$\frac{2}{5}$ is a rational number and a real number.

0 is a whole number, an integer, a rational number, and a real number.

$\sqrt{2}$ is an irrational number and a real number.

$0.29 = \frac{29}{100}$ is a rational number and a real number.

	Whole Number	Integer	Rational Number	Irrational Number	Real Number
−5		X	X		X
$\frac{2}{5}$			X		X
0	X	X	X		X
$\sqrt{2}$				X	X
0.29			X		X

PRACTICE PROBLEM FOR EXAMPLE 2

Check all boxes that are appropriate for each number in the following table.

	Whole Number	Integer	Rational Number	Irrational Number	Real Number
8.3					
$\frac{-4}{3}$					
56					
π					
−15					

In Section R.3, we learned how to convert between fractions and decimals. We now look at those problems again, in the context of the real number system.

Example 3 Converting between fractions and decimals

a. Convert 0.635 to a fraction in simplest form. Is this number a rational number or an irrational number? Explain.

b. Convert $\frac{1}{6}$ to a decimal. Is this number a rational number or an irrational number? Explain.

SOLUTION

a. The number 0.635 can be written as

$$0.635 \qquad \text{The last place value is thousandths.}$$

$$= \frac{635}{1000} \qquad \text{Rewrite over 1000.}$$

$$= \frac{\cancel{5} \cdot 127}{\cancel{5} \cdot 200} \qquad \text{Reduce to simplest form.}$$

$$= \frac{127}{200}$$

The number 0.635 is a rational number because it has a finite number of nonzero decimal digits and can be written as a ratio of integers.

b. The number $\frac{1}{6}$ can be written as

$$\frac{1}{6} \quad \textit{Divide 6 into 1.}$$

$$\begin{array}{r} 0.166 \\ 6\overline{)1.000} \\ -6 \\ \hline 40 \\ -36 \\ \hline 40 \\ -36 \\ \hline 4 \end{array}$$

Therefore, $\frac{1}{6} = 0.1666\ldots = 0.1\overline{6}$. The number $\frac{1}{6}$ is a rational number because it is a fraction. It can also be said that $\frac{1}{6}$ is rational because it has an infinite, repeating decimal expansion.

PRACTICE PROBLEM FOR EXAMPLE 3

a. Convert 0.255 to a fraction in simplest form. Is this number a rational number or an irrational number? Explain.

b. Convert $\frac{1}{9}$ to a decimal. Is this number a rational number or an irrational number? Explain.

Exact and Approximate Answers

It is important to pay careful attention to the difference between the *exact answer* and an *approximate answer*. The number π is an irrational number, which is approximated when used in problems. The value of π is $\pi = 3.1415926535\ldots$, where the decimal expansion continues indefinitely. When computing with π, many times students are told to use 3.14 as an approximation. Likewise, we have seen that $\sqrt{2}$ is an irrational number. The decimal expansion for $\sqrt{2}$ is $\sqrt{2} = 1.41421356\ldots$, where the decimal expansion continues indefinitely. An approximate value of $\sqrt{2}$ is 1.41. Whenever a number is rounded or truncated, the resulting value is an approximation of the original number. In this book, we will use only rounding.

Approximate values for rational numbers can be found as well. Since $\frac{1}{3} = 0.333\ldots$, an approximation for $\frac{1}{3}$ is 0.3. Write $\frac{1}{3} \approx 0.3$.

Exact Value	An Approximate Value
π	3.14
$\sqrt{2}$	1.41

> **What's That Mean?**
>
> **Truncate**
>
> To *truncate* a number means to approximate the number by just cutting off the last decimal digits.
>
> For example, the fraction $\frac{2}{3}$ has the decimal expansion $\frac{2}{3} = 0.666\ldots$.
>
> *Truncating* $\frac{2}{3}$ to two decimal digits gives 0.66. *Rounding* $\frac{2}{3}$ to two decimal digits gives 0.67. Note that truncation and rounding can give different results. In this book, we will use only rounding.

Example 4 Rounding to approximate values

Round each number to the given place value.

a. Round to the thousandths place: $\sqrt{5}$

b. Round to the tenths place: $\frac{1}{9}$

c. Round to the ten-thousandths place: π

SOLUTION

a. Using a calculator, $\sqrt{5} \approx 2.23606797\ldots$. To round to the thousandths place, underline the thousandths place: $2.236\underline{0}6797\ldots$. The digit to the right of the 6 in the thousandths place is 0, so round down. Therefore, $\sqrt{5} \approx 2.236$.

b. Using a calculator, $\frac{1}{9} = 0.11111111\ldots$. Recall that to write a repeating decimal, put a bar over the repeating part: $\frac{1}{9} = 0.11111111\ldots = 0.\overline{1}$. To round to the tenths place, underline the tenths place: $0.\underline{1}1111111\ldots$. The digit to the right of the 1 in the tenths place is 1, so round down. Therefore, $\frac{1}{9} \approx 0.1$.

c. Using a calculator, $\pi \approx 3.141592654\ldots$. To round to the ten-thousandths place, underline the ten-thousandths place: $3.141\underline{5}92654\ldots$. The digit to the right of the 5 in the ten-thousandths place is 9, so round up. Therefore, $\pi \approx 3.1416$.

PRACTICE PROBLEM FOR EXAMPLE 4

Round each number to the given decimal place.

a. Round to the tenths place: $\sqrt{7}$

b. Round to the hundredths place: $\frac{2}{7}$

The grocery store is a place where approximations are often used. To help you compare prices on items, many grocery stores will provide the unit price for each item. The unit price is the cost for one unit of that item, such as $0.20 for 1 ounce of juice or $0.88 for 1 pound of oranges. To find a unit price, take the price for the item and divide by the number of units.

Junial Enterprises/shutterstock.com

Example 5 Unit prices

Find the unit price for each item. Round answers to the nearest cent.

a. A 14-ounce box of cereal for $3.79

b. A 12-ounce package of raisins for $2.00

SOLUTION

a. To find the unit price, divide $3.79 by 14 ounces. To round to the nearest cent, divide out to the thousandths place.

$$
\begin{array}{r}
0.270 \\
14\overline{)3.790} \\
-28 \\
\hline
99 \\
-98 \\
\hline
10 \\
\end{array}
$$

Therefore, the unit price for this box of cereal is approximately $0.27 per ounce.

b. Divide $2.00 by 12 ounces.

$$
\begin{array}{r}
0.166 \\
12\overline{)2.000} \\
-12 \\
\hline
80 \\
-72 \\
\hline
80 \\
-72 \\
\hline
80 \\
\end{array}
$$

Divide out to the thousandths place.

Round to the nearest cent. Therefore, the unit price for these raisins is approximately $0.17 per ounce.

PRACTICE PROBLEM FOR EXAMPLE 5

Find the unit price for each item. Round answers to the nearest cent.

a. A 16-ounce package of bologna for $1.99

b. A 28-ounce jar of peanut butter for $5.99

R.4 Exercises

For Exercises 1 and 2, check all boxes that are appropriate for each number in the table.

1.

	Whole Number	Integer	Rational Number	Irrational Number	Real Number
1.47					
$\frac{16}{49}$					
-7					
$\sqrt{5}$					
9					

2.

	Whole Number	Integer	Rational Number	Irrational Number	Real Number
$\frac{1}{9}$					
-21.3					
55					
π					
5.001					

For Exercises 3 through 14, determine the set(s), integers or rational numbers, to which all possible numbers described by the statement could belong.

3. The ratio of boys to girls in a calculus course.

4. The ratio of girls to boys in a philosophy course.

5. The ratio of flour to water in a bread recipe.

6. The ratio of water to rice when cooking steamed rice.

7. The daily high temperature in Milwaukee, Wisconsin, over the course of a year.

8. The daily low temperature in Portland, Maine, over the course of a year.

9. The amount owed on an electricity bill for a month.

10. The amount owed on a cable TV bill for a month.

11. The number of people who attend a college football game.

12. The number of people who attend a college basketball game.

13. The elevation of Death Valley, California. See Practice Problem for Example 10 in Section R.1 for the elevation.

14. The elevation of Mount Everest, which is on the border of Nepal, Tibet, and China.

For Exercises 15 through 24, list all the given numbers requested from the set.

15. All the rational numbers in the set $\left\{-3, 0, \pi, \frac{5}{2}, \sqrt{2}\right\}$

16. All the rational numbers in the set $\left\{-\frac{1}{2}, 0, 4, \frac{9}{4}, \pi\right\}$

17. All the irrational numbers in the set $\left\{-3, 0, \pi, \frac{5}{2}, \sqrt{2}\right\}$

18. All the irrational numbers in the set $\left\{-\frac{1}{2}, 0, 4, \frac{9}{4}, \pi\right\}$

19. All the whole numbers in the set $\left\{16, -5, \frac{9}{2}, \sqrt{5}, 0, 2\right\}$

20. All the whole numbers in the set $\left\{-3.5, -21, 5, \sqrt{2}, 10, 0.5\right\}$

21. All the integers in the set $\left\{-5.9, 8.6, \frac{7}{25}, 3, 111, \pi\right\}$

22. All the integers in the set $\left\{\frac{9}{77}, 8, \frac{3}{2}, -71, 4\right\}$

23. All the natural numbers in the set $\left\{-9, 0, \frac{2}{3}, 56, \sqrt{2}\right\}$

24. All the natural numbers in the set $\left\{\frac{4}{5}, \pi, 96, -4.2, 12\right\}$

For Exercises 25 through 32, convert each number to the requested form. Is the given number a rational number or an irrational number? Explain.

25. Convert $\frac{5}{8}$ to a decimal. Is $\frac{5}{8}$ a rational number or an irrational number? Explain.

26. Convert $\frac{3}{4}$ to a decimal. Is $\frac{3}{4}$ a rational number or an irrational number? Explain.

27. Convert 1.34 to a fraction in simplest form. Is 1.34 a rational number or an irrational number? Explain.

28. Convert 2.78 to a fraction in simplest form. Is 2.78 a rational number or an irrational number? Explain.

29. Convert $\frac{1}{11}$ to a decimal. Is $\frac{1}{11}$ a rational number or an irrational number? Explain.

30. Convert $\frac{1}{15}$ to a decimal. Is $\frac{1}{15}$ a rational number or an irrational number? Explain.

31. Convert 0.0133 to a fraction in simplest form. Is 0.0133 a rational number or an irrational number? Explain.

32. Convert 0.0527 to a fraction in simplest form. Is 0.0527 a rational number or an irrational number? Explain.

For Exercises 33 through 38, find a decimal approximation for the given number and round to the given place value. Is the given number a rational number or an irrational number? Explain.

33. Round $\frac{3}{11}$ to the thousandths place. Is $\frac{3}{11}$ a rational number or an irrational number? Explain.

34. Round $\frac{5}{21}$ to the ten-thousandths place. Is $\frac{5}{21}$ a rational number or an irrational number? Explain.

35. Round $\sqrt{11}$ to the ten-thousandths place. Is $\sqrt{11}$ a rational number or an irrational number? Explain.

36. Round $\sqrt{13}$ to the tenths place. Is $\sqrt{13}$ a rational number or an irrational number? Explain.

37. Round π to the millionths place. Is π a rational number or an irrational number? Explain.

38. Round π to the tenths place. Is π a rational number or an irrational number? Explain.

For Exercises 39 through 44, find the unit price for each item. Round answers to the nearest cent.

39. A 21-ounce container of mixed nuts for $9.99.

40. A 4.5-ounce package of sunflower seeds for $1.18.

41. A 12-ounce package of angel hair pasta for $0.75.

42. A 16-ounce package of elbow macaroni for $0.75.

43. A 24-ounce jar of marinara sauce for $2.59.

44. A 24-ounce jar of pasta sauce for $3.00.

For Exercises 45 through 56, identify the number of terms. Then use the order-of-operations agreement to simplify the expression.

45. $\frac{3}{5} \cdot \frac{1}{6} + \frac{1}{2}$

46. $\frac{4}{3} \div \frac{5}{6} - \frac{1}{2}$

47. $1.2 \cdot 2 - 6.2 \div 2 + 12.1$

48. $106 - 2.4 \div 4 + 6.9 \cdot 3$

49. $\frac{3}{5} + 1.5 \cdot 3$

50. $3.3 \cdot 5 - \frac{1}{8}$

51. $26.1 \div 6 - \frac{17}{5} \cdot \frac{1}{20}$

52. $\frac{1}{9} \cdot \frac{3}{4} + 11.25 \cdot 0.8$

53. $5 - 6.75 + \frac{2}{3} \div 4$

54. $\frac{6}{7} \div \frac{3}{14} + 8.95 - 12$

55. $\frac{1}{4} + \frac{3}{8} \cdot \frac{16}{21} - 4 \div \frac{2}{3}$

56. $\frac{1}{6} + \frac{3}{5} \cdot \frac{20}{21} - 5 \div \frac{10}{3}$

Chapter Summary

R

Section R.1 Operations with Integers

- The **natural numbers** are the set $\{1, 2, 3, \ldots\}$.
- The **whole numbers** are the set $\{0, 1, 2, 3, \ldots\}$.
- The **integers** are the set $\{\ldots, -2, -1, 0, 1, 2, \ldots\}$.
- A **number line** is used to visually represent numbers.

- The **scale** of a number line is the distance between the tick marks on the number line.
- Numbers have order, and both equalities and **inequalities** are used to represent the order relationship between numbers.
- The **absolute value** of a number is the distance between that number and 0. It is always nonnegative.
- **Opposites** have the same absolute value but differ only in sign.
- **Terms** are numbers or expressions that are added or subtracted.
- The **order-of-operations agreement** is used to compute the value of an expression that contains multiple operations.

  1. Circle or underline the terms (remember: terms are parts that are added or subtracted).
  2. Evaluate the operations (multiplications and divisions) inside of each term, working from left to right.
  3. Add and subtract the simplified terms, working from left to right.

Example 1   Place the appropriate inequality symbol, $<$ or $>$, between the two numbers.

a. $-3 \qquad -7$

b. $-6 \qquad -(-6)$

SOLUTION   a. $-3 > -7$

b. $-6 < -(-6)$

Example 2   Find the absolute value of each of the following numbers.

a. $|9|$

b. $|-6|$

SOLUTION   a. 9

b. 6

Example 3

Identify the terms. Then simplify using the order-of-operations agreement.

a. $-12 + 3(-5)$

b. $7 + 5 \cdot 4 - 12 \div 2 \cdot 7$

SOLUTION

a. $\boxed{-12} + \boxed{3(-5)}$ There are two terms.

$= -12 + (-15)$ Do the multiplication in the second term.

$= -27$ Add the integers.

b. $\boxed{7} + \boxed{5 \cdot 4} - \boxed{12 \div 2 \cdot 7}$ There are three terms.

$= 7 + 20 - 6 \cdot 7$ Do the operations in the second and third terms, working from left to right.

$= 7 + 20 - 42$ Add and subtract, working from left to right.

$= 27 - 42$

$= -15$

Section R.2   Operations with Fractions

- **Prime numbers** are natural numbers greater than 1 that are evenly divisible only by themselves and 1.
- To find the **prime factorization** of a number, first write any factorization of the number. Continue to factor all composite numbers until there is only a product of primes left.
- Fractions are parts of a whole number and should always be **reduced to lowest terms.**
- **Equivalent fractions** represent the same quantity: $\frac{1}{2} = \frac{5}{10}$.
- **To add or subtract fractions that have like denominators**, just add or subtract their numerators. Reduce to lowest terms.
- **To add or subtract fractions with unlike denominators**, first find the least common denominator. Then rewrite each fraction over the least common denominator. Finally, add or subtract the numerators and reduce to lowest terms.
- **To multiply fractions**, multiply numerators and multiply denominators. Reduce to lowest terms.
- The **reciprocal** of a is $\frac{1}{a}$, if $a \neq 0$.
- **To divide fractions**, find the reciprocal of the second fraction and multiply. Reduce to lowest terms.
- **The order-of-operations agreement** is used with fractions the same way it is used with integers.

Example 4

Write the prime factorization of the number 24.

SOLUTION

$24 = 2 \cdot 2 \cdot 2 \cdot 3$

Example 5

Add or subtract the following fractions.

a. $-\frac{5}{4} + \frac{3}{4}$ **b.** $\frac{2}{3} + \frac{1}{2}$

SOLUTION

a. $-\frac{5}{4} + \frac{3}{4} = -\frac{2}{4} = -\frac{1}{2}$

b. $\frac{2}{3} + \frac{1}{2} = \frac{4}{6} + \frac{3}{6} = \frac{7}{6} = 1\frac{1}{6}$

Example 6   Multiply or divide the following fractions.

a. $\dfrac{4}{9} \cdot \dfrac{3}{8}$ b. $\dfrac{2}{3} \div \dfrac{5}{6}$

SOLUTION   a. $\dfrac{4}{9} \cdot \dfrac{3}{8} = \dfrac{12}{72} = \dfrac{1}{6}$

b. $\dfrac{2}{3} \div \dfrac{5}{6} = \dfrac{2}{3} \cdot \dfrac{6}{5} = \dfrac{12}{15} = \dfrac{4}{5}$

Section R.3   Operations with Decimals and Percents

- The numbers to the right of the decimal point have **place value** that accords with a multiple of ten. The names of place values to the right of a decimal point will end with "ths."
- **Place value** can be used to convert decimals to fractions. Find the rightmost place value in the given decimal. Removing the decimal point, write the number over the rightmost place value to give the fractional form. Reduce to lowest terms.
- **Decimals can be added or subtracted** by lining them up vertically by place value. Then add or subtract, carrying or borrowing as necessary.
- **Decimals can be multiplied or divided** like whole numbers. Pay close attention to where the decimal point goes in the final answer.
- The **order-of-operations** agreement is used in the same way when decimals are involved.
- Decimals can be **rounded** to a given place value. If the next digit to the right is 0, 1, 2, 3, or 4, round down. If the next digit to the right is 5, 6, 7, 8, or 9, round up.
- **Percent** means "a part of 100."
- **Percents** may be converted to either decimal or fraction form. To convert to fraction form, put the percent over 100. To convert to decimal form, divide the percent by 100 (move the decimal point two places to the left) and drop the percent symbol.
- **When using a percent in a problem**, first convert to decimal form.

Example 7   Answer as indicated.

a. Find the digit in the thousandths place: 1067.52943

b. Round the number to the tenths place: 3.259

c. Find 7% of 65.

SOLUTION   a. The digit in the thousandths place is 9. 1067.52943

b. 3.$\underline{2}$59   *The digit to the right is 5 or more: round up.*

3.3

c. 7% of 65 = $0.07 \cdot 65 = 4.55$

Example 8   Add or subtract as indicated.

a. $8.20597 + 31.451$

b. $16.0243 - 9.951$

SOLUTION   a. $8.20597 + 31.451 = 39.65697$

b. $16.0243 - 9.951 = 6.0733$

Example 9 Multiply or divide as indicated.

 a. $3.6(2.7)$

 b. $4.34 \div 1.4$

SOLUTION a. $3.6(2.7) = 9.72$

 b. $4.34 \div 1.4 = 3.1$

Section R.4 The Real Number System

- The **rational numbers** are the set of numbers that are ratios of integers. Natural numbers, whole numbers, integers, finite decimals, and infinite repeating decimals are all part of the rational numbers.

- The **irrational numbers** are the set of numbers that cannot be expressed as ratios of integers. Irrational numbers are infinite, nonrepeating decimals.

- The **real numbers** consist of the set of all rational and irrational numbers.

- **Approximate answers** can be found by rounding to a desired place value.

Example 10 List all the rational numbers in the set $\left\{-3, \frac{5}{6}, 0.22, \pi, 9\frac{2}{3}\right\}$.

SOLUTION The rational numbers are $-3, \frac{5}{6}, 0.22$, and $9\frac{2}{3}$.

Example 11 Find a decimal approximation for $\sqrt{85}$. Round your answer to the thousandths place.

SOLUTION Using a calculator, we find $\sqrt{85} \approx 9.21954$, and rounding to the thousandths place gives $\sqrt{85} \approx 9.220$.

Chapter Review Exercises

R

At the end of each exercise, the section number in brackets indicates where the material is covered.

For Exercises 1 through 4, classify each number as a natural number, a whole number, or an integer. If a number belongs to more than one set, list all possible sets it belongs to.

1. a. -12 **b.** 0 **c.** 17 [R.1]

2. a. 9 **b.** -1 **c.** 0 [R.1]

3. The number of students in a chemistry lab.   [R.1]

4. The number of trees in a public park.   [R.1]

5. List all numbers in the set. All the whole numbers between -3 and 4, including -3 and 4.   [R.1]

6. List all the numbers in the set. All the integers between -6 and -3, including -6 and -3.   [R.1]

7. Determine the scale of the number line.   [R.1]

8. Determine the scale of the number line.   [R.1]

9. Plot the numbers on a number line.
$$-3, \frac{1}{2}, 0, \frac{-4}{2}, 4.25 \qquad \text{[R.2]}$$

10. Plot the numbers on a number line.
$$2.5, \frac{-1}{3}, -2, \frac{5}{2}, -0.8 \qquad \text{[R.2]}$$

11. Place the appropriate inequality symbol ($<$ or $>$) between the two numbers.
$$-3 \qquad -5 \qquad \text{[R.1]}$$

12. Place the appropriate inequality symbol ($<$ or $>$) between the two numbers.
$$-9 \qquad -2 \qquad \text{[R.1]}$$

13. Find the value of the absolute value expression:
$$|-9| \qquad \text{[R.1]}$$

14. Find the value of the absolute value expression:
$$|-6.7| \qquad \text{[R.1]}$$

15. Place the list of numbers in increasing order, from smallest to largest.
$$3 \quad -2 \quad \frac{2}{5} \quad |-7| \qquad \text{[R.2]}$$

16. Place the list of numbers in increasing order, from smallest to largest.
$$-4 \quad \left|\frac{-2}{3}\right| \quad 1.8 \quad -0.1 \qquad \text{[R.2]}$$

17. Rewrite the math expression in phrase form and then find the value: $-(-8)$ [R.1]

18. Rewrite the math expression in phrase form and then find the value: $-(-1)$ [R.1]

19. Add or subtract as indicated.
   a. $-22 + (-45)$ b. $-9 - 17$
   c. $-18 + 8$ d. $-16 - (-11)$ [R.1]

20. Add or subtract as indicated.
   a. $-13 + (-5)$ b. $50 - (-18)$
   c. $4 - 18$ d. $-19 + 12$ [R.1]

21. Multiply or divide as indicated.
   a. $-5(-10)(-3)$ b. $-2(4)(-1)$
   c. $64 \div (-4)$ d. $-55 \div (-11)$ [R.1]

22. Multiply or divide as indicated.
   a. $(-3)(-5)(2)$ b. $-(-3)(-6)$
   c. $27 \div (-9)$ d. $-24 \div (-3)$ [R.1]

23. Identify the number of terms in the expression:
$$-9 \cdot 4 \div 6 + 18 - 3 \qquad \text{[R.1]}$$

24. Identify the number of terms in the expression:
$$-12 + 8 \div 2 - 1 \qquad \text{[R.1]}$$

25. Identify the number of terms. Then simplify, using the order-of-operations agreement.
$$-48 \div (-12) \cdot 5 + 4 \cdot 3 - 7 \qquad \text{[R.1]}$$

26. Identify the number of terms. Then simplify, using the order-of-operations agreement.
$$9 \cdot (-2) + 17 + 32 \div (-16) \cdot 3 \qquad \text{[R.1]}$$

27. Find the prime factorization of 27. [R.2]

28. Find the prime factorization of 45. [R.2]

29. Find the GCF for the set of numbers.
   8 and 28 [R.2]

30. Find the GCF for the set of numbers.
   15 and 45 [R.2]

31. Reduce the fraction to lowest terms.
$$\frac{20}{44} \qquad \text{[R.2]}$$

32. Reduce the fraction to lowest terms.
$$\frac{12}{30} \qquad \text{[R.2]}$$

33. Rewrite the fraction as an equivalent fraction with the given denominator.
$$\frac{5}{8} = \frac{?}{56} \qquad \text{[R.2]}$$

34. Rewrite the fraction as an equivalent fraction with the given denominator.
$$\frac{3}{7} = \frac{?}{42} \qquad \text{[R.2]}$$

35. Classify each number as an integer or a rational number or both.
   a. $\frac{3}{5}$ b. -5 c. 16.1 [R.4]

36. Classify each number as an integer or a rational number or both.
   a. -0.7 b. $\frac{-1}{9}$ c. 0 [R.4]

37. Add or subtract as indicated. Reduce the answer to lowest terms.
   a. $\frac{1}{6} + \frac{3}{6}$ b. $\frac{1}{6} + \frac{1}{4}$
   c. $\frac{1}{2} - \frac{2}{3}$ d. $3\frac{1}{2} - 1\frac{1}{3}$ [R.2]

38. Add or subtract as indicated. Reduce the answer to lowest terms.
   a. $\frac{5}{8} - \frac{1}{8}$ b. $\frac{1}{5} + \frac{1}{15}$
   c. $\frac{1}{4} - \frac{2}{5}$ d. $4\frac{1}{5} - 3\frac{1}{2}$ [R.2]

39. Find the reciprocal of each number.
   a. 6 b. $\frac{1}{4}$ [R.2]

40. Find the reciprocal of each number.
   a. -5 b. $\frac{3}{2}$ [R.2]

41. Multiply or divide as indicated. Reduce the answer to lowest terms.

    a. $\dfrac{2}{7} \cdot \dfrac{14}{22}$ **b.** $\dfrac{1}{5} \div 9$ **c.** $\dfrac{3}{8} \div \dfrac{9}{16}$ [R.2]

42. Multiply or divide as indicated. Reduce the answer to lowest terms.

    a. $\dfrac{4}{5} \cdot \dfrac{15}{28}$ **b.** $\dfrac{3}{7} \div 2$ **c.** $\dfrac{5}{6} \div \dfrac{10}{9}$ [R.2]

43. Identify the number of terms. Simplify, using the order-of-operations agreement.

$$\frac{1}{3} \div \frac{2}{9} - 7 \qquad \text{[R.2]}$$

44. Identify the number of terms. Simplify, using the order-of-operations agreement.

$$3 - \frac{4}{5} \cdot \frac{10}{3} \qquad \text{[R.2]}$$

45. Identify the place value of the digit 9 in the number 2.497031.   [R.3]

46. Identify the place value of the digit 5 in the number 8.26571.   [R.3]

47. Write the decimal as a fraction in lowest terms.

$$2.75 \qquad \text{[R.3]}$$

48. Write the decimal as a fraction in lowest terms.

$$4.68 \qquad \text{[R.3]}$$

49. Write the fraction as a decimal. Put a bar over any repeating decimal part.

$$\frac{4}{9} \qquad \text{[R.3]}$$

50. Write the fraction as a decimal. Put a bar over any repeating decimal part.

$$\frac{5}{8} \qquad \text{[R.3]}$$

51. Add or subtract as indicated.

    a. $3.625 + 7.019$ **b.** $4.061 - 3.987$ [R.3]

52. Add or subtract as indicated.

    a. $4.073 + 16.998$ **b.** $5.072 - 3.826$ [R.3]

53. Multiply or divide as indicated.

    a. $(4.7)(1.03)$ **b.** $14.58 \div 5.4$ [R.3]

54. Multiply or divide as indicated.

    a. $(9.2)(3.8)$ **b.** $40.85 \div 4.3$ [R.3]

55. Identify the terms. Simplify using the order-of-operations agreement.

$$9.6 - 11.73 \div 5.1 - 3.2 \qquad \text{[R.3]}$$

56. Identify the terms. Simplify using the order-of-operations agreement.

$$0.92 \div (-0.1) + 6.3 - 4.75 \qquad \text{[R.3]}$$

57. Round 0.01996 to the hundredths place.   [R.3]

58. Round 5.409999 to the tenths place.   [R.3]

59. Convert 8.75% to a decimal.   [R.3]

60. Convert 5.45% to a decimal.   [R.3]

61. Convert 28% to a fraction in lowest terms.   [R.3]

62. Convert 45% to a fraction in lowest terms.   [R.3]

63. Convert 0.0456 to a percent.   [R.3]

64. Convert 0.0775 to a percent.   [R.3]

65. Convert 1.905 to a percent.   [R.3]

66. Convert 2.01 to a percent.   [R.3]

67. Convert $\dfrac{4}{5}$ to a percent.   [R.3]

68. Convert $\dfrac{3}{50}$ to a percent.   [R.3]

69. Convert $1\dfrac{1}{5}$ to a percent.   [R.3]

70. Convert $3\dfrac{1}{3}$ to a percent.   [R.3]

71. Find 8.25% of 45.   [R.3]

72. Find 3.45% of 9.   [R.3]

73. Find 5.5% of 20.   [R.3]

74. Find 10.2% of 16.   [R.3]

75. Find the sales tax on a \$235 purchase if the sales tax rate is 8.5%.   [R.3]

76. List all rational numbers in the set.

$$\left\{ \frac{4}{3}, -16.9, \sqrt{5}, 0 \right\} \qquad \text{[R.4]}$$

77. List all rational numbers in the set.

$$\left\{ -7.5, 2, \frac{5}{4}, \pi \right\} \qquad \text{[R.4]}$$

78. List all irrational numbers in the set.

$$\left\{ \frac{4}{3}, -16.9, \sqrt{5}, 0 \right\} \qquad \text{[R.4]}$$

79. List all irrational numbers in the set.

$$\left\{ -7.5, 2, \frac{5}{4}, \pi \right\} \qquad \text{[R.4]}$$

80. Find a decimal approximation for the number. Round to the hundredths place: $\dfrac{3}{7}$ [R.4]

81. Find a decimal approximation for the number. Round to the thousandths place: $\sqrt{21}$ [R.4]

For Exercises 82 through 91, use the order-of-operations agreement to simplify the expression.

82. $\dfrac{1}{2} \div 5 + 5.2 - 7.9$ [R.4]

83. $6 \div \dfrac{3}{5} - 5.69 + 8.4$ [R.4]

84. $\dfrac{3}{5} \div \dfrac{9}{10} - \dfrac{3}{2} + 4$ [R.4]

85. $7 - \dfrac{4}{7} \div \dfrac{1}{14} + \dfrac{1}{3}$ [R.4]

86. $0.35 + \dfrac{5}{4} \cdot \dfrac{3}{125}$ [R.4]

87. $1.27 - \dfrac{2}{10} \cdot \dfrac{3}{20}$ [R.4]

88. $44.2 \div 2 + 5 \cdot 7.1 - 5 \div \dfrac{5}{2}$ [R.4]

89. $25.15 \div 5 + 7 \div 0.2 - 6 \div 12$ [R.4]

90. $\dfrac{4}{5} \div \dfrac{8}{15} \cdot \dfrac{4}{9}$ [R.4]

91. $3 \div \dfrac{6}{11} \cdot \dfrac{2}{5}$ [R.4]

Chapter Test

R

The following chapter test should take approximately one hour to complete. Read each question carefully. Show all of your work.

1. Check all boxes that apply for each number listed below.

	Whole Number	Integer	Rational Number	Irrational Number	Real Number
2.25					
$\dfrac{2}{3}$					
-6					
$\sqrt{2}$					
10					

2. Determine the scale of the number line.

$-25 \quad -20 \quad -15 \quad -10 \quad -5 \quad 0 \quad 5 \quad 10 \quad 15 \quad 20 \quad 25$

3. Place the numbers on a number line.

$$4, \quad -5.5, \quad \dfrac{7}{2}, \quad 0, \quad -0.9$$

4. Place the list of numbers in increasing order, from smallest to largest.

$$-4, \quad \dfrac{13}{5} \quad -(-6.8) \quad |-11|$$

5. Use the appropriate inequality symbol ($<$ or $>$) between the two numbers.

   a. $-9 \quad -11$ **b.** $\dfrac{1}{3} \quad 0.3$

6. Find the value of each of the following.

   a. $-(-(-3))$ **b.** $|-6|$

7. Find the prime factorization of 36.

8. Add or subtract as indicated.

   a. $-5 - (-9)$ **b.** $-0.3 - 1.5 + 0.75$

   c. $-2 + (-8) - (-6)$

9. Multiply or divide as indicated.

   a. $(-4)(-6)(-2)$ **b.** $(-36) \div (-4)$

   c. $(32.2) \div (3.5)$

For Exercises 10 through 15, identify the number of terms. Then simplify each expression.

10. $-6 + 3 \cdot 4 - (-5) + 12 \div (-3)$

11. $24 \div 2 \cdot 3 + (-2) - (-1)$

12. $(-64) \div 16 \cdot 5 - 9$

13. $|-18| - (-5)(-7) + 36 \cdot 4$

14. $\dfrac{6}{5} \div \dfrac{2}{15} - \dfrac{1}{3} + 2$

15. $(1.2)(3.5) - 6.4 + 7$

16. Find the prime factorization of 50.

17. Find the GCF for 18 and 36.

18. Reduce to lowest terms. $\dfrac{48}{56}$

19. Write an equivalent fraction with the given denominator.

$$\dfrac{2}{7} = \dfrac{?}{63}$$

20. Add as indicated. Reduce the answer to lowest terms.

$$\dfrac{3}{5} + \dfrac{12}{5}$$

21. Subtract as indicated. Reduce the answer to lowest terms.

$$\dfrac{9}{5} - \dfrac{3}{4}$$

22. Multiply or divide as indicated. Reduce the answer to lowest terms.

   a. $\dfrac{-2}{5} \cdot \dfrac{15}{4}$ **b.** $\dfrac{3}{4} \div \dfrac{-9}{16}$

23. What is the place value of the digit 4 in the number 6.02478?

24. Round 5.02317 to the thousandths place.

25. Complete the table by filling in the missing values.

Percent	Decimal	Fraction
1.05%		

26. Find 9% of 206.

Chapter R Projects

What Kind of Number Is That?

Class Project

4–5 people in a group

What you will need

- Set of 20 index cards from your instructor
- Set of five containers from your instructor
- Response sheet to record the answers

Your instructor will give you five buckets labeled "natural numbers," "whole numbers," "integers," "rational numbers," and "irrational numbers." You will also receive a set of 20 index cards and a sheet of paper on which to record your results. Each card has a number written on it.

1. With your group members, decide which of the five buckets represents the smallest set to which the number belongs. Place the card in that bucket.

2. When your group is done with all 20 cards, write the answers on the sheet of paper your instructor has given you.

How Did the Ancients Record Their Counting?

Research Project

One or more people

What you will need

- Information from a Web search of the Ishango Bone
- Follow the MLA Style Guide for all citations. If your school recommends another style guide, use it.

Research the Ishango Bone artifact online. Write a one-page paper on the Ishango Bone. Include the age, what kind of bone was used, what continent it was found on, and how the Ishango Bone is thought to have been used for counting and possibly arithmetic. Clearly state which Websites you used as a part of your paper.

© Museum of Natural Science – Brussels

Pricing Your Trip to a Professional Sporting Event

Research Project

One or more people

What you will need

- Find data online to make your estimates.
- Follow the MLA Style Guide for all citations. If your school recommends another style guide, use it.

You are planning a trip for four friends and family to attend a professional sporting event. The cost of the event will be determined by a number of factors, such as the type of sporting event you are going to see, whether you have to travel out of town or see a local event, and lodging. To come up with an estimate of the total cost of your trip, use the following steps. Do your research online and provide printouts of the cost estimates you used.

1. Select which professional sporting event you want to arrange the trip to see. Some selections are events of the National Football League (NFL), the National Basketball Association (NBA), the Major League Soccer Association (MLS), and Major League Baseball (MLB).

2. How much are the tickets per person? For four people?

3. Decide which city you want to see the event in. Is the city local, or do you need to arrange to travel out of town?

4. If you have to travel out of town, decide on the mode of travel. Will you arrange to fly and then rent a car? Will you travel by private car (drive)? Will you take a train and then a taxi? Will you take a bus and then a taxi? Estimate the cost of travel for four people. Note: If you are arranging to drive by private car, look up the IRS mileage reimbursement rate and use that to estimate the driving cost.

5. Do you need to make reservations at a hotel? For how many rooms (at least two) and how many days?

6. If your trip requires travel, estimate the food cost per person per day.

7. How much does it cost to park at the stadium or arena if you are driving?

8. How much does it cost to eat and drink at the sporting event? Remember, you are taking four people.

9. Add up all the costs above.

10. What is the cost per person?

Write a Review of a Section for Presentation

Research Project

One or more people

What you will need:

- This presentation may be done in-class or as an online video.
- If it is done as a video, post it on a Website where it may be easily viewed by the class.
- You may want to use homework or other review problems from the book.
- Make it creative and fun.

Create a five-minute review presentation of one section from this chapter. The format of the presentation can be a poster presentation, a blackboard presentation from notes, an online video, or a game format (e.g., math jeopardy). The presentation should include the following:

1. Any important formulas in the chapter.

2. Important skills in the chapter, backed up by examples.

3. Explanation of terms used. For example, what is modeling?

4. Common mistakes and how to avoid them.

Building Blocks of Algebra

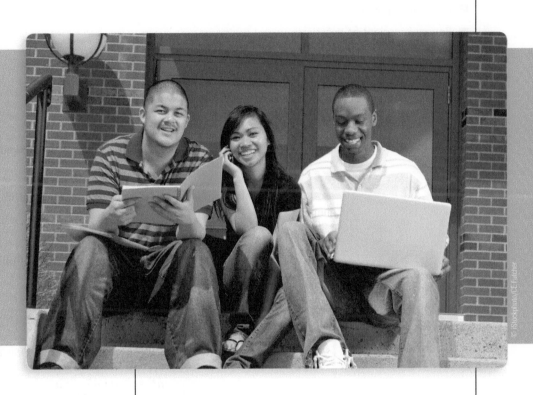

1.1 Exponents, Order of Operations, and Properties of Real Numbers

1.2 Algebra and Working with Variables

1.3 Simplifying Expressions

1.4 Graphs and the Rectangular Coordinate System

Many colleges charge students by credit hour (or unit) taken. To figure out how much tuition he or she owes for a semester (or quarter), the student must multiply the number of credit hours by the cost per credit hour. Then any additional fees, such as health fees or parking fees, must be added on. Algebra can be used to represent this calculation in a way that allows for different numbers of credit hours to be taken. In this chapter, we will start to study the foundations of algebra.

1.1   Exponents, Order of Operations, and Properties of Real Numbers

LEARNING OBJECTIVES

■ Evaluate exponents.

■ Recognize scientific notation.

■ Simplify using the order-of-operations agreement.

■ Use the properties of real numbers.

Exponents

Multiplication of natural numbers is a way to write a repeated addition.

$$6 + 6 + 6 + 6 = 6 \cdot 4$$

A natural number exponent is a way to write a repeated multiplication of natural numbers.

$$2 \cdot 2 \cdot 2 \cdot 2 = 2^4$$

Here, 2 is said to be the **base** (the number repeatedly multiplied), and 4 is said to be the **exponent** (the number of repeated multiplications).

DEFINITION

Natural Number Exponent   If a is a real number and n is a natural number, then

$$a^n = \underbrace{a \cdot a \cdot a \cdot \ldots \cdot a}_{n}$$

(a is multiplied by itself n times).

a is called the **base,** and n is called the **exponent.**

When working with natural number exponents, we say that $(2 \cdot 2 \cdot 2 \cdot 2)$ is in **expanded form** and (2^4) is in **exponential form**.

Example 1   Working with natural number exponents

Write each value as indicated.

a. Write in expanded form. 5^4

b. Write in exponential form. $7 \cdot 7 \cdot 7 \cdot 7 \cdot 7 \cdot 7$

c. Find the value without a calculator. $(-3)^4$

d. Find the value with a calculator. 6^5

SOLUTION

a. The base is 5, and the exponent of 4 tells us we are multiplying 5 by itself four times. The expanded form is $5 \cdot 5 \cdot 5 \cdot 5$.

b. The base is 7, and we are multiplying 7 by itself 6 times. So the exponent is 6. The exponential form is 7^6.

c. The base is -3, and we are multiplying -3 by itself four times.
$$(-3) \cdot (-3) \cdot (-3) \cdot (-3) = 81$$

d. Using a calculator, we have that $6^5 = 7776$.

PRACTICE PROBLEM FOR EXAMPLE 1

Write each value as indicated.

a. Write 16^5 in expanded form.

b. Write $29 \cdot 29 \cdot 29 \cdot 29$ in exponential form.

c. Find the value of $(-2)^5$ without a calculator.

d. Find the value of 5^6 with a calculator.

When calculating exponents, be very careful with negative signs. The expression -5^2 means the *opposite* of 5^2. Therefore,

$$-5^2 = -25$$

To raise a negative number to an exponent, the negative number *must be in parentheses*. The expression $(-5)^2$ means to square the number -5. Therefore,

$$(-5)^2 = (-5)(-5) = 25$$

Use the Concept Investigation to see what happens when we raise a number to the zero power.

■ CONCEPT INVESTIGATION

What happens when 0 is the exponent?

1. Fill in the following table, using your calculator.

2. What do you think that a number raised to the 0 power is in general?

3. Now try 0^0 in your calculator. Does this give the result you expected? Explain.

Exponential Expression	Calculator Value
4^0	1
3^0	
2^0	
1^0	

> ### DEFINITION
>
> **Zero as an Exponent** $a^0 = 1$ for all $a \neq 0$.
>
> $$3^0 = 1 \qquad (-8)^0 = 1$$
>
> The expression 0^0 does not exist (or is said to be undefined).

Calculator Details

On some scientific calculators, look for the key of the form or $\boxed{y^x}$. To enter 4^3, you first enter 4, hit the exponent key, then enter the exponent 3.

$$\boxed{4} \quad \boxed{x^y} \quad \boxed{3}$$

You may then have to hit the $\boxed{=}$ key to get a display of the answer, 64.

The exponent key on other scientific calculators looks like the symbol. To enter 4^3, first enter 4, then $\boxed{\wedge}$, and then the exponent of 3.

$$\boxed{4} \quad \boxed{\wedge} \quad \boxed{3} \quad \boxed{\text{ENTER}}$$

This will display the answer of 64.

Calculator Details

Most scientific calculators have an $\boxed{x^2}$ key. To find the value of 15^2 on a calculator, enter 15, then the $\boxed{x^2}$ key. To enter the square of a negative number such as $(-11)^2$ will depend on the programming of your calculator. To be safe, you can use the parentheses keys, usually located above the number 8 and 9 keys.

Enter $\boxed{(}\ \boxed{-}\ \boxed{11}$ $\boxed{)}$, and then hit the $\boxed{x^2}$ key. The display should read 121.

Example 2   Exponents on negative numbers and zero as an exponent

Evaluate the following expression.

a. -6^4 **b.** $(-8)^2$ **c.** 124^0 **d.** $(-2)^3$

SOLUTION

a. In the expression -6^4, the negative is not being raised to the power of 4, so the negative will wait, and the result will still be negative. $-6^4 = -1296$.

b. In the expression $(-8)^2$, the negative is being squared, so the result is positive. $(-8)^2 = 64$.

c. Any number raised to the zero power is 1 except zero to the zero power. Therefore, $124^0 = 1$.

d. The negative is being raised to the third power in the expression $(-2)^3$. Because there will be three negative numbers multiplied together, the result will still be negative. $(-2)^3 = (-2)(-2)(-2) = -8$.

PRACTICE PROBLEM FOR EXAMPLE 2

Evaluate the following expression.

a. $(-4)^2$ **b.** $(-5)^3$ **c.** 38^0 **d.** -7^2

Scientific Notation

When using positive exponents, we may encounter very large numbers. Large numbers are often displayed on a calculator in a special format. This format is a version of what is called **scientific notation.**

■ CONCEPT INVESTIGATION

What happened to my calculator display?

1. Use your calculator to fill in the following table.

Exponential Expression	Numerical Value
8^4	4096
8^5	
8^7	
8^{10}	
8^{13}	

2. What do you notice about the number your calculator displayed for 8^{13}?

Notice the appearance of the calculator display for the value of 8^{13}. Most calculators will commonly show one of the three answers below. All three forms of the following calculator display have the same meaning: that is, the value of 8^{13}.

Input	Calculator Display	
8^{13}	5.497558139E11	Notice the E just before the 11.
8^{13}	5.497558139 ^{11}	Notice the space between the number and the exponent.
8^{13}	5.497558139 $\times$ 10^{11}	

A calculator display like those above means that the calculator has gone into scientific notation mode. This means that this number is so large that it cannot be displayed all at once on the screen. The calculator goes into a special format to display as much of the number as it can.

When a calculator displays 5.497558139E11 or 5.497558139 ^{11}, it means

$$5.497558139 \times 10^{11} = 549{,}755{,}813{,}900$$

When a calculator displays 5.497558139E11, the number 11 to the right of the E represents the exponent on 10.

$$5.497558139E11 = 5.497558139 \times 10^{11}$$

A different calculator might display the value as 5.497558139 ^{11}.

In this display, the number 11 in the superscript represents the exponent on 10. The spacing between the number 5.497558139 and the exponent of 11 indicates scientific notation.

$$5.497558139\ ^{11} = 5.497558139 \times 10^{11}$$

Remember that we work in a number system in base 10. This means each place value is a *power* of 10. For example, 400 can be written as $400 = 4 \times 100$. Because $100 = 10^2$, 400 in scientific notation would be written as $400 = 4 \times 10^2$. A calculator may display this as 4E2 or 4 ^{2}. Be very careful to read 4 ^{2} correctly when there is a space between the 4 and the exponent of 2 on a calculator. It means 4×10^2, not 4 squared. The form that we use when we write it by hand is 4×10^2. We say that 400 is in standard form and 4×10^2 is written by using scientific notation.

What's That Mean?

Power

Exponents are sometimes referred to as *powers*. In the expression 5^3, 3 is referred to as the *exponent* or the *power* of 5.

> **DEFINITION**
>
> **Scientific Notation**   A number in the form $a \times 10^n$ where $1 \le |a| < 10$ and n is an integer is said to be in scientific notation.

We now will learn how to change scientific notation into standard form.

> **Steps to Convert a Number Written in Scientific Notation to Standard Form**
>
> **The exponent on 10 is positive n:** Multiply by 10^n, which is equivalent to moving the decimal point n places to the right.

Example 3   Converting scientific notation to standard form

Write each of the following numbers in standard form.

a. 4.53×10^5 **b.** 9.32×10^7

SOLUTION

a. The exponent on 10 is 5. Move the decimal point five places to the right.

$$4.53 \times 10^5 = 4.53 \cdot 100{,}000 = 453{,}000$$

Therefore, 4.53×10^5 has the standard form 453,000.

b. The exponent on 10 is 7. Move the decimal point seven places to the right.

$$9.32 \times 10^7 = 9.32 \cdot 10{,}000{,}000 = 93{,}200{,}000$$

Therefore, 9.32×10^7 has the standard form 93,200,000.

PRACTICE PROBLEM FOR EXAMPLE 3

Write each of the following numbers in standard form.

a. 1.02×10^6 **b.** 4.51×10^9

In Chapter 5, we will study scientific notation more closely, as we learn more about exponents. For now, it is important to be able to read these numbers correctly from a calculator.

Order of Operations

In Chapter R, we studied four operations used to combine real numbers. Those operations were addition, subtraction, multiplication, and division. We have just learned a new way to combine numbers, namely, *exponentiation*. The list of basic operations now includes these five operations, which are used throughout algebra.

What's That Mean?

Exponentiation

The operation of finding a power of a number is called *exponentiation*.

DEFINITIONS

Basic Operations The basic operations used in algebra are as follows:

1. **Addition** The two (or more) quantities we are adding are called **addends** or **terms.** The result of an addition is called a **sum.**

2. **Subtraction** The two (or more) quantities we are subtracting are called **terms.** The result of a subtraction is called a **difference.**

3. **Multiplication** The two (or more) quantities we are multiplying are called **factors.** The result of a multiplication is called a **product.**

4. **Division** The result of a division is called a **quotient.**

5. **Exponentiation** Exponential notation takes the form a^n, where a is called the **base** and n is the **exponent.**

The order-of-operations agreement must be updated to include this new operation, exponentiation. Recall that to use the order-of-operations agreement, terms are first identified. In an expression, terms are identified as the things that are added or subtracted. Now we will also see terms that include exponents.

Example 4 Identifying terms

Identify the terms in each expression.

a. $\dfrac{8}{4} - 16 + 9 \cdot 3 - 5^2$ **b.** $2^3 + 16 \div 4 \cdot 3$

SOLUTION

a. This expression has four terms. Remember that the terms are parts added or subtracted, so they are separated by addition and subtraction symbols. The terms are circled.

$$\left(\frac{8}{4}\right) \left(- 16\right) + \left(9 \cdot 3\right) \left(- 5^2\right)$$

b. This expression has two terms. There are two terms separated by an addition symbol. The terms are circled.

$$\left(2^3\right) + \left(16 \div 4 \cdot 3\right)$$

PRACTICE PROBLEM FOR EXAMPLE 4

Identify the terms in each expression.

a. $3^4 - \dfrac{10}{2} + 5 \cdot 4$ **b.** $9^4 - 16 \cdot 3 + 9 - 6$

The order-of-operations agreement has been expanded to include exponents. In general, the order-of-operations agreement remains the same as in Chapter R.

Steps to Use the Order-of-Operations Agreement

1. Evaluate any exponents inside each term, working from left to right.
2. Evaluate all of the operations (multiplications and divisions) inside of each term, working from left to right.
3. Add and subtract the terms, working from left to right.

Steps 2 and 3 of the order-of-operations agreement call for working on the multiplications and divisions in order from left to right, then working on the additions and subtractions in order from left to right. Think of evaluating an expression in the same order as English is read, from left to right, and it will seem natural to do the operations in the same order.

Example 5   Ordering the operations

Evaluate each expression.

a. $75 - 7^2$ **b.** $5^3 - 16 \div 8 - (-3)$ **c.** $4^3 \div 8 \cdot 7$

SOLUTION

Circle the terms to help focus on doing the correct operations.

a. This expression has two terms.

$\quad$ (75) $($ $- 7^2$ $)$ $\qquad$ *Circle the terms.*

$\quad = 75 - 49$ $\qquad$ *Do the exponent first.*

$\quad = 26$ $\qquad$ *Do the subtraction last.*

b. This expression has three terms.

$\quad$ $($ 5^3 $)($ $- 16 \div 8$ $)($ $- (-3)$ $)$ $\qquad$ *Circle the terms.*

$\quad = 125 - 16 \div 8 - (-3)$ $\qquad$ *Do the exponent.*

$\quad = 125 - 2 - (-3)$ $\qquad$ *Do the division.*

$\quad = 123 - (-3)$ $\qquad$ *Do the additions and subtractions from left to right.*

$\quad = 126$

c. This expression has one term.

$\quad$ $($ $4^3 \div 8 \cdot 7$ $)$ $\qquad$ *Do the exponent.*

$\quad = 64 \div 8 \cdot 7$ $\qquad$ *Do the division.*

$\quad = 8 \cdot 7$ $\qquad$ *Do the multiplication.*

$\quad = 56$

PRACTICE PROBLEM FOR EXAMPLE 5

Evaluate each expression.

a. $6 + 3 \cdot 4 - 2 \div 2$ **b.** $8 \div 2 + 6 \cdot 3 - 3 \cdot 3 + 28 \div 4$ **c.** $5^2 - 16 + 9$ ■

Now try to enter all of these expressions, exactly as they are written, all at once on a calculator. Do not hit Enter or = until the entire expression has been typed in. The results will be the same as those in Example 5. This is because calculators are programmed with the order-of-operations agreement in mind.

In evaluating expressions, more complicated expressions involving grouping symbols, such as parentheses or absolute value bars, can appear. Therefore, the order-of-operations agreement has been expanded to include grouping symbols.

Steps to Perform the Order-of-Operations Agreement with Grouping Symbols

1. Evaluate everything inside the grouping symbols first, inside to outside working from left to right, using the basic order-of-operations agreement.
2. Evaluate all exponents, inside to outside working from left to right.
3. Do all multiplications and divisions in the order they occur, working from left to right.
4. Do all additions and subtractions in the order they occur, working from left to right.

■ Calculator Details

Scientific calculators have been programmed with the order-of-operations agreement. If the expression is entered *exactly* the way it is written in the problem, the calculator will evaluate it correctly. For example, to enter $4^3 \div 8 \cdot 7$, enter

The calculator will display the correct answer of 56.

■ Connecting the Concepts

What are grouping symbols?

Grouping symbols can include any of the following.

Parentheses: $(9 - 16)$

Square Brackets: $[4 \cdot 12 - 10]$

Curly Braces: $\{2 \div 14 + 7\}$

Absolute Value Bars: $|-2 + 5|$

Fraction Bar: $\dfrac{(6(-5) + 8)}{2}$

Square Root: $\sqrt{6 + 3}$

Example 6 Evaluating expressions

Evaluate each expression using the order-of-operations agreement.

a. $8 \cdot 5 \div (12 - 10 \div 5) + 8 \cdot 4$

b. $(7 - 2)^3$

c. $(26 - 10 \cdot 2) \div 3 + \dfrac{18 - 3 \cdot 2}{2 + 1}$

d. $|17 - 4|^2 + \dfrac{10 \cdot 4}{2 \cdot 6 - 4} \cdot 3$

SOLUTION

a. Remember to evaluate grouping symbols first.

$8 \cdot 5 \div (12 - 10 \div 5) + 8 \cdot 4$	Do the operations inside the parentheses first.
$= 8 \cdot 5 \div (12 - 2) + 8 \cdot 4$	Divide inside the parentheses, then subtract.
$= 8 \cdot 5 \div 10 + 8 \cdot 4$	
$= 40 \div 10 + 8 \cdot 4$	Do multiplications and divisions next.
$= 4 + 32$	
$= 36$	Do the addition last.

b.

$(7 - 2)^3$	Do the operations inside the parentheses first.
$= 5^3$	Do the exponent second.
$= 125$	

c. The key to doing this problem correctly is to recall that a fraction bar is considered a grouping symbol. Work out the numerator and denominator separately. Then evaluate the division indicated by the fraction bar.

$(26 - 10 \cdot 2) \div 3 + \dfrac{18 - 3 \cdot 2}{2 + 1}$	Evaluate inside the parentheses and the fraction bar first.
$= (26 - 20) \div 3 + \dfrac{18 - 6}{3}$	
$= 6 \div 3 + \dfrac{12}{3}$	Do multiplications and divisions.
$= 2 + 4$	Do the addition.
$= 6$	

d. $|17 - 4|^2 + \dfrac{10 \cdot 4}{2 \cdot 6 - 4} \cdot 3$	Evaluate within the absolute value and the fraction first.
$= |13|^2 + \dfrac{40}{12 - 4} \cdot 3$	Do the exponent next.
$= 169 + \dfrac{40}{8} \cdot 3$	Do the multiplications and divisions in order from left to right.
$= 169 + 5 \cdot 3$	
$= 169 + 15$	Do the addition.
$= 184$	

PRACTICE PROBLEM FOR EXAMPLE 6

Evaluate each expression using the order-of-operations agreement.

a. $16 \div (-8) \cdot 3 - (5 \cdot 3) + 12 \cdot 5$

b. $(-3 - 4)^2$

c. $|9 - 2 \cdot 3| + (-6) \div (-18 \div 3)$

d. $\dfrac{(-2)^2 + 4 \cdot 3}{7 - 2 \cdot 3} - [10 \div 2]$

Properties of Real Numbers

There are three very important properties about the operations of addition, subtraction, multiplication, and division. These properties allow us to perform operations on numbers quickly.

What's That Mean?

PEMDAS

There is a handy mnemonic to help remember the order-of-operations agreement. It is PEMDAS, which can be remembered as Please Excuse My Dear Aunt Sally. The letters in PEMDAS stand for:

P = Parentheses (evaluate grouping symbols first, working from left to right)

E = Exponents (evaluate exponents second, working from left to right)

MD = multiplications and divisions (evaluate multiplications and divisions in the order in which they occur, working from left to right)

AS = additions and subtractions (evaluate additions and subtractions in the order in which they occur, working from left to right).

If the order in which an operation is performed does not matter (that is, does not change the result), then the operation is said to be **commutative.** For example, in the morning, most of us brush our hair and brush our teeth. It does not matter which brushing we perform first: The order does not matter. This, mathematically, is a commutative operation.

Addition is commutative: $5 + 10 = 10 + 5$. The result is 15 regardless of which way 10 and 5 are added. Rearrangement of the problem can also be helpful in a multiplication problem. The commutative properties state that real numbers can be added or multiplied in any order.

> ## COMMUTATIVE PROPERTY
>
> If a and b are any real numbers, then the commutative properties are as follows:
>
> The **commutative property of addition** is $a + b = b + a$
>
> $$8 + 5 = 5 + 8$$
>
> The **commutative property of multiplication** is $a \cdot b = b \cdot a$
>
> $$7 \cdot 9 = 9 \cdot 7$$

Suppose Natalie wants to buy a piece of candy for \$0.40, a bag of chips for \$0.75, and a soda for \$1.25. If she adds the numbers in the given order using the order-of-operations agreement (PEMDAS) to compute $0.40 + 0.75 + 1.25$, she will first add \$0.40 and \$0.75, to get \$1.15. Then Natalie has to add on \$1.25 to get the final result of \$2.40. But if she first adds \$0.75 (chips) and \$1.25 (soda) in her head to get \$2.00, then adds on the additional \$0.40 (candy), Natalie will get the same answer of \$2.40. This alternative calculation can be written by using parentheses to group the cost for the chips and soda.

$$0.40 + (0.75 + 1.25)$$

It can be easier to combine the \$1.25 and \$0.75 to get \$2.00 first, then add on the \$0.40 at the end. This is an example of the **associative property of addition.** The associative property of addition tells us that it is permissible to group the order of addition in any convenient way and get the same result.

> ## ASSOCIATIVE PROPERTY
>
> If a, b, and c are any real numbers, then the associative properties are as follows:
>
> The **associative property of addition** is $a + (b + c) = (a + b) + c$
>
> $$(0.40 + 0.75) + 1.25 = 0.40 + (0.75 + 1.25)$$
>
> The **associative property of multiplication** is $a \cdot (b \cdot c) = (a \cdot b) \cdot c$
>
> $$2(3 \cdot 5) = (2 \cdot 3) \cdot 5$$

Example 7   Identifying properties

Identify the property used in each statement.

a. $2 + 7 = 7 + 2$

b. $3(-2 \cdot 6) = (3 \cdot (-2)) \cdot 6$

c. $(3 + 5) + 10 = 3 + (5 + 10)$

d. $6(-41) = (-41) \cdot 6$

What's That Mean?

Property

In mathematics, the word *property* means an essential attribute or characteristic of something. This is different from the everyday use of the word *property*, which means something you own, such as land or a car.

What's That Mean?

Commutative

The word *commutative* comes from a French word that means "to switch or substitute." The commutative property says that we can switch the order of terms in an operation and get the same result.

SOLUTION

a. $2 + 7 = 7 + 2$

This is an example of the commutative property of addition, because the order of the terms has been changed.

b. $3(-2 \cdot 6) = (3 \cdot (-2)) \cdot 6$

This is an example of the associative property of multiplication, because the order of the numbers was not changed but how they are grouped was changed.

c. $(3 + 5) + 10 = 3 + (5 + 10)$

This is an example of the associative property of addition, because the order of the numbers was not changed but how they are grouped was changed.

d. $6(-41) = (-41) \cdot 6$

This is an example of the commutative property of multiplication because the order of the numbers was changed.

PRACTICE PROBLEM FOR EXAMPLE 7

Identify the property used in each statement.

a. $29 + (15 + 29) = (29 + 15) + 29$

b. $(-6) \cdot (-3) = (-3) \cdot (-6)$

c. $(5 \cdot 17) \cdot 3 = 5 \cdot (17 \cdot 3)$

d. $-100 + 46 = 46 + (-100)$

CONCEPT INVESTIGATION

Which properties are not commutative?

1. Subtract the following integers. In the third column, note whether the results in the first column and second column are the same or different.

Subtract	Subtract	Same or Different?
$6 - 3 = 3$	$3 - 6 = -3$	Different
$10 - 5 =$	$5 - 10 =$	
$25 - 9 =$	$9 - 25 =$	
$8 - 9 =$	$9 - 8 =$	
$14 - 3 =$	$3 - 14 =$	

2. Do you get the same answer when you reverse the order of subtraction?

3. Is subtraction commutative?

4. Perform the following division problems. In the third column, note whether the results in the first column and second column are the same or different.

Division	Division	Same or Different?
$10 \div 2 = 5$	$2 \div 10 = 0.2$	Different
$16 \div 2 =$	$2 \div 16 =$	
$(-3) \div 1 =$	$1 \div (-3) =$	
$45 \div (-5) =$	$(-5) \div 45 =$	
$5 \div 2 =$	$2 \div 5 =$	

5. Do you get the same answer when you reverse the order of division?

6. Is division commutative?

Notice that both the commutative properties and associative properties are defined only for addition and multiplication. They do not work for subtraction and division. Order matters in problems involving these operations.

In the next Concept Investigation, we are going to explore another important property, called the **distributive property.** The goal is to understand when it is appropriate to use the distributive property.

CONCEPT INVESTIGATION

When is it okay to distribute?

1. Complete the following table using the first two rows as examples. In the third column, compare whether or not the results in the first two columns are the same or different. Make sure you use the order-of-operations agreement correctly.

		Same or Different?
$6(2 + 3)$ $= 6(5)$ $= 30$	$6 \cdot 2 + 6 \cdot 3$ $= 12 + 18$ $= 30$	Same
$4(5 + 6)$ $= 4(11)$ $= 44$	$4 \cdot 5 + 4 \cdot 6$ $= 20 + 24$ $= 44$	Same
$2(3 + 5)$	$2 \cdot 3 + 2 \cdot 5$	
$5(7 + 11)$	$5 \cdot 7 + 5 \cdot 11$	
$-2(8 - 4)$	$-2 \cdot 8 - (-2) \cdot 4$	

2. Do you always get the same value for columns 1 and 2?

3. Can you "distribute" a factor over the operation of addition or subtraction?

4. Complete the following table using the first two rows as examples. In the third column, compare whether or not the results in the first two columns are the same or different. Make sure you use the order-of-operations agreement correctly.

		Same or Different?
$3(2 \cdot 5)$ $= 3(10)$ $= 30$	$(3 \cdot 2)(3 \cdot 5)$ $= 6 \cdot 15$ $= 90$	Different
$4(3 \cdot 2)$ $= 4(6)$ $= 24$	$(4 \cdot 3)(4 \cdot 2)$ $= (12)(8)$ $= 96$	Different
$-6(4 \div 2)$	$-6(4) \div -6(2)$	
$-3(-2 \cdot 5)$	$-3(-2) \cdot (-3)(5)$	
$5(9 \div 3)$	$(5 \cdot 9) \div (5 \cdot 3)$	

5. Do you always get the same value for columns 1 and 2?

6. Can you "distribute" a factor over the operation of multiplication or division?

Calculator Details

To enter an expression such as $6(2 + 3)$ correctly on your calculator, enter it as it is written, including parentheses and the implied multiplication.

Your calculator will display 30.

If you do not enter the parentheses for the expression $6(2 + 3)$, the calculator will compute

The calculator will multiply the 6 and 2 and then add 3 to get the result 15.

To enter $6 \cdot 2 + 6 \cdot 3$, enter it exactly as written, including the operations.

The calculator will display 30.

In many problems, several operations are combined. The distributive property helps to simplify problems that combine multiplication and addition (or subtraction). You might want to remember that the distributive property says that each term in the group must be multiplied.

■ Skill Connection

Area of a Rectangle

The area of a rectangle with a length of l and a width of w is

$$l \cdot w$$

DISTRIBUTIVE PROPERTY

If a, b, and c are real numbers, then the **distributive property** states

$$a(b + c) = a \cdot b + a \cdot c$$
$$a(b - c) = a \cdot b - a \cdot c$$

Example 8 Using the distributive property

There are two bedrooms, side by side, that have to be carpeted. See the figure. This requires that the total square footage of both rooms be calculated.

a. Compute (separately) the areas of the two rooms. Find the total area by adding the areas of the two individual rooms.

b. Consider the two rooms to be one large room. First compute the total length (of both rooms). What is the width? Find the total area by multiplying the length times the width.

c. This is an example of which property?

SOLUTION

a. The area of the room on the right of the diagram is

$$(16 \text{ ft})(10 \text{ ft}) = 160 \text{ ft}^2$$

The area of the room on the left of the diagram is

$$(12 \text{ ft})(10 \text{ ft}) = 120 \text{ ft}^2$$

Therefore, the total area is

$$(16 \text{ ft})(10 \text{ ft}) + (12 \text{ ft})(10 \text{ ft})$$
$$= 160 \text{ ft}^2 + 120 \text{ ft}^2$$
$$= 280 \text{ ft}^2$$

b. The total length is 12 ft + 16 ft. The total area is

$$10 \text{ ft} \cdot (12 \text{ ft} + 16 \text{ ft}) = 10 \text{ ft} \cdot 28 \text{ ft} = 280 \text{ ft}^2$$

c. Notice that we get the same total area using either method. This is an example of the distributive property.

Example 9 The distributive property versus the order-of-operations agreement

Evaluate the expression $7(9 + 3)$ as indicated.

a. Use the distributive property.   **b.** Use the order-of-operations agreement.

c. Are the answers to parts a and b the same?

SOLUTION

a. Use the distributive property to evaluate.

$$7(9 + 3) = 7 \cdot 9 + 7 \cdot 3 \qquad \text{Distribute the 7.}$$
$$= 63 + 21 \qquad \text{Add.}$$
$$= 84$$

b. Use the order-of-operations agreement to evaluate the expression.

$$7(9 + 3) \qquad \text{Simplify inside the parentheses first.}$$
$$= 7(12) \qquad \text{Multiply.}$$
$$= 84$$

c. The answers to parts a and b are the same. It does not matter whether we use the distributive property first or follow the order of operations when we evaluate a problem like this one.

PRACTICE PROBLEM FOR EXAMPLE 9

Evaluate the expression $5(16 - 7)$ as indicated.

a. Use the distributive property.   **b.** Use the order-of-operations agreement.

c. Are the answers to parts a and b the same?

Example 10 The distributive property

Evaluate the expression using the distributive property.

a. $4(3 + 6) - 10$ **b.** $-(4 - 11) + 34$

SOLUTION

a. First, distribute the 4 through the addition inside the parentheses.

$$4(3 + 6) - 10 = 4(3) + 4(6) - 10 \qquad \text{Distribute the 4.}$$
$$= 12 + 24 - 10 \qquad \text{Multiply.}$$
$$= 36 - 10 \qquad \text{Add and subtract.}$$
$$= 26$$

b. Because $-(4 - 11) = -1(4 - 11)$, distribute the negative 1 through the subtraction inside the parentheses. Watch your signs carefully.

$$-(4 - 11) + 34 = -(4) - (-11) + 34 \qquad \text{Distribute the negative 1.}$$
$$= -4 + 11 + 34 \qquad \text{Multiply.}$$
$$= 7 + 34 \qquad \text{Add.}$$
$$= 41$$

PRACTICE PROBLEM FOR EXAMPLE 10

Evaluate the expression using the distributive property.

a. $7(2 + 8) - 25$ **b.** $-(17 - 8) + 5$

1.1 Exercises

1. Write in exponential form: $7 \cdot 7 \cdot 7 \cdot 7 \cdot 7$

2. Write in exponential form: $9 \cdot 9 \cdot 9 \cdot 9 \cdot 9 \cdot 9 \cdot 9$

3. Write in expanded form: 5^3

4. Write in expanded form: 3^4

5. Write in expanded form: $(-7)^3$

6. Write in expanded form: $(-1)^4$

7. Write in exponential form:

$$(-3) \cdot (-3) \cdot (-3) \cdot (-3) \cdot (-3)$$

8. Write in exponential form: $(-2)(-2)(-2)$

9. Write in exponential form: $\dfrac{2}{3} \cdot \dfrac{2}{3} \cdot \dfrac{2}{3}$

10. Write in exponential form: $\dfrac{4}{5} \cdot \dfrac{4}{5} \cdot \dfrac{4}{5} \cdot \dfrac{4}{5}$

11. Write in expanded form: $\left(\dfrac{5}{8}\right)^3$

12. Write in expanded form: $\left(\dfrac{6}{11}\right)^4$

For Exercises 13 through 20, find the value without a calculator.

13. 2^3

14. 3^3

15. $(-2)^4$

16. $(-4)^2$

17. -5^2

18. -3^2

19. 15^0

20. 10^0

For Exercises 21 through 34, use a calculator to calculate the value of the exponential expression.

21. 3^7

22. 8^5

23. $(-5)^2$

24. $(-3)^5$

25. -7^4

26. -5^4

27. $(-1)^3$

28. $(-1)^4$

29. $\left(\dfrac{3}{4}\right)^3$

30. $\left(\dfrac{1}{6}\right)^4$

31. $(0.35)^2$

32. $(1.42)^3$

33. -6^3

34. -4^3

For Exercises 35 through 42, convert each value in scientific notation to standard notation.

35. 1.034×10^6

36. 4.29×10^8

37. 9.3×10^7

38. 5.31×10^5

39. 4.001×10^9

40. 1.0095×10^8

41. -5.487×10^4

42. -1.295×10^{11}

For Exercises 43 through 52, identify the terms in the expression. Do not evaluate the expression.

43. $4 \div 2 + 3 \cdot 27 - |-27|$

44. $15 + \dfrac{18}{3} - |-9 \cdot 4| - 22$

45. $8 \cdot 9 - 4 \cdot 16^2$

46. $9^3 - \dfrac{4 \cdot 3}{16}$

47. $\dfrac{3}{7} - \dfrac{1}{2} \div 8$

48. $\dfrac{6}{5} + \dfrac{5}{2} \cdot 6 - 12$

49. $(-4)^5 \cdot 2 \div 32$

50. $(-15)^2 \div 5 \cdot 7$

51. $(-64) \div 4 \div 2$

52. $81 \div (-9) \div 3$

For Exercises 53 through 66, evaluate each expression using the order-of-operations agreement.

53. $16 + 8 \div 2$

54. $9 - 18 \div 2$

55. $\dfrac{4}{5} - \dfrac{2}{3} \cdot \dfrac{9}{5}$

56. $8 \div \dfrac{16}{3} + \dfrac{4}{7}$

57. $3 \cdot 12 - 16 \div 4 + 1$

58. $4 \cdot 3 - (-7) + 16 \div 4$

59. $1 + \dfrac{7}{10} \cdot \dfrac{4}{5} - \dfrac{2}{5}$

60. $6 \div \dfrac{2}{5} + 4 \cdot \dfrac{3}{8} - 2$

61. $(-2)^3 + 4 \cdot (-6)$

62. $32 \div 8 + (-3)^2$

63. $-9 + 7 \cdot 3 - 15 \div 3 - 4^2 + (-8)$

64. $-(-6)^2 \cdot 3 + 16 \div (-4) - (-7)$

65. $-9 \cdot 3 + 5 - 15 \div 3 - 2^3$

66. $(-1)^4 + 9 \cdot (-2) - 6 \div 3$

For Exercises 67 through 80, evaluate each expression using the order-of-operations agreement. Pay attention to the grouping symbols.

67. $|16 - (3 \cdot 8)| + 9$

68. $4 + |-24 - 6|$

69. $\dfrac{4 \cdot 5 - 4}{6 - 4}$

70. $\dfrac{6 + 3 \cdot 5 - 7}{9 - 2}$

71. $3 \cdot \dfrac{-4 + 6 \cdot 8}{15 - 2^2} - 3^2$

72. $-5 + \dfrac{9 - 3}{2 \cdot 3} + (-2)^2$

73. $(18 - 2 \cdot 3)^3$

74. $10 + (-4 + 5 \cdot 2)^3$

75. $4 \div (-3 - 14 \div 2) - (-2)^2$

76. $-5 \cdot 4 - 2 + 3 \cdot 5^2 + |15 - 27|$

77. $(49 - 7 \cdot 2) \div 5 + \dfrac{30 - (-6) \cdot 2}{-4 + 2}$

78. $\dfrac{27 \cdot 2 + 3}{|3 - (6 \cdot 3)|}$

79. $|3 - 5 \cdot 6| + (-3 - 5)^2$

80. $(5 - 8)^3 + |-6 - 7 \cdot 2|$

For Exercises 81 through 92, identify the property used: the commutative property of addition or multiplication, the associative property of addition or multiplication, or the distributive property.

81. $3 + (2 + 5) = (3 + 2) + 5$

82. $(16 + 9) + 2 = 16 + (9 + 2)$

83. $\dfrac{3}{5} \cdot 24 = 24 \cdot \dfrac{3}{5}$

84. $61\left(\dfrac{-5}{16}\right) = \left(\dfrac{-5}{16}\right) \cdot 61$

85. $-3(14 + 7) = -3 \cdot 14 + (-3) \cdot 7$

86. $2(5 + 3) = 2 \cdot 5 + 2 \cdot 3$

87. $(-11) + 19 = 19 + (-11)$

88. $3 + 9 = 9 + 3$

89. $3(9 - 2) = 3 \cdot 9 - 3 \cdot 2$

90. $-7(25 - 16) = -7 \cdot 25 - (-7) \cdot 16$

91. $(5 \cdot 3) \cdot 10 = 5(3 \cdot 10)$

92. $(9 \cdot 8)(-3) = 9(8(-3))$

93. Complete the following table by placing a check in each box that is true.

Operation	Commutative Property	Associative Property
Addition		
Subtraction		
Multiplication		
Division		

94. Complete the following table by answering true or false.

Equation	True or False?
$4(8 - 5) = 4 \cdot 8 - 4 \cdot 5$	
$2(3 \cdot 6) = 2 \cdot 3 \cdot 2 \cdot 6$	
$3(9 + 7) = 3 \cdot 9 + 3 \cdot 7$	
$8(4 \div 2) = 8 \cdot 4 \div 8 \cdot 2$	

For Exercises 95 through 104, use the distributive property to rewrite the expression. Do not evaluate the expression.

95. $2(5 + 9)$ **96.** $2(8 + 7)$

97. $16(9 - 5)$ **98.** $9(8 - 10)$

99. $-2(8 + 7)$ **100.** $-2(5 + 10)$

101. $-2(7 - 16)$ **102.** $-1(-3 - 7)$

103. $\dfrac{7}{9}(11 + 15)$ **104.** $\dfrac{5}{8}(29 - 17)$

For Exercises 105 through 114, evaluate the expression using either the order-of-operations agreement or the distributive property.

105. $6(3 + 17)$ **106.** $8(14 + 9)$

107. $-5(6 + 27)$ **108.** $-7(15 + 3)$

109. $6(7 - 16) + 12$ **110.** $3(8 - 24) + 18$

111. $-(7 - 28) - 9$ **112.** $-(16 - 30) - 7$

113. $\dfrac{1}{2}(5 - 17)$ **114.** $\dfrac{3}{5}(-16 + 31)$

1.2 Algebra and Working with Variables

LEARNING OBJECTIVES

- Work with variables.
- Evaluate expressions.
- Convert units.
- Define variables.
- Translate phrases into algebraic expressions.
- Generate expressions from tables.

Constants and Variables

People have always wanted to solve problems that involved quantities that are unknown or that can vary. The need to solve these types of problems created the field of mathematics that we call *algebra*. In this course, we will study algebra, which is the branch of mathematics that solves problems involving quantities that are unknown or can change.

Algebra has been used since ancient times to solve problems. Ancient civilizations, such as those of Babylonia, Egypt, Greece, India, and China, stated problems using words and sentences and solved those problems using techniques that we will study. One example is to be found in the Rhind Papyrus (a paper document from Egypt, written in 1650 B.C.E.), which states:

Rhind Papyrus

Divide 100 loaves among 10 men including a boatman, a foreman and a doorkeeper, who receive double portions. What is the share of each?

Source: http://vmoc.museophile.com/algebra/

In this problem, the number of loaves for each man is unknown. One of the arithmetic operations involved is division. Like this problem, many algebra problems contain both arithmetic operations and an unknown quantity. Since algebra builds on arithmetic and arithmetic depends on numbers, the first topic we studied in Chapter R was sets of numbers.

In algebra, we use letters to represent quantities that can change, or vary. These letters are called **variables.** A value that cannot change is called a **constant.** Often the letters x, y, and z are used as variables, but be aware that any letter may be used. In application problems ("real-world" problems that come out of a situation), other letters that connect to the meaning of the quantity that is changing are often used. The letter o is avoided as a variable, though, because it can be confused with the number 0.

> ### DEFINITIONS
>
> **Variable**   A variable is a symbol, usually a letter, used to represent a quantity that can change (vary).
>
> **Constant**   A constant is a value that does not change.

Frequently, variables are used in a problem in which a quantity is repeatedly computed. For example, suppose we are interested in computing your weekly salary over a period of nine weeks. Since your pay is dependent on the number of hours you worked and the number of hours might vary each week, it would be efficient to introduce a variable in this situation. We might use the variable h to represent the number of hours that you worked in a particular week.

In problems that come out of a real-world circumstance, we use letters that prompt us as to what the variable represents (such as h for hours).

Example 1   Varying the weekly pay

Kevin works for Patio Furniture Plus. He currently earns $8.75 an hour. His weekly pay can be computed as $8.75h$, where h is the number of hours he worked for a week. Here, $8.75h$ means 8.75 multiplied by h.

a. If Kevin works 18 hours in a week, what is his weekly pay?

b. If Kevin works 29 hours in a week, what is his weekly pay?

SOLUTION

a. If Kevin works 18 hours in a week, then we can substitute 18 for h, and we get

$$8.75(18) = 157.50$$

If Kevin works 18 hours in a week, his weekly pay is $157.50.

b. If Kevin works 29 hours in a week, then we can substitute 29 for h, and we get

$$8.75(29) = 253.75$$

If Kevin works 29 hours in a week, his weekly pay is $253.75.

■ Connecting the Concepts

How can the product of a variable and constant be written?

A product of a variable and constant can be written in several ways.

$$8.75h$$
$$8.75 \cdot h$$
$$8.75(h)$$
$$(8.75)h$$
$$(8.75)(h)$$

The first way, $8.75h$, is the most common. When there is no operation symbol between a constant and a variable, the operation is a multiplication.

PRACTICE PROBLEM FOR EXAMPLE 1

The Cruz family is planning a driving trip. They figure that with occasional rest stops, they will drive an average of 50 miles an hour. The distance they drive can be computed by $50t$, where t is the number of hours for which they drive.

a. What is the distance they will drive if they travel for 4.5 hours?

b. What is the distance they will drive if they travel for 7.25 hours?

In all application problems, write the answer using complete sentences as in Example 1.

In Example 1, Kevin's weekly pay was given by $8.75h$. The number 8.75 (the multiplier of h) has a special name. It is called the **coefficient** of h.

> ### DEFINITION
>
> **Coefficient**   The coefficient of a variable term is the numerical factor of the term.
>
> The coefficient of the term $4x$ is 4.

Example 2   **Managing the monthly budget**

Rebecca gets paid monthly from her employer. The amount she makes each month depends on the number of hours she worked that month. Let d be the dollar amount of her paycheck for a month. Rebecca has to pay $550 a month for rent. After paying her rent, Rebecca has $d - 550$ left.

i love images/Jupiterimages

a. If Rebecca earns $1200 in a month, how much money does she have left after paying her rent?

b. If Rebecca earns $1450 in a month, how much money does she have left after paying her rent?

SOLUTION

a. If Rebecca earns $1200 in a month, then substitute in $d = 1200$ and get

$$1200 - 550 = 650$$

If Rebecca earns $1200 in a month, she will have $650 left after paying her rent.

b. If Rebecca earns $1450 in a month, then substitute in $d = 1450$ and get

$$1450 - 550 = 900$$

If Rebecca earns $1450 in a month, she will have $900 left after paying her rent.

Evaluating Expressions

In Examples 1 and 2, we substituted in a value for the variable and then simplified the remaining expression. This process is called **evaluating an expression.** We are now going to further investigate what it means to evaluate an expression.

> ### Steps to Evaluate an Expression
>
> 1. Substitute the given value of the variable into the expression.
> 2. Simplify, using the order-of-operations agreement.

Example 3 Evaluating an expression

Evaluate each of the variable expressions for the given value(s) of the variable.

a. The fees for taking u credits at Grossmont College are $13 + 26u$ dollars. Find the fees for taking 6 credits, 9 credits, or 12 credits.

b. The cost for renting a 29-foot U-Haul truck for a 1-day rental is $29.95 + 0.79m$ dollars, where m is the number of miles driven. Find the cost for renting the truck if you drive 25 miles. Find the cost for renting the truck if you drive 72 miles.

© iStockphoto/track 5

SOLUTION

a. To find the cost of taking 6 credits, substitute $u = 6$ into the expression and evaluate.

$$13 + 26(6) = \$169$$

The cost of taking 6 credits is $169.00.

To find the cost of taking 9 credits, substitute $u = 9$ into the expression and evaluate.

$$13 + 26(9) = \$247$$

The cost of taking 9 credits is $247.00.

To find the cost of taking 12 credits, substitute $u = 12$ into the expression and evaluate.

$$13 + 26(12) = \$325$$

The cost of taking 12 credits is $325.00.

b. To find the cost for renting the truck if you drive 25 miles, substitute $m = 25$ into the expression and evaluate.

$$29.95 + 0.79(25) = \$49.70$$

The cost of renting the truck and driving 25 miles is $49.70.

To find the cost for renting the truck if you drive 72 miles, substitute $m = 72$ into the expression and evaluate.

$$29.95 + 0.79(72) = \$86.83$$

The cost of renting the truck and driving 72 miles is $86.83.

Note that we round to the cents (hundredths) place, since the units are dollars.

PRACTICE PROBLEM FOR EXAMPLE 3

Evaluate each of the following expressions.

a. The cost in dollars of printing n pages at Palomar College is $0.10n$ when it costs $0.10 a page to print. Find the cost of printing 5, 10, and 25 pages.

b. The average home air conditioner uses $3500h$ watt-hours of electricity when it runs for h hours. Find the number of watt-hours of electricity used by the average home air conditioner in 4, 8, and 24 hours.

Source: http://michaelbluejay.com/electricity/cooling.html.

Example 4 Evaluating algebraic expressions

Evaluate each of the following expressions for the given value of the variable.

a. $6n + 8$ for $n = -2$

b. $2y^2 - \dfrac{12}{y} + 4$ for $y = 3$

c. $-4(t \div 6) + (9 - 2)^2$ for $t = -18$

SOLUTION

a.

$$6n + 8$$ Substitute in $n = -2$.

$$= 6(-2) + 8$$ Simplify.

$$= -12 + 8$$

$$= -4$$

b.

$$2y^2 - \dfrac{12}{y} + 4$$ Substitute in $y = 3$ for every y in the expression.

$$= 2(3)^2 - \dfrac{12}{3} + 4$$ Simplify using the order-of-operations agreement.

$$= 2(9) - 4 + 4$$

$$= 18 - 4 + 4$$

$$= 14 + 4$$

$$= 18$$

c.

$$-4(t \div 6) + (9 - 2)^2$$ Substitute in $t = -18$.

$$= -4[(-18) \div 6] + (9 - 2)^2$$ Add brackets to distinguish from parentheses.

$$= -4(-3) + 7^2$$ Simplify using the order-of-operations agreement.

$$= 12 + 49$$

$$= 61$$

PRACTICE PROBLEM FOR EXAMPLE 4

Evaluate each of the following expressions for the given value of the variable.

a. $-3h + 12$ for $h = 7$

b. $-3x^2 + 6x + 1$ for $x = -2$

c. $|-t + 6| + 2t^2 - 1$ for $t = 5$

▮ Connecting the Concepts

When do we use brackets?

In Example 4c, we can use either two sets of parentheses

$$((-18) \div 6)$$

or a pair of brackets and then parentheses:

$$[(-18) \div 6]$$

Often, we use the second form, $[(-18) \div 6]$, because it is easier to read.

Unit Conversions

We often have to convert from one system of units to another. For example, suppose you take a trip to Mexico. As of this writing, $1.00 (U.S.) is equivalent to 13.2343 MXN (Mexican pesos) (*Source: www.XE.com*). You want to buy a gift for your mother on a trip to Mexico, and it costs 142 pesos. How many U.S. dollars is that equivalent to? To convert from one system of units (in this example, pesos) to another (U.S. dollars), we rely on the concept of a unity fraction.

© Gary/Fotolia.

▮ What's That Mean?

Units

The *units* of a quantity refer to the way the quantity is being measured. When we say that 5 meters has the units of meters, we mean that the quantity 5 is being measured in meters.

▮ What's That Mean?

Unity Fraction

In fields such as chemistry and physics, unity fractions are called *conversion factors*.

DEFINITION

Unity Fraction A unity fraction is a fraction that has units in the numerator and denominator and whose simplified value is equal to 1.

What's That Mean?

Unit Abbreviations

Here is a list of abbreviations for commonly used units.

Length:
in. = inch
ft = foot
mi = mile
cm = centimeter
m = meter
km = kilometer

Weight:
lb = pound
kg = kilogram
g = gram

Capacity:
qt = quart
gal = gallon
oz = ounce
l = liter

Dry Measurement:
tsp = teaspoon
tbl = tablespoon

Area:
ft² = square foot
yd² = square yard

For example, 3 feet = 1 yard, so $\frac{3 \text{ feet}}{1 \text{ yard}}$ is a unity fraction (since the value of the fraction is 1). To convert units, we multiply the given quantity by the appropriate unity fraction. Place the units we are converting to in the numerator and the units we want to change in the denominator. Units can be divided out when multiplying fractions just as factors. Therefore, to convert 142 pesos to U.S. dollars, we would multiply as follows:

$$142 \text{ pesos} \cdot \frac{1 \text{ dollar}}{13.2343 \text{ pesos}}$$

$$= \frac{142 \text{ pesos}}{1} \cdot \frac{1 \text{ dollar}}{13.2343 \text{ pesos}} \approx 10.73 \text{ dollars}$$

Steps to Convert Units

1. Find the appropriate unity fraction needed for the problem. Put the units that are wanted in the final answer in the numerator and the units to be converted from in the denominator.
2. Multiply the given value by the unity fraction. Divide out the common units.
3. Reduce the fraction to lowest terms.

Note: Common unit conversions are found on the inside back cover.

Example 5   Convert units

Convert units as indicated. Round to the hundredths place if necessary.

a. Convert 56 cm (centimeters) to inches (in.). *Note:* There are 2.54 cm in 1 in.

b. Convert 2640 ft (feet) to miles (mi). *Note:* There are 5280 ft in 1 mi.

c. Convert 80 qt (quarts) to gallons (gal). *Note:* There are 4 qt in 1 gal.

d. Convert 60 kg (kilograms) to pounds (lb). *Note:* There are approximately 2.2 lb in 1 kg.

SOLUTION

First, form the unity fraction from the relationship between the two quantities. Then multiply the given quantity by the unity fraction and simplify.

a. First, form the unity fraction. We want to convert from the units of centimeters, so the units of centimeters will go into the denominator. We want to convert to the units of inches, so inches will go in the numerator. There are 2.54 cm in 1 inch, so the unity fraction is $\frac{1 \text{ in}}{2.54 \text{ cm}}$. Multiply 56 cm by this unity fraction, and simplify the expression as follows:

$$56 \text{ cm} \cdot \frac{1 \text{ in}}{2.54 \text{ cm}}$$

$$= \frac{56 \text{ cm}}{1} \cdot \frac{1 \text{ in}}{2.54 \text{ cm}}$$

$$= \frac{56 \text{ in}}{2.54} \approx 22.05 \text{ in}$$

Therefore, 56 cm is equal to approximately 22.05 in.

b. First, form the unity fraction. We want to convert to the units of miles, so miles will go into the numerator. We want to convert from the units of feet, so feet will go into the denominator. There are 5280 ft in 1 mi, so the unity fraction is $\frac{1 \text{ mi}}{5280 \text{ ft}}$.

Multiply 2640 ft by this unity fraction, and simplify the expression as follows:

Connecting the Concepts

What's in the denominator?

A value that does not have a denominator, such as 80, can be rewritten as a fraction with a denominator of 1.

$$80 = \frac{80}{1}$$

$$2640 \text{ ft} \cdot \frac{1 \text{ mi}}{5280 \text{ ft}}$$

$$= \frac{2640 \text{ ft}}{1} \cdot \frac{1 \text{ mi}}{5280 \text{ ft}} = 0.5 \text{ mi}$$

Therefore, 2640 ft is equal to 0.5 mi.

c. First, form the unity fraction. We want to convert to the units of gallons, so gallons will go in the numerator. We want to convert from the units of quarts, so quarts will go in the denominator. There are 4 qt in 1 gal, so the unity fraction is $\frac{1 \text{ gal}}{4 \text{ qt}}$.

Multiply 80 qt by this unity fraction, and simplify the expression as follows:

$$80 \text{ qt} \cdot \frac{1 \text{ gal}}{4 \text{ qt}}$$

$$= \frac{80 \text{ qt}}{1} \cdot \frac{1 \text{ gal}}{4 \text{ qt}} = 20 \text{ gal}$$

Therefore, 80 qt is equal to 20 gal.

d. First, form the unity fraction. We want to convert to the units of pounds, so pounds will go into the numerator. We want to convert from the units of kilograms, so kilograms will go into the denominator. There are approximately 2.2 lb in 1 kg, so the unity fraction is $\frac{2.2 \text{ lb}}{1 \text{ kg}}$. Multiply 60 kg by this unity fraction, and simplify the expression as follows:

$$60 \text{ kg} \cdot \frac{2.2 \text{ lb}}{1 \text{ kg}}$$

$$= \frac{60 \text{ kg}}{1} \cdot \frac{2.2 \text{ lb}}{1 \text{ kg}} = 132 \text{ lb}$$

Therefore, 60 kg is approximately equal to 132 lb.

PRACTICE PROBLEM FOR EXAMPLE 5

Convert units as indicated. Round to the hundredths place if necessary.

a. 500 feet (ft) to meters (m). There are approximately 3.28 ft in 1 m.

b. 42 oz (ounces) to grams (g). There are approximately 28.35 g in 1 oz.

c. 156 pounds (lb) to kilograms (kg). There are approximately 2.2 lb in 1 kg.

Defining Variables

Recall that a variable is a quantity that can change or is unknown. By defining variables and translating the problem statement into an expression, we can evaluate the expression for any value of the variable. In an application problem that represents a situation, to define a variable means to write a statement of what the variable represents including units. We represent a variable with shorthand notation, such as x.

Example 6   Defining the variables

Define variables for each problem situation below. This means to write a sentence that explains what the variable represents. Include the units of the variable.

a. Your weekly paycheck depends on how many hours you worked for that week.

b. You are driving to San Francisco from San Diego. How far you have driven since you left San Diego depends on your speed and how long you have been driving.

SOLUTION

Here are some reasonable definitions for the variables.

a. In this problem, there are two quantities that can change. One quantity is the number of hours worked for a given week, and the second is the amount of that week's paycheck. Let

$$h = \text{time worked each week in hours}$$
$$P = \text{amount of the weekly paycheck in dollars}$$

b. The three quantities that can change are the distance you have traveled, the speed of the car, and the number of hours spent driving. Let

$$d = \text{distance traveled in miles}$$
$$h = \text{time driven in hours}$$
$$s = \text{speed of the car in miles per hour (mph)}$$

PRACTICE PROBLEM FOR EXAMPLE 6

Define variables for each problem situation.

a. The temperature depends on the time of day.

b. The cost of your tuition for the semester depends on how many credits you are taking.

Translating Phrases into Algebraic Expressions

Once we have defined variables for a problem situation, we then translate the problem into an algebraic expression. When translating applications into algebraic expressions, it helps to know how to translate some commonly used phrases. The following tables give algebraic translations of some often used phrases.

Addition

Phrases Used for Addition	Translation
The sum of n and 4	$n + 4$
The total of 7 and x	$7 + x$
f increased by 16	$f + 16$
9 plus c	$9 + c$
100 more than t	$t + 100$
exceeds c by 50	$c + 50$
P added to 3	$3 + P$

Because addition is a commutative operation, we could have written any of the above in the opposite order. Thus, the statement *P added to 3* translates as both $3 + P$ and $P + 3$.

Connecting the Concepts

When do we reverse the order in subtraction?

Be very careful when translating *less than* and *subtracted from*. Notice that these are the only phrases we have seen so far for which you reverse the order of the terms. Ask yourself what number is being subtracted, and always put that number after the minus sign.

Subtraction

Phrases Used for Subtraction	Translation
92 minus y	$92 - y$
The difference of 24 and n	$24 - n$
9 subtracted from t	$t - 9$
W reduced by 8	$W - 8$
n decreased by 8	$n - 8$
100 less than x	$x - 100$

Subtraction is *not* a commutative operation, so the order does matter in the above statements. In subtraction, the terms cannot be rearranged. Remember that $5 - 3 = 2$ is different from $3 - 5 = -2$.

Multiplication

Phrases Used for Multiplication	Translation
The product of 6 and m	$6m$
4 times r	$4r$
Twice z	$2z$
Half of x	$\frac{1}{2}x$
30% of n	$0.30n$

Multiplication is a commutative operation, so order does not matter in the above translations. For this reason, $6m$ is equal to $m6$. However, it is traditional in algebra to write the number part first and the variable part last, so always write the final answer in the form $6m$. Recall that in the expression $6m$, 6 is called the coefficient of m.

Division

Phrases Used for Division	Translation
The quotient of n and 17	$\frac{n}{17}$
The ratio of 5 and x	$\frac{5}{x}$
Q divided by 12	$\frac{Q}{12}$

Division is *not* a commutative operation, so order matters in the above translations. Remember that $6 \div 3 = 2$ is different from $3 \div 6 = \frac{1}{2}$.

Example 7   Translating a phrase

Translate each of the following phrases into expressions. Note that *a number* translates as a variable (an unknown).

a. Twice a number added to 6

b. The product of 3 and the difference of a number and 5

c. The quotient of 8 and a number

d. 9 less than a number

SOLUTION

Let $x = $ a number.

a. Twice a number means to multiply a number by 2. So "twice a number" translates as $2x$. Then we add this to 6. The phrase translates as $6 + 2x$ or $2x + 6$.

b. We are told to find the product of 3 and something. So we know we need to multiply 3 by something. That something is "the difference of a number and 5." This translates as $x - 5$. So the product of 3 and the difference of a number and 5 translates as $3(x - 5)$.

c. Quotient means to divide, and order matters. We divide 8 by a number. Therefore, the translation is $\dfrac{8}{x}$.

d. Remember that "less than" translates as a subtraction, but it is done in reverse order. So this translates as something minus 9. The "something" is a number, which is x. The translation is $x - 9$.

PRACTICE PROBLEM FOR EXAMPLE 7

Translate each of the following phrases into expressions. Note that *a number* translates as a variable (an unknown).

a. 5 times a number

b. The sum of 4 times a number and 9

c. The ratio of 6 and a number

d. 16 subtracted from twice a number

Example 8   Defining variables and translating sentences

Define the variables. Translate each sentence into an expression.

a. As of 2009, the fees at Oregon Coast Community College in Newport, Oregon, are $62.00 per credit hour. Find an expression for the total cost of taking a variable number of units.
Source: www.occc.cc.or.us

b. As of 2010, the Internal Revenue Service set the standard mileage rate for the cost of operating a car for business at $0.50 a mile. Find an expression for the total cost of operating a car for a variable number of miles driven.
Source: www.irs.gov

c. 16 less than a number.

SOLUTION

First, define the variables.

a. Let c = number of credit hours a student is registered for. The total cost will be the expense of taking c credit hours. The cost per credit hour is $62.00, so the total cost of taking c credits is

$$62c \text{ dollars}$$

b. Let m = number of miles driven for business. The total cost of operating a car will be the expense of driving m miles. The cost per mile is $0.50, so the cost of driving m miles is

$$0.50m \text{ dollars}$$

c. Let x = an unknown number. The sentence translates as

$$x - 16$$

Remember that *less than* translates in expression form in reverse order from the phrase form.

PRACTICE PROBLEM FOR EXAMPLE 8

Define the variables. Translate each sentence into an expression.

a. 29 subtracted from a number.

b. At Grand Valley State University, an adult ticket to a basketball game costs $7. Find an expression for the total cost of buying a variable number of tickets.

c. The total of 150 and three times a number.

d. The cost of the Nationwide Select plan with Verizon Wireless is $59.95 for 450 anytime minutes plus $0.45 per additional minute. Find an expression for the monthly cost of your phone bill. *Hint:* Let m = minutes over 450.
Source: www.verizonwireless.com.

In converting units, it sometimes makes sense to use a variable if we need to repeatedly convert the same units in a problem situation.

Example 9   Defining variables and converting units

Define the variables. Write expressions for each of the following unit conversions.

a. Convert a variable number of feet to miles. There are 5280 ft in 1 mi.

b. Convert a variable number of kilograms (kg) into pounds (lb). There are 2.2 lb in 1 kg.

c. Convert a variable number of square feet (ft²) into square yards (yd²). There are 9 ft² in 1 yd².

SOLUTION

a. Let x = number of feet.

$$x \text{ ft} = \frac{x \text{ ft}}{1} \cdot \frac{1 \text{ mi}}{5280 \text{ ft}} = \frac{x}{5280} \text{ mi}$$

Notice that the units of the final output are in miles.

b. Let x = number of kilograms.

$$x \text{ kg} = \frac{x \text{ kg}}{1} \cdot \frac{2.2 \text{ lb}}{1 \text{ kg}} = 2.2x \text{ lb}$$

Notice that the units of the final answer are in pounds.

c. Let x = number of square feet.

$$x \text{ ft}^2 = \frac{x \text{ ft}^2}{1} \cdot \frac{1 \text{ yd}^2}{9 \text{ ft}^2} = \frac{x}{9} \text{ yd}^2$$

Notice that the units of the final answer are in square yards.

PRACTICE PROBLEM FOR EXAMPLE 9

Define the variables. Write expressions for each of the following unit conversions.

a. Convert a variable number of miles to kilometers. There are 1.609 km (kilometers) in 1 mile.

b. Convert a variable number of teaspoons (tsp) to tablespoons (tbl). There are 3 teaspoons in 1 tablespoon.

Example 10   Using units at home

You want to estimate the cost of installing new sod on your front lawn. You measure your front yard and find that it is 20 ft by 15 ft.

© Horticulture/Fotolia.

a. What is the area of your front yard? (Recall that the area of a rectangle is length times width.)

b. What are the units on your answer to part a?

c. Sod is sold by the square foot. The type of sod that you decide on, Marathon, costs $0.47 per square foot. How much will it cost you to buy the sod for your lawn?
Source: www.supergarden.com.

SOLUTION

a. To find the area of a rectangle, multiply length times width. The area is (20 feet)(15 feet) = 300 feet². The area of the front yard is 300 feet².

b. The units are square feet, or ft² = feet².

c. The cost will be

$$\left(\frac{300 \; \cancel{ft^2}}{1}\right)\left(\frac{\$0.47}{1 \; \cancel{ft^2}}\right) = \$141.00$$

The cost for 300 square feet of sod will be $141.00. Notice that when we multiply, the units of square feet divide out and the final units are dollars ($).

PRACTICE PROBLEM FOR EXAMPLE 10

You want to estimate the cost of installing laminate flooring in your living room. Your living room is 15 ft by 18 ft.

a. What is the area of your living room? (Recall that the area of a rectangle is length times width.)

b. What are the units on your answer in part a?

c. The laminate flooring that you decide on costs $2.38 per square foot. What is the total cost of flooring for your living room?

Generating Expressions from Input-Output Tables

What's That Mean?

Independent and Dependent

The independent variable is not changed or controlled by another variable. The dependent variable tends to be changed by the independent variable.

Many times, a table may be used to help generate an expression for a problem situation. These tables are often called **input-output** tables. The *input*, or *independent variable*, may be thought of as the data or information that we are entering into the problem. The *output*, or *dependent variable*, is the information that results from, or is produced from, the problem. In a table, the input variable is placed in the left-hand column, and the output variable is placed in the right-hand column. In generating expressions from an input-output table, we must substitute enough values for the input variable so that a pattern emerges in the calculation of the output variable. To see the pattern, write out all the operations in the output column. Don't just write the simplified result.

Steps to Generate Expressions from Input-Output Tables

1. Determine the input variable and the output variable. Put the input variable in the left column and output variable in the right column.
2. Select four or more reasonable values for the input variable. Think carefully about the problem situation. The last row of the input column should be the general variable used for the input (*n, x,* and so forth).
3. Calculate the value of the outputs for the chosen inputs. Make sure to write out all of the operations involved in computing the output.
4. Find the pattern used to calculate the outputs from the inputs.
5. Write the general algebraic expression in the last row.

Example 11 Generating expressions from input-output tables

Use an input-output table to generate expressions for the following problem situations.

a. Convert h hours into days by completing the input-output table.

h = number of hours	d = number of days
12	
24	
36	
72	
h	

b. There is 1 inch of rain in 1 foot of snow. Convert inches of snow into inches of rain by completing the input-output table.

s = inches of snow	r = inches of rain
12	
24	
36	
42	
s	

© iStockphoto.com/rotofrank

c. Rex's Shipping Company boxes 1-quart cans of paint and 1-quart cans of glaze to ship to home improvement stores. Each shipping box can hold 24 1-quart cans. Determine how many cans of glaze (g) you can include in one shipping box if you ship 0, 1, 2, 3, 10, or p 1-quart cans of paint. Remember that one shipping box can hold only 24 1-quart cans.

p = cans of paint	g = cans of glaze
0	
1	
2	
3	
10	
p	

SOLUTION

Notice in the solutions that the variables are defined and that the operations used to compute the output are clearly written out. Doing so lets us see the pattern from the inputs to the outputs. Once we know what operations and constants are used in the pattern, we can generalize the pattern to find the general variable expression.

a.

h = number of hours	d = number of days
12	$\dfrac{12}{24} = 0.5$
24	$\dfrac{24}{24} = 1$
36	$\dfrac{36}{24} = 1.5$
72	$\dfrac{72}{24} = 3$
h	$\dfrac{h}{24}$

Take the number of hours and divide it by 24 (there are 24 hours in a day) to get the number of days. The general variable expression is $\dfrac{h}{24}$.

b.

s = inches of snow	r = inches of rain
12	$\dfrac{12}{12} = 1$
24	$\dfrac{24}{12} = 2$
36	$\dfrac{36}{12} = 3$
42	$\dfrac{42}{12} = 3.5$
s	$\dfrac{s}{12}$

To get the number of inches of rain, divide the number of inches of snow by 12. The general variable expression is $\dfrac{s}{12}$.

c.

p = cans of paint	g = cans of glaze
0	$24 - 0 = 24$
1	$24 - 1 = 23$
2	$24 - 2 = 22$
3	$24 - 3 = 21$
10	$24 - 10 = 14$
p	$24 - p$

To get the number of cans of glaze, subtract the number of cans of paint from 24. The general variable expression is $24 - p$.

Example 12 Using tables to explore tuition costs

The Virginia Community College system charges a fee of $87.20 per credit hour plus a $5.50 technology fee per credit hour.

a. Fill in the following input-output table with some reasonable inputs to determine an expression for the total cost (tuition) for one semester.

n = number of credits	T = total cost (tuition)
n	

b. Suppose that a student has $930 budgeted for tuition for one semester. Approximately how many credits can the student take?

SOLUTION

a. Here are some reasonable inputs.

n = number of credits	T = total cost (tuition)
0	0
3	$87.20(3) + 5.50(3) = 278.10$
6	$87.20(6) + 5.50(6) = 556.20$
12	$87.20(12) + 5.50(12) = 1112.40$
n	$87.20(n) + 5.50(n)$

b. Notice that 6 credits cost $556.20 and 12 credits cost $1112.40. The number $930 is between these two values and a bit closer to $1112.40. Extend the table to get a good estimate of how many credits a student can take for $930.

n = number of credits	T = total cost of tuition (in dollars)
11	$87.20(11) + 5.50(11) = 1019.70$
10	$87.20(10) + 5.50(10) = 927.00$

On the basis of this information, a student can enroll in 10 or fewer credits.

PRACTICE PROBLEM FOR EXAMPLE 12

Carla and Don are getting married and are trying to figure out how many people they can invite to their reception. They have determined that they have no more than $3500 to pay for the food at the reception. They have also decided on a no-host bar, so liquor costs will not be paid for by the bride and groom. The New Day Catering Co. charges $425.00 for the cake and $22.00 per person for the reception dinner.

a. Generate an expression for the reception costs per person for Carla and Don. Remember that you can use an input-output table to help generate the expression.

b. Approximately how many people can Carla and Don invite?

1.2 Exercises

For Exercises 1 through 12, find the value of the expression for the given value of the variable.

1. Sarah's hourly wage is $11.25 working as a mathematics tutor. Her weekly pay can be computed as $11.25h$, where h is the number of hours she worked for a week. What would Sarah's weekly pay be if she worked 15 hours in a week?

2. Josh's hourly wage is $14.25 working as a biology lab assistant. His weekly pay can be computed as $14.25h$, where h is the number of hours he worked for a week. What would Josh's weekly pay be if he worked 13 hours in a week?

3. Thomas sells wrapping paper to raise money for his elementary school. The wrapping paper costs $5.00 per roll. The total revenue Thomas earns for his school can be computed as $5.00p$, where p is the number of rolls of wrapping paper he sells. How much revenue would Thomas earn if he sells 53 rolls of wrapping paper?

4. Brin sells Girl Scout cookies that cost $4.00 a box. The total revenue Brin earns for the Girl Scouts can be computed as $4.00b$, where b is the number of boxes she sells. How much revenue would Brin earn if she sells 400 boxes of cookies?

5. Marcus works in sales at an electronics store. His commission is 7% of his total sales for the week. His commission can be computed as $0.07s$, where s is his total weekly sales in dollars. What will Marcus's commission be if he sells $1045 worth of merchandise in a week?

6. Keesha works in sales at a jewelry store. Her commission is 6.75% of her total sales for the week. Her commission can be computed as $0.0675s$, where s is her total weekly sales in dollars. What will Keesha's commission be if she sells $2,750 worth of jewelry in a week?

7. Vinny runs at a pace of 7.5 miles per hour. His total miles run for a day can be computed as $7.5h$, where h is the number of hours he runs that day. How many miles will Vinny run if he runs for 2.5 hours?

8. Frank rides his road bike at a pace of 18 miles per hour. His total miles for the day can be computed as $18h$, where h is the number of hours he rode his bike. How many miles will Frank ride if he rides for 4.25 hours?

9. Judy sells real estate and estimates that for each house she is listing, she spends $250.00 in advertising. The total amount she spends in advertising may be computed as $250l$, where l is the number of houses she is listing. How much does Judy estimate that she will spend on advertising if she is currently listing five houses?

10. Tomas sells real estate and estimates that for each property he is listing, he spends $550.00 in advertising. The total amount he spends in advertising may be computed as $550l$, where l is the number of houses he is listing. How much does Tomas estimate that he will spend on advertising if he is currently listing 12 houses?

11. Fusako is taking a road trip and drives at an average speed of 75 miles per hour. The total distance she travels in one day can be computed as $75h$, where h is the number of hours she drives for that day. How many miles does Fusako drive if she drives for 6.5 hours?

12. Hiroyoshi is taking a road trip and drives at an average speed of 68 miles per hour. The total distance he travels in one day can be computed as $68h$, where h is the number of hours he drives that day. How many miles does Hiroyoshi drive if he drives for 9.25 hours?

For Exercises 13 through 32, evaluate each expression for the given values of the variables.

13. $-6x + 9$ for $x = 4$

14. $15x - 24$ for $x = 3$

15. $\frac{2}{5}n + 7$ for $n = -10$

16. $\frac{-7}{4}n + 11$ for $n = -8$

17. $x^2 - 6x + 7$ for $x = -1$

18. $2t^2 - 3t + 11$ for $t = -2$

19. $-y^2 + 7$ for $y = -4$

20. $-n^2 + 2n$ for $n = -1$

21. $\frac{6y - 3}{2y + 8}$ for $y = 5$

22. $\frac{-2x + 9}{4x - 3}$ for $x = 5$

23. Evaluate $36x^2 + 4y^2$ for $x = -5$ and $y = -2$.

24. Evaluate $-16st + 7s - 2t$ for $s = 3$ and $t = 0$.

25. Evaluate $-22a - 8b$ for $a = 10$ and $b = -10$.

26. Evaluate $t + h$ for $t = \frac{1}{2}$ and $h = \frac{3}{5}$.

27. Evaluate $\frac{x - y}{x + 2y}$ for $x = 3$ and $y = -4$.

28. Evaluate $\frac{2a - b}{2a + b}$ for $a = -1$ and $b = 8$.

29. Evaluate $-9x + 51$ for $x = -6$.

30. Evaluate $2xy + y$ for $x = 3$ and $y = -3$.

31. Evaluate $2x^2 - 6x + 5$ for $x = 3$.

32. Evaluate $4 - 16c + 2t$ for $c = -3$ and $t = -9$.

For Exercises 33 through 50, convert units as indicated.

33. The unity fraction to convert feet to yards is $\frac{1 \text{ yd}}{3 \text{ ft}}$. Convert 22 feet to yards.

34. The unity fraction to convert miles per hour to feet per second is $\frac{5280 \text{ ft}}{3600 \text{ sec}}$. Convert 75 miles per hour to feet per second.

35. Convert 1057 feet to miles. *Note:* There are 5280 ft in 1 mi.

36. Convert 692 centimeters to meters. *Note:* There are 100 cm in 1 m.

37. Convert 254 feet to meters. *Note:* There are 3.28 ft in 1 m.

38. As of this writing, 1.00 euro is equal to 1.49 U.S. dollars. Convert 149.00 euros to U.S. dollars. *Source: www.XE.com.*

39. Convert 7.89 kilograms to pounds. *Note:* There are 2.2 lb in 1 kg.

40. Convert 60 square feet to square yards. *Note:* There are 9 ft² in 1 yd².

41. Convert 15 gallons to liters. *Note:* There are 3.785 l in 1 gal.

42. Convert 22 quarts to gallons. *Note:* There are 4 qt in 1 gal.

43. Convert 22,000 square feet to acres. *Note:* There are 43,560 ft² in 1 acre.

44. Convert 6780 milliliters to liters. *Note:* There are 1000 ml in 1 l.

45. Convert 601 million to thousands. *Hint:* 1 million = 1000 thousands.

46. Convert 10,011 thousands to millions.

47. Convert 5397 million to billions. *Hint:* 1 billion = 1000 million.

48. Convert 8.6 billion to millions.

49. Convert 9 trillion to billions. *Hint:* 1 trillion = 1000 billion.

50. Convert 8375 billion to trillions.

For Exercises 51 through 60, define variables for each problem situation.

51. The amount owed on a monthly electricity bill depends on how many kilowatt-hours of electricity were used during that month.

52. The height of the ocean tide (in feet) at high tide depends on the phase of the moon.

53. The amount you pay (in dollars) yearly in federal taxes depends on your income (in dollars) for that year.

54. The amount of money (in dollars) a family spends a week on gas depends on the number of miles they drive that week.

55. The temperature outdoors (in degrees Fahrenheit) depends on the time of day.

56. The amount of revenue (in dollars) a theater makes depends on the number of tickets sold.

57. The amount of first-class postage you owe (in dollars) for a package depends on the weight of the package you are shipping (in pounds).

58. The amount (in milliliters) of IV fluids a hospitalized patient requires depends on the patient's weight (in kilograms).

59. The cost of attending a community college depends on how many credits a student enrolls in per semester.

60. The amount of money you earn weekly depends on the number of hours you worked that week.

For Exercises 61 through 80, translate each of the following phrases into an expression.

61. The sum of a number and 62.

62. The sum of -19 and a number.

63. 9 more than twice a number.

64. Three times a number plus -7.

65. The quotient of 16 and a number.

66. Five times a number divided by 12.

67. 7 less than $\frac{1}{3}$ times a number.

68. 9 subtracted from $\frac{1}{2}$ a number.

69. The difference between 8 times a number and 12.

70. The difference between -7 times a number and 18.

71. The product of -5 and the square of a number.

72. The product of a number squared and -1.

73. 16 increased by the quotient of a number and 4.

74. The sum of 7 divided by a number and 3.

75. The quotient of 6 and the difference of a number and 2.

76. The quotient of a number minus 2 and 3.

77. Half of a number added to 6.

78. One-third of a number minus 16.

79. The difference between 7 and twice a number.

80. The difference between -3 times a number and 8.

For Exercises 81 through 86, define the variable (include units). Then translate each phrase into an expression.

81. Cayuga County Community College (in upstate New York) charges part-time resident students (10 credit hours or less) $132.00 per credit plus a $7.00 per credit activity fee plus a $7.00 per credit technology fee plus a $4.00 records fee each semester. Write an expression that gives the cost of attending Cayuga County Community College for one semester.
Source: www.cayuga-cc.edu

82. A car repair shop quotes a rate of $60.00 an hour for labor. Write an expression that gives the labor cost for a car repair.

83. A house-painting company quotes a price to paint a house. The quote includes the price of the paint, which is $175.00, plus labor, which costs $17.00

an hour. Write an expression that determines the cost of painting this house.

84. A local horse-boarding facility buys alfalfa hay to feed the horses. At the time of this writing, the average price of a small square bale of alfalfa hay in California is $1.00 a bale. The hay distributor also charges a $75.00 delivery fee. Find the cost of purchasing and delivering the hay.
Source: www.hayexchange.com

85. As of this writing, the cost of first-class (letter) mail in the United States is $0.44 for the first ounce plus $0.17 per each additional ounce. Write an expression for the cost of mailing a first-class letter.
Source: www.usps.gov

86. A movie theater charges $9.00 a ticket for an adult ticket. Write an expression for the amount of money (revenue) the theater will take in if it sells t tickets.

For Exercises 87 through 96, first define a variable. Then write an expression for the unit conversion.

87. Convert a variable number of pounds to kilograms.

88. Convert a variable number of ounces to pounds.

89. Convert a variable number of miles to feet.

90. Convert a variable number of meters to feet.

91. Convert a variable number of liters to gallons.

92. Convert a variable number of quarts to gallons.

93. Convert a variable number of acres to square feet.

94. Convert a variable number of square yards to square feet.

95. Convert a variable number of seconds to minutes.

96. Convert a variable number of days to years.

For Exercises 97 through 100, use the information given in each exercise to answer the questions.

97. Bill wants to estimate the cost to recarpet his living room. Bill measures his living room and finds that its length is 20 feet and its width is 15 feet.
   a. Find the area of Bill's living room. What are the units?
   b. Carpet is sold by the square yard. Convert the area of Bill's living room to units of square yards. Round up to the nearest full square yard.

c. The Berber carpet that Bill wants costs $19.38 per square yard. How much will the carpet cost?

d. Bill is quoted a shipping price of $1.75 per square yard. How much will it cost to ship his carpet?

e. What will the total cost of the carpet and shipping be?

98. JoAnn wants to estimate the cost to repaint her living room. JoAnn measures her living room and finds that its length is 15 feet and its width is 15 feet. The walls are 10 feet tall.

a. Find the area of her living room walls. What are the units? *Hint:* You must find the total area of all four walls. For the purpose of the estimate, don't worry about doors or windows.

b. The paint JoAnn wants covers 200 square feet per gallon. How many gallons of paint does JoAnn need to buy?

c. The paint costs $16.98 per gallon. How much will it cost JoAnn to buy the paint?

99. You and some friends are going on a seven-night cruise. The cruise ship company only allows each passenger to bring a total of 75 pounds (lb) of luggage on board. You want to bring some clothing and toiletries for your trip. Let c = amount in pounds of clothing you will pack, l = weight of your suitcase in pounds, and t = amount in pounds of toiletries that you will pack. The total weight of your luggage is

$$c + l + t$$

a. Suppose that you take 50 lb of clothes and 10 lb of toiletries and that your suitcase weighs 12 lb. What is the total weight of your luggage?

b. Suppose that you take 54.6 lb of clothes and 9.6 lb of toiletries and that your suitcase weighs 10 lb. What is the total weight of your luggage?

100. You want to go on a backpacking trip. In your backpack, you will have to carry all your food and equipment. Let f = number of pounds of food you will pack, and let e = number of pounds of equipment (including the backpack) you will pack. The total weight you will have to carry is

$$f + e$$

© Anton Gvozdikov/Fotolia

a. Suppose that you take 14 lb of food and 16 lb of equipment. What is the total weight you will have to carry?

b. Suppose that you take 12.6 lb of food and 18.9 lb of equipment. What is the total weight you will have to carry?

c. Suppose that you can pack only a total of 24 lb. Fill in the following table to determine various combinations of food and equipment you could take on the trip.

f	e	$f + e$
10		24
	15	24
13		24
	12	24

For Exercises 101 through 106, use input-output tables to generate expressions for the problem.

101. John drives from San Diego to Los Angeles and back in a total time (round trip) of 4.5 hours. If he spends t hours driving from San Diego to Los Angeles, find an expression for the time it takes him to drive back.

Time to Drive from San Diego to Los Angeles	Time to Drive from Los Angeles to San Diego
1	
2	
2.5	
3	
t	

102. Sean rides his bike from his home to school daily. One day, it takes him a total time of 90 minutes for the round trip. If he spends m minutes riding his bike to school, find an expression for the time it takes him to ride from school to home.

Time to Ride Bike from Home to School	Time to Ride Bike from School to Home
20	
30	
40	
45	
m	

103. Rebecca has a total of $2500 to invest. She is going to invest part of the money in an account earning 3.5% interest and part of the money in a stock fund earning 7% interest. If Rebecca invests d dollars in the 3.5% account, find an expression for the amount of money she invests in the 7% account.

Amount Invested in the 3.5% Account	Amount Invested in the 7% Account
0	
500	
100	
1500	
d	

104. Tom has 40 feet of lumber that he needs to cut into two pieces. If Tom cuts *f* feet of lumber for the first piece, find an expression for the remaining amount of lumber in the second piece.

First Piece of Lumber	Second Piece of Lumber
5	
10	
20	
35	
f	

105. Heather, owner of Cup to Go Coffee, wants 65 lb total of coffee in a coffee blend of Kenyan and Colombian. If Heather includes *c* lb of Colombian coffee in her blend, find an expression for the amount (in pounds) of Kenyan coffee she will need to include.

Pounds of Colombian Coffee	Pounds of Kenyan Coffee
0	
10	
20	
50	
c	

106. Anya, a chemist at Bio-chem, Inc., is mixing a 5% saline solution with a 7.5% saline solution for a total of 10 gallons in the mix. If Anya uses *g* gallons of the 5% saline solution, find an expression for the amount (in gallons) of the 7.5% solution she will need to include.

Amount of 5% Saline Solution	Amount of 7.5% Saline Solution
0	
2	
4	
6	
g	

For Exercises 107 through 110, use the information given in each exercise to answer the questions.

107. Sandy is throwing a 25th anniversary party for her parents. She is trying to figure out how many people she can invite to the party. She has budgeted $500.00 to pay for the food at the party. Sheila's Catering Company says they will charge Sandy $12.00 per person for the food.

   a. Generate an expression for the food cost for the party based on the number of people. Remember to use an input-output table to help generate the expression if needed.

   b. Approximately how many people can Sandy invite?

108. Gerry and Maureen want to throw a fifth birthday party for their daughter. They plan to serve take-out fried chicken, which will cost $1.49 per child. They also figure that the party favors will cost $3.50 per child. They have budgeted $90.00 for food and party favors.

   a. Generate an expression for the total cost of food and party favors, based on the number of children. Remember to use an input-output table to help generate the expression if needed.

   b. Approximately how many children can Gerry and Maureen invite?

109. Tricia is a professional event planner. She has been hired to set up a business reception at a conference. Tricia has been told that her budget for food is $1700.00. Jeff's Catering Affair has quoted Tricia $18.00 per person for drinks and $15.00 per person for appetizers.

   a. Generate an expression for the total food and drink cost based on the number of people attending. Remember to use an input-output table to help generate the expression if needed.

   b. Approximately how many people can attend the conference reception and stay within Tricia's budget?

110. Casey sets up paid phone interviews with industry professionals for his corporate clients. His clients hire him to ask industry professionals for their opinions about products and services. Casey is setting up interviews for a client who has given him a budget of $4000.00. Each interviewee will be paid $110.00 for participation.

   a. Generate an expression for the cost for all the interviews. Remember to use an input-output table to help generate the expression if needed.

   b. Approximately how many people can Casey have participate in the phone interview to stay within his $4000 budget?

1.3   Simplifying Expressions

LEARNING OBJECTIVES

- Recognize like terms.
- Use the addition and subtraction properties.
- Use the multiplication and distributive properties.
- Simplify expressions.

Like Terms

Terms are the building blocks of expressions. Expressions may involve the four main operations that we are already familiar with. In this section, we are going to review the concept of a term and learn the basic operations for combining terms that are used throughout algebra.

> **DEFINITION**
>
> **Term**   A constant (a number) or a product of a constant and a variable (or variables) is called a **term**.
>
> $$3 \qquad -4a \qquad \frac{2}{3}km^2 \qquad x$$
>
> *Note*   The numerical part of a term is called the **coefficient.**

What's That Mean?

Terms

Two phrases are used in discussing terms.

Constant term: A constant is a number by itself.

Variable term: A term with a variable.

We can combine more than one term together with the operations of addition or subtraction to create expressions. One of the more useful concepts in algebra is that of **like terms.** Two or more terms are "like" if they have the same variable part, where the variables are raised to the same exponents. Notice that the coefficients do not need to be the same for two terms to be "like."

> **DEFINITION**
>
> **Like Terms**   Two or more terms that have the same variable part, where the variables are raised to the same exponents, are called **like terms.**
>
> $$3x \text{ and } 5x \text{ are like terms}$$
> $$-25a^2bc^3 \text{ and } 10a^2bc^3 \text{ are like terms}$$

Example 1   Identifying like terms

Identify the number of terms. Then circle the like terms (if any) in each expression.

a. $5x^2 + 4x - 7$

b. $3a - 4b + 7a + 2$

c. $105 + 8m^2 + 7m - 4m^2 - 17$

d. $14x^2y + 3xy^2 + 4x^2y - 19y^2$

SOLUTION

a. $5x^2 + 4x - 7$. There are three terms in this expression. There are no like terms in this expression. None of the terms in this expression have the same variable raised to the same exponent. The first two terms have the same variable x, but in the first term, x is raised to the second power, and in the second term, x is raised to the first power.

b. $\overparen{3a} - 4b + \overparen{7a} + 2$. There are four terms in this expression. The like terms are $3a$ and $7a$ because they both have a raised to the first power.

c. $\overparen{105} + \overparen{8m^2} + 7m \overparen{- 4m^2} \overparen{- 17}$. There are five terms in this expression. Both 105 and -17 are constant terms and are like terms. The terms $8m^2$ and $-4m^2$ are also like terms. Notice that the sign in front of a term is part of the term. This is why we have the term -17 and not 17 and $-4m^2$ not $4m^2$.

d. $\overparen{14x^2y} + 3xy^2 + \overparen{4x^2y} - 19y^2$. There are four terms in this expression. The like terms are $14x^2y$ and $4x^2y$. Notice that the variables are the same and that each is raised to the same power.

PRACTICE PROBLEM FOR EXAMPLE 1

Identify the number of terms. Then circle the like terms (if any) in each expression.

a. $-5x^2 + 7c + 4d^2 + 8c$ **b.** $45x^2 + 7x - 9$

c. $23g^2k + 45g^2k^2 - 16g^2k + 57g^2k^2$

Addition and Subtraction Properties

One of the powerful characteristics of algebra is the ability to simplify complicated expressions. A calculation that takes several operations to complete can often be simplified to just a few operations.

The reason why recognizing like terms is so important is that like terms are the basic components of addition and subtraction in algebra. Often, we can simplify an expression using addition or subtraction. To add or subtract any two or more terms in an expression, they must be like terms. When adding or subtracting like terms, we add or subtract their coefficients.

The distributive property that we learned in Section 1.1 validates why like terms can be added or subtracted. In the same way that we can multiply a constant through an addition or subtraction, we can also take out a common variable and combine the coefficients.

$$2x + 3x = (2 + 3)x \qquad \textit{The distributive property is used to rewrite}$$
$$= 5x \qquad\qquad \textit{the problem. Combine the coefficients.}$$

Throughout this text, we will say to add or subtract like terms, but remember that this is justified by the distributive property. Just add or subtract the coefficients.

$$2x + 3x = 5x$$

> ### ADDITION AND SUBTRACTION PROPERTY
>
> Two or more terms can be added or subtracted only if they are like terms. Add or subtract the coefficients of the like terms. The variable part will remain the same.
>
> $$5x + 7x = 12x \qquad 9x^2 - 13x^2 = -4x^2$$

Example 2   Simplifying expressions by combining like terms

Simplify each expression by combining like terms.

a. $14x + 6x$ **b.** $12a - 3a$ **c.** $8m + 5n - 3m + 14n$

d. $7a + 10b - 15$ **e.** $4x^2 + 5x - x^2 + 9$

SOLUTION

a. $14x + 6x$ *Combine like terms by adding the coefficients.*
   $= 20x$

b. $12a - 3a$ *Combine like terms by subtracting the coefficients.*

   $= 9a$

c. $8m + 5n - 3m + 14n$ *Rearrange terms using the commutative property.*

   $= 8m - 3m + 5n + 14n$ *Note that the negative sign in front of the $3m$ term goes with that term.*

   $= 5m + 19n$ *Combine like terms by adding or subtracting the coefficients.*

d. $7a + 10b - 15$ *There are no like terms, so this expression is already simplified.*

e. $4x^2 + 5x - x^2 + 9$ *Rearrange terms using the commutative property.*

   $= 4x^2 - x^2 + 5x + 9$ *Combine like terms.*

   $= 3x^2 + 5x + 9$

PRACTICE PROBLEM FOR EXAMPLE 2

Simplify each expression by combining like terms.

a. $8p + 5p$ **b.** $2w + 7 - 9w + 3$

c. $3x^2y + 4xy - 7xy + 15x^2y$ **d.** $8z^2 + 5x - 2z - 20$

It is conventional that the terms in an expression are ordered alphabetically, with descending exponents and with constant terms last. Writing terms with descending exponents means that the term with the highest power exponent should go first, the next highest power second, and so on. When simplifying an expression, write the final answer using this convention.

Example 3   Writing the expression in conventional form

Write each expression in conventional form. This means that terms are ordered alphabetically, have descending exponents, and end with the constant terms.

a. $2b + 5a$ **b.** $-5x + 3x^2 + 6$ **c.** $3y - 3x + 11 + 6x^2$

SOLUTION

a. This expression is not in alphabetical order, reading left to right. We use the commutative property of addition to reorder the terms.

$$2b + 5a = 5a + 2b$$

b. This expression is not written with descending exponents, reading left to right. The term with the exponent of the highest power is $3x^2$, and it should go first. The term with the second highest power exponent is $-5x$, and it goes second. The only remaining term is the constant term 6, and it is placed last.

$$-5x + 3x^2 + 6$$
$$= 3x^2 - 5x + 6$$

c. This expression is not in alphabetical order. The x-terms are not in descending order. Rearranging the expression yields the answer below.

$$3y - 3x + 11 + 6x^2$$
$$= 6x^2 - 3x + 3y + 11$$

PRACTICE PROBLEM FOR EXAMPLE 3

Write each expression in conventional form. This means the terms are ordered alphabetically, have descending exponents, and end with the constant terms.

a. $-3d + 9c$ **b.** $16 - 2x + 3x^2$ **c.** $7 - 4b^2 - 2a + 3a^2$

Example 4   Combining like terms that represent cost

Debra is the captain of the Leffingwell Lions cheerleading squad. She wants to buy T-shirts for all the squad members. Debra called a local shirt company and was given the following information:

$6 per T-shirt
$2 per T-shirt for the school logo to be printed on the back of a shirt
$0.50 per letter for a name to be embroidered on the front of the shirt

These prices include all taxes.
Debra defined the following variables:

s = number of T-shirts ordered
n = number of letters in a squad member's name.

a. Write an expression for the cost to buy s T-shirts.

b. Write an expression for the cost to print the logo on the back of s T-shirts.

c. Use your expressions from part a and b to write an expression for the total cost to buy and print the logos on s T-shirts. Simplify the expression if possible.

d. Write an expression for the cost to embroider a name with n number of letters on the front of the T-shirt.

e. Would it make sense to add the expression you found in part c to the expression in part d? Explain why or why not.

SOLUTION

a. The problem states that s = number of T-shirts ordered.
It will cost $6 to buy each shirt, and we have to pay for every shirt, so 6 times the number of shirts, $6s$, is an expression for the cost in dollars to buy the shirts. The expression is

$$6s$$

b. To print the logo on the back of the shirts, we pay $2 for each logo, so $2s$ is an expression for the cost in dollars to print the logos. The expression is

$$2s$$

c. In Section 1.2, we learned that *total* means to *add*. Adding these two expressions together gives us the expression $6s + 2s$. This expression represents the total cost to buy the shirts and print the logos. We can simplify this expression because both of these costs are per T-shirt and the terms are like terms. Since we pay $6 for the shirt and $2 more for the logo, we pay a total of $8 for each shirt with a logo printed on it. Therefore, combining $6s + 2s$ gives us the simplified expression $8s$ for the total cost in dollars to buy and print the logo on s T-shirts. The expression is

$$6s + 2s = 8s$$

d. The problem states that n = number of letters. It costs $0.50 per letter for the embroidery, so a name with n letters will cost $0.50n$ dollars to be embroidered. The expression is

$$0.50n$$

e. It does not make sense to add these expressions together. If we added these two expressions, $8s$ and $0.50n$, we would be adding the cost for all the shirts and logos to the cost for only one name to be embroidered. We also could not add these two terms, since the $8 is a cost per T-shirt and the $0.50 is a cost per letter embroidered. If we did try to add these together, we would get $8.50, but the units would not make sense. $8s$ and $0.50n$ are not like terms and cannot be added together.

PRACTICE PROBLEM FOR EXAMPLE 4

Murray's Hitch installs trailer hitches on cars and trucks. When ordering supplies for the shop, Murray must order hitches as well as wiring kits and bolt kits. Murray's costs for these items are as follows:

$125 per standard hitch
$23 per wiring kit
$2 per bolt kit (Some hitches require two or three bolt kits to be installed properly.)

All of these prices include shipping and applicable taxes.

a. Write an expression for the cost to buy h standard hitches.

b. Write an expression for the cost to buy wiring kits for h hitches.

c. Use your expressions from part a and b to write an expression for the total cost to buy h standard hitches and wiring kits. Simplify the expression if possible.

d. Write an expression for the cost to buy b bolt kits.

e. Would it make sense to add the expression you found in part c to the expression in part d? Explain why or why not.

Example 5   Ordering parts to manufacture a bicycle

A custom bike shop produces bikes for small bike stores across the country. When an order is placed for bikes, the supply manager must order the right amount of tubing for the production process. To save money, the supply manager orders tubing in standard lengths of 2.5 ft.

a. The top tube of a bike uses one 2.5-ft piece of tubing, and the down tube takes an additional 2.5-ft piece of tubing. Write an expression for the number of 2.5-ft tubes the supply manager should order to make the top tubes and down tubes for b bikes.

b. The seat tube and head tube of each bike can be made from the same 2.5-ft tube. Write an expression for the number of 2.5-ft tubes the supply manager should order to make the seat tubes and head tubes for b bikes.

c. Use the expressions from parts a and b to find an expression that will represent the total number of 2.5-ft pieces of tubing that need to be ordered for b bikes. Simplify the expression if possible.

SOLUTION

a. Let b = number of bikes ordered. Since each bike will need two tubes, one for the top tube and one for the down tube, the supply manager should order $2b$ 2.5-ft tubes for an order of b bikes.

b. Since the seat and head tubes can be made from one 2.5-ft tube, the supply manager needs to order one tube for each bike so $1b$ or b tubes should be ordered for an order of b bikes.

c. To find the total number of 2.5-ft tubes, the supply manager needs to add the order for the top and down tubes to the order for the seat and head tubes. Since the two expressions are both orders for 2.5-ft tubes, the supply manager can add them together and therefore should order $2b + b$ or $3b$ 2.5-ft tubes for the b bikes.

These last examples should help us see that to add two terms together, they must be like terms.

Multiplication and Distributive Properties

In multiplying a term or expression by a constant, we must know what to multiply together. Use the following Concept Investigation to determine the difference between multiplying one term by a constant and multiplying several terms by a constant.

CONCEPT INVESTIGATION

What do I multiply by?

Use the order-of-operations agreement or use your calculator to evaluate the expressions in each column, substituting in the values given. If you use your calculator, be sure to enter the expressions on your calculator in the same order as they appear in the columns below. Then determine which columns result in the same value and which result in a different value.

First, consider multiplying a single term by a constant.

a. $x = 5$ $y = 4$	$2(3xy)$ $2(3(5)(4)) = 120$ *Original expression*	$6xy$ $6(5)(4) = 120$ *Same value as the original expression.*	$(6x)(2y)$ $(6(5))(2(4)) = 240$ *Different value from the original expression*
b. $x = 7$ $y = 3$	$4(xy)$ $4((7)(3)) = 84$ *Original expression*	$4xy$	$(4x)(4y)$
c. $g = 2$ $h = 5$	$-4(3gh)$	$-12gh$	$(-12g)(-4h)$

Calculator Details

When evaluating an expression for different values of a variable, use parentheses around the value you are substituting in for the variable. Using parentheses helps to eliminate some calculator errors. This is especially important in substituting in negative values. To substitute in $x = -2$ in the expression $3x^2 + 1$, enter it as

$$3(-2)^2 + 1$$

1. What column gave the same result as the original expression?

2. What does your answer to question 1 imply about what you should multiply together when multiplying a **single term** by a constant?

Now consider the result when multiplying the sum or difference of terms by a constant.

a. $x = 5$ $y = 4$	$2(3x + y)$ $2(3(5) + (4)) = 38$ *Original expression*	$6x + y$ $6(5) + (4) = 34$ *Different value from the original expression.*	$6x + 2y$ $6(5) + 2(4) = 38$ *Same value as the original expression.*
b. $x = 7$ $y = 3$	$4(5x + 3y)$	$20x + 3y$	$20x + 12y$
c. $g = 2$ $h = 5$	$-4(3g - 8h)$	$-12g - 8h$	$-12g + 32h$

3. What column gave the same result as the original expression?

4. What does the result in question 3 tell you about what to multiply together when multiplying **several terms** by a constant?

This Concept Investigation shows that in multiplying a **single** term by a constant, simply multiply the constant by the coefficient of the term. This rule is called the **multiplication property.**

MULTIPLICATION PROPERTY

When multiplying a single term by a constant, multiply the coefficient by the constant, and the variable parts stay the same.

$$5(4x^2y) = 20x^2y$$

If there are several terms in the parentheses, we multiply the coefficient of each term by the constant. In Section 1.1, we learned how to use the distributive property to multiply expressions such as $a(b + c) = a \cdot b + a \cdot c$, where a, b, and c are real numbers. The distributive property is now extended to the case in which a *variable expression* is in the parentheses.

DISTRIBUTIVE PROPERTY

When multiplying a multiple term expression by a constant, multiply the coefficient of each term by the constant, and the variable parts will stay the same.

$$a(b + c) = a \cdot b + a \cdot c \qquad \text{or} \qquad a(b - c) = a \cdot b - a \cdot c$$

$$3(2x - 7y) = 6x - 21y$$

Example 6 Using the multiplication and distributive properties

State whether the multiplication property or the distributive property should be used. Then simplify the following expressions by multiplying.

a. $4(7x)$ **b.** $-3(5w + 7)$ **c.** $5(7x^2 + 8x - 3)$

d. $-\dfrac{2}{3}(9t)$ **e.** $-(m^2 - 6m + 3)$

SOLUTION

The property that is used will depend on the number of terms in the parentheses. The multiplication property is used if only one term is in the parentheses. The distributive property is used if multiple terms are in the parentheses.

a. $4(7x)$ *A single term. Multiplication property.*

$\quad = 28x$ *Multiply the 4 by the coefficient 7.*

b. $-3(5w + 7)$ *Several terms. Distributive property.*

$\quad = -3(5w) + (-3)(7)$ *Distribute the –3 to both terms, and multiply.*

$\quad = -15w - 21$

c. $5(7x^2 + 8x - 3)$ *Several terms. Distributive property.*

$\quad = 5(7x^2) + 5(8x) - 5(3)$ *Distribute the 5 to all the terms, and multiply each coefficient.*

$\quad = 35x^2 + 40x - 15$

d. $-\dfrac{2}{3}(9t)$ *A single term. Multiplication property.*

$\quad = -\dfrac{18}{3}t$ *Multiply the coefficient.*

$\quad = -6t$ *Reduce the fraction.*

e. $-(m^2 - 6m + 3)$ *A negative sign in front of the parenthesis is the same as multiplying by –1.*

$\quad = -1(m^2 - 6m + 3)$ *Several terms. Distributive property.*

$\quad = -1(m^2) - 1(-6m) - 1(3)$ *Distribute the –1 to each term.*

$\quad = -m^2 + 6m - 3$ *Distributing the –1 changed the signs of all the terms enclosed in the parentheses.*

PRACTICE PROBLEM FOR EXAMPLE 6

State whether the multiplication property or the distributive property should be used. Then simplify the following expressions by multiplying.

a. $-9(4m^3)$

b. $7(-4x + 6y)$

c. $-\dfrac{4}{5}(25c^2 + 5c - 10)$

d. $0.4(3x - 6)$

Simplifying Expressions

The properties discussed in this section can be used to simplify expressions that have a combination of operations. When simplifying more complicated expressions, follow the order-of-operations agreement. Therefore, simplify anything inside grouping symbols first, then multiply or divide, and finally add or subtract. The mnemonic for the order of operations is PEMDAS, as discussed in Section 1.1. Always keep in mind that only like terms can be added or subtracted.

Example 7 Simplifying expressions

Simplify the following expressions.

a. $3(5x + 7) + 2x - 9$

b. $-3m + 4n + 2(5m + 7)$

c. $0.5(3x - 8) + 2(x + 6)$

SOLUTION

a. Using PEMDAS, first consider the parentheses. The inside of the parentheses cannot be simplified because the terms are not like. There are no exponents, so multiply first by using the distributive property.

$3(5x + 7) + 2x - 9$	Multiply first. Distribute the 3 to each term inside the parentheses.
$= 15x + 21 + 2x - 9$	
$= 15x + 2x + 21 - 9$	Rearrange terms using the commutative property.
$= 17x + 12$	Combine like terms.

b.

$-3m + 4n + 2(5m + 7)$	Multiply first by distributing the 2 to each term in the parentheses.
$= -3m + 4n + 10m + 14$	
$= -3m + 10m + 4n + 14$	Rearrange terms using the commutative property.
$= 7m + 4n + 14$	Combine like terms.

c.

$0.5(3x - 8) + 2(x + 6)$	Multiply first by distributing the 0.5 and 2.
$= 1.5x - 4 + 2x + 12$	
$= 1.5x + 2x - 4 + 12$	Rearrange the terms.
$= 3.5x + 8$	Combine like terms.

PRACTICE PROBLEM FOR EXAMPLE 7

Simplify the following expressions.

a. $5(4x - 9) + 8x + 20$

b. $1.5(2w + 7) + 3.5(4w - 6)$

When simplifying expressions using the distributive property, be careful to keep track of the signs involved. Whenever the distributive property is applied using a negative number, each sign inside the grouping symbol will change.

Example 8 Simplifying more complex expressions

Simplify the following expressions.

a. $5(10w + 7) - (20w + 15)$ **b.** $6(3a^2c + 2a) - (5a^2c - 7a)$

c. $4(2x + 7y) + 3(5x - 4) - 2(-6x - 8)$

SOLUTION

a. $5(10w + 7) - (20w + 15)$ Recall that a negative sign in front of an expression or term is the same as a -1 coefficient.

$= 5(10w + 7) - 1(20w + 15)$ Multiply by distributing the 5 and the negative sign.

$= 50w + 35 - 20w - 15$ The negative sign changes the sign of both terms in the second parentheses.

$= 50w - 20w + 35 - 15$

$= 30w + 20$ Rearrange and combine the like terms.

b. $6(3a^2c + 2a) - (5a^2c - 7a)$ Multiply first by distributing the 6 and the negative 1.

$= 6(3a^2c + 2a) - 1(5a^2c - 7a)$

$= 18a^2c + 12a - 5a^2c + 7a$ The negative 1 changes the sign of both terms in the second parentheses.

$= 18a^2c - 5a^2c + 12a + 7a$

$= 13a^2c + 19a$ Rearrange and combine the like terms.

c. $4(2x + 7y) + 3(5x - 4) - 2(-6x - 8)$ Multiply first by distributing the 4, 3, and -2.

$= 8x + 28y + 15x - 12 + 12x + 16$

$= 8x + 15x + 12x + 28y - 12 + 16$ Rearrange the terms.

$= 35x + 28y + 4$ Combine like terms.

PRACTICE PROBLEM FOR EXAMPLE 8

Simplify the following expressions.

a. $(4x^2 + 5x) - (x^2 - 3x)$ **b.** $4(8t + 9u) - 3(6t - 5u)$

1.3 Exercises

For Exercises 1 through 10, identify the number of terms and the like terms (if any) in each expression.

1. $2x + 8 + 7x$

2. $4p - 5p + 3$

3. $3 + 2h - 5 + 7h$

4. $4b + 5 - 6b + 2$

5. $3x^2 + 5x + 7x^2 + 3x$

6. $t^5 + 4t^3 + 3t^5 - t^3$

7. $2x^2 + 5x - 9$

8. $2n^4 + n^3 + 2n + 1$

9. $7xy + 8x - 2xy - 3y$

10. $4ab + 2a - 3b + 7ab$

For Exercises 11 through 20, simplify each expression by combining like terms.

11. $13x + 7x$

12. $7y + 20y$

13. $3p - 9p$

14. $10q - 16q$

15. $4x + 5y - 6x - y$

16. $a - 4b - 6a + 5b$

17. $-18n - 3 + 7n - 5$ **18.** $-3b + 11 - 7b - 9$

19. $3x^2 + 9x - 1 - 4x^2 + 2x - 5$

20. $5y^2 - 3y - 2 + 8y^2 - 7y - 9$

For Exercises 21 through 30, write each expression in conventional form. This means that terms are ordered alphabetically and have descending exponents and that constant terms are last in the expression.

21. $-8y + 3x$

22. $15b - 29a$

23. $7n - 8m + 12$

24. $9y + 7 - 8x$

25. $5 - x + 7x^2$

26. $8 - 6y - y^2$

27. $8 + 5x - 7x^5 - 3x^2$

28. $4y - 6 - y^3 - 2y^2$

29. $a - \frac{7}{5}b + 3a^2 - \frac{1}{2}a^6$

30. $3y - \frac{4}{5}x^2 + 5x + \frac{2}{5}x^4$

For Exercises 31 through 36, use the information given in each exercise to answer the questions.

31. Julie owns Children's Paradise Preschool and wants to order supplies for the children in the 4- to 5-year-old class for a project. Julie researches on the Internet and finds the following prices:

> Birdhouse kit: $4.19 each
> Paint-with-brush set: $1.39 each

The Bird House Kit

Tools not included

Instructions Enclosed

a. If Julie needs supplies for k children in the class, write an expression for the cost in dollars to order each child a birdhouse kit.

b. Write an expression for the cost in dollars to order each child a paint-with-brush set.

c. Use the expressions you wrote from parts a and b to write an expression for the total cost in dollars to buy each child a birdhouse kit and a paint-with-brush set.

d. Simplify the expression from part c if possible.

32. Ms. Binkinz is buying her first kindergarten class gifts for the end of the school year. She wants to order a book for each student that costs $1.25. Ms. Binkinz also wants to buy each student an educational toy that costs $2.35.

a. If Ms. Binkinz has s students in her kindergarten class, write an expression for the cost in dollars to buy each student a book.

b. Write an expression for the cost in dollars to buy each student an educational toy.

c. Use the expressions you wrote from parts a and b to write an expression for the total cost in dollars to buy each student a book and educational toy.

d. Simplify the expression from part c if possible.

33. Julie, from Exercise 31, decides to have the 4- to 5-year-old children do another project and build pinewood derby cars. Julie again finds the prices for the supplies on the Internet:

Mark Clark. By permission.

> Pinewood derby complete car kit: $8.79 each
> Sandpaper and sealer: $1.19 each
> Paint-with-brush set: $1.39 each

a. If Julie needs supplies for k children in the class, write an expression for the cost to order each child a pinewood derby car kit.

b. Write an expression for the cost to order each child sandpaper and sealer.

c. Write an expression for the cost to order each child a paint-with-brush set.

d. Use the expressions you wrote from parts a, b, and c to write an expression for the total cost to buy each child all the supplies needed for this project. Simplify the expression if possible.

34. A local Boy Scout troop is going to build model rockets to launch on their next adventure weekend. The scout leader looks up the following prices for the parts for each rocket they build:

> BT-50 9″ body tube: $0.89
> Plastic nose cone: $1.39
> Fin kit: $1.49
> Engine mount kit: $5.29
> 3 pack D engine pack: $7.79
> 24″ parachute kit: $3.49

a. If the scout leader wants to make r rockets with the scouts, write an expression for the cost to buy the body tubes for the rockets.

b. Write expressions for the cost for each of the remaining parts listed.

c. Using the expressions you found in parts a and b, write an expression for the total cost of buying the parts to make r rockets for the scouts. Simplify the expression if possible.

35. When doing his taxes, Steve discovers that he is in the 15% tax bracket for federal taxes and in the 8% tax bracket for his state.

a. If I is Steve's taxable income in dollars, write an expression for the amount Steve pays in federal taxes.

b. Write an expression for the amount Steve pays for his state taxes.

c. Use the expressions you found in parts a and b to write an expression for the total amount Steve pays in both federal and state taxes. Simplify the expression if possible.

36. Perry looked at his first paycheck and noticed that money was withheld from his pay for taxes. Perry figured out the following withholdings:

> Federal tax 17%
> Social Security tax 6%
> Medicare tax 1.5%
> State tax 5%

a. If T is Perry's taxable income in dollars, write expressions for the amount of each tax that is taken out of his paycheck.

b. Use the expressions you found in part a to write an expression for the total amount taken out of Perry's paycheck for taxes. Simplify the expression if possible.

For Exercises 37 through 50, simplify each expression by combining like terms.

37. $3x + 7 + 5x$

38. $9m + 4m + 8$

39. $7t + 9 - 3t + 5$

40. $4h - 8 - 9h + 6$

41. $2x^2 + 3x + 5x^2 + 6x$

42. $w^3 + 5w^3 + 3w^3 - w^2$

43. $4k^2 + 5k - 9$

44. $3g^5 + 5g^3 + 2g + 6$

45. $2xy + 5x - 3xy + 7y$

46. $8st + 5t^2 + 4st + 9s$

47. $5a^2b^3 + 4ab^2 + 8a^2b^2 + 2ab^2$

48. $-7n^3p^2 + 5n^2p + 4n^2p + 13n^3p^2$

49. $s^5t^3 + 4s^3t^5 + 7s^2t + 6s^5t^3 + 2s^2t$

50. $4xy + 2xz - xy + 3yz + 5xz$

For Exercises 51 through 60:
   a. State whether the multiplication property or the distributive property will be used.
   b. Simplify each expression.

51. $2(3x + 7)$

52. $6(10m^2 + 2m + 3)$

53. $5(2xy)$

54. $-3(4mn^2)$

55. $-4(7x^2 + 9x - 6)$

56. $6(9w^3)$

57. $-5(4a^2bc)$

58. $7(3g^5 + 5g^3 + 2g - 8)$

59. $-2(-3xy + 7y)$

60. $-3(12st + 5t^2 - 9s)$

For Exercises 61 through 70, a problem and a student's solution are given.
   a. Determine whether the student simplified correctly or incorrectly.
   b. If the student simplified the expression incorrectly, give the correct simplification.

61. $2(3xy)$

Bill
$6x2y$

62. $4(3x + 5)$

James
$12x + 20$

63. $3(2k - 4)$

Mandee
$6k - 4$

64. $5(2ab)$

Erin
$10a5b$

65. $7(3mn)$

Cynthia
$21m21n$

66. $3(5xy)$

Eve
$15xy$

67. $\frac{1}{5}(25ab)$

Jennifer
$5ab$

68. $\frac{1}{2}(10xy)$

Rita
$5x\frac{1}{2}y$

69. $\frac{2}{3}(6x + 9)$

Joanne
$4x + 9$

70. $\frac{3}{4}(8y - 12)$

Chad
$6y - 9$

For Exercises 71 through 96, simplify each expression.

71. $5(4x + 8) + 3x - 10$

72. $-2(5x - 4) + 10$

73. $-3(4g + 7) + 2g + 9$

74. $7(8d + 3) - 20d - 15$

75. $(2x + 5) - (5x - 7)$

76. $(5w + 9) - (-3w + 8)$

77. $(4k^2 + 5) - 3(2k^2 + 5k)$

78. $3(2a + 7) + (3a^2 + 5)$

79. $2xy + 5x + 2(3xy + 7)$

80. $-5(2st + 3) + 4st + 9$

81. $3(2x^2 + 3x) - 2(5x^2 + 6x)$

82. $4(3a^2 + 5a) - 7(6a^2 + 9a)$

83. $4(5w^2 + 6w - 3) + 3(2w^2 + 4w + 1)$

84. $2(3y^2 + 4y - 1) + 5(6y^2 + 8y + 3)$

85. $-2(4r^2 + 6r - 9) - 3(-5r^2 - 5r + 3)$

86. $-7(9x^2 - 5x + 1) - (-2x^2 + 7x - 2)$

87. $1.3(2t + 6) + 6.3t + 8$

88. $2.1(3b + 5) + 6.1b + 10$

89. $2.5(4h + 6) - 3.5(2h - 8)$

90. $3.2(4m - 3) - 6.3(2m + 8)$

91. $\frac{1}{2}(4x - 8) + 7x - 3$

92. $\frac{1}{2}(10 - 2x) - 7x + 12$

93. $\frac{1}{3}(9a - 6) + 8a - 14$

94. $\frac{1}{3}(12 - 3b) - 2b - 1$

95. $\frac{1}{5}(10a - 5b) + \frac{1}{2}(-4a + 12b)$

96. $\frac{1}{3}(6b - 15a) - \frac{1}{4}(16a - 8b)$

For Exercises 97 through 106, use the given figures to find expressions for the perimeter of the shapes. Simplify the expressions if possible. Note: Perimeter is the sum of the lengths of the sides.

97. Perimeter of a rectangle:

98. Perimeter of a square:

99.

100.

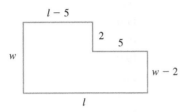

101. Perimeter of a rectangle:

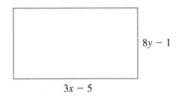

102. Perimeter of a rectangle:

103. Perimeter of an equilateral triangle:

104. Perimeter of an equilateral triangle:

105. Perimeter of a square:

106. Perimeter of a square:

1.4 Graphs and the Rectangular Coordinate System

LEARNING OBJECTIVES

- Interpret data tables.
- Read and create bar graphs and scatterplots.
- Plot points on the rectangular coordinate system.
- Describe scale.
- Graph real-world data.

Data Tables

In Section 1.3, we saw that algebraic expressions may be derived from input-output tables. Tables are also used to organize and display data. In many fields, such as health organizations and corporations, information is often presented in tables.

Example 1 Reading a table

The following table gives data on the influenza season from the first 10 weeks in 2003. The first column of the table (the input) is the week number in 2003. The second column (the output) gives the percentage of positive isolates (tests) for the influenza virus from testing labs across the United States. This percentage means the number of people who actually had the flu out of those who were tested for the flu.

Week	Percentage of Positive Isolates
1	5.5
2	8.6
3	11.6
4	16.1
5	19.9
6	24.7
7	23.7
8	21.2
9	20.8
10	18.4

Source: Centers for Disease Control and Prevention
(www.cdc.gov/flu).

If we examine these data carefully, we can see that the percentage is increasing to its highest level through week 6 and then starts to decrease.

a. What is the maximum percentage of positive isolates recorded? When does this occur?

b. What is the minimum percentage of positive isolates recorded? When does this occur?

SOLUTION

a. The maximum percentage of positive isolates is 24.7%, and it occurs in week 6.

b. The minimum percentage of positive isolates is 5.5%, and it occurs in week 1.

PRACTICE PROBLEM FOR EXAMPLE 1

The following table gives the number of bachelor's degrees awarded in the United States to science and engineering majors for the years 2000 thru 2004.

Year	Number of Science and Engineering Degrees
2000	398,622
2001	400,206
2002	415,611
2003	439,434
2004	454,978

Source: www.nsf.gov

a. What was the maximum number of bachelor's degrees awarded? When did this occur?

b. What was the minimum number of bachelor's degrees recorded? When did this occur?

Bar Graphs

Often, data are easier for many people to examine if they are visually presented in a graph. The **horizontal axis,** sometimes called the x-axis, is where the input values are plotted. The **vertical axis,** sometimes called the y-axis, is where the output values are plotted. The height of each bar represents the value of the output for the corresponding value of the input. The bars are of uniform width and evenly spaced along the horizontal axis.

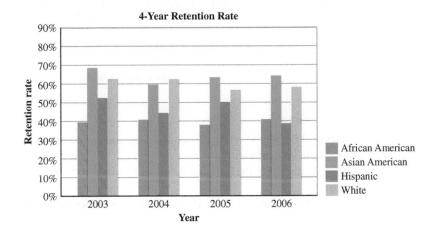

Example **2**   Reading a bar chart

The following graph is a bar chart giving the numbers of immigrants to the United States during the years 1820–2010 (projected values for 1991–2010).

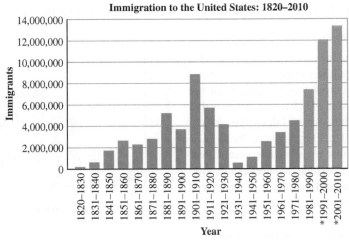

Source: Population Environment Balance.

a. For what years was the number of immigrants to the United States about 4,000,000 (four million)?

b. For what time period is the number of immigrants to the United States the largest?

SOLUTION

a. For the years 1921–1930, the bar is about (just slightly above) 4,000,000.

b. The highest bar is for the years 2001–2010, so that is the time period when the number of immigrants to the United States was the largest.

PRACTICE PROBLEM FOR EXAMPLE 2

The following graph is a bar chart showing the cost of asthma, in billions of U.S. dollars, in the United States for the years 1980–2000. These costs include both the direct ▼

cost of treating asthma (such as hospitalizations) and the indirect cost due to factors such as lost income.

a. What was the estimated cost of asthma in the United States in the year 1994?

b. During what year is the cost of asthma projected to be the highest?

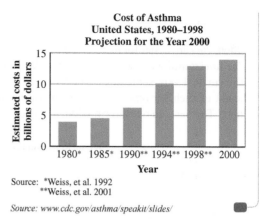

**Cost of Asthma
United States, 1980–1998
Projection for the Year 2000**

Source: *Weiss, et al. 1992
**Weiss, et al. 2001

Source: *www.cdc.gov/asthma/speakit/slides/*

Week	Percentage of Positive Isolates
1	5.5
2	8.6
3	11.6
4	16.1
5	19.9
6	24.7
7	23.7
8	21.2
9	20.8
10	18.4

Source: Centers for Disease Control and Prevention (www.cdc.gov/flu).

Steps to Create a Bar Graph

1. The input values will be plotted on the horizontal axis, and the output values will be plotted on the vertical axis.
2. Evenly and consistently space the horizontal axis so that it includes the input values (data).
3. Evenly and consistently space the vertical axis so that it includes the output values (data).
4. Draw vertical bars of uniform width. Center each bar over the appropriate input value. Draw the bars of height corresponding to the output value.

Example 3 Drawing a bar chart

Make a bar chart for the influenza data presented in Example 1 on page 106.

SOLUTION

The input values are weeks 1 through 10, so we plot these values on the horizontal axis. The output values range from the smallest value of 5.5 to the largest value of 24.9. Thus, we will draw the vertical axis from 0 to 30 by counting by fives.

   Notice that each bar is centered over the week to which it corresponds (the input value) and that the bars are evenly spaced along the horizontal axis. The heights of the bars represent the output value (the percent of positive isolates).

Example 4 Drawing a bar chart that includes negative values

The following table gives the quarterly earnings for the Kmart Corporation from July 2003 to July 2004. Draw a bar chart for this data set.

SOLUTION

Notice that the output values take on both positive and negative values. When the output values take on negative values, draw the bar *upside down* under the horizontal axis.

Quarters Since July 2003	Kmart Earnings (millions of dollars)
1	−5
2	−23
3	279
4	93
5	155

Source: www.fidelity.com

The horizontal axis will be scaled by 1, which will accommodate the quarters 1 through 5. The vertical axis will be scaled by 50. This will accommodate the smallest output value of -23 and the largest output value of 279.

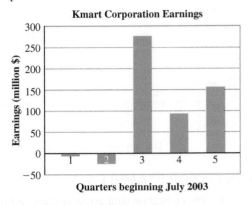

Kmart Corporation Earnings

PRACTICE PROBLEM FOR EXAMPLE 4

The following table shows the average daily high temperature at Vostok Research Station in Antarctica. Draw a bar chart for this data set.

Month	Average High Temperature (°F)
January	$-20°F$
February	$-39°F$
March	$-63°F$
April	$-77°F$
May	$-75°F$

Source: Wikipedia

Scatterplots

Another important type of graph is a scatterplot. The horizontal and vertical axes are scaled as they were for bar graphs. Instead of having a bar represent the height (or output value), use a large dot where the top of the bar would be.

Example **5**   Drawing a scatterplot

Draw a scatterplot for Kmart data given in Example 4.

SOLUTION

Quarters Since July 2003	Kmart Earnings (millions of dollars)
1	-5
2	-23
3	276
4	93
5	155

Source: www.fidelity.com

A reasonable vertical axis for these data would range between -50 and 300, with a scale of 50. A negative value for Kmart's earnings means that the company lost money that quarter and will be graphed below the horizontal axis. For a scatterplot, instead of using a bar to represent the height, use a large dot.

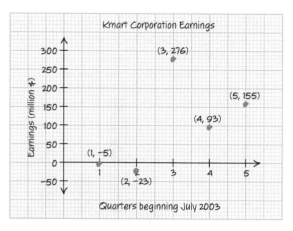

Month	Average High Temperature (°F)
January	−20°F
February	−39°F
March	−63°F
April	−77°F
May	−75°F

Source: Wikipedia.

PRACTICE PROBLEM FOR EXAMPLE 5

Draw a scatterplot for the Vostok Station data given in Practice Problem for Example 4.

Rectangular Coordinate System

In Section 1.2, we learned how to generate relationships between two variables, an input and an output, from tables and expressions. For example, we developed the following table, which gave us the relationship between the number of inches of snow (*s*) and the number of inches of rain (*r*).

The data consist of values for the input variable (*s*) and values for the output variable (*r*). We write individual data items as **ordered pairs** (*input, output*) = (*s, r*). For example, the ordered pair (12, 1) for this equation means that *s* = 12 inches of snow

s = inches of snow	*r* = inches of rain
12	$\frac{12}{12} = 1$
24	$\frac{24}{12} = 2$
36	$\frac{36}{12} = 3$
42	$\frac{42}{12} = 3.5$
s	$\frac{s}{12}$

converts to *r* = 1 inch of rain. The order matters in an ordered pair. We cannot swap the input and output variables. In math, we often use the variables *x* and *y* and have ordered pairs (*x, y*).

> ### DEFINITION
>
> **Ordered Pair**   An ordered pair is of the form (*x, y*), where *x* is the value of the input variable and *y* is the value of the output variable.

What's That Mean?

What's That Mean?

Cartesian Coordinate System

The rectangular coordinate system is also called the Cartesian coordinate system. It is named after the French mathematician, philosopher, and scientist René Descartes.

What's That Mean?

Coordinates

A point is described by an ordered pair (*x, y*). The values of *x* and *y* are called the *coordinates* of that point.

To graph data, we use what is called the **rectangular coordinate system.** The input data are graphed on the horizontal axis (or *x*-axis), and the output data are graphed on the vertical axis (or *y*-axis). We will graph each ordered pair as a point. The input, or *x*-coordinate, will tell us how many units the point is located to the right (*x* is positive) or to the left (*x* is negative) of the *y*-axis. The output, or *y*-coordinate, will tell us how many units the point is located above (*y* is positive) the *x*-axis, or below (*y* is negative) the *x*-axis. The point where the *x*-axis and *y*-axis cross is written as (0, 0) and is called the **origin.**

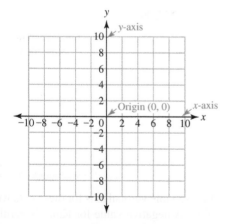

Notice that on the graph above, the scale on the *x*-axis is 2. The scale on the *y*-axis is also 2.

Example 6   **Writing the ordered pairs shown on the graph**

On the following graph, there are eight different points. Write the ordered pairs that give the coordinates of each point.

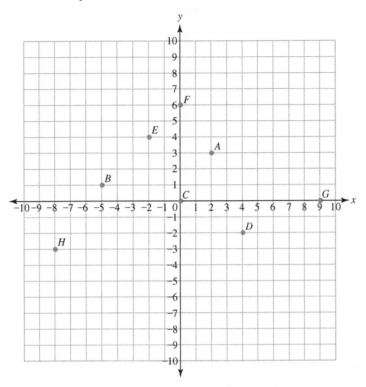

SOLUTION

To determine the coordinates of point A, we need to find the values of the x- and y-coordinates. Point A is located 2 units to the right of the y-axis, so the x-coordinate is $x = 2$. Point A is located 3 units above the x-axis, so the y-coordinate is $y = 3$. The coordinates of Point A are $(2, 3)$.

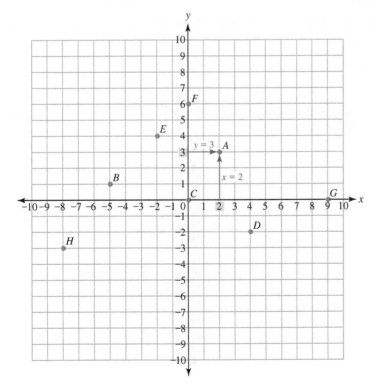

Point *B* is located 5 units to the left of the *y*-axis, so the *x*-coordinate is $x = -5$. Point *B* is located 1 unit above the *x*-axis, so the *y*-coordinate is $y = 1$. The coordinates of Point *B* are $(-5, 1)$.

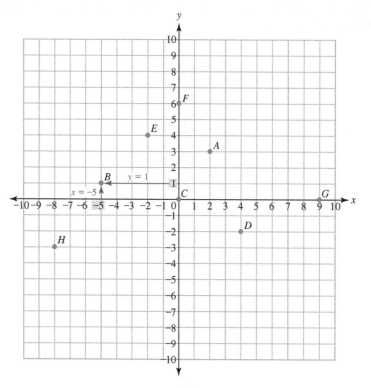

We find the coordinates of the rest of the points in a similar fashion.

Point *C* has coordinates $(0, 0)$: Point *C* is located at the origin.

Point *D* has coordinates $(4, -2)$.

Point *E* has coordinates $(-2, 4)$.

Point *F* has coordinates $(0, 6)$. Point *F* is located on the *y*-axis, which passes through $x = 0$.

Point *G* has coordinates $(9, 0)$. Point *G* is located on the *x*-axis, which passes through $y = 0$.

Point *H* has coordinates $(-8, -3)$.

PRACTICE PROBLEM FOR EXAMPLE 6

On the following graph, there are eight different points. Write the ordered pairs that give the coordinates of each point.

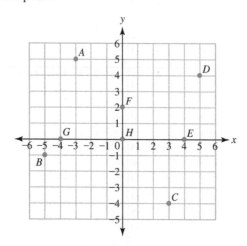

In Example 6, point *D* has coordinates $(4, -2)$, and point *E* has coordinates $(-2, 4)$. We can see from the graph that points *D* and *E* are not the same. This means that $(4, -2) \neq (-2, 4)$. This is why we call them *ordered* pairs. The order matters.

It is very important to pay attention to reading the scale from a graph. The scales on the axes are not always 1 and can be different from one another. This is demonstrated in the following example.

Example 7   Looking for the horizontal and vertical scales

Determine the scales of the *x*-axis and *y*-axis in the following graph.

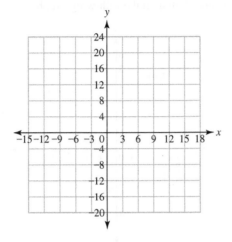

SOLUTION

The *x*-axis has a scale of 3 because the even spacing on the *x*-axis is by 3's. The *y*-axis has a scale of 4 because the even spacing on the *y*-axis is by 4's. Here, the two axes have different scales from each other, but the scale on a single axis must be consistent.

PRACTICE PROBLEM FOR EXAMPLE 7

Determine the scales of the *x*-axis and *y*-axis in the following graph.

Steps to Create a Graph in the Rectangular Coordinate System

1. Evenly and consistently space and scale the horizontal axis so that it includes the input values (data).
2. Evenly and consistently space and scale the vertical axis so that it includes the output values (data). *Note:* The scale of the vertical and horizontal axes may be different.
3. Plot each ordered pair (point) by first finding the intersection of the input value and the output value and then drawing a dot.

■ Skill Connection

When $x = 0$, the point will be located on the *y*-axis. It will have the form $(0, y)$. When $y = 0$, the point will be located on the *x*-axis. It will have the form $(x, 0)$.

Example 8 Graphing ordered pairs

Graph the following ordered pairs on the same axes. Clearly label and scale your axes.

a. $(-3, 4)$ **b.** $(5, -2)$ **c.** $(3, 3)$

d. $(-4, -1)$ **e.** $(2, 0)$ **f.** $(0, -3)$

SOLUTION

The input values range from -4 to 5. It is reasonable to scale the horizontal axis by 1's. Likewise, the output values range from -3 to 4 so it will also be reasonable to scale the y-axis by 1's. The points are plotted on the following graph.

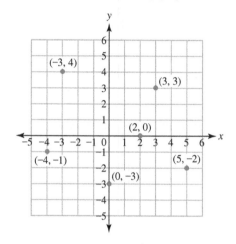

PRACTICE PROBLEM FOR EXAMPLE 8

Graph the following ordered pairs on the same axes. Clearly label and scale your axes.

a. $(2, 6)$ **b.** $(-5, 12)$ **c.** $(-1, 15)$

d. $(-6, -10)$ **e.** $(0, 20)$ **f.** $(-5, 0)$

When graphing real data from a problem situation, consider the scale to be used on the axes. Remember that the scale on an axis must be consistent. This means that values on that particular axis must be evenly spaced. However, the horizontal axis and the vertical axis may have different scales.

Example 9 Graphing data

Graph the following ordered pairs on the same axes. Clearly label and scale your axes.

s = inches of snow	r = inches of rain
12	1
24	2
36	3
42	3.5

SOLUTION

To graph the data, we first should decide on the scale to use. For the horizontal axis, the data values are increasing by 12, so we will plot starting at 0, with a scale of 12. The output values, which are plotted on the vertical axis, range from 1 to 3.5. So plotting from 0 to 5 with a scale of 0.5 should graph these values effectively.

When ordered pairs appear in a table, we pair them by row. In the first row, we are given that $s = 12$ and $r = 1$. This row represents the ordered pair $(s, r) = (12, 1)$.

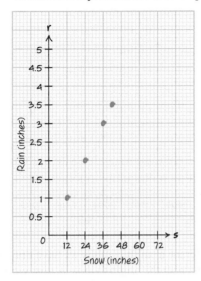

Sometimes the data presented to us do not start anywhere near the zero value of either axis. When we do not start graphing an axis at zero, we use a *zigzag* pattern to show there is a break in the numbering. This zigzag is called a *break* in the graph. This is shown in Example 10.

Example 10   Graphing data and adjusting axes

For the following data set, graph the points. Clearly scale and label the axes. The table lists the number of bank robbery incidents reported in the Bank Crime Statistics (BCS) database for the years 1990–2001.

Year	Bank Robbery Incidents
1990	8042
1991	9532
1992	9540
1993	8561
1994	7081
1995	6986
1996	8362
1997	8082
1998	7711
1999	6813
2000	7310
2001	8516

SOLUTION

We will graph the input values along the horizontal axis. Since the years begin not at zero but at 1990, we place a zigzag in the graph along the lower left corner to indicate the break in time, and we start with the year 1988 and end at 2002, with a scale of 1 year. The vertical axis is where we graph the output data, which have a minimum value of 6813 and a maximum value of 9540. We put a zigzag in the graph to indicate that the vertical axis does not start at zero, and we graph from 6000 to 10,500 with a scale of 500. The scale of 500 was selected because it is easy to count by 500's and the data were spread out by several thousand.

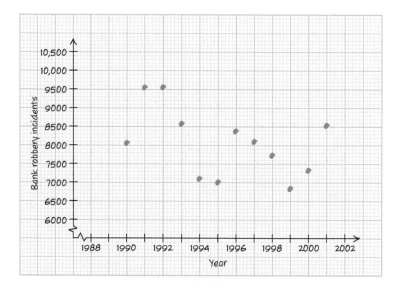

Year	Burglaries (per 1000 households)
1999	34.1
2000	31.8
2001	28.7
2002	27.7
2003	29.8
2004	29.6
2005	29.6

Source: www.ojp.usdoj.gov

This graph is a bit different from the graphs we have drawn previously. First of all, there is a break in the graph near the origin to indicate that we are not starting to count at 0. The second difference is that the output values in the data table do not exactly match up with the values on the vertical axis. This is common with real-world data, and we often have to make a best estimate of where the point lies on the graph.

PRACTICE PROBLEM FOR EXAMPLE 10

For the accompanying data set, graph the points. Clearly scale and label the axes. The table lists the number of burglaries per 1000 households in the United States during the years 1999–2005.

1.4   Exercises

For Exercises 1–4, use the data table given in each exercise to answer the questions.

1. The table lists the percentage of crimes reported to the police.

	Violent Crime	Property Crime
Average	44.7%	35.5%
1992–1993	42.7%	33.4%
1994–1995	41.2%	33.4%
1996–1997	43.6%	34.9%
1998–1999	45%	34.6%
2000–2001	48.6%	36.4%
2002–2003	48%	39.3%
2004–2005	48.7%	39.3%

Source: www.ojp.usdoj.gov/bjs

a. What is the maximum percentage of violent crime reported to the police? When did this happen?

b. What is the minimum percentage of property crime reported to the police? When did this happen?

2. The table lists the total number of firearm incidents and victims in the United States.

Years	Firearm Incidents	Firearm Victims
1993	1,054,820	1,248,250
1994	1,060,800	1,286,860
1995	902,680	1,050,900
1996	845,220	989,930
1997	680,900	795,560
1998	557,200	670,480
1999	457,150	562,870
2000	428,670	533,470
2001	467,880	524,030
2002	353,880	430,930
2003	366,840	449,150
2004	280,890	331,630
2005	419,640	477,040

Source: www.ojp.usdoj.gov/bjs

a. What is the maximum number of firearm incidents? When did this happen?

b. What is the minimum number of firearm victims? When did this happen?

3. The world record times for the men's marathon are listed in the table.

Chris Mole/shutterstock.com

Time	Athlete	Country	Date
2h03:59	Haile Gebrselassie	Ethiopia	28-Sep-08
2h04:55	Paul Tergat	Kenya	28-Sep-03
2h04:56	Sammy Korir	Kenya	28-Sep-03
2h05:15	Martin Lel	Kenya	13-Apr-08
2h05:24	Samuel Wanjiru	Kenya	13-Apr-08
2h05:30	Abderrahim Goumri	Morocco	13-Apr-08
2h05:35	James Kwambai	Kenya	28-Sep-08
2h05:38	Khalid Khannouchi	United States	14-Apr-02
2h05:49	William Kipsang	Kenya	13-Apr-08
2h05:50	Evans Rutto	Kenya	12-Oct-03

Source: en.wikipedia.org/wiki/Marathon

a. What is the fastest marathon time? In what year did this happen?

b. What country do most of the top 10 runners come from?

4. The world record times for the women's 100-meter dash are listed in the table.

Rank	Time (seconds)	Athlete	Nation	Date
1	10.49	Florence Griffith Joyner	United States	16-Jul-88
2	10.65A*	Marion Jones	United States	12-Sep-98
3	10.73	Christine Arron	France	19-Aug-98
4	10.74	Merlene Ottey	Jamaica	7-Sep-96
5	10.76	Evelyn Ashford	United States	22-Aug-84
6	10.77	Irina Privalova	Russia	6-Jul-94
		Ivet Lalova	Bulgaria	19-Jun-04
8	10.78A*	Dawn Sowell	United States	3-Jun-89
	10.78	Torri Edwards	United States	28-Jun-08
		Shelly-Ann Fraser	Jamaica	17-Aug-08

*A denotes a time set at high altitude.

Source: en.wikipedia.org/wiki/100_metres

a. What is the fastest women's 100-meter dash time? In what year did it happen?

b. Most of the top runners on this list are from which country?

For Exercises 5 through 8, use the graph given in each exercise to answer the questions.

5. The graph gives the percentage of obese adults in the United States for the years 1998–2004.

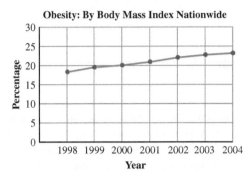

Obesity: By Body Mass Index Nationwide

Source: www.cdc.gov

a. During which year(s) was the percentage of obese adults the highest? Approximately what percentage of the adult population was obese that year?

b. During which year(s) was the percentage of obese adults the lowest? Approximately what percentage of the adult population was obese that year?

6. The graph shows the number of named storms and hurricanes from 1944 to 2005 in the Atlantic Ocean. The strong storms are in red, and the weak storms are in blue.

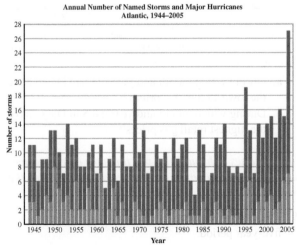

Annual Number of Named Storms and Major Hurricanes Atlantic, 1944–2005

Source: commons.wikimedia.org/wiki/

a. Which year(s) had the lowest number of Atlantic named storms and hurricanes? Approximately how many storms and hurricanes occurred during that year(s)?

b. Which year(s) had the highest number of Atlantic named storms and hurricanes? Approximately how many storms and hurricanes occurred during that year(s)?

7. The graph below shows sales of new homes in the United States from 1963 to 2009.

Historical New Home Sales: 1963–2009

Source: U.S. Census Bureau.

a. In which year were new home sales at their lowest point? Approximately how many sales were made?

b. In which year were new home sales at their highest point? Approximately how many sales were made?

8. The graph shows gasoline prices in San Diego, California, during 2005–2008.

36-Month Average Retail Price Chart

Source: http://www.sandiegogasprices.com/

a. During which month and year did San Diego have the lowest retail gas prices?

b. During which month and year did San Diego have the highest retail gas prices?

For Exercises 9 through 14, use the table given in each exercise to make a bar chart. Clearly label and scale the axes.

9. The table gives Gina's personal income over a five-year period.

Year	Personal Income
2000	$27,000
2001	$29,000
2002	$30,500
2003	$31,000
2004	$31,500

10. The table lists the cost of attending Cayuga County Community College (in upstate New York), as determined by the number of units a resident part-time student enrolls in.

Number of Units	Cost (dollars)
3	$353.00
6	$704.00
8	$938.00
9	$1055.00
10	$1172.00

11. The table lists the relationship between the number of years and the number of centuries. Note that a century is a 100-year time period.

Number of Years	Number of Centuries
100	1
150	1.5
200	2
250	2.5
300	3

12. The table lists the relationship between the number of centuries and the number of millennia. Note that a century is a 100-year time period and a millennium is a 1000-year time period.

Number of Centuries	Number of Millennia
10	1
15	1.5
20	2
25	2.5
30	3

13.

t	P
0	23
2	17
4	11
6	5
8	−7
10	−25

14.

x	y
0	−4
0.5	−1
1	5
1.5	6
2	3
2.5	1

For Exercises 15–20, use the data given in each exercise to create a scatterplot. Clearly label and scale the axes.

15. Use the table from Exercise 9.

16. Use the table from Exercise 10.

17.

x	y
−50	−20
−25	−10
0	0
10	4
40	16
50	20

18.

x	y
−2	−4
−1.5	−1
−1.0	5
−0.5	6
0	3
0.5	1

19. The average high monthly temperature in San Diego, California, for the months of January through June is listed in the table. *Hint:* Let January = 1, February = 2, and so on.

Month	Average Monthly High Temperature
January	66°F
February	66°F
March	66°F
April	69°F
May	69°F
June	72°F

20. The average high monthly temperature in St. Paul, Minnesota, for the months of January through June is listed in the table.

Month	Average Monthly High Temperature
January	23°F
February	30°F
March	42°F
April	58°F
May	71°F
June	79°F

For Exercises 21 through 24, write the coordinates of each ordered pair shown on the graph.

21.

22.

23.

24.

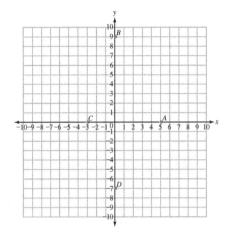

For Exercises 25 through 28, state the scale on both the x- and y-axes.

25.

26.

27.

28.

For Exercises 29 and 30, write the coordinates of each ordered pair shown on the graph.

29.

30.

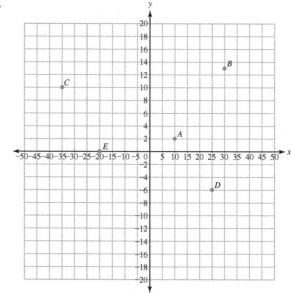

For Exercises 31 through 38, graph the given ordered pairs on the same axes. Clearly label and scale the axes.

31. $\{(3, 2), (5, 4), (-2, 1), (-3, 6)\}$

32. $\{(-16, -8), (-8, -4), (0, 0), (8, 4)\}$

33. $\{(0.5, 1.0), (1.0, 0.5), (1.5, 0), (2.0, -0.5)\}$

34. $\{(-0.8, 3), (-0.4, 3.5), (0, 4.0), (0.4, 4.5)\}$

35.

x	y
0	−2
10	−4
20	16
30	−8
40	0
50	12

36.

x	y
−9	5
0	−10
3	15
6	−20
9	10
15	20

37.

x	y
−50	60
−25	40
0	10
50	−20
75	50
125	−30

38.

x	y
4	2.5
3	1.5
2	0
1	−2
0	−0.5
−3	1

For Exercises 39 through 44, use the data given in each exercise to create a scatterplot. Clearly label and scale the axes.

39. The table gives the total Christmas holiday spending in the United States for the years 1994–2003.

Year	Total Spending (billions of dollars)
1994	$133.43
1995	$144.64
1996	$149.20
1997	$159.33
1998	$168.66
1999	$182.56
2000	$190.49
2001	$201.20
2002	$205.63
2003	$217.40

Source: www.nrf.com

40. The table gives United States consumer debt (in billions of dollars) for the years 1992–2001.

Year	Consumer Debt (billions of dollars)
1992	$778
1993	$785
1994	$845
1995	$973
1996	$1103
1997	$1191
1998	$1235
1999	$1315
2000	$1409
2001	$1523

Source: www.npr.org

41. The table lists the conversion between the number of hours and the number of days.

h = number of hours	d = number of days
12	0.5
24	1
36	1.5
48	2
72	3

42. The table lists the conversion between pounds and kilograms.

P = number of pounds	K = number of kilograms
2.2	1
4.4	2
6.6	3
8.8	4
13.2	6

43. The table gives the U.S. federal debt (total amount owed) during the years 1990–2005.

Year	U.S. Debt (trillions of dollars)
1990	$3.23
1995	$4.97
2000	$5.67
2005	$7.93

Source: www.colorado.edu/.../lewis/ecology/struct.htm

44. The table gives new privately owned housing starts for the year 2005. The units are in thousands.

Month	Number of New Housing Starts (thousands)
January	2136
February	2093
March	2021
April	2148
May	2062
June	2132
July	2171
August	2138
September	2219
October	2103
November	2163
December	2075

Source: www.census.gov/indicator

For Exercises 45 through 50, find the mistake in the student work shown.

45. Graph the point (3, 4).

Mark

46. Graph the point (−5, −2).

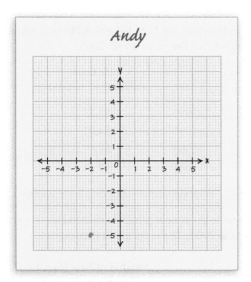

Andy

47. Graph the points in the table.

x	y
2	5
0	−2
5	−1
−3	−4

Joy

48. Graph the points in the table.

x	y
3	−1
6	0
−2	−4
4	1

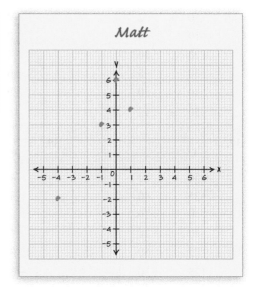

Matt

49. Graph the points in the table.

x	y
5	40
−20	−2

Erin

50. Graph the points in the table.

x	y
−4	50
0.5	−20

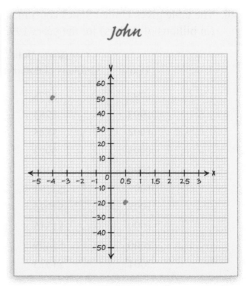

John

Chapter Summary

Section **1.1** Exponents, Order of Operations, and Properties of Real Numbers

- A **natural number exponent** is a way of writing a repeated multiplication. **Exponentiation** is another operation on real numbers.
- $a^0 = 1$ for all $a \neq 0$. 0^0 does not exist.
- **Scientific notation** is used to write extremely large or small numbers in a more compact form. For $1 \leq |a| < 10$, $a \times 10^n$ is written using scientific notation.
- The **basic arithmetic operations** are addition, subtraction, multiplication, division, and exponentiation.
- In arithmetic the two (or more) quantities being added or subtracted are called **terms.**
- The **order-of-operations agreement** is used to simplify expressions with multiple operations. **PEMDAS** is an acronym to help memorize the order-of-operations agreement.
- When **grouping symbols** appear in an expression to be simplified, they must be evaluated first.
- The **commutative property** tells us that we may add or multiply in any order.
- The **associative property** tells us that how we group terms (factors) in an addition (multiplication) problem does not change the result.
- The **distributive property** allows us to distribute the operation of multiplication over addition (or subtraction).

Example 1

Answer as indicated.

a. Write in exponential form: $(-5) \cdot (-5) \cdot (-5)$

b. Write in expanded form: 4^6

c. Find the value without a calculator: $(-2)^4$

SOLUTION

a. $(-5) \cdot (-5) \cdot (-5) = (-5)^3$

b. $4^6 = 4 \cdot 4 \cdot 4 \cdot 4 \cdot 4 \cdot 4$

c. $(-2)^4 = 16$

Example 2

Simplify each expression using the order-of-operations agreement.

a. $-16 + \dfrac{12}{4} + 3 \cdot (-2) - 8$ **b.** $|4 - 2 \cdot 6| + (-4 - 3)^2$

SOLUTION

a. $-16 + \dfrac{12}{4} + 3 \cdot (-2) - 8 = -27$ **b.** $|4 - 2 \cdot 6| + (-4 - 3)^2 = 57$

Example 3

Identify the property used to rewrite the expression: the commutative property, the associative property, or the distributive property.

   a. $3(5 - 4) = 3(5) - 3(4)$

   b. $46 \cdot 2 = 2 \cdot 46$

   c. $3 + (4 + 19) = (3 + 4) + 19$

SOLUTION

   a. This is an example of the distributive property.

   b. This is an example of the commutative property.

   c. This is an example of the associative property.

Section 1.2   Algebra and Working with Variables

- **Variables** are used to represent an unknown quantity or a quantity that can change (vary).
- A **constant** is a quantity that cannot change.
- A **term** is a constant or the product of a constant and a variable(s). An **algebraic expression** is a combination of variables and constants under algebraic operations.
- To **evaluate an expression** means to substitute in the given value of the variable and simplify the expression using the order-of-operations agreement.
- To form a **unity fraction,** find a relationship between the two quantities. Put the units required in the final answer in the numerator, and the units that are being converted from in the denominator.
- To **convert units** (from one set of units to another), multiply by the unity fraction and simplify. Remember that units can be divided out.
- When **translating a phrase into an algebraic expression,** first **define** the variables. Then translate the phrases into an algebraic expression.
- **Input-output tables** can be used to help translate phrases into algebraic expressions. Be careful to write out all the operations used in the output column. Doing so helps in finding the general pattern of the relationship between the input variable and the output variable.

Example 4

Convert units as indicated. Convert 25 kilograms to pounds. There are 2.2 lb in 1 kg.

SOLUTION

$$25 \text{ kg} \cdot \frac{2.2 \text{ lb}}{1 \text{ kg}} = 55 \text{ lb}$$

Example 5

Evaluate the algebraic expression for the given value of the variable. $-3x^2 + 12x$ for $x = -2$.

SOLUTION

$$-3x^2 + 12x$$
$$= -3(-2)^2 + 12(-2) \qquad \text{Substitute in } x = -2.$$
$$= -3(4) + (-24) \qquad \text{Simplify.}$$
$$= -12 + (-24)$$
$$= -36$$

Example 6 Define the variables and translate into an expression.
A house-cleaning service quotes a rate of $15.00 an hour for labor. Write an expression that gives the labor cost for house cleaning.

SOLUTION Let h = number of hours worked cleaning a home. The total cost in dollars for labor will be $15h$.

Section 1.3   Simplifying Expressions

- A **term** is a constant, a variable, or the product of any number of constants and variables.
- The **coefficient** is the numerical factor of a term.
- Terms are called **like** if they have the same variables and those variables are raised to the same exponents.
- Only **like terms** can be added or subtracted. To add or subtract like terms, add or subtract their coefficients.
- When multiplying a single term by a constant, use the **multiplication property** to multiply the coefficient of the term by the constant.
- When multiplying several terms by a constant, use the **distributive property** to multiply the coefficient of each term by the constant.
- To **simplify** an expression means to use arithmetic or algebraic properties to rewrite the expression in simplest form. To simplify an expression, first multiply or distribute constants if necessary, and then combine like terms, all the while following the order of operations.

Example 7 Identify the number of terms in the expression. Simplify. $-3y^2 + 4y + 7 - y^2 + 9$

SOLUTION There are five terms in this expression. They are circled. $\widehat{-3y^2} + \widehat{4y} + \widehat{7} - \widehat{y^2} + \widehat{9}$
To simplify, add like terms.

$$-3y^2 + 4y + 7 - y^2 + 9 \qquad \text{Add } y^2 \text{ terms (like).}$$
$$= -4y^2 + 4y + 7 + 9 \qquad \text{Add 7 and 9 (like terms).}$$
$$= -4y^2 + 4y + 16$$

Example 8 Multiply each expression.

   a. $-3(-2a)$ **b.** $-2(3x^2 - 5x + 1)$

SOLUTION **a.** $-3(-2a) = 6a$ Use the multiplication property.

               b. $-2(3x^2 - 5x + 1) = -6x^2 + 10x - 2$ Use the distributive property.

Example 9 Simplify the expression. $-2(4x - 3) - (-5x + 7)$

SOLUTION
$$-2(4x - 3) - (-5x + 7)$$
$$= -8x + 6 + 5x - 7$$
$$= -3x - 1$$

Section **1.4** Graphs and the Rectangular Coordinate System

- **Data tables** are often used to organize and display data.
- **Graphs** are a visual way to look at tabular data or an equation in two variables.
- The most common kinds of graphs are **bar graphs and scatterplots.**
- The **input** (independent) variable is plotted on the horizontal or *x*-axis, and the **output** (dependent) variable is plotted on the vertical or *y*-axis.
- An **ordered pair** has the form (x, y), where x is the value of the input and y is the value of the output. The values of x and y are also called the **coordinates** of the ordered pair or point.

Example 10 Graph the given ordered pairs on the same axes. Clearly label and scale the axes.
$(-6, 20)$ $(-4, -20)$ $(12, -50)$ $(10, 40)$ $(0, 12)$

SOLUTION

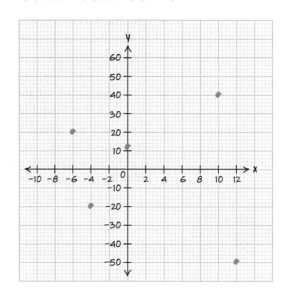

Example 11 Determine the scale on the *x*- and *y*-axes.

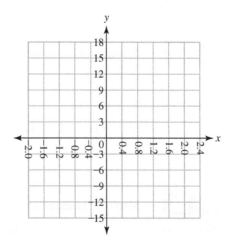

The *x*-axis has a scale of 0.4 because the tick marks are evenly and consistently 0.4 unit apart. Likewise, the *y*-axis has a scale of 3.

Chapter Review Exercises

1. Write in exponential form: $6 \cdot 6 \cdot 6 \cdot 6 \cdot 6$ [1.1]

2. Write in exponential form: $8 \cdot 8 \cdot 8 \cdot 8$ [1.1]

3. Write in exponential form: $\left(\frac{3}{8}\right) \cdot \left(\frac{3}{8}\right) \cdot \left(\frac{3}{8}\right)$ [1.1]

4. Write in exponential form:
$\left(\frac{-4}{5}\right) \cdot \left(\frac{-4}{5}\right) \cdot \left(\frac{-4}{5}\right) \cdot \left(\frac{-4}{5}\right) \cdot \left(\frac{-4}{5}\right)$ [1.1]

5. Write in expanded form: 5^6 [1.1]

6. Write in expanded form: $(-2)^3$ [1.1]

7. Write in expanded form: $\left(\frac{-2}{5}\right)^4$ [1.1]

8. Write in expanded form: $\left(\frac{1}{11}\right)^3$ [1.1]

9. Find the value without a calculator: $(-3)^3$ [1.1]

10. Find the value without a calculator: $(-6)^2$ [1.1]

11. Find the value without a calculator: $\left(\frac{4}{9}\right)^2$ [1.1]

12. Find the value without a calculator: $\left(\frac{-2}{3}\right)^3$ [1.1]

13. Write using standard notation: 2.07×10^5 [1.1]

14. Write using standard notation: 5.67×10^6 [1.1]

15. Underline or circle the terms. Then simplify using the order-of-operations agreement:
$-3 + 4 \cdot (-2) + 24 \div 8 - 3^2 + (-2)$ [1.1]

16. Underline or circle the terms. Then simplify using the order-of-operations agreement:
$27 \div 3 - 5^2 + (-10) + 20 - 3 \cdot (-5)$ [1.1]

17. Underline or circle the terms. Then simplify using the order-of-operations agreement: $5 \div \frac{15}{7} + \frac{2}{3} - 1$ [1.1]

18. Underline or circle the terms. Then simplify using the order-of-operations agreement: $-4 - \frac{1}{5} + \frac{3}{2} \cdot \frac{4}{15}$ [1.1]

For Exercises 19 through 30, simplify the expression using the order-of-operations agreement.

19. $6 \div (-2) \cdot 5 + (-3)^2$ [1.1]

20. $(-2)^3 - 36 \div 9 \cdot 7$ [1.1]

21. $\frac{3}{2} \cdot \frac{4}{9} - 5 + \frac{2}{3}$ [1.1]

22. $\frac{-1}{4} \cdot \frac{12}{5} + 3 \div \frac{5}{2} - 1$ [1.1]

23. $-7 \cdot (-4) \div 2 + (-1)^4 + \frac{6 \cdot 3}{5 - 2}$ [1.1]

24. $\frac{8 - 5}{4 + 2} + 16 \cdot (-3) \div 12 + (-3)^2$ [1.1]

25. $-5 + 7 \cdot (-3) + 44 \div 2 - 6^2 + (-8)$ [1.1]

26. $(-5)^2 - 24 \div (-3) \cdot 2 - (-6 - 4) + 9$ [1.1]

27. $5 + \frac{22 - 4 \cdot 2}{16 - 3^2} - (-2)^2$ [1.1]

28. $\frac{-2 + 6 \cdot 2}{14 - 3^2} - (3 \cdot 2 - 7)$ [1.1]

29. $\left| -2 + 3 \cdot (-4) \right| + (-7)^2$ [1.1]

30. $\left| -8 + (-3)(-2) \right| + 3^3$ [1.1]

For Exercises 31 through 38, identify the property (commutative, associative, or distributive) used to rewrite the statement.

31. $(-2)(-8) = (-8)(-2)$ [1.1]

32. $-3 + (-8) = -8 + (-3)$ [1.1]

33. $-3(4 + 5) = -3 \cdot 4 + (-3) \cdot 5$ [1.1]

34. $2 \cdot (3 - 7) = 2 \cdot 3 - 2 \cdot 7$ [1.1]

35. $(-3) + (-4 + 9) = (-3 + (-4)) + 9$ [1.1]

36. $(5 \cdot 3)(-2) = 5 \cdot (3 \cdot (-2))$ [1.1]

37. $\frac{4}{5} + \frac{8}{9} = \frac{8}{9} + \frac{4}{5}$ [1.1]

38. $\frac{5}{7} \cdot \frac{3}{25} = \frac{3}{25} \cdot \frac{5}{7}$ [1.1]

39. Define the variables: The amount of money you earn in a month depends on the number of hours you work in a month. [1.2]

40. Define the variables: The amount of money (revenue) a local playhouse earns for a night depends on the number of tickets sold for that night. [1.2]

For Exercises 41 through 44, translate the phrase into a variable expression.

41. Six less than three times a number. [1.2]

42. Eight more than five times a number. [1.2]

43. One-half of the difference between a number and 4. [1.2]

44. The quotient of the sum of a number and 12, and 16. [1.2]

For Exercises 45 through 50, convert units as indicated. Round to the hundredths place if necessary.

45. Convert 9 inches to centimeters. [1.2]

46. Convert 55 kilometers to miles. [1.2]

47. Convert 185 pounds to kilograms. [1.2]

48. Convert 100 kilograms to pounds. [1.2]

49. Convert 55 grams to ounces. [1.2]

50. Convert 5 ounces to grams. [1.2]

For Exercises 51 through 60, evaluate the expression for the given values of the variables.

51. $\dfrac{-5h}{18} + 9$ for $h = -3$ [1.2]

52. $-4r + \dfrac{r}{2}$ for $r = 8$ [1.2]

53. $5x - 2y$ for $x = -3, y = -5$ [1.2]

54. $5y - 6x$ for $x = -2, y = -7$ [1.2]

55. $3xy + 2x - y$ for $x = -2$ and $y = 3$ [1.2]

56. $l + k - 10$ for $l = 4$ and $k = -3$ [1.2]

57. $0.25a + 1.75b$ for $a = 0.8, b = 4.6$ [1.2]

58. $0.5h - 2.5k$ for $h = 8, k = -10$ [1.2]

59. $15ab + c$ for $a = 2, b = -3, c = 4$ [1.2]

60. $a + b + c$ for $a = 3, b = 4, c = 5$ [1.2]

61. Wang Li is going to invest $4500.00 in two different accounts. He invests d dollars in the first account. Fill out the input-output table to write an expression for the amount of money he invests in the second account. [1.2]

Amount Invested in the First Account	Amount Invested in the Second Account
0	
1000	
2000	
3500	
d	

62. Colin has to cut a 20-foot board into two pieces. He cuts x feet of lumber in the first piece. Fill out the input-output table to write an expression for the length of the second piece. [1.2]

First Piece	Second Piece
0	
4	
8	
16	
x	

63. Convert 800 million to thousands. *Hint:* There are 1000 thousands in 1 million. [1.2]

64. Convert 700 billion into millions. *Hint:* There are 1000 millions in 1 billion. [1.2]

65. The table gives the total paid circulation for Sunday newspapers in the United States for the years 1960 through 2008. Use the given table to make a bar chart. Clearly label and scale the axes. [1.4]

Year	Total Paid Sunday Circulation (thousands)
1960	47,699
1970	49,217
1980	54,676
1990	62,635
2000	59,421
2008	49,115

Source: www.naa.org

66. Use the given table to make a scatterplot. Clearly label and scale the axes. [1.4]

x	y
-20	-3.5
-10	1
-5	4.5
0	-2.5
20	0.5
25	4.5

For Exercises 67 through 70, identify the number of terms and the like terms (if any) in each expression.

67. $-6p + 4 + 7p - 9$ [1.3]

68. $5x + 16 - \dfrac{2}{3}x + 12$ [1.3]

69. $-3x^2 + 2x - 4x^2 + 1$ [1.3]

70. $-\dfrac{2}{5}y + y^2 - 6y + 12$ [1.3]

71. Ms. Welch is buying her first grade class gifts for the end of the school year. She wants to order a book that costs $3.25 for each student. Ms. Welch also wants to buy each student a candy bar that costs $1.25. [1.3]

a. If Ms. Welch has s students in her first grade class, write an expression for the cost in dollars to buy each student a book.

b. Write an expression for the cost in dollars to buy each student a candy bar.

c. Use the expressions you wrote from parts a and b to write an expression for the total cost in dollars to buy each student a book and a candy bar.

d. Simplify the expression if possible.

72. Yong Park has to pay $500 monthly for his part of the rent. He also pays $85.00 a week for groceries. **[1.3]**

    a. If Yong Park makes a monthly salary of d dollars, write an expression for how much money he has left after paying his rent.

    b. Write an expression for how much he pays for groceries each month. (Assume that there are 4 weeks in a month.)

    c. Use the expressions you wrote from parts a and b to write an expression for the total amount of money he has left over each month after he pays his rent and purchases groceries.

    d. Simplify the expression if possible.

For Exercises 73 through 80, simplify each expression by combining like terms.

73. $y^2 - 4y^3 + 3y^2 - 8y^3$ **[1.3]**

74. $-8a^2b + 3ab - 16ab + 12a^2b$ **[1.3]**

75. $-\dfrac{3}{4}x + 7 - \dfrac{1}{4}x - 12$ **[1.3]**

76. $-5 + \dfrac{2}{3}x - 7 + \dfrac{1}{3}x$ **[1.3]**

77. $1.25a - 6b - 7.5a + 8.1b$ **[1.3]**

78. $4.7x + 3.2y - 5x - 1.3y$ **[1.3]**

79. $5x^2 - 6x + 4 - 3x^2 + 7x + 8$ **[1.3]**

80. $12 - y + 3y^2 - 6y - 2y^2 + 7$ **[1.3]**

For Exercises 81 through 86:
    a. State whether the multiplication property or the distributive property can be used on the problem.
    b. Simplify each expression.

81. $16(-3ab^2)$ **[1.3]**

82. $-4(3xy)$ **[1.3]**

83. $-5(3x - 6y)$ **[1.3]**

84. $2(3a - 8b)$ **[1.3]**

85. $-(-13x)$ **[1.3]**

86. $-(5y - 7)$ **[1.3]**

For Exercises 87 through 96, simplify each expression.

87. $9 - 3(2x - 6)$ **[1.3]**

88. $-2(3x - 4) + 7x - 1$ **[1.3]**

89. $-(-2x + 3)$ **[1.3]**

90. $-(9y - 5)$ **[1.3]**

91. $(-2a + 3b) - (4a - 5b)$ **[1.3]**

92. $3x + 2y - 4(-x + 5y)$ **[1.3]**

93. $\dfrac{1}{2}(4x - 12) + 9x - 3$ **[1.3]**

94. $3h - 2k + \dfrac{1}{4}(4h - 16k)$ **[1.3]**

95. $-0.2(10x - 5) + 2x - 1$ **[1.3]**

96. $0.25(7x - 6y) - 1.25x + 9.8y$ **[1.3]**

For Exercises 97 and 98, use the given figures to find expressions for the perimeter of the shapes. Simplify the expressions if possible. Note: *The perimeter is the lengths of all the sides added together.*

97. **[1.3]**

98. **[1.3]**

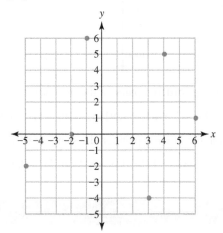

99. Write the coordinates of each ordered pair shown on the graph. **[1.4]**

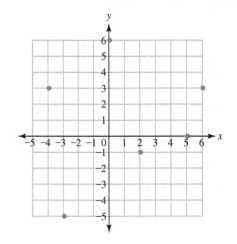

100. Write the coordinates of each ordered pair shown on the graph. **[1.4]**

101. State the scales on both the x- and y-axes. **[1.4]**

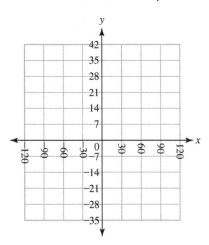

102. State the scales on both the x- and y-axes. **[1.4]**

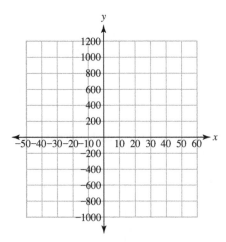

103. Graph the ordered pairs on the same set of axes. **[1.4]**

$(4, -7)(-2, -5)(-3, 9)(1, 6)(0, -3)(-5, 0)$

104. Graph the ordered pairs on the same set of axes. **[1.4]**

$(-2, -5)(1, -1)(4, 1)(-9, 2)(0, 5)(-2, 0)$

105. Use the given data to create a bar graph. Clearly label and scale the axes. **[1.4]**

State	Unemployment Rate as of Dec. 2009
Michigan	14.6%
Rhode Island	12.9%
California	12.4%
Texas	8.3%
South Carolina	12.6%
Ohio	10.9%
Illinois	11.1%
Nevada	13.0%

Source: www.bls.gov

106. Use the given data to create a bar graph. Clearly label and scale the axes. **[1.4]**

Year	U.S. National Unemployment Rate
2000	3.99%
2001	5.7%
2002	6.0%
2003	5.7%
2004	5.4%
2005	4.8%
2006	4.4%
2007	5.0%

Source: www.bls.gov

Chapter Test

1

The following chapter test should take approximately one hour to complete. Read each question carefully. Show all of your work.

1. Write in exponential form: $3 \cdot 3 \cdot 3 \cdot 3 \cdot 3 \cdot 3$

2. Write in expanded form: $\left(\dfrac{-5}{8}\right)^3$

3. Find the value without a calculator: $(-2)^3$

4. Write in standard form: 4.299×10^7

For Exercises 5 through 8, identify the number of terms. Then simplify each expression.

5. $-6 + 3 \cdot 4 - (-5) + 12 \div (-3)$

6. $24 \div 2 \cdot 3 + (-2)^2 - (-1)$

7. $\dfrac{12 - 3 \cdot 2}{4 - 2} + 8 \div 4$

8. $-3 + |7 \cdot (-2)| - (-5) + 3 \cdot 6$

For Exercises 9 through 11, identify the property used to rewrite the expression: the commutative property of addition or multiplication, the associative property of addition or multiplication, or the distributive property.

9. $(-3 + 9) + (-6) = -3 + (9 + (-6))$

10. $4(59 - 11) = 4 \cdot 59 - 4 \cdot 11$

11. $72(-89) = (-89) \cdot 72$

12. Lucas's hourly wage is $13.75 working as an office assistant. His weekly salary can be computed as 13.75h, where h is the number of hours he worked for a week. What would Lucas's weekly salary be if he worked 24 hours in a week?

13. Define the variables. Translate into an expression. A plumber quotes a homeowner a price of $20.00 plus $65.00 an hour for labor. Write an expression that gives the cost to the homeowner for this plumber's services.

14. Convert 100 yards to meters. Note that 1 m $\approx$ 1.09 yd.

15. Evaluate the expression for the given value of the variable. $x^2 + 2x - 1$ for $x = -3$

16. Simplify the expression: $-3(-2x^2 + 5x - 1)$

17. Simplify the expression:
$-5hk + 3k^2 - 2h + 7 + 2hk + 9h + 15$

18. Simplify the expression: $-2(x + 3y) + 4(2y) + 5x$

19. The graph shows the U.S. Productivity Index (major sectors, non-farm) for the years 2001–2008.

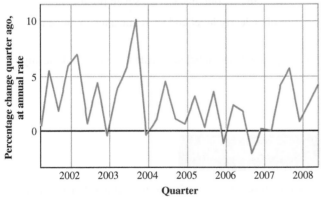

Source: www.bls.gov

  a. Approximately when was the index at its highest?
  b. Approximately when was the index at its lowest?
  c. What is the scale on the vertical axis?
  d. What is the scale on the horizontal axis?

20. What are the scales of both the *x*- and *y*-axes?

21. Graph the ordered pairs on the same axes. Clearly label and scale the axes.

x	y
-50	4.5
-30	2.5
-15	0.5
0	-1.0
20	-2.5
40	-3.0

22. Write the coordinates of each ordered pair on the graph.

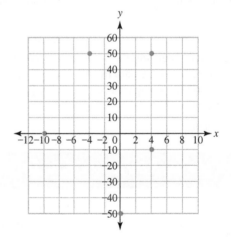

Chapter 1 Projects

How Many Miles Are in a Light Year?

Written Project

One or more people

What you will need

- A scientific calculator.

Light travels at the speed of 186,000 miles per second. The number of miles light travels in one year is called a *light-year*. To find out how many miles are in a light-year, use the following steps:

[2010] © PVMPIX. Image from BigStockPhoto.com.

1. Convert the speed of light of 186,000 miles per second to miles per minute. *Hint:* To find the unity fraction, write down how many seconds are in 1 minute.

2. Convert the speed of light in miles per minute from step 1 to miles per hour. *Hint:* To find the unity fraction, write down how many minutes are in 1 hour.

3. Convert the speed of light in miles per hour from step 2 to miles per day. *Hint:* To find the unity fraction, write down how many hours are in 1 day.

4. Convert the speed of light in miles per day from step 3 to miles per year. *Hint:* To find the unity fraction, write down how many days are in 1 year. Assume it is not a leap year.

Creating a Bar Graph and a Scatterplot

Research Project

One or more people

What you will need

- Find data for a real-world situation. You may use data from an online source, a magazine, or a newspaper.

- Graph paper.

In this project, you will find a data set and display it in various ways.

1. Find a data set, either from print media or an online source. Include a copy of the data set with your project. Make sure it contains at least seven points.

2. Graph the data set in a bar graph. Clearly label and scale the axes. Include any necessary breaks.

3. Graph the data set in a scatterplot. Clearly label and scale the axes. Include any necessary breaks.

Write a Review of a Section for Presentation

Research Project

One or more people

What you will need

- This presentation may be done in class or as an online video.

- If it is done as a video, post it on a Website where it may be easily viewed by the class.

- You might want to use homework or other review problems from the book.

- Make it creative and fun.

Create a five-minute review presentation of one section from Chapter 1. The format of the presentation can be a poster presentation, a blackboard presentation from notes, an online video, or a game format (e.g., Math Jeopardy). The presentation should include the following:

1. Any important formulas in the chapter.

2. Important skills in the chapter, backed up by examples.

3. Explanation of terms used. For example, what is modeling?

4. Common mistakes and how to avoid them.

Linear Equations and Inequalities with One Variable

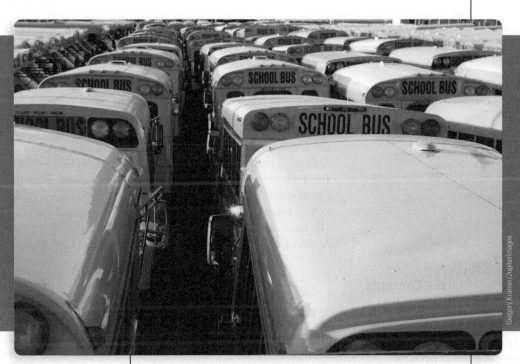

Gregory Kramer/Jupiterimages

When determining the number of school buses needed, school districts must take into account the capacity of each school bus. The *capacity* of the bus means how many students can ride on the bus. The capacity of a school bus seat is determined by dividing the width of the seat by 13 and rounding the result down to the nearest whole number. The school district can then multiply this result by the number of seats in the bus to determine how many students can be transported in each bus.

2.1 Addition and Subtraction Properties of Equality

LEARNING OBJECTIVES

▪ Recognize an equation and a solution.

▪ Use the addition and subtraction properties of equality.

▪ Solve literal equations.

Recognizing Equations and Their Solutions

In Chapter 1, we worked with applications using expressions that represented situations in real life. Recall that the expression $8.75h$ represented the weekly salary of an employee who is making $8.75 an hour with $h =$ number of hours worked for that week. This expression can be used repeatedly to calculate different weekly salaries for any employee who makes $8.75 an hour. Since the result of the calculation will change depending on what number of hours is substituted into the variable h, the salary could also be represented by a variable. Using the variable S for the salary will result in the equation $S = 8.75h$. This equation states that the salary S (the output) in dollars is equal to 8.75 times the number of hours, h (the input), that the employee worked that week. The equal sign $(=)$ is used to indicate that the value of the two expressions is the same. A statement that two expressions are equal is called an **equation.**

> **DEFINITION**
>
> **Equation** A statement that two expressions are equal is called an **equation.**
> $$125 = 125 \qquad 5x + 7 = 205$$

Many applications in algebra generate equations. These equations can be used to determine the value of the output for a given value of the input. Using the equation $S = 8.75h$, we can evaluate this equation for different values of h, hours worked, to find the corresponding values of S, salary earned. If someone worked 30 hours in a week, substitute 30 for h to determine his or her salary.

$$S = 8.75(30)$$
$$S = 262.50$$

Someone who works 30 hours will earn a salary of $262.50. This equation can calculate the weekly salary for any number of hours that a person works. Any combination of hours and salary that makes this equation true is said to be a **solution** to the equation.

Example 1 Is it an expression or an equation?

Identify each of the following as an expression or an equation. Do not solve or simplify.

a. $5x - 2(4 + 3x)$ **b.** $-x + 3(4 - 2x) = 7$

c. $7 = 7$ **d.** $-x$

SOLUTION

a. This is an expression. There is no equal sign.

b. This is an equation. There is an equal sign.

c. This is an equation. There is an equal sign.

d. This is an expression. There is no equal sign.

PRACTICE PROBLEM FOR EXAMPLE 1

Identify each of the following as an expression or an equation. Do not solve or simplify.

a. $-9x = 7x$　　　　　　**b.** $3y - 1$

DEFINITION

Solution　　The **solution(s)** is/are any value(s) of the variable(s) that make the equation true (when evaluated).

Note:　The equation is true when both sides are equal.

For the equation $S = 8.75h$, the values $h = 20$ and $S = 175.00$ are a solution to the equation. When we substitute 175 for S and 20 for h, the two sides are equal, $175.00 = 8.75(20)$. In this case, these values represent a salary of $175.00 for 20 hours of work. To **check** whether certain values for the variables are solutions, substitute in the given value(s) of the variable(s) and determine whether both sides are equal.

Steps to Check a Solution

1. Substitute in the given value(s) of the variable(s).
2. Evaluate both sides of the equation. Simplify using the order-of-operations agreement.
3. If both sides are equal (the equation is true) then those value(s) of the variable(s) is (are) solutions to the equation.

Example 2　Checking whether the given values are solutions

Determine whether or not the given values of the variables are solutions to the given equation.

a. $S = 8.75h$, where S is the salary in dollars (output) if h hours (input) are worked in a week; $h = 15$ and $S = 131.25$. Explain what these values mean in terms of this situation.

b. $D = 50t$, where D is the distance traveled in miles (output) when you have been driving for t hours (input); $t = 3$ and $D = 200$. Explain what these values mean in terms of this situation.

c. $3x + 25 = 55; x = 10$

d. $5r - 40 = 8r; r = 4$

SOLUTION

a. To check whether the given values of the variables are a solution to the equation, evaluate each side of the equation and see whether the two sides are equal.

$$S = 8.75h \qquad \text{Original equation.}$$
$$131.25 \overset{?}{=} 8.75(15) \qquad \text{Substitute 131.25 for } S \text{ and 15 for } h.$$
$$131.25 = 131.25 \qquad \text{This statement is true.}$$

Because the final statement is true, $h = 15$ and $S = 131.25$ is a solution to the equation $S = 8.75h$. If a person works 15 hours, then the person will earn a salary of $131.25 for the week.

b.　$D = 50t$ 　　　　　　　　*Original equation.*
$$200 \overset{?}{=} 50(3) \qquad \text{Substitute 200 for } D \text{ and 3 for } t.$$
$$200 \overset{?}{=} 150 \qquad \text{This statement is false.}$$
$$200 \neq 150$$

What's That Mean?

$\overset{?}{=}$

The $\overset{?}{=}$ symbol will be used when checking solutions. It means that we are trying to determine whether or not the two sides of the equation are equal.

Because the final results are not equal, $t = 3$ and $D = 200$ do not give a solution to the equation $D = 50t$. These values state that if a person drives for 3 hours, then that person will travel 200 miles. These values do not make the equation true, so they do not make sense in this situation.

c. $3x + 25 = 55$ Original equation.

$3(10) + 25 \stackrel{?}{=} 55$ Substitute 10 for x.

$30 + 25 \stackrel{?}{=} 55$ Simplify both sides.

$55 = 55$ This statement is true.

Because the final statement is true, $x = 10$ is a solution to the equation $3x + 25 = 55$.

d. $5r - 40 = 8r$ Original equation.

$5(4) - 40 \stackrel{?}{=} 8(4)$ Substitute 4 for r.

$20 - 40 \stackrel{?}{=} 32$ Simplify both sides.

$-20 \stackrel{?}{=} 32$ This statement is false.

$-20 \neq 32$

Because the final results are not equal, $r = 4$ is not a solution to the equation $5r - 40 = 8r$.

PRACTICE PROBLEM FOR EXAMPLE 2

Determine whether or not the given values of the variables are solutions to the given equation.

a. $P = 25n$ if P is the profit in dollars (output) when n car batteries (input) are sold; $n = 120$ and $P = 4000$. Explain what these values mean in this situation.

b. $7x + 34 = 10x - 11; x = 15$

c. $4(x + 6) - 2x = x + 15; x = -10$

Addition and Subtraction Properties of Equality

We now study the process of solving equations. In solving an equation, the goal is to isolate the variable on one side of the equal sign. Most of the equations in this chapter have only one variable. Some equations in this chapter may have more variables, but the values of the additional variables will be given, so the one unknown variable can be solved for. In this section, we will introduce some of the properties of equations that will be used throughout algebra.

An equation can be thought of as similar to an old-fashioned balance scale used to weigh objects. Someone wanting to weigh gold, for instance, would put the gold object in the pan on one side of the balance scale and then place known weights in the pan on the other side of the balance scale until the two pans were balanced. When the pans are balanced, there is equal weight on both sides. Using a balance scale is how the weight of the gold was determined. The weight of the gold was equal to the standard weight in the pan on the other side.

An equation is similar in that both sides of an equation must represent the same *amount* or value. The equal sign represents the balance. This is easy to see with numbers.

$$5 = 5 \quad \text{or} \quad 2 + 8 = 10$$

If a variable is in the equation, it is the unknown value. Be very careful to keep the two "pans" in the "balance" of the equation true when solving for the variable. Consider the equation $x - 5 = 12$ and think of the equal sign as a balance.

What's That Mean?

Solve an Equation

To solve an equation means to find the value(s) of the variable(s) that make the equation true.

What's That Mean?

Mathematical Verbs

Simplify: Use arithmetic and basic algebra rules to make an expression simpler. *We simplify expressions.*

Evaluate: Substitute any given values for variables and simplify the resulting expression or equation.

Solve: Isolate the given variable in an equation on one side of the equal sign using the properties of equality. This will result in a value that the isolated variable is equal to. *We solve equations.*

Because this is an equation, the two pans are in balance—both sides are equal. If 5 is added to the left side, it becomes out of balance because equal "weight" must be added to both sides.

The scales are out of balance because 5 has been added to only the left side. When out of balance, the equation is no longer true. To keep the sides balanced, add 5 to the scale on the right side as well.

Now the pans are back in balance, and the equation is again true. Simplify the expressions on both sides of the scale and get

This last scale shows that $x = 17$. To check that this is the solution to the equation, substitute 17 for x in the original equation and make sure the equation is still true.

$$x - 5 = 12 \qquad \text{Original equation.}$$
$$(17) - 5 \stackrel{?}{=} 12 \qquad \text{Substitute 17 for } x.$$
$$12 = 12 \qquad \text{This statement is true.}$$

Using the idea of a balance scale, if a quantity is added to the scale on one side, the same quantity must be added to the other side for the scale to remain in balance.

A balance scale is a conceptual way to think about the **addition property of equality.** A similar property states that if a quantity is taken away from one side of the balance scale, the same quantity must be taken away from the other side to keep the two sides in balance. This property is called the **subtraction property of equality.**

ADDITION PROPERTY OF EQUALITY

When the same real number or algebraic expression is added to **both** sides of an equation, the solution to the equation is unchanged.

$$\text{If } a = b, \text{ then } a + c = b + c$$

SUBTRACTION PROPERTY OF EQUALITY

When the same real number or algebraic expression is subtracted from **both** sides of an equation, the solution to the equation is unchanged.

$$\text{If } a = b, \text{ then } a - c = b - c$$

■ Connecting the Concepts

Why do we check?

Checking an answer(s) is an important step in solving an equation. We are all capable of making mistakes. Common mistakes are adding incorrectly and giving a number the wrong sign.

Every time we solve an equation, we check the answers to be sure we did not make any mistakes.

These two properties can be used to solve equations that involve addition or subtraction. When solving an equation, the goal will be to isolate the variable (get the variable by itself) on one side of the equation. This allows us to determine what that variable is equal to. To use these properties it is helpful to ask what operation is being performed on the variable and then use the reverse operation to *undo* that operation. To undo addition, subtract the same number from both sides of the equation. To undo subtraction, add the same number to both sides of the equation. Always remember to perform the same operation on **both** sides of the equation.

Steps to Undoing an Operation Using the Properties of Equality

1. To undo an operation, do the reverse operation on both sides of the equal sign.
2. To undo addition, use subtraction.
3. To undo subtraction, use addition.

Note: Another way to think about undoing is to "add the opposite."

Example 3   Finding the total weight

Mark, one of the authors of this book, went on a hike to the top of Mount Whitney in California during the summer of 2005. He planned to be gone for two nights and three days and had to carry a backpack with all the equipment and food he would need on the hike. The total weight of the backpack depended on the weight of the food and equipment he carried. The total weight can be represented by the equation

$$W = e + f$$

where W is the total weight in pounds of the backpack, e is the weight in pounds of the equipment, and f is the weight in pounds of the food. Use this equation to answer the following questions.

a. If Mark wanted the total weight of the backpack to be 25 pounds and his equipment weighed 15 pounds, how heavy could the food be?

b. If the total weight of the backpack could be 30 pounds and the food weighed 12 pounds, how heavy could the equipment be?

SOLUTION

a. The total weight of the backpack is given as 25 pounds and the weight of the equipment as 15 pounds, so first substitute these values into the given equation.

$$W = e + f \qquad \text{\textit{Original equation.}}$$
$$(25) = (15) + f \qquad \text{\textit{Substitute 25 for W and 15 for e.}}$$

To solve for f, isolate the variable f on one side of the equation. To do so, we must remove 15 from the right side of the equation. Because 15 is being added to f, undo adding 15 by subtracting 15 from both sides of the equation.

$$
\begin{array}{ll}
25 = 15 + \boxed{f} & \text{\textit{Identify the variable term.}} \\
\underline{-15 \quad -15} & \text{\textit{Subtract 15 from both sides.}} \\
10 = f & \text{\textit{f is isolated, so we have an answer.}}
\end{array}
$$

Now check the answer to be sure that it works in the original equation and makes sense in the context of the problem.

$$
\begin{array}{ll}
W = e + f & \text{\textit{Substitute the values for each variable.}} \\
(25) \stackrel{?}{=} (15) + (10) & \\
25 = 25 & \text{\textit{This statement is true, so our answer is}} \\
& \text{\textit{mathematically correct.}}
\end{array}
$$

Carrying 15 pounds of equipment and 10 pounds of food gives the total weight of the backpack of 25 pounds. This is a correct solution. The final answer should be written in a complete sentence as follows:

Mark should carry 10 pounds of food with his 15 pounds of equipment to keep his backpack weight at 25 pounds.

b. The total weight of the backpack is 30 pounds, and the food weighs 12 pounds, so substitute these values into the given equation.

$$
\begin{array}{ll}
W = e + f & \text{\textit{Original equation.}} \\
(30) = e + (12) & \text{\textit{Substitute 30 for W and 12 for f.}}
\end{array}
$$

To solve, we must isolate e. To do so, remove the term of 12 from the right side of the equation. Because 12 is being added to e, subtract 12 from both sides of the equation.

$$
\begin{array}{ll}
30 = \boxed{e} + 12 & \text{\textit{Identify the variable term.}} \\
\underline{-12 \quad -12} & \text{\textit{Subtract 12 from both sides.}} \\
18 = e & \text{\textit{e is isolated, so we have an answer.}}
\end{array}
$$

Check this answer in the original equation and determine whether it makes sense in the context of the problem.

$$
\begin{array}{ll}
W = e + f & \text{\textit{Substitute the values for each variable.}} \\
(30) \stackrel{?}{=} (18) + (12) & \\
30 = 30 & \text{\textit{This statement is true, so our answer is}} \\
& \text{\textit{mathematically correct.}}
\end{array}
$$

Since carrying 12 pounds of equipment and 18 pounds of food gives us a total of 30 lb, the solution checks. The final answer should be written in a complete sentence as follows:

Mark should carry 18 pounds of equipment with his 12 pounds of food to keep his backpack at 30 total pounds.

In Example 3, note that the solution to the equation has to be checked by substituting it back into the original equation. Something else to check is whether or not the solution makes sense in light of the original information, units of measurement, and data given in the problem. An answer in the form of a complete sentence is always required for problems that involve an application.

PRACTICE PROBLEM FOR EXAMPLE 3

Katie is a new college student and has to take 15 credits per semester to stay on her parents' health insurance plan as a full-time student. Katie wants to take a combination

---

■ Skill Connection

Checking a solution

Check the answer by substituting the value(s) found back into the *original* problem. Then simplify the equation and see whether it is true (both sides are equal). If the equation is true, then the solution checks.

of general education classes (English, math, and science) and some electives (sports and art). If Katie does not want to take more than 15 credits a semester, she can represent the credits she takes using the equation

$$G + E = 15$$

where G = the number of general education credits Katie takes and E = the number of elective credits Katie takes.

a. If Katie takes 11 general education credits this semester, how many elective credits should she take?

b. If Katie takes 2.5 credits of electives this semester, how many general education credits should she take?

The equations we are now going to study have a special form and name. They are called *linear equations in one variable*.

DEFINITION

Linear Equation in One Variable A linear equation in one variable may be written in the form $mx + b = 0$, where m and b are real numbers and $m \neq 0$.

Example 4 — Solving equations using the addition and subtraction properties

Solve the equation. Check the answer.

a. $x + 20 = 55$ **b.** $t - 6 = 9$ **c.** $13.48 + k = 21.52$

SOLUTION

a. 20 is being added to x, so subtract 20 from both sides of the equation.

$\widehat{x} + 20 = 55$	Identify the variable term.
$\underline{-20 \quad -20}$	Subtract 20 from both sides of the equation.
$x = 35$	x is isolated. This is the answer.
$(35) + 20 \stackrel{?}{=} 55$	Check the answer.
$55 = 55$	The answer works.

b. 6 is being subtracted from t, so add 6 to both sides of the equation.

$\widehat{t} - 6 = 9$	Identify the variable term.
$\underline{+6 \quad +6}$	Add 6 to both sides of the equation.
$t = 15$	t is isolated. This is the answer.
$(15) - 6 \stackrel{?}{=} 9$	Check the answer.
$9 = 9$	The answer works.

c. 13.48 is being added to k, so subtract 13.48 from both sides of the equation.

$13.48 + \widehat{k} = 21.52$	Identify the variable term.
$\underline{-13.48 \qquad -13.48}$	Subtract 13.48 from both sides of the equation.
$k = 8.04$	k is isolated. This is the answer.
$13.48 + (8.04) \stackrel{?}{=} 21.52$	Check the answer.
$21.52 = 21.52$	The answer works.

PRACTICE PROBLEM FOR EXAMPLE 4

Solve the equation. Check the answer.

a. $r + 9 = 24$ **b.** $p - 15.7 = 16.9$

> ## Example 5   Solving an equation from business

The amount of profit a company makes is found by subtracting the company's costs from its revenue. This relationship can be written as the following equation:

$$P = R - C$$

where P is the profit in dollars, R is the revenue in dollars, and C is the cost in dollars for the company.

a. If a company has monthly revenue of $425,000 and monthly costs of $195,000, what is its profit?

b. If this company wants a profit of $21,000 for the month and has costs of $25,000, what revenue will this company have to generate?

SOLUTION

a. If the revenue is $425,000, then $R = 425,000$. If the costs are $195,000, then $C = 195,000$. Substituting these values into the equation $P = R - C$ yields the profit:

$$P = R - C$$
$$P = 425,000 - 195,000$$
$$P = 230,000$$

Therefore, the monthly profit $P = 230,000$.

A company with $425,000 in revenue and $195,000 in costs has $230,000 in profit.

b. If the profit is $21,000, then $P = 21,000$. If the costs are $25,000, then set $C = 25,000$. Substituting these values into the equation $P = R - C$ yields

$$P = R - C$$
$$21,000 = R - 25,000$$

To solve this equation for R, add 25,000 to both sides.

$$21,000 = R - 25,000$$
$$\underline{+25,000 \qquad +25,000} \qquad \text{Add 25,000 to both sides of the equation.}$$
$$46,000 = R$$

$$21,000 \overset{?}{=} 46,000 - 25,000 \qquad \text{Check the answer.}$$
$$21,000 = 21,000 \qquad \text{The answer works.}$$

Therefore, the monthly revenue $R = \$46,000$.

If a company wants $21,000 profit and has $25,000 in costs, it must generate $46,000 of revenue.

PRACTICE PROBLEM FOR EXAMPLE 5

The amount of profit a company makes is found by subtracting the company's costs from its revenue. This relationship can be written as the following equation:

$$P = R - C$$

where P is the profit in dollars, R is the revenue in dollars, and C is the cost in dollars for the company.

a. If a company has monthly revenue of $65,000 and monthly costs of $22,500, what is its profit?

b. If this company wants a profit of $135,000 for the month and has costs of $75,000, what revenue will this company have to generate?

What's That Mean?

Profit, Revenue, and Cost

In business, revenue is the amount of money a company earns, such as from sales. The cost refers to both fixed costs (such as rent) and variable costs (such as electricity) that a company must pay. The profit a company makes is equal to the difference between the revenue and the cost.

> ### Example 6 Solving equations involving fractions
>
> Solve the equation. Check the answer.
>
> **a.** $n - \dfrac{2}{9} = \dfrac{7}{9}$
>
> **b.** $x + \dfrac{4}{5} = \dfrac{7}{10}$
>
> **SOLUTION**
>
> **a.** The number $\dfrac{2}{9}$ is being subtracted from n, so add $\dfrac{2}{9}$ to both sides of the equation.
>
> $$\textcircled{n} - \dfrac{2}{9} = \dfrac{7}{9}$$ Identify the variable term.
>
> $$\dfrac{+\dfrac{2}{9} \qquad +\dfrac{2}{9}}{n = \dfrac{9}{9}}$$ Add $\dfrac{2}{9}$ to both sides of the equation.
>
> $$n = 1$$ Simplify the fraction.
>
> $$(1) - \dfrac{2}{9} \overset{?}{=} \dfrac{7}{9}$$ Check the answer.
>
> $$\dfrac{9}{9} - \dfrac{2}{9} \overset{?}{=} \dfrac{7}{9}$$ Find like denominators.
>
> $$\dfrac{7}{9} = \dfrac{7}{9}$$ The answer works.
>
> **b.** The number $\dfrac{4}{5}$ is being added to x, so subtract $\dfrac{4}{5}$ from both sides of the equation.
>
> $$\textcircled{x} + \dfrac{4}{5} = \dfrac{7}{10}$$ Identify the variable term.
>
> $$\dfrac{-\dfrac{4}{5} \qquad -\dfrac{4}{5}}{x = \dfrac{7}{10} - \dfrac{4}{5}}$$ Subtract $\dfrac{4}{5}$ from both sides of the equation.
>
> Find like denominators to subtract the fractions.
>
> $$x = \dfrac{7}{10} - \dfrac{8}{10}$$
>
> $$x = -\dfrac{1}{10}$$
>
> $$\left(-\dfrac{1}{10}\right) + \dfrac{4}{5} \overset{?}{=} \dfrac{7}{10}$$ Check the answer.
>
> $$-\dfrac{1}{10} + \dfrac{8}{10} \overset{?}{=} \dfrac{7}{10}$$ Find like denominators.
>
> $$\dfrac{7}{10} = \dfrac{7}{10}$$ The answer works.

■ Skill Connection

Find the LCD

In Section R.2, we learned that to find the least common denominator, or LCD, involves two steps.

1. Find the prime factorization of each denominator.

2. The LCD equals the product of the distinct factors from step 1. If a factor occurs more than once, include the highest power of that factor in the LCD.

PRACTICE PROBLEM FOR EXAMPLE 6

Solve the equation. Check the answer. $x + \dfrac{2}{3} = \dfrac{5}{6}$

When using the addition and subtraction properties of equality to solve equations, we are trying to undo an addition or subtraction that is on the variable side of the equation. Look at an equation that has to be solved and ask which operation will undo the number or expression on the variable side. In many cases, this is clear. Subtract to undo addition, and add to undo subtraction. Exercise caution when isolating a variable that is not the leftmost term. For example, in the equation $-5 + x = 3$, add 5 to both sides because that will isolate x on the left side of the equation.

$$-5 + \textcircled{x} = 3$$ Identify the variable term.

$$\dfrac{+5 \qquad\quad +5}{x = 8}$$ Add 5 to both sides of the equation.

This is the answer.

Remember to include the sign in front of the term when considering whether to use the addition or subtraction property to isolate the variable.

Example 7   Solving equations

Solve the equation. Check the answer.

a. $3 + t = 15$

b. $12 = -9 + w$

c. $8 + c = 19$

d. $-20 + x = -50$

SOLUTION

a.
$$3 + \widehat{t} = 15$$
$$\underline{-3 \qquad -3}$$
$$t = 12$$

Identify the variable term.

The 3 is positive, so subtract 3 from both sides.

$$3 + (12) \overset{?}{=} 15$$
$$15 = 15$$

Check the answer.

The answer works.

b.
$$12 = -9 + \widehat{w}$$
$$\underline{+9 \quad +9}$$
$$21 = w$$

Identify the variable term.

The 9 is negative, so add 9 to both sides.

$$12 \overset{?}{=} -9 + (21)$$
$$12 = 12$$

Check the answer.

The answer works.

c.
$$8 + \widehat{c} = 19$$
$$\underline{-8 \qquad -8}$$
$$c = 11$$

Identify the variable term.

Subtract 8 from both sides.

$$8 + (11) \overset{?}{=} 19$$
$$19 = 19$$

Check the answer.

The answer works.

d.
$$-20 + \widehat{x} = -50$$
$$\underline{+20 \qquad +20}$$
$$x = -30$$

Identify the variable term.

Add 20 to both sides.

$$-20 + (-30) \overset{?}{=} -50$$
$$-50 = -50$$

Check the answer.

The answer works.

PRACTICE PROBLEM FOR EXAMPLE 7

Solve the equation. Check the answer.

a. $7 + m = 20$

b. $-5 = -8 + c$

Solving Literal Equations

In many applications, equations or **formulas** are used to represent common calculations. Many of these come from science and geometry, but others come from daily life. Several examples from geometry are the formulas for perimeter, area, and volume. Some examples from science are the position of an object and velocity. A formula from daily life is $d = r \cdot t$. Here, d stands for distance, r stands for the rate (speed), and t stands for time. We use this formula to estimate travel distances and times. If a person drives 50 miles an hour for 2 hours, then the distance traveled is

$$d = r \cdot t$$
$$d = 50 \cdot 2$$
$$d = 100 \text{ miles}$$

Several of these frequently used formulas are given inside the back cover. In mathematics, equations or formulas that have several variables are called **literal equations**.

> **DEFINITIONS**
>
> **Formula** An equation that expresses a general relationship between quantities is called a **formula.**
>
> **Literal Equation** An equation or formula that contains several variables is called a **literal equation.**

To solve a literal equation means to solve for only one of the variables. Solving literal equations is similar to solving other equations we have seen in this section. The properties of equality are used to isolate the variable we wish to solve for. When solving literal equations for a variable, we are not finding a single value for the variable. Instead, we find a new formula with the variable being solved for isolated on one side of the equal sign.

Example 8 Solving literal equations

Solve the following literal equations for the indicated variable.

a. Sum of angle measures in a triangle: $A + B + C = 180$; for A.

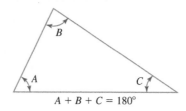

$$A + B + C = 180°$$

b. Slope-intercept form of a linear equation: $y = mx + b$; for b.

c. $H = r - p$; for r.

SOLUTION

a. To solve for A means to isolate A on one side of the equal sign. Since B is being added to A, remove B from the left side by using the reverse operation of subtraction.

$$\begin{array}{ll} \circled{A} + B + C = 180 & \text{Identify the variable term being solved for.} \\ \underline{\quad -B \qquad\quad -B} & \text{Subtract } B \text{ from both sides of the equation.} \\ \circled{A} + C = 180 - B & \end{array}$$

To finish solving this literal equation for A, move C from the left side by subtracting it from both sides of the equation.

$$\begin{array}{ll} \circled{A} + C = 180 - B & \\ \underline{\quad -C \qquad\quad -C} & \text{Subtract } C \text{ from both sides of the equation.} \\ A = 180 - B - C & \end{array}$$

The variable A has been solved for. Notice that we have not found a specific value for A but instead have found a formula for A. This formula for A states that the measure of angle A of a triangle is 180 degrees minus the measures of the two other angles, B and C.

b. To solve for b, remove the expression mx from the right side of the equation. Since it is being added to b, use the subtraction property of equality to remove it.

$$\begin{array}{ll} y = mx + \circled{b} & \text{Identify the variable term being solved for.} \\ \underline{\quad -mx \quad -mx} & \text{Subtract } mx \text{ from both sides of the equation.} \\ y - mx = b \text{ or } b = y - mx & \end{array}$$

This equation is now solved for b.

■ **Connecting the Concepts**

How do I write the answer?

The two equations in Example 8b are equivalent: $y - mx = b$ or $b = y - mx$. Ask your instructor whether he or she prefers the variable being solved for on the left side of the equal sign. Many instructors do prefer the variable being isolated on the left.

c. To solve, isolate the r on one side of the equal sign.

$$H = \textcircled{r} - p \qquad \text{Identify the variable term being solved for.}$$
$$\underline{+p \qquad +p} \qquad \text{Add } p \text{ to both sides of the equation.}$$
$$H + p = r \text{ or } r = H + p$$

r is isolated on one side of the equal sign, so the literal equation has been solved for r.

PRACTICE PROBLEM FOR EXAMPLE 8

Solve the following literal equations for the indicated variable.

a. Weight of a backpack: $W = e + f$; for e.

b. $M + N - P = 200$; for N.

2.1 Exercises

For Exercises 1 through 12, identify each problem as an expression or an equation.

1. $3x - 2$

2. $5 - 2a$

3. $b = 1$

4. $n = 0$

5. -6

6. $-2x$

7. $-5x^2 + 10 = 0$

8. $7 - 2y + y^2 = 2$

9. $2l + 2w = P$

10. $C = 2\pi r$

11. $x^2 + 4x - 9$

12. $-x^2 + 2x - 1$

For Exercises 13 and 14, answer the questions about each problem situation.

13. Joe has a job at a local hotel that pays $9.50 an hour. Joe's weekly salary can be represented by the equation $S = 9.5h$, where S is Joe's weekly salary in dollars when he works h hours a week.

    a. Use the equation to find Joe's salary if he works 20 hours in a week.

    b. Determine whether or not the following values are a solution to the equation $S = 332.50$ when $h = 35$. Explain what these values mean in this situation.

    c. Determine whether or not the following values are a solution to the equation $S = 240$ when $h = 25$. Explain what these values mean in this situation.

    d. Determine whether or not the following values are a solution to the equation $S = 380$ when $h = 40$. Explain what these values mean in this situation.

14. Danny works on the assembly line at a local golf club manufacturer. If it takes Danny 7 minutes to put together the parts for a golf club, then the amount of time it takes Danny to assemble g golf clubs can be represented by the equation $t = 7g$, where t is the total time in minutes it takes for him to assemble g golf clubs.

    a. Use the equation to find how long it will take Danny to assemble 45 golf clubs.

    b. Determine whether or not the following values are a solution to the equation $t = 340$ when $g = 50$. Explain what these values mean in this situation.

    c. Determine whether or not the following values are a solution to the equation $t = 329$ when $g = 47$. Explain what these values mean in this situation.

For Exercises 15 through 24:

    a. *Determine whether or not the given values of the variables are solutions to the equations.*

    b. *Explain what the values mean in this situation.*

15. $D = 60t$, where D is the distance traveled in miles when driving for t hours; $t = 4$ and $D = 240$.

16. $D = 65t$, where D is the distance traveled in miles when driving for t hours; $t = 30$ and $D = 1950$.

17. $C = 2\pi r$, where C is the circumference of a circle with radius r; $C = 37.7$ and $r = 6$. (Answers rounded to one decimal place.)

18. $C = 2\pi r$, where C is the circumference of a circle with radius r; $C = 163.4$ and $r = 26$. (Answers rounded to one decimal place.)

19. $F = 15L$, where F is the origination fee in dollars paid for a loan of L thousand dollars; $F = 4500$ and $L = 300$. (*Note:* An origination fee in a mortgage is the fee paid to the company originating your loan to cover costs associated with creating, processing, and closing your mortgage.)

20. $F = 20L$, where F is the origination fee in dollars paid for a loan of L thousand dollars; $F = 9000$ and $L = 450$.

21. $F = 10L$, where F is the origination fee in dollars paid for a loan of L thousand dollars; $F = 2000$ and $L = 225$.

22. $F = 12.5L$, where F is the origination fee in dollars paid for a loan of L thousand dollars; $F = 4500$ and $L = 400$.

23. $S = 77.8f$, where S is the number of cubic yards of sand needed to fill a sand volleyball court f feet deep; $S = 155.6$ and $f = 2$.

24. $S = 77.8f$, where S is the number of cubic yards of sand needed to fill a sand volleyball court f feet deep; $S = 200$ and $f = 3$.

For Exercises 25 through 44, determine whether or not the given value(s) of the variable(s) are solutions to the equations.

25. $2x + 8 = 30; x = 11$

26. $4g + 23 = 80; g = 10$

27. $7m + 15 = 10m; m = 8$

28. $-4y + 7 = -25; y = -6$

29. $\frac{3}{4}x - 13 = 8; x = 28$

30. $7 = \frac{-5}{3}y + \frac{1}{3}; y = -4$

31. $\frac{1}{2}x - 10 = \frac{-15}{2}; x = 5$

32. $-1 = \frac{2}{3}x + 1; x = -3$

33. $0.15x + 1.2 = 1.35; x = 1$

34. $-1.4x - 6 = -14.4; x = 5$

35. $0.5t + 3.2 = 1.7; t = 3$

36. $-6.1 + 3y = -10.3; y = 1.4$

37. $3x + 5y = 20; x = 5$ and $y = 1$

38. $4x - 9y = 30; x = 3$ and $y = -2$

39. $-x + 2y = 4; x = -4$ and $y = 0$

40. $-3x + 4y = -12; x = 0$ and $y = -3$

41. $25m + 15 = 10n + 40; m = 3$ and $n = 5$

42. $-3x + 7 = 4y + 9; x = 0$ and $y = -2$

43. $-5x + 3y = -15; x = 0$ and $y = 5$

44. $4x + 3y = -12; x = -4$ and $y = 1$

45. The maximum weight limit on the roof of a 2001 Volvo V70 station wagon is 220 lb. If you consider the weight of a cargo storage system and the luggage and other cargo, you can represent the maximum weight using the equation

$$s + l + c = 220$$

where s is the weight in pounds of the cargo storage system, l is the weight in pounds of the luggage, and c is the weight in pounds of any additional cargo.
Source: Volvo V70 2001 owner's manual.

a. If the cargo storage system weighs 75 pounds and the luggage that you want to store on the roof weighs 100 pounds, how many pounds of other cargo can you store on the roof of the car?

b. If the cargo storage system weighs 75 pounds and the additional cargo you want to store on the roof weighs 60 pounds, how many pounds of luggage can you store on the roof of the car?

46. Alex has budgeted his expenses for the month and does not want to spend more than he makes at work. Alex needs to pay rent and other bills and wants some money for entertainment. Alex's total expenses can be represented by the equation

$$E = r + b + e$$

where E is the total monthly expenses in dollars, r is the amount he pays for rent in dollars, b is the amount of his other bills in dollars, and e is the amount of money he has for entertainment in dollars.

a. If Alex has $1200 this month for expenses and pays $600 in rent and $230 for other bills, how much does he have left for entertainment?

b. If Alex has only $1000 this month but still pays $600 for rent and needs $350 for other bills, how much does he have left for entertainment?

For Exercises 47 through 52, use the following information.

The amount of profit a company makes is found by subtracting the company's costs from its revenue. This relationship can be written as the following equation:

$$P = R - C$$

where P is the profit in dollars, R is the revenue in dollars, and C is the cost in dollars for the company.
Note: *Revenue is the amount of money a company brings in from sales.*

47. If a company has monthly revenue of $47,000 and monthly costs of $39,000 what is the profit?

48. If a company has monthly revenue of $180,000 and monthly costs of $165,000, what is the profit?

49. If a company has monthly revenue of $38,000 and monthly costs of $41,000, what is the profit?

50. If a company has monthly revenue of $430,000 and monthly costs of $500,000, what is the profit?

51. If a company wants a profit of $4000 for the month and has costs of $25,000, what revenue does this company have to generate?

52. If this company wants a profit of $11,000 for the month and has costs of $156,000, what revenue will this company have to generate?

For Exercises 53 through 82, solve the equation. Check the answer.

53. $x + 5 = 30$

54. $w + 12 = 28$

55. $x + 20.5 = 45$

56. $4.2 + t = -7.3$

57. $m - 14 = 5$

58. $k - 8 = 22$

59. $-4 + p = 23$

60. $-4 + y = 9$

61. $-1 + k = -16$

62. $-3 + w = -9$

63. $5 = -3 + x$

64. $-8 = -2 + r$

65. $a + 0.25 = 2.75$

66. $-1.35 + b = 7.60$

67. $\dfrac{3}{2} = \dfrac{1}{2} + x$

68. $\dfrac{5}{3} = -\dfrac{1}{3} + y$

69. $m + \dfrac{2}{3} = \dfrac{7}{3}$

70. $t - \dfrac{9}{5} = \dfrac{6}{5}$

71. $\dfrac{4}{9} + m = \dfrac{5}{9}$

72. $\dfrac{1}{3} + y = \dfrac{5}{3}$

73. $5 + x = 14$

74. $7 + z = 5$

75. $d - 1.75 = 6.5$

76. $-2.8 + k = 12.3$

77. $-1.3 + x = -4.7$

78. $13.5 = -7.8 + y$

79. $\dfrac{2}{5} + x = \dfrac{3}{7}$

80. $\dfrac{1}{2} + x = \dfrac{2}{3}$

81. $\dfrac{4}{5} + y = \dfrac{3}{10}$

82. $\dfrac{6}{11} + a = \dfrac{1}{22}$

For Exercises 83 through 100, solve the given literal equation for the indicated variable.

83. Profit: $P = R - C$; solve for R.

84. Sale price: $S = P - D$; solve for P.

85. Maximum weight limit for the roof of a car: $s + l + c = 220$; solve for l.

86. Retail price: $R = C + M$; solve for C.

87. Sum of the measures of the angles in a right triangle: $A + B + 90 = 180°$; solve for A.

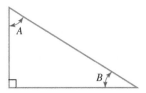

88. Sum of the angles in a quadrilateral: $A + B + C + D = 360°$; solve for C.

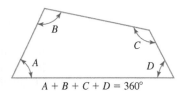

$A + B + C + D = 360°$

89. $T = 45 + M$; solve for M.

90. $g = 3f + h$; solve for h.

91. $x + y = -4$; solve for y.

92. $2x + y = 7$; solve for y.

93. $D + 10 = 3F + G - 20$; solve for G.

94. $5a - 8 = b + 2c + 15$; solve for b.

95. $t = -3u + w$; solve for w.

96. $y = -4x + z - 20$; solve for z.

97. $P = a + b + c$; solve for b.

98. $P = a + b + c + d$; solve for d.

99. $3y = x - 5$; solve for x.

100. $-4y = x + 9$; solve for x.

For Exercises 101 through 110, identify each problem as an expression or equation. Simplify any expressions, and solve any equations.

101. $23 = x + 9$

102. $14 + m = 45$

103. $5x + 7 - 3x$

104. $8h - 3h + 14 + 2h$

105. $20a^2 + 6a - 3a^2 + 10$

106. $-11n^2 + 8 - 5n^2 + 7n$

107. $-14 + c = -10$

108. $-16 + y = -4$

109. $p - 14 = 20$

110. $r - 27 = 41$

2.2 Multiplication and Division Properties of Equality

LEARNING OBJECTIVES

- Use the multiplication and division properties of equality.
- Solve multiple-step equations.
- Generate equations from applications.
- Solve more literal equations.

Multiplication and Division Properties of Equality

In Section 2.1, we studied the addition and subtraction properties of equality and learned how to use them to solve some types of equations. In this section, two more properties of equality are presented. Keep in mind the visual example of scales in balance. Think of scales that are balanced: If we put twice as much weight on each side, then the two scales are still balanced.

If a scale is in balance and you double both sides, the scale will remain in balance.

This is the same as multiplying both sides of an equation by 2.

The same would be true if we took half of the weight away from both sides of the balance scale. It would still be in balance. In these two examples, we are demonstrating that when multiplying or dividing both sides of an equation by the same nonzero real number, the equation will stay true.

This leads us to the **multiplication and division properties of equality.**

■ Connecting the Concepts

How do we show multiplication?

Multiplication can be shown in several ways. Multiplication is the only operation that does not need a separate symbol. When a number, variable, or parentheses are next to a variable or parentheses, it means to multiply.

$$9h = 9 \cdot h$$
$$2(3x + 5) = 6x + 10$$
$$(2)(4x) = 8x$$

MULTIPLICATION PROPERTY OF EQUALITY

When **both** sides of an equation are multiplied by the same nonzero real number or nonzero algebraic expression, the solution to the equation is unchanged.

If $a = b$ and $c \neq 0$, then $a \cdot c = b \cdot c$

DIVISION PROPERTY OF EQUALITY

When **both** sides of an equation are divided by the same nonzero real number or nonzero algebraic expression, the solution to the equation is unchanged.

If $a = b$ and $c \neq 0$, then $\dfrac{a}{c} = \dfrac{b}{c}$

From this definition, there is only one number by which we should not multiply or divide both sides of an equation. That number is zero. Division by zero is undefined. Likewise, both sides of an equation are not multiplied by 0. To see why, multiply both sides of the following equation by 0.

$$x + 5 = 7$$
$$0(x + 5) = 0(7) \qquad \text{Multiply both sides by 0.}$$
$$0 = 0$$

Multiplying both sides by 0 only shows that $0 = 0$. This does not help solve the equation at all. Therefore, do not multiply both sides of an equation by 0.

Example 1 Hourly pay

José has a job at a local Post and Pack store and gets paid about $9 an hour after taxes are taken out of his paycheck. José can calculate his weekly take-home salary using the equation

$$S = 9h$$

where S represents his weekly take-home salary in dollars and h is the number of hours he works that week.

a. Calculate José's weekly take-home salary if he works 15 hours.

b. How many hours does José have to work if he needs $180 to pay his car payment?

c. How many hours does José have to work if he needs $300 to pay his part of the rent at the end of the week?

SOLUTION

a. Because we are given that José worked 15 hours that week, we can substitute $h = 15$ and calculate his weekly take-home salary.

$$S = 9(15)$$
$$S = 135$$

José will take home about $135 for working 15 hours a week.

b. In this situation, José needs $180 for his car payment, and we want to find out how many hours he has to work to earn that much. Since he wants his take-home salary to be $180, substitute $S = 180$, and solve for h to find the hours he has to work.

$$S = 9h$$
$$180 = 9h$$

Since h is being multiplied by 9, undo the multiplication by dividing both sides of the equation by 9.

$180 = 9h$	The variable term is already by itself, so isolate the variable.
$\dfrac{180}{9} = \dfrac{9h}{9}$	Divide both sides by 9.
$20 = \dfrac{\cancel{9}h}{\cancel{9}}$	Reduce.
$20 = h$	

Check the answer by substituting both 180 and 20 into the equation and checking that the statement is true.

$$180 \overset{?}{=} 9(20)$$
$$180 = 180$$

The answer checks and seems like a reasonable number of hours for this situation.

José has to work 20 hours this week to make enough money to pay his $180 car payment.

Connecting the Concepts

Should you give an answer using a fraction?

There is more than one way in which you can answer a question with a fraction result.

Always reduce fractions to lowest terms. When the question is not an application, put answers in the same form as the original question.

When working with applications, read the problem to see if a decimal approximation is more appropriate. For example, if the problem is given in dollars, round the answer to two decimal places (the cents place).

c. This week, José also has to earn \$300 to pay his rent, so set $S = 300$. Solve for h.

$$300 = 9h \qquad \text{The variable term is already by itself, so isolate the variable.}$$

$$\frac{300}{9} = \frac{9h}{9} \qquad \text{Divide both sides by 9.}$$

$$33\frac{1}{3} = \frac{\cancel{9}h}{\cancel{9}} \qquad \text{Reduce.}$$

$$33\frac{1}{3} = h \text{ or } 33.\overline{3} = h$$

Again, check the answer using the original equation and think about whether or not this many hours makes sense in this situation. José needs more money than he did in part b, so he should have to work more hours. This answer seems to make sense.

$$300 \stackrel{?}{=} 9\left(33\frac{1}{3}\right)$$

$$300 = 300 \qquad \text{The answer checks and makes sense in this situation.}$$

José has to work $33\frac{1}{3}$ hours this week to pay \$300 for his rent.

PRACTICE PROBLEM FOR EXAMPLE 1

Ann sells subscriptions to a local newspaper door to door. For every subscription she sells, she earns \$6. The amount Ann gets paid for selling subscriptions can be represented by using the equation

$$P = 6s$$

where P is the amount Ann gets paid in dollars for selling s newspaper subscriptions.

a. How much does Ann get paid for 20 subscriptions?

b. Find how many subscriptions Ann must sell to make \$240.

Example 2 Solving equations using the division property of equality

Solve the equation. Check the answer.

a. $5b = 140$ **b.** $14 = -3.5x$ **c.** $-x = 3.5$

SOLUTION

a. To solve for b, isolate the variable b on one side of the equation. In this case, we have to undo the multiplication by 5 to isolate b on the left side of the equation. To undo the multiplication, divide both sides by 5.

$$5b = 140 \qquad \text{The variable term is already by itself, so isolate the variable.}$$

$$\frac{5b}{5} = \frac{140}{5} \qquad \text{Isolate } b \text{ by dividing both sides by 5.}$$

$$\frac{\cancel{5}b}{\cancel{5}} = 28 \qquad \text{Reduce.}$$

$$b = 28$$

$$5(28) \stackrel{?}{=} 140 \qquad \text{Check the answer.}$$

$$140 = 140 \qquad \text{The answer works.}$$

b. Since x is multiplied by -3.5, undo the multiplication by dividing both sides of the equation by -3.5.

$$14 = -3.5x \qquad \text{The variable term is already by itself, so isolate the variable.}$$

$$\frac{14}{-3.5} = \frac{-3.5x}{-3.5} \qquad \text{Isolate } x \text{ by dividing both sides by } -3.5.$$

$$-4 = x$$

$$14 \stackrel{?}{=} -3.5(-4) \qquad \text{Check the answer.}$$

$$14 = 14 \qquad \text{The answer works.}$$

c. The variable term is $-x = -1 \cdot x$, so the coefficient of x is -1. To solve this equation, divide both sides by -1.

$$-x = 3.5 \qquad \text{Rewrite the left side with a coefficient of } -1.$$

$$\frac{-1 \cdot x}{-1} = \frac{3.5}{-1} \qquad \text{Divide both sides by } -1.$$

$$x = -3.5$$

$$-(-3.5) \overset{?}{=} 3.5 \qquad \text{Check the answer.}$$

$$3.5 = 3.5 \qquad \text{The answer works.}$$

PRACTICE PROBLEM FOR EXAMPLE 2

Solve the equation. Check the answer.

a. $6d = 78$ **b.** $-7m = -45.5$ **c.** $8.42 = -n$

> ### ■ Connecting the Concepts
>
> **Which operations undo others?**
>
> Remember that the four properties of equality help us to isolate the variable by undoing operations that are on the same side of the equation as the variable.
>
> Use the table to help remember how operations undo each other.
>
> | Do | Undo |
> |---|---|
> | Add | Subtract |
> | Subtract | Add |
> | Multiply | Divide |
> | Divide | Multiply |

Example 3 Solving equations with fractional coefficients

Solve the equation. Check the answer.

a. $\dfrac{w}{4} = 7$ **b.** $\dfrac{3}{8}y = -6$

SOLUTION

a. w is being divided by 4, so undo the division by multiplying both sides of the equation by 4.

$$\frac{w}{4} = 7 \qquad \text{The variable term is already by itself, so isolate the variable.}$$

$$4\left(\frac{w}{4}\right) = 4(7) \qquad \text{Isolate } w \text{ by multiplying both sides by 4.}$$

$$\cancel{4}\left(\frac{w}{\cancel{4}}\right) = 28 \qquad \text{Reduce.}$$

$$w = 28$$

$$\frac{28}{4} \overset{?}{=} 7 \qquad \text{Check the answer.}$$

$$7 = 7 \qquad \text{The answer works.}$$

b. The coefficient of y is $\dfrac{3}{8}$. Undo multiplication by $\dfrac{3}{8}$ by dividing both sides of the equation by $\dfrac{3}{8}$.

$$\frac{3}{8}y = -6$$

$$\frac{\frac{3}{8}y}{\frac{3}{8}} = \frac{-6}{\frac{3}{8}} \qquad \text{Divide both sides by the coefficient.}$$

$$\frac{\frac{3}{8}y}{\frac{3}{8}} = -6 \cdot \frac{8}{3} \qquad \text{To divide by a fraction, invert and multiply by the reciprocal.}$$

$$y = -\overset{2}{\cancel{6}} \cdot \frac{8}{\cancel{3}} \qquad \text{Divide out like factors.}$$

$$y = -16$$

■ **Connecting the Concepts**

How do we write a coefficient of $\frac{1}{2}$?

If a problem says to find one-half of a number, then it translates as $\frac{1}{2}x$. This can also be written as

$$\frac{1}{2}x = \frac{1}{2} \cdot x = \frac{1}{2} \cdot \frac{x}{1} = \frac{x}{2}$$

Likewise, $\frac{3}{8}y$ can be written as $\frac{3y}{8}$.

Notice that in the above problem, we divided both sides by the fraction $\frac{3}{8}$. Dividing by $\frac{3}{8}$ is equivalent to inverting $\frac{3}{8}$ and multiplying both sides by $\frac{8}{3}$.

$$\frac{3}{8}y = -6$$

$$\frac{8}{3} \cdot \frac{3}{8}y = \frac{8}{3} \cdot (-6) \qquad \text{Multiply both sides by the reciprocal.}$$

$$\frac{\cancel{8}}{\cancel{3}} \cdot \frac{\cancel{3}}{\cancel{8}}y = \frac{8}{\cancel{3}} \cdot (-\overset{2}{\cancel{6}}) \qquad \text{Divide out like factors.}$$

$$y = -16$$

To check, substitute $y = -16$ into the original problem.

$$\frac{3}{8}(-16) \overset{?}{=} -6$$

$$\frac{3}{\cancel{8}}(-\overset{2}{\cancel{16}}) \overset{?}{=} -6$$

$$-6 = -6 \qquad \text{The answer works.}$$

PRACTICE PROBLEM FOR EXAMPLE 3

Solve the equation. Check the answer.

a. $\dfrac{n}{5} = -\dfrac{3}{10}$ **b.** $\dfrac{2}{3}x = -8$

■ **Connecting the Concepts**

Why circle the variable term?

When solving an equation that has several operations to be undone, visualize a present that is in a box and has been gift-wrapped.

If you want to get to your present, you must open the package. You cannot get to the present without first taking off the wrapping paper and then opening the box. You cannot open the box first and then take off the wrapping paper. This is similar to an equation that has more than one operation involved. You should typically undo any operations that are farther away from the variable (the present) you are trying to isolate. This is why we often circle the variable term so that we can concentrate on isolating it first. Then work toward the variable by undoing one layer of operations at a time.

Solving Multiple-Step Equations

Remember that to solve a linear equation in one variable, the variable must be isolated on one side of the equation. So far, we have solved only equations that involved one operation. One of the four properties of equality has been used to undo the operation and isolate the variable.

Many equations contain more than one operation. This means that we will use more than one property of equality to isolate the variable. In solving equations with more than one operation, a combination of the properties of equality studied so far will be applied. In general, first isolate the variable term of an equation, and then isolate the variable itself. In the equation $3x + 9 = 21$, first isolate the variable term $3x$ by subtracting 9 from both sides, and then isolate x by dividing both sides by 3.

$$\boxed{3x} + 9 = 21 \qquad \text{Identify the variable term.}$$

$$\underline{\quad -9 \quad -9} \qquad \begin{array}{l}\text{Isolate the variable term by subtracting} \\ \text{9 from both sides of the equation.}\end{array}$$

$$3x = 12$$

$$\frac{3x}{\cancel{3}} = \frac{12}{3} \qquad \text{Now isolate the variable by dividing both sides by 3.}$$

$$x = 4$$

$$3(4) + 9 \overset{?}{=} 21 \qquad \text{Check the answer.}$$

$$12 + 9 \overset{?}{=} 21$$

$$21 = 21 \qquad \text{The answer works.}$$

When solving multiple-step problems, be sure to consider one step at a time. Right now we only have four basic properties of equality to use. In later chapters, we will use other techniques to solve more complicated equations. To stay focused on the variable term, it is useful to circle the variable term and then work to isolate it on one side of the equation.

Example 4 Cost of T-shirts

The local YMCA wants to order T-shirts for kids who attend its summer day camps. After calling a few local shirt printers, the staff members find one that will charge a $350 setup fee for the design and $4 per shirt for the T-shirt with design printed on it. Using this information, the staff at the YMCA can estimate costs using the formula

$$C = 350 + 4s$$

where C represents the total cost in dollars for s T-shirts.

a. What will it cost the YMCA to purchase 100 T-shirts?

b. How many T-shirts can the YMCA purchase if the budget for T-shirts is $1250?

SOLUTION

a. Since the staff members want to purchase 100 T-shirts, $s = 100$. Substitute this into the equation and evaluate to find the cost.

$$C = 350 + 4(100) \qquad \text{Substitute 100 for } s.$$
$$C = 350 + 400$$
$$C = 750$$

If the YMCA purchases 100 T-shirts, it will cost $750.

b. The YMCA has $1250 to spend on T-shirts, so we let $C = 1250$ and solve for s.

$$1250 = 350 + \boxed{4s} \qquad \text{Substitute in 1250 for } C. \text{ Identify the variable term.}$$
$$1250 = 350 + \boxed{4s} \qquad \text{Isolate the variable term by subtracting 350 from both sides.}$$
$$\underline{-350 \quad -350}$$
$$900 = 4s$$
$$\frac{900}{4} = \frac{4s}{4} \qquad \text{Isolate } s \text{ by dividing both sides by 4.}$$
$$225 = s$$
$$1250 \overset{?}{=} 350 + 4(225) \qquad \text{Check the answer.}$$
$$1250 \overset{?}{=} 350 + 900$$
$$1250 = 1250 \qquad \text{The answer works.}$$

If the YMCA has $1250 to spend on T-shirts, the staff can purchase 225 shirts.

PRACTICE PROBLEM FOR EXAMPLE 4

The annual passenger-miles of travel on public transportation in Raleigh-Durham, North Carolina, can be estimated by using the equation

$$M = 2t + 37$$

where $M =$ the annual passenger-miles of travel in millions of miles on public transportation in the Raleigh-Durham area and $t =$ the number of years since 1995.
Source: 2005 Urban Mobility Study, Texas Transportation Institute at Texas A&M University.

a. Estimate the number of annual passenger-miles of travel on public transportation in the Raleigh-Durham area in 2005.

b. Find what year the number of annual passenger-miles of travel on public transportation in the Raleigh-Durham area reached 45 million miles.

From Example 4, we see that in solving equations with more than one operation involved, a combination of properties is used to isolate the variable. In general, concentrate first on isolating the variable on one side of the equal sign. Since it does not matter which side the variable is on, do not bother moving the variable to the other side of the equal sign. Instead, move the other terms away from the variable.

> **Steps to Solving Linear Equations**
> 1. **Simplify** both sides of the equation independently, if needed, using the distributive property and combining like terms.
> 2. **Isolate the variable term.** Circle the variable term. Use the addition or subtraction properties of equality to isolate the variable term on one side of the equation.
> 3. **Isolate the variable.** Use the multiplication or division properties of equality to isolate the variable on one side of the equation.
> 4. **Check the answer.** Substitute the answer into the original equation, and simplify both sides to check that they give the same result.

Example 5 Solving multiple-step equations

Solve the equation. Check the answer.

a. $3x + 8 = 44$

b. $75 = \dfrac{p}{2} - 25$

c. $4k + 20 + 6k = 30$

d. $84 = 6x - 12 - 10x$

SOLUTION

a. To undo the addition, subtract 8 from both sides. Then undo the multiplication by dividing both sides by 3.

$$\boxed{3x} + 8 = 44 \qquad \text{Identify the variable term.}$$

$$\underline{ -8 \quad -8} \qquad \text{Isolate the variable term by subtracting}$$
$$3x = 36 \qquad \text{8 from both sides of the equation.}$$

$$\frac{3x}{3} = \frac{36}{3} \qquad \text{Isolate } x \text{ by dividing both sides by 3.}$$

$$x = 12$$

$$3(12) + 8 \stackrel{?}{=} 44 \qquad \text{Check the answer.}$$

$$36 + 8 \stackrel{?}{=} 44$$

$$44 = 44 \qquad \text{The answer works.}$$

b. First isolate the variable term on one side of the equal sign. Begin by adding 25 to both sides of the equation to undo the subtraction by 25. Then multiply both sides by 2 to undo the division.

$$75 = \boxed{\frac{p}{2}} - 25 \qquad \text{Identify the variable term.}$$

$$\underline{+25 \qquad\qquad +25} \qquad \text{Isolate the variable term by adding 25 to both sides.}$$

$$100 = \frac{p}{2}$$

$$2(100) = 2\left(\frac{p}{2}\right) \qquad \text{Isolate } p \text{ by multiplying both sides by 2.}$$

$$200 = p$$

$$75 \stackrel{?}{=} \frac{(200)}{2} - 25 \qquad \text{Check the answer.}$$

$$75 \stackrel{?}{=} 100 - 25$$

$$75 = 75 \qquad \text{The answer works.}$$

c. When necessary, first simplify both sides of the equation before starting to solve. In this case, the left side can be simplified by combining like terms.

$$4k + 20 + 6k = 30$$ *Simplify the left side by combining like terms.*

$$\boxed{10k} + 20 = 30$$ *Identify the variable term.*

$$\underline{\quad -20 \qquad -20 \quad}$$ *Isolate the variable term by subtracting 20 from both sides.*

$$10k = 10$$

$$\frac{10k}{10} = \frac{10}{10}$$ *Isolate k by dividing both sides by 10.*

$$k = 1$$

$$4(1) + 20 + 6(1) \overset{?}{=} 30$$ *Check the answer.*

$$4 + 20 + 6 \overset{?}{=} 30$$

$$30 = 30$$ *The answer works.*

d. In this equation, simplify the right side by combining like terms.

$$84 = 6x - 12 - 10x$$ *Simplify the right side by combining like terms.*

$$84 = \boxed{-4x} - 12$$ *Identify the variable term.*

$$\underline{+12 \qquad\qquad +12}$$ *Isolate the variable term by adding 12 to both sides.*

$$96 = -4x$$

$$\frac{96}{-4} = \frac{-4x}{-4}$$ *Isolate x by dividing both sides by −4.*

$$-24 = x$$

$$84 \overset{?}{=} 6(-24) - 12 - 10(-24)$$ *Check the answer.*

$$84 \overset{?}{=} -144 - 12 + 240$$

$$84 = 84$$ *The answer works.*

PRACTICE PROBLEM FOR EXAMPLE 5

Solve the equation. Check the answer.

a. $8b - 7 = 41$ **b.** $55 = \dfrac{x}{3} + 30$ **c.** $7x + 13 + 3x = 188$

Generating Equations from Applications

In Chapter 1, we studied how to translate sentences into expressions. In this chapter, we are now discussing equations and how to solve them. When a problem is given in a sentence form, first translate it into an algebraic equation and then solve it. The most common phrases used for the operations are reviewed in the What's That Mean? feature on this page. The phrases that represent an equal sign are in the following table.

Phrases	Translation
x is equal to 10	$x = 10$
15 is the same as n	$15 = n$
p is 4	$p = 4$
t was -8	$t = -8$

Any words or phrases that mean equal or the same will represent an equal sign. The words *is*, *are*, *were*, and *was* also represent an equal sign when translated. In some situations, we may be able to use a known formula or information to write the equation needed to find the value of the variable.

What's That Mean?

Operations

Recall from Chapter 1 that the common phrases for addition, subtraction, multiplication, and division are as follows:

Addition:
sum
total
increased by
plus
more than
exceeds by
added to

Subtraction:
minus
difference
decreased by
less than
subtracted from
reduced by

Multiplication:
product
times
twice
doubled
tripled
half of

Division:
quotient
ratio
divided by

Example **6** Translating sentences into equations and solving

Translate each of the following sentences into an equation. Solve the equation. Check the answer.

a. Twice a number added to 10 is equal to 20.

b. The quotient of a number and 5 is 30.

c. Five times the sum of a number and 6 is equal to 40.

d. The perimeter of a rectangle is 40 inches, and its length is 12 inches. Find the rectangle's width.

SOLUTION

In these solutions, let x = a number.

a. "Twice" means to multiply by 2, and "is equal to" translates as the equal sign. This yields the equation

$$10 + 2x = 20$$

Solve the equation.

$10 + 2x = 20$	Identify the variable term.
$\underline{-10 \qquad\quad -10}$	Isolate the variable term by subtracting 10 from both sides.
$2x = 10$	
$\dfrac{2x}{2} = \dfrac{10}{2}$	Isolate x by dividing both sides by 2.
$x = 5$	
$10 + 2(5) \overset{?}{=} 20$	Check the answer.
$20 = 20$	The answer works.

b. *Quotient* represents division, and *is* represents the equal sign. Remember that the order of division is important. Read from left to right. Write the quotient in the same order as it is read. The equation translates as

$$\frac{x}{5} = 30$$

The variable term is by itself. To isolate x, multiply both sides of the equation by 5.

$\dfrac{x}{5} = 30$	
$5\left(\dfrac{x}{5}\right) = 5(30)$	Isolate x by multiplying both sides by 5.
$x = 150$	
$\dfrac{150}{5} \overset{?}{=} 30$	Check the answer.
$30 = 30$	The answer works.

c. *Times* means to multiply and *times the sum* means to multiply an addition that has already been done. To show the addition, include a set of parentheses around the sum. This grouping gives us the equation

$$5(x + 6) = 40$$

Solve the equation.

$5(x + 6) = 40$	Simplify the left side by distributing the 5.
$5x + 30 = 40$	Identify the variable term.
$\underline{\quad -30 \quad\; -30}$	Isolate the variable term by subtracting 30 from both sides.
$5x = 10$	

Connecting the Concepts

Does it matter which side of the equal sign the variable is on?

The equation $15 = n$ is the same as $n = 15$. It is okay to switch both sides of the equality.

Connecting the Concepts

Is order important when translating?

With addition and multiplication, the order in which you add or multiply is not important, since these operations are commutative. In subtracting or dividing, the order matters a great deal. Subtraction and division are not commutative. In subtracting, the phrases *less than* and *subtracted from* are translated in the reverse order of the way they are stated.

6 less than 20 is

$$20 - 6$$

10 subtracted from 30 is

$$30 - 10$$

$$\frac{5x}{5} = \frac{10}{5} \qquad \text{Isolate } x \text{ by dividing both sides by 5.}$$

$$x = 2$$

$$5((2) + 6) \stackrel{?}{=} 40 \qquad \text{Check the answer.}$$

$$5(8) \stackrel{?}{=} 40$$

$$40 = 40 \qquad \text{The answer works.}$$

d. Recall that the perimeter of a rectangle can be calculated by using the formula

$$P = 2l + 2w$$

where P is the perimeter of the rectangle with length l and width w. We are given the perimeter and length of the rectangle, so substitute $P = 40$ and $l = 12$. After substituting in these values, solve the equation for w.

$$40 = 2(12) + 2w \qquad \text{Substitute the given values and simplify.}$$

$$40 = 24 + \boxed{2w} \qquad \text{Identify the variable term.}$$

$$\underline{-24 \quad -24} \qquad \text{Isolate the variable term by subtracting 24 from both sides.}$$

$$16 = 2w$$

$$\frac{16}{2} = \frac{2w}{2} \qquad \text{Isolate } w \text{ by dividing both sides by 2.}$$

$$8 = w$$

$$40 \stackrel{?}{=} 2(12) + 2(8) \qquad \text{Check the answer.}$$

$$40 \stackrel{?}{=} 24 + 16$$

$$40 = 40 \qquad \text{The answer works.}$$

A rectangle with a perimeter of 40 inches and length 12 inches has a width of 8 inches.

PRACTICE PROBLEM FOR EXAMPLE 6

Translate each of the following sentences into an equation. Solve the equation. Check the answer.

a. Half a number minus 13 is equal to 7.

b. The product of 3 and a number plus 8 is 23.

In some problems, an equation is translated from the situation described in the problem. In an application problem, be sure to verify that the solution makes sense as well as checks in the equation. Remember that sometimes we round the answers to make them reasonable for the situation. For example, a solution that represents dollars should be rounded to the cents (hundredths) place. Any solution to an application problem should also be written in a complete sentence using units.

Example 7 Translating application problems

Define the variables, and translate each sentence into an equation. Solve the equation. Check the answer for accuracy and reasonableness.

a. The fees at Grossmont College are $26.00 per credit plus a $13.00 health fee. If Fred paid $221.00 in fees this semester, how many credits did he take?

b. The cost of renting a 17-foot truck from U-Haul is $29.95 for one day and $0.79 per mile. If it cost Mandel $91.57 to rent the truck for one day, how many miles did he drive it?

Using tables to generate equations

In Section 1.2, we learned how to use input-output tables to generate expressions. In Example 7a, we can use a table as follows. The problem tells us that the fees are $26 a credit plus a $13 health fee. Using this information, we can generate a table for several values of the number of credits taken, c.

c = no. of credits	F = fees paid
0	13
1	26 + 13
2	$26 \cdot 2 + 13$
3	$26 \cdot 3 + 13$
c	$26 \cdot c + 13$

Therefore, from the last row, we have that $F = 26.00c + 13.00$.

SOLUTION

a. There are two quantities involved in this problem: the fees Fred pays and the number of credits he takes. Define two variables to represent this situation.

Let F = the fees paid in dollars to Grossmont College.

Let c = the number of credits taken this semester.

Multiply the number of credits by the per credit charge and add the health fee. The equation is

$$F = 26.00c + 13.00$$

Since Fred paid $221.00 in fees this semester, $F = 221.00$. Substitute this value into the equation and solve for c (the number of credits).

$F = 26.00c + 13.00$	Substitute 221 for F.
$221.00 = \boxed{26.00c} + 13.00$	Identify the variable term.
$\underline{-13.00 \quad -13.00}$	Isolate the variable term by subtracting 13 from both sides.
$208 = 26.00c$	
$\dfrac{208}{26.00} = \dfrac{26.00c}{26.00}$	Isolate c by dividing both sides by 26.00.
$8 = c$	
$221.00 \overset{?}{=} 26.00(8) + 13.00$	Check the answer.
$221.00 = 221.00$	The answer works.

Many students take between 6 and 15 credits a semester, so 8 credits is a reasonable answer. The quantity 8 checks in the equation. Fred paid $221.00 to take 8 credits at Grossmont College this semester.

b. Let C = the cost in dollars to rent a 17-foot truck from U-Haul for one day. Let m = the miles the truck is driven. Mandel must pay the one-day fee of $29.95 and a per mile charge of $0.79 per mile. The equation is

$$C = 29.95 + 0.79m$$

If it cost Mandel $91.57 to rent the truck for a day, then $C = 91.57$. Substitute this amount into the equation and solve for the number of miles driven.

$C = 29.95 + 0.79m$	Substitute 91.57 for C.
$91.57 = 29.95 + \boxed{0.79m}$	Identify the variable term.
$\underline{-29.95 \quad -29.95}$	Isolate the variable term by subtracting 29.95 from both sides.
$61.62 = 0.79m$	
$\dfrac{61.62}{0.79} = \dfrac{0.79m}{0.79}$	Isolate m by dividing both sides by 0.79.
$78 = m$	
$91.57 \overset{?}{=} 29.95 + 0.79(78)$	Check the answer.
$91.57 = 91.57$	The answer works.

If the truck rental cost Mandel $91.57, then he drove the truck 78 miles. This is a reasonable amount of miles for a one-day truck rental, and it checks in the equation.

PRACTICE PROBLEM FOR EXAMPLE 7

Define the variables and translate the sentence into an equation. Solve the equation. Check the answer for accuracy and reasonableness.

The value of a used backhoe loader decreases by an average of $5000 per year. A particular used backhoe loader is worth $61,000. After how many years will the backhoe loader be worth only $36,000?

More on Solving Literal Equations

Solving literal equations uses the same properties of equality that are used to isolate a variable in a formula or equation. Start by isolating the term that contains the variable to be solved for. Then isolate that variable. In this section, we assume that a variable expression does not equal zero so that division will not result in an undefined answer.

Example 8 Solving literal equations for a variable

Solve each literal equation for the indicated variable.

a. Distance: $D = rt$; solve for r.

b. Slope-intercept form of a linear equation: $y = mx + b$; solve for x.

c. Perimeter of a rectangle: $P = 2l + 2w$; solve for w.

SOLUTION

a.
$$D = rt$$
$$\frac{D}{t} = \frac{rt}{t} \qquad \text{Isolate } r \text{ by dividing both sides by } t.$$
$$\frac{D}{t} = \frac{r\cancel{t}}{\cancel{t}} \qquad \text{Reduce.}$$
$$\frac{D}{t} = r$$

b.
$$y = \boxed{mx} + b \qquad \text{Identify the } x\text{-term.}$$
$$\underline{-b \qquad\qquad -b} \qquad \text{Isolate the } x\text{-term by subtracting } b \text{ from both sides.}$$
$$y - b = mx \qquad \text{Because } y \text{ and } b \text{ are not like terms, the subtraction on the left side cannot be simplified.}$$
$$\frac{y - b}{m} = \frac{mx}{m}$$
$$\frac{y - b}{m} = \frac{\cancel{m}x}{\cancel{m}} \qquad \text{Isolate } x \text{ by dividing both sides by } m \text{ and reduce.}$$
$$\frac{y - b}{m} = x$$

c.
$$P = 2l + \boxed{2w} \qquad \text{Identify the } w\text{-term.}$$
$$\underline{-2l \qquad -2l} \qquad \text{Isolate the } w\text{-term by subtracting } 2l \text{ from both sides.}$$
$$P - 2l = 2w \qquad \text{Because } P \text{ and } 2l \text{ are not like terms, the subtraction on the left side cannot be simplified.}$$
$$\frac{P - 2l}{2} = \frac{2w}{2} \qquad \text{Isolate } w \text{ by dividing both sides by 2. Reduce.}$$
$$\frac{P - 2l}{2} = w$$

■ Skill Connection

Reducing Fractions

When reducing a fraction, always be careful to divide out factors, not terms.

Correct	Wrong
$\dfrac{2 + 3}{4}$	$\dfrac{\cancel{2}+3}{\cancel{4}}^{\,2}$
$= \dfrac{5}{4}$ *vs.*	$= \dfrac{3}{2}$
$= 1.25$	$= 1.5$

We can divide out like factors in the numerator and denominator (multiplication) but not through additions or subtractions.

When the fraction contains only factors, we can multiply first or reduce the fraction first.

Correct	Also Correct
$\dfrac{2 \cdot 3}{4}$	$\dfrac{\cancel{2} \cdot 3}{\cancel{4}}^{\,2}$
$= \dfrac{6}{4}$ *vs.*	$= \dfrac{3}{2}$
$= 1.5$	$= 1.5$

PRACTICE PROBLEM FOR EXAMPLE 8

Solve each literal equation for the indicated variable.

a. Volume of a rectangular solid: $V = lwh$; solve for w.

b. Area of a trapezoid: $A = \frac{1}{2}h(b_1 + b_2)$; solve for h.

Example 9 Solving more literal equations for a variable

Solve each equation for the indicated variable.

a. $-6x + 3y = -18$: solve for y.

b. $y - 2 = \frac{2}{3}(6x - 9)$: solve for x.

SOLUTION

a. To solve the equation for y, isolate the variable y on one side of the equal sign.

$$-6x + 3y = -18 \qquad \text{Isolate } y \text{ by adding } 6x \text{ to both sides.}$$

$$\underline{+6x \qquad\qquad +6x}$$

$$3y = -18 + 6x \qquad \text{Rewrite with the } x\text{-term first.}$$

$$3y = 6x - 18$$

$$\frac{3y}{3} = \frac{6x}{3} - \frac{18}{3} \qquad \text{Divide each term by 3 to solve for } y.$$

$$y = 2x - 6$$

b. To solve this equation for x, first multiply out the right side.

$$y - 2 = \frac{2}{3}(6x - 9) \qquad \text{Multiply out the right side.}$$

$$y - 2 = \frac{2}{\cancel{3}}(^2\cancel{6}x) - \frac{2}{\cancel{3}}(^3\cancel{9}) \qquad \text{Divide out like factors.}$$

$$y - 2 = 4x - 6$$

$$\underline{+6 \qquad\qquad +6} \qquad \text{Add 6 to both sides to isolate the } x\text{-term.}$$

$$y + 4 = 4x$$

$$4x = y + 4 \qquad \text{Rewrite the equation with the } x\text{-term on the left.}$$

$$\frac{4x}{4} = \frac{y}{4} + \frac{4}{4} \qquad \text{Divide each term by 4 to solve for } x.$$

$$x = \frac{y}{4} + 1$$

PRACTICE PROBLEM FOR EXAMPLE 9

Solve each equation for the indicated variable.

a. $-5x + 15y = -45$: solve for y.

b. $y + 1 = \frac{4}{5}(-10x + 5)$: solve for x.

2.2 Exercises

For Exercises 1 through 22, solve each equation and check the answer. If the problem has decimals in it, then answer in decimal form. Otherwise, write any fractional answers as reduced fractions.

1. $3x = -81$

2. $4x = -48$

3. $-10y = -55$

4. $-6y = -27$

5. $7g = 91$

6. $14k = 84$

7. $-x = -9$

8. $17 = -n$

9. $42 = 2.8x$

10. $3.7m = 31.45$

11. $15.25 = 6.1n$

12. $49.68 = 5.4n$

13. $-6c = 42$

14. $-4x = 45$

15. $\frac{t}{5} = 14$

16. $\frac{p}{3} = 9$

17. $\frac{2}{3}x = -10$

18. $\frac{-4}{5}x = 8$

19. $\frac{5n}{7} = \frac{-2}{5}$

20. $\frac{3n}{4} = \frac{-9}{5}$

21. $\frac{k}{-3.5} = -4$

22. $\frac{g}{-7} = 4.6$

23. Victoria works part time as a legal assistant and makes $17 per hour after taxes. Victoria can calculate her monthly salary using the equation:

$$S = 17h$$

where S is the monthly salary in dollars that Victoria makes if she works h hours that month.

  a. Find Victoria's monthly salary if she works 80 hours.

  b. How many hours does Victoria have to work a month to make $2040 a month?

  c. How many hours does Victoria have to work a month if she only wants to earn $700 a month?

24. Emily is taking a driving trip across the country to go to college and plans to average a speed of about 60 miles per hour. The distance Emily can go in a day can be calculated by using the equation

$$D = 60t$$

where D is the distance in miles Emily can travel in a day that she drives for t hours.

a. How far will Emily travel in a day if she drives for 12 hours?

b. If Emily wants to drive about 450 miles a day, how many hours will she have to drive?

c. How many hours will Emily have to drive to make it the approximately 2450 miles from Charlotte, North Carolina, to San Diego, California?

25. Pablo works for a discount mortgage broker who advertises home loans that cost only 1.5 points (1.5%) of the loan amount. No other fees will be charged. When a customer calls, Pablo uses the equation

$$F = 0.015L$$

where F is the fee in dollars the customer will be charged and L is the loan amount in dollars requested by the customer.

a. If a customer calls and requests a loan for $180,000, how much will the fees be?

b. If Pablo wants to keep the fees for a customer down to only $2000, what is the maximum loan amount he can suggest?

26. The LEGO Group makes LEGO toys around the world. They make approximately 1.7 million items an hour, 24 hours a day, 365 days a year. That means about 15 billion LEGO bricks and other components are made every year. A certain machine can make 50 bricks every 7 seconds. The number of bricks B that this machine can produce after m minutes can be represented by the equation

Mark Clark

$$B = 429m$$

Source: LEGO Company profile 2005. www.lego.com.

a. How many bricks can this machine make in 1 minute?

b. How many bricks can this machine make in 1 hour?

c. If the company has an order for 15 million bricks, how long will it take this machine to produce them?

27. The LEGO Group requires such accuracy in its production process that only 18 elements in every million produced do not meet the company's high quality standards. The number of elements that do not meet the quality standards of the company can be represented by the equation

$$D = 18b$$

where D is the number of bricks that do not meet the quality standards when b *million* bricks are produced.
Source: LEGO Company profile 2005. www.lego.com.

a. If 500 million bricks are produced, how many will not meet the quality standards?

b. If LEGO makes about 40.8 million bricks a day, how many of those do not meet the quality standards?

c. If 21,600 bricks do not meet the company's standards, how many bricks did Lego produce?

28. The "rated maximum capacity" of a school bus seat gives the number of people who can sit on the seat. It is determined by dividing the width of the seat by the number 13. Using this calculation, the seat capacity can be determined by using the formula

Susan Law Cain/shutterstock.com

$$C = \frac{w}{13}$$

where C is the rated maximum capacity in number of students when the bus seat is w inches wide.
Source: National Association of State Directors of Pupil Transportation Services. http://www.nasdpts.org/ paperSeatCap.html.

a. Use this formula to determine the rated maximum capacity of a bus seat that is 39 inches wide.

b. What is the smallest width a bus seat would have to be to have a maximum capacity of 2 people?

c. What is the smallest width a bus seat would have to be to have a maximum capacity of 4 people?

d. If a bus has 24 seats in it that are 39 inches wide, what is the maximum capacity for the bus?

29. If the average bus can seat 60 people, then the number of buses needed to transport a group of people can be calculated by using the formula

$$B = \frac{p}{60}$$

where B is the number of buses needed to transport a group of p people.

a. How many buses are needed to transport 300 people?

b. If a city has 350 buses, how many people can public transport handle at a time?

c. If a city has 600 buses, how many people can the city transport at a time?

30. Rachel is applying for a home loan and wants to calculate the fees she will pay. The mortgage broker she is working with says that Rachel will pay 2.5 percent (2.5 points) of the amount of the loan in fees. With this information, Rachel can calculate the fees for her home loan using the equation

Andy Dean Photography/ shutterstock.com

$$F = 0.025L$$

where F is the fee in dollars paid for a home loan of L dollars.

a. Find the fees Rachel will pay if her home loan is for $300,000.

b. If Rachel has $5000 she is willing to pay in fees for her home loan, what is the most she can borrow from this broker?

31. The amount of money taken out in mortgages for single-family and multi-family homes in the United States can be found by using the formula

$$M = -237t + 3796$$

where M is the amount in billions of dollars of single-family and multi-family home mortgages taken out in the United States during the tth year since 2000. (2000 is $t = 0$, 2001 is $t = 1$, 2005 is $t = 5$ etc.)

a. Find the total amount of money in mortgages for single-family and multi-family homes in the United States taken out in the year 2006.

b. Find what year the total amount of money in mortgages for single-family and multi-family homes in the United States was only $1900 billion.

32. An online store shows the following chart for shipping charges within the United States.

Option	Delivery	Tracking	Flat Fee	Per Item
USPS	3–7 days	No	$2.99	$0.99
UPS Ground	3–5 days	Yes	$6.99	$1.99
UPS 2nd Day	2 days	Yes	$13.98	$0.00

The total cost to ship items from this store using the U.S. Postal Service (USPS) option can be found by using the formula

$$C = 2.99 + 0.99n$$

where C is the total cost in dollars for shipping n items from the online store using the USPS.

a. Find the cost to ship five items via USPS.

b. If the total shipping cost through the USPS is $5.96, how many items were shipped?

c. If the total shipping cost through the USPS is $12.89, how many items were shipped?

33. Business or industrial capital equipment includes items such as tractors, farm machinery, and manufacturing equipment. When business or industrial capital equipment is sold on eBay, the seller is charged an insertion fee of $20 for posting the item and a final value fee of 1% of the final price of the item. The total fee can be calculated by using the formula

$$f = 0.01p + 20$$

where f is the total fee in dollars charged by eBay for selling a business or industrial capital equipment item for a final price of p dollars.
Source: www.ebay.com.

a. What will the fee be if the final price of a John Deere tractor was $15,250?

b. If someone was charged a total fee of $124 for selling a log splitter, what was the final price of the item on eBay?

c. If a company was charged a total fee of $270 for selling a Kubota tractor, what was the final price for this item on eBay?

34. Fidelity Investments charges online customers commissions for buying stock options using the following formula:

$$C = 19.95 + 0.75n$$

where C is the commission in dollars when a customer orders n options contracts.
Source: www.Fidelity.com.

a. Find the commission Fidelity Investments will charge if the customer orders 20 options contracts online.

b. If the total commission a customer paid for an online options order was $94.95, how many contracts did the customer order?

c. If the total commission a customer paid for an online options order was $46.20, how many contracts did the customer order?

35. zShops pays Amazon $0.25 plus 2.5% of the sale price, including shipping and handling. The total fee paid by the zShop for an Amazon payments transaction can be calculated by using the formula

$$F = 0.25 + 0.025p$$

where F is the fee paid by the zShop to Amazon when a transaction of p dollars is charged using the Amazon payments option.
Source: www.Amazon.com.

a. What is the fee for a $100 transaction?

b. If the zShop is charged a $9.25 fee for an Amazon payments transaction, how much was the total transaction?

c. If the zShop is charged a $37.75 fee for an Amazon payments transaction, how much was the total transaction?

36. Maria is a realtor who charges a flat fee of $1500 plus 1.5% of the sales price of the home. The total commission that Maria earns on the sale of a home can be calculated by using the formula

$$C = 1500 + 0.015p$$

where C is the total commission in dollars from selling a home for a sales price of p dollars.

a. Find the commission on a home that sold for $145,000.

b. If the total commission paid was $4875, what was the sales price of the home?

c. If the total commission paid was $9450, what was the sales price of the home?

For Exercises 37 through 64, solve each equation, and check the answer. Reduce all fractions. For problems given with decimals, if necessary, round to two decimal places.

37. $5x + 20 = 60$

38. $8m + 34 = 154$

39. $-3p + 50 = -85$

40. $-2q + 25 = -45$

41. $-2.5c + 15 = -5$

42. $-6.5h - 64 = -93.25$

43. $-2.3t + 20 = 26.9$

44. $21.2 = 4.8k + 50$

45. $48 = 12m - 30$

46. $-20 = 8d - 56$

47. $-251.8 = -8.6h + 14.8$

48. $-46.8 = -2.3y - 12.3$

49. $-134.0 = -4.7x - 16.5$

50. $4v - 52.2 = -3$

51. $-2n + 3.8 = 4.85$

52. $-5 + 2.5m = -16.25$

53. $7m + 8 = 31.8$

54. $6k - 56 = -11.6$

55. $-5z + 16 = 32$

56. $-4x + 26 = 84$

57. $\dfrac{x}{4} + 6 = 9$

58. $\dfrac{t}{3} + 14 = -8$

59. $20.1 = \dfrac{w}{8} + 17$

60. $-8.75 = -14 - \dfrac{b}{2}$

61. $\dfrac{x}{-16} + 5 = 2.5$

62. $\dfrac{s}{1.5} - 6 = -3$

63. $\dfrac{2x}{3} + \dfrac{1}{5} = \dfrac{4}{5}$

64. $\dfrac{-5x}{7} - \dfrac{2}{3} = \dfrac{5}{3}$

65. In Exercise 32, we were told that the online store charges a flat fee of $6.99 and an additional $1.99 per item to ship using UPS Ground.

   a. Define the variables. Write an equation for the cost to ship items purchased using UPS Ground.

   b. What does it cost to ship 5 items UPS Ground?

   c. How many items can be shipped UPS Ground for $12.96?

66. Fidelity Investments charges its Silver-level online customers commissions of $10.95 plus $0.75 per option contract for all option orders.
Source: www.Fidelity.com.

   a. Define the variables. Write an equation for the total commission when buying option contracts.

   b. Find the commission a Silver-level customer will be charged if the customer orders 20 option contracts.

   c. If a Silver-level customer is charged $48.45 in commissions for an online options order, how many option contracts did she order?

67. A local machine shop gets an order from a gardening supply manufacturer to create a crank for a portable composter. The production foreman determines that it will take about 6 hours to set up the manufacturing process and about 5 minutes per crank to manufacture.

   a. Define the variables. Write an equation for the total time in *minutes* it will take to set up and produce the cranks.

   b. How long will it take to set up and produce 50 cranks?

   c. If it takes the machine shop 1175 minutes to produce the cranks, how many did they make?

68. Richard copies CDs for local bands. Each CD that he burns takes 12 minutes to create. The total time it takes for Richard to process an order for CDs depends on how many are requested.

   a. Define the variables. Write an equation for the total time it takes Richard to process an order of CDs.

   b. How long will it take Richard to create 250 CDs?

   c. If Richard has 4 hours today to spend creating CDs, how many can he get done? (*Hint:* Change 4 hours into minutes first.)

   d. If Richard spends 6 hours a day creating CDs and works 5 days a week, how many CDs can he make in a week?

For Exercises 69 through 86, define variables and translate each sentence into an equation. Then solve that equation. Check the answer for accuracy and reasonableness.

69. Three times a number is 45.

70. The sum of 20 and 4 times a number is equal to 44.

71. The perimeter of a rectangular garden is 56 feet, and its width is 8 feet. Find the length of the garden.

72. The perimeter of a volleyball court is 180 feet, and its width is 30 feet. Find the length of the volleyball court.

73. The area of a triangle is 40 square inches, and its base is 8 inches. Find the height of the triangle.

74. The area of a triangle is 75 square inches, and its height is 15 inches. Find the base of the triangle.

75. The quotient of a number and 7 is 13.

76. The quotient of a number and 5 added to 12 is 19.2.

77. Six plus the product of 7 and a number is equal to 62.

78. Four times the sum of a number and 3 is equal to 68.

79. One third of a number minus 8 is 28.

80. Half a number plus 18 is 15.

81. The difference between twice a number and 15 is 40.

82. The difference between three times a number and 7 is 17.

83. An unknown number subtracted from 8 is 19.

84. An unknown number subtracted from 36 is −5.

85. Seven less than twice a number is 11.

86. 8 less than three times a number is −23.

For Exercises 87 through 106, solve each literal equation for the indicated variable.

87. Perimeter of a rectangle: $P = 2l + 2w$; solve for l.

88. Circumference of a circle: $C = 2\pi r$; solve for r.

89. Volume of a cylinder: $V = \pi r^2 h$; solve for h.

90. Volume of a cone: $V = \frac{1}{3}\pi r^2 h$; solve for h.

91. Area of a triangle: $A = \frac{1}{2}bh$; solve for b.

92. Area of a trapezoid: $A = \frac{1}{2}h(b_1 + b_2)$; solve for h.

93. $W = 3t - 20$; solve for t.

94. $H = rt + 50$; solve for r.

95. $P = 2b + 2B$; solve for B.

96. $V = lwh$; solve for w.

97. $5x - 3y = -15$; solve for y.

98. $-3x + 4y = 24$; solve for y.

99. $x - 5y = 9$; solve for y.

100. $\frac{1}{3}x + 6y = -4$; solve for y.

101. $y - 2 = 3(x + 7)$; solve for x.

102. $y - 3 = -2(x - 5)$; solve for x.

103. $y + 1 = \frac{3}{4}(12x + 8)$; solve for x.

104. $y - 6 = \frac{1}{6}(12x + 6)$; solve for x.

105. Simple interest: $I = Prt$; solve for r.

106. Simple interest: $I = Prt$; solve for t.

For Exercises 107 through 116, identify each problem as an expression or equation. Simplify any expressions, and solve any equations.

107. $5a^2 + 6a - 8 + 12a + 3$

108. $10m^2 - 3n + 10 - 4m^2 + 4$

109. $2x + 7 = 21$

110. $-6x + 14 = -46$

111. $\frac{1}{3}r + 8 - \frac{5}{6}r = -2$

112. $\frac{3}{10}d + 15 - \frac{4}{5}d = -8$

113. $5n + 7 - 8n + 20m + 4$

114. $8w - 6 + 4v - 14w + 23$

115. $3.4y + 4 - 2.1y = 11.28$

116. $-4.6h - 8.7 + 1.2h = -32.84$

2.3 Solving Equations with Variables on Both Sides

LEARNING OBJECTIVES

- Solve equations with variables on both sides.
- Solve equations that contain fractions.
- Recognize equations that are identities or have no solution.
- Translate sentences into equations and solve.

Solving Equations with Variables on Both Sides

Some equations have the same variable appearing in terms on both sides of the equal sign. In this type of equation, it is best to simplify each side of the equation first. If a term has to be moved to the other side of the equation, use the addition or subtraction property of equality to move it. Putting the variable terms together on one side allows us to combine the like variable terms together so that we can solve for the variable.

> **Steps to Solving Equations with Variables on Both Sides**
>
> 1. Simplify each side of the equation independently by performing any arithmetic and combining any like terms.
> 2. Move the variable terms to one side of the equation by using the addition or subtraction property of equality. Combine like terms.
> 3. Isolate the variable term by using the addition or subtraction property of equality.
> 4. Isolate the variable by using the multiplication or division property of equality.
> 5. Check the answer in the original problem.

Example **1**   Solving equations with variables on both sides

Solve each equation. Check the answer.

a. $5w + 3 = 2w + 78$

b. $3(4x - 7) = 7x - 9 - x$

c. $0.25(3t + 6) = 1.25t - 3$

d. $2m + 15 - 3m = 28$

SOLUTION

a. Both sides of the equation $5w + 3 = 2w + 78$ are already simplified, so first move the like terms that are on opposite sides of the equation. Since the terms $5w$ and $2w$ are on opposite sides of the equation, move one of these terms to the other side so that we can combine the variable terms. Either variable term can be moved, because doing so will not change the solution. To move the term $2w$, subtract it from both sides of the equation.

$$
\begin{array}{r}
5w + 3 = 2w + 78 \\
\underline{-2w \qquad\quad -2w} \\
3w + 3 = 78 \\
\underline{-3 \quad -3} \\
3w = 75
\end{array}
$$

Combine the like variable terms by subtracing $2w$ from both sides.

Isolate the variable term by subtracting 3 from both sides.

$$\frac{3w}{3} = \frac{75}{3}$$

$$w = 25$$

Isolate w by dividing both sides by 3.

$$5(25) + 3 \overset{?}{=} 2(25) + 78$$

Check the answer.

$$125 + 3 \overset{?}{=} 50 + 78$$

$$128 = 128$$

The answer works.

b.

$$3(4x - 7) = 7x - 9 - x$$

Distribute 3, and simplify both sides.

$$
\begin{array}{r}
12x - 21 = 6x - 9 \\
\underline{-6x \qquad\quad -6x} \\
6x - 21 = -9 \\
\underline{+21 \quad +21} \\
6x = 12
\end{array}
$$

Combine the like variable terms by subtracting $6x$ from both sides.

Isolate the variable term by adding 21 to both sides.

$$\frac{6x}{6} = \frac{12}{6}$$

$$x = 2$$

Isolate x by dividing both sides by 6.

$$3(4(2) - 7) \overset{?}{=} 7(2) - 9 - (2)$$

Check the answer.

$$3(8 - 7) \overset{?}{=} 14 - 9 - 2$$

$$3(1) \overset{?}{=} 5 - 2$$

$$3 = 3$$

The answer works.

c.

$$0.25(3t + 6) = 1.25t - 3$$

Simplify the left side by distributing 0.25.

$$
\begin{array}{r}
0.75t + 1.5 = 1.25t - 3 \\
\underline{-0.75t \qquad\quad -0.75t} \\
1.5 = 0.5t - 3 \\
\underline{+3 \qquad\quad +3} \\
4.5 = 0.5t
\end{array}
$$

Combine the like variable terms by subtracting $0.75t$ from both sides.

Isolate the variable term by adding 3 to both sides.

$$\frac{4.5}{0.5} = \frac{0.5t}{0.5}$$

$$9 = t$$

Isolate the variable by dividing both sides by 0.5.

Skill Connection

Answer as a fraction or decimal

A problem that is given with fractions is answered using fractions.
A problem that is given with decimals is answered using decimals.

$$0.25(3(9) + 6) \overset{?}{=} 1.25(9) - 3 \qquad \text{Check the answer.}$$
$$0.25(27 + 6) \overset{?}{=} 11.25 - 3$$
$$0.25(33) \overset{?}{=} 8.25$$
$$8.25 = 8.25 \qquad \text{The answer works.}$$

d.
$$2m + 15 - 3m = 28 \qquad \text{Combine like terms to simplify the left side.}$$
$$-m + 15 = 28 \qquad \text{Isolate the variable by subtracting 15 from both sides.}$$
$$\underline{-15 \quad -15}$$
$$-m = 13$$
$$\frac{-m}{-1} = \frac{13}{-1} \qquad \text{Isolate the variable by dividing both sides by } -1.$$
$$m = -13$$
$$2(-13) + 15 - 3(-13) \overset{?}{=} 28 \qquad \text{Check the answer.}$$
$$-26 + 15 + 39 \overset{?}{=} 28$$
$$28 = 28 \qquad \text{The answer works.}$$

PRACTICE PROBLEM FOR EXAMPLE 1

Solve each equation. Check the answer.

a. $4x + 80 = 2x + 40$ **b.** $2.5(6x + 8) = -4x + 59$ **c.** $20 = 7k - 9 - 8k$

Solving Equations That Contain Fractions

When an equation involves fractions, we can approach the problem in several ways. To solve the equation using the fractions, common denominators are required whenever adding or subtracting fractions. Another way to solve an equation with fractions is to clear the equation of fractions at the beginning of the problem. This is done by multiplying both sides of the equation by a common denominator and using the distributive property. This results in a problem without fractions that can be solved. Either method is appropriate to use. Multiplying by a common denominator to clear the fractions from the equation may be an easier method when the fractions are more complicated or do not have the same denominator.

Example 2 Solving equations with fractions

Solve each equation. Check the answer.

a. $\dfrac{2}{3}x + \dfrac{1}{3} = 5$ **b.** $\dfrac{3}{5}k + 7 = 8 - \dfrac{1}{5}k$ **c.** $\dfrac{1}{3}(m + 4) = \dfrac{2}{5}m - 4$

SOLUTION

a. This equation starts with fractions that have a denominator of 3. Eliminate the fractions in the problem by multiplying both sides of the equation by 3.

$$\frac{2}{3}x + \frac{1}{3} = 5 \qquad \text{Clear the fractions by multiplying both sides by the common denominator 3.}$$

$$3\left(\frac{2}{3}x + \frac{1}{3}\right) = 3(5)$$

$$3\left(\frac{2}{3}x\right) + 3\left(\frac{1}{3}\right) = 15 \qquad \text{Distribute the 3 and simplify.}$$

$$2x + 1 = 15$$

$$\underline{-1 \quad -1} \qquad \text{Isolate the variable term by subtracting 1 from both sides.}$$

$$2x = 14$$

$$\frac{2x}{2} = \frac{14}{2} \qquad \text{Isolate the variable by dividing both sides by 2.}$$

$$x = 7$$

$$\frac{2}{3}(7) + \frac{1}{3} \overset{?}{=} 5 \qquad \text{Check the answer.}$$

$$\frac{14}{3} + \frac{1}{3} \overset{?}{=} 5$$

$$\frac{15}{3} \overset{?}{=} 5$$

$$5 = 5 \qquad \text{The answer works.}$$

b. This equation has fractions, but this time, we leave the fractions and solve the equation.

$$\frac{3}{5}k + 7 = 8 - \frac{1}{5}k \qquad \text{Combine the like variable terms by adding } \frac{1}{5}k \text{ to both sides.}$$

$$\underline{+\frac{1}{5}k \qquad\qquad +\frac{1}{5}k}$$

$$\frac{4}{5}k + 7 = 8 \qquad \text{Isolate the variable term by subtracting 7 from both sides.}$$

$$\underline{\quad -7 \ -7}$$

$$\frac{4}{5}k = 1$$

$$\frac{5}{4}\left(\frac{4}{5}k\right) = \frac{5}{4}(1) \qquad \text{Isolate } k \text{ by multiplying both sides by } \frac{5}{4} \text{ (the reciprocal).}$$

$$k = \frac{5}{4} = 1\frac{1}{4} \qquad \text{Write the answer as either a reduced improper fraction or a mixed number.}$$

$$\frac{3}{5}\left(\frac{5}{4}\right) + 7 \overset{?}{=} 8 - \frac{1}{5}\left(\frac{5}{4}\right) \qquad \text{Check the answer.}$$

$$\frac{3}{4} + 7 \overset{?}{=} 8 - \frac{1}{4}$$

$$\frac{3}{4} + \frac{28}{4} \overset{?}{=} \frac{32}{4} - \frac{1}{4} \qquad \text{Find common denominators.}$$

$$\frac{31}{4} = \frac{31}{4} \qquad \text{The answer works.}$$

c. This equation starts with fractions. First, simplify both sides, and then clear the fractions by multiplying by the common denominator.

$$\frac{1}{3}(m + 4) = \frac{2}{5}m - 4 \qquad \text{Simplify the left side by distributing the } \frac{1}{3}.$$

$$\frac{1}{3}m + \frac{4}{3} = \frac{2}{5}m - 4$$

$$15\left(\frac{1}{3}m + \frac{4}{3}\right) = 15\left(\frac{2}{5}m - 4\right) \qquad \text{Multiply both sides by the common denominator 15.}$$

$$\overset{5}{15}\left(\frac{1}{3}m\right) + \overset{5}{15}\left(\frac{4}{3}\right) = \overset{3}{15}\left(\frac{2}{5}m\right) - 15(4) \qquad \text{Distribute and simplify.}$$

$$5m + 20 = 6m - 60 \qquad \text{Combine the variable terms by subtracting } 5m \text{ from both sides.}$$

$$\underline{-5m \qquad\qquad -5m}$$

$$20 = m - 60$$

$$\underline{+60 \qquad\quad +60} \qquad \text{Isolate the variable by adding 60 to both sides.}$$

$$80 = m$$

$$\frac{1}{3}((80) + 4) \overset{?}{=} \frac{2}{5}(80) - 4 \qquad \text{Check the answer in the original equation.}$$

$$\frac{1}{3}(84) \overset{?}{=} 32 - 4$$

$$28 = 28 \qquad \text{The answer works.}$$

PRACTICE PROBLEM FOR EXAMPLE 2

Solve each equation. Check the answer.

a. $\frac{3}{4}x + 7 = \frac{1}{4}x - 5$

b. $\frac{1}{2}(c + 3) = \frac{2}{5}c - \frac{3}{4}$

Equations That Are Identities or Have No Solution

When solving equations, we may run into two special situations. All of the equations we have solved so far have had one solution. Some equations can have many solutions, while other equations may have no solution at all. Use the following Concept Investigation to discover how these situations come about.

CONCEPT INVESTIGATION

What happened to the answer?

Solve each of the following equations for the variable, if possible. If this is not possible, state whether the equation is a true statement or a false statement.

1. $3 + 4 - x = 3x - 4x + 7$

2. $2x - 1 = 5(x + 1) - 3(x + 2)$

3. $-5x + 4 = -10x + 5x + 1$

4. $\frac{1}{2}(6y) = 3(y + 3)$

This Concept Investigation has revealed that we can get two other situations while solving equations, besides a solution for the variable. We can get an equation that is always true (such as $0 = 0$ or $x = x$), or we can get an equation that is always false (such as $0 = 9$).

The simple equation

$$x = x$$

is true for any value of x.

$$x = x \qquad \text{if} \qquad x = 5$$
$$5 = 5 \qquad\qquad \text{Checks.}$$
$$x = x \qquad \text{if} \qquad x = -29$$
$$-29 = -29 \qquad \text{Checks.}$$

so the solution set is all real numbers. An equation that has all real numbers as the solution set is called an **identity.**

DEFINITION

Identity An equation that has the solution set all real numbers is called an **identity.** An identity can often be simplified so that both sides are exactly the same (identical).

Some equations have **no solution.** The equation

$$x = x + 2$$

has no solution because there are no numbers that are equal to themselves plus 2. If we solve this equation, it will lead to a false statement.

$$x = x + 2$$
$$\underline{-x \quad -x} \qquad\qquad \text{Subtract } x \text{ from both sides of the equation.}$$
$$0 \overset{?}{=} 2 \qquad\qquad \text{This is always a false statement. This equation has no solution.}$$

This equation simplified to a false statement, $0 = 2$, which has no variables left and is not true. The equation has no solutions.

What's That Mean?

All real numbers and no solution

There are several ways to state the solution set of an identity or a problem with no solution. All real numbers can be represented by any of the following notations.

$$\mathbb{R}$$
$$(-\infty, \infty)$$
All real numbers

The solution set of an equation that has no solution can be written as

No solution
$\varnothing$ = empty set
{ } = empty set

Do not confuse the empty set symbol $\varnothing$ with the number zero. Zero is a number and is a possible solution to an equation. The empty set means that there are no solutions to the equation.

It is common not to recognize at first that an equation is an identity or has no solution. When solving an equation, one of the following situations will occur at the very end.

$x = 3$ This is a solution.

$3 = 3$ This is a true statement without variables, so the solution set will be all real numbers.

$3 \overset{?}{=} 7$ This is a false statement without variables, so there is no solution.

Example 3   Recognizing equations that either are identities or have no solution

Solve. If the equation has no solution, write, "No solution." If it is an identity, write, "All real numbers."

a. $3x + 15 = 3(x + 6) - 3$

b. $4x + 6 - x = 2x + 5 + x$

c. $2x + 5 = 5$

SOLUTION

a. Solve as usual.

$$3x + 15 = 3(x + 6) - 3 \qquad \text{Use the distributive property.}$$
$$3x + 15 = 3x + 18 - 3$$
$$3x + 15 = 3x + 15 \qquad \text{Combine the variable terms.}$$
$$\underline{-3x \qquad\quad -3x}$$
$$15 = 15 \qquad \text{A true statement (identity).}$$

This equation simplifies to an identity, so the solution set is all real numbers.

b.
$$4x + 6 - x = 2x + 5 + x \qquad \text{Simplify both sides.}$$
$$3x + 6 = 3x + 5$$
$$\underline{-3x \qquad\quad -3x}$$
$$6 \overset{?}{=} 5 \qquad \text{This is a false statement.}$$

This equation simplifies to a false statement, so there are no solutions to this equation.

c.
$$2x + 5 = 5 \qquad \text{Isolate the variable term by subtracting 5 from both sides.}$$
$$\underline{-5 \quad -5}$$
$$2x = 0$$
$$\frac{2x}{2} = \frac{0}{2} \qquad \text{Isolate the variable by dividing both sides by 2.}$$
$$x = 0 \qquad \text{Zero divided by 2 is zero, so we have a solution.}$$
$$2(0) + 5 \overset{?}{=} 5 \qquad \text{Check the answer.}$$
$$5 = 5 \qquad \text{The answer works.}$$

PRACTICE PROBLEM FOR EXAMPLE 3

Solve. If the equation has no solution, write, "No solution." If it is an identity, write, "All real numbers."

a. $4(2x + 3) - 8 = 8x + 6$

b. $2(x + 1) - 3 = -1 - 5x$

c. $5x + 7 - 3x = \frac{1}{2}(4x + 12) + 1$

Note that an equation with "no solution" is *not* the same as having the number zero as a solution. For instance, $x = 0$ can be a solution to an equation just as the amount of money in our checking account can be zero. "No solution" means that there are no values of the variable that will be a solution to the equation.

Translating Sentences into Equations and Solving

> **Example 4** Translating and solving
>
> Translate each of the following sentences into an equation and solve. Check the answer.
>
> **a.** Three times a number is equal to twice the sum of the number and 5.
>
> **b.** Half a number is equal to the number minus 14.

SOLUTION

Let $x =$ a number.

a. "Three times a number" translates as $3x$. "Twice" means to multiply by two, but "twice the sum" means to multiply a sum by 2, so put the sum in parentheses. Using these translations yields the equation

$$3x = 2(x + 5)$$

Now solve this equation.

$3x = 2(x + 5)$	Distribute the 2 to simplify the right side.
$3x = 2x + 10$	
$\underline{-2x \quad -2x}$	Combine the like variable terms by subtracting $2x$ from both sides.
$x = 10$	
$3(10) \stackrel{?}{=} 2((10) + 5)$	Check the answer.
$30 = 30$	The answer works.

b. "Half a number" translates as $\frac{1}{2}x$, and "the number minus 14" means $x - 14$. Translating yields the equation

$$\frac{1}{2}x = x - 14$$

Now solve the equation.

$\frac{1}{2}x = x - 14$	
$2\left(\frac{1}{2}x\right) = 2(x - 14)$	Clear the fraction by multiplying both sides by 2.
$x = 2x - 28$	Combine the like variable terms by subtracting $2x$ from both sides.
$\underline{-2x \quad -2x}$	
$-x = -28$	
$-1(-x) = -1(-28)$	Multiply both sides by -1 to remove the negative in front of x and isolate the variable.
$x = 28$	
$\frac{1}{2}(28) \stackrel{?}{=} (28) - 14$	Check the answer.
$14 = 14$	The answer works.

PRACTICE PROBLEM FOR EXAMPLE 4

Translate each of the following sentences into equations and solve. Check the answer.

a. $\frac{2}{3}$ of a number plus 8 equals -2 times the number plus 40.

b. A number plus twice the difference between the number and 10 is equal to 5 times the number.

Geometry is a subject in which many formulas and relationships are found that are used in everyday life. People in construction and manufacturing use many volume, area, and perimeter formulas to calculate costs and material needs. Architects and designers use some of the basic relationships from geometry to calculate and check different shapes that they design. We see area when buying tables (square feet) or volume when considering the capacity of a refrigerator (cubic feet). Most of the formulas we will use are found inside the back cover.

Example 5   Using a geometric formula

Given the following triangle, find the measure of each angle.

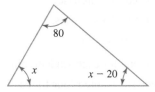

SOLUTION

The measures of the angles in a triangle must sum to 180 degrees. This yields the equation

$$(x) + (80) + (x - 20) = 180$$

Solve this equation.

$$
\begin{aligned}
x + 80 + x - 20 &= 180 & &\text{Simplify each side independently.} \\
2x + 60 &= 180 & &\text{Isolate the variable term by subtracting} \\
\underline{-60 \quad -60} & & &\text{60 from both sides.} \\
2x &= 120 \\
\frac{2x}{2} &= \frac{120}{2} & &\text{Isolate } x \text{ by dividing both sides by 2.} \\
x &= 60 \\
(60) + 80 + (60) - 20 &\stackrel{?}{=} 180 & &\text{Check the answer.} \\
180 &= 180 & &\text{The answer works.}
\end{aligned}
$$

Since $x = 60$, the angles measure $80°$, $60°$, and $60° - 20° = 40°$.

PRACTICE PROBLEM FOR EXAMPLE 5

Given the following triangle, find the measure of each angle.

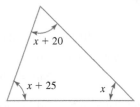

In some problems, it might seem that more than one variable should be defined. Because we have not introduced the process to solve for more than one variable, represent each problem using only one variable. Look at each problem carefully and determine what missing quantity is used to describe the other missing quantities. Be careful not to define variables for things that are already given in the problem. For example, if the problem states that gas costs $4.75 per gallon, don't define a variable for the cost of gas. Simply use 4.75 in that equation or calculation.

Example 6   Buying supplies

Amy, an elementary school teacher, wants to order supplies for her classroom. She plans to get each student an art kit each filled with a box of crayons, four colored pencils, and a watercolor paint set. It costs $2.50 for a box of crayons, $0.50 for each colored pencil, and $4.00 for each watercolor paint set. Amy wants to purchase the supplies to fill an art kit for each student plus three extra boxes of crayons and five extra paint sets. If Amy has a $240.00 budget for this year, for how many students can she purchase kits?

SOLUTION

We first consider how many of each item Amy wants to buy. We should not define different variables for each item. We will instead use the number of students to describe how many of each item she needs to purchase.

Let s = the number of students in Amy's class.

Amy should buy the following art supplies:

- $s + 3$ boxes of crayons, one for each student, plus the three extra she wanted.
- $4s$ colored pencils, since she wanted four for each student with no extras.
- $s + 5$ watercolor paint sets, one for each student and five extras.

Now we multiply each of these expressions by how much they cost and then add those costs together to get the total of $240.00. Translating will give us the following costs as terms and then an equation.

- $2.50(s + 3)$ dollars for the crayons
- $0.50(4s)$ dollars for the colored pencils
- $4(s + 5)$ dollars for the watercolor paint sets
- The total cost will be all these costs added together. In this case, we have to get a total of $240.00, Amy's budget, so we write out the following equation:

$$2.50(s + 3) + 0.50(4s) + 4(s + 5) = 240.00$$

We can solve this equation by first simplifying the left side and then solving for s.

$$2.50(s + 3) + 0.50(4s) + 4(s + 5) = 240.00$$

$$2.50s + 7.50 + 2.00s + 4s + 20 = 240.00$$ Distribute to simplify the left side.

$$8.50s + 27.50 = 240.00$$

$$\underline{-27.50 \quad -27.50}$$ Isolate the variable term by subtracting 27.50 from both sides.

$$8.50s = 212.5$$

$$\frac{\cancel{8.50}s}{\cancel{8.50}} = \frac{212.5}{8.50}$$ Isolate s by dividing both sides by 8.50.

$$s = 25$$

$$2.50((25) + 3) + 0.50(4(25)) + 4((25) + 5) \stackrel{?}{=} 240.00$$ Check the answer.

$$2.50(28) + 0.50(100) + 4(30) \stackrel{?}{=} 240$$

$$240 = 240$$ The answer works.

With a budget of $240.00, Amy can purchase art kits for 25 students.

In Example 6, it is important to attack or approach the problem in parts so that we do not become overwhelmed by the amount of information presented. Read the problem carefully, and break it up into pieces to help build the equation, and then solve it.

PRACTICE PROBLEM FOR EXAMPLE 6

The Clarks are throwing a party and plan to serve their famous ribs, but they must stay within their budget of $500.00. For each person they invite, they will buy ribs, drinks, and paper goods. From past parties, the Clarks know that they will need about two drinks and an average of 1.5 sets of paper goods per person (the ribs can be spicy and messy). The ribs cost $5 per person. Each drink costs $0.50. Each set of paper goods costs $0.20. If they spend their entire budget, how many people can attend the Clarks' party?

2.3 Exercises

For Exercises 1 through 16, translate each sentence and solve. Check the answer.

1. Four times a number is equal to the number plus 33.

2. A number added to eight is equal to five times the number.

3. 5 times a number plus 8 is equal to 3 times the number minus 4.

4. 7 times a number plus 10 is equal to 4 times the number minus 18.

5. Twice a number is equal to 5 times the sum of the number and 6.

6. The product of 7 and a number is equal to 2 times the difference of the number and 5.

7. Twenty minus 3 times a number is equal to 4 times the number minus 22.

8. Twice the difference between a number and 6 is equal to three times the sum of the number and two.

9. Half of a number is equal to the number plus 5.

10. One third of a number plus 5 is equal to the number minus seven.

11. The quotient of a number and 2 added to 5 is equal to the number minus seven.

12. The quotient of a number and 3 is equal to the sum of five times the number and 28.

13. 8 less than a number is equal to five times the number plus 4.

14. 29 is equal to seven less than twice a number.

15. One fourth of a number minus 8 is equal to twice the number minus 29.

16. Half of a number plus 20 is equal to 3 times the number plus 5.

For Exercises 17 through 46, solve each equation. Check the answer. If the equation is an identity, write the answer as "All real numbers." If there is no solution, write, "No solution."

17. $3x + 12 = 7x - 28$

18. $6x + 20 = 10x - 36$

19. $12t - 50 = 4t + 14$

20. $7m - 30 = 3m - 10$

21. $4b + 36 = 9b + 66$

22. $15p - 20 = 4p - 64$

23. $2c + 5 + c = 3c - 4$

24. $5f - 7 = 8f + 2 - 3f$

25. $4t + 5 = 3t + 5 + t$

26. $2z + 8 - 5z = -3z + 8$

27. $3.5h = 2h - 12$

28. $4.8d + 20 = 7.3d$

29. $15 - x = 8$

30. $8x + 5 - 9x = 20$

31. $3h + 8 - 4h = 13$

32. $14 = 5m - 8 - 6m$

33. $2(3x + 5) = 4x + 22$

34. $3(8x - 9) = 30x - 99$

35. $5(2c + 3) - 8 = 3(4c + 2) - 2c$

36. $2(6w - 5) = 3(4w - 2) - 7$

37. $7d + 20 - 3d = 9d + 50$

38. $12r - 15 - 5r = 3r - 51$

39. $\frac{1}{2}x + 5 = 3x - 45$

40. $\frac{1}{2}z - 4 = 5z - 31$

41. $\frac{1}{3}x + 20 = 2x + 20$

42. $\frac{1}{7}h + 8 = 8$

43. $9y - 2.1 = 5y + 3.5$

44. $15y + 3.6 = 8y - 11.8$

45. $35t + 10.2 = 5t + 9.9$

46. $3w - 7.9 = -4.75 - 4w$

47. A triangle has angles with measures x, $2x$, and $5x$. Find the measure of each angle.

48. A triangle has angles with measures y, $3y$, and $6y$. Find the measure of each angle.

49. A rectangular yard has sides which measure $3x + 1$ feet and $5x$ feet. The perimeter is 66 feet. Find the length of each side of the yard.

50. A rectangular yard has sides which measure $4x + 2$ feet and $3x$ feet. The perimeter is 88 feet. Find the length of each side of the yard.

51. A square yard has sides which measure $3x - 2$ feet. The perimeter is 83 feet. Find the length of each side of the yard.

52. A square yard has sides which measure $6x - 3$ feet. The perimeter is 60 feet. Find the length of each side of the yard.

53. A rectangular lawn has sides which measure $x - 5$ feet and $4x$ feet. The perimeter is 100 feet. Find the length of each side of the lawn.

54. A rectangular lawn has sides which measure $x - 7$ feet and $3x$ feet. The perimeter is 58 feet. Find the length of each side of the lawn.

55. A triangle has angles with measures x, $2x$, and $2x$. Find the measure of each angle.

56. A triangle has angles with measures x, $2x$, and $3x$. Find the measure of each angle.

For Exercises 57 through 70, solve each equation. Check the answer. If the equation is an identity, write the answer as "All real numbers." If there is no solution, write, "No solution."

57. $3(x - 0.5) + 1 = 3x - 0.5$

58. $2.1(x + 2) - 3 = 2.1x + 1.2$

59. $0.3x + 0.3 = 0.5x + 0.1 - 0.2x$

60. $0.9x - 0.2 = 0.5(3x + 1) - 0.6x$

61. $\frac{1}{2}r + 5 = \frac{7}{5}r + 5$

62. $\frac{1}{4}w + 50 = 3w + 50$

63. $\frac{3}{5}d - 1 = \frac{1}{10}(6d - 10)$

64. $\frac{2}{3}n + 6 = \frac{1}{3}(2n + 18)$

65. $\frac{1}{5}g + 7 = 2 + \frac{2}{5}g$

66. $\frac{2}{7}t - 5 = 15 - \frac{3}{7}t$

67. $\frac{1}{2}x + 7 = \frac{2}{5}x + 9$

68. $\frac{1}{3}v + 4 = \frac{1}{4}v + \frac{9}{2}$

69. $\frac{1}{2}x + 5 = \frac{1}{2}x + 3$

70. $\frac{1}{3}(3x + 6) = 2\left(\frac{1}{2}x + 4\right)$

For Exercises 71 through 76, solve each geometry problem.

71. Given the following triangle, find the measure of each angle.

72. Given the following triangle, find the measure of each angle.

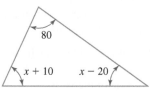

73. Given the following triangle, find the measure of each angle.

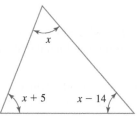

74. Given the following triangle, find the measure of each angle.

Geometry gives us the following property of quadrilaterals.

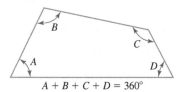

$$A + B + C + D = 360°$$

The measures of the four angles of a quadrilateral always add up to 360 degrees.

75. Given the following quadrilateral, find the measures of each angle.

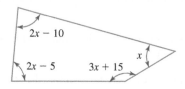

76. Given the following quadrilateral, find the measures of each angle.

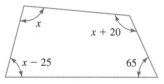

For Exercises 77 through 80, use the drawing of land plots below to answer each application problem. The figure is not drawn to scale.

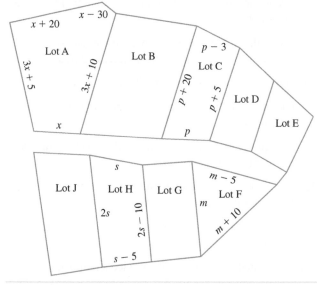

77. The perimeter of Lot C above is 342 feet. Find the length of each side.

78. The perimeter of Lot F is 335 feet. Find the length of each side.

79. The perimeter of Lot H is 345 feet. Find the length of each side.

80. The perimeter of Lot A is 500 feet. Find the length of each side.

81. A group of college students is taking a bike tour through Europe this summer. Carlotta is organizing the supplies for the trip. For each person, Carlotta must rent a bike, and she must also buy two water bottles and three food sacks for meals on the road. Carlotta calls the bike tour company and finds that each bike will cost $145 to rent, each water bottle is $2, and each food sack is $4.50. How many students can Carlotta supply if she has $2275.00 to spend?

82. Bill's EduToys manufactures educational toys for kids. For each Alphabet Car that Bill manufactures, he ships a few extra parts to reduce customer requests for replacements. For each Alphabet Car that Bill manufactures, he wants to order four wheels, two axles, and five hubcaps. Each wheel costs him $0.27, each axle costs $0.78, and each hubcap costs $0.06. If Bill budgets $14,700 a year for these parts, how many Alphabet Cars can he build?

83. The North Oceanside Home Depot is sponsoring a Kids Workshop in which the kids are going to build wood desk calendars for their parents. Each kit requires 1 foot of a pine 2 × 2 to make the month and dates blocks, 1.5 feet of a pine 1 × 3 for the holder, and a set of nails and some glue to put it together with. For mistakes that happen, the Kids Workshop manager always wants about 8 feet of extra 2 × 2, an extra 10 feet of 1 × 3, and 12 extra sets of nails. The 2 × 2 pine costs $0.45 per foot, the 1 × 3 pine costs $0.55 per foot, and the sets of nails are $0.05 each.

Mark Clark. By permission.

    a. Write an equation for the total amount spent on supplies for these calendars if k kids come to build the project.

    b. Use your equation to find the cost if 75 kids come to build the project.

    c. If the manager has $310 left in his budget, for how many projects can he buy the supplies?

84. Quality Landscaping Co. contracts to put front yard sprinkler systems into each home in a new development. For each system installed in a yard,

Quality Landscaping calculates that the supplies required are 12 10-foot PVC pipes, 9 sprinkler heads, and a set of miscellaneous PVC parts. The project manager decides that he should also order 15 extra 10-foot PVC pipes, 6 extra sprinkler heads, and 2 extra sets of miscellaneous PVC parts. Each 10-foot PVC pipe costs $1.50, each sprinkler costs $2.50, and each set of PVC parts costs $15.

    a. Write an equation for the total the landscaping company will pay for the supplies needed to install sprinkler systems in y yards.

    b. If the company installs 12 sprinkler systems during the first phase of the development, how much will it cost for the supplies?

    c. If the manager budgets $6006 for the entire project, how many sprinkler systems can be installed?

For Exercises 85 through 94, identify each problem as an expression or equation. Simplify any expressions, and solve any equations.

85. $5ab + 6a^2 - 4a + 12ab + 3$

86. $10mn^2 + 9n + 1 - 7mn^2 + 4$

87. $0.5x - 4 = 2x + 7$

88. $-0.25r + 12 = 4.5r - 15$

89. $\frac{1}{8}n + 12 = \frac{3}{24}n - 2$ **90.** $\frac{3}{4}d + 14 = \frac{12}{16}d - 20$

91. $2x + 11 - 4x + 8$ **92.** $7y^3 - 10y + 3y^2 + 2y$

93. $\frac{1}{2}(3x + 4) = \frac{1}{3}x + 20$ **94.** $\frac{1}{4}(5w + 2) = 11 - \frac{5}{18}w$

2.4 Solving and Graphing Linear Inequalities on a Number Line

LEARNING OBJECTIVES

- Solve inequalities.
- Write a solution set using interval notation.
- Graph a solution set on a number line.
- Solve compound inequalities.

Introduction to Inequalities

There are many situations in which quantities are less than or greater than another value. For example, we want our bills to be less than the money we make, or we want to spend less than our budget for a project. In school, students like their grades to be greater than the minimum to pass. For health reasons, it is desirable to have one's weight in the normal range, between underweight and overweight. Doctors want their patients to have less bad (LDL) cholesterol and more good (HDL) cholesterol. Many relationships such as these can be mathematically expressed as *inequalities*.

Most of the equations that we have been solving thus far have had one solution for the variable that makes the equation true. When working with inequalities, it is common to end up with a solution set that contains many possible solutions. Consider how many days we can rent a car and stay within our budget. The result will be anywhere from no days to the maximum number of days that will fit within our budget. To rent a bus for a school trip, the number of people who go on the bus must be less than or equal to the maximum occupancy of the bus. All of these situations have many possible answers that are mathematically correct as well as reasonable in the situation. The solution set to an inequality is an interval that includes all the possible solutions.

Solving inequalities is much like solving equations, with one difference in the solving process. To discover this difference in the solving process, we start by looking at the properties of equality and see whether they hold true for inequalities.

CONCEPT INVESTIGATION

Do the properties of equality work with inequalities?

Use the given inequality to test whether each property of equality is also true for inequalities. Test different kinds of numbers such as small, big, positive, or negative numbers. In this investigation, we will consider the resulting inequality true if the original inequality symbol is still the correct symbol to use.

a. Addition Property

The addition property of equality says that we can add the same real number to both sides of an equation and the equation will remain true. Fill in the table below to test if the property is true for inequalities.

	Add a Small Positive Number	Add a Large Positive Number	Add a Negative Number Close to Zero	Add a Negative Number Far from Zero	Add a Decimal or Fraction
$5 > 2$	$5 + \underline{4} > 2 + \underline{4}$ $\underline{9} > \underline{6}$	$5 + \_ > 2 + \_$ $\_ > \_$	$5 + \_ > 2 + \_$ $\_ > \_$	$5 + \_ > 2 + \_$ $\_ > \_$	$5 + \_ > 2 + \_$ $\_ > \_$
True or False	True				

b. Subtraction Property

The subtraction property of equality says that we can subtract the same real number from both sides of an equation and the equation will remain true. Fill in the table below to test if the property is true for inequalities.

	Subtract a Small Positive Number	Subtract a Large Positive Number	Subtract a Negative Number Close to Zero	Subtract a Negative Number Far from Zero	Subtract a Decimal or Fraction
$6 < 100$	$6 - \underline{2} < 100 - 2$ $\underline{4} < \underline{98}$	$6 - \_ < 100 - \_$ $\_ < \_$	$6 - \_ < 100 - \_$ $\_ < \_$	$6 - \_ < 100 - \_$ $\_ < \_$	$6 - \_ < 100 - \_$ $\_ < \_$
True or False	True				

c. Multiplication Property

The multiplication property says that we can multiply both sides of an equation by any nonzero real number and the equation will remain true. Fill in the following table to test if the property is true for inequalities.

	Multiply by a Small Positive Number	Multiply by a Large Positive Number	Multiply by a Negative Number Close to Zero	Multiply by a Negative Number Far from Zero	Multiply by a Negative Decimal or Fraction
$3 < 5$	$\underline{2}(3) < \underline{2}(5)$ $\underline{6} < \underline{10}$	$\_ (3) < \_ (5)$ $\_ < \_$	$\_ (3) < \_ (5)$ $\_ < \_$	$\_ (3) < \_ (5)$ $\_ < \_$	$\_ (3) < \_ (5)$ $\_ < \_$
True or False	True				

d. Division Property

The division property says that we can divide both sides of an equation by any non-zero real number and the equation will remain true. (You might want to use decimals to compare the results.) Fill in the table below to test if the property is true for inequalities.

	Divide by a Small Positive Number	Divide by a Large Positive Number	Divide by a Negative Number Close to Zero	Divide by a Negative Number Far from Zero	Divide by a Negative Decimal or Fraction
$40 > 30$	$\frac{40}{2} > \frac{30}{2}$ $20 > 15$	$\frac{40}{\_} > \frac{30}{\_}$ $\_ > \_$	$\frac{40}{\_} > \frac{30}{\_}$ $\_ > \_$	$\frac{40}{\_} > \frac{30}{\_}$ $\_ > \_$	$\frac{40}{\_} > \frac{30}{\_}$ $\_ > \_$
True or False	True				

Answer the following questions that refer to this Concept Investigation.

1. Which operations always keep the inequality true?

2. Which operations do not always keep the inequality true?

3. When do these operations fail to keep the inequality true? When do they still work?

4. When an inequality is *not* true, how can you change the inequality symbol to make the inequality true again?

This Concept Investigation can be summarized by the following properties for inequalities.

ADDITION PROPERTY OF INEQUALITIES

If the same real number or algebraic expression is added to **both** sides of an inequality, the solution to the inequality is unchanged.

$$\text{If } a < b, \quad \text{then} \quad a + c < b + c$$
$$\text{If } a > b, \quad \text{then} \quad a + c > b + c$$

SUBTRACTION PROPERTY OF INEQUALITIES

If the same real number or algebraic expression is subtracted from **both** sides of an inequality, the solution to the inequality is unchanged.

$$\text{If } a < b, \quad \text{then} \quad a - c < b - c$$
$$\text{If } a > b, \quad \text{then} \quad a - c > b - c$$

MULTIPLICATION PROPERTY OF INEQUALITIES

When both sides of an inequality are multiplied by a positive real number, the solution to the inequality is unchanged.

Continued

$$\text{If } a < b \text{ and } c \text{ is positive, then } a \cdot c < b \cdot c$$
$$\text{If } a > b \text{ and } c \text{ is positive, then } a \cdot c > b \cdot c$$

When both sides of an inequality are multiplied by a **negative** real number, the direction of the inequality symbol must be reversed.

$$\text{If } a < b \text{ and } c \text{ is negative, then } a \cdot c > b \cdot c$$
$$\text{If } a > b \text{ and } c \text{ is negative, then } a \cdot c < b \cdot c$$

DIVISION PROPERTY OF INEQUALITIES

When both sides of an inequality are divided by a positive real number, the solution to the inequality is unchanged.

$$\text{If } a < b \text{ and } c \text{ is positive, then } \frac{a}{c} < \frac{b}{c}$$

$$\text{If } a > b \text{ and } c \text{ is positive, then } \frac{a}{c} > \frac{b}{c}$$

When both sides of an inequality are divided by a **negative** real number, the direction of the inequality symbol must be reversed.

$$\text{If } a < b \text{ and } c \text{ is negative, then } \frac{a}{c} > \frac{b}{c}$$

$$\text{If } a > b \text{ and } c \text{ is negative, then } \frac{a}{c} < \frac{b}{c}$$

What's That Mean?

Endpoint

In the inequality $x \geq 2$, we call 2 the *endpoint*. In the inequality $x < -1$, we call -1 the *endpoint*.

Solving Inequalities

With these properties, we can solve most inequalities. We will solve inequalities in the same way that we solved equations except that we will reverse the inequality symbol whenever we multiply or divide by a negative number. Checking a solution for an inequality requires two steps. First, we check the **endpoint(s)** of the interval, and then we check the direction of the inequality symbol. The endpoint(s) is/are the number(s) at which the solution set starts or ends.

> ### Steps to Solving Inequalities
>
> 1. Solve inequalities the same way as equations, except that when both sides are **multiplied or divided** by a negative number, reverse the inequality symbol.
>
> ### Steps to Checking the Solution to an Inequality
>
> 1. Substitute the endpoint into the inequality. Both sides should be equal (not unequal).
> 2. Pick a number other than the endpoint from the solution set. Substitute this value in the original inequality. The original inequality should remain true.

Example 1 Weekly salary

In Example 1 of Section 2.2, we considered José, who worked for Post and Pack and earned $9 per hour. Let h be the number of hours José works in a week.

a. Write an inequality to show that José needs to earn at least $180 this week for his car payment.

b. Solve the inequality found in part a. Write the solution as a complete sentence.

c. Find the number of hours José must work to earn at least $250 a week.

SOLUTION

a. Because h is the number of hours José works a week, his salary is $9h$. His salary should be "at least $180," so we want it to be greater than or equal to 180. This gives us the inequality

$$9h \geq 180$$

b. Solve the inequality from part a in a similar way to solving an equation by dividing both sides by 9.

$$9h \geq 180$$

$$\frac{9h}{9} \geq \frac{180}{9}$$ *Divide both sides by 9.*

$$h \geq 20$$ *This means that any values greater than or equal to 20 will be a solution. $h = 20$ is called the endpoint of the solution set.*

$$9(20) \stackrel{?}{=} 180$$ *Check the endpoint 20 for equality.*

$$180 = 180$$ *The endpoint works.*

$$9(21) \stackrel{?}{\geq} 180$$ *Now check a number greater than 20 to check the direction of the inequality symbol. The direction of the inequality works.*

$$189 \geq 180$$

José has to work at least 20 hours a week to earn enough money to make his car payment.

c. José's salary needs to be at least $250, so we have the inequality

$$9h \geq 250$$

$$9h \geq 250$$ *We can solve this inequality.*

$$\frac{9h}{9} \geq \frac{250}{9}$$ *Divide both sides by 9.*

$$h \geq \frac{250}{9} \approx 27.8$$ *The rounded approximation will help us to interpret the answer.*

$$9\left(\frac{250}{9}\right) \stackrel{?}{=} 250$$ *Check the endpoint for equality.*

$$250 = 250$$ *The endpoint works.*

$$9(28) \stackrel{?}{\geq} 250$$ *Check a number larger than 27.8 to check the direction of the inequality symbol. The direction of the inequality works.*

$$252 \geq 250$$

José needs to work 28 hours or more a week to earn at least $250. This result means that José could work 28, 29, 30, or more hours a week and earn at least $250. ■

What's That Mean?

At Least and At Most

"at least"
"I need *at least* $20 for the day," implies that $20 would be enough for the day but that more money would come in handy. Writing it as an inequality, we include the value 20 or more, so we use a symbol for greater than or equal to.

$$x \geq 20$$

"at most"
"Mom, I will need *at most* $100 for my trip," implies that less than $100 would probably be enough, but the trip could run as much as $100. Writing it as an inequality, we include the possibility that you will need $100 or less, which we express as a "less than or equal to" symbol.

$$x \leq 100$$

Connecting the Concepts

Do we need to write the inequality symbol when solving inequalities?

When solving an inequality, keep writing the inequality symbol throughout the solving process. This is similar to solving an equation, in which we keep writing the equal sign.

Example 2   Solving inequalities

Solve the following inequalities. Check the answer.

a. $5x + 7 < 62$ **b.** $-2x + 8 \geq 20$

c. $4(x - 9) < 7x + 51$ **d.** $\frac{x}{3} + 9 \leq 4$

SOLUTION

Remember that we solve inequalities in the same way that equations are solved, except that we reverse the inequality symbol whenever we multiply or divide both sides by a negative number.

a. $5x + 7 < 62$ *Subtract 7 from both sides.*

$$\frac{-7 \quad -7}{5x < 55}$$

$$\frac{5x}{5} < \frac{55}{5}$$ *Divide both sides by 5.*

$$x < 11$$ *$x = 11$ is the endpoint of the solution set. All numbers less than 11 are elements of the solution set.*

Check the answer. To do so, check the endpoint and the direction of the inequality symbol. In this case, the endpoint is $x = 11$. To check the endpoint, we are checking whether $x = 11$ will make both sides of the inequality equivalent. After checking the endpoint, check whether the inequality symbol is facing the correct way by picking a number less than 11 to test.

$$5(11) + 7 \overset{?}{=} 62 \qquad \text{Check the endpoint } x = 11.$$

$$55 + 7 \overset{?}{=} 62$$

$$62 = 62 \qquad \text{The endpoint works.}$$

$$5(10) + 7 \overset{?}{<} 62 \qquad \text{Check a number less than 11 } (x = 10) \text{ to test the direction}$$

$$57 < 62 \qquad \text{of the inequality symbol. The direction of the inequality works.}$$

Both checks worked, so $x < 11$ is the solution set.

Skill Connection

The location of negative numbers on the number line

A number to the left of a number is less than that number. A number to the right of a number is greater than that number.

$$-10\,-9\,-8\,-7\,-6\,-5\,-4\,-3\,-2\,-1\ 0\ 1\ 2\ 3$$

$$-7 < -5$$

-7 is less than -5 because it is to the left of -5 on the number line.

$$-10\,-9\,-8\,-7\,-6\,-5\,-4\,-3\,-2\,-1\ 0\ 1\ 2\ 3$$

$$-3 > -6$$

-3 is greater than -6 because it is to the right of -6 on the number line.

b.
$$-2x + 8 \geq 20 \qquad \text{Subtract 8 from both sides.}$$
$$\underline{-8 \quad -8}$$
$$-2x \geq 12$$
$$\frac{-2x}{-2} \leq \frac{12}{-2} \qquad \text{Divide both sides by } -2. \text{ When dividing by a negative,}$$
$$\text{reverse the inequality symbol.}$$
$$x \leq -6$$
$$-2(-6) + 8 \overset{?}{=} 20 \qquad \text{Check the endpoint using } x = -6.$$
$$12 + 8 \overset{?}{=} 20$$
$$20 = 20 \qquad \text{The endpoint works.}$$
$$-2(-7) + 8 \overset{?}{\geq} 20 \qquad \text{Check a number less than } -6 (x = -7) \text{ to test the}$$
$$14 + 8 \overset{?}{\geq} 20 \qquad \text{direction of the inequality symbol.}$$
$$22 \overset{?}{\geq} 20 \qquad \text{The direction of the inequality works.}$$

Both checks worked, so $x \leq -6$ is the solution set.

c.
$$4(x - 9) < 7x - 51 \qquad \text{Distribute the 4 to simplify.}$$
$$4x - 36 < 7x - 51 \qquad \text{Subtract } 7x \text{ from both sides.}$$
$$\underline{-7x \qquad -7x}$$
$$-3x - 36 < -51 \qquad \text{Add 36 to both sides.}$$
$$\underline{+36 \quad +36}$$
$$-3x < -15$$
$$\frac{-3x}{-3} > \frac{-15}{-3} \qquad \text{Divide both sides by } -3. \text{ When dividing by a negative,}$$
$$\text{reverse the inequality symbol.}$$
$$x > 5$$
$$4((5) - 9) \overset{?}{=} 7(5) - 51 \qquad \text{Use } x = 5 \text{ to check the value of the endpoint.}$$
$$4(-4) \overset{?}{=} 35 - 51$$
$$-16 = -16 \qquad \text{The endpoint works.}$$
$$4((6) - 9) \overset{?}{<} 7(6) - 51 \qquad \text{Check a number larger than } 5 (x = 6) \text{ to test the direction}$$
$$4(-3) \overset{?}{<} 42 - 51 \qquad \text{of the inequality symbol.}$$
$$-12 < -9 \qquad \text{The direction of the inequality works.}$$

Both checks worked, so $x > 5$ is the solution set.

d.
$$\frac{x}{3} + 9 \leq 4$$
$$3\left(\frac{x}{3} + 9\right) \leq 3(4) \qquad \text{Multiply both sides by 3. Be sure to use the distributive}$$
$$\text{property to divide out the denominator.}$$
$$x + 27 \leq 12$$
$$x + 27 \leq 12$$
$$\underline{-27 \quad -27} \qquad \text{Subtract 27 from both sides.}$$
$$x \leq -15$$

$$\frac{-15}{3} + 9 \overset{?}{=} 4$$

Use x = −15 to check the value of the endpoint.

$$-5 + 9 \overset{?}{=} 4$$

$$4 = 4$$

The endpoint works.

$$\frac{-18}{3} + 9 \overset{?}{\leq} 4$$

Check a number less than −15 (x = −18) to test the direction of the inequality symbol.

$$-6 + 9 \overset{?}{\leq} 4$$

$$3 \leq 4$$

The direction of the inequality works.

Both checks worked, so $x \leq -15$ is the solution set.

PRACTICE PROBLEM FOR EXAMPLE 2

Solve the following inequalities. Check the answer.

a. $-6x + 12 > 36$ **b.** $2(x + 5) \leq 7x + 75$

When solving inequalities, always remember to reverse the inequality symbol when multiplying or dividing by a negative number. Also, keep in mind that an answer that is negative does not reverse the symbol. Only the operation of multiplying or dividing by a negative number reverses the symbol.

Do Not Reverse the Inequality	Reverse the Inequality
$2x < -4$	$-2x < 4$
$\dfrac{2x}{2} < \dfrac{-4}{2}$	$\dfrac{-2x}{-2} > \dfrac{4}{-2}$
$x < -2$	$x > -2$

Students often find it simplest to interpret inequalities correctly if the **variable is on the left side** of the inequality symbol. Notice that all inequalities in this textbook are solved this way. It is not wrong for a variable to be on the right side of the inequality, but be careful with the direction of the inequality symbol.

$$x < 5 \text{ is the same as } 5 > x$$

The inequality symbol was reversed when expressions on the sides were switched. If x is less than 5, then 5 must be greater than x.

Example 3   Writing the variable on the left

Rewrite each inequality so that the variable appears on the left side. Solve the inequality.

a. $16 > x$ **b.** $-4 \leq y$ **c.** $-15 < 5x$

SOLUTION

a. If $16 > x$, then x must be less than 16. This means that we can rewrite the inequality as

$$x < 16$$

b. If $-4 \leq y$, then y must be greater than or equal to -4. This means that we can rewrite the inequality as

$$y \geq -4$$

c. If $-15 < 5x$, then $5x$ must be greater than -15. Rewriting the inequality yields

$$5x > -15$$

Dividing both sides by 5 to solve the inequality for x yields

$$\frac{5x}{5} > \frac{-15}{5}$$

$$x > -3$$

Example 4   Solving inequalities that arise from applications

Alice's cell phone company charges $40 per month for the first 400 minutes of use and $0.40 per minute beyond 400. Let m be the number of minutes Alice goes over her 400 minutes allowed in a month.

a. Write an inequality to show that Alice must keep her monthly cell phone bill to at most $45. (This is within her budget.)

b. Solve the inequality from part a. Write the solution in a complete sentence.

SOLUTION

a. Since m is the number of minutes over 400, the monthly cell phone charges for Alice are given by the expression $40 + 0.40m$. The inequality that represents Alice keeping her monthly cell phone bill to at most $45 is

$$40 + 0.40m \leq 45$$

b. To solve the inequality, we isolate the term with m on the left side.

$$40 + 0.40m \leq 45$$

$$\underline{-40 \qquad\qquad -40} \qquad \text{Subtract 40 from both sides.}$$

$$0.40m \leq 5$$

$$\frac{0.40m}{0.40} \leq \frac{5}{0.40} \qquad \text{Divide both sides by 0.40 to isolate } m.$$

$$m \leq 12.5$$

Alice can use at most an extra 12 minutes to keep her monthly bill to at most $45.00.

PRACTICE PROBLEM FOR EXAMPLE 4

Amy's wireless carrier charges $5.00 per month for the first 250 texts sent or received. She is charged $0.20 per text beyond 250. Let t be the number of texts Amy goes over her 250 texts allowed per month.

a. Write an inequality to show that Amy must keep her monthly texting bill to at most $10. (This is within her budget.)

b. Solve the inequality from part a. Write the solution in a complete sentence.

Interval Notation and Number Lines

The solution set for an inequality is usually a set of numbers that can be represented in several ways. So far in this section, we have worked all the examples using inequalities. Interval notation and number lines are also used to represent the solution set of an inequality. The inequality $x < 5$ can be represented in any of the following three ways.

In Words	Mathematical Representation
As an inequality.	$x < 5$
Using interval notation.	$(-\infty, 5)$
Graphed on a number line.	<p style="text-align:center">⟵┼┼┼┼┼┼┼┼┼┼┼┼┼┼)┼┼┼┼⟶</p><p style="text-align:center">-10 -9 -8 -7 -6 -5 -4 -3 -2 -1 0 1 2 3 4 5 6 7 8 9 10</p>

Connecting the Concepts

Is there more than one way to write the solution set?

The solution set to an inequality may be written in one of three ways.

1. Inequality notation $x < -2$

2. Interval notation $(-\infty, -2)$

3. Number line

-7 -6 -5 -4 -3 -2 -1 0 1

In interval notation, use either parentheses ( ) or brackets [ ] to indicate the ends of the interval. Parentheses are used when the endpoint is **not** included in the interval. When either a "less than" symbol or a "greater than" symbol is used in the inequality, parentheses are used in writing the solution set as an interval. If the endpoint is included in the interval, then a bracket is used. This happens when an "equal to" part is included with the inequality, such as "greater than or equal to."

The infinity symbol, ∞, is used to indicate that the interval does not stop in that direction and gets increasingly larger. Many intervals in this book will continue either to positive infinity or to negative infinity. Always use a parenthesis next to an infinity symbol. As an example, the inequality $x > -1$ is written as $(-1, \infty)$. Remember that we always write intervals starting with the left endpoint and ending with the right endpoint.

[left endpoint, right endpoint]

Number lines also use parentheses or brackets to indicate whether an endpoint of an interval is included or not. If an endpoint is *not* included, a parenthesis is used. If the endpoint is included in the interval, then a bracket is used. Some math instructors and textbooks will use open dots and closed dots with number lines instead of parentheses and brackets. If an interval goes to ∞ or $-\infty$ an arrowhead is used to indicate the line goes on forever. Following are some examples of the three types of notation being used.

> **■ Connecting the Concepts**
>
> **Why don't we write $[-3, \infty]$?**
>
> A square bracket, [or], next to a number means that the interval will stop at and include that number in the interval. Infinity, ∞, is not a number on a number line. Since ∞ is not a value we ever get to on a number line, we never include it using square brackets. We always write parentheses next to ∞.

	Endpoint Not Included
Inequality $<$ or $>$	$x < -3$ or $x > -3$
Interval Notation Parentheses	$(-\infty, -3)$ or $(-3, \infty)$
Number Line Parentheses	

	Endpoint Included
Inequality $\leq$ or $\geq$	$x \leq -3$ or $x \geq -3$
Interval Notation Bracket	$(-\infty, -3]$ or $[-3, \infty)$
Number Line Bracket	

Example 5 Writing the solution set using interval notation and graphing it on a number line

Solve the following inequalities. Write the solution set using both interval notation and a number line.

a. $\dfrac{x}{7} > 3$ **b.** $-2x \geq -12$

SOLUTION

a. $\dfrac{x}{7} > 3$

$7\left(\dfrac{x}{7}\right) > 7(3)$ Multiply both sides by 7.

$x > 21$

$\dfrac{21}{7} \overset{?}{=} 3$ Use $x = 21$ to check the value of the interval's endpoint.

$3 = 3$ The endpoint works.

$\dfrac{28}{7} \overset{?}{>} 3$ Check a number greater than 21 to verify the direction of the inequality symbol. The direction of the inequality works.

$4 > 3$

Using interval notation, the answer is written as $(21, \infty)$. Use a parenthesis next to the 21 because the inequality does not have an "equal to" part. Always use a parenthesis next to the infinity symbol.

Using a number line:

b. $-2x \geq -12$

$\dfrac{-2x}{-2} \leq \dfrac{-12}{-2}$ Divide both sides by -2. Reverse the inequality symbol.

$x \leq 6$

$-2(6) \overset{?}{=} -12$ Use $x = 6$ to check the value of the endpoint of the interval.

$-12 = -12$ The endpoint works.

$-2(5) \overset{?}{\geq} -12$ Check a number less than 6 to verify the direction of the inequality symbol. The direction of the inequality works.

$-10 \geq -12$

Using interval notation, write the answer as $(-\infty, 6]$. Use a bracket next to the 6 because of the "equal to" part of the inequality symbol. This means that 6 is part of the solution set.

Using a number line:

PRACTICE PROBLEM FOR EXAMPLE 5

Solve the following inequalities. Write the solution set using both interval notation and a number line.

a. $-4x + 7 \leq 35$ **b.** $\dfrac{x}{2} > -4$

Example 6   Graphing from the interval notation

Given the interval form of an inequality, graph the solution set on a number line. Then rewrite using inequality notation.

a. $[3, \infty)$ **b.** $(-\infty, -5)$

SOLUTION

a. The graph of this interval is given in the following graph.

The values that are shown start at 3, include 3, and include all numbers greater than 3. This is equivalent to the inequality $x \geq 3$.

b. The graph of this interval is given in the following graph.

The values that are shown start at -5, do not include -5, and include all numbers less than -5. This is equivalent to the inequality $x < -5$.

PRACTICE PROBLEM FOR EXAMPLE 6

Given the interval form of an inequality, graph the solution set on a number line. Then rewrite using inequality notation.

a. $(-\infty, 7]$ **b.** $(-6, \infty)$

Compound Inequalities

In many areas of daily life, we face situations that require values to be within a certain range. A Boeing 787-9 Dreamliner, for example, can hold up to a maximum of 259 passengers. *Source: Boeing.com.*

Because it does not make sense to have a negative number of passengers, we say that the number of passengers must be between 0 and 259 inclusive. If we let $p =$ the number of passengers, we can write this range of values using inequality symbols as $0 \le p \le 259$. In this example, we interpret p as a whole number because it is representing the number of passengers on a jet. Because both 0 and 259 are possible values, include both endpoints for the set. This is an example of a **compound inequality** because it uses two inequalities together to represent the set. This set can be written in interval notation as [0, 259] and as a number line as follows:

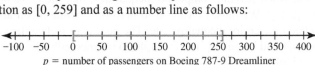

p = number of passengers on Boeing 787-9 Dreamliner

DEFINITION

Compound Inequalities   When two inequalities are used together to show that a quantity lies between two values, the inequality is called a **compound inequality.**

$$5 < x < 20$$

means that x is between 5 and 20.

$$5 \le x \le 20$$

means that x is between 5 and 20 including the endpoints.

Note: Write the compound inequality from left to right and from the smaller value to the larger, just like in interval notation.

Example 7   Writing compound inequalities given in an application

Write a compound inequality for the following statements.

a. The number of passengers on a tour bus must not exceed 60.

b. The amount of open space on a certain computer hard drive is limited to 80 gigabytes.

c. To work correctly, an Aqua Star 250SX tankless water heater must have natural gas pressure between 5 inches and 14 inches water column (a unit of pressure).

SOLUTION

a. We cannot have a negative number of passengers on a tour bus, so we must have between 0 and 60 passengers. Since capacity cannot exceed 60, include the number 60 in our interval. Let $p =$ the number of passengers on the tour bus.

$$0 \le p \le 60$$

b. A computer hard drive cannot have a negative amount of open space, but it can be full. Include 0 to allow for no open space and 80 for the maximum open space. Let $s =$ the amount of open space in gigabytes on this computer hard drive.

$$0 \le s \le 80$$

c. Between 5 inches and 14 inches water column are required, and the problem does not indicate whether it can equal 5 or 14. Therefore, we should not use "equal to" parts on the endpoints. Let $p =$ the gas pressure in inches of water column.

$$5 < p < 14$$

Note: $5 \le p \le 14$ might be valid, but since it was not explicitly stated in the problem that we include the endpoints, we will leave it as "less than" symbols.

PRACTICE PROBLEM FOR EXAMPLE 7

Write a compound inequality for the following statements.

a. The normal height for boys at 5 years of age is between 40 and 47 inches tall.
Source: FPnotebook.com (Family Practice Notebook, a Family Medicine Resource).

b. The Walt Disney Concert Hall in Los Angeles, California, can seat up to 2265 people.
Source: www.wdch.laphil.com.

Keep in mind, when solving compound inequalities, that there are more than two sides to the inequality. We must be careful to perform operations on all sides of the inequalities to keep the entire inequality true. The goal is to isolate the variable in the *middle* of the compound inequality. For example, in the inequality $5 \le p \le 14$, the variable p is in the middle.

Example 8   Solving compound inequalities

Solve each compound inequality. Write the answer in the requested form.

a. $20 < 2x + 6 < 30$ Answer using a number line.

b. $-50 \le -5x - 20 \le 40$ Answer using interval notation.

c. $8 < \dfrac{x}{2} \le 12$ Answer using a number line and interval notation.

SOLUTION

a. $20 < 2x + 6 < 30$ *Isolate the x-term by subtracting 6 from all sides.*
$\quad \underline{-6 \qquad -6 \quad -6}$

$14 < 2x < 24$

$\dfrac{14}{2} < \dfrac{2x}{2} < \dfrac{24}{2}$ *Isolate the x by dividing all sides by 2.*

$\quad 7 < x < 12$

$20 \overset{?}{=} 2(7) + 6$ *Check the left endpoint using x = 7.*

$20 = 20$ *This endpoint works.*

$2(12) + 6 \overset{?}{=} 30$ *Check the right endpoint using x = 12.*

$\quad\quad 30 = 30$ *This endpoint works.*

$20 \overset{?}{<} 2(10) + 6 \overset{?}{<} 30$ *Check the direction of the inequality symbols by using a number between 7 and 12. The direction of the inequality symbols works.*

$20 < 26 < 30$

Since x is between 7 and 12 and there is no "equal to" part, we have a line from 7 to 12 with parentheses on both ends.

b. $-50 \le -5x - 20 \le 40$ *Isolate the x-term by adding 20 to all sides.*
$\underline{+20 \qquad\quad +20 \ +20}$

$-30 \le -5x \le 60$

$\dfrac{-30}{-5} \ge \dfrac{-5x}{-5} \ge \dfrac{60}{-5}$ *Isolate the x by dividing all the sides by −5. Reverse the inequality symbols.*

$\quad 6 \ge x \ge -12$

or

$-12 \le x \le 6$ *Usually, write compound inequalities from left to right and from small to large.*

$-50 \overset{?}{=} -5(6) - 20$ Check the right endpoint using $x = 6$.

$-50 = -50$ This endpoint works.

$-5(-12) - 20 \overset{?}{=} 40$ Check the left endpoint using $x = -12$.

$\qquad\qquad 40 = 40$ This endpoint works.

$-50 \overset{?}{\leq} -5(0) - 20 \overset{?}{\leq} 40$ Check the direction of the inequality symbols using a number

$-50 \leq -20 \leq 40$ between -12 and 6. The direction of the inequality symbols works.

Since both sides have "equal to" parts, we will use brackets for both sides. Always write intervals from lowest to highest numbers, so we get the interval [–12, 6].

c. $8 < \dfrac{x}{2} \leq 12$

$2(8) < 2\left(\dfrac{x}{2}\right) \leq 2(12)$ Isolate the x by multiplying all sides by 2.

$16 < x \leq 24$

$8 \overset{?}{=} \dfrac{16}{2}$ Check the left endpoint using $x = 16$.

$8 = 8$ This endpoint works.

$\dfrac{24}{2} \overset{?}{=} 12$ Check the right endpoint using $x = 24$.

$12 = 12$ This endpoint works.

$8 \overset{?}{<} \dfrac{20}{2} \overset{?}{\leq} 12$ Check the direction of the inequality symbols using a number

$8 < 10 \leq 12$ between 16 and 24. The direction of the inequality symbols works.

In interval notation, the solution set will have a parenthesis on the left side, since it is less than, and a bracket on the right side, since it has a "less than or equal to" sign.

$$(16, 24]$$

Using a number line, we have the following:

PRACTICE PROBLEM FOR EXAMPLE 8

Solve the following inequalities. Write the answer in the requested form.

a. $10 < 7x - 4 < 31$ Answer using interval notation.

b. $-8 \geq \dfrac{x}{-4} - 12 > -12$ Answer using a number line.

2.4 Exercises

For Exercises 1 through 22, solve each inequality. Check the answer. Write the solution set using inequality symbols.

1. $3x \geq 21$

2. $5w \geq 300$

3. $2d < 15$

4. $8z < 56$

5. $-4x \geq 48$

6. $-3y \leq 15$

7. $-a < -61$

8. $-x > -55$

9. $2g + 5 \leq 35$

10. $3x - 8 \geq 4$

11. $5m - 13 > 33$

12. $6x + 15 < 42$

13. $-2x + 9 \leq 25$

14. $4 - 3y > -13$

15. $4x + 7 > 6x + 3$

16. $3t - 14 < 4t - 20$

17. $-4x + 7 \geq 5x + 25$

18. $2 - 5y \leq y + 20$

19. $2(k + 5) - 3 < k + 18$

20. $4(z - 3) + 8 \geq 7z + 20$

21. $7(x - 2) + 1 > 8x - 6$

22. $9(x + 2) - 3 < 10x + 13$

For Exercises 23 through 34, solve each application problem. Round to the hundredths place if necessary.

23. Kati works for the school bookstore and gets paid $11 per hour. Let h be the number of hours Kati works per week.

    a. Write an inequality to show that Kati needs to earn at least $275 this week so she can pay her rent.
    b. Solve the inequality you found in part a, and write the solution as a complete sentence.
    c. Rewrite the inequality, and find the number of hours Kati must work to earn at least $400 in a week. Write the solution as a complete sentence.

24. Tyler works for a local coffee shop and earns $9.75 per hour. Let h be the number of hours Tyler works per week.

    a. Write an inequality to show that Tyler is required to earn less than $200 per week if he wants to continue getting financial aid at his college.
    b. Solve the inequality you found in part a, and write the solution as a complete sentence.
    c. Rewrite the inequality, and find the number of hours Tyler has to work to earn at least $150 per week. Write the solution as a complete sentence.

25. Kevin's cell phone company charges $30 per month for the first 200 minutes of use and $0.50 per minute beyond 200. Let m be the number of minutes Kevin goes over his 200 minutes allowed in a month.

    a. Write an inequality to show that Kevin must keep his monthly cell phone bill to at most $45. (This is within his budget.)
    b. Solve the inequality from part a. Write the solution in a complete sentence.
    c. Rewrite the inequality, and find how many minutes a month Kevin can talk if he needs to keep his bill to at most $40. Write the solution as a complete sentence.

26. Amy called a local truck rental company and was told that it will charge her $20 for the day and $0.60 per mile to rent a truck. Let m be the number of miles Amy drives the truck in a day.

    a. Write an inequality to show that Amy has to keep the cost of her truck rental less than or equal to $95.
    b. Solve the inequality you wrote in part a, and write the solution in a complete sentence.
    c. Rewrite the inequality, and find how many miles Amy can drive the truck if she must limit the rental costs to at most $125. Write the solution as a complete sentence.

27. Warren's wireless company charges $9 per month for the first 200 texts and $0.10 per text beyond 200. Let t be the number of texts Warren goes over his 200 texts allowed in a month.

    a. Write an inequality to show that Warren must keep his monthly texting bill to at most $18. (This is within his budget.)
    b. Solve the inequality from part a. Write the solution in a complete sentence.
    c. Rewrite the inequality, and find how many texts a month Warren can send if he needs to keep his bill to at most $15. Write the solution as a complete sentence.

28. Crystal's cell phone company charges $50 per month for the first 300 minutes of use and $0.40 per minute beyond 300. Let m be the number of minutes Crystal goes over her 300 minutes allowed in a month.

    a. Write an inequality to show that Crystal must keep her monthly cell phone bill to at most $65. (This is within her budget.)
    b. Solve the inequality from part a. Write the solution in a complete sentence.
    c. Rewrite the inequality, and find how many minutes a month Crystal can talk if she needs to keep her bill to at most $60. Write the solution as a complete sentence.

29. Alicia calls Reliable Towing to tow her car after it broke down. Reliable Towing charges a $75.00 hook-up fee for towing and $3.00 a mile after the first 10 miles towed. Let m be the number of miles towed over 10 miles.

    a. Write an inequality to show that Alicia must keep her tow bill to at most $115.00. (This is within her budget.)
    b. Solve the inequality from part a. Write the solution in a complete sentence.

30. Ricardo calls Quality Carpet Cleaning to get a quote on cleaning his carpets. They quote him a price of $100 to clean three rooms and then $40.00 for each room over three. Let n be the number of rooms over three that Ricardo needs to have cleaned.

    a. Write an inequality to show that Ricardo must keep his carpet cleaning bill to $220.00. (This is within his budget.)
    b. Solve the inequality from part a. Write the solution in a complete sentence.

31. Solve the inequality

    $$0.02t + 2.67 \geq 3$$

    where t is years since 2000, to determine what year the population of Arkansas will be 3 million or more. Write the solution as a complete sentence.
    Source: Model derived from data from Census Bureau 2003.

32. Solve the inequality

    $$0.07t + 19.01 \geq 20$$

    where t is years since 2000, to determine what year the population of New York will be 20 million or more. Write the solution as a complete sentence.
    Source: Model derived from data from Census Bureau 2003.

33. Solve the inequality

$$0.35t + 16.01 \geq 18$$

where t is years since 2000, to determine what year the population of Florida will be 18 million or more. Write the solution as a complete sentence.
Source: Model derived from data from Census Bureau 2003.

34. Solve the inequality

$$2p - 400 > 0$$

where p is the number of pieces of jewelry sold to find how many pieces of jewelry Juanita must sell to make a profit. Write the solution as a complete sentence.

For Exercises 35 through 44, rewrite each inequality so the variable appears on the left. Solve the inequality if necessary.

35. $4 > x$

36. $5 > y$

37. $-9 < n$

38. $-16 > m$

39. $0 \geq t$

40. $10 \leq t$

41. $6 > 2x$

42. $4 < -8x$

43. $5 \leq 2x + 1$

44. $-3 \geq 3x + 6$

For Exercises 45 through 62, solve each inequality. Check the answer. Write the solution set using both interval notation and a number line.

45. $4x > 20$

46. $2x > 16$

47. $\dfrac{m}{3} < -2$

48. $\dfrac{h}{4} < 1.5$

49. $-3x \geq 12$

50. $-6x \geq -30$

51. $-\dfrac{2}{5}x < -\dfrac{1}{10}$

52. $-\dfrac{5y}{7} > \dfrac{3}{5}$

53. $\dfrac{-a}{3} \leq -4$

54. $\dfrac{-b}{5} \geq -11$

55. $2(k + 5) \leq k + 13$

56. $-(p + 4) + 5 \leq 3p + 9$

57. $2.5z + 8 \geq 3.5z - 4$

58. $-0.5x + 11 \geq -x - 4$

59. $2c + 7 \leq 6c + 17$

60. $-5z - 16 \leq 9z - 44$

61. $5w - 12 \geq 2(5w - 10) - 30$

62. $4(3g + 8) < 5(4g - 10) + 26$

For Exercises 63 through 70, given the interval form of an inequality, graph the solution set on a number line. Then rewrite using inequality notation.

63. $[-1, \infty)$

64. $[-7, \infty)$

65. $(-\infty, 9)$

66. $(-\infty, -12)$

67. $(69, \infty)$

68. $(42, \infty)$

69. $(-\infty, -16]$

70. $(-\infty, 0]$

For Exercises 71 through 80, write a compound inequality for each statement.

71. The maximum enrollment in a beginning algebra class on a college campus is 38. The class will be canceled if it does not have at least 16 students in it.

72. A Boeing 717-200 can hold a maximum of 106 passengers.
Source: www.boeing.com.

73. School bus #12 has a capacity of at most 71 students.

74. Oakbridge, a Young Life camp in southern California, can accommodate up to 177 people.
Source: www.younglife.org.

75. Another Young Life camp, Timber Wolf Lake, can accommodate up to 450 people. The minimum group size is 200.
Source: www.younglife.org.

76. A local certified public accountant charges her clients between $150 and $500 to prepare tax returns depending on the complexity of the return.

77. At LEGOLAND California, to ride on some attractions, a child between 42 inches and 52 inches tall must have an adult ride with them.

78. College-level courses at Palomar College are numbered between 100 and 300 including 100 but not including 300.

79. The average adult has a normal resting heart rate of 66 to 100 beats per minute.

80. The average newborn baby has a normal resting heart rate of 100 to 160 beats per minute.

For Exercises 81 through 104, solve the given inequality. Write the solution set using both interval notation and a number line.

81. $6 < 2x < 8$

82. $25 < 5x < 55$

83. $-7 < y - 1 < -3$

84. $-4 < b + 5 < 6$

85. $12 < 3x + 3 < 21$

86. $20 < 2x + 10 < 36$

87. $3 < \dfrac{k}{2} < 5$

88. $-2 < \dfrac{n}{4} < 3$

89. $40 \leq 6x + 4 \leq 64$

90. $-25 \leq 8x - 1 \leq 15$

91. $-1.5 \leq \dfrac{m}{6} \leq -0.5$

92. $3 \leq \dfrac{w}{4} + 2 \leq 5$

93. $-12 \leq \dfrac{1}{2}x - 2 \leq 0$

94. $0 \leq \dfrac{1}{3}x + 1 \leq 16$

95. $4 < \dfrac{x}{2} < 30$

96. $5 < \dfrac{x}{15} < 25$

97. $-7 < \dfrac{3x}{4} < -1$

98. $-25 < \dfrac{5x}{7} < -2$

99. $3.5 \le 2x - 2 \le 8.5$

100. $-12.3 \le 6x + 4 \le 6.6$

101. $-9 \le 3v + 6 < 3$

102. $5 < 2x - 4 \le 8$

103. $-7 < \dfrac{5a}{3} - 8 \le 3$

104. $-3 < 4x - 9 \le 17$

For Exercises 105 through 120, identify each problem as an expression, equation, or inequality. Simplify each expression, and solve each inequality or equation. Write the solution set of each inequality, using interval notation.

105. $2x + 7 > 41$ **106.** $6c - 10 < 32$

107. $4x + 7 - 12x$

108. $2m^2 + 3 - 4m - 7m^2$

109. $5h + 12 = 3h - 16$

110. $2(4n - 7) = -5n + 19$

111. $3a + 4 \ge 7a - 20$ **112.** $-5t - 14 \le 3t + 2$

113. $\dfrac{2}{3}x + \dfrac{4}{3} = \dfrac{1}{3}x + 7$

114. $\dfrac{4}{7}d - \dfrac{2}{7} = 2d + \dfrac{3}{7}$

115. $-20 < 4a + 2 < 12$ **116.** $8 \le \dfrac{y}{4} + 10 < 16$

117. $\dfrac{2}{3}b + 5 + \dfrac{4}{9}b - 2$ **118.** $\dfrac{3}{5}x - 8 + \dfrac{3}{10}x + \dfrac{1}{2}$

119. $4 < -\dfrac{g}{2} \le 7$ **120.** $-8 \le \dfrac{x}{3} \le 4$

Chapter Summary

$$\boxed{2}$$

Section **2.1**	Addition and Subtraction Properties of Equality

- An **equation** is a statement that two expressions are equal. Equations have equal signs.
- **Solutions to an equation** are the values for the variables that make the equation true.
- **To check solutions** to an equation, substitute the values for the variables into the equation and determine if both sides are equal.
- The **addition property of equality:** If the same real number or algebraic expression is added to **both** sides of an equation, the solution to the equation is not changed.
- The **subtraction property of equality:** If the same real number or algebraic expression is subtracted from **both** sides of an equation, the solution to the equation is not changed.
- To solve an equation for a variable, **isolate** the variable on one side of the equation.
- **To isolate a variable on one side** of the equation, use the reverse operation ("undo") to move any expressions being added to or subtracted from the variable.
- An equation that involves several variables or is a formula is called a **literal equation.** Solve literal equations using the same process as for solving other equations.

Example 1   Solve. Check the answer. $-8 + x = -16$

SOLUTION

$$-8 + x = -16 \quad \text{Add 8 to both sides.}$$
$$\underline{+8 \qquad\quad +8}$$
$$x = -8$$
$$-8 + (-8) \stackrel{?}{=} -16 \quad \text{Check the answer.}$$
$$-16 = -16 \quad \text{The answer works.}$$

Example 2   Solve. Check the answer. $x - \dfrac{2}{5} = \dfrac{1}{2}$

SOLUTION

$$x - \frac{2}{5} = \frac{1}{2} \qquad \text{Add } \frac{2}{5} \text{ to both sides.}$$
$$\underline{+\frac{2}{5} \quad +\frac{2}{5}}$$
$$x = \frac{1}{2} + \frac{2}{5} \qquad \text{Find the LCD} = 10.$$
$$x = \frac{5}{10} + \frac{4}{10} \qquad \text{Rewrite fractions over LCD.}$$
$$x = \frac{9}{10}$$
$$\frac{9}{10} - \frac{2}{5} \stackrel{?}{=} \frac{1}{2} \qquad \text{Check the answer.}$$
$$\frac{9}{10} - \frac{4}{10} \stackrel{?}{=} \frac{1}{2}$$
$$\frac{5}{10} \stackrel{?}{=} \frac{1}{2}$$
$$\frac{1}{2} = \frac{1}{2} \qquad \text{The answer works.}$$

Example 3   Solve the literal equation for b: $2a + b = c$

SOLUTION

$$2a + \textcircled{b} = c$$
$$\underline{-2a \qquad -2a}$$
$$b = c - 2a$$

To isolate b, subtract $2a$ from both sides.

Section 2.2   Multiplication and Division Properties of Equality

- The **Multiplication Property of Equality:** If *both* sides of an equation are multiplied by the same nonzero real number or nonzero algebraic expression, the solution to the equation is not changed.

- The **Division Property of Equality:** If *both* sides of an equation are divided by the same nonzero real number or nonzero algebraic expression, the solution to the equation is not changed.

- **Simplify both sides of an equation before** isolating the variable.

- **When solving equations with several operations** involved, undo the addition or subtraction first to isolate the variable term, and then undo any multiplication or division to isolate the variable.

- When **solving literal equations,** assume that all variables represent nonzero real numbers so that multiplying or dividing both sides of the equation by the variable will not make the equation undefined.

Example 4   Solve the equation for the variable. Check the answer. $-5d = -55$

SOLUTION

$$\frac{-5d}{-5} = \frac{-55}{-5}$$ Divide both sides by -5.
$$d = 11$$
$$-5(11) \overset{?}{=} -55$$ Check the answer.
$$-55 = -55$$ The answer works.

Example 5   Solve the equation for the variable. Check the answer. $-3x + 8 + 9x = 44$

SOLUTION

$$-3x + 8 + 9x = 44$$ Simplify the left side.
$$6x + 8 = 44$$ Subtract 8 from both sides.
$$\underline{-8 \quad -8}$$
$$6x = 36$$

$$\frac{6x}{6} = \frac{36}{6}$$ Divide both sides by 6.

$$x = 6$$
$$-3(6) + 8 + 9(6) \overset{?}{=} 44$$ Check the answer.
$$-18 + 8 + 54 \overset{?}{=} 44$$
$$44 = 44$$ The answer works.

Example 6   Translate the following sentences into equations and solve. Check the answer.
The difference between 8 and three times a number is 32.

SOLUTION   The sentence translates as

$$8 - 3x = 32$$

Solving the equation yields

$$8 - 3x = 32$$ Subtract 8 from both sides.
$$\underline{-8 \qquad\ -8}$$
$$\frac{-3x}{-3} = \frac{24}{-3}$$ Divide both sides by -3.
$$x = -8$$
$$8 - 3(-8) \overset{?}{=} 32$$ Check the answer.
$$8 + 24 \overset{?}{=} 32$$
$$32 = 32$$ The answer works.

Section 2.3   Solving Equations with Variables on Both Sides

- **Solving equations with variables on both sides:**
  1. **Simplify** each side of the equation by performing any arithmetic and combining any like terms.
  2. Move the variable terms to one side of the equation using the addition or subtraction property of equality. **Combine** like terms.
  3. **Isolate** the variable term by using the addition or subtraction property of equality.
  4. **Isolate** the variable by using the multiplication or division property of equality.
  5. **Check the answer** in the original problem.

- When **solving equations that contain fractions,** eliminate the fractions by multiplying both sides of the equation by the common denominator. Use the distributive property.

- An **identity** is an equation that is true for all possible values of the variable. Equations that are identities will have all real numbers as the solution set. Identities simplify to a statement that is always true, such as $0 = 0$.

- **Some equations have no solutions.** If an equation simplifies to a false statement, then it has no solution. An example of a false statement is $0 = 5$.

- When **translating sentences into equations,** use only one variable to describe the missing quantities.

- **Read an application problem carefully,** breaking it up into smaller pieces to solve the entire problem.

- Some applications will require you to use a **known formula or relationship.** Often, these are geometry formulas. Many formulas are available inside the back cover.

Example 7   Solve for the variable. Check the answer. $5x - 4 = 3x + 8$

SOLUTION
$$5x - 4 = 3x + 8$$ Combine x-terms by subtracting 3x from both sides.
$$\underline{-3x \qquad\ -3x}$$
$$2x - 4 = 8$$

$$2x - 4 = 8$$
$$\underline{+4 \quad +4}$$
$$2x = 12$$

Isolate the variable term by adding 4 to both sides.

$$\frac{2x}{2} = \frac{12}{2}$$
$$x = 6$$

Divide both sides by 2 to isolate x.

$$5(6) - 4 \overset{?}{=} 3(6) + 8$$

Check the answer.

$$30 - 4 \overset{?}{=} 18 + 8$$

$$26 = 26$$

The answer works.

Example 8 Solve for the variable. Check the answer. $\frac{1}{5}x + 4 = -3 + \frac{6}{5}x$

SOLUTION

$$\frac{1}{5}x + 4 = -3 + \frac{6}{5}x$$

$$5\left(\frac{1}{5}x + 4\right) = 5\left(-3 + \frac{6}{5}x\right)$$

Eliminate the fractions by multiplying both sides by 5.

$$5\left(\frac{1}{5}x\right) + 20 = -15 + 5\left(\frac{6}{5}x\right)$$

Distribute and reduce.

$$x + 20 = -15 + 6x$$

$$\underline{-x \qquad\qquad\quad -x}$$

Combine variable terms by subtracting x from both sides.

$$20 = -15 + 5x$$

Isolate the variable term by adding 15 to both sides.

$$\underline{+15 \quad +15}$$

$$35 = 5x$$

$$\frac{35}{5} = \frac{5x}{5}$$

Isolate the variable by dividing both sides by 5.

$$7 = x$$

$$\frac{1}{5}(7) + 4 \overset{?}{=} -3 + \frac{6}{5}(7)$$

Check the answer.

$$\frac{7}{5} + 4 \overset{?}{=} -3 + \frac{42}{5}$$

$$\frac{7}{5} + \frac{20}{5} \overset{?}{=} -\frac{15}{5} + \frac{42}{5}$$

$$\frac{27}{5} = \frac{27}{5}$$

The answer works.

Example 9 Solve. If the equation has no solution, answer "no solution." If it is an identity, answer "all real numbers."

a. $5(x - 2) = 5x - 10$ 　　　　　　**b.** $4x + 3 = 4x - 5$

SOLUTION 　**a.** $5(x - 2) = 5x - 10$ 　　　　Use the distributive property to multiply.

$$5x - 10 = 5x - 10$$

Move the x-terms to the left.

$$\underline{-5x \qquad -5x}$$

$$-10 = -10$$

This is a true statement.

Because this statement is always true, the equation is an identity. The solution set is all real numbers.

b. 　$4x + 3 = 4x - 5$ 　　　　Move the x-terms to the left.

$$\underline{-4x \qquad -4x}$$

$$3 = -5$$

This is a false statement.

Because this equation is false, there is no solution.

Section **2.4**   Solving and Graphing Linear Inequalities on a Number Line

- **Inequalities** will usually have a set of values that represent all possible solutions.
- **Inequalities are solved** by using the same properties as equations except that we **reverse the inequality symbol when multiplying or dividing** both sides by a negative number.
- When writing using **interval notation,** use parentheses when the endpoint is not included in the interval. Use brackets when there is an "equal to" part and you want to include the endpoint in the interval.
- When **drawing a number line,** use parentheses to indicate that the endpoint is not included in the interval and brackets to indicate the "equal to" part that includes the endpoint of the interval.
- **Whenever infinity or negative infinity** is part of a solution set written in interval notation, you **must use a parenthesis** next to the infinity symbol. The symbol for infinity is ∞.
- **When drawing a number line, use arrowheads** on the end of the line to indicate that the set continues toward ∞ or $-\infty$.
- **Compound inequalities** involve more than one inequality.
- **Steps to Checking the Solution to an Inequality**

  1. Substitute the endpoint into the inequality. Both sides should be equal (not unequal).
  2. Pick a number other than the endpoint from the solution set. Substitute this value in the original inequality. The original inequality should remain true.

Example 10   Solve the following inequality. Check the answer. $4 - 2x < -10$

SOLUTION

$$4 - 2x < -10$$
$$\underline{-4 \qquad\quad -4}$$
$$-2x < -14$$

$$\frac{-2x}{-2} > \frac{-14}{-2}$$ *Reverse the inequality when dividing by a negative number.*
$$x > 7$$

$$4 - 2(7) \overset{?}{=} -10$$ *Check the endpoint for equality.*
$$-10 = -10$$ *The endpoint works.*
$$4 - 2(8) \overset{?}{<} -10$$ *Check the direction of the inequality symbol*
$$4 - 16 \overset{?}{<} -10$$ *using a number greater than 7.*
$$-12 < -10$$ *The direction of the inequality works.*   ■

Example 11   Solve the inequality and write the solution in interval notation and graph it on a number line. $-3x + 1 > -17$

SOLUTION

$$-3x + 1 \geq -17$$
$$\underline{-1 \qquad -1}$$
$$-3x \geq -18$$

$$\frac{-3x}{-3} \leq \frac{-18}{-3}$$ *Reverse the inequality.*
$$x \leq 6$$

$$-3(6) + 1 \overset{?}{=} -17$$ Check the endpoint for equality.

$$-18 + 1 \overset{?}{=} -17$$

$$-17 = -17$$ The endpoint works.

$$-3(0) + 1 \overset{?}{\geq} -17$$ Check the direction of the inequality symbol using

$$0 + 1 \overset{?}{\geq} -17$$ a number less than 6.

$$1 \geq -17$$ The direction of the inequality works.

In interval notation, the solution is $(-\infty, 6]$.

Example 12

Solve the inequality. Graph the solution on a number line. $-4 < 2x - 4 < 16$

SOLUTION

$$-4 < 2x - 4 < 16$$ Add 4 to all sides.

$$\underline{+4 \qquad +4 \quad +4}$$

$$0 < 2x < 20$$

$$\frac{0}{2} < \frac{2x}{2} < \frac{20}{2}$$ Divide all sides by 2.

$$0 < x < 10$$

$$-4 \overset{?}{=} 2(0) - 4$$ Check the left endpoint using $x = 0$.

$$-4 = -4$$ This endpoint works.

$$2(10) - 4 \overset{?}{=} 16$$ Check the right endpoint using $x = 10$.

$$16 = 16$$ This endpoint works.

$$-4 \overset{?}{<} 2(3) - 4 \overset{?}{<} 16$$ Check the direction of the inequality symbols by

$$-4 \overset{?}{<} 6 - 4 \overset{?}{<} 16$$ using a number between 0 and 10.

$$-4 < 2 < 16$$ The direction of the inequality symbols works.

Chapter Review Exercises

2

For Exercises 1 and 2,

a. Determine whether or not the given values of the variables are solutions to the equations.

b. Explain what the values mean in the problem situation.

1. $D = 75t$, where D is the distance traveled in miles when driving for t hours; $t = 3.5$ and $D = 262.5$. **[2.1]**

2. $F = 11.5L$, where F is the origination fee in dollars paid for a loan of L thousand dollars; $F = 6900$ and $L = 600$. **[2.1]**

For Exercises 3 and 4, determine whether or not the given value(s) of the variable(s) are solutions to the equations.

3. $-2x + 4y = -8$; $x = -2$ and $y = 3$ **[2.1]**

4. $y = -3x + 5$; $x = -3$ and $y = 14$ **[2.1]**

For Exercises 5 and 6, use the following information.

The amount of profit a company makes is found by subtracting the company's costs from its revenue. This relationship can be written as the following equation:

$$P = R - C$$

where P is the profit in dollars, R is the revenue in dollars, and C is the cost in dollars for the company. Note: Revenue is the amount of money a company brings in from sales.

5. If a company has monthly revenue of $49,000 and monthly costs of $26,000, what is the profit?   [2.1]

6. If a company has monthly revenue of $225,000 and monthly costs of $186,000, what is the profit?   [2.1]

For Exercises 7 through 14, solve for the variable. Check the answer.

7. $x - 3 = -9$ [2.1]

8. $p - 16 = -9$ [2.1]

9. $-8 = a + 9$ [2.1]

10. $-16 = b + 7$ [2.1]

11. $k - \dfrac{1}{2} = \dfrac{3}{2}$ [2.1]

12. $\dfrac{-2}{5} + x = \dfrac{4}{5}$ [2.1]

13. $y - 9.8 = 4.6$ [2.1]

14. $0.02 + h = 1.04$ [2.1]

For Exercises 15 through 18, solve the given literal equation for the indicated variable.

15. $2p + q = 9$ for q [2.1]

16. $x - y = 2$ for x [2.1]

17. $8x - 24y = 48$ for y [2.2]

18. $3p - 5q = -30$ for p [2.2]

For Exercises 19 through 28, solve the equation for the variable. Check the answer. Round to the hundredths place, if necessary.

19. $7y = 84$ [2.2]

20. $4x = -64$ [2.2]

21. $-a = 7$ [2.2]

22. $-8 = -x$ [2.2]

23. $-2b = -22$ [2.2]

24. $-5y = 35$ [2.2]

25. $\dfrac{2}{3}x = -16$ [2.2]

26. $\dfrac{-3}{4}n = -9$ [2.2]

27. $6.2t = -8.4$ [2.2]

28. $-0.5k = -16.5$ [2.2]

29. The average short-haul jet airplane (such as a Boeing 737) can seat 126 people. The number of these airplanes needed to transport a group of people can be calculated by using the formula

$$J = \dfrac{P}{126}$$

where J is the number of airplanes needed to transport a group of P people.   [2.2]

   a. How many airplanes are needed to transport 520 people?

   b. If an airline carrier has 15 planes, how many people can the carrier transport at a time?

30. Devora works as a medical assistant and makes $14 per hour after taxes. Devora can calculate her monthly salary using the equation

$$S = 14h$$

where S is the monthly salary in dollars that Devora makes if she works h hours that month.   [2.2]

   a. Find Devora's monthly salary if she works 140 hours.

   b. How many hours does Devora have to work a month to make $2100 a month?

   c. How many hours does Devora have to work a month if she wants to earn only $1330 a month?

For Exercises 31 through 38, solve the equation. Check the answer.

31. $6x - 9 = -63$ [2.2]

32. $5y - 17 = 33$ [2.2]

33. $-2a + 9 = -5$ [2.2]

34. $-8k - 19 = 5$ [2.2]

35. $\dfrac{x}{2} - 1 = -11$ [2.2]

36. $\dfrac{-x}{3} + 2 = -4$ [2.2]

37. $-8.6 - 1.2x = 10.6$ [2.2]

38. $0.25y - 1 = -7$ [2.2]

For Exercises 39 through 46, define variables and translate each sentence into an equation. Then solve that equation and check the answer.

39. Nine times a number is 76.   [2.2]

40. 12 is equal to the product of a number and -2.   [2.2]

41. The sum of twice a number and 16 is -44.   [2.2]

42. The sum of one-half a number and 4 is -18.   [2.2]

43. The quotient of a number and 4 is 0.25.   [2.2]

44. The quotient of a number and -3 is 0.75.   [2.2]

45. The difference of 8 and 3 times a number is 17. **[2.2]**

46. Nine less than twice a number is 7. **[2.2]**

For Exercises 47 through 52, solve the literal equations for the indicated variable.

47. Solve $D = cma$ for m. **[2.2]**

48. Solve $V = lwh$ for h. **[2.2]**

49. Solve $C = \pi \cdot d$ for d. **[2.2]**

50. Solve $A = \frac{1}{2}b \cdot h$ for h. **[2.2]**

51. Solve $9x - 3y = -12$ for y. **[2.2]**

52. Solve $-8x + 4y = -24$ for y. **[2.2]**

For Exercises 53 and 54, translate each sentence and solve. Check the answer.

53. The sum of twice a number and 1 is equal to the difference between three times the number and 4. **[2.2]**

54. The sum of half a number and ten is equal to the difference between that number and 4. **[2.2]**

For Exercises 55 through 62, solve each equation. Check the answer. If the equation is an identity, write the answer as "All real numbers." If there is no solution, write, "No solution."

55. $4x - 8 = -3x + 20$ **[2.3]**

56. $9y + 12 = 7y + 6$ **[2.3]**

57. $5(a + 5) = 12a - 13$ **[2.3]**

58. $11 + 7x + 7 = 5x - 2$ **[2.3]**

59. $4k + 1 = -5k + 3(3k - 1)$ **[2.3]**

60. $9h - 7(h + 1) = 2h + 9$ **[2.3]**

61. $-5x + 3 = 13 - 5(x + 2)$ **[2.3]**

62. $7y - 10 + 2(-3y + 2) = y - 6$ **[2.3]**

63. Given the following triangle, find the measure of each angle. **[2.3]**

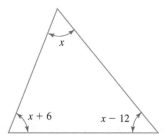

64. Given the following triangle, find the measure of each angle. **[2.3]**

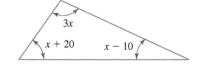

For Exercises 65 through 78, solve each inequality. Check the answer. Write the solution set in each of the following ways: using inequality symbols, using interval notation, and graphing the solution on a number line.

65. $4x + 1 > 49$ **[2.4]**

66. $3x - 2 \le 19$ **[2.4]**

67. $-x \le 7$ **[2.4]**

68. $-y \ge 3$ **[2.4]**

69. $-5y + 1 \ge -16$ **[2.4]**

70. $-6x - 7 < -3$ **[2.4]**

71. $\frac{-1}{4}y + 3 \le -2$ **[2.4]**

72. $4 - \frac{2}{5}t > -8$ **[2.4]**

73. $-3x - 3 < -2x + 9$ **[2.4]**

74. $-8y - 1 > -3y + 9$ **[2.4]**

75. $-3 < 2x + 3 < 11$ **[2.4]**

76. $-1 < 5x - 6 < 24$ **[2.4]**

77. $-2 < \frac{x}{3} < 9$ **[2.4]**

78. $-8 < \frac{y}{2} + 11 < -5$ **[2.4]**

For Exercises 79 through 82, given the interval form of an inequality, graph the solution set on a number line. Then rewrite using inequality notation.

79. $[-3, \infty)$ **[2.4]**

80. $(5, \infty)$ **[2.4]**

81. $(-\infty, 6)$ **[2.4]**

82. $(-\infty, -12]$ **[2.4]**

For Exercises 83 and 84, rewrite the inequality with the variable on the left side.

83. $-6 > x$ **[2.4]**

84. $0 \le y$ **[2.4]**

85. Solve the inequality **[2.4]**

$$80n - 2400 > 0$$

where n is the number of stained-glass windows that Kiano must sell to make a profit. Write the solution as a complete sentence.

86. Solve the inequality **[2.4]**

$$32.49d + 21.65 \le 119.12$$

where d is the number of days Jessie can rent a car if she wants to spend only up to \$119.12. Write the solution as a complete sentence.

87. Karyn's wireless carrier charges $7.50 per month for the first 200 texts and $0.10 per text beyond 200. Let t be the number of texts Karyn goes over her 200 texts allowed in a month. [2.4]

   a. Write an inequality to show that Karyn must keep her monthly texting bill to at most $10. (This is within her budget.)

   b. Solve the inequality from part a. Write the solution in a complete sentence.

88. Trey purchases a flat-screen TV at a local electronics store. The store tells him that the minimum delivery charge is $50.00 plus $1.50 per mile. Let m be the number of miles that Trey lives from the store. [2.4]

   a. Write an inequality to show that Trey must keep his shipping charge to at most $65. (This is within his budget.)

   b. Solve the inequality from part a. Write the solution in a complete sentence.

Chapter Test

2

The following chapter test should take approximately one hour to complete. Read each question carefully. Show all of your work.

1. Is $b = -2$ a solution of $5b + 8 = 2$?

2. Is $t = 4.2$ and $D = 294$ a solution to $D = 70t$, where D is the distance traveled in miles when driving for t hours?

3. Solve and check the answer: $-5 + x = -17$

4. Solve the literal equation for the variable c:
   $P = a + b + c$

5. Use the equation $P = R - C$, where P represents the profit, R represents the revenue, and C is the cost. If a company has monthly revenue of $250,000 and monthly costs of $88,000, what is the profit?

6. Solve and check the answer: $-5w = 450$

7. Solve and check the answer: $-4p + 25 = -119$

8. Solve and check the answer: $\frac{x}{3} + 7 = -5$

9. Solve and check the answer. If the equation is an identity, write the answer as "All real numbers." If there is no solution, write, "No solution."
   $4(x + 4) - 5 = 4x + 11$

10. Solve and check the answer. If the equation is an identity, write the answer as "All real numbers." If there is no solution, write, "No solution."
    $3x + 20 = 20 + 3(x - 5)$

11. Define your variables and translate the problem into an equation. Solve the equation and check the answer. The perimeter of a rectangular building lot is 330 feet. The width of the lot is 40 feet. Find the length of the lot.

12. Solve the literal equation for the variable x. $y = mx + b$.

13. Translate the sentence into an equation and solve. The sum of four times a number and 7 is negative seventeen.

14. Solve the equation and check the answer:
    $10x - 15 = 7x - 9$

15. Solve the equation and check the answer:
    $4x + 3 = 4(x - 1) + 7$

16. A triangle has angles that measure x, $11x$, and $6x$ degrees. Find the measure of each angle of the triangle.

17. Rewrite the inequality with the variable on the left side. $-16 \leq x$

18. Solve the inequality. Graph the solution set on a number line. $2x + 1 > 4x - 3$

19. Solve the inequality. $5 \leq 2x - 7 \leq 15$

20. Aiden works for a large retailer and earns $10.25 per hour. Let h be the number of hours Aiden works per week.

   a. Write an inequality that shows that Aiden needs to earn more than $287.00 a week to meet his expenses.

   b. Solve the inequality from part a, and write the solution set using a complete sentence.

Chapter 2 Projects

What Is That Pattern?

Written Project

One or more people

a. Look at the pattern in the following table.

$n = 1$	***
$n = 2$	*****
$n = 3$	*******
$n = 4$	*********
$n = 5$	***********
$n = 6$	
$n = 7$	

1. Using the pattern you observe, fill in the last two rows of the table, continuing the pattern.
2. Let n represent the row number. Write a general expression for the number of asterisks in the table in terms of n.
3. Suppose there are 107 asterisks in a row. In what row number does that occur? *Hint:* Find n using the expression you found in step 2.

b. Look at the pattern in the following table.

$n = 1$	**
$n = 2$	*****
$n = 3$	********
$n = 4$	***********
$n = 5$	
$n = 6$	
$n = 7$	

1. Using the pattern you observe, fill in the last three rows of the table, continuing the pattern.
2. Let n represent the row number. Write a general expression for the number of asterisks in the table in terms of n.
3. Suppose there are 107 asterisks in a row. In what row number does that occur? *Hint:* Find n using the expression you found in step 2.

Men's Boxing Weight Classes at the Summer Olympics

Research Project

One or more people

What you will need

- Find data for this situation. You may use data from online, a magazine, or a newspaper.

In this project, you will search online for the weight classes for men's Olympic boxing. Using that information, you will rewrite each weight class as an inequality.

1. Search online for a list of the weight classes for men's boxing at the Olympics. Print out the list, and turn it in with your report.
2. Rewrite each weight class as an inequality. Make sure that you consider the endpoints of each weight class as part of the inequality.
3. List all weight classes in which a 65-kg man could participate.

Write a Review of a Section for Presentation

Research Project

One or more people

What you will need

- This presentation may be done in class or as an online video.
- If it is done as a video, post it on a Website where it may be easily viewed by the class.
- You might want to use homework or other review problems from the book.
- Make it creative and fun.

Create a five-minute review presentation of one section from Chapter 2. The format of the presentation can be a poster presentation, a blackboard presentation from notes, an online video, or a game format (e.g., Math Jeopardy). The presentation should include the following:

a. Any important formulas in the chapter.

b. Important skills in the chapter, backed up by examples.

c. Explanation of terms used. For example, what is modeling?

d. Common mistakes and how to avoid them.

Linear Equations

Distributive Property	Use when an equation contains grouping symbols.	$2(x + 4) = 3x - 5$	Section 1.3
Addition and Subtraction Properties of Equality	Use to isolate a term.	$x + 7 = 20$	Section 2.1
Multiplication and Division Properties of Equality	Use to isolate a variable.	$5x = 13$	Section 2.2

1. Write in exponential form: $\dfrac{9}{4} \cdot \dfrac{9}{4} \cdot \dfrac{9}{4} \cdot \dfrac{9}{4} \cdot \dfrac{9}{4} \cdot \dfrac{9}{4}$

2. Write in expanded form: $(-4)^3$

3. Find the value without a calculator: $(-1)^5$

4. Write using standard notation: 3.045×10^8

5. Underline or circle the terms, and simplify using the order-of-operations agreement:
$$\dfrac{84}{(10 - 6)} \cdot 3 - 2^2 - (-5) + 20 \div 4 \cdot (-3)$$

6. Simplify the expression using the order-of-operations agreement: $18 \div (-2) + \left|6 - 7 \cdot (-2)\right| + (-3)^2$

7. Identify the property (commutative, associative, or distributive) used to rewrite the statement:
$$(-16) + (3 - 7) = (3 - 7) + (-16)$$

8. Define the variables: A local youth soccer club is selling candy bars. The amount of money (revenue) the club makes depends on the number of candy bars sold.

9. Translate the sentence into a variable expression: Seven less than 8 times a number.

10. Convert 95 feet to meters. There is 0.3048 meter in 1 foot.

11. Evaluate the expression for the given value of the variable: $\dfrac{-x}{3} + 7x$ for $x = -6$.

12. Lisa has a box of 50 dog biscuits she is going to divide up between her two dogs, Scout and Shadow. Fill in the input-output table to generate an expression for the problem situation.

Number of Biscuits for Scout	Number of Biscuits for Shadow
0	
5	
10	
15	
n	

13. Simplify: $7xy - 3x^2 + 6x - 9x^2 + 8xy - x$

14. Simplify: $6x - (3x - 5) + 8$

15. Simplify: $(3b - c) - (-b + 7c)$

16. Write the coordinates of each ordered pair shown on the graph.

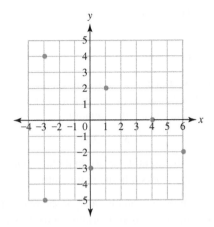

17. Graph the ordered pairs on the same set of axes:
$(5, 6)(-1, -2)(7, -4)(-3, -3)(0, 4)(-1, 0)$

18. The following table gives the world record progression for the men's long jump. Use the given data to create a scatterplot. Clearly label and scale the axes.

Year	Distance Traveled in Meters (Athlete's Name in Parentheses)
1960	8.21 m (Ralph Boston, USA)
1961	8.24 m (Ralph Boston, USA)
1961	8.28 m (Ralph Boston, USA)
1962	8.31 m (Igor Ter-Ovanesyan, URS)
1964	8.31 m (Ralph Boston, USA)
1964	8.34 m (Ralph Boston, USA)
1965	8.34 m (Ralph Boston, USA)
1967	8.35 m (Igor Ter-Ovanesyan, URS)
1968	8.90 m (Bob Beamon, USA)
1991	8.95 m (Mike Powell, USA)

Source: www.track-and-field-jumpers.com.
Prior to 1960 the world record was 8.13 m by Jesse Owens of the United States.

19. Are the values of the variables solutions to the equation? $4x - 7y = -6$: $x = -1.5$ and $y = 0$

20. Solve: $-2 + y = -7$

21. Solve: $x - \dfrac{1}{3} = \dfrac{5}{6}$

22. Solve: $-0.051 + n = 4.006$

23. Solve for the indicated value of the variable:
$3x - 5y = -30$ for y

24. Solve: $-7x = -21$

25. Solve: $\frac{2}{3}n = -8$

26. Solve: $-5z = 7.95$

27. Corinthia works as a dental assistant and makes $12 per hour after taxes. Corinthia can calculate her monthly salary using the equation:

$$S = 12h$$

where S is the monthly salary in dollars that Corinthia makes if she works h hours that month.

  a. Find Corinthia's monthly salary if she works 120 hours.
  b. How many hours does Corinthia have to work a month to make $1680 a month?
  c. How many hours does Corinthia have to work a month if she wants to earn only $1200 a month?

28. Solve: $8y - 11 = 21$

29. Solve: $\frac{x}{5} - 4 = -9$

30. Solve: $-1.2 + 3.7x = 15.45$

31. Translate and solve: The sum of twice a number and 20 is 6.

32. Solve: $P = rgm$ for m.

33. Solve: $6x - 3y = -30$ for y.

34. Translate and solve: The sum of twice a number and 8 is equal to the difference between four times the number and 18.

35. Solve: $8y + 4 = 12y + 20$

36. Solve: $7n + 8 = -3n + 2(4n - 12)$

37. Solve: $5w - 6 + 3(-4w + 9) = w + 5$

38. Given the following triangle, find the measure of each angle.

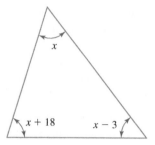

39. Solve the inequality: $6x + 1 > 49$

40. Solve the inequality: $\frac{-1}{7}r + 5 \le 9$

41. Solve the inequality: $14 < 3x + 5 < 26$

42. Solve the inequality: $10 - \frac{3}{8}t > -4$

43. Write a compound inequality for the statement: The maximum enrollment in an English class on a college campus is 25. The class will be canceled if it does not have at least 15 students in it.

44. Write a compound inequality for the statement. At a state university, upper-division courses are labeled beginning with 200 to less than 400.

Linear Equations with Two Variables

Robert Glusic/Jupiterimages

The relationship between the sighting of a flash of lightning and the distance the lightning is away from the observer can be represented by a linear equation. After seeing the lightning flash, count the seconds until you hear the bang of thunder. Divide this value by 5. The result will give an estimate of how many miles the lightning is away from you.

3.1 # Graphing Equations with Two Variables

LEARNING OBJECTIVES

- Use tables to represent ordered pairs and data.
- Graph equations by plotting points.
- Graph nonlinear equations by plotting points.
- Graph vertical and horizontal lines.

Skill Connection

Input-Output Tables

In Section 1.2, we learned that we put the input in the left column of the table and the output in the right column of the table. Recall that the input is the data entering a problem, and the output is the value being generated by the problem.

Using Tables to Represent Ordered Pairs and Data

Many of the equations and problems we have studied so far have involved more than one variable. When the value of the input variable changes, the output value may change as well. In many problems, we are actually interested in more than one possible situation at a time. For example, if you work a part-time job, you might be interested in how much money (output) you will earn if you work different numbers of hours per week (input). A nutritionist might be interested in how different numbers of calories (input) affect a person's weight gain or loss (output).

In Chapter 1, we studied input-output tables relying on one variable, the input. We are now going to assign the output a variable as well because its value depends on the input. Recall that we sometimes call the input the *independent variable* and the output the *dependent variable*. We will now create input-output tables with two variables.

If Robin earns $9.50 per hour at her job as a receptionist, we could represent her weekly pay as

$$P = 9.50h$$

where P is the weekly pay in dollars when Robin works h hours per week. Because Robin may work a different number of hours each week, she may also earn a different amount of money each week. In this situation, we would say that Robin's pay depends on how many hours she works. Therefore, P would be the dependent variable, and h would be the independent variable.

We can list some possibilities in a table of values such as the following.

h = Hours worked	P = Weekly pay (dollars)
1	9.50
5	47.50
20	190.00
30	285.00
40	380.00

We can easily fill a table such as this one by evaluating the given equation for several values of the input variable. In this case, we used the number of hours given in the table and calculated Robin's weekly pay using the given equation.

Example 1 — Filling a table with data

Maria's monthly salary from her sales job includes $700 per month in base pay and 3% commission on all sales she makes. We can calculate Maria's monthly salary using the equation

$$M = 700 + 0.03s$$

where M is Maria's monthly salary in dollars when she makes s dollars in sales during the month. Use this equation to fill the following table with possible sales and salaries. Fill in the last two rows with any sales amounts you think are reasonable.

s = Sales made (dollars)	M = Monthly salary (dollars)
0	
1000	
5000	
10,000	
20,000	

SOLUTION

We are given some sales values to start with, so we use the equation to calculate the monthly salary for the given sales amounts. In the last two rows, we will put any sales amounts that we think are reasonable for Maria in a month and then calculate the monthly salary using the equation.

s = Sales made (dollars)	M = Monthly salary (dollars)	Using the equation to find M
0	700	$M = 700 + 0.03(0)$ $M = 700$
1000	730	$M = 700 + 0.03(1000)$ $M = 730$
5000	850	$M = 700 + 0.03(5000)$ $M = 850$
10,000	1000	$M = 700 + 0.03(10,000)$ $M = 1000$
20,000	1300	$M = 700 + 0.03(20,000)$ $M = 1300$
50,000	2200	$M = 700 + 0.03(50,000)$ $M = 2200$
100,000	3700	$M = 700 + 0.03(100,000)$ $M = 3700$

The last two rows could have been filled with any sales amounts. The ones listed were just two possibilities.

PRACTICE PROBLEM FOR EXAMPLE 1

The Rocky Mountain White Water Rafting Company keeps track of costs for the rafting season using the equation

$$C = 50r + 4000$$

where C is the cost in dollars for the rafting season when r riders take a rafting trip during the season. Use this equation to fill the following table with possible riders and costs. Fill in the last two rows with other reasonable values for the number of riders.

r = riders	C = Costs (dollars)
0	
50	
100	
150	
200	

Graphing Equations by Plotting Points

Problems can be presented with verbal statements, equations, or data tables. Often, we would like to represent these problems visually using a graph. It is often easier to see trends in data by looking at a graph than by looking at a table or equation. This ability to gain information quickly from visual representations is what makes graphing important in mathematics.

We will use the rectangular coordinate system first introduced in Section 1.4 to graph the information given by an equation or table of data. When considering a table of data, we have points, or coordinates, that can be plotted on a graph. Each table or equation that we have looked at so far has had an input and an output that are traditionally the x and y coordinates on the graph.

$$(\text{input, output}) = (x, y)$$

If we look at the equation $P = 9.50h$ and the table that represented Robin's weekly pay and hours worked, we have an input of hours worked and an output of weekly pay. The variable h is the input variable (sometimes called the independent variable). It will take place of the x in each coordinate. The variable P is the output variable (sometimes called the dependent variable). It will take place of the y in each coordinate. The table of data can be used to write coordinates for points on the graph.

h = Hours worked	P = Weekly pay (dollars)	Points on the graph (h, P)
1	9.50	(1, 9.50)
5	47.50	(5, 47.50)
20	190.00	(20, 190.00)
30	285.00	(30, 285.00)
40	380.00	(40, 380.00)

In Section 1.4, we learned that the order used in the coordinates is important. The input must be the first part of the coordinate, and the output is always the second part. The input of each coordinate represents the horizontal position, and the output of each coordinate represents the vertical position of the point. These points can now be plotted on a graph using the rectangular coordinate plane. Connect these points with a smooth curve. The line represents many more of the possible combinations of hours worked and the associated weekly pay.

Steps to Sketch a Graph by Plotting Points

1. Create a table of points using the equation.
2. Plot the points on a set of axes. Clearly label and scale the axes.
3. Connect the points with a smooth curve.

Example 2   Creating a graph given a table

Use the table to write coordinates for points and graph them. Connect the points with a smooth curve. The equation is $y = 2x + 3$.

x	$y = 2x + 3$	(x, y)
-2	-1	
-1	1	
0	3	
1	5	
2	7	

SOLUTION

In this case, we are given an equation and a table already filled in with x- and y-values. Complete the table by writing coordinates using the given values. Then plot the points on a graph and connect them with a smooth curve.

x	$y = 2x + 3$	(x, y)
-2	-1	$(-2, -1)$
-1	1	$(-1, 1)$
0	3	$(0, 3)$
1	5	$(1, 5)$
2	7	$(2, 7)$

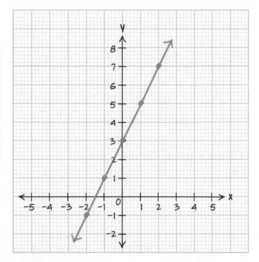

All these points lie on a straight line.

PRACTICE PROBLEM FOR EXAMPLE 2

Use the table to write coordinates for points and graph them. Connect the points with a smooth curve. The equation is $y = -3x + 6$.

x	$y = -3x + 6$	(x, y)
-2	12	
-1	9	
0	6	
1	3	
2	0	

When building a table of points from an equation, we can choose any points we want. In most situations, it is best to pick at least one negative number, zero, and at least one positive number.

Example 3   Generating a table to create a graph

Use the equation $y = x - 2$ to create a table of points, and graph them. Connect the points with a smooth curve.

x	$y = x - 2$	(x, y)

SOLUTION

To fill in the table, select values for x and calculate y. We can choose any values for x. Select a few negative values, zero, and a few positive values that are easy to work with.

x	$y = x - 2$	(x, y)
-4	-6	$(-4, -6)$
-2	-4	$(-2, -4)$
0	-2	$(0, -2)$
2	0	$(2, 0)$
4	2	$(4, 2)$

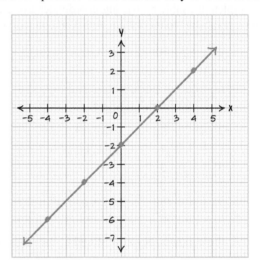

All these points lie on a straight line.

Skill Connection

Using graph paper

In algebra, we use graph paper to graph equations because we can draw a very accurate graph on it. Graph paper is readily available online.

PRACTICE PROBLEM FOR EXAMPLE 3

Use the equation $y = 3x - 6$ to create a table of points, and graph them. Connect the points with a smooth curve.

Example 4   Graphing Camille's weekly pay

Camille earns $10 per hour at her job and can represent her weekly pay with the equation $P = 10h$, where P is Camille's weekly pay in dollars when she works h hours.

a. Create a table of points that make sense in this situation.

b. Graph the points, and connect the points with a smooth curve.

SOLUTION

a. The number of hours that Camille works is our input, so h is the independent variable and will go on the horizontal axis. The weekly pay in dollars is the output, so P is the dependent variable and will go on the vertical axis. Select different numbers of hours for Camille to work during a week and calculate the different weekly pay she would earn from each of these hours.

h	$P = 10h$	(h, P)
10	100	$(10, 100)$
15	150	$(15, 150)$
20	200	$(20, 200)$
30	300	$(30, 300)$
40	400	$(40, 400)$

b. Negative numbers of hours or a negative amount of pay does not make sense, so we will graph only positive values on both axes. In this situation, think about the scale that we should use on the axes. The horizontal axis should include values that go from zero to about 50, so we use a scale of 5. The vertical axis should include values from zero to about 500, so we use a scale of 50. These scales will make sure we include all the values we found in the table. Label the axes with what each variable represents in the situation.

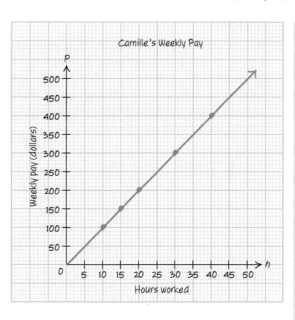

Camille's Weekly Pay

The *x*-axis is labeled *h* for hours worked. The *y*-axis is labeled *P* for weekly pay in dollars.

All the points on this line represent possible hours that Camille might work in a week and the weekly pay she would earn. The table shows only a few specific examples, but the graph makes visible many more possibilities. Notice that the graph also shows the overall trend of Camille's pay increasing when she works more hours in a week.

PRACTICE PROBLEM FOR EXAMPLE 4

Over the course of an 8-week weight-loss diet, Philip's weight could be estimated by using the equation

$$W = 210 - 5n$$

where *W* is Philip's weight in pounds after *n* weeks on the diet.

a. Create a table of points that make sense in this situation.

b. Graph the points, and connect the points with a smooth curve.

All of the equations above graphed as straight lines. These graphs are called *linear*. An equation that generates a graph that is not a straight line is said to be *nonlinear*.

Graphing Nonlinear Equations by Plotting Points

When working with more complicated equations, we still graph them by creating a table of points, plotting the points, and connecting the points with a smooth curve. In these cases, plot additional points on the graph to be certain about the shape of the curve.

| Example 5 | Creating a nonlinear graph using a table |

Use each equation to create a table of points and graph. Connect the points with a smooth curve.

a. $y = x^2 + 3$

b. $y = |x|$

Connecting the Concepts

How many values make a good display?

In Section 1.4, we discussed scaling the axes of graphs. We generally place between 5 and 20 tick marks on each axis. Any more than 20 is too much detail to look at. Fewer than 5 may not give enough detail. Therefore, adjust the scale so that neither too many nor too few values sit on an axis. Be sure that all the input and output values will be included in the graph.

Connecting the Concepts

How many points do we graph?

In Examples 2 through 4, we plotted five points for each equation. For more complicated equations, such as those involving an x^2 or $|x|$ term, graph nine or more points. These additional points will help to make the graph more accurate.

SOLUTION

a. This equation is more complicated than previous ones because it includes a term with x^2. To make the graph more accurate, we will find more points to plot for the graph. Begin by building a table of points using a few positive and negative x-values, as well as $x = 0$. Although we can pick any input values, we will select x-values between -4 and 4 to make graphing easier. Then, we plot the points and connect them with a smooth curve.

x	$y = x^2 + 3$	(x, y)
-4	19	$(-4, 19)$
-3	12	$(-3, 12)$
-2	7	$(-2, 7)$
-1	4	$(-1, 4)$
0	3	$(0, 3)$
1	4	$(1, 4)$
2	7	$(2, 7)$
3	12	$(3, 12)$
4	19	$(4, 19)$

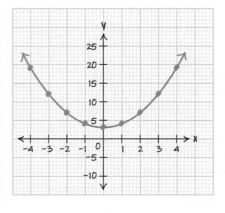

b. This equation includes an absolute value, so we generate a table of more points to plot for the graph. We build a table of points using some positive and negative x-values, as well as $x = 0$.

x	$y = |x|$	(x, y)
-5	5	$(-5, 5)$
-4	4	$(-4, 4)$
-3	3	$(-3, 3)$
-2	2	$(-2, 2)$
-1	1	$(-1, 1)$
0	0	$(0, 0)$
1	1	$(1, 1)$
2	2	$(2, 2)$
3	3	$(3, 3)$
4	4	$(4, 4)$
5	5	$(5, 5)$

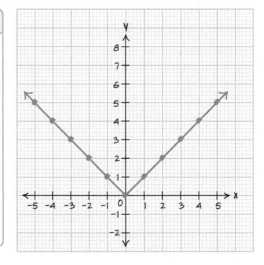

PRACTICE PROBLEM FOR EXAMPLE 5

Use each equation to create a table of points and graph. Connect the points with a smooth curve.

a. $y = x^2 - 5$

b. $y = |x + 4|$

What's That Mean?

Horizontal and Vertical

The word *horizontal* has the word *horizon* in it. This will help you remember that a horizontal line opens left and right, like the horizon. A vertical line opens straight up and down.

Vertical and Horizontal Lines

All of the equations that we have graphed in this section have two variables. To create a graph for an equation with one variable, we generate a table of points. However, the table of points will be very simple. If $y = 5$ is the equation, then y will always be 5 no matter what value x is. Equations that have only one variable will result in horizontal or vertical lines.

DEFINITIONS

Vertical Line   The graph of an equation of the form $x = c$, where c is a real number, is a **vertical line.**

Horizontal Line   The graph of an equation of the form $y = b$, where b is a real number, is a **horizontal line.**

Example 6   Graphing horizontal and vertical lines

Use each equation to create a table of points and graph. Connect the points with a smooth curve.

a. $y = 5$

b. $x = -2$

SOLUTION

a. The value of y is constantly 5, so the values for x do not affect y. For any values of x selected, the value of y will always equal 5.

x	$y = 5$	(x, y)
-3	5	$(-3, 5)$
-1	5	$(-1, 5)$
0	5	$(0, 5)$
1	5	$(1, 5)$
3	5	$(3, 5)$

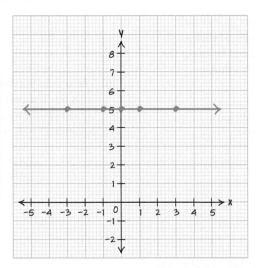

b. The value of x is always -2, so the values for y do not affect the value of x. Therefore, we can choose any values of y we want, and x will equal -2.

$x = -2$	y	(x, y)
-2	-3	$(-2, -3)$
-2	-1	$(-2, -1)$
-2	1	$(-2, 1)$
-2	2	$(-2, 2)$
-2	4	$(-2, 4)$

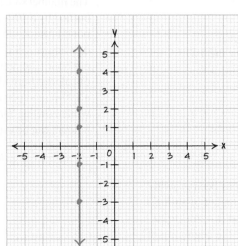

3.1 Exercises

For Exercises 1 through 8, fill in the given table. Complete the last two rows with values that are reasonable in the context of the given situation.

1. Martina earns a base salary of $300 per month and 5% commission on all sales she makes. Martina's monthly pay in dollars can be calculated by using the equation $P = 0.05s + 300$ if she sells s dollars of merchandise.

s = Sales (dollars)	P = Monthly pay (dollars)
0	
1000	
8000	

2. Maizie earns a base salary of $250 per month and 6% commission on all sales she makes. Maizie's monthly pay in dollars can be calculated by using the equation $P = 0.06s + 250$ if she sells s dollars of merchandise.

s = Sales (dollars)	P = Monthly pay (dollars)
0	
2000	
6000	

3. The total number of customers who visit a local sports equipment store can be estimated by using the equation $C = 8h + 2$, where h is the number of hours after opening for the day.

h = Hours since opening	C = Number of customers for the day
0	
1	
3	

4. The number of animals at the shelter has been growing since the beginning of the year. The number of animals can be calculated by using the equation $A = 4w + 20$, where w is the number of weeks since the beginning of the year.

w = Weeks since the beginning of the year	A = Animals in the shelter
0	
2	
6	

5. The cost in dollars to purchase one 2×4 stud is $3.50. The cost for framing a wall can be calculated by using the equation $C = 3.5n$ when n studs are purchased.

n = Number of studs purchased	C = Cost (dollars)
4	
6	
8	

6. The cost to purchase one plant in a 2-gallon container is $8.50. The cost to purchase plants in 2-gallon containers for a garden can be calculated by using the equation $C = 8.5n$ when n plants are purchased.

n = Number of plants purchased	C = Cost (dollars)
2	
4	
8	

7. The number of calories burned by a 190-pound person while bowling is 259 calories per hour. The number of calories burned by a 190-pound person while bowling for h hours can be estimated by the equation $C = 259h$.

© iStockphoto.com/krausphoto

h = Hours of bowling	C = Calories burned
1	
2	
3	

8. The number of calories burned by a 190-pound person while bicycling is 406 per hour. The number of calories burned by a 190-pound person while bicycling with a moderate effort for h hours can be estimated by the equation $C = 406h$.

h = Hours of bicycling	C = Calories burned
1	
2	
3	

For Exercises 9 through 16, graph the given set of points using graph paper. Clearly label and scale the axes. Connect the points with a smooth curve.

9. Graph the points in the table from Exercise 1, and connect them with a smooth curve.

10. Graph the points in the table from Exercise 2, and connect them with a smooth curve.

11. Graph the points in the table from Exercise 3, and connect them with a smooth curve.

12. Graph the points in the table from Exercise 4, and connect them with a smooth curve.

13. Graph the points in the table from Exercise 5, and connect them with a smooth curve.

14. Graph the points in the table from Exercise 6, and connect them with a smooth curve.

15. Graph the points in the table from Exercise 7, and connect them with a smooth curve.

16. Graph the points in the table from Exercise 8, and connect them with a smooth curve.

For Exercises 17 through 24, fill in the given table using the equation. Graph the points. Connect the points with a smooth curve. Clearly label and scale the axes. Determine whether the graph is linear or nonlinear.

17.

t	$P = -8t + 17$
-4	
-2	
0	
2	
4	

18.

n	$C = 42n - 250$
-100	
-50	
0	
50	
100	

19.

x	$y = \lvert x - 2 \rvert$
-6	
-3	
0	
2	
3	
6	

20.

x	$y = \lvert 5 - x \rvert$
-16	
-8	
0	
5	
8	
16	

21.

s	$R = s^2 + 7$
-2	
-1	
0	
1	
2	

22.

s	$V = 3s^2$
-2	
-1	
0	
1	
2	

23.

x	$y = -2x^2 + 3$
-2	
-1	
0	
1	
2	

24.

x	$y = -x^2 + 1$
-2	
-1	
0	
1	
2	

For Exercises 25 through 42, use the given equation to create a table of five or more points and graph them. Connect the points with a smooth curve. Clearly label and scale the axes. Determine whether the graph is linear or nonlinear.

25. $y = 2x - 8$

26. $y = 3x - 9$

27. $y = 0.5x + 3$

28. $y = 0.25x + 1$

29. $y = -2x + 10$

30. $y = -5x + 15$

31. $y = -0.4x + 2$

32. $y = -0.75x + 4$

33. $y = 3x$

34. $y = 5x$

35. $y = -3x$

36. $y = -4x$

37. $y = \frac{1}{2}x + 3$

38. $y = \frac{1}{2}x - 4$

39. $y = \frac{2}{3}x - 5$

40. $y = \frac{3}{4}x + 1$

41. $y = -\frac{1}{5}x - 2$

42. $y = -\frac{1}{3}x + 4$

For Exercises 43 through 48, use the given information to answer the question.

43. When lightning strikes, the time that it will take to hear thunder depends on the distance of the lightning strike from a location. The "flash to bang" rule says that the time delay is 5 seconds per mile. The time delay can be estimated by the equation $T = 5d$, where T is the time delay in seconds when lightning strikes d miles away. Create a table of points that make sense in this situation, and graph them. Connect the points with a smooth curve.

44. The average American uses about 90 gallons of water per day. The amount of water the average person will use during d days can be estimated by using the equation $G = 90d$, where G is the total number of gallons of water the average person uses during d days. Create a table of points that make sense in this situation, and graph them. Connect the points with a smooth curve.

45. The outside temperature can be estimated by using the equation $T = 75 - 3h$, where T is the outside temperature in degrees Fahrenheit h hours after 12 noon. Create a table of points that make sense in this situation, and graph them. Connect the points with a smooth curve.

46. The distance that Marissa is from home after h hours of riding her bike can be estimated by using the equation $D = 8h + 2$, where D is her distance from home in miles. Create a table of points that make sense in this situation, and graph them. Connect the points with a smooth curve.

47. The amount of grass still to be mowed at a park after m minutes of mowing can be estimated by using the equation $g = 24,000 - 100m$, where g is the number of square feet of grass still to be mowed. Create a table of points that make sense in this situation, and graph them. Connect the points with a smooth curve.

48. The amount of money, m (in dollars), left in Choung's savings account w weeks after starting a home improvement project can be calculated by using the equation $m = 45,000 - 7500w$. Create a table of points that make sense in this situation, and graph them. Connect the points with a smooth curve.

For Exercises 49 through 62, use the given equation to create a table of nine or more points and graph them. Connect the points with a smooth curve. Clearly label and scale the axes. Determine whether the graph is linear or nonlinear.

49. $y = x^2 + 1$

50. $y = x^2 + 5$

51. $y = x^2 - 4$

52. $y = x^2 - 2$

53. $y = (x + 3)^2$

54. $y = (x + 1)^2$

55. $y = (x - 2)^2$

56. $y = (x - 5)^2$

57. $y = |x| + 2$

58. $y = |x| - 3$

59. $y = |x + 2|$

60. $y = |x + 5|$

61. $y = |x - 3|$

62. $y = |x - 1|$

For Exercises 63 through 72, use the given equation to create a table of five or more points and graph them. Connect the points with a smooth curve. Clearly label and scale the axes. Determine whether the graph is linear or nonlinear.

63. $y = 6$

64. $y = 3$

65. $x = 7$

66. $x = 2$

67. $y = -3.5$

68. $y = -7$

69. $x = -1.5$

70. $x = -4$

71. $x = 0$

72. $y = 0$

3.2 Finding and Interpreting Slope

LEARNING OBJECTIVES

■ Interpret graphs.

■ Describe the rate of change.

■ Calculate slope.

■ Interpret slope.

Interpreting Graphs

When we examine graphs, there are several characteristics of the graph that give us information about the situation portrayed in the graph. The height of the line or curve tells us about the value of the outputs. The direction the curve goes in, reading from left to right, tells us about the kind of change that occurs over a unit change in input.

Consider a graph that compares the populations of two cities in the United States.

Which city has the larger population? Looking at the graph, we see that Lansing–East Lansing, Michigan, has a larger population than Anchorage, Alaska, over this time period. The line for Lansing–East Lansing is above the line for Anchorage.

Which city's population is growing faster? Since the line representing Anchorage is going up (reading from left to right) faster than the line for Lansing, we can tell that the population of Anchorage is growing more rapidly than the population of Lansing.

Source: Models derived from data found in the Statistical Abstract of the United States, 2004–2005, Table 24.

> ■ **Connecting the Concepts**
>
> **How do we read a graph?**
>
> Remember that in math, we most often read graphs from left to right. This is because the x-values increase from left to right.

Example 1   Interpreting graphs

Use the graphs to answer the following questions.

a.

Source: Models derived from data found in the Statistical Abstract of the United States, 2004–2005, Table 24.

1. Which city has the smaller population? Explain your response.

2. Which city's population is growing faster? Explain your response.

b.

Percentage of 15- to 19-Year-Old Women Who Tested Positive in Family Planning Clinics for Chlamydia

Source: Models derived from data found at www.cdc.gov.

1. Which of these regions of the United States has a higher percentage of 15- to 19-year-old women testing positive for chlamydia in family planning clinics?

2. Are the percentages in both of these regions increasing? Explain your response.

3. If these trends continue, how will the percentages of positive tests in these two regions compare in the future?

SOLUTION

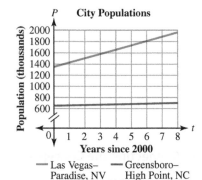

City Populations

Source: Models derived from data found in the Statistical Abstract of the United States, 2004–2005, Table 24.

a. 1. Greensboro–High Point, North Carolina, has a much smaller population than Las Vegas–Paradise, Nevada. The graph shows the line representing Greensboro as being much lower on the vertical axis.

2. Las Vegas–Paradise, Nevada, is growing much more quickly than Greensboro–High Point. The Las Vegas line is much steeper, so its population growth is greater.

b. 1. The Southeast has a higher percentage of 15- to 19-year-old women who test positive for chlamydia in family planning clinics. The graph for the Southeast is higher than the graph for the Northwest.

2. The percentage in the Southeast is decreasing because the graph is going down from left to right. The percentage in the Northwest is increasing.

3. If these trends continue, the Southeast will eventually have a smaller percentage of 15- to 19-year-old women who test positive for chlamydia in family planning clinics than the Northwest.

PRACTICE PROBLEM FOR EXAMPLE 1

Use the graph to answer the following questions.

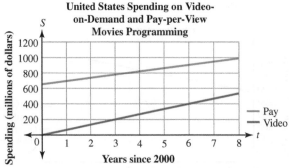

United States Spending on Video-on-Demand and Pay-per-View Movies Programming

Source: Models derived from data found in USA Today, May 23, 2005.

a. Do Americans spend more money on pay-per-view movies or on video-on-demand? Explain how you know.

b. Which is growing at the faster rate? Explain.

Determining a Rate of Change

How fast is a disease spreading?

How fast is the amount of affordable housing decreasing?

How quickly is a population growing?

How slowly is your salary increasing?

These are all questions about how quickly something is changing. In mathematics, how fast a quantity is changing is called a **rate of change.** All around us, change is occurring. Being able to measure that change is a powerful tool that can help us to better understand a situation.

In many areas of life, we want to know how fast something is changing. Businesses want to know how to get their revenues and profits to increase more quickly. Governments want to know how quickly populations are growing so that they can predict the resources they will need for schools, public safety programs, and other services.

A familiar example of a rate of change is speed. When you are traveling in a car at 50 miles per hour, the distance from the starting place is increasing by 50 miles for every hour driven. A possible table of values of your driving distance from a location, traveling at an average speed of 50 mph, is as follows.

t (hours)	Distance (miles)
0	0
1	50
2	100
3	150
4	200

© marilynv/Big Stock Photo

> ### What's That Mean?
>
> **Rate**
>
> A *rate* is a ratio of two different kinds of quantities. The units for a rate are often written with the word *per*, which indicates the division of the two quantities.
>
> mph = miles per hour
>
> $$\frac{\text{miles}}{\text{hour}}$$
>
> m/s² = meters per second squared
>
> $$\frac{\text{meters}}{\text{second}^2}$$

From the table, we see that for each one hour increase in time, the distance in the second column increases by 50 miles. However, also notice that the one hour represents the *difference* between two consecutive inputs (time). The 50 miles also represents the *difference* between two consecutive outputs (distance). Recalling that a *difference* means to *subtract*, we can write out this calculation by finding the changes using subtraction and then dividing the two values to get a speed in miles per hour.

t (hours)	Distance (miles)
0	0
1	50
2	100
3	150
4	200

Change in distance.
$100 - 50 = 50$

Change in time.
$2 - 1 = 1$

Divide the changes to find the rate of change, which is speed.

$$\frac{50 \text{ miles}}{1 \text{ hour}} = 50 \text{ mph}$$

Try again with two different rows.

$$\frac{\text{Change in distance}}{\text{Change in time}} = \frac{200 - 150}{4 - 3} = \frac{50 \text{ miles}}{1 \text{ hour}} = 50 \text{ mph}$$

Keep in mind that two quantities are compared in computing speed: the change in distance and the change in time. If we know the distance but do not know how long it took to travel that distance (that is, the time), then we cannot determine the speed. Because speed can be measured by using different units such as feet per second, miles per hour, meters per second, or kilometers per hour, we must be sure to use units when discussing speed or other rates of change. Notice that when calculating the speeds, we first calculate the difference in distance. Then calculate the difference in time, and finally, divide these two quantities.

This discussion of *speed* explains why in math and science, speed is often called the *rate*. Therefore, speed is the rate of change in a distance problem.

> **DEFINITION**
>
> **Rate of Change** The rate of change between two points is the change in outputs divided by the change in inputs.
>
> $$\frac{\text{change in outputs}}{\text{change in inputs}}$$

Let's investigate the idea of speed a little more, using the following Concept Investigation.

CONCEPT INVESTIGATION

Are the speeds the same?

Use the tables to determine the average speed that each car was driving. Check more than one set of rows to verify any speed you find.

a.

t (hours)	Distance (miles)	Speed (mph)	
1	60	$\dfrac{120 - 60}{2 - 1}$	*Change in distance*
2	120		*Change in time*
		$= \dfrac{60}{1} = 60$	
3	180		
4	240		
5	300		

b.

t (hours)	Distance (miles)	Speed (mph)
1	75	$\dfrac{225 - 75}{3 - 1}$
3	225	
		$= \dfrac{150}{2} = 75$
5	375	
7	525	
9	675	

c.

t (hours)	Distance (miles)	Speed (mph)
2	50	
3	75	
4	100	
6	150	
7	175	

d.

t (hours)	Distance (miles)	Speed (mph)
1	65	
2	100	
3	140	
4	200	
5	300	

What's That Mean?

Constant

In mathematics, the word *constant* is used to describe something that does not change.

In an expression or equation, we call numbers by themselves *constant terms*.

When we are discussing a rate of change, a *constant rate* means the rate is not varying.

Do all of these tables represent cars that are traveling at a constant (not changing) speed? If not, which table(s) represents constant speeds?

Using the table given before the preceding Concept Investigation and graphing the points, we get the following graph.

t (hours)	Distance (miles)
0	0
1	50
2	100
3	150
4	200

The distance is constantly changing as time increases. We can represent this constant change by drawing a smooth curve through the points, as we did in Section 3.1. Connecting the points on this graph yields a straight line.

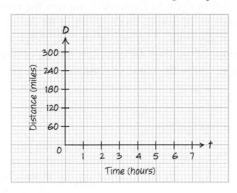

Now let's consider the data from the first Concept Investigation.

CONCEPT INVESTIGATION

Do these points make a line?

1. Plot the data from the following tables. Draw a smooth curve through the points.

a.

t (hours)	Distance (miles)
1	60
2	120
3	180
4	240
5	300

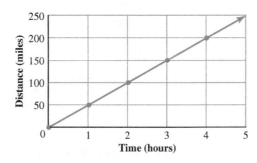

b.

t (hours)	Distance (miles)
1	75
3	225
5	375
7	525
9	675

c.

t (hours)	Distance (miles)
2	50
3	75
4	100
6	150
7	175

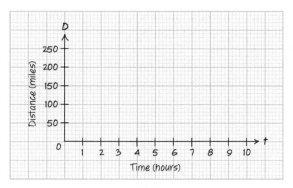

d.

t (hours)	Distance (miles)
1	65
2	100
3	140
4	200
5	300

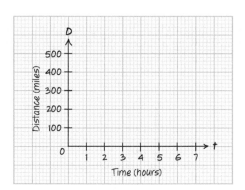

2. Connect the data points in each plot. Does each of the graphs look like a straight line? If not, which ones are not straight?

3. Do the two Concept Investigations in this section show a connection between a constant speed and the graph of a straight line? Explain your response.

The rate of change or speed in the preceding Concept Investigation is seen on the graph as the steepness of the line and whether the graph is rising or falling when read from left to right. In Example 1, we saw the rate of change of the populations and the percentages of women testing positive for chlamydia.

In mathematics, the rate of change, steepness, and direction of the line are called the **slope** of the line. An important feature of a linear graph is that the slope, or rate of change, will be the same, or constant, for the entire line.

DEFINITION

Slope   The slope of a line is the rate of change of a line.

$$\text{slope} = \frac{\text{change in outputs}}{\text{change in inputs}}$$

Calculating Slope

We now learn how to calculate the slope of a line using a graph or using any two points on a line. The basic components of rate of change are finding differences and then dividing them. The difference in outputs can be seen on a graph as the vertical change between the two points, reading from left to right. The vertical change is called the **rise.** The difference in inputs can be seen on the graph as horizontal change between the two points, reading from left to right. The horizontal change is called the **run.** To compute the slope correctly, we must be very specific in the order in which we divide the two differences. Use one of the following descriptions of slope to help you remember the order correctly.

$$\text{slope} = \frac{\text{change in outputs}}{\text{change in inputs}} = \frac{\text{rise}}{\text{run}}$$

In looking at a graph, the idea that slope is $\frac{\text{rise}}{\text{run}}$ is usually the best way to understand and remember how to calculate slope. Working from left to right, pick two points on a line. The rise is how far the graph goes up or down to get to the next point. The run is how far the graph goes left to right to get to the next point. If we use the distance and time graph that we worked with earlier, the rise and run are the change in distance and the change in time, respectively.

Steps to Calculate Slope Using a Graph

1. Pick two points on the line with coordinates that are easy to read.
2. Start with one point, and draw a right triangle to the other point.
3. Determine the rise and run from one point to the other.
4. Divide the rise by the run.

$$\text{slope} = \frac{\text{change in outputs}}{\text{change in inputs}} = \frac{\text{rise}}{\text{run}}$$

Example 2 Using the graph to find slope

Use the graph to estimate the slope of the line. Make sure to work from left to right.

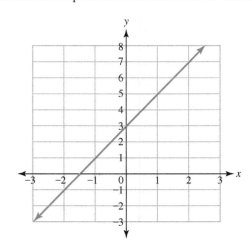

SOLUTION

When you look at a graph of a line, you can think of $\frac{\text{rise}}{\text{run}}$ as the template of how to calculate slope. First, look for two points on the line that are easy to read. Usually, ▼

points are easier to read when the line crosses an intersection on the grid. Then, working from left to right, count the rise (how far up or down it is from one point to the next) and the run (how far across it is from one point to the next).

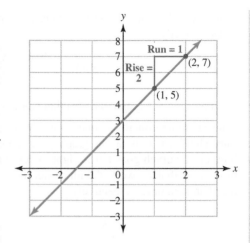

In this case, we chose the points $(1, 5)$ and $(2, 7)$. Looking at the graph, you can see that we have a rise of 2 and a run of 1, so when we divide to find slope, we get

$$\text{slope} = \frac{\text{rise}}{\text{run}} = \frac{2}{1} = 2$$

Notice that this slope is positive, which indicates that the line increases from left to right. If we pick any other two points to calculate slope, we get the same value for slope. For example, the following graph uses the points $(-2, -1)$ and $(1, 5)$.

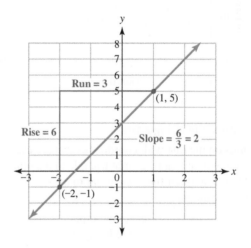

Therefore, any two points on the line can be used to calculate slope.

PRACTICE PROBLEM FOR EXAMPLE 2

Use the graph to estimate the slope of the line. Make sure to work from left to right.

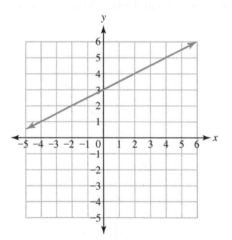

Example   3   The slope of decreasing lines

Use the graph to estimate the slope of the line. Make sure to work from left to right. Remember to select two points on the line to calculate slope.

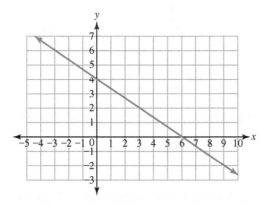

SOLUTION

Using the points $(-3, 6)$ and $(0, 4)$ gives a rise of -2 and a run of 3. In this case, the line is going down, so the rise is negative because the line is falling from left to right. When dividing the rise and run, we get that the

$$\text{slope} = \frac{-2}{3}$$

Note that the negative sign indicates that the line is decreasing, going downward, when we read the graph from left to right.

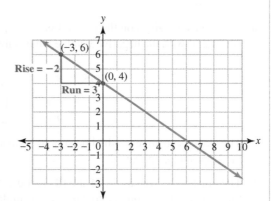

> ### ■ Connecting the Concepts
>
> **What is an increasing or decreasing line?**
>
> We say that a line **increases** if it goes up from left to right. A positive slope indicates an increasing line.
>
> We say that a line **decreases** if it goes down from left to right. A negative slope indicates a decreasing line.

PRACTICE PROBLEM FOR EXAMPLE 3

Use the graph to estimate the slope of the line.

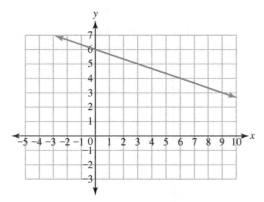

Sometimes, using a graph is not convenient, or the graph is not given. In this case, we can find the slope using any two points on the line using the formula definition for slope.

> **Slope Formula**   The slope of a line can be found by using the formula
>
> $$\text{slope} = \frac{\text{change in } y}{\text{change in } x} = \frac{y_2 - y_1}{x_2 - x_1}$$
>
> when (x_1, y_1) and (x_2, y_2) are any two points on the line.

Example 4 Using two points to find the slope

a. Find the slope of the line.

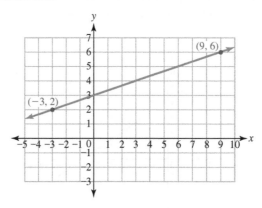

b. Find the slope of the line that goes through points $(5, 7)$ and $(8, 3)$.

SOLUTION

a. The points are given on the graph. Let $(x_1, y_1) = (-3, 2)$ and $(x_2, y_2) = (9, 6)$. Be careful with the negative x-value when subtracting.

$$\text{slope} = \frac{y_2 - y_1}{x_2 - x_1} = \frac{6 - 2}{9 - (-3)}$$

$$= \frac{4}{9 + 3} = \frac{4}{12} = \frac{1}{3}$$

The slope is positive, so the line should be increasing. From the graph we see that the slope and graph agree.

b. The points are given as $(5, 7)$ and $(8, 3)$. Let $(x_1, y_1) = (5, 7)$ and $(x_2, y_2) = (8, 3)$. Substituting these points into the slope formula yields

$$\text{slope} = \frac{y_2 - y_1}{x_2 - x_1} = \frac{3 - 7}{8 - 5}$$

$$= \frac{-4}{3} = -\frac{4}{3}$$

This slope is negative, so the line should be decreasing. Graphing these two points and connecting them with a line, we get a line that goes down from left to right.

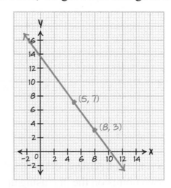

PRACTICE PROBLEM FOR EXAMPLE 4

Find the slope of the line that goes through the points $(2, -5)$ and $(7, 9)$.

Example 5 Using any two points from a table to find slope

Use any two points from the table to find the slope of the line that passes through the points.

Connecting the Concepts

Does the slope formula give the same slope as rise/run?

In Example 4a, the slope formula gives the slope of $m = \frac{1}{3}$. Using the $\dfrac{\text{rise}}{\text{run}}$ method, we have that

$$m = \frac{\text{rise}}{\text{run}} = \frac{4}{12} = \frac{1}{3}$$

The slope is the same no matter which method is used to calculate it.

a.

x	y
1	10
3	18
7	34
8	38
10	46

b.

x	y
3	−1
3	0
3	1
3	2
3	5

c.

x	y
−2	1
−1	1
0	1
2	1

SOLUTION

a. We can choose any two points in the table. Selecting the second and last points yields

$$\text{slope} = \frac{46 - 18}{10 - 3} = \frac{28}{7} = 4$$

Check this calculation by selecting two other points and substituting them into the slope formula.

$$\text{slope} = \frac{38 - 34}{8 - 7} = \frac{4}{1} = 4$$

b. We can choose any two points in the table. Selecting the first and fourth points yields

$$\text{slope} = \frac{2 - (-1)}{3 - 3} = \frac{3}{0} \qquad \text{\textit{This is undefined;}} \\ \text{\textit{cannot divide by 0.}}$$

The slope of this line is undefined.

c. We can choose any two points in the table. Selecting the first and second points yields

$$\text{slope} = \frac{1 - 1}{(-1) - (-2)} = \frac{0}{1} = 0$$

The slope of this line is 0.

PRACTICE PROBLEM FOR EXAMPLE 5

Use any two points from the table to find the slope of the line that passes through the points.

a.

x	y
0	24
2	23.5
8	22
10	21.5
20	19

b.

x	y
7	−3
7	0
7	8
7	11
7	15

In Example 5, we saw two special cases of slope. If we look at the rise and run of horizontal and vertical lines, we get the following.

Horizontal Line $y = 2$

$$\text{slope} = \frac{0}{3} = 0$$

Vertical Line $x = 3$

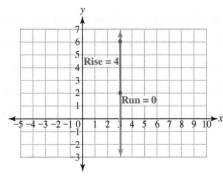

$$\text{slope} = \frac{4}{0} = \text{undefined}$$

These results are true for horizontal and vertical lines in general.

> **DEFINITIONS (TWO SPECIAL CASES)**
>
> **Slope of a Horizontal Line**   The slope of a horizontal line is zero.
> **Slope of a Vertical Line**   The slope of a vertical line is undefined.

Connecting the Concepts

How can we convert units in thousands?

Recall from Section 1.2 that the units are very important.

   2.5 thousand people is the same as

   $2.5(1000) = 2500$ people

The thousand can be in words or multiplied out to be represented in number form.

Interpreting Slope

Recall Example 1 comparing the populations of Anchorage and Lansing–East Lansing. In the following population graph, two points are given on each line, and the calculation of slope is carried out.

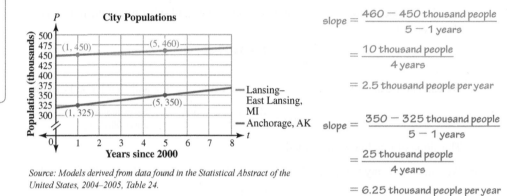

Source: Models derived from data found in the Statistical Abstract of the United States, 2004–2005, Table 24.

$$\text{slope} = \frac{460 - 450 \text{ thousand people}}{5 - 1 \text{ years}}$$

$$= \frac{10 \text{ thousand people}}{4 \text{ years}}$$

$$= 2.5 \text{ thousand people per year}$$

$$\text{slope} = \frac{350 - 325 \text{ thousand people}}{5 - 1 \text{ years}}$$

$$= \frac{25 \text{ thousand people}}{4 \text{ years}}$$

$$= 6.25 \text{ thousand people per year}$$

The population of Lansing–East Lansing is growing at a rate of about 2500 people per year, while the population of Anchorage is growing at a rate of about 6250 people per year. Graphically, this correlates with the visual sense that the blue line that represents Anchorage is "steeper" than the red line that represents Lansing–East Lansing.

When you are interpreting the slope in an application, it is important to include all the following information:

1. What the output represents

2. Whether the output is increasing or decreasing

3. The value of the slope

4. The units of the output variable per the units of the input variable

The explanation for the slope of the Lansing–East Lansing line above is:

   The population of Lansing–East Lansing is increasing at a rate of about 2500 people per year.

In this sentence, we have all four components of an interpretation for slope:

1. The output represents: **The population of Lansing–East Lansing**

2. The output is increasing or decreasing: **is increasing**

3. The value of the slope: **at a rate of about 2500**

4. The units of the output per the units of the input: **people per year**

Example **6**   Interpreting slope

Calculate the slope of the lines in the given graph. Interpret the meaning of each slope in the context of the problem situation.

Source: Models derived from data found in the Statistical Abstract of the United States, 2004–2005, Table 24.

SOLUTION

Start with the Las Vegas–Paradise line. As we calculate the slope, include the units for the input and output values.

$$\text{slope} = \frac{1650 - 1420 \text{ thousand people}}{4 - 1 \text{ years}}$$

$$= \frac{230 \text{ thousand people}}{3 \text{ years}}$$

$$\approx 76.67 \text{ thousand people per year.}$$

Calculating the slope for the Greensboro–High Point line yields

$$\text{slope} = \frac{680 - 650 \text{ thousand people}}{5 - 0 \text{ years}}$$

$$= \frac{30 \text{ thousand people}}{5 \text{ years}}$$

$$\approx 6 \text{ thousand people per year.}$$

The population of Las Vegas is increasing at a rate of about 76,670 people per year. The population of Greensboro is increasing at a rate of about 6000 people per year.

PRACTICE PROBLEM FOR EXAMPLE 6

Calculate the slope of the line in the given graph. Interpret the meaning of the slope in terms of the ticket sales.

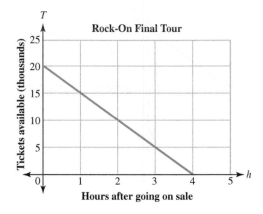

CONCEPT INVESTIGATION

Which line has the greater slope?

Consider the following graph.

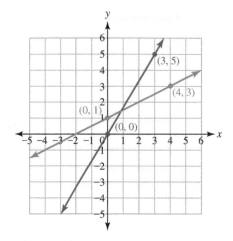

1. Compute the slope for the blue line.

2. Compute the slope for the red line.

3. Which line has the greater slope? (*Hint*: Compare the two numbers you got in parts a and b.)

4. Which line is steeper? Another way to say this is, Which line is increasing faster? Read the graph from left to right.

5. How does the slope of the line relate to which line is steeper?

The preceding Concept Investigation shows that for lines with positive slope, the greater the slope means the steeper the line.

Example 7 Comparing slopes of lines

Examine the graphs given below. Which line has the greater slope? Explain how you know.

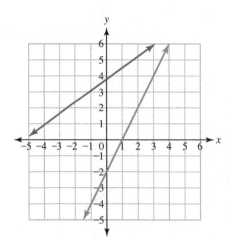

SOLUTION

The red line is steeper than the blue line, reading from left to right. Therefore, the red line has the greater slope.

3.2 Exercises

For Exercises 1 through 8, use the given graphs to answer the questions. Do not calculate any values.

1.

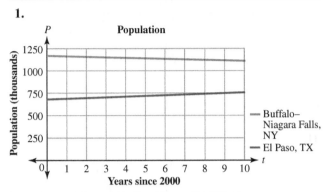

Source: *Statistical Abstract of the United States, 2008, Table 20.*

a. Which city has the larger population during these years? Explain how you conclude that from the graph.

b. Which city is growing faster during these years? Explain how you conclude that from the graph.

2.

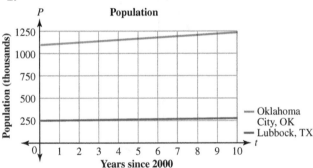

Source: *Statistical Abstract of the United States, 2008, Table 20.*

a. Which city has the larger population during these years? Explain how you conclude that from the graph.

b. Which city is growing faster during these years? Explain how you conclude that from the graph.

3.

Source: *Nutristrategy.com.*

Which kind of exercise burns more calories per hour? Explain how you conclude that from the graph.

4.

Source: *Nutristrategy.com.*

Which kind of exercise burns more calories per hour? Explain how you conclude that from the graph.

5.

Source: *Centers for Disease Control and Prevention.*

a. Which state has more adults who have diagnosed diabetes? Explain how you conclude that from the graph.

b. Which state's number of adults with diagnosed diabetes is growing more slowly? Explain how you conclude that from the graph.

6.

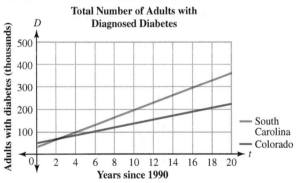

Source: *Centers for Disease Control and Prevention.*

a. Which state had more adults who had diagnosed diabetes in 1990? Explain how you conclude that from the graph.

b. Which state currently has more adults who have diagnosed diabetes? Explain how you conclude that from the graph.

c. Which state's number of adults with diagnosed diabetes is growing more slowly? Explain how you conclude that from the graph.

7.

Concert Tickets Available

Rock-On Live Tour
Classics Rule Tour

Hours after going on sale

a. Which tour had more tickets available at the start of sales? Explain how you conclude that from the graph.
b. Which tour sold out first? Explain how you conclude that from the graph.
c. Which tour's available tickets decreased faster? Explain how you conclude that from the graph.

8.

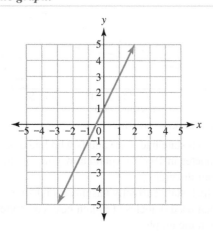

Fund-Raising for Breast Cancer

Deb
Christine

Days after starting to fund-raise

a. Who had the higher fund-raising goal? Explain how you conclude that from the graph.
b. Who finished fund-raising first? Explain how you conclude that from the graph.
c. Whose fund-raising came in at a faster rate? Explain how you conclude that from the graph.

For Exercises 9 through 22, find the slope of the line given in the graph.

9.

10.

11.

12.

13.

14.

15.

16.

17.

18.

19.

20.

21.

22.

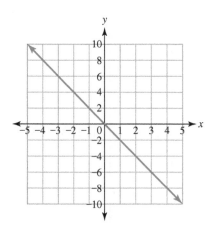

23. Find the slope of the line that goes through points $(2, 5)$ and $(6, 13)$.

24. Find the slope of the line that goes through points $(3, 7)$ and $(5, 17)$.

25. Find the slope of the line that goes through points $(0, 2)$ and $(4, 3)$.

26. Find the slope of the line that goes through points $(1, 3)$ and $(7, 5)$.

27. Find the slope of the line that goes through points $(-4, -7)$ and $(2, 11)$.

28. Find the slope of the line that goes through points $(-2, -14)$ and $(1, -2)$.

29. Find the slope of the line that goes through points $(4, 8)$ and $(1, 8)$.

30. Find the slope of the line that goes through points $(-4, -3)$ and $(2, -3)$.

31. Find the slope of the line that goes through points $(-3, -7.5)$ and $(1, -5.5)$.

32. Find the slope of the line that goes through points $(-4, -9)$ and $(2, -7.5)$.

33. Find the slope of the line that goes through points $(2, 5)$ and $(2, 6)$.

34. Find the slope of the line that goes through points $(-8, 9)$ and $(-8, 7)$.

35. Find the slope of the line that goes through points $(-3, 18)$ and $(3, -6)$.

36. Find the slope of the line that goes through points $(-5, 22)$ and $(5, -8)$.

For Exercises 37 through 40, use the graph to answer the following questions.

37. Which line has slope closer to zero: the red line or the blue line? Explain.

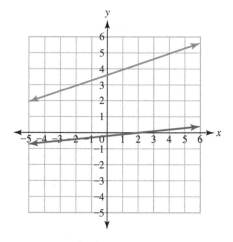

38. Which line has slope closer to zero: the red line or the blue line? Explain.

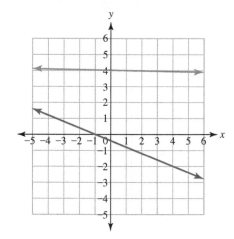

39. Which line has slope closer to being undefined: the red line or the blue line? Explain.

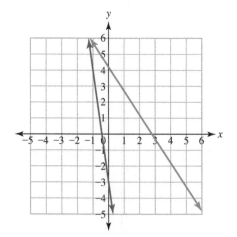

40. Which line has slope closer to being undefined: the red line or the blue line? Explain.

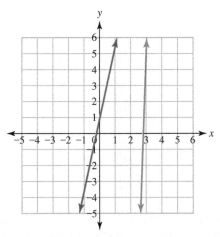

For Exercises 41 through 54, use any two points from the table to calculate the slope of the line that passes through the points.

41.

x	y
1	−17
2	−14
3	−11
5	−5

42.

x	y
1	−3
5	5
6	7
8	11

43.

x	y
2	−2
5	2.5
7	5.5
10	10

44.

x	y
1	−6.75
5	−1.75
7	0.75
10	4.5

45.

x	y
−4	2
−4	−3
−4	−7
−4	−12

46.

x	y
6	−2
6	−1
6	3
6	11

47.

x	y
3	8
9	10
12	11
15	12

48.

x	y
2	−7.5
6	−6.5
10	−5.5
18	−3.5

49.

x	y
1	2
3	−6
8	−26
11	−38

50.

x	y
2	−11
8	−29
11	−38
16	−53

51.

x	y
1	10
7	10
12	10
22	10

52.

x	y
−8	−2
−1	−2
3	−2
7	−2

53.

x	y
−3	9.5
−1	8.5
2	7
5	5.5

54.

x	y
−5	12.5
−2	11.6
0	11
5	9.5

55. a. Calculate the slope for the Buffalo–Niagara Falls, New York, line given in the graph in Exercise 1 on page 231. Use the points (0, 1169) and (6, 1138).
b. Interpret the meaning of the slope you found in part a.

56. a. Calculate the slope for the El Paso, Texas, line given in the graph in Exercise 1 on page 231. Use the points (0, 682) and (4, 712).
b. Interpret the meaning of the slope you found in part a.

57. a. Calculate the slope for the Oklahoma City, Oklahoma, line given in the graph in Exercise 2 on page 231. Use the points (1, 1107) and (5, 1154).
b. Interpret the meaning of the slope you found in part a.

58. a. Calculate the slope for the Lubbock, Texas, line given in the graph in Exercise 2 on page 231. Use the points (2, 254) and (6, 261).
b. Interpret the meaning of the slope you found in part a.

59. a. Calculate the slope for the archery line given in the graph in Exercise 3 on page 231.
b. Interpret the meaning of the slope you found in part a.

60. a. Calculate the slope for the billiards line given in the graph in Exercise 3 on page 231.
b. Interpret the meaning of the slope you found in part a.

61. a. Calculate the slope for the competitive badminton line given in the graph in Exercise 4 on page 231.
b. Interpret the meaning of the slope you found in part a.

62. a. Calculate the slope for the volleyball line given in the graph in Exercise 4 on page 231.
b. Interpret the meaning of the slope you found in part a.

63. a. Calculate the slope for the California line given in the graph in Exercise 5 on page 231.
b. Interpret the meaning of the slope you found in part a.

64. a. Calculate the slope for the Florida line given in the graph in Exercise 5 on page 231.
b. Interpret the meaning of the slope you found in part a.

65. a. Calculate the slope for the South Carolina line given in the graph in Exercise 6 on page 231.
b. Interpret the meaning of the slope you found in part a.

66. **a.** Calculate the slope for the Colorado line given in the graph in Exercise 6 on page 231.
   b. Interpret the meaning of the slope you found in part a.

67. **a.** Calculate the slope for the Rock-On Live Tour line given in the graph in Exercise 7 on page 232.
   b. Interpret the meaning of the slope you found in part a.

68. **a.** Calculate the slope for the Classics Rule Tour line given in the graph in Exercise 7 on page 232.
   b. Interpret the meaning of the slope you found in part a.

69. **a.** Calculate the slope for the Deb line given in the graph in Exercise 8 on page 232.
   b. Interpret the meaning of the slope you found in part a.

70. **a.** Calculate the slope for the Christine line given in the graph in Exercise 8 on page 232.
   b. Interpret the meaning of the slope you found in part a.

For Exercises 71 through 74, state which line (red or blue) has the greater slope. Do not calculate the slope. See Example 7 on page 230 for help. Explain how you know.

71.

72.

73.

74.

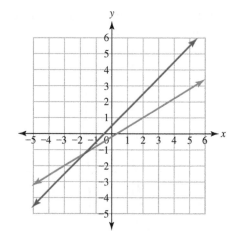

For Exercises 75 through 80, state whether the line is increasing, decreasing, or neither. Explain how you know.

75.

76.

77.

78.

79.

80.

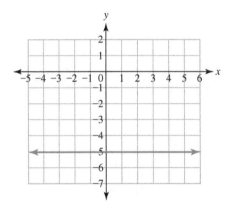

For Exercises 81 through 86, state whether the line is increasing, decreasing, or neither. Explain how you know. (Hint: Graph the line.)

81. $y = -3x + 19$

82. $y = -0.5x - 12$

83. $y = \dfrac{-5}{4}$

84. $y = \dfrac{-2}{3}$

85. $y = \dfrac{6}{5}x - 7$

86. $y = 8x - 21$

For Exercises 87 through 94, state whether the output quantity is increasing, decreasing, or neither.

87. Mallory's weekly pay P can be computed by the formula $P = 12.5h$, where h is the number of hours she works per week.

88. Jonas's weekly pay P can be computed by the formula $P = 11.75h$, where h is the number of hours he works per week.

89. The temperature T outside after 2:00 P.M. may be computed by $T = 89 - 3h$, where h is the number of hours after 2:00 P.M.

90. The temperature T outside after noon may be computed by $T = 65 - 2h$, where h is the number of hours after noon.

91. Patrick's weight W while dieting can be computed by the formula $W = 189 - 2t$, where t is the number of weeks that he has been on the diet.

92. Larissa's weight W while dieting can be computed by the formula $W = 165 - t$, where t is the number of weeks that she has been on the diet.

93. The distance D that Minh drives in h hours can be computed by the formula $D = 66h$.

94. The distance D that Trevor drives in h hours can be computed by the formula $D = 71h$.

For Exercises 95 and 96, answer the questions on the basis of the given information.

95. Use the graph to answer the following questions.

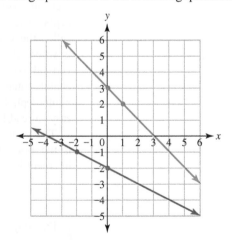

a. Which line appears to be decreasing more rapidly: the red line or the blue line?

b. Compute the slopes of both lines.

c. Look at your answers from parts a and b. Does the line that is decreasing more rapidly (part a) have a slope that is greater than or less than the slope of the other line (part b)?

96. Use the graph to answer the following questions.

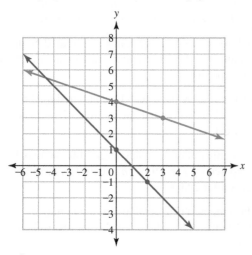

a. Which line appears to be decreasing more rapidly: the red line or the blue line?

b. Compute the slopes of both lines.

c. Look at your answers from parts a and b. Does the line that is decreasing more rapidly (part a) have a slope that is greater than or less than the slope of the other line (part b)?

3.3   Slope-Intercept Form of Lines

LEARNING OBJECTIVES

■ Find and interpret intercepts from graphs.

■ Find and interpret intercepts from equations.

■ Recognize and use the slope-intercept form of a line.

Finding and Interpreting Intercepts from Graphs

The places where a curve intersects the axes are called **intercepts.** The vertical intercept is called the *y*-intercept because it is where the curve touches the vertical axis or *y*-axis. The horizontal intercept is called the *x*-intercept. Intercepts are often easy to read from a graph.

The *y*-intercept on this graph is the point (0, 4), and the *x*-intercept is the point (6, 0).

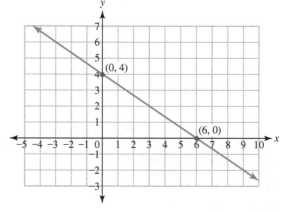

DEFINITIONS

y-**intercept**   The point where the curve touches the *y*-axis (vertical axis) is called the *y*-**intercept** or **vertical intercept.**

y-intercepts are points on the graph and should always be written as a coordinate point (0, *b*).

x-**intercept**   The point where the curve touches the *x*-axis (horizontal axis) is called the *x*-**intercept** or **horizontal intercept.**

x-intercepts are points on the graph and should always be written as a coordinate point (*c*, 0).

Example 1   **Reading intercepts from graphs**

a. Find the *x*-intercept and *y*-intercept of the following line.

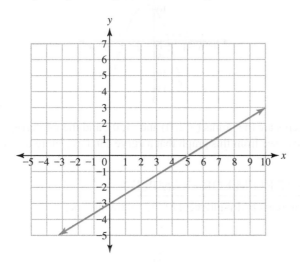

b. Find the *x*-intercepts and *y*-intercept of the following curve.

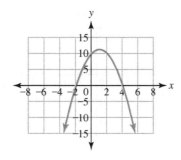

SOLUTION

a. Reading the graph, we find the following intercepts.

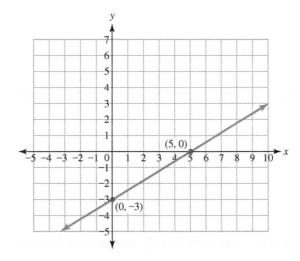

The *y*-intercept is the point $(0, -3)$, and the *x*-intercept is the point $(5, 0)$.

b. This curve has two *x*-intercepts and one *y*-intercept.

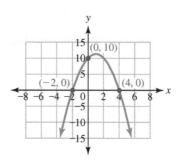

The *x*-intercepts are the points $(-2, 0)$ and $(4, 0)$, and the *y*-intercept is the point $(0, 10)$. We can see from this graph that a curve can have more than one *x*- or *y*-intercept.

PRACTICE PROBLEM FOR EXAMPLE 1

a. Find the *x*-intercept and *y*-intercept of the following line.

■ Connecting the Concepts

What are other ways to discuss intercepts?

The following words or phrases all mean the same thing.

y-intercept:

- Vertical intercept
- Can take on the name of the dependent variable that is represented on the vertical axis.

x-intercept:

- Horizontal intercept
- Can take on the name of the independent variable that is represented on the horizontal axis.

We will use *horizontal* and *vertical* intercept when the variables in the problem are not *x* and *y*. Most often, this will be when we are working with applications.

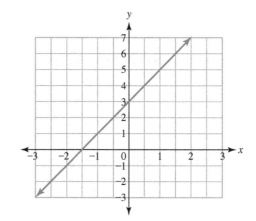

b. Find the *x*-intercepts and *y*-intercept of the following curve.

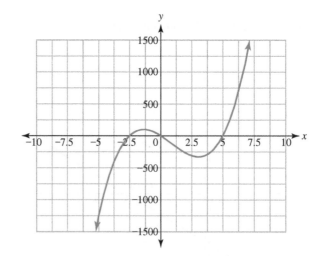

When a graph represents an application, the intercepts can be interpreted in the terms of the problem.

Source: Models derived from data found in the Statistical Abstract of the United States, 2004–2005, Table 24.

From this graph, we can see that the Anchorage, Alaska, line crosses the vertical axis at about the point (0, 320). This indicates that zero years since 2000, the year 2000, the population was about 320 thousand. Notice that both the zero and the 320 have meaning in the context of the situation.

The vertical intercept for the Lansing–East Lansing, Michigan, line is approximately (0, 448). The meaning of this point is that in the year 2000, the population was about 448 thousand. Both of these points are approximations, since reading an exact value from this graph is difficult.

The horizontal intercepts on the city population graph above cannot be seen on the graph and would not make sense in this situation. The horizontal intercept would indicate the year in which the population of the city was zero. In some applications, one or both of the intercepts might not make sense.

Example 2 Interpreting intercepts from graphs

a. Estimate and interpret the vertical intercepts for the lines in this graph.

Source: Models derived from data found in the Statistical Abstract of the United States, 2004–2005, Table 24.

b. Estimate and interpret the vertical and horizontal intercepts for the line in this graph.

SOLUTION

a. We can estimate the vertical intercepts from this graph. Then we will interpret what the points represent in this situation.

Source: Models derived from data found in the Statistical Abstract of the United States, 2004–2005, Table 24.

The vertical intercept for the Greensboro–High Point, North Carolina, line is approximately the point (0, 650) and represents a population of about 650 thousand in the year 2000. The vertical intercept for the Las Vegas–Paradise, Nevada, line is approximately the point (0, 1390) and represents a population of about 1390 thousand in the year 2000.

b. We first read both intercepts from the graph. Then we will interpret what they mean in the context of the situation.

The vertical intercept is the point (0, 20) and means that when they started selling tickets, there were 20,000 tickets available for the Rock-On final tour. The horizontal intercept is the point (4, 0) and means that 4 hours after going on sale, no more tickets were available for the Rock-On final tour.

PRACTICE PROBLEM FOR EXAMPLE 2

a. Find and interpret the vertical intercept for the line in this graph.

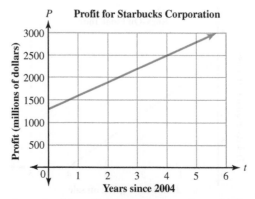

Source: Graph derived from data found at http://finance.Google.com.

b. Find and interpret the vertical and horizontal intercepts for the line in this graph.

Finding and Interpreting Intercepts from Equations

When you look for *x*- and *y*-intercepts on a graph, notice that every intercept has a zero as part of the point. The *zero* is always the value of the *other* variable. Therefore, the *y*-intercept always has a zero for the *x*-value, and the *x*-intercept always has a zero for the *y*-value.

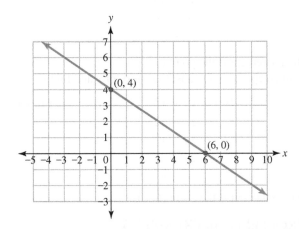

The fact that an intercept will always have a zero allows us to find intercepts from equations. If we are given an equation and want to find a *y*-intercept, we can substitute zero for *x* and solve for *y*. Remember that an intercept is a point on a graph, so it will have a coordinate with both an *x*-value and a *y*-value.

> ### Steps to Finding Intercepts from Equations
>
> **y-intercept:**
>
> **1.** Substitute zero for *x*, $x = 0$, and find the value of *y*.
> **2.** Write the intercept as a coordinate in the form $(0, b)$.
>
> **x-intercept:**
>
> **1.** Substitute zero for *y*, $y = 0$, and find the value of *x*.
> **2.** Write the intercept as a coordinate in the form $(c, 0)$.

Example 3   Finding intercepts from equations

Find the *x*- and *y*-intercepts of the following equations.

a. $y = 5x + 20$ **b.** $2x + 3y = 12$

SOLUTION

a. To find the y-intercept, we will substitute zero for x and find y.

$$y = 5(0) + 20 \qquad \text{Substitute in } x = 0.$$
$$y = 20 \qquad \text{Simplify.}$$

Therefore, the y-intercept is the point $(0, 20)$.
To find the x-intercept, we will substitute zero for y and find x.

$$0 = 5x + 20 \qquad \text{Substitute in } y = 0.$$
$$\underline{-20 \qquad\qquad -20} \qquad \text{Solve for } x.$$
$$-20 = 5x$$
$$\frac{-20}{5} = \frac{5x}{5}$$
$$-4 = x$$

Therefore, the x-intercept is the point $(-4, 0)$.

b. To find the y-intercept, we will substitute zero for x and find y.

$$2(0) + 3y = 12 \qquad \text{Substitute in } x = 0.$$
$$3y = 12 \qquad \text{Solve for } y.$$
$$\frac{3y}{3} = \frac{12}{3}$$
$$y = 4$$

Therefore, the y-intercept is the point $(0, 4)$.
To find the x-intercept, we will substitute zero for y and find x.

$$2x + 3(0) = 12 \qquad \text{Substitute in } y = 0.$$
$$2x = 12 \qquad \text{Solve for } x.$$
$$\frac{2x}{2} = \frac{12}{2}$$
$$x = 6$$

Therefore, the x-intercept is the point $(6, 0)$.

PRACTICE PROBLEM FOR EXAMPLE 3

Find the x- and y-intercepts of the following equations.

a. $y = -7x + 21$ **b.** $-4x + 7y = -56$

When you are working with a word problem, intercepts are found in the same way. Pay close attention to the meaning of the variables, and use that information to understand the intercepts. Remember that each intercept has two parts. Include the meaning of both parts in the interpretation.

Example 4   Finding and interpreting intercepts from equations

Paulo started a diet plan two months ago to help him make weight for his next boxing match. Paulo's weight in pounds n weeks after starting the diet can be approximated by the equation

$$W = -1.5n + 175$$

a. Find and interpret the W-intercept for this equation.

b. Find and interpret the n-intercept.

c. Do the intercepts make sense in this situation?

SOLUTION

a. To find the W-intercept, we will substitute zero for n and find W.

$$W = -1.5(0) + 175 \qquad \text{Substitute in } n = 0.$$
$$W = 175 \qquad \text{Simplify.}$$

Therefore, the W-intercept is the point $(0, 175)$ and means that when the diet started, Paulo weighed 175 pounds.

b. To find the n-intercept, we will substitute zero for W and solve for n.

$$0 = -1.5n + 175 \qquad \text{Substitute in } W = 0.$$
$$\underline{-175 \qquad\qquad -175} \qquad \text{Solve for } n.$$
$$-175 = -1.5n$$
$$\frac{-175}{-1.5} = \frac{-1.5n}{-1.5}$$
$$116.7 \approx n$$

Therefore, the n-intercept is the point $(116.7, 0)$, which means that after about 117 weeks on the diet, Paulo will weigh zero pounds. Since n is weeks after starting the diet, we will round to a whole week.

c. The n-intercept does not make sense because Paulo cannot weigh zero pounds. The W-intercept seems reasonable, as 175 pounds is a fairly normal weight.

PRACTICE PROBLEM FOR EXAMPLE 4

Deb and Christine are walking in the 60-mile Breast Cancer 3Day Walk and want to keep track of the number of miles they still have to walk. They will use the equation

$$D = -3h + 60$$

where D is the distance in miles they still have to walk after h hours of walking.

Mark Clark

a. Find and interpret the D-intercept for this equation.

b. Find and interpret the h-intercept.

c. Do the intercepts make sense in this situation?

Slope-Intercept Form of a Line

CONCEPT INVESTIGATION

How are the y-intercepts and slopes connected to the equation?

1. Find the y-intercept for the following equations. Write as the point $(0, b)$.

   a. **Equation:** $y = 4x + 9$ \qquad **y-intercept:**

   b. **Equation:** $y = \dfrac{1}{2}x + 3$ \qquad **y-intercept:**

   c. **Equation:** $y = 1.25x - 2.5$ \qquad **y-intercept:**

2. What is the relationship between the y-intercept and the equation?

3. Find the slopes of the following equations using any two points given in each table.

   a. **Equation:** $y = 4x + 9$ **Slope:**

x	$y = 4x + 9$
1	13
3	21
7	37
10	49

   b. **Equation:** $y = \frac{1}{2}x + 3$ **Slope:**

x	$y = \frac{1}{2}x + 3$
2	4
6	6
10	8
16	11

   c. **Equation:** $y = 1.25x - 2.5$ **Slope:**

x	$y = 1.25x - 2.5$
2	0
4	2.5
5	3.75
6	5

4. What is the relationship between the slope and the equation?

■ **Connecting the Concepts**

Are there other forms of lines?

In this section, we study the slope-intercept form of a line. There are several other forms of lines, which we will study in Sections 3.4 and 3.5.

All of the equations in the Concept Investigation are in what is called the **slope-intercept form** of a line. The slope-intercept form of a line is written as

$$y = mx + b$$

where m and b are real numbers. When an equation is written in this form, we can read the slope and the y-intercept of the line directly from the equation. In the first half of the Concept Investigation, we noticed that the point $(0, b)$ is the y-intercept for each line. In the second half of the Concept Investigation, we noticed that the slope for each equation is m, the coefficient of the x-term.

DEFINITION

Slope-Intercept Form of a Line   The slope-intercept form of a line is

$$y = mx + b$$

where m and b are real numbers. The slope of the line is m, and the y-intercept is the point $(0, b)$.

Using this information, we can find the slope and y-intercept of any line that is in the slope-intercept form.

Example **5**   Finding the slope and the intercepts from the slope-intercept form

Find the slope, x-intercept, and y-intercept for each of the following linear equations.

a. $y = 2x + 4$ **b.** $y = \dfrac{2}{3}x - \dfrac{1}{3}$ **c.** $y = -0.5x + 7.5$

SOLUTION

a. This equation is in slope-intercept form, so the slope is the coefficient of the x-term, and the y-intercept is the point $(0, b)$. Therefore, the slope is 2, and the y-intercept is $(0, 4)$. To find the x-intercept, substitute zero for y and solve for x.

$$0 = 2x + 4 \qquad \text{\small Substitute in } y = 0.$$
$$\underline{-4 \qquad\quad -4} \qquad \text{\small Solve for x.}$$
$$-4 = 2x$$
$$\frac{-4}{2} = \frac{2x}{2}$$
$$-2 = x$$

Therefore, the x-intercept is the point $(-2, 0)$.

b. This equation is in slope-intercept form, so the slope is $\dfrac{2}{3}$ and the y-intercept is $\left(0, -\dfrac{1}{3}\right)$. To find the x-intercept, substitute zero for y and solve for x.

$$0 = \frac{2}{3}x - \frac{1}{3} \qquad \text{\small Substitute in } y = 0.$$
$$\underline{+\frac{1}{3} \qquad\quad +\frac{1}{3}} \qquad \text{\small Solve for x.}$$
$$\frac{1}{3} = \frac{2}{3}x$$
$$\frac{3}{2}\left(\frac{1}{3}\right) = \frac{3}{2}\left(\frac{2}{3}x\right) \qquad \text{\small Multiply both sides by the}$$
$$\qquad\qquad\qquad\qquad \text{\small reciprocal } \frac{3}{2}.$$
$$\frac{1}{2} = x$$

Therefore, the x-intercept is the point $\left(\dfrac{1}{2}, 0\right)$.

c. This equation is in slope-intercept form, so the slope is -0.5 and the y-intercept is $(0, 7.5)$. To find the x-intercept, substitute zero for y and solve for x.

$$0 = -0.5x + 7.5$$
$$\underline{-7.5 \qquad\qquad -7.5}$$
$$-7.5 = -0.5x$$
$$\frac{-7.5}{-0.5} = \frac{-0.5x}{-0.5}$$
$$15 = x$$

Therefore, the x-intercept is the point $(15, 0)$.

PRACTICE PROBLEM FOR EXAMPLE 5

Find the slope, x-intercept, and y-intercept for each of the following linear equations.

a. $y = -\dfrac{2}{3}x + 4$

b. $y = \dfrac{1}{4}x - \dfrac{2}{5}$

■ Skill Connection

Dividing Fractions

To divide by a fraction, we multiply by the reciprocal of that fraction.

$$8 \div \frac{2}{5} =$$
$$8 \cdot \frac{5}{2} =$$
$$\overset{4}{\cancel{8}} \cdot \frac{5}{\cancel{2}} = 20$$

Example 6 Finding and interpreting slopes and intercepts from applications

The cost in dollars to have the carpets cleaned in your home can be calculated by using the equation

$$C = 25r + 15$$

where C is the cost in dollars to have the carpet in r rooms cleaned.

a. Find and interpret the C-intercept for this equation.

b. Find and interpret the slope of this equation.

SOLUTION

a. This equation is in slope-intercept form, so the C-intercept is $(0, 15)$. If you have no carpet cleaned, the company will charge you $15. This could be a base fee for coming out to the home.

b. The slope of this equation is 25. Since slope can be thought of as the change in outputs over the change in inputs, we can represent this slope as

$$25 = \frac{25 \text{ dollars}}{1 \text{ room}}$$

Therefore, the slope means that the cost for cleaning the carpets goes up $25 for each room cleaned.

PRACTICE PROBLEM FOR EXAMPLE 6

peresanz/shutterstock.com

The time it takes to manufacture f bicycle frames for a certain type of bike can be calculated by using the equation

$$T = 0.5f + 2$$

where T is the time in hours it takes to produce f bicycle frames.

a. Find and interpret the T-intercept for this equation.

b. Find and interpret the slope of this equation.

Whenever a given equation is not in slope-intercept form, we cannot directly read the slope and y-intercept. Therefore, when an equation is not given in slope-intercept form, solve the equation for y to put the equation into slope-intercept form. Then we can read the slope and y-intercept directly from the equation.

Example 7 Finding slopes and intercepts from equations

Find the slope and y-intercept for each of the following linear equations.

a. $2x + y = 6$ **b.** $y + 5 = 4(x - 3)$ **c.** $2x - 5y = 3$

Skill Connection

Solutions to Literal Equations

Solving an equation for a variable is known as solving a literal equation. We studied this in Sections 2.1 and 2.2.

SOLUTION

a. This equation is not in slope-intercept form, so we first put the equation into slope-intercept form.

$$2x + y = 6 \qquad \text{Solve for } y.$$
$$\underline{-2x \qquad\quad -2x}$$
$$y = -2x + 6$$

Now that the equation is in slope-intercept form, we can see that the slope is -2 and the y-intercept is $(0, 6)$.

b. This equation is not in slope-intercept form, so we first put the equation into slope-intercept form.

$$y + 5 = 4(x - 3) \qquad \text{Distribute on the right.}$$
$$y + 5 = 4x - 12 \qquad \text{Solve for } y.$$
$$\underline{-5 \qquad\quad -5}$$
$$y = 4x - 17$$

Now that the equation is in slope-intercept form, we can see that the slope is 4 and the y-intercept is $(0, -17)$.

c. This equation is not in slope-intercept form, so we first put the equation into slope-intercept form.

$$2x - 5y = 3 \qquad\qquad \text{Solve for } y.$$
$$\underline{-2x \qquad\qquad -2x}$$
$$-5y = -2x + 3$$
$$\frac{-5y}{-5} = \frac{-2x + 3}{-5} \qquad \text{Divide each term by } -5.$$
$$y = \frac{2}{5}x - \frac{3}{5}$$

Now that the equation is in slope-intercept form, we can see that the slope is $\frac{2}{5}$ and the y-intercept is $\left(0, -\frac{3}{5}\right)$.

PRACTICE PROBLEM FOR EXAMPLE 7

Find the slope and y-intercept of the given equations.

a. $y = 3x - 10$ **b.** $2y = 8x + 5$

c. $y - 8 = \frac{2}{3}(x + 6)$ **d.** $4x + 3y = 1$

3.3 Exercises

For Exercises 1 through 10, use the graphs to find the x-intercept(s) and y-intercept for each line or curve.

1.

2.

3.

4.

5.

6.

7.

8.

9.

10.

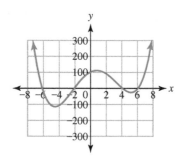

For Exercises 11 through 18, use the given information to answer the questions.

11.

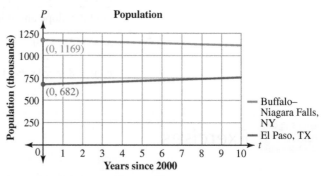

Source: Statistical Abstract of the United States, 2008, Table 20.

a. Interpret the vertical intercept for the Buffalo–Niagara Falls, New York, line.

b. Interpret the vertical intercept for the El Paso, Texas, line.

12.

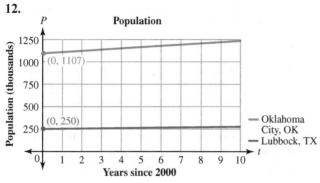

Source: Statistical Abstract of the United States, 2008, Table 20.

a. Interpret the vertical intercept for the Oklahoma City, Oklahoma, line.

b. Interpret the vertical intercept for the Lubbock, Texas, line.

13.

Source: Nutristrategy.com.

Interpret the intercept for these lines.

14.

Source: Nutristrategy.com.

Interpret the intercept for these lines.

15.

Source: Centers for Disease Control and Prevention.

a. Interpret the vertical intercept for the California line.

b. Interpret the vertical intercept for the Florida line.

16.

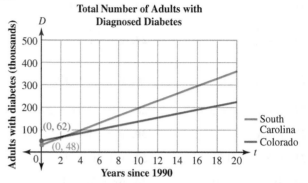

Source: Centers for Disease Control and Prevention.

a. Interpret the vertical intercept for the South Carolina line.

b. Interpret the vertical intercept for the Colorado line.

17.

a. Interpret the vertical and horizontal intercepts for the Rock-On Live Tour line.

b. Interpret the vertical and horizontal intercepts for the Classics Rule Tour line.

18.

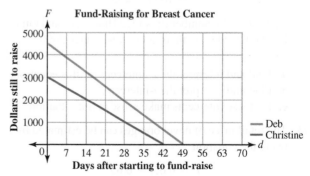

a. Interpret the vertical and horizontal intercepts for the line that represents Deb's fund-raising.

b. Interpret the vertical and horizontal intercepts for the line that represents Christine's fund-raising.

For Exercises 19 through 40, find the x-intercept and y-intercept of the given equations.

19. $y = 5x + 20$

20. $y = 2x + 12$

21. $y = 4x - 36$

22. $y = 3x - 12$

23. $y = \frac{1}{2}x + 3$

24. $y = \frac{1}{2}x - 5$

25. $y = \frac{2}{3}x + 6$

26. $y = \frac{4}{5}x + 10$

27. $y = 0.25x + 3.75$

28. $y = -1.4x + 2.8$

29. $y = x$

30. $y = -x$

31. $x + 5y = 15$

32. $x + 4y = 20$

33. $4x - 2y = 10$

34. $6x - 3y = 15$

35. $4x + 3y = 30$

36. $2x - 3y = 12$

37. $y = 6$

38. $y = -3$

39. $x = -5$

40. $x = 2$

For Exercises 41 through 48, use the given information to answer the questions.

41. The number of American Indians and Alaska Natives in the United States can be estimated by using the equation

$$P = 38t + 2674$$

where P is the number of American Indians and Alaska Natives in thousands t years since 2000.
Source: Statistical Abstract of the United States, 2008, Table 6.

a. Find and interpret the P-intercept for this equation.
b. Find and interpret the t-intercept.
c. Do these intercepts make sense in this situation?

42. The number of Native Hawaiians and Other Pacific Islanders in the United States can be estimated by using the equation

$$P = 10.6t + 465$$

where P is the number of Native Hawaiians and Other Pacific Islanders in thousands t years since 2000.
Source: Statistical Abstract of the United States, 2008, Table 6.

a. Find and interpret the P-intercept for this equation.
b. Find and interpret the t-intercept.
c. Do these intercepts make sense in this situation?

43. The retail price of navel oranges can be estimated by using the equation

$$P = 0.05t + 0.65$$

where P is the price of navel oranges in dollars per pound t years since 2000.
Source: Statistical Abstract of the United States, 2008, Table 709.

a. Find and interpret the P-intercept for this equation.
b. Find and interpret the t-intercept.
c. Do these intercepts make sense in this situation?

44. The average price of residential natural gas can be estimated by using the equation

$$P = 1.5t + 5.0$$

where P is the average price of residential natural gas in dollars per 1000 cubic feet t years since 2000.
Source: Statistical Abstract of the United States, 2008, Table 710.

a. Find and interpret the P-intercept for this equation.
b. Find and interpret the t-intercept.
c. Do these intercepts make sense in this situation?

45. The number of cars sold at Big Jim's Car Lot can be estimated by using the equation

$$C = -2w + 25$$

where C is the number of cars sold during week w of the year.

a. Find and interpret the C-intercept for this equation.
b. Find and interpret the w-intercept.
c. Do these intercepts make sense in this situation?

46. The amount of time it takes to create personalized candy bars can be estimated by using the equation

$$T = 2c + 40$$

where T is the time in minutes it takes to make c personalized candy bars.

a. Find and interpret the T-intercept for this equation.
b. Find and interpret the c-intercept.
c. Do these intercepts make sense in this situation?

47. The amount of credit card debt that José has can be estimated by using the equation

$$D = -250m + 12{,}500$$

where D is the credit card debt in dollars m months after he starts to pay his credit cards off.

a. Find and interpret the D-intercept for this equation.
b. Find and interpret the m-intercept.
c. Do these intercepts make sense in this situation?

48. The amount of credit card debt that Svetlana has can be estimated by using the equation

$$D = -100m + 5400$$

where D is the credit card debt in dollars m months after starting to pay her credit cards off.

a. Find and interpret the D-intercept for this equation.
b. Find and interpret the m-intercept.
c. Do these intercepts make sense in this situation?

For Exercises 49 through 64, find the slope, x-intercept, and y-intercept of the given equations.

49. $y = -3x + 27$

50. $y = -4x + 12$

51. $y = 8x - 16$

52. $y = 5x - 10$

53. $y = \frac{1}{2}x + 6$

54. $y = \frac{1}{2}x - 4$

55. $y = -\dfrac{1}{3}x + 5$ **56.** $y = -\dfrac{1}{5}x + 2$

57. $y = \dfrac{2}{3}x - 4$ **58.** $y = \dfrac{3}{4}x - 18$

59. $y = 1.5x - 3$ **60.** $y = 0.25x - 5$

61. $y = -5$ **62.** $y = 4$

63. $x = 6$ **64.** $x = -2$

65. Find and interpret the slope of the equation from Exercise 41.

66. Find and interpret the slope of the equation from Exercise 42.

67. Find and interpret the slope of the equation from Exercise 43.

68. Find and interpret the slope of the equation from Exercise 44.

69. Find and interpret the slope of the equation from Exercise 45.

70. Find and interpret the slope of the equation from Exercise 46.

71. The total revenue earned by Cisco Systems, Inc. can be estimated by the equation

$$R = 5t + 29.4$$

where R is the total revenue in billions of dollars t years since 2005.
Source: http://finance.google.com, accessed October 2008.

a. Find and interpret the R-intercept for this equation.
b. Find and interpret the slope of this equation.

72. The total gross profit earned by Cisco Systems, Inc. can be estimated by the equation

$$P = 3t + 19.3$$

where P is the total gross profit in billions of dollars t years since 2005.
Source: http://finance.google.com, accessed October 2008.

a. Find and interpret the P-intercept for this equation.
b. Find and interpret the slope of this equation.

For Exercises 73 through 86, find the slope and y-intercept of the given equations. (Hint: Put in $y = mx + b$ form as in Example 7.)

73. $3x + y = 18$ **74.** $2x + y = 4$

75. $3x + 2y = 6$ **76.** $4x + 5y = 10$

77. $2x - 7y = 21$ **78.** $5x - 6y = 42$

79. $x - 2y = -7$ **80.** $5x - 4y = -15$

81. $y + 3 = 2(x - 5)$ **82.** $y + 7 = 3(x + 4)$

83. $y - 2 = \dfrac{1}{2}(x + 20)$

84. $y - 6 = \dfrac{1}{5}(x + 55)$

85. $y - 7 = 0$

86. $y + 2 = 0$

3.4 Linear Equations and Their Graphs

LEARNING OBJECTIVES

- Graph from slope-intercept form.
- Graph from general form.
- Describe a linear equation.
- Discern and graph parallel lines.
- Distinguish and graph perpendicular lines.

Graphing from Slope-Intercept Form

Now that we know how to find the slope and y-intercept of a line from an equation in slope-intercept form, $y = mx + b$, we want to use this information to make graphing lines easier. The y-intercept is a point on the line that can be used as a starting point. The slope will then tell us in what direction to go from that point. The idea of slope as rise over run becomes the basis for finding other points on the line that we can use to draw the line.

Steps to Graphing Lines Using the Slope and y-Intercept

1. Determine the slope and y-intercept from the equation $y = mx + b$.
2. Plot the y-intercept $(0, b)$ on the graph.
3. Write the slope in fraction form. Use the slope to count the rise and run from the y-intercept to another point on the line. Repeat the rise and run process to find a third point. Work from left to right.
4. Draw a straight line through the points.

Example 1 Graphing lines using the slope and y-intercept

Graph the following linear equations using the slope and y-intercept. Graph at least three points.

a. $y = \dfrac{2}{3}x + 1$ **b.** $y = -2x + 3$

SOLUTION

a. From the equation $y = \dfrac{2}{3}x + 1$, we see that the slope is $m = \dfrac{2}{3} = \dfrac{\text{rise}}{\text{run}}$ and the y-intercept is the point $(0, 1)$. Start by plotting the y-intercept, $(0, 1)$, and then use the slope to rise 2 and run 3 from the y-intercept. Repeat the rise/run process twice to find two additional points on the line and then connect them with a straight line.

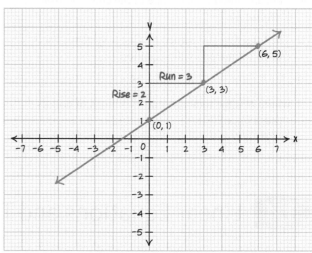

b. From the equation $y = -2x + 3$, we see that the slope is $-2 = \dfrac{-2}{1} = \dfrac{\text{rise}}{\text{run}}$ and the y-intercept is the point $(0, 3)$. Start by plotting the y-intercept, $(0, 3)$, and then use the slope to rise -2 and run 1 from the y-intercept. Since the rise is negative, we go down 2 instead of up. Repeating this process twice yields two more points on the graph.

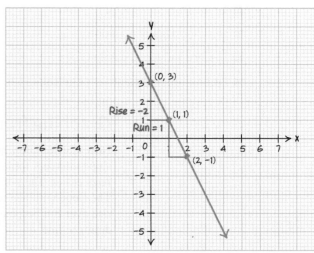

PRACTICE PROBLEM FOR EXAMPLE 1

Graph the following linear equations using the slope and y-intercept. Graph at least three points.

a. $y = 3x - 4$ **b.** $y = -\dfrac{3}{4}x - 3$

Using the slope and y-intercept of a line to graph is like giving someone directions to your house. First, you must know where they are coming from (use as a starting point the y-intercept) so that you can give them correct directions (a slope). The slope does no good without a starting point and vice versa.

Some linear equations are not already in slope-intercept form. When we are given an equation not in slope-intercept form, we start by putting the equation into slope-intercept form. We will then determine the slope and the y-intercept and use this information to graph the line.

Example 2   Graphing lines from a different form

Graph the linear equation $y + 3 = \dfrac{1}{5}(x + 10)$ using the slope and y-intercept. Graph at least three points.

SOLUTION

The equation $y + 3 = \dfrac{1}{5}(x + 10)$ is not in slope-intercept form, so before we start graphing, we will solve for y and put the equation into slope-intercept form.

$$y + 3 = \frac{1}{5}(x + 10) \qquad \text{Distribute on the right side.}$$

$$y + 3 = \frac{1}{5}x + 2 \qquad \text{Solve for } y.$$

$$\underline{-3 \qquad\quad -3}$$

$$y = \frac{1}{5}x - 1$$

Now we can see that the slope is $\dfrac{1}{5}$ and the y-intercept is the point $(0, -1)$. First plotting the y-intercept of $(0, -1)$ and then using the slope $m = \dfrac{1}{5} = \dfrac{\text{rise}}{\text{run}}$, we get the following graph.

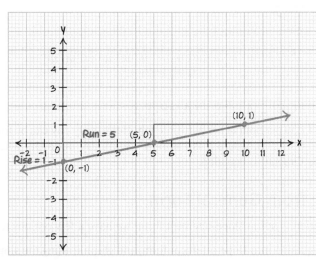

PRACTICE PROBLEM FOR EXAMPLE 2

Graph the linear equation $y - 8 = \dfrac{2}{3}(x - 6)$ using the slope and y-intercept. Graph at least three points.

Example 3 Graphing a cost equation

It costs $7 for admission to the local carnival and $1.50 for each game or ride ticket. The cost for someone who pays for admission and purchases t tickets can be found with the equation

$$C = 1.5t + 7$$

where C is the cost in dollars for admission and tickets at the local carnival when t tickets are purchased. Graph the cost equation.

SOLUTION

This equation is in slope-intercept form, so the slope is 1.5 and the vertical intercept is the point $(0, 7)$. With a decimal value of slope, it is easier to convert the decimal to a fraction to determine the rise and run.

$$m = 1.5 = \frac{15}{10} = \frac{3}{2} = \frac{\text{rise}}{\text{run}}$$

Starting at the vertical intercept, $(0, 7)$, we rise 3 and run over 2. In this case, the horizontal axis is scaled by twos to include more numbers of tickets. We also scaled the vertical axis by fives to include enough costs. When counting the rise, notice that each little box on the graph paper represents 1, so we rise 3 little boxes. When counting the run, each tick mark represents 2.

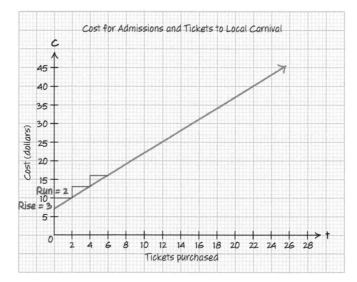

PRACTICE PROBLEM FOR EXAMPLE 3

Fatima earns $11.50 per hour at her part-time job. Her weekly pay can be found by using the equation $P = 11.50h$, where P is Fatima's weekly pay in dollars when she works h hours a week. Graph this equation.

Graphing from General Form

When an equation is not in slope-intercept form, we have a few options to graph it.

- Put the equation into slope-intercept form, and graph it using the slope and y-intercept.
- Build a table of points, as in Section 3.1.
- Find the x- and y-intercepts for the equation, and use those to graph the line.

Skill Connection

Converting decimals to fractions

Recall from Section R.3 how to convert a decimal to a fraction. Remove the decimal, and divide the number by the place value of the last decimal digit.

Convert 1.5 to a fraction.

   Because the 5 is in the tenths place, we divide by 10. This fraction can then be reduced.

$$1.5 = \frac{15}{10} = \frac{3}{2}$$

Convert 2.37 to a fraction.

   Because the 7 is in the hundredths place, we divide by 100.

$$2.37 = \frac{237}{100}$$

Another form that linear equations are often written in is called the **general form** of a line. The general form is

$$Ax + By = C$$

where A, B, and C are real numbers and both A and B are not zero. One of the differences between the slope-intercept form and general form of a line is that all lines can be represented with the general form, but the slope-intercept form cannot represent vertical lines. We will see the general form of a line used extensively in Chapter 4.

> ### DEFINITION
>
> **The General Form of a Line**   The general form of a line is
>
> $$Ax + By = C$$
>
> where A, B, and C are real numbers and both A and B are not zero.

When an equation is in general form, we cannot read the slope and y-intercept directly from the equation. Instead, we will find the x- and y-intercepts and use these points to draw the graph. Up until now, we have required at least three points to graph a line. Now that we have become more proficient at graphing lines, we will use a fact from geometry that states that two points uniquely determine a line.

> ### Steps to Graphing a Linear Equation Using Intercepts
>
> **1.** Find the x-intercept by substituting zero for y and solving for x.
> **2.** Find the y-intercept by substituting zero for x and solving for y.
> **3.** Plot both intercepts, and draw a line through the points.

> ### Connecting the Concepts
>
> **How do we write a line in general form?**
>
> When we write a line in general form, the values of A, B, and C are usually written as integers. To put the equation $\frac{1}{2}x + y = -3$ in general form, we clear out the fraction. Both sides of the equation are multiplied by 2 (the least common denominator). This gives the equation
>
> $$2\left(\frac{1}{2}x + y\right) = 2(-3)$$
> $$x + 2y = -6$$
>
> This last equation is in the general form of the line.

Example 4   Graphing lines using intercepts

Graph the following linear equations using the x- and y-intercepts. Label the intercepts.

a. $3x + 2y = 12$

b. $2x - 5y = 15$

SOLUTION

a. The equation $3x + 2y = 12$ is in general form, so we will find the intercepts and graph the line. To find the y-intercept, substitute in $x = 0$ and solve for y.

$$3(0) + 2y = 12$$
$$2y = 12$$
$$y = 6$$

Therefore, the point $(0, 6)$ is the y-intercept. To find the x-intercept, substitute in $y = 0$ and solve for x.

$$3x + 2(0) = 12$$
$$3x = 12$$
$$x = 4$$

Therefore, the point $(4, 0)$ is the x-intercept. Use these two points to graph the line.

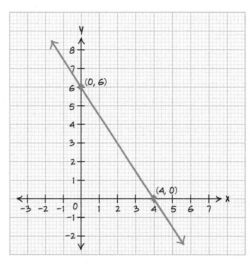

b. The equation $2x - 5y = 15$ is in general form, so we will find the intercepts and graph the line. To find the y-intercept, substitute in $x = 0$ and solve for y.

$$2(0) - 5y = 15$$
$$-5y = 15$$
$$y = -3$$

Therefore, the point $(0, -3)$ is the y-intercept. To find the x-intercept, substitute in $y = 0$ and solve for x.

$$2x - 5(0) = 15$$
$$2x = 15$$
$$x = 7.5$$

Therefore, the point $(7.5, 0)$ is the x-intercept. Use these two points to graph the line.

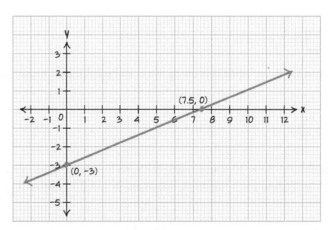

PRACTICE PROBLEM FOR EXAMPLE 4

Graph the following linear equations using the x- and y-intercepts. Label the intercepts.

a. $x + 5y = 20$ **b.** $3x - 4y = 8$

Example 5   Graphing lines using intercepts

To stay within budget, Antonio must not spend more than $300 on incentives for the next sales meeting. Antonio plans to buy a combination of $30 and $15 gift cards. If Antonio spends the entire $300 budget, the possible numbers of each kind of gift card can be found by using the equation $30T + 15F = 300$. Here, T is the number of $30 gift cards and F is the number of $15 gift cards purchased.

a. Graph the given equation.

b. Using the graph, determine how many $15 gift cards can be purchased if five $30 gift cards are purchased.

SOLUTION

a. Begin by finding the intercepts for the graph. In this case, either variable can be used on the horizontal or vertical axis. We select T on the horizontal axis and F on the vertical axis.

$$30T + 15F = 300$$
$$30(0) + 15F = 300$$
$$15F = 300$$
$$F = 20$$
$$(0, 20) \qquad \text{The vertical intercept.}$$

$$30T + 15(0) = 300$$
$$30T = 300$$
$$T = 10$$
$$(10, 0) \qquad \text{The horizontal intercept.}$$

Using these intercepts, we get the following graph.

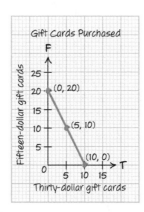

b. On the graph, we can see that the point (5, 10) is on the line. This point means that if five $30 cards are purchased, then ten $15 cards can be bought.

PRACTICE PROBLEM FOR EXAMPLE 5

Amanda has two credit cards, one charging 15% interest and the other charging 20% interest. Amanda paid $1135 in interest this year. The possible balances on each credit card can be found by using the equation $0.15A + 0.20B = 1135$, where A is the amount in dollars owed on the credit card that charges 15% interest and B is the amount in dollars owed on the credit card that charges 20% interest.

a. Graph the given equation.

b. Using the graph, estimate the amount Amanda owes on the card charging 20% if she owes $4500 on the card charging 15%.

There are several ways to graph a line given in general form. One is by using the intercepts, as we just learned. Another way is to create a table of values and graph the points, as in Section 3.1. Yet a third way is to put the equation of the line into $y = mx + b$ form and then graph using the slope and y-intercept.

> **Example 6** Converting general form into slope-intercept form for graphing

Graph the line $12x - 3y = -6$ by completing the following steps.

a. Put the equation $12x - 3y = -6$ into $y = mx + b$ form.

b. Graph the line using the slope and y-intercept.

SOLUTION

a. Solve the equation $12x - 3y = -6$ for y.

$$12x - 3y = -6$$

$$\underline{-12x \qquad\qquad -12x} \qquad\qquad \text{Subtract } 12x \text{ from both sides.}$$

$$-3y = -12x - 6$$

$$\frac{-3y}{-3} = \frac{-12x}{-3} - \frac{6}{-3} \qquad \text{Divide each term by } -3 \text{ on both sides.}$$

$$y = 4x + 2$$

b. The equation of the line $y = 4x + 2$ is now in $y = mx + b$ form. We see that the y-intercept is the point $(0, 2)$ and the slope is $m = 4 = \dfrac{4}{1}$. Graphing the line yields the following graph.

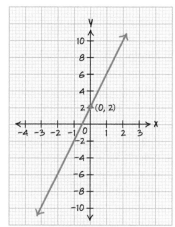

Recognizing a Linear Equation

When we are working with equations, it is helpful to recognize which equations are linear. The two forms of linear equations that we have studied so far give us some information about what a linear equation will or will not contain.

$$y = mx + b \qquad \text{and} \qquad Ax + By = C$$

Both have variables that have an exponent of 1 and are not multiplied or divided by each other. Any equation of two variables that can be simplified into one of these forms is linear.

■ Connecting the Concepts

What is not in a linear equation?

Linear equations have x and y raised only to the first power. The variables x and y cannot be inside an absolute value, under a square root, or in a denominator. The variables x and y are in separate terms, never combined into the same term.

DEFINITION

Linear Equation An equation that can be put into one of the following forms is called a **linear equation.**

$$y = mx + b \qquad \text{and} \qquad Ax + By = C$$

where m, b, A, B, and C are real numbers and both A and B are not zero.

The graph of a linear equation will be a straight line.

Note: The exponents on x and y in a linear equation can only be 1.

| Example 7 | Determining linear equations |

Determine whether the following equations are linear equations. If the equation is linear, put it into slope-intercept or general form.

a. $y + 3 = 2(x + 5)$ **b.** $y = 3x^2 + 5$

c. $3y - 4x = -5x + 7$ **d.** $5xy = 30$

SOLUTION

a. This equation can be simplified to slope-intercept form, so it is a linear equation.

$$y + 3 = 2(x + 5)$$
$$y + 3 = 2x + 10$$
$$\underline{ -3 \qquad\quad -3}$$
$$y = 2x + 7$$

b. This equation has the variable x raised to the second power, so this is not a linear equation.

c. This equation can be simplified to the general form, so it is a linear equation.

$$3y - 4x = -5x + 7$$
$$-4x + 3y = -5x + 7$$
$$\underline{+5x \qquad\qquad\quad +5x}$$
$$x + 3y = 7$$

d. This equation has the variables x and y *multiplied* together, so this is not a linear equation.

PRACTICE PROBLEM FOR EXAMPLE 7

Determine whether the following equations are linear equations. If the equation is linear, put it into slope-intercept or general form.

a. $y - 8 = 4(x - 2) - 7$ **b.** $20 = 2xy + 7$

Parallel and Perpendicular Lines

CONCEPT INVESTIGATION

Are those lines parallel?

1. Graph the two lines on the same axes.

$y = -2x + 3$

$y = -2x - 4$

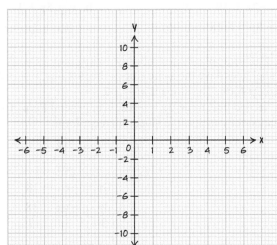

2. Are the two lines in part 1 parallel?

3. Find the slopes of the two lines in part 1. Are the slopes the same or different?

4. Graph the two lines on the same axes.

$$y = \frac{1}{2}x + 3$$

$$y = 0.5x - 4$$

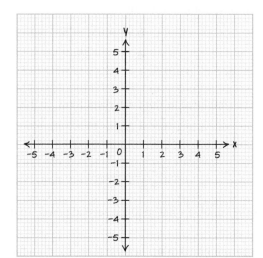

5. Are the two lines in part 4 parallel?

6. Find the slopes of the two lines in part 4. Are the slopes the same or different?

7. Make a conjecture about the slopes of parallel lines.

In the preceding Concept Investigation, we saw that the lines graphed were parallel and had the same slope. In fact, this is always true.

DEFINITION

Parallel Lines   Two lines that have the same slope are parallel. If the slope of the first line is m_1 and the slope of the second line is m_2, then the two lines are parallel when $m_1 = m_2$.

Example 8   Determine whether the lines are parallel

Determine whether or not the two lines are parallel.

a. $y = -2x + 10$

  $6x + 3y = -18$

b. $y = 5x + 1$

  $40x + 8y = 3$

SOLUTION

a. Parallel lines have the same slope. The first line, $y = -2x + 10$, is in slope-intercept form. The slope is $m = -2$.

The second line, $6x + 3y = -18$, is in general form. To find the slope, solve this equation for y to put it in slope-intercept form.

$$
\begin{array}{ll}
6x + 3y = -18 & \text{Isolate } y \text{ by subtracting } 6x \\
\underline{-6x \qquad\qquad -6x} & \text{from both sides.} \\
3y = -6x - 18 & \\
\dfrac{3y}{3} = \dfrac{-6x}{3} - \dfrac{18}{3} & \text{Divide both sides by 3 to} \\
& \text{solve for } y. \\
y = -2x - 6 & \text{This is in slope-intercept form.}
\end{array}
$$

The slope of this second line is $m = -2$. Because the two lines have the same slope, they are parallel lines.

b. Parallel lines have the same slope. The first line, $y = 5x + 1$, is in slope-intercept form. The slope is $m = 5$.
The second line, $40x + 8y = 3$, is in general form. To find the slope, solve this equation for y to put it in slope-intercept form.

$$40x + 8y = 3$$

Isolate y by subtracting $40x$ from both sides.

$$\underline{-40x \qquad\qquad -40x}$$

$$8y = -40x + 3$$

$$\frac{8y}{8} = \frac{-40x}{8} + \frac{3}{8}$$

Divide both sides by 8 to solve for y.

$$y = -5x + \frac{3}{8}$$

This is in slope-intercept form.

The slope of this second line is $m = -5$. Because the two lines have different slope, they are not parallel lines.

PRACTICE PROBLEM FOR EXAMPLE 8

Determine whether or not the two lines are parallel.

a. $y = 5x + 3$

$-20x + 4y = 1$

b. $y = -\dfrac{3}{5}x + 8$

$3x - 5y = 5$

Another type of special lines to be aware of are **perpendicular** lines. Perpendicular lines meet at 90°, or right, angles.

DEFINITION

Perpendicular Lines   Two lines that have slopes that are negative reciprocals of each other are said to be perpendicular. If the slope of the first line is m_1 and the slope of the second line is m_2, then the two lines are perpendicular when $m_1 = \dfrac{-1}{m_2}$.

Example 9   **Determining whether lines are perpendicular**

Determine whether or not the two lines are perpendicular.

a. $y = 3x + 7$

$x + 3y = 15$

b. $y = 4x - 2$

$x - 4y = -24$

SOLUTION

a. Perpendicular lines have slopes that are negative reciprocals. The first line, $y = 3x + 7$, is in slope-intercept form. The slope is $m = 3$.
The second line, $x + 3y = 15$, is in general form. To find the slope, we solve this equation for y to put it in slope-intercept form.

$$x + 3y = 15$$

Isolate y by subtracting x from both sides.

$$\underline{-x \qquad\qquad -x}$$

$$3y = -x + 15$$

$$\frac{3y}{3} = \frac{-x}{3} + \frac{15}{3}$$

Divide both sides by 3 to solve for y.

$$y = \frac{-x}{3} + 5$$

This is in slope-intercept form.

$$y = \frac{-1}{3}x + 5$$

The coefficient on x is $\frac{-1}{3}$.

▮ Skill Connection

Negative Reciprocals

Recall that a reciprocal means to "flip" a fraction over. The reciprocal of $\dfrac{3}{5}$ is $\dfrac{5}{3}$. To find a negative reciprocal, flip the fraction over *and* change the sign. The negative reciprocal of $\dfrac{3}{5}$ is $-\dfrac{5}{3}$.

The slope of this second line is $m = \dfrac{-1}{3}$. Take this slope, $m = \dfrac{-1}{3}$, and find the negative reciprocal.

$$\dfrac{-1}{3}$$ Flip over the fraction, and change the sign.

$$-\left(\dfrac{3}{-1}\right) = \dfrac{3}{1} = 3$$

Because this yields the slope of the first line, 3, the two lines are perpendicular.

b. Perpendicular lines have slopes that are negative reciprocals. The first line, $y = 4x - 2$, is in slope-intercept form. The slope is $m = 4$.
The second line, $x - 4y = -24$, is in general form. To find the slope, we solve this equation for y to put it in slope-intercept form.

$$x - 4y = -24$$ Isolate y by subtracting x from both sides.

$$\underline{-x \qquad\qquad -x}$$

$$-4y = -x - 24$$

$$\dfrac{-4y}{-4} = \dfrac{-x}{-4} - \dfrac{24}{-4}$$ Divide both sides by -4 to solve for y.

$$y = \dfrac{x}{4} + 6$$ This is in slope-intercept form.

$$y = \dfrac{1}{4}x + 6$$ The coefficient on x is $\dfrac{1}{4}$.

The slope of this second line is $m = \dfrac{1}{4}$. The negative reciprocal of $\dfrac{1}{4}$ is $-\dfrac{4}{1} = -4$. Since this does not equal the slope of the first line, $m = 4$, the two lines are not perpendicular.

PRACTICE PROBLEM FOR EXAMPLE 9

Determine whether or not the two lines are perpendicular.

a. $y = \dfrac{5}{2}x + 1$

$2x - 5y = 35$

b. $y = x$

$x + y = 1$

3.4 Exercises

For Exercises 1 through 4, match the equations to the given graphs.

1. $y = 2x + 3$
$y = -2x + 3$
$y = 2x - 3$

Graph A

Graph B

Graph C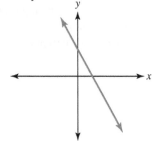

2. $y = -3x + 5$

$y = 3x - 5$

$y = -3x - 5$

Graph A

Graph B

Graph C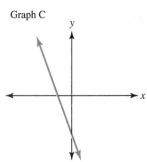

3. $y = \frac{1}{2}x + 2$

$y = \frac{1}{2}x - 3$

$y = \frac{1}{2}x + 5$

Graph A

Graph B

Graph C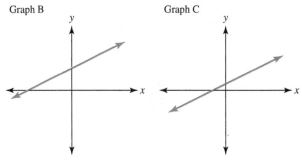

4. $y = -\frac{2}{3}x + 1$

$y = -\frac{2}{3}x + 4$

$y = -\frac{2}{3}x - 6$

Graph A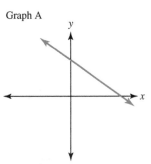

Graph B

Graph C

For Exercises 5 through 22, graph the equation using the slope and y-intercept. Graph at least three points. Clearly label and scale the axes.

5. $y = \frac{1}{2}x - 3$ **6.** $y = \frac{2}{5}x - 4$

7. $y = \frac{1}{3}x + 2$ **8.** $y = \frac{2}{3}x + 1$

9. $y = -\frac{3}{5}x + 6$ **10.** $y = -\frac{3}{4}x + 5$

11. $y = 3x - 8$ **12.** $y = 4x - 10$

13. $y = -2x + 4$ **14.** $y = -3x + 7$

15. $y + 5 = \frac{1}{2}(x + 26)$

16. $y + 3 = \frac{1}{3}(x + 15)$

17. $y + 6 = -2(x + 1)$

18. $y + 4 = -3(x + 2)$

19. $5y = 4x - 30$ **20.** $2y = 3x - 8$

21. $-4y = 3x - 12$ **22.** $-y = x + 3$

For Exercises 23 through 30, an equation is given with a student's graph. Each graph has a mistake in it. Explain what the student did wrong when graphing the given equation.

23. $y = \frac{1}{2}x + 2$

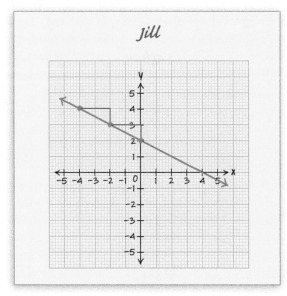

24. $y = \frac{2}{3}x + 1$

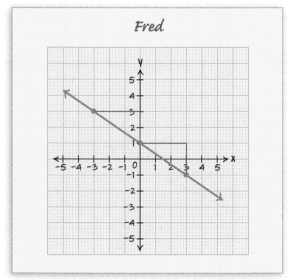
Fred

25. $y = -2x - 3$

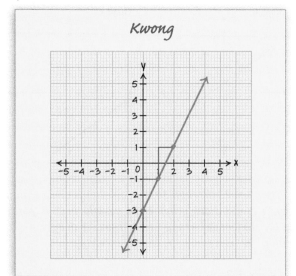
Kwong

26. $y = -\frac{1}{2}x - 1$

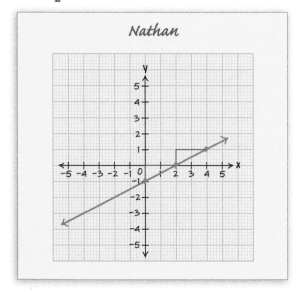
Nathan

27. $y = 2x + 2$

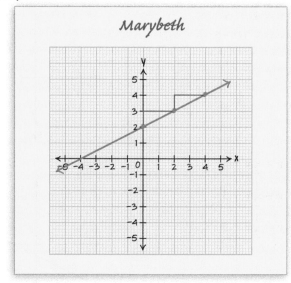
Marybeth

28. $y = -\frac{3}{2}x + 1$

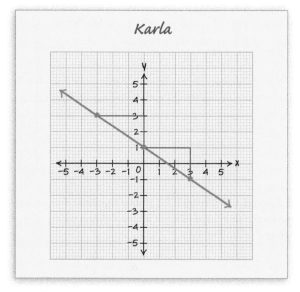
Karla

29. $y = \frac{1}{2}x + 2$

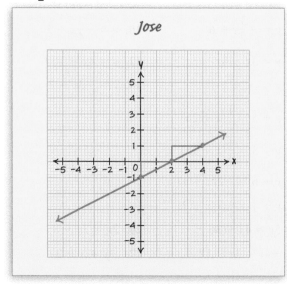
Jose

30. $y = -\dfrac{2}{3}x + 3$

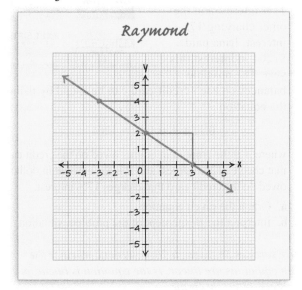

For Exercises 31 through 40, use the given problem situation to graph the equation. Clearly label and scale the axes.

31. The number of cars sold at Big Jim's Car Lot can be estimated by using the equation

$$C = -2w + 25$$

where C is the number of cars sold during week w of the year. Graph this equation.

32. The amount of time it takes to create personalized candy bars can be estimated by using the equation

$$T = 2c + 40$$

where T is the time in minutes it takes to make c personalized candy bars. Graph this equation.

33. The amount of credit card debt that Jose has can be estimated by using the equation

$$D = -250m + 12{,}500$$

where D is the credit card debt in dollars m months after starting to pay his credit cards off. Graph this equation.

34. The amount of credit card debt that Svetlana has can be estimated by using the equation

$$D = -100m + 5400$$

where D is the credit card debt in dollars m months after starting to pay her credit cards off. Graph this equation.

35. The average price of residential natural gas can be estimated by using the equation

$$P = 1.5t + 5.0$$

where P is the average price of residential natural gas in dollars per 1000 cubic feet t years since 2000. Graph this equation.

36. The cost for Hamid to make CDs for his new garage band can be calculated by using the equation

$$C = 1.25n + 100$$

where C is the cost in dollars to make n CDs. Graph this equation.

37. The total revenue for Deere and Company, the makers of John Deere tractors and other agricultural equipment, can be estimated by using the equation

$$R = 1.6t + 13$$

where R is the revenue in billions of dollars t years since 2000. Graph this equation.
Source: http://finance.google.com, accessed October 2008.

38. The total revenue for Apple, Inc. can be estimated by using the equation

$$R = 5.25t + 13.75$$

where R is the revenue in billions of dollars t years since 2005. Graph this equation.
Source: http://finance.google.com, accessed October 2008.

39. The gross profit for Papa John's International, Inc. can be estimated by the equation

$$P = 25t + 238$$

where P is the gross profit in millions of dollars t years since 2005. Graph this equation.
Source: http://finance.google.com, accessed October 2008.

40. The gross profit for McDonald's Corporation can be estimated by the equation

$$P = 0.7t + 6$$

where P is the gross profit in billions of dollars t years since 2005. Graph this equation.
Source: http://finance.google.com, accessed October 2008.

For Exercises 41 through 50, graph the given linear equations using the x- and y-intercepts. Clearly label and scale the axes. Label the intercepts.

41. $2x + 5y = 20$

42. $3x + 4y = 24$

43. $x + 2y = 6$

44. $x + 3y = 12$

45. $4x - 2y = 10$

46. $5x - 7y = 14$

47. $4x - 5y = 15$

48. $3x - 8y = 12$

49. $10x + 35y = 210$

50. $15x - 25y = 300$

For Exercises 51 through 54, use the given information to answer the questions.

51. The number of lawn mowers and tillers that a factory can produce is limited by the amount of time available. It takes 2 hours to make a lawn mower and 3 hours to make a tiller. If there are 80 hours a week when the production line can be run, the number of lawn mowers and tillers that can be produced can be found by using the equation

$$2m + 3t = 80$$

where m is the number of lawn mowers and t is the number of tillers that the plant can produce.

a. Graph the given equation.
b. Using the graph, determine how many lawn mowers the factory can produce if the workers make 12 tillers that week.

52. The number of sets of 20-inch wheels and 24-inch wheels that a custom shop can produce is limited by the amount of time available. It takes 4.5 hours to make a set of 20-inch wheels and 6 hours to make a set of 24-inch wheels. If there are 36 hours a week to run the production equipment, the number of sets of 20-inch wheels and 24-inch wheels that can be produced can be found by using the equation

$$4.5t + 6f = 36$$

where t is the number of 20-inch wheel sets and f is the number of 24-inch wheel sets that the shop can produce.

a. Graph the given equation.
b. Using the graph, determine how many 24-inch wheel sets the shop can produce if the workers make four sets of 20-inch wheel sets that week.

53. Maggie has two credit cards, one charging 16% interest and the other charging 24% interest. Maggie paid $800 in interest this year. The possible balances on each credit card can be found by using the equation

$$0.16A + 0.24B = 800$$

where A is the amount in dollars owed on the credit card that charges 16% interest and B is the amount in dollars owed on the credit card that charges 24% interest.

a. Graph the given equation.
b. Interpret the A-intercept of the problem situation.

54. Irina has two credit cards, one charging 12% interest and the other charging 17% interest. Irina paid $1204 in interest this year. The possible balances on each credit card can be found by using the equation

$$0.12A + 0.17B = 1204$$

where A is the amount in dollars owed on the credit card that charges 12% interest and B is the amount in dollars owed on the credit card that charges 17% interest.

a. Graph the given equation.
b. Interpret the B-intercept of the problem situation.

For Exercises 55 through 70, determine whether the given equations are linear. If the equation is linear, put it into slope-intercept form.

55. $2y + 7 = 3x + 21$ **56.** $3y - 6 = 4x + 8$

57. $12 = 3xy + 9$ **58.** $8 = -2xy - 10$

59. $y = |3x + 1|$ **60.** $y = |2x - 4|$

61. $2x + 3 = 4(y + 8)$ **62.** $5x - 8 = 7(2 - y)$

63. $y = 3x^2 + 5$ **64.** $y = -2x^2 + 10$

65. $y = \dfrac{5}{x} + 2$ **66.** $y = \dfrac{2}{x} - 7$

67. $3x + 8 = 4y - 9$ **68.** $x + 5 = 8 - 7y$

69. $y = x^3 + 2$ **70.** $y = -x^3 + 1$

For Exercises 71 through 82, decide whether you would graph the given equation by using the slope and y-intercept, by using the x- and y-intercepts, or by building a table of points to plot. Do not graph these equations. There are several possible correct answers.

71. $y = \dfrac{2}{9}x + 5$ **72.** $y = \dfrac{7}{3}x - 8$

73. $2x + 8y = 93$ **74.** $5x - 3y = 24$

75. $y = 2x^2 + 5$ **76.** $y = -x^2 + 3$

77. $y + 5 = 2(x - 9)$ **78.** $y - 7 = -3(x + 8)$

79. $y = 2.45x - 3.75$ **80.** $3.5y = 1.78x - 4.26$

81. $y = |x - 4|$ **82.** $y = |7 - x|$

For Exercises 83 through 94, determine whether the lines are parallel, perpendicular, or neither. Do not graph the equations.

83. $y = -3x + 5$ **84.** $y = \dfrac{5}{2}x - 1$

        $y = -3x$ $y = 2.5x + 6$

85. $y = -7x + 2$

$y = \frac{1}{7}x - 44$

86. $y = x - 17$

$y = -x + 9$

91. $2x - 12y = 12$

$y = \frac{1}{6}x + 2$

92. $-4x + 5y = 20$

$y = \frac{4}{5}x - 3$

87. $y = \frac{2}{5}x + 3.5$

$y = \frac{5}{2}x - 3.5$

88. $y = 8x - 12$

$y = \frac{1}{8}x + 11$

93. $x - 6y = 12$

$y = 6x + 7$

94. $y = \frac{3}{8}x - 4$

$8x - 3y = -3$

89. $y = \frac{1}{2}x - 7$

$6x + 3y = 27$

90. $4x + 3y = 15$

$y = \frac{3}{4}x - 2$

3.5 Finding Equations of Lines

LEARNING OBJECTIVES

- ▦ Find equations of lines using slope-intercept form.
- ▦ Solve applications.
- ▦ Find equations of lines using the point-slope form.
- ▦ Find equations of parallel and perpendicular lines.

Finding Equations of Lines Using Slope-Intercept Form

In Section 3.3, we saw that $y = mx + b$ is the equation of a line in slope-intercept form. We will now learn how to use the slope-intercept form of a line to write the equation of a line. To do so, we must determine the value of the slope, m, and the y-intercept $(0, b)$.

Example 1 Finding the equation of a line from a graph with a known y-intercept

Use the graph to find the equation of the line.

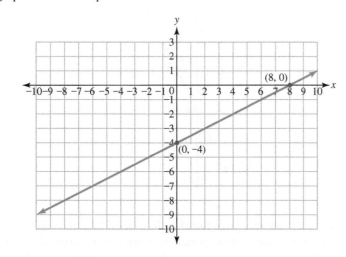

SOLUTION

We have to find the slope, m, and the y-intercept, $(0, b)$, of this line. To find the slope, select two points on the line, and use the definition of slope. Recall that one form of the definition of slope is $m = \dfrac{\text{rise}}{\text{run}}$. Two points on the line are $(0, -4)$ and $(8, 0)$.

Therefore, the slope is

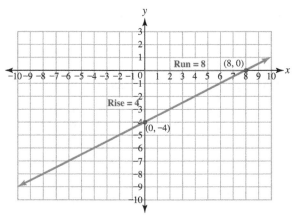

$$m = \frac{\text{rise}}{\text{run}} = \frac{4}{8} = \frac{1}{2}$$

Substitute this value of slope into the slope-intercept form of a line.

$$y = mx + b$$

$$y = \frac{1}{2}x + b \qquad \text{Substitute in } m = \frac{1}{2}.$$

The point where the graph crosses the y-axis is the y-intercept $(0, b)$. That point is $(0, -4)$ so $b = -4$. Substituting this value into our equation yields

$$y = \frac{1}{2}x + b \qquad \text{The linear equation.}$$

$$y = \frac{1}{2}x + (-4) \qquad \text{Substitute in } b = -4.$$

$$y = \frac{1}{2}x - 4 \qquad \text{Simplify.}$$

Therefore, the equation of the line is $y = \dfrac{1}{2}x - 4$.

PRACTICE PROBLEM FOR EXAMPLE 1

Use the following graph to find the equation of the line.

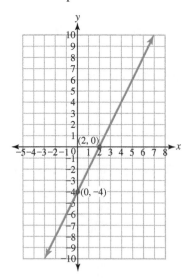

In Example 1, the y-intercept was found by inspection from the graph. However, we cannot always determine the y-intercept exactly by inspection. In problems in which the y-intercept is unknown, use the slope and substitute any point on the line to find the value of the y-intercept b.

> **Steps to Finding the Equation of a Line Using the Slope-Intercept Form**
>
> 1. Using two points on the line, find the slope m.
> 2. To find the y-intercept $(0, b)$, substitute any point on the line in for x and y into $y = mx + b$ and solve for b.
> 3. Write the equation of the line $y = mx + b$ with the specific values for m and b found in steps 1 and 2.
>
> *Note:* x and y will remain variables in the final answer.

Example 2   **Finding the equation of a line from a graph with an unknown y-intercept**

Use the graph to find the equation of the line.

a.

b.

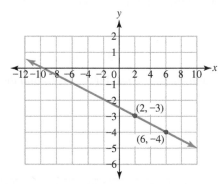

SOLUTION

a. Two points on the graph are $(-7, -3)$ and $(2, 3)$. To find the slope, we use the $m = \dfrac{\text{rise}}{\text{run}}$ definition.

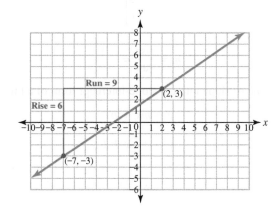

Therefore, the slope is

$$m = \frac{\text{rise}}{\text{run}} = \frac{6}{9} = \frac{2}{3}$$

Substitute this value of slope into the slope-intercept form of a line.

$$y = mx + b$$

$$y = \frac{2}{3}x + b$$

To find the y-intercept, $(0, b)$, substitute either point into the equation. Selecting $(2, 3)$ and substituting it into the equation, we get

$$y = \frac{2}{3}x + b$$

$$3 = \frac{2}{3}(2) + b \qquad \text{Substitute } x = 2, y = 3, \text{ and simplify.}$$

$$3 = \frac{4}{3} + b \qquad \text{Solve for } b.$$

$$\underline{-\frac{4}{3} \qquad -\frac{4}{3}}$$

$$3 - \frac{4}{3} = b \qquad \text{Find like denominators.}$$

$$\frac{9}{3} - \frac{4}{3} = b$$

$$\frac{5}{3} = b$$

Now that we have found the slope $m = \frac{2}{3}$ and $b = \frac{5}{3}$, write the equation of the line using these values.

$$y = \frac{2}{3}x + \frac{5}{3}$$

b. Two points on the graph are $(2, -3)$ and $(6, -4)$. To find the slope, use the $m = \frac{\text{rise}}{\text{run}}$ definition.

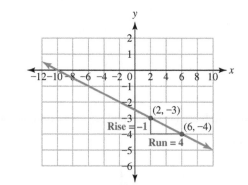

$$m = \frac{\text{rise}}{\text{run}} = \frac{-1}{4}$$

Substitute this value of slope into the slope-intercept form of a line.

$$y = mx + b$$

$$y = -\frac{1}{4}x + b$$

To find the y-intercept, $(0, b)$, substitute either point into the equation. Selecting $(2, -3)$ and substituting it into the equation, we get

$$y = -\frac{1}{4}x + b$$

$$-3 = -\frac{1}{4}(2) + b \quad \textit{Substitute } x = 2, y = -3, \textit{ and simplify.}$$

$$-3 = -\frac{1}{2} + b \quad \textit{Solve for } b.$$

$$\underline{+\frac{1}{2} \quad +\frac{1}{2}}$$

$$-3 + \frac{1}{2} = b$$

$$-\frac{6}{2} + \frac{1}{2} = b \quad \textit{Find like denominators.}$$

$$-\frac{5}{2} = b$$

Now that we have found the slope $m = -\frac{1}{4}$ and $b = -\frac{5}{2}$, write the equation of the line using these values.

$$y = -\frac{1}{4}x - \frac{5}{2}$$

PRACTICE PROBLEM FOR EXAMPLE 2

Use the graph to find the equation of the line.

a.

b.

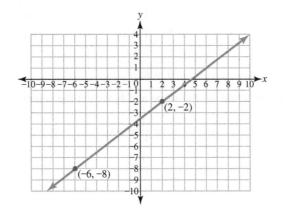

Finding Equations of Lines from Applications

If we know that the relationship between the variables in an application is linear, then we can use any two points to find the value of the slope and y-intercept. Using these, we can generate the equation of the line.

Example 3 · Inches of rain from snow

In Section 1.2, we examined the relationship in the conversion between the inches of snowfall into the inches of rainfall. There is a linear relationship between the inches of snow, s, and the inches of rain, r. Find the equation of the line that passes through these points.

$s =$ Inches of snow	$r =$ Inches of rain
12	$\dfrac{12}{12} = 1$
24	$\dfrac{24}{12} = 2$
36	$\dfrac{36}{12} = 3$
42	$\dfrac{42}{12} = 3.5$

Mark Clark

SOLUTION

Two points on the line are (12, 1) and (24, 2). Because we were not given the graph, use the formula definition of slope to compute the slope of this line.

$$m = \frac{y_2 - y_1}{x_2 - x_1} = \frac{2 - 1}{24 - 12} = \frac{1}{12}$$

Substitute this value of slope into the slope-intercept form of a line.

$$y = mx + b \qquad \textit{Slope-intercept form of a line.}$$

$$r = ms + b \qquad \textit{Use the variables from the problem.}$$

$$r = \frac{1}{12}s + b$$

To find the y-intercept, $(0, b)$, substitute either point into the equation. Selecting (12, 1) and substituting it into the equation, we get

$$r = \frac{1}{12}s + b$$

$$1 = \frac{1}{12}(12) + b \qquad \textit{Substitute } s = 12, r = 1,$$
$$\textit{and simplify.}$$

$$1 = 1 + b \qquad \textit{Solve for b.}$$

$$\underline{-1 \quad\ -1}$$

$$0 = b$$

Using the values we found for the slope and b, we get the equation of the line

$$r = \frac{1}{12}s + 0$$

$$r = \frac{1}{12}s$$

PRACTICE PROBLEM FOR EXAMPLE 3

The conversion between the number of hours, h, and the number of days, d, is given in the following table. A linear relationship exists between the variables h and d. Find the equation of the line that passes through these points.

h = Number of hours	d = Number of days
12	$\dfrac{12}{24} = 0.5$
24	$\dfrac{24}{24} = 1$
36	$\dfrac{36}{24} = 1.5$
72	$\dfrac{72}{24} = 3$

   In some applications, the two points are given in the wording of the problem. We have to read the problem carefully to find the relationship between the two variables. These relationships can be written as points and used to find the slope and the value of b. We can then write the equation of the line that describes the linear relationship between the variables.

Example 4 Converting from Celsius to Fahrenheit

Two methods of measuring temperature are degrees Fahrenheit (°F) and degrees Celsius (°C). Water freezes at 32°F, which is the same as 0°C. Water boils at 212°F, which is equal to 100°C. The two quantities (°F and °C) have a linear relationship.

a. Find the equation of the line that describes this relationship. Let the input C represent degrees Celsius, and let the output F represent degrees Fahrenheit.

b. Interpret the slope of the linear equation.

c. Find and interpret the intercepts of the linear equation.

d. Find F when $C = 20$. Interpret the solution in the context of measuring temperature.

SOLUTION

a. First, define the variables. The input variable C represents the degrees Celsius. The output variable F represents the degrees Fahrenheit. Two points on the line are $(C, F) = (0, 32)$ and $(C, F) = (100, 212)$. Notice that we could switch the input and output in this situation, but we will select the input variable C and the output variable F. Therefore, in the slope-intercept form of a line,

$$y = mx + b$$

we will have

$$F = mC + b$$

The slope of this line can be calculated by using the slope formula.

$$m = \frac{y_2 - y_1}{x_2 - x_1} \qquad \text{We are using } x = C \text{ and } y = F.$$

$$m = \frac{F_2 - F_1}{C_2 - C_1}$$

$$m = \frac{F_2 - F_1}{C_2 - C_1} = \frac{212 - 32}{100 - 0} = \frac{180}{100} = \frac{9}{5}$$

Substituting $m = \dfrac{9}{5}$ into $F = mC + b$ yields

$$F = \dfrac{9}{5}C + b$$

To determine the value of b, we may substitute in either point. Selecting $(C, F) = (0, 32)$ and substituting these values in, we get

$$F = \dfrac{9}{5}C + b$$

$$32 = \dfrac{9}{5}(0) + b \qquad\qquad F = 32, C = 0$$

$$32 = 0 + b$$

$$32 = b$$

Because the point $(0, 32)$ represents the vertical intercept, we could have known that $b = 32$ without substituting any points into the equation. Using the slope $m = \dfrac{9}{5}$ and $b = 32$, we get the equation of the line.

$$F = \dfrac{9}{5}C + 32$$

b. The slope is $m = \dfrac{9}{5}$. To interpret the slope, recall that

$$m = \dfrac{9}{5} = \dfrac{\text{change in } F}{\text{change in } C}$$

Attaching units to the numerator and denominator will allow us to interpret the slope in terms of the problem.

$$m = \dfrac{9 \text{ degrees Fahrenheit}}{5 \text{ degrees Celsius}}$$

Therefore, the interpretation of the slope is that for an increase of 9 degrees Fahrenheit, there is an increase of 5 degrees Celsius.

c. One point on the line is $(C, F) = (0, 32)$. This point is the F-intercept because $C = 0$. The interpretation of this point is that it is 32°F when it is 0°C. To find the C-intercept, let $F = 0$ and solve for C.

$$F = \dfrac{9}{5}C + 32$$

$$0 = \dfrac{9}{5}C + 32 \qquad\qquad \text{Substitute } F = 0.$$

$$\underline{-32 \qquad\qquad -32} \qquad\qquad \text{Solve for } C.$$

$$-32 = \dfrac{9}{5}C$$

$$\dfrac{5}{9}(-32) = \dfrac{\cancel{5}}{\cancel{9}}\left(\dfrac{\cancel{9}}{\cancel{5}}C\right) \qquad\qquad \text{Multiply both sides by the reciprocal.}$$

$$-\dfrac{160}{9} = C$$

$$-17.8 \approx C$$

Therefore, 0°F is equivalent to approximately -17.8°C.

d. When $C = 20$, we have

$$F = \dfrac{9}{5}(20) + 32 \qquad \text{Substitute in } C = 20.$$

$$F = 36 + 32$$

$$F = 68$$

Therefore, 20°C is equivalent to 68°F.

Example 5   **Manufacturing toys**

A toy manufacturer is currently producing 2000 toys a week. Beginning in October, the manufacturer will begin to increase production each week by 500 more toys during each week of the Christmas production season. A linear relationship exists between the week w and the number of toys produced, P. Here, $w = 1$ is the first week in October, $w = 2$ is the second week in October, and so on.

Feng Li/Staff/Getty Images Entertainment

a. Find the equation of the line that describes this relationship. Let the input w represent the week number beginning with the first week in October, and let the output P represent the production level of toys in week w.

b. Interpret the slope of the linear equation.

c. Find and interpret the intercepts of the linear equation.

d. Find P when $w = 5$. Interpret the solution in terms of toy production.

SOLUTION

a. In this problem, the toy production is being increased by 500 toys per week. This rate is how fast the production is changing and, therefore, is also the slope of the line. The production of toys depends on the week, so the input is w, and the output is P. Substituting $m = 500$ into $P = mw + b$ yields

$$P = 500w + b$$

When $w = 0$, the plant is producing $P = 2000$ toys. To determine b, we can substitute these values into the linear equation to get

$$P = 500w + b$$

$$2000 = 500(0) + b \qquad w = 0, P = 2000$$

$$2000 = b \qquad \text{Solve for } b.$$

Therefore, the linear equation is

$$P = 500w + 2000$$

b. The slope (from above) is $m = 500$. To interpret the slope, attach the proper units to the numerator and denominator.

$$m = \frac{500}{1} = \frac{\text{change in } P}{\text{change in } w}$$

$$m = \frac{500 \text{ toys}}{1 \text{ week}}$$

Therefore, the plant is producing 500 more toys per week.

c. From part a, we have that when $w = 0$, the plant is producing $P = 2000$ toys. This is the P-intercept, the point $(0, 2000)$, and it means that at the start of the Christmas production season, the plant is producing 2000 toys a week.

d.
$$P = 500(5) + 2000 \qquad \text{Substitute in } w = 5.$$
$$P = 4500$$

Therefore, during the fifth week of the Christmas production season, the plant is producing 4500 toys for that week.

PRACTICE PROBLEM FOR EXAMPLE 5

a. There is a "flash to bang" method for computing the distance that lightning is from you. When you see lightning (the flash), count the number of seconds until you hear the thunder (the bang). Divide the number of seconds by 5 to get the number of miles that the lightning is from you. Let the input s be the number of seconds you count from flash to bang and the output d represent the distance in miles the lightning is from you. There is a linear relationship between s and d. Find the equation of the line that describes this relationship.

Source: http://www.srh.noaa.gov/jetstream/lightning/lightning_safety.htm.

b. Kaito plans to lose weight on his diet. He currently weighs 195 pounds (week 0). He would like to lose 1 pound a week for w weeks. Let the input w represent the week number that he has been on his diet. Let the output N represent the number of pounds that Kaito weighs that week. There is a linear relationship between w and N. Find the equation of the line that describes this relationship.

Finding Equations of Lines Using Point-Slope Form

We have been finding equations of lines using the slope-intercept form, $y = mx + b$. From the formula for slope, we can get another form for the equation of a line called the **point-slope form.**

To derive the equation for the point-slope form, start with the slope formula. Replace (x_2, y_2) with (x, y) so the resulting equation will have the variables (x, y) in it.

$$m = \frac{y_2 - y_1}{x_2 - x_1} \qquad \text{Replace } (x_2, y_2) \text{ with } (x, y).$$

$$m = \frac{y - y_1}{x - x_1}$$

Using this equation for slope, we can derive the point-slope form of a line.

$$m = \frac{y - y_1}{x - x_1}$$

$$(x - x_1)m = \frac{y - y_1}{x - x_1}(x - x_1) \qquad \text{Multiply both sides of the equation by } (x - x_1).$$

$$(x - x_1)m = \frac{y - y_1}{x - x_1}(x - x_1) \qquad \text{Reduce.}$$

$$(x - x_1)m = y - y_1 \qquad \text{Switch the two sides.}$$

$$y - y_1 = m(x - x_1) \qquad \text{This is point-slope form.}$$

> **DEFINITION**
>
> **The Point-Slope Form of the Equation of a Line**   Given the slope of a line, m, and a point on the line, (x_1, y_1), the point-slope form of the line is
>
> $$y - y_1 = m(x - x_1)$$

Example 6   Finding equations using the point-slope form

a. Find the equation of the line with slope $m = \dfrac{-2}{5}$ that passes through the point $(5, 1)$. Put the final answer in slope-intercept form, $y = mx + b$.

b. Using point-slope form, find the equation of the line passing through the points $(3, -4)$ and $(-3, -8)$. Put the final answer in slope-intercept form, $y = mx + b$.

SOLUTION

a. Notice that we have been given a point on the line and the slope. This is a situation in which the point-slope form of a line generates the equation efficiently. We have that $m = \dfrac{-2}{5}$ and $(x_1, y_1) = (5, 1)$. Substituting these values into the point-slope form of a line yields

$$(x_1, y_1) = (5, 1)$$

$$y - 1 = \dfrac{-2}{5}(x - 5) \qquad \text{Substitute } m = \dfrac{-2}{5}$$
$$\text{and } (x_1, y_1) = (5, 1).$$

$$y - 1 = \dfrac{-2}{5}x - \dfrac{-2}{5}(5) \qquad \text{Distribute and simplify.}$$

$$y - 1 = \dfrac{-2}{5}x + 2 \qquad \text{Solve for } y.$$

$$\underline{+1 \qquad\qquad +1}$$

$$y = \dfrac{-2}{5}x + 3$$

Therefore, the equation of the line is $y = \dfrac{-2}{5}x + 3$.

b. As before, first determine the slope of the line.

$$m = \dfrac{y_2 - y_1}{x_2 - x_1} = \dfrac{-8 - (-4)}{-3 - 3}$$

$$m = \dfrac{-8 + 4}{-6} = \dfrac{-4}{-6} = \dfrac{2}{3}$$

Substituting this value in for the slope in the point-slope form yields

$$y - y_1 = \dfrac{2}{3}(x - x_1)$$

We can choose either of the two given points to substitute in for (x_1, y_1). Choosing $(x_1, y_1) = (3, -4)$ and substituting this into our equation, we get

$$y - (-4) = \dfrac{2}{3}(x - 3) \qquad \text{Substitute in } (x_1, y_1) = (3, -4).$$

$$y + 4 = \dfrac{2}{3}(x - 3) \qquad \text{Distribute and simplify.}$$

$$y + 4 = \dfrac{2}{3}x - \dfrac{2}{3}(3)$$

$$y + 4 = \dfrac{2}{3}x - 2 \qquad \text{Solve for } y.$$

$$\underline{-4 \qquad\qquad -4}$$

$$y = \dfrac{2}{3}x - 6$$

Therefore, the equation of the line is $y = \dfrac{2}{3}x - 6$.

PRACTICE PROBLEM FOR EXAMPLE 6

a. Using point-slope form, find the equation of the line passing through the points $(-2, 5)$ and $(2, 3)$. Put the final answer in slope-intercept form, $y = mx + b$.

b. Find the equation of the line with slope $m = \dfrac{1}{6}$ that passes through the point $(6, -1)$. Put the final answer in slope-intercept form, $y = mx + b$.

Finding Equations of Parallel and Perpendicular Lines

We can use the techniques of this section to find the equations of parallel and perpendicular lines.

Example 7 Finding the equation of a line parallel to a given line

Find the equation of the line parallel to $y = \dfrac{-3}{5}x + 1$ passing through the point $(5, 3)$.

SOLUTION

To find the equation of a line, we need both the slope and a point. Parallel lines have the same slope. Therefore, since the slope of the given line is $m = \dfrac{-3}{5}$, the slope of the line for which we are trying to find the equation is also $m = \dfrac{-3}{5}$. Substituting this into slope-intercept form yields

$$y = mx + b \qquad \text{Substitute in } m = \dfrac{-3}{5}.$$

$$y = \dfrac{-3}{5}x + b$$

To find the value of b, substitute in the given point $(5, 3)$ and solve for b.

$$y = \dfrac{-3}{5}x + b \qquad \text{Substitute in the given point (5, 3).}$$

$$3 = \dfrac{-3}{5}(5) + b \qquad \text{Simplify the right side.}$$

$$3 = -3 + b \qquad \text{Solve for } b.$$

$$\underline{+3 \qquad +3}$$

$$6 = b$$

$$y = \dfrac{-3}{5}x + 6 \qquad \text{The equation of the line.}$$

PRACTICE PROBLEM FOR EXAMPLE 7

Find the equation of the line parallel to $y = \dfrac{-1}{2}x - 17$ passing through the point $(-6, 1)$.

Example 8 Finding the equation of a line perpendicular to a given line

Find the equation of the line perpendicular to $y = -3x + 12$ passing through the point $(-9, 2)$.

SOLUTION

To find the equation of a line, we need both the slope and a point. Perpendicular lines have slopes that are negative reciprocals. The slope of the given line is $m = -3$. The slope can be written as

$$-3 = \dfrac{-3}{1}$$

The negative reciprocal is

$$-\left(\dfrac{1}{-3}\right) = \dfrac{1}{3}$$

The slope of the line we are trying to find is $m = \dfrac{1}{3}$.

Substituting this into slope-intercept form yields

$$y = mx + b \qquad \text{Substitute in } m = \frac{1}{3}.$$

$$y = \frac{1}{3}x + b$$

To find the value of b, substitute in the given point $(-9, 2)$ and solve for b.

$$y = \frac{1}{3}x + b \qquad \text{Substitute in the given point } (-9, 2).$$

$$2 = \frac{1}{3}(-9) + b \qquad \text{Simplify the right side.}$$

$$2 = -3 + b \qquad \text{Solve for } b.$$

$$\underline{+3 \quad\;\; +3}$$

$$5 = b$$

$$y = \frac{1}{3}x + 5 \qquad \text{The equation of the line.}$$

PRACTICE PROBLEM FOR EXAMPLE 8

Find the equation of the line perpendicular to $y = \frac{3}{7}x - 1$ passing through the point $(6, -1)$.

3.5   Exercises

For Exercises 1 through 10, use the graph to find the equation of the line. Put the answer in $y = mx + b$ form.

1.

2.

3.

4.

5.

6.

7.

8.

9.

10.

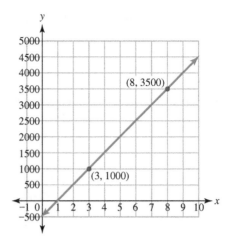

11. There is a linear relationship between the number of years, y, and the number of centuries, c. The accompanying table lists some conversions between the number of years and the number of centuries. Find the equation of the line that describes this relationship.

y = Number of years	c = Number of centuries
0	0
100	1
150	1.5
200	2

12. There is a linear relationship between the number of yards, y, and the number of feet, f. The accompanying table lists some conversions between the number of yards and the number of feet. Find the equation of the line that describes this relationship.

y = Number of yards	f = Number of feet
0	0
1	3
2	6
3	9

13. The temperature drops from 1:00 P.M. onward. Let the input t represent the time of the day, and let the output F represent the temperature in degrees Fahrenheit. At 1:00 P.M. ($t = 1$), the temperature is $F = 75$. At 3:00 P.M. ($t = 3$), the temperature is $F = 71$. Find the linear relationship between t and F.

14. The temperature increases from 6:00 A.M. onward. Let the input t represent the time of the day, and let the output F represent the temperature in degrees Fahrenheit. At 6:00 A.M. ($t = 6$), the temperature is $F = 54$. At 10:00 A.M. ($t = 10$), the temperature is $F = 68$. Find the linear relationship between t and F.

15. Irina goes on a diet to lose weight. Let the input t represent the week of her diet and the output W represent Irina's weight in pounds (lb). At the start of her diet ($t = 0$), Irina weighed 165 pounds. After 4 weeks on her diet, she weighed 157 pounds. Find the linear relationship between t and W.

16. Peter goes on a diet to lose weight. Let the input t represent the week of his diet, and let the output W represent Peter's weight in pounds. At the start of his diet ($t = 0$), Peter weighed 225 pounds. After 6 weeks on his diet, he weighed 207 pounds. Find the linear relationship between t and W.

For Exercises 17 through 22, find and interpret the slope in the context of the given problem.

17. Interpret the slope in terms of the problem situation for Exercise 11.

18. Interpret the slope in terms of the problem situation for Exercise 12.

19. Interpret the slope in terms of the problem situation for Exercise 13.

20. Interpret the slope in terms of the problem situation for Exercise 14.

21. Interpret the slope in terms of the problem situation for Exercise 15.

22. Interpret the slope in terms of the problem situation for Exercise 16.

For Exercises 23 through 28, find and interpret the intercepts in the context of the given problem.

23. Find and interpret the intercepts in terms of the problem situation for Exercise 11.

24. Find and interpret the intercepts in terms of the problem situation for Exercise 12.

25. Find and interpret the intercepts in terms of the problem situation for Exercise 13.

26. Find and interpret the intercepts in terms of the problem situation for Exercise 14.

27. Find and interpret the intercepts in terms of the problem situation for Exercise 15.

28. Find and interpret the intercepts in terms of the problem situation for Exercise 16.

29. The 2009 Toyota Prius has average highway mileage as given in the following table. Let the input g represent the number of gallons of gas used, and let the output d represent the distance in (highway) miles driven.

a. Find the equation of the line that describes this relationship.

b. Interpret the slope in terms of the problem situation.

g = Number of gallons of gas	d = Number of miles driven
2	90
3	135
4	180
5	225

c. Interpret the intercepts in terms of the problem situation.

30. The 2009 Honda Civic has average city mileage as given in the following table. Let the input g represent the number of gallons of gas used, and let the output d represent the distance in (city) miles driven.

a. Find the equation of the line that describes this relationship.

b. Interpret the slope in terms of the problem situation.

g = Number of gallons of gas	d = Number of miles driven
2	46
3	69
4	92
5	115

c. Interpret the intercepts in terms of the problem situation.

31. A local gym is advertising memberships that cost $45.00 a month plus an initial $125 sign-up fee. Let the input m represent the number of months, and let the output c represent the cost. Find the linear relationship between m and c.

a. Find the equation of the line that describes this relationship.

b. Interpret the slope in terms of the problem situation.

c. Interpret the intercepts in terms of the problem situation.

32. A community college charges $26.00 per unit plus a $50.00 health fee. Let the input u represent the number of units enrolled in, and let the output T represent the tuition (charges) for that semester.

a. Find the equation of the line that describes this relationship.

b. Interpret the slope in terms of the problem situation.

c. Interpret the intercepts in terms of the problem situation.

For Exercises 33 through 42, determine the equation of the line that passes through the given points. Put the final answer in $y = mx + b$ form.

33. Points: $(0, -9)$ and $(4, -5)$

34. Points: $(0, 6)$ and $(3, 15)$

35. Points: $(-3, -1)$ and $(0, 1)$

36. Points: $(0, -2)$ and $(-5, -3)$

37. Points: $(1, -6)$ and $(-1, 2)$

38. Points: $(-2, -3)$ and $(3, -13)$

39. Points: $(3, 5)$ and $(-4, 5)$

40. Points: $(6, -1)$ and $(3, -1)$

41. Points: $(6, 3)$ and $(7, 6)$

42. Points: $(-3, 6)$ and $(-1, 2)$

For Exercises 43 through 58, determine the equation of the line by using the point-slope form. Put the final answer in $y = mx + b$ form.

43. $m = -2$ and point $(0, -7)$

44. $m = -4$ and point $(0, 9)$

45. $m = 6$ and point $(2, 3)$

46. $m = 5$ and point $(3, -1)$

47. $m = \dfrac{2}{3}$ and point $(6, 4)$

48. $m = \dfrac{1}{2}$ and point $(-8, -1)$

49. $m = 0$ and point $(-3, 5)$

50. $m = 0$ and point $(4, 6)$

51. Points: $(1, 5)$ and $(-1, -1)$

52. Points: $(2, 3)$ and $(4, 11)$

53. Points: $(-1, 7)$ and $(3, -5)$

54. Points: $(-1, 6)$ and $(1, -4)$

55. Points: $(2, 2)$ and $(-2, 0)$

56. Points: $(4, -1)$ and $(8, -4)$

57. Points: $(3, -6)$ and $(-2, -6)$

58. Points: $(0, 18)$ and $(-5, 18)$

For Exercises 59 through 66, rewrite each linear equation in the requested form.

59. Write in general form: $y = \dfrac{-2}{3}x + 7$

60. Write in general form: $y = \dfrac{2}{5}x - 3$

61. Write in slope-intercept form: $-3x + 4y = -24$

62. Write in slope-intercept form: $7x - 14y = 21$

63. Write in slope-intercept form: $y - 3 = -6(x + 11)$

64. Write in slope-intercept form: $y + 9 = -4(x - 5)$

65. Write in general form: $y - 2 = 7(x + 1)$

66. Write in general form: $y + 12 = -\dfrac{1}{2}(x + 16)$

For Exercises 67 through 70, write the equation of the line through the given points. (Hint: Graph the two points and connect them with a line. Review Section 3.1 if necessary.)

67. Points: $(5, 15)$ and $(5, 3)$

68. Points: $(7, 3)$ and $(7, -3)$

69. Points: $(0, -6)$ and $(0, -10)$

70. Points: $(-12, 5)$ and $(-12, 0)$

For Exercises 71 through 78, find the equation of the requested line. See Examples 7 and 8 for help.

71. Find the equation of the line parallel to $y = 6x - 10$ passing through the point $(-7, 0)$.

72. Find the equation of the line parallel to $y = -11x + 3$ passing through the point $(0, -5)$.

73. Find the equation of the line parallel to $x - 5y = 9$ passing through the point $(-10, 2)$.

74. Find the equation of the line parallel to $2x + 3y = -1$ passing through the point $(-6, -1)$.

75. Find the equation of the line perpendicular to
$y = \dfrac{3}{8}x - 15$ passing through the point $(-12, 4)$.

76. Find the equation of the line perpendicular to
$y = \dfrac{6}{7}x - 9$ passing through the point $(-6, 5)$.

77. Find the equation of the line perpendicular to
$-5x + 4y = -9$ passing through the point $(-5, 1)$.

78. Find the equation of the line perpendicular to
$-2x + 9y = -7$ passing through the point $(-4, 1)$.

For Exercises 79 through 86, find the equation of the line using the given information. (Hint: Draw the graph to help yourself visualize the situation.)

79. Find the equation of the line parallel to $y = 4$ passing through the point $(-3, 6)$.

80. Find the equation of the line parallel to $y = 0$ passing through the point $(5, -3)$.

81. Find the equation of the line perpendicular to $x = 3$ passing through the point $(2, 5)$.

82. Find the equation of the line perpendicular to $x = -1$ passing through the point $(0, 2)$.

83. Find the equation of the line parallel to $x = -5$ passing through the point $(1, -3)$.

84. Find the equation of the line parallel to $x = 4$ passing through the point $(6, -1)$.

85. Find the equation of the line perpendicular to $y = -3$ passing through the point $(5, 2)$.

86. Find the equation of the line perpendicular to $y = 7$ passing through the point $(0, 4)$.

Chapter Summary

3

Section 3.1   Graphing Equations with Two Variables

- **Tables** can be used to represent data or ordered pairs.
- **Equations** with two variables may be **graphed** by generating a table of points and then plotting the points and connecting them with a smooth curve.
- **Both the x- and y-axes should be scaled** so that all points in the table are displayed on the graph. Each axis should have 5 to 20 values listed.
- To **graph simpler equations in two variables,** graph five or more points.
- To **graph more complicated equations in two variables,** such as those with an exponent of 2 on one of the variables or with absolute values, graph nine or more points.
- A **vertical line** is the graph of an equation of the form $x = c$.
- A **horizontal line** is the graph of an equation of the form $y = b$.

Example 1   Use the table to write coordinates for points, and then graph them. Connect the points with a smooth curve. The equation is $y = -3x + 5$.

x	$y = -3x + 5$	(x, y)
-3	14	
-2	11	
-1	8	
1	2	
2	-1	

SOLUTION

x	$y = -3x + 5$	(x, y)
-3	14	$(-3, 14)$
-2	11	$(-2, 11)$
-1	8	$(-1, 8)$
1	2	$(1, 2)$
2	-1	$(2, -1)$

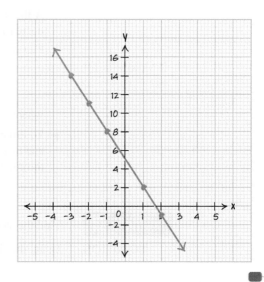

Example 2   Use each equation to create a table of points, and then graph them. Connect the points with a smooth curve. The equation is $y = |x - 1|$.

SOLUTION

x	$y = |x - 1|$	(x, y)
-5	6	$(-5, 6)$
-4	5	$(-4, 5)$
-3	4	$(-3, 4)$
-2	3	$(-2, 3)$
-1	2	$(-1, 2)$
0	1	$(0, 1)$
1	0	$(1, 0)$
2	1	$(2, 1)$
3	2	$(3, 2)$
4	3	$(4, 3)$
5	4	$(5, 4)$

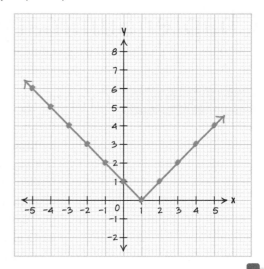

Section 3.2   Finding and Interpreting Slope

- **Graphs** give information about the output values from the height of the graph.
- **Graphs** are most often read from left to right.
- **The rate of change** between two points is the change in the outputs divided by the change in the inputs.
- **Speed** is the rate of change of a distance (output) versus time (input) graph.
- The rate of change of a linear graph is called the **slope of the line.**
- **The slope of a line may be found from the graph** by using the formula slope $= \dfrac{\text{rise}}{\text{run}}$. Here, the rise is the vertical change in the outputs, and the run is the horizontal change in the inputs.
- **A line is said to be increasing** if it goes up, reading from left to right. A line is increasing when its slope is positive.
- **A line is said to be decreasing** if it goes down, reading from left to right. A line is decreasing when its slope is negative.
- The **slope of a line between two points may be found by using the formula**

$$\text{slope} = \frac{\text{change in } y}{\text{change in } x} = \frac{y_2 - y_1}{x_2 - x_1}$$

  where (x_1, y_1) and (x_2, y_2) are any two points on the line.
- To **interpret slope in the context of an application,** we compute the slope first and then attach the units of the output to the numerator and the units of the input to the denominator. We then write the slope as a rate, including the units.

Example 3   Find the slope of the line that passes through the two points $(-3, -1)$ and $(4, 6)$.

SOLUTION   Using the slope formula, we find that the slope of the line is 1.

$$m = \frac{6 - (-1)}{4 - (-3)} = \frac{7}{7} = 1$$

Example 4

The population of San Diego, California, in 1990 was 1,110,549. The population of San Diego in 2000 was 1,223,400. Find and interpret the slope of the line between these two points.

Source: wikipedia.

SOLUTION

Using the slope formula, we find that the slope of the line is 11,285.1.

$$m = \frac{1,223,400 - 1,110,549}{2000 - 1990} = \frac{112,851}{10} = \frac{11,285.1 \text{ people}}{1 \text{ year}}$$

This means that the population of San Diego is increasing at the rate of 11,285.1 people per year.

Section 3.3 Slope-Intercept Form of Lines

- The **y-intercept** is the point(s) where the curve touches the y-axis. It is written in the form $(0, b)$.
- The **x-intercept** is the point(s) where the curve touches the x-axis. It is written in the form $(c, 0)$.
- **Interpreting intercepts in a problem** may or may not make sense in the problem situation.
- **To find the y-intercept,** substitute in $x = 0$, and solve the equation for y. Write the intercept in the form $(0, b)$.
- **To find the x-intercept,** substitute in $y = 0$, and solve the equation for x. Write the intercept in the form $(c, 0)$.
- **The slope-intercept form** of a line is $y = mx + b$, where m and b are real numbers. The slope of the line is m, and the y-intercept is the point $(0, b)$.

Example 5

Find the x- and y-intercepts of the equation $-2x + 5y = 20$.

SOLUTION

To find the x-intercept, let $y = 0$, and solve for x.

$$-2x + 5(0) = 20 \qquad \text{Substitute in } y = 0.$$

$$\frac{-2x}{-2} = \frac{20}{-2} \qquad \text{Solve for } x.$$

$$x = -10$$

The x-intercept is the point $(-10, 0)$.
To find the y-intercept, let $x = 0$, and solve for y.

$$-2(0) + 5y = 20 \qquad \text{Substitute in } x = 0.$$

$$\frac{5y}{5} = \frac{20}{5} \qquad \text{Solve for } y.$$

$$y = 4$$

The y-intercept is the point $(0, 4)$.

Example 6

Find the slope and y-intercept of the line $y = -\frac{1}{2}x + 7$.

SOLUTION

This line is in the form $y = mx + b$. Read the slope from the equation, $m = \frac{-1}{2}$.
The value of b is $b = 7$. Therefore, the y-intercept is the point $(0, 7)$.

Section **3.4** | Linear Equations and Their Graphs

- **To graph a line from slope-intercept form,** $y = mx + b$, first plot the y-intercept $(0, b)$ on the graph. Then, beginning at the y-intercept, use the fact that the slope $= \dfrac{\text{rise}}{\text{run}}$ to determine two more points on the graph. Work from left to right. Connect the points with a straight line.

- The **general form of the equation of a line** is $Ax + By = C$, where A, B, and C are real numbers, and both A and B are not zero.

- **To graph a line using the intercepts,** first find both the x- and y-intercepts. Then plot both intercepts on the graph, and connect the two points with a line.

- **A linear equation in two variables** is an equation that may be put into either form,

$$y = mx + b \qquad \text{or} \qquad Ax + By = C$$

- Two lines are **parallel** if they have the same slope: $m_1 = m_2$.

- Two lines are **perpendicular** if their slopes are negative reciprocals: $m_1 = \dfrac{-1}{m_2}$.

Example 7 | Graph the line using the slope and y-intercept.

$$y = \frac{2}{3}x - 5$$

SOLUTION The y-intercept of this line is the point $(0, -5)$. The slope is $m = \dfrac{2}{3} = \dfrac{\text{rise}}{\text{run}}$. First, graph the y-intercept $(0, -5)$, and then use the slope to get two more points on the line.

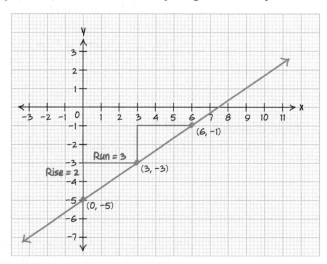

Example 8 | Graph the line by finding and graphing the x- and y-intercepts. $-3x + 4y = -12$

SOLUTION To find the x-intercept, let $y = 0$, and solve for x.

$$-3x + 4(0) = -12 \qquad \text{Let } y = 0.$$

$$\frac{-3x}{-3} = \frac{-12}{-3} \qquad \text{Solve for } x.$$

$$x = 4$$

Therefore, the x-intercept is the point $(4, 0)$.
To find the y-intercept, let $x = 0$, and solve for y.

$$-3(0) + 4y = -12 \qquad \text{Let } x = 0.$$

$$\frac{4y}{4} = \frac{-12}{4} \qquad \text{Solve for } y.$$

$$y = -3$$

Therefore, the y-intercept is the point $(0, -3)$.

Graphing these two points and connecting them with a line, we get the following graph.

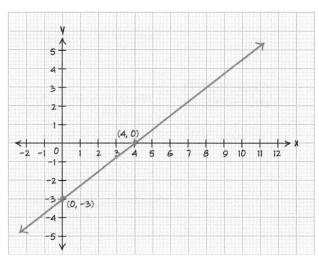

Example 9

Determine whether the following equations are linear or not. If it is linear, put it in $y = mx + b$ form.

a. $y = x^2 + 6$ b. $-2x + y = 7$

SOLUTION

a. This equation is NOT linear. The variable x has an exponent of 2, which is not a characteristic of a linear equation.

b. This equation is linear. It is in general form, $Ax + By = C$. To put it in slope-intercept form, we must solve this equation for y. Remember, to solve for y means to isolate y on one side of the equal sign.

$$-2x + y = 7$$
$$\underline{+2x \qquad\qquad +2x}$$
$$y = 2x + 7$$

Section **3.5**   Finding Equations of Lines

- **To find the slope-intercept form of the equation of a line,** first use two points to find the slope. Then substitute any point on the line in for x and y and solve for b. Write the equation of the line as $y = mx + b$.
- **The point-slope form of a line** is $y - y_1 = m(x - x_1)$, where (x_1, y_1) is any point on the line and m is the slope of the line.

Example 10

Find the equation of the line that passes through the points $(5, 1)$ and $(-5, -3)$.

SOLUTION

The slope of the line is

$$m = \frac{-3 - 1}{-5 - 5} = \frac{-4}{-10} = \frac{2}{5}$$

Substituting this result into $y = mx + b$ yields $y = \frac{2}{5}x + b$. To find the value of b, substitute either point into the equation for x and y and solve for b.

$$1 = \frac{2}{5}(5) + b \qquad\qquad \textit{Substitute in } (x, y) = (5, 1).$$

$$1 = 2 + b$$
$$\underline{-2 \quad -2}$$
$$-1 = b$$

Therefore, the equation of the line is $y = \dfrac{2}{5}x - 1$.

Example 11   Using point-slope form, find the equation of the line passing through the points $(1, -3)$ and $(-2, -15)$. Put the final answer in slope-intercept form, $y = mx + b$.

SOLUTION   The slope of the line is

$$m = \frac{-15 - (-3)}{-2 - 1} = \frac{-12}{-3} = 4$$

Substituting the slope and the point $(x_1, y_1) = (1, -3)$ into the point-slope form yields

$$y - (-3) = 4(x - 1)$$
$$y + 3 = 4x - 4$$
$$\underline{-3 \qquad -3}$$
$$y = 4x - 7$$

Chapter Review Exercises
3

In Exercises 1 and 2, fill in the given table. Complete the last two rows with values that you think are reasonable in the problem situation.

1. The number of calories burned by a 160-pound person while walking at the rate of 2.5 mph for h hours can be estimated by the equation $C = 87h$. [3.1]

h = Hours of walking	C = Calories burned
1	
2	
3	

2. The cost to purchase a plant in a one-gallon container for a garden can be calculated by using the equation $C = 5.25n$ when n plants are purchased. [3.1]

n = Number of plants purchased	C = Cost (dollars)
2	
4	
8	

3. Graph the points from Exercise 1, and connect them with a smooth curve. [3.1]

4. Graph the points from Exercise 2, and connect them with a smooth curve. [3.1]

For Exercises 5 through 12, use the given equation to create a table of five or more points. Graph the points. Clearly label and scale the axes. Connect the points with a smooth curve.

5. $y = -3x + 8$
6. $y = -5x - 3$ [3.1]

7. $y = \dfrac{3}{4}x + 1$
8. $y = \dfrac{-1}{5}x - 6$ [3.1]

9. $y = 5$
10. $y = -4$ [3.1]

11. $x = -3$
12. $x = 5$ [3.1]

For Exercises 13 through 16, use the given equation to create a table of nine or more points. Graph the points. Clearly label and scale the axes. Connect the points with a smooth curve.

13. $y = x^2 + 2$
14. $y = -x^2 + 5$ [3.1]

15. $y = |9 - 3x|$
16. $y = |x + 2|$ [3.1]

17.   [3.2]

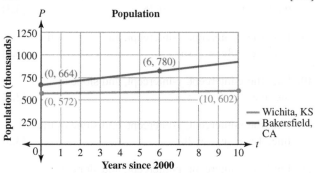

Source: Models derived from data found in the Statistical Abstract of the United States, 2007.

a. Which city has the larger population during these years? Explain your response.

b. Which city is growing faster during these years? Explain your response.

18.   [3.2]

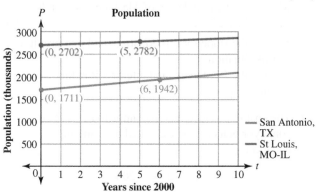

Source: Models derived from data found in the Statistical Abstract of the United States, 2007.

a. Which city has the larger population during these years? Explain your response.

b. Which city is growing faster during these years? Explain your response.

For Exercises 19 and 20, find the slope of the line given in the graph.

19.   [3.2]

20.   [3.2]

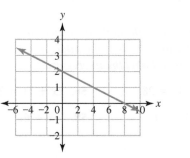

21. Find the slope of the line that goes through the points $(-3, 4)$ and $(5, -2)$.   [3.2]

22. Find the slope of the line that goes through the points $(-8, 2)$ and $(0, 5)$.   [3.2]

23. Use two points from the table to find the slope of the line that passes through the points.   [3.2]

x	y
-10	-11
-5	-9
0	-7
5	-5

24. Use two points from the table to find the slope of the line that passes through the points.   [3.2]

x	y
-6	-6
-3	-5
0	-4
3	-3

25. Calculate the slope for Bakersfield, California, given in Exercise 17. Interpret the meaning of the slope in terms of the problem situation.   [3.2]

26. Calculate the slope for San Antonio, Texas, given in Exercise 18. Interpret the meaning of the slope in terms of the problem situation.   [3.2]

27. Use the graph to find the x-intercept(s) and y-intercept of the curve.   [3.3]

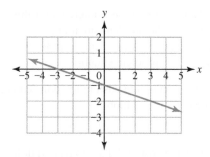

28. Use the graph to find the x-intercept(s) and y-intercept of the curve.   [3.3]

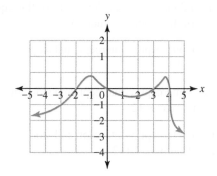

29. a. Interpret the vertical intercept for the Bakersfield line in Exercise 17 in terms of the problem situation.

b. Interpret the vertical intercept for the Wichita line in Exercise 17 in terms of the problem situation. [3.3]

30. [3.3]

a. Interpret the vertical intercept for the line in terms of the problem situation.
b. Interpret the horizontal intercept for the line in terms of the problem situation.

31. Find the x- and y-intercepts of the equation

$$y = -\frac{3}{4}x + 3.$$ [3.3]

32. Find the x- and y-intercepts of the equation $-6x + 3y = -18$. [3.3]

33. The time it takes to hand-paint toy dolls can be estimated by the equation

$$T = 1.5d + 1$$

where T is the time in hours it takes to paint d dolls.
a. Find and interpret the T-intercept for this equation in terms of the problem situation.
b. Find and interpret the d-intercept for this equation in terms of the problem situation. [3.3]

34. The cost to hand-paint custom toy dolls can be estimated by the equation

$$C = 25d + 10$$

where C is the cost in dollars to paint d dolls.
a. Find and interpret the C-intercept for this equation in terms of the problem situation.
b. Find and interpret the d-intercept for this equation in terms of the problem situation. [3.3]

35. Find the x-intercept, y-intercept, and slope of the line: $y = -3x + 9$ [3.3]

36. Find the x-intercept, y-intercept, and slope of the line: $y = 2x + 12$ [3.3]

37. Find the x-intercept, y-intercept, and slope of the line: $y = 1.005x - 7.112$ [3.3]

38. Find the x-intercept, y-intercept, and slope of the line: $y = -0.25x + 9.75$ [3.3]

39. Find the x-intercept, y-intercept, and slope of the line: $4x + 8y = -16$ [3.3]

40. Find the x-intercept, y-intercept, and slope of the line: $-x - 3y = 12$ [3.3]

41. Find the x-intercept, y-intercept, and slope of the line: $4x - 5y = -20$ [3.3]

42. Find the x-intercept, y-intercept, and slope of the line: $2x - 10y = -20$ [3.3]

43. The population of Alaska can be estimated by using the equation

$$P = 7.4t + 626$$

where P is the population of Alaska in thousands t years since 2000. [3.3]
a. Find the slope for this equation, and interpret it in this situation.
b. Find the P-intercept and interpret it in this situation.

44. The cost to produce sets of clamps to be used on conveyor belts can be estimated by using the equation

$$C = 2.5s + 200$$

where C is the cost in dollars for s sets of clamps. [3.3]
a. Find the slope for this equation, and interpret it in this situation.
b. Find the C-intercept, and interpret it in this situation.

For Exercises 45 through 54, graph the equation using the slope and y-intercept. Graph at least three points. Clearly label and scale the axes.

45. $y = \frac{1}{4}x - 5$ **46.** $y = \frac{2}{3}x - 6$ [3.4]

47. $y = -\frac{1}{6}x + 2$ **48.** $y = -\frac{2}{7}x + 3$ [3.4]

49. $y = 4x - 9$ **50.** $y = -4x + 8$ [3.4]

51. $y + 3 = \frac{1}{2}(x + 12)$ **52.** $y - 5 = -3(x + 4)$ [3.4]

53. $3y = 2x - 30$ **54.** $-6y = 3x - 18$ [3.4]

For Exercises 55 through 58, graph the given linear equations using the x- and y-intercepts. Clearly label and scale the axes. Label the intercepts.

55. $3x + 4y = 28$ **56.** $2x + 5y = 30$ [3.4]

57. $x + 3y = 9$ **58.** $-x + 6y = 24$ [3.4]

For Exercises 59 and 60, use the graph to find the equation of the line. Put the answer in the slope-intercept form (y = mx + b form).

59.   [3.5]

60.   [3.5]

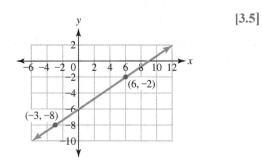

For Exercises 61 and 62, find the equation of the line that describes the given linear relationship.

61. The number of calories burned every hour by a 160- to 170-pound person while running is 852. (*Note:* This is at a pace of 8 mph.)   [3.5]

62. The number of calories a 160- to 170-pound person burns each hour while golfing using a handcart is 264.   [3.5]

63. Interpret the slope of the line in Exercise 61 in terms of the problem situation.   [3.5]

64. Interpret the slope of the line in Exercise 62 in terms of the problem situation.   [3.5]

For Exercises 65 through 72, determine the equation of the line that passes through the given points. If possible, put the final answer in y = mx + b form.

65. Points $(6, 2)$ and $(11, -3)$ [3.5]

66. Points $(6, 1)$ and $(9, -1)$ [3.5]

67. Points $(-10, 4)$ and $(0, 5)$ [3.5]

68. Points $(-2, -8)$ and $(2, -6)$ [3.5]

69. Points $(3, -11)$ and $(-2, -11)$ [3.5]

70. Points $(-10, 12)$ and $(16, 12)$ [3.5]

71. Points $(1, -8)$ and $(1, 7)$ [3.5]

72. Points $(-4, -3)$ and $(-4, 17)$ [3.5]

For Exercises 73 through 76, determine the equation of the line by using the point-slope form and then putting the final answer in y = mx + b form.

73. $m = \dfrac{1}{2}$ and $(-6, 3)$ **74.** $m = \dfrac{-1}{3}$ and $(9, -1)$ [3.5]

75. $(-4, 5)$ and $(4, -1)$ **76.** $(-6, 4)$ and $(6, 2)$ [3.5]

For Exercises 77 through 80, determine whether the two lines are parallel, perpendicular, or neither.

77. $y = -3x + 7$ **78.** $y = \dfrac{1}{3}x - 13$ [3.5]

  $6x + 2y = 11$ $5x - 15y = 19$

79. $5x + 2y = 6$ **80.** $y = -3x + 9$ [3.5]

  $y = \dfrac{2}{5}x - 1$ $x - 3y = -15$

For Exercises 81 through 84, find the equation of the requested line.

81. Find the equation of the line parallel to $-x + 8y = 1$ passing through the point $(-8, 3)$.   [3.5]

82. Find the equation of the line parallel to $5x - 2y = 7$ passing through the point $(10, -1)$.   [3.5]

83. Find the equation of the line perpendicular to $y = \dfrac{-4}{3}x + 1$ passing through the point $(12, -5)$. [3.5]

84. Find the equation of the line perpendicular to $y = \dfrac{-x}{2} + 16$ passing through the point $(-3, -7)$. [3.5]

For Exercises 85 through 92, put the equation of the line in the requested form.

85. Put in general form: $y = \dfrac{-5}{6}x + 7$ [3.5]

86. Put in general form: $y = \dfrac{-4}{5}x - 9$ [3.5]

87. Put in slope-intercept form: $-6x + 5y = -30$ [3.5]

88. Put in slope-intercept form: $5x - 10y = -100$ [3.5]

89. Put in general form: $y - 1 = -2(x + 4)$ [3.5]

90. Put in general form: $y + 3 = -7(x - 5)$ [3.5]

91. Put in slope-intercept form: $y + 4 = \dfrac{2}{3}(x - 6)$ [3.5]

92. Put in slope-intercept form: $y - 7 = \dfrac{-5}{7}(x + 14)$ [3.5]

Chapter Test

3

This test should take approximately one hour to complete. Read each question carefully. Show all of your work.

1. For the given equation, create a table of five or more points and graph them. Connect the points with a smooth curve. $y = -5x + 2$

2. For the given equation, create a table of nine or more points and graph them. Connect the points with a smooth curve. $y = x^2 - 1$

3. Find the slope of the line that goes through the points $(3, 7)$ and $(-4, 0)$.

4. In 1999, there were 66,043 children in the United States diagnosed with autism. In 2003, there were 141,022 children in the United States with autism. These values correspond to the points (1999, 66,043) and (2003, 141,022). Find the slope of the line between these points. Interpret the slope in terms of the problem situation.

   Source: http://fightingautism.org/idea/autism.php?.

5. Find the x- and y-intercepts of the equation $-2x + 3y = -6$.

6.

   E   Net Electricity Generation by Source

   Source: *Models derived from data found at U.S. Energy Information Administration.*

   a. Interpret the vertical intercept for the line representing electricity generation by wind.
   b. Interpret the vertical intercept for the line representing electricity generation by geothermal.

7. Find the slope and the x- and y-intercepts of the equation $y = \dfrac{3}{5}x - \dfrac{2}{5}$.

8. Graph the line using the slope and y-intercept. Graph at least three points.

$$y = -\frac{1}{2}x + 7$$

9. Ahmed earns $12.00 an hour as a tutor. His wages can be computed by using the equation $W = 12h$, where h represents the number of hours Ahmed works and W represents his wages. Graph this line by graphing at least three points.

10. Graph the line by finding the x- and y-intercepts and plotting them. $4x + y = -7$

11. Determine whether each equation is linear. If the equation is linear, put it in $y = mx + b$ form.

    a. $y = 6 - x^2$ b. $y - 2 = 3(x + 4)$

12. Find the equation of the line that passes through the points $(1, -2)$ and $(-2, -17)$. Put the final answer in $y = mx + b$ form.

13. Use the graph to find the equation of the line. Put the final answer in $y = mx + b$ form.

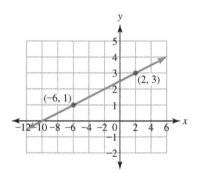

14. Paul goes on a diet to lose weight. Let the input t represent the week of his diet, and let the output W represent Paul's weight in pounds. At the start of his diet ($t = 0$), Paul weighed 235 pounds. After 5 weeks on his diet, he weighed 210 pounds. Find the linear relationship between t and W.

15. Interpret the slope of the line in Problem 14 in terms of the problem situation (weight loss).

16. Determine the equation of the line that passes through the points by using point-slope form. Put your final answer in $y = mx + b$ form. The points are $(4, -2)$ and $(-8, -11)$.

17. Are the lines parallel, perpendicular, or neither?

$$y = -7x + 11$$
$$2x - 14y = 3$$

18. Find the equation of the line parallel to $y = \dfrac{2}{5}x + 9$ passing through the point $(-5, -3)$.

Chapter 3 Projects

Solving Linear Equations Using Tables

Written Project

One or more people

Suppose we want to solve the linear equation $5x + 6 = 12 - x$ using tables. We generate two tables using the following steps.

1. Let y = left side of the equation, and let y = right side of the equation.
2. For each equation from step 1, fill in the table.

x	$y = 5x + 6$
-1	
0	
1	
2	
3	

x	$y = 12 - x$
-1	
0	
1	
2	
3	

3. For which point (x, y) are the two tables the same?
4. To solve $5x + 6 = 12 - x$, we are trying to find x. What is the value of x from step 3?

How Old Is the Grand Canyon?

Written Project

One or more people

The Grand Canyon is a steep canyon located in the state of Arizona. It is about 277 miles long and is anywhere from 4 to 18 miles wide. The Grand Canyon has been cut into the landscape by the Colorado River, which is gradually eroding the rocks. The central region of the canyon is about 5000 feet deep. Measurements show that the Colorado River is cutting into the canyon at the approximate rate of 1 inch deeper every 80 years. Suppose the river has been cutting (eroding) the canyon at a constant rate.
Source: Dr. Steve Spear, Palomar College.

© Steve Cukrov. By permission.

1. How deep is the central part of the Grand Canyon?
2. What is the rate of erosion by the Colorado River?
3. How long did it take for the Colorado River to erode the current depth of the canyon?
4. How old (approximately) is the Grand Canyon?

Write a Review of a Section for Presentation

Research Project

One or more people

What you will need

- This presentation may be done in class or as an online video.
- If it is done as a video, post it on a Website where it may be easily viewed by the class.
- You may want to use homework or other review problems from the book.
- Make it creative and fun.

Create a five-minute review presentation of one section from Chapter 3. The format of the presentation can be a poster presentation, a blackboard presentation from notes, an online video, or a game format (e.g., Math Jeopardy). The presentation should include the following:

a. Any important formulas in the chapter

b. Important skills in the chapter, backed up by examples

c. Explanation of terms used. For example, what is slope?

d. Common mistakes and how to avoid them

Systems of Linear Equations

4

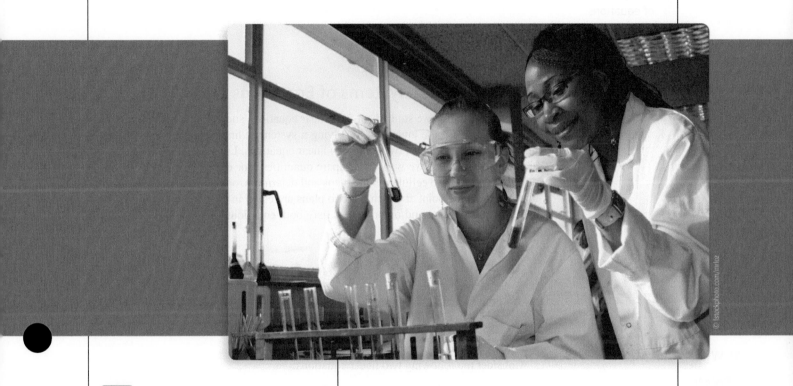

4.1 Identifying Systems of Linear Equations

4.2 Solving Systems Using the Substitution Method

4.3 Solving Systems Using the Elimination Method

4.4 Solving Linear Inequalities in Two Variables Graphically

Students in chemistry and nursing often have to mix solutions containing different amounts of saline or acid. They have to be careful that the mixture contains the desired amount of saline or acid after mixing. To determine how much of each type of solution to mix together, algebra can be used to solve a system of equations.

4.1   Identifying Systems of Linear Equations

LEARNING OBJECTIVES

- Identify a system of equations.
- Interpret solutions to systems of equations.
- Solve systems graphically.

Introduction to Systems of Equations

In Chapters 2 and 3, we studied solving linear equations and graphing linear equations. In this chapter, we are interested in solving a system of linear equations. A system of linear equations is a set of two (or more) linear equations. Linear systems arise in many applications in which we want to compare quantities. For example, a consumer might want to compare two cellular phone plans and determine, on the basis of the number of minutes used, the point at which the two plans are equal in cost. In general, the goal is to determine an input and output that satisfy both equations. This point is the solution of the system.

> **DEFINITION**
>
> **System of Linear Equations**   A **system of linear equations** is a set of two (or more) linear equations.

What's That Mean?

System

In different fields, the meaning of the word *system* may vary. A biological system is an arrangement of many parts that work together. An example is the circulatory system. The parts include the heart, the veins, and the arteries. In mathematics, the term *system* has a slightly different meaning. A system of equations is a set of simultaneous equations. This means that two or more equations are being considered at the same time.

Consider the following two linear equations:

$$y = 2x$$
$$y = -3x + 10$$

These two equations are an example of a system of linear equations. A table of values for each of these two lines is given below.

x	$y = 2x$
-1	-2
0	0
1	2
2	4
3	6

x	$y = -3x + 10$
-1	13
0	10
1	7
2	4
3	1

From these two tables, we see that the two lines have one input and output pair that are the same: $(2, 4)$. Many systems can be investigated in numerical (table) form.

Example 1   Comparing rental fees

Grace is moving to Seattle, and she has to rent a truck. She compares the rental costs for two companies. For a small truck, Vince's Truck Rentals quotes her $19.99 a day plus a one-time fee of $15.00. Gina's Rent-a-Truck quotes her $24.99 a day plus a one-time fee of $5.00.

© iStockphoto.com/rjane

a. Find equations for the cost for each of the two companies for renting a small truck for n days. Let V = cost in dollars of renting a truck from Vince's, and let G = cost in dollars of renting a truck from Gina's.

b. Fill in the following tables for Vince's Truck Rentals and Gina's Rent-a-Truck.

n = number of days	V = total cost of rental
0	
1	
2	
3	
4	

n = number of days	G = total cost of rental
0	
1	
2	
3	
4	

c. After how many days is the rental cost (approximately) the same?

d. If Grace has to rent a truck for 4 days, which company should she choose?

SOLUTION

a. First find the equation for the cost of renting from Vince's. The cost of renting a truck is $15.00 in fees plus $19.99 a day. The equation for the cost of renting from Vince's is

$$V = 15 + 19.99n$$

Find the equation of the cost for renting a truck from Gina's Rent-a-Truck. The cost of renting the truck is $5.00 plus $24.99 a day. The equation for the cost of renting a truck from Gina's is

$$G = 5 + 24.99n$$

b. Use the equations from part a to fill in the tables.

n = number of days	V = total cost of rental from Vince's
0	$15.00
1	$34.99
2	$54.98
3	$74.97
4	$94.96

n = number of days	G = total cost of rental from Gina's
0	$5.00
1	$29.99
2	$54.98
3	$79.97
4	$104.96

c. Remember that the solution to a system of equations is the point at which the two equations are equal. For 2 days, the rental cost is the same to rent a truck from Vince's Truck Rentals as to rent a truck from Gina's Rent-a-Truck. The rental cost is $54.98 for both companies. The solution is 2 days and a cost of $54.98.

d. It costs $94.96 to rent from Vince's for 4 days and $104.96 to rent from Gina's. So for a 4-day rental, Vince's Truck Rentals is cheaper.

PRACTICE PROBLEM FOR EXAMPLE 1

Angelica makes belts and handbags, which she sells to local clothing boutiques. A major cost that concerns her is shipping. She must send the items to her customers using a local delivery service. Her customers currently all live in the same city that she does but are located more than 15 miles away from her studio. The first local shipping company she contacts, Ship Quick, quotes her a base rate of $55.00 plus $2.30 per mile for delivery beyond 15 miles. The second local shipping company, In Town Shipping, quotes Angelica $50.00 plus $2.50 per mile for delivery beyond 15 miles.

■ **Connecting the Concepts**

How do we estimate a reasonable value?

In Example 1, Grace is interested in renting a truck. To make a quick estimate of the cost, she should round the values to make the calculations easy. For example, for Vince's Truck Rentals, the quote of $19.99 a day rounds to $20.00. If Grace needs to rent a truck for 3 days, she can estimate $3 \cdot 20 = 60$ and then add on the $15.00 fee to get $75.00.

a. Find equations for the cost (in dollars) for shipping a box m miles beyond 15 miles. Let S = cost in dollars of shipping with Ship Quick, and let I = cost in dollars of shipping with In Town Shipping.

b. Fill in the following tables for Ship Quick and In Town Shipping.

m = number of miles over 15 miles	S = cost of shipping for Ship Quick
0	
5	
10	
15	
20	
25	
30	

m = number of miles over 15 miles	I = cost of shipping for In Town Shipping
0	
5	
10	
15	
20	
25	
30	

c. After how many miles over 15 miles is the shipping cost the same for both companies? That is, find the solution to the system of equations.

d. If Angelica has to ship a package 20 miles (i.e., 5 miles beyond 15 miles), which company should she use?

Solutions to Systems of Equations

In Example 1, we are interested in finding the point at which the number of days and cost were the same for Vince's and Gina's truck rentals. In more formal language, we are trying to find what value of the input (n) makes both outputs (cost) the same for the two equations. The solution to this system is $n = 2$ days and cost = $54.98. Notice that this point is a solution that works in both linear equations. This point is called the **solution of the system of equations.**

> **DEFINITION**
>
> **Solution to a System of Linear Equations**   A **solution to a system of linear equations** is one (or more) point that is a solution to every linear equation in the system.
>
> **Note:** The solution to a system of linear equations must be written as the ordered pair (x, y). The values of *both* variables must be written down.

To *check* a solution of a system, substitute the coordinates of the point into *both* original equations, and determine whether it makes both equations true (or satisfies both equations).

> **Example 2**   Checking solutions of a system of equations

Check the solution of each system of equations.

a. Is $(1, 1)$ a solution of the system?

$$5x - 2y = 3$$
$$-20x + 8y = -12$$

b. The solution to Example 1 was $(2, 54.98)$. The equations are below. Check the solution.

$$V = 15 + 19.99n \qquad G = 5 + 24.99n$$

c. Is $(0, -3)$ a solution of the system?

$$3x - 2y = 6$$
$$-2x + y = 8$$

SOLUTION

a. Substitute $x = 1$ and $y = 1$ into both equations to see whether they both are true.

First Equation		**Second Equation**
$5(1) - 2(1) \overset{?}{=} 3$	Substitute the values for x and y.	$-20(1) + 8(1) \overset{?}{=} -12$
$5 - 2 \overset{?}{=} 3$		$-20 + 8 \overset{?}{=} -12$
$3 = 3$	Both statements are true.	$-12 = -12$

Therefore, the point $(1, 1)$ is a solution of the system.

b. Substituting $n = 2$, $V = 54.98$, and $G = 54.98$ into Vince's and Gina's cost equations yields the following:

Vince's Cost Equation		**Gina's Cost Equation**
$54.98 \overset{?}{=} 15 + 19.99(2)$		$54.98 \overset{?}{=} 5 + 24.99(2)$
$54.98 = 54.98$	Both statements are true.	$54.98 = 54.98$

The point $(2, 54.98)$ is a solution of the system.

c. Substitute $x = 0$ and $y = -3$ into both equations to see whether they both are true.

First Equation		**Second Equation**
$3(0) - 2(-3) \overset{?}{=} 6$	Substitute in the values for x and y.	$-2(0) + (-3) \overset{?}{=} 8$
$0 - (-6) \overset{?}{=} 6$		$0 - 3 \overset{?}{=} 8$
$6 = 6$	Only one statement is true.	$-3 \neq 8$ False.

The point is on the first line but not on the second. Since $(0, -3)$ does not make the second equation a true statement, it is *not* a solution of the system.

PRACTICE PROBLEM FOR EXAMPLE 2

Check the solution of each system of equations.

a. Is $(-2, -2)$ a solution of the system?

$$x + y = -4$$
$$y = \frac{5}{2}x + 3$$

b. Is $(25, 112.50)$ a solution of the system?

$$C = 55 + 2.30m$$
$$C = 50 + 2.50m$$

c. Is $(4, 9)$ a solution of the system?

$$2x - y = -1$$
$$-3x + 7y = 4$$

Solving Systems Graphically

We are now going to look at some systems graphically and determine the solution using the graph. Recall that the solution to a system is a point that satisfies both linear equations. Graphically, this point lies on both lines: it is the intersection point of both lines.

At the start of this section, we examined the following two linear equations.

$$y = 2x$$
$$y = -3x + 10$$

We found, using a table of values, that a solution to this system is (2, 4). Graphing both lines on the same axes yields the accompanying graph.

The two lines intersect at (2, 4), which is the same point that we found using the tables. Therefore, when solving a linear system graphically, we are looking for the point where the lines intersect.

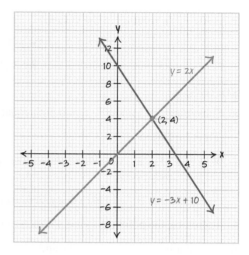

Example 3 Graphical solutions from real data

Unintentional injuries were the leading cause of death for people 15–24 years of age in the United States for the years 1950–2000. The following graph give the rates for the other leading causes of death for people 15–24 years of age in the United States for the years 1950–2000. Use this graph to answer the questions below.

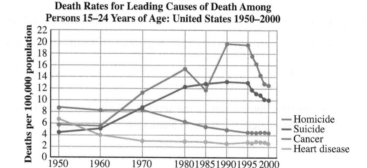

Death Rates for Leading Causes of Death Among Persons 15–24 Years of Age: United States 1950–2000

a. During which years did the same number of young Americans die from cancer as died from homicides? Estimate the deaths per 100,000 at the point(s) of intersection.

b. During which years did the same number of young Americans die from heart disease as died from suicide? Estimate the deaths per 100,000 at the point(s) of intersection.

SOLUTION

Using the graph above, we see the following.

a. Cancer death rates were equal to homicide death rates in the late 1960s. We could estimate the year as approximately 1965. From the graph, we estimate the deaths per 100,000 to be approximately 8.2 for the point of intersection.

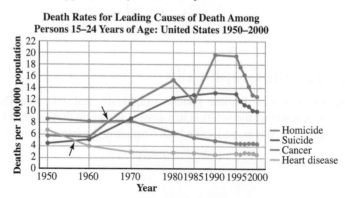

Death Rates for Leading Causes of Death Among Persons 15–24 Years of Age: United States 1950–2000

b. Heart disease death rates were equal to suicide death rates in the late 1950s. We could estimate the year as approximately 1957 and the deaths per 100,000 to be approximately 5.

PRACTICE PROBLEM FOR EXAMPLE 3

Using the graph in Example 3, answer the following questions about the leading causes of death for young Americans during the years 1950–2000.

a. During which years did the same number of young Americans die from suicides as died from homicides? Estimate the deaths per 100,000 at the point(s) of intersection.

b. During which years did the same number of young Americans die from cancer as died from suicide? Estimate the deaths per 100,000 at the point(s) of intersection.

In Example 3, we used the graphs to determine the solution(s) to a system. Typically in these problems, there are just two lines, and we are looking for the intersection point. In the next example, we will use a graph to find the intersection point.

Example 4   **Reading the solution to a system from a graph**

Use the graph to determine the solution to each system of equations.

a.

$y = x - 1$

$y = -\dfrac{1}{2}x - 4$

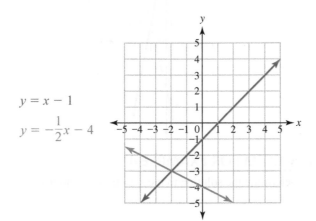

b.

$y = -5x + 6$

$y = 4x - 3$

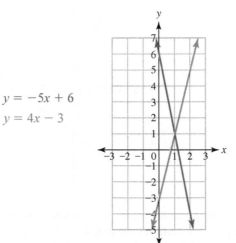

SOLUTION

a. To find the solution to this system, look for the intersection of the two lines. Looking at the graph, we see that the point of intersection seems to be at $x = -2$ and $y = -3$ or, as an ordered pair, $(-2, -3)$.

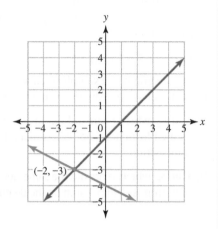

b. To find the solution to this system, again look for the intersection of the two lines. When we look at the graph, it is clear that the two lines intersect with the x-coordinate $x = 1$. The y-coordinate is $y = 1$. The solution is $(1, 1)$.

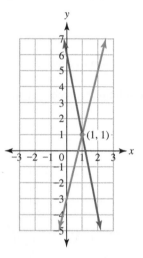

PRACTICE PROBLEM FOR EXAMPLE 4

Use the graph to determine the solution to the system of equations.

$$y = \frac{3}{2}x - 6$$

$$y = -3x + 3$$

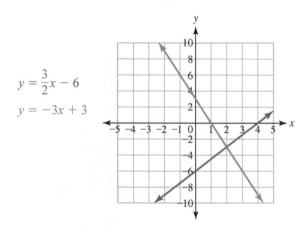

In Example 4, we were given the graph, and our task was to examine the graph and find the intersection point. Sometimes the graph is not given. In that case, first graph the system of equations, and then use that graph to find the solution. To solve a system accurately using a graph, it is important to use graph paper and to draw the lines using a straightedge or ruler.

Steps to Solving a System of Equations Graphically

1. On graph paper, carefully graph both lines on the same pair of axes.
   a. Scale the axes so that both lines can be graphed simultaneously.
   b. Use a ruler to draw in the lines.
2. Find the point of intersection. This is the solution to the system.
3. Write the solution as an ordered pair (x, y).
4. Check the answer by substituting the solution into *both* of the original equations.

Example 5   Solving a system graphically

Solve the system graphically. Check the solution.

$$y = 2x + 3$$
$$2x + y = -1$$

SOLUTION

To begin, carefully graph both lines. The first line has a y-intercept of $(0, 3)$, so graph the point $(0, 3)$. The slope is $2 = \dfrac{2}{1} = \dfrac{\text{rise}}{\text{run}}$, so from the point $(0, 3)$, go up 2 and over 1 to get to another point on the line, which is $(1, 5)$. Draw in the line.

   The second line is not in slope-intercept form. To put this line in slope-intercept form, solve for y.

$$2x + y = -1 \qquad \text{Isolate } y \text{ by subtracting } 2x \text{ from both sides.}$$
$$\underline{-2x \qquad\quad -2x}$$
$$y = -2x - 1 \qquad \text{This is in } y = mx + b \text{ form.}$$

The y-intercept is $(0, -1)$, and the slope is $-2 = \dfrac{-2}{1} = \dfrac{\text{rise}}{\text{run}}$. Start at the point $(0, -1)$, and go down 2 units and over 1 unit to get to another point on the line, $(1, -3)$. Draw in the line.

   The two lines intersect at the point $(-1, 1)$.

   Now check the answer $(-1, 1)$. Start by substituting it into the first equation.

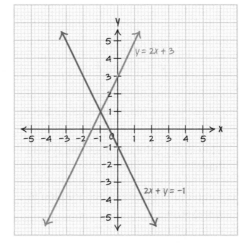

First Equation		**Second Equation**
$y = 2x + 3$		$y = -2x - 1$
$1 \stackrel{?}{=} 2(-1) + 3$	Substitute in $x = -1$ and $y = 1$.	$1 \stackrel{?}{=} -2(-1) - 1$
$1 = 1$	Both statements are true.	$1 = 1$

Therefore, the point $(-1, 1)$ is a solution to the system of linear equations.

PRACTICE PROBLEM FOR EXAMPLE 5

Solve the system graphically. Check the answer.

$$y = -2x - 16$$
$$y = 4x - 4$$

Types of Systems

In the following Concept Investigation, we explore how many solutions a system of linear equations can have. Remember that we are trying to determine the number of intersection points that two lines can have.

■ CONCEPT INVESTIGATION

How many answers are there?

Graph each system on the axes provided, and answer the question.

a. Graphically determine the solution to the system

$$y = 8x - 4$$
$$y = -2x + 6$$

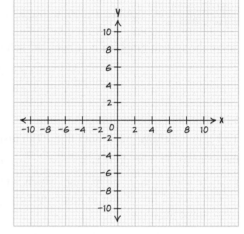

How many solutions does this system have?

b. Graphically determine the solution to the system

$$y = -3x + 5$$
$$y = -3x - 3$$

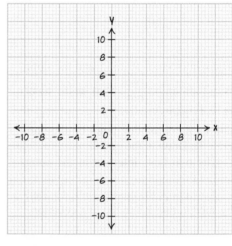

How many solutions does this system have?

c. Graphically determine the solution to the system

$$6x + 2y = 10$$
$$y = -3x + 5$$

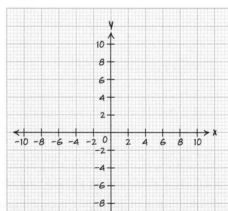

How many solutions does this system have?

In the Concept Investigation, we saw that two lines can intersect at exactly one point, never intersect, or intersect everywhere on the line as they are the same line. The following terms are used to describe the number of solutions a system of equations has.

DEFINITIONS

Consistent System A system of linear equations is said to be consistent if it has at least one solution. This means that the two lines can intersect at exactly one point or intersect at infinitely many points on the same line.

Inconsistent System A system of linear equations is said to be inconsistent if it has no solutions.

We summarize this new terminology and the number of solutions to linear systems in the following box.

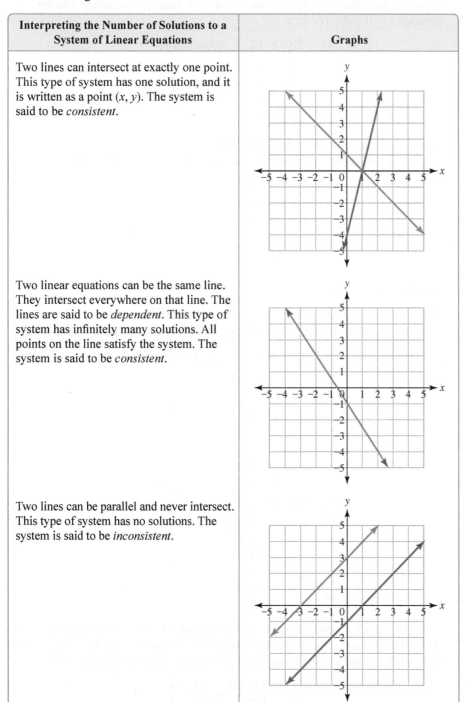

Interpreting the Number of Solutions to a System of Linear Equations	Graphs
Two lines can intersect at exactly one point. This type of system has one solution, and it is written as a point (x, y). The system is said to be *consistent*.	
Two linear equations can be the same line. They intersect everywhere on that line. The lines are said to be *dependent*. This type of system has infinitely many solutions. All points on the line satisfy the system. The system is said to be *consistent*.	
Two lines can be parallel and never intersect. This type of system has no solutions. The system is said to be *inconsistent*.	

> ### Example 6 Consistent or inconsistent systems?

Solve each system graphically. Identify each system as consistent or inconsistent. Clearly label and scale the axes. Check the solution(s), when possible, by substituting into the original problem.

a. $4x - 3y = 12$

$y = \dfrac{4}{3}x + 5$

b. $y = \dfrac{3}{2}x - 4$

$y = \dfrac{-x}{4} + 3$

c. $2x + 5y = 25$

$y = \dfrac{-2}{5}x + 5$

SOLUTION

a. The equation of the first line is $4x - 3y = 12$. This equation is in general form. To graph it requires two points on the line. For this particular line, it is fairly easy to find the two intercepts. Recall that to find the x-intercept, substitute into the equation $y = 0$ and solve for x.

$$4x - 3(0) = 12 \qquad \text{Substitute in } y = 0.$$
$$4x = 12$$
$$\frac{4x}{4} = \frac{12}{4} \qquad \text{Divide both sides by 4.}$$
$$x = 3$$

Therefore, the x-intercept is the point $(3, 0)$.
To find the y-intercept, substitute into the equation $x = 0$ and solve for y.

$$4(0) - 3y = 12 \qquad \text{Substitute in } x = 0.$$
$$-3y = 12$$
$$\frac{-3y}{-3} = \frac{12}{-3} \qquad \text{Divide both sides by } -3.$$
$$y = -4$$

Therefore, the y-intercept is $(0, -4)$. Graph the line using these two points. The equation of the second line is $y = \dfrac{4}{3}x + 5$. The second line is given in slope-intercept form. The y-intercept is the point $(0, 5)$, and we can use the slope to find another point on the graph. The slope is $m = \dfrac{4}{3} = \dfrac{\text{rise}}{\text{run}}$. The graph looks like the following:

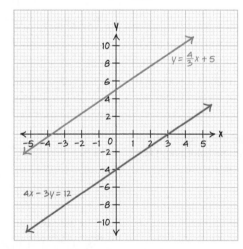

From the graph, it appears that the lines are parallel. To determine whether the lines are parallel, find and compare the slopes of both lines. The first line, $4x - 3y = 12$, has intercepts $(3, 0)$ and $(0, -4)$. Using the slope formula, we find the slope as follows:

$$m = \frac{-4 - 0}{0 - 3} = \frac{-4}{-3} = \frac{4}{3}$$

The second line is given in slope-intercept form, $y = \frac{4}{3}x + 5$, and the slope is $\frac{4}{3}$. Because the two slopes are equal but the y-intercepts are different, the lines are parallel. There are no solutions to this system of equations. The system is inconsistent.

b. Both lines are given in the slope-intercept form. To graph them, use the y-intercept and then use the slope to find an additional point on the line. The equation of the first line is $y = \frac{3}{2}x - 4$. From this equation, we see that $b = -4$. Therefore, the y-intercept is $(0, -4)$, so we graph this point first. The slope is

$$m = \frac{3}{2} = \frac{\text{rise}}{\text{run}}$$

Starting from the y-intercept of -4, we go up 3 and over 2 to get to another point on the graph, $(2, -1)$.

The equation of the second line is $y = \frac{-x}{4} + 3$. Using the same technique on the second line as above, we have that the y-intercept is the point $(0, 3)$ and the slope is

$$m = \frac{-1}{4} = \frac{\text{rise}}{\text{run}}$$

Starting from the y-intercept of 3, go down 1 and over 4 to get to another point on the line, $(4, 2)$. Graphing both lines carefully on the same axes yields the following graph.

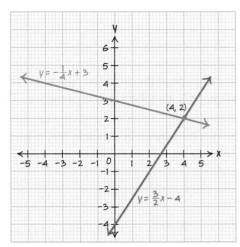

The two lines intersect at the point $(4, 2)$. Check the solution $(4, 2)$ by substituting $x = 4$ and $y = 2$ into both equations to see that they are true.

First Equation

$2 \stackrel{?}{=} \frac{3}{2}(4) - 4$ Substitute in $x = 4$, $y = 2$.

$2 \stackrel{?}{=} 6 - 4$

$2 = 2$ Both equations are true.

Second Equation

$2 \stackrel{?}{=} \frac{-(4)}{4} + 3$

$2 \stackrel{?}{=} -1 + 3$

$2 = 2$

The solution checks in both equations. The system is consistent.

c. The equation of the first line is $2x + 5y = 25$ and is in general form. We will graph this line using its intercepts. To find the x-intercept, make $y = 0$ and solve for x.

$2x + 5(0) = 25$ Substitute zero for y.

$2x = 25$ Solve for x.

$x = \frac{25}{5} = 12.5$

Connecting the Concepts

How do we use slope to find parallel lines?

Recall from Chapter 3 that two lines are parallel if they have the same slope but different y-intercepts. Therefore, to determine whether two lines are parallel, find their slopes and check to see whether they are equal. To find the slope, either put each line in the $y = mx + b$ form, or select two points on the line and use the slope formula,

$$m = \frac{y_2 - y_1}{x_2 - x_1}$$

The *x*-intercept is (12.5, 0). Find the *y*-intercept by making $x = 0$ and solve for *y*.

$$2(0) + 5y = 25 \qquad \text{Substitute zero for x.}$$
$$5y = 25 \qquad \text{Solve for y.}$$
$$y = 5$$

The *y*-intercept is the point (0, 5).

The equation of the second line is $y = \dfrac{-2}{5}x + 5$ and is in slope-intercept form ($y = mx + b$). The *y*-intercept is (0, 5), and the slope is $m = \dfrac{-2}{5} = \dfrac{\text{rise}}{\text{run}}$. Starting from the *y*-intercept of 5, use the slope to get to another point on the graph, which is (5, 3).

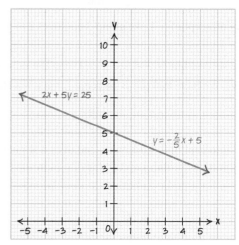

The two linear equations graph as the same line. Therefore, the two equations intersect everywhere, so there are infinitely many solutions. This system is consistent.

To show that these two lines are really the same line, solve the first equation for *y*.

$$2x + 5y = 25$$
$$\underline{-2x \qquad\qquad -2x} \qquad \text{Subtract 2x from both sides.}$$
$$5y = -2x + 25$$
$$\frac{5y}{5} = \frac{-2x}{5} + \frac{25}{5} \qquad \text{Divide both sides by 5, and simplify.}$$
$$y = \frac{-2}{5}x + 5$$

This is equal to the second linear equation, $y = \dfrac{-2}{5}x + 5$.

When solving a system of equations that result from an application problem, there is an additional first step of determining the two linear equations that result from the problem. Then proceed as before by graphing the two lines carefully and using the graph to determine the point(s) of intersection (if any).

Example 7 Comparing salaries

Renee is considering two part-time jobs in sales. One job, at Electronics-4-U, offers her $100 a week plus a 4% commission on her weekly sales. The other job, at Clothes to Go, offers her a weekly base salary of $90 plus a 5% commission on her weekly sales.

a. Determine the equations for Renee's weekly salary for each of the two jobs.

b. Graph the two lines on graph paper. Think carefully about how to scale the axes.

c. What is the solution to the system of equations? Interpret the solution in terms of her salary and weekly sales.

d. If Renee estimates that her weekly sales will be $550, which job should she take?

SOLUTION

a. Let w = weekly sales in dollars, and let S = weekly salary in dollars. The equation for Renee's weekly salary at Electronics-4-U is

$$S = 100 + 0.04w$$

Make sure to write the percentage as a decimal in the problem. The equation for Renee's weekly salary at Clothes to Go is given by

$$S = 90 + 0.05w$$

b. Notice that the y-intercepts are $(0, 100)$ and $(0, 90)$. A reasonable starting scale for the vertical axis would be from 0 to 200 by an increment of 20. Since the input is w, which represents weekly sales, a reasonable scale for the horizontal axis would be from 0 to 2500, with an increment of 500. One way to graph these two lines is to generate a table of values for each equation.

	Electronics-4-U			Clothes to Go
w	$S = 100 + 0.04w$		w	$S = 90 + 0.05w$
0	100		0	90
1000	140		1000	140
2000	180		2000	190

This is an estimate of what her weekly sales in clothing or electronics would be.

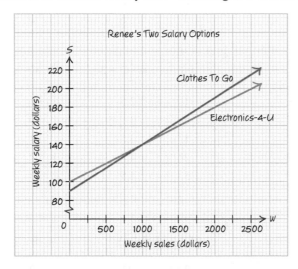

c. From the graph, the two lines intersect at $(1000, 140)$. This means that if Renee's weekly sales are $1000, her weekly salary will be $140.00 at both companies.

d. Substitute 550 into w in each equation to find the weekly salaries.

Electronics-4-U	Clothes to Go
$S = 100 + 0.04w$	$S = 90 + 0.05w$
$S = 100 + 0.04(550)$	$S = 90 + 0.05(550)$
$S = 122.00$	$S = 117.50$

Since she earns more at Electronics-4-U, she should work there.

What's That Mean?

Commission

Sales jobs are sometimes paid on a base salary plus a *commission.* The commission is a percentage of the sales that is paid back to the salesperson. If a salesperson sells $1000.00 and earns a 5% commission, the pay would be $0.05 \cdot 1000 = 50$, or $50.00.

■ Skill Connection

Set the Scale

Recall from Chapter R that the consistent and even spacing along an axis is called the scale. To scale an axis, find the smallest and largest values to be plotted along that axis. Round these values as needed, remembering that it is easy to count in multiples of twos, fives, and tens. Then decide on the scale, aiming for about ten tick marks on the axis.

PRACTICE PROBLEM FOR EXAMPLE 7

You are moving and want to store some of your things temporarily. You contact two local storage companies and get quotes on a 10-foot by 10-foot storage space. Help-U-Stor gives you a quote of $160.00 per month with a one-time $10.00 administration fee. Local Storage Solutions quotes you $150.00 per month with a one-time $30.00 administration fee.

a. Determine the equations for the cost of renting a 10-foot × 10-foot storage unit for each of the two companies. Let m = number of months, and let C = total monthly rental cost.

b. Graph the two lines on graph paper. Think carefully about how to scale the axes.

c. What is the solution to the system of equations? Interpret the solution in terms of the cost of renting the two units.

d. If you have to rent the storage space for 3 months, which company should you store your things with?

4.1 Exercises

For Exercises 1 through 8, use the table of values to solve the system.

1.

x	$y = \dfrac{-2}{5}x + 4$
-7	6.8
-6	6.4
-5	6
-4	5.6
-3	5.2

x	$y = \dfrac{-8}{5}x - 2$
-7	9.2
-6	7.6
-5	6
-4	4.4
-3	2.8

2.

x	$y = -x + 1$
-5	6
-4	5
-3	4
-2	3
-1	2

x	$y = \dfrac{1}{3}x + 5$
-5	$3\dfrac{1}{3}$
-4	$3\dfrac{2}{3}$
-3	4
-2	$4\dfrac{1}{3}$
-1	$4\dfrac{2}{3}$

3.

x	$y = 5.5x - 5$
-2	-16
-1	-10.5
0	-5
1	0.5
2	6

x	$y = -1.5x + 9$
-2	12
-1	10.5
0	9
1	7.5
2	6

4.

x	$y = 2x - 1$
-1	-3
0	-1
1	1
2	3
3	5

x	$y = -x + 8$
-1	9
0	8
1	7
2	6
3	5

5.

x	$y = \dfrac{1}{2}x + 3$
-1	2.5
0	3
1	3.5
2	4
3	4.5

x	$y = \dfrac{3}{2}x + 3$
-1	1.5
0	3
1	4.5
2	6
3	7.5

6.

x	$y = -2x + 7$
-2	11
0	7
2	3
4	-1
6	-5

x	$y = 3x + 7$
-2	1
0	7
2	13
4	19
6	25

7.

x	y = −x + 10
6	4
7	3
8	2
9	1
10	0

x	y = x − 8
6	−2
7	−1
8	0
9	1
10	2

8.

x	y = −3x + 2
−1	5
0	2
1	−1
2	−4
3	−7

x	y = 3x − 10
−1	−13
0	−10
1	−7
2	−4
3	−1

For Exercises 9 through 20, determine whether or not the given point is a solution of the system.

9.
$$C = 3x − 11$$
$$C = −2x + 14$$
a. Is $(x, C) = (−3, 2)$ a solution of the system?
b. Is $(x, C) = (5, 4)$ a solution of the system?

10.
$$y = 4x$$
$$y = −7x − 22$$
a. Is $(x, y) = (1, 4)$ a solution of the system?
b. Is $(x, y) = (−2, −8)$ a solution of the system?

11.
$$5a + 3b = −15$$
$$a + 3b = 3$$
a. Is $(a, b) = (0, 3)$ a solution of the system?
b. Is $(a, b) = (3, 0)$ a solution of the system?

12.
$$5t − 3P = −33$$
$$t + 2P = −4$$
a. Is $(t, P) = (−5, 1)$ a solution of the system?
b. Is $(t, P) = (1, −6)$ a solution of the system?

13.
$$−12x + 3y = −24$$
$$4x − y = 8$$
a. Is $x = 0, y = −8$ a solution of the system?
b. Is $x = 1, y = −4$ a solution of the system?

14.
$$−3c + d = 5$$
$$6c − 2d = −10$$
a. Is $c = \dfrac{−5}{3}, d = 0$ a solution of the system?
b. Is $c = 0, d = 5$ a solution of the system?

15.
$$−2x + y = −12$$
$$y = 2x + 16$$

a. Is $x = 6, y = 0$ a solution of the system?
b. Is $x = −8, y = 0$ a solution of the system?

16.
$$s + 3r = 3$$
$$3r = −s − 9$$
a. Is $s = 0, r = 1$ a solution of the system?
b. Is $s = 3, r = 1$ a solution of the system?

17.
$$x = 3$$
$$y = −1$$
a. Is $(3, 1)$ a solution of the system?
b. Is $(3, −1)$ a solution of the system?

18.
$$x = 0$$
$$y = −7$$
a. Is $(0, 0)$ a solution of the system?
b. Is $(0, −7)$ a solution of the system?

19.
$$y = −5x + 6$$
$$5x + y = 6$$
a. Is $(1, 1)$ a solution of the system?
b. Is $(2, −4)$ a solution of the system?

20.
$$y = \dfrac{1}{3}x − 4$$
$$x − 3y = 12$$
a. Is $(3, −3)$ a solution of the system?
b. Is $(0, −4)$ a solution of the system?

For Exercises 21 and 22, use the given graph to answer the questions. The graph below shows the death rates (percentage) involving CHD, which is short for coronary heart disease, in various countries organized by serum cholesterol level.

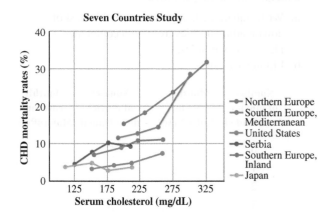

21. For which serum cholesterol level are the CHD mortality rates for Serbia and Japan equal?

22. For which serum cholesterol level are the CHD mortality rates for Northern Europe and the United States equal?

For Exercises 23 through 26, fill in the given tables. Answer the corresponding questions.

23. You are interested in two different services to download music on the Internet. Music OnLine charges $10.00 per month plus $0.80 per track downloaded. GotTunes charges $8.00 per month plus $1.00 per track downloaded.

   a. Write equations for the monthly cost of downloading music from each company. Define the variables.

   b. Fill in each table below.

Number of tracks downloaded	Monthly cost for Music OnLine
0	
2	
4	
6	
8	
10	
12	

Number of tracks downloaded	Monthly cost for GotTunes
0	
2	
4	
6	
8	
10	
12	

   c. Examine the tables to find the number of tracks downloaded that makes the costs of the two services equal.

   d. If you download an average of eight tracks a month, which company will be cheaper for you to use?

24. You are interested in comparing two video-on-demand services on the Internet. VideoNow charges $15.00 per month plus $3.00 per movie. MoviesPlus charges $5.00 a month plus $8.00 per movie.

   a. Write equations that give the monthly cost of downloading movies from both companies. Define the variables.

   b. Fill in each table.

Number of movies downloaded	Monthly cost for VideoNow
0	
1	
2	
3	
4	
5	

Number of movies downloaded	Monthly cost for MoviesPlus
0	
1	
2	
3	
4	
5	

   c. Examine the tables to find the number of movies downloaded that makes the monthly cost of the two services equal.

   d. If you download an average of five movies a month, which service will be cheaper for you to use?

25. You want to join a fitness club and are considering two options in your area. The first club, Fitness Plus, charges a start-up fee of $100.00 plus $15.00 per month. The second club, Rock's Gym, charges an initial fee of $80.00 plus $20.00 per month.

   a. Write equations for the cost of joining each gym. Define the variables.

   b. Fill in each table.

Number of months	Cost of Fitness Plus
0	
1	
2	
3	
4	
5	
6	

Number of months	Cost of Rock's Gym
0	
1	
2	
3	
4	
5	
6	

   c. After how many months will the cost of joining the two fitness clubs be equal?

   d. If you plan on joining for 6 months, which fitness club will be cheaper for you to use?

26. The cost to a retailer for each small bottle of water she sells is $0.37. She sells each small bottle for $1.50.

   a. Write equations for the cost that the retailer pays to purchase the water and the revenue the retailer takes in from selling the water. Define the variables.

   b. Fill in each table below.

Number of small bottles of water	Cost to retailer
0	
2	
4	
6	
8	
10	
12	

Number of bottles of water	Revenue retailer earns from sale of water
0	
2	
4	
6	
8	
10	
12	

   c. How many bottles of water does the retailer have to sell for her cost to equal her revenue?

   d. Does your answer to part c make sense in the context of this problem? Explain.

For Exercises 27 through 34, use the graph to determine the solution to the system of equations.

27.

28.

29.

30.

31.

32.

33.

34.

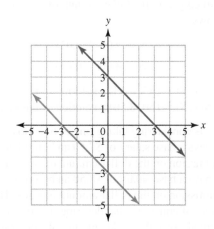

For Exercises 35 through 38, use the given information to answer the questions.

35. Ayesha is moving and gets quotes from two truck rental companies for a cargo van. The first company quotes her a one-day rental price of $19.95 plus $0.79 per mile. The second company quotes a one-day rental price of $21.95 plus $0.59 per mile. The system of equations that describes the cost C for a one-day rental given the number of miles m driven is as follows:

$$C = 19.95 + 0.79m$$
$$C = 21.95 + 0.59m$$

a. Is $(m, C) = (10, 27.85)$ a solution of the system?
b. Is $(m, C) = (15, 31.80)$ a solution of the system?

36. Amir is moving and gets two quotes from two rental companies for a 14-foot truck. The first company quotes him a one-day rate of $29.95 plus $0.79 per mile. The second company quotes the one-day rental price of $34.95 plus $0.59 per mile. The system of equations that describes the cost C for a one-day rental given the number of miles m driven is as follows:

$$C = 29.95 + 0.79m$$
$$C = 34.95 + 0.59m$$

a. Is $(m, C) = (30, 52.65)$ a solution of the system?
b. Is $(m, C) = (25, 49.70)$ a solution of the system?

37. Verena is considering taking one of two jobs. The first job pays a base salary of $7.00 an hour plus 3% commission on the dollar amount of sales. The second job pays a base salary of $8.00 an hour plus 1% commission on the dollar amount of sales. The system of equations that describes the hourly salary S earned given the dollar amount of sales x is as follows:

$$S = 7.00 + 0.03x$$
$$S = 8.00 + 0.01x$$

a. Is $(x, S) = (45, 8.45)$ a solution of the system?
b. Is $(x, S) = (50, 8.50)$ a solution of the system?

38. Alex is considering taking one of two jobs. The first job pays a base salary of $7.50 an hour plus 2% commission on the dollar amount of sales. The second job pays a base salary of $8.50 an hour plus 1% commission on the dollar amount of sales. The system of equations that describes the hourly salary S earned given the dollar amount of sales x is as follows:

$$S = 7.50 + 0.02x$$
$$S = 8.50 + 0.01x$$

a. Is $(x, S) = (100, 9.5)$ a solution of the system?
b. Is $(x, S) = (75, 9.25)$ a solution of the system?

For Exercises 39 through 62, graphically determine the solution to the system of equations. Identify each system as consistent or inconsistent. Clearly label and scale all graphs. Check the solution by substituting into the original system.

39. $y = 3x - 6$
    $y = -6x + 3$

40. $y = -5x + 10$
    $y = 10x - 5$

41. $y = 4x - 20$
    $y = -2x + 10$

42. $y = \frac{-1}{2}x + 6$
    $y = 2x - 4$

43. $y = \frac{1}{2}x - 1$
    $-x + 2y = -2$

44. $y = \frac{1}{6}x + 2$
    $y = \frac{1}{6}x - 4$

45. $x + y = 1$
    $x + y = -5$

46. $4x + y = 7$
    $4x + y = -1$

47. $-2x + y = 4$
    $4x + y = -2$

48. $-x + 2y = 2$
    $3x + 4y = -16$

49. $-9x + y = 6$
    $2x + y = -5$

50. $2x + 3y = 21$
    $-4x + 3y = 3$

51. $y = 5$
    $x = -4$

52. $x = 3$
    $y = -1$

53. $x = -9$
    $y = -2.5$

54. $y = -3.8$
    $x = 5.7$

55. $y = \frac{-1}{3}x + 2$
    $2x + 6y = 4$

56. $\frac{x}{3} + y = 7$
    $-3x + y = -3$

57. $-3x + 5y = 7$
    $y = \frac{3}{5}x + 2$

58. $y = \frac{x}{3}$
    $y = x + 2$

59. $y = \frac{4}{5}x + 3$
    $5y = 4x + 15$

60. $x - 4y = 12$
    $y = \frac{1}{4}x - 3$

61. $y = \frac{2}{3}x + 3$
    $y = -2x + 19$

62. $y = \frac{-1}{2}x + 7$
    $x + 2y = 14$

For Exercises 63 through 66, solve the application problems graphically. Clearly label and scale all graphs. Check the solution by substituting into the original system. Recall that the break-even point is the point at which revenue equals cost.

63. Jason's mobile auto repair has the following weekly revenue and cost equations for his business:

$$R = 75h$$
$$C = 50h + 300$$

where R represents the weekly revenue in dollars and C represents the weekly costs in dollars when he does *h* hours of repair work a week. Find the break-even point for Jason's mobile auto repair.

64. Gourmet Apples sells chocolate- and caramel-covered apples at local farmers' markets. Their weekly revenue and cost equations are

$$R = 15a$$
$$C = 3a + 600$$

where *R* represents the weekly revenue in dollars and *C* represents the weekly costs in dollars when Gourmet Apples sells *a* apples a week. Find the break-even point for Gourmet Apples.

65. Hummus R Us sells specialty hummus products at small grocery stores. Their weekly revenue and cost equations are

$$R = 6n$$
$$C = 2n + 460$$

where *R* represents the weekly revenue in dollars and *C* represents the weekly costs in dollars when Hummus R Us sells *n* hummus products a week. Find the break-even point for Hummus R Us.

66. Eve knits scarves to sell at craft fairs. Her monthly revenue and cost equations are

$$R = 40n$$
$$C = 25n + 300$$

where *R* represents the monthly revenue in dollars and *C* represents the monthly cost in dollars when Eve sells *n* scarves a month. Find the break-even point for Eve.

67. Janelle wants to hire a handyman for one day to do some repairs to her condo. A handyman named Mike advertises an hourly rate of $60.00 plus a $10.00 travel fee. Josh, another handyman, advertises an hourly rate of $55 plus a $15.00 travel fee.

   a. Find an equation for the cost of hiring Mike for one day.
   b. Find an equation for the cost of hiring Josh for one day.
   c. Carefully graph both lines on the same graph. Determine the point at which the cost of hiring Mike is equal to the cost of hiring Josh.

68. One plumber, Rocco, advertises that his labor rate is $65.00 an hour plus a $20.00 travel fee. A second plumber, Marco, advertises his labor rate at $60.00 an hour plus a $25.00 travel fee.

   a. Find an equation for the cost of hiring Rocco for one day.
   b. Find an equation for the cost of hiring Marco for one day.
   c. Carefully graph both lines on the same graph. Determine the point at which the cost of hiring Rocco is equal to the cost of hiring Marco.

69. An oven and microwave combination costs $960.00. Purchased individually, the oven costs twice as much as the microwave. Find the cost of the oven and microwave.

70. A washer and dryer combination costs $1300. If each is bought separately, the dryer costs $\frac{7}{6}$ times as much as the washer. Find the cost of the washer and dryer.

71. The perimeter of a rectangle is 24 centimeters. The length is three times the width. Find the length and the width of the rectangle.

72. The perimeter of a rectangle is 40 inches. The length is twice the width. Find the length and the width of the rectangle.

73. The local high school track team is holding a luncheon fund-raiser. They rented space in a nearby hotel for $255.00 for one afternoon. The catering company tells them that it will cost $5.75 per person for lunch. They plan to sell tickets to the fund-raiser for $10.00 per person.

   a. Find an equation for the total cost. This will include both the cost of renting the space and the cost of providing lunch.
   b. Find an equation for the total revenue. This will be all the money they take in for their fund-raiser.
   c. Carefully graph both lines on the same graph. Determine the break-even point, where cost = revenue.
   d. How many tickets do they have to sell to break even?

74. The Women's Charity League wants to hold a charity fund-raiser. They plan on a dinner and dancing. A local church has offered them space for free. The League plans to spend $9.50 per person for dinner. The band they hired is charging $715 for the evening. The League plans to sell tickets to the fund-raiser for $16.00 per person.

   a. Find an equation for the total cost. This will include both the cost of hiring the band and the cost of dinner.
   b. Find an equation for the total revenue. This will include all the money the League takes in for their fund-raiser.
   c. Carefully graph both lines on the same graph. Determine the break-even point, where the cost = revenue.
   d. How many tickets do they have to sell to break even?

For Exercises 75 through 84, determine whether the pair of lines is parallel, perpendicular, or neither. See Section 3.4 to review as needed.

75. $y = -3x + 5$

$y = -3x$

76. $y = \frac{2}{3}x + 7$

$y = \frac{2}{3}x - 1$

77. $y = -7x + 16$

$y = \dfrac{-1}{7}x - 24$

78. $y = \dfrac{3}{4}x + 5$

$y = \dfrac{4}{3}x - 12$

79. $y = \dfrac{-5}{6}x + 7$

$y = \dfrac{6}{5}x - 14$

80. $y = -9x + 71$

$y = \dfrac{1}{9}x + 19$

81. $x + y = 3$

$y = -x - 8$

82. $x - 2y = -4$

$y = \dfrac{1}{2}x + 9$

83. $2x + 5y = 5$

$6x + 15y = -3$

84. $x + y = -9$

$x = 15 - y$

For Exercises 85 through 90, determine how many solutions to the system there are. You do NOT have to find the solution to the system.

85.

86.

87.

88.

89.

90.

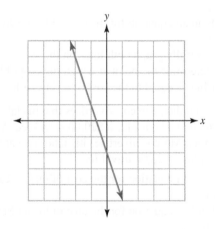

4.2 Solving Systems Using the Substitution Method

LEARNING OBJECTIVES

▪ Use the substitution method.

▪ Identify inconsistent and dependent systems.

▪ Solve practical applications of systems of linear equations.

Substitution Method

In Section 4.1, we learned that a system of linear equations can be solved by graphing both lines and determining the point of intersection (the solution). However, graphing by hand can be slow, and finding an accurate scale can be difficult. Also, if the two lines intersected at a point such as $\left(\dfrac{1}{3}, \dfrac{-3}{8}\right)$, it would be very hard to tell from the graph what the actual coordinates of the intersection point are. Therefore, algebraic methods have been developed to more efficiently solve such systems. One such method is called the **substitution method.**

Suppose we want to solve the following linear system.

$$2x + y = 7 \qquad \textit{The first linear equation.}$$
$$x - y = 5 \qquad \textit{The second linear equation.}$$

Solve the first equation for the variable y.

$$2x + y = 7 \qquad \textit{Solve the first equation for y.}$$
$$\underline{-2x \qquad\quad -2x}$$
$$y = 7 - 2x$$

Substitute $7 - 2x$ in for y in the second equation.

$$x - (7 - 2x) = 5$$

This equation contains only the variable x, so solve for x.

$$x - (7 - 2x) = 5 \qquad \textit{Use the distributive property.}$$
$$x - 7 + 2x = 5 \qquad \textit{Combine like terms.}$$
$$3x - 7 = 5 \qquad \textit{Solve for x.}$$
$$\underline{+7 \quad +7}$$
$$3x = 12$$
$$\dfrac{3x}{3} = \dfrac{12}{3}$$
$$x = 4$$

To determine where these two lines intersect requires that we find both the x and y coordinates. Substituting $x = 4$ into the second linear equation yields

$$x - y = 5 \qquad \textit{Substitute in x = 4.}$$
$$4 - y = 5 \qquad \textit{Solve for y.}$$
$$\underline{-4 \qquad\quad -4}$$
$$-y = 1$$
$$y = -1$$

Therefore, the solution is $(4, -1)$. To check, substitute $x = 4$ and $y = -1$ into both original equations.

Equation 1		Equation 2
$2(4) + (-1) \stackrel{?}{=} 7$	Substitute in $x = 4, y = -1$.	$4 - (-1) \stackrel{?}{=} 5$
$8 + (-1) \stackrel{?}{=} 7$		$4 + 1 \stackrel{?}{=} 5$
$7 = 7$	Both equations are true.	$5 = 5$

To determine where two lines intersect requires that we find a solution that is an ordered pair (x, y). The steps involved in solving a system using the substitution method are as follows.

Steps to Solve a System of Equations Using the Substitution Method

1. Solve one of the two equations for one of the variables. (*Hint:* Whenever possible, solve for a variable with a coefficient of ± 1 to avoid introducing fractions.)
2. Substitute the expression from step 1 in for the value of the variable in the other equation. Use parentheses.
3. Simplify the equation in step 2, and solve for the remaining variable.
4. Substitute the answer from step 3 into either of the original equations, and solve for the remaining variable.
5. Check the solution by substituting into both original equations.

Example 1 Trying out the substitution method

Solve each of the following linear systems using the substitution method. Check the solution.

a. $7x - 2y = 4$

$y = x + 3$

b. $2x + 3y = 24$

$y = \dfrac{2}{3}x$

c. $4x - y = -4$

$3x - 2y = 12$

SOLUTION

a. The second equation, $y = x + 3$, already has y isolated. Substitute $x + 3$ for y into the first equation.

$$7x - 2y = 4 \qquad \text{Substitute in } y = x + 3 \text{ for } y.$$
$$7x - 2(x + 3) = 4 \qquad \text{Distribute.}$$
$$7x - 2x - 6 = 4 \qquad \text{Simplify.}$$
$$5x - 6 = 4$$
$$\underline{+6 \quad +6}$$
$$5x = 10 \qquad \text{Solve for } x.$$
$$x = 2$$
$$y = x + 3$$
$$y = (2) + 3 \qquad \text{Substitute in } x = 2 \text{ to find } y.$$
$$y = 5$$
$$(x, y) = (2, 5) \qquad \text{This is the solution.}$$

To check, substitute the point $(x, y) = (2, 5)$ into both equations. Check $(x, y) = (2, 5)$ in both equations.

Equation 1	Equation 2
$7x - 2y = 4$	$y = x + 3$
$7(2) - 2(5) \stackrel{?}{=} 4$	$5 \stackrel{?}{=} (2) + 3$
$14 - 10 \stackrel{?}{=} 4$	$5 = 5$
$4 = 4$	

Since both equations are true, the solution checks.

b. The two equations are

$$2x + 3y = 24$$

$$y = \frac{2}{3}x$$

Notice that the second equation has been solved for y. Substitute $\frac{2}{3}x$ for y into the first equation to get

$$2x + 3\left(\frac{2}{3}x\right) = 24 \qquad \textit{Substitute } y = \frac{2}{3}x \textit{ in for } y.$$

$$2x + 2x = 24 \qquad \textit{Simplify.}$$

$$4x = 24$$

$$\frac{4x}{4} = \frac{24}{4} \qquad \textit{Divide both sides by 4.}$$

$$x = 6$$

Now find the value of the variable y. Substitute $x = 6$ into the second equation to get

$$y = \frac{2}{3}(6)$$

$$y = 2(2)$$

$$y = 4$$

The solution is the point $(6, 4)$.
Check $(x, y) = (6, 4)$ in both equations.

Equation 1	**Equation 2**
$2x + 3y = 24$	$y = \frac{2}{3}x$
$2(6) + 3(4) \stackrel{?}{=} 24$	$4 \stackrel{?}{=} \frac{2}{3}(6)$
$12 + 12 \stackrel{?}{=} 24$	$4 \stackrel{?}{=} 2(2)$
$24 = 24$	$4 = 4$

Since both equations are true, the solution checks. The two lines intersect at the point $(6, 4)$.

c. To avoid introducing fractions into the problem, solve the first equation for y, since it has a coefficient of -1.

$$4x - y = -4 \qquad \textit{Solve the first equation for } y.$$

$$\underline{+y \quad +y}$$

$$4x = -4 + y \qquad \textit{Add 4 to both sides.}$$

$$\underline{+4 \quad +4}$$

$$4x + 4 = y$$

$$y = 4x + 4$$

Substituting $4x + 4$ in for y in the second equation results in

$$3x - 2(4x + 4) = 12 \qquad \textit{Substitute in } y = 4x + 4.$$

$$3x - 8x - 8 = 12 \qquad \textit{Distribute and simplify.}$$

$$-5x - 8 = 12$$

$$\underline{+8 \quad +8} \qquad \textit{Add 8 to both sides.}$$

$$-5x = 20$$

$$\frac{-5x}{-5} = \frac{20}{-5} \qquad \textit{Divide both sides by } -5.$$

$$x = -4$$

Now find the value for y. Substituting $x = -4$ into the first equation yields

$$4(-4) - y = -4 \qquad \text{Substitute in } x = -4.$$

$$-16 - y = -4$$

$$\underline{+16 \qquad\qquad +16} \qquad \text{Add 16 to both sides.}$$

$$-y = 12$$

$$\frac{-y}{-1} = \frac{12}{-1} \qquad \text{Divide both sides by } -1.$$

$$y = -12$$

The solution is the point $(-4, -12)$.
Check $(x, y) = (-4, -12)$ in both equations.

Equation 1	**Equation 2**
$4x - y = -4$	$3x - 2y = 12$
$4(-4) - (-12) \stackrel{?}{=} -4$	$3(-4) - 2(-12) \stackrel{?}{=} 12$
$-16 + 12 \stackrel{?}{=} -4$	$-12 + 24 \stackrel{?}{=} 12$
$-4 = -4$	$12 = 12$

Since both equations are true, the solution checks.

PRACTICE PROBLEM FOR EXAMPLE 1

Solve each linear system using the substitution method. Check the solution.

a. $x - 2y = 7$
$\quad -3x + y = 24$

b. $3x - 6y = 12$
$\quad -2x + 8y = 10$

Example 2 Using the substitution method to solve the truck rental problem

In Example 1 of Section 4.1, we generated the equations for Vince's Truck Rentals and Gina's Rent-a-Truck. The cost for renting a truck from Vince's was given by

$$V = 15 + 19.99n$$

where $n =$ number of days the truck is rented. The cost for renting a truck from Gina's was given by

$$G = 5 + 24.99n$$

Use the substitution method to solve this system.

SOLUTION

Notice that in both equations, the variable representing cost (V or G) has been isolated. Since we are trying to determine where the cost of renting from Vince's equals the cost of renting from Gina's, we can *set the two costs equal* and solve for n. Setting the two costs equal is the same as setting these two equations equal.

$$V = G \qquad \text{Set } V \text{ equal to } G.$$

$$15 + 19.99n = 5 + 24.99n$$

$$\underline{-5 \qquad\qquad -5} \qquad \text{Subtract 5 from both sides.}$$

$$10 + 19.99n = 24.99n$$

$$10 + 19.99n = 24.99n$$

$$\underline{-19.99n \quad -19.99n} \qquad \text{Subtract } 19.99n \text{ from both sides.}$$

$$10 \qquad\quad = 5n$$

$$\frac{10}{5} = \frac{5n}{5} \qquad \text{Divide both sides by 5.}$$

$$n = 2$$

Substituting $n = 2$ into the two equations yields the following:

Vince's Cost	Gina's Cost
$V = 15 + 19.99(2)$	$G = 5 + 24.99(2)$
$V = 54.98$	$G = 54.98$

So the cost for renting a truck from Vince's is the same as the cost of renting a truck from Gina's when a truck is rented for 2 days.

PRACTICE PROBLEM FOR EXAMPLE 2

In Practice Problem 7 of Section 4.1, we generated equations for the cost of renting a 10-foot by 10-foot storage space. The cost C for Help-U-Stor was

$$C = 160m + 10$$

and the cost for Local Storage Solutions was

$$C = 150m + 30$$

where m = number of months. Solve this system using the substitution method.

Inconsistent and Consistent Systems

When using the substitution method, we typically don't look at the graphs of the two lines in the system. Therefore, we cannot see if the two lines are parallel (no solution) or the same line (infinitely many solutions). Recall from Section 4.1 that a consistent system has at least one solution. A consistent system may consist of two lines that intersect exactly once or two lines that intersect in infinitely many points along the line because they are the same line. When the two lines can be graphed as the same line, the system is consistent and the lines are *dependent*.

In the next example, we look at how the substitution method behaves when there are no solutions or infinitely many solutions.

> ### What's That Mean?
>
> **Dependent**
>
> A definition of the word *dependent* is reliant. In mathematics, two lines are dependent if they are exactly reliant on each other. The points overlap each other on the lines.

Example 3   Using the substitution method to explore solutions

Solve each of the following systems using the substitution method. If there is a solution, check the answer.

a. $2x + 5y = 40$

$y = \dfrac{-2}{5}x - 3$

b. $-3x + 4y = 4$

$6x - 8y = -8$

SOLUTION

a. $2x + 5y = 40$

$y = \dfrac{-2}{5}x - 3$

Notice that the second equation has been solved for y. Substitute $\dfrac{-2}{5}x - 3$ in for y in the first equation.

$$2x + 5\left(\frac{-2}{5}x - 3\right) = 40 \qquad \text{Substitute into the first equation.}$$

$$2x + 5\left(\frac{-2x}{5}\right) - 15 = 40 \qquad \text{Distribute and simplify.}$$

$$2x - 2x - 15 = 40 \qquad \text{The variable terms add to zero.}$$

$$-15 \stackrel{?}{=} 40 \qquad \text{This statement is false.}$$

Since this is a false statement ($-15 = 40$), there are no solutions to the system. The lines are parallel. This is similar to Section 2.3, in which we saw that some

Connecting the Concepts

How many possibilities are there for the solution?

In Section 4.1, we learned that there are three possibilities for the number of solutions to a system of two linear equations in two unknowns. The possibilities are a single solution, no solutions (parallel lines), and infinitely many solutions (the same line).

equations have no solutions. To prove that these two lines are parallel, show that their slopes are equal. The second line has slope $m = \dfrac{-2}{5}$, since this line is given in slope-intercept form. To find the slope of the first line, rewrite this equation in slope-intercept form.

$$2x + 5y = 40$$
$$\underline{-2x \qquad\quad -2x}$$
$$5y = 40 - 2x \qquad \text{Switch the order of the terms.}$$
$$5y = -2x + 40$$
$$\frac{5y}{5} = \frac{-2x}{5} + \frac{40}{5} \qquad \text{Divide both sides by 5.}$$
$$y = \frac{-2x}{5} + 8$$

The slope of both lines is $m = \dfrac{-2}{5}$. Because the slopes are equal and the y-intercepts are different, the lines are parallel. This is an example of the inconsistent case. The graphs of these two lines are shown on the following graph. They confirm that the lines are indeed parallel and thus never intersect. The lines being parallel tells us that the answer to the system is no solution.

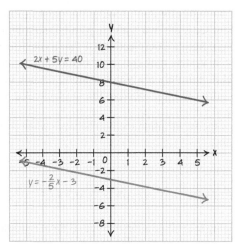

The system has no solutions.

b. Neither equation has a variable with coefficient ± 1, so there will be no way to avoid coefficients that are in fraction form. Solving the first equation for y yields

$$-3x + 4y = 4$$
$$\underline{+3x \qquad\quad +3x} \qquad \text{Add } 3x \text{ to both sides.}$$
$$4y = 3x + 4$$
$$\frac{4y}{4} = \frac{3x}{4} + \frac{4}{4} \qquad \text{Divide both sides by 4.}$$
$$y = \frac{3x}{4} + 1$$

Substituting $\dfrac{3x}{4} + 1$ for y into the second equation yields

$$6x - 8\left(\frac{3x}{4} + 1\right) = -8 \qquad \text{Distribute and simplify.}$$
$$6x - 8\left(\frac{3x}{4}\right) - 8 = -8$$
$$6x - 6x - 8 = -8 \qquad \text{The variable terms add to zero.}$$
$$-8 = -8 \qquad \text{This statement is true.}$$

Because this equation is always true ($-8 = -8$), there are infinitely many solutions. These two equations graph as the same line. This is an example of the dependent case.

To prove that these really are the same lines, put both lines in slope-intercept form. The first equation was put into slope-intercept form above, with

$$y = \frac{3}{4}x + 1$$

Rewriting the second line in slope-intercept form yields

$$6x - 8y = -8$$

$$\underline{-6x \qquad\quad -6x} \qquad\qquad \text{Subtract } 6x \text{ from both sides.}$$

$$-8y = -6x - 8$$

$$\frac{-8y}{-8} = \frac{-6x}{-8} - \frac{8}{-8} \qquad \text{Divide both sides by } -8 \text{ to solve for } y.$$

$$y = \frac{3x}{4} + 1$$

These two lines are the same line. This is an example of the dependent case. The graphs of these two lines are on the following graph. They confirm that the lines are the same and intersect at each point on the line.

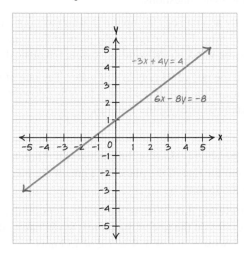

PRACTICE PROBLEM FOR EXAMPLE 3

Solve each of the systems using the substitution method. If there is a solution, check the answer.

a. $10x - 15y = 30$
$\quad -2x + 3y = -6$

b. $7x + y = 10$
$\quad -14x - 2y = 10$

Interpreting Results From the Substitution Method

- There is a **unique solution** (x, y) to the system when a value can be determined for both x and y. This is also known as a **consistent** system. Graphically, this means the two lines intersect at exactly one point.
- There are **infinitely many solutions** to the system when all the **variables add to zero** and a true statement remains (for example, $-8 = -8$). This is also known as a **consistent** system, and the lines are **dependent**. Graphically, this means the two lines graph as the same line and intersect at all points on that line.
- There are **no solutions** to the system when all the **variables add to zero** and a **false statement** remains (for example, $0 = -1$). This is also known as an **inconsistent** system. Graphically, this means the two lines are parallel: There are no points of intersection.

Practical Applications of Systems of Linear Equations

We have looked at various applications that result in a system of equations. These systems have been solved by using the graphical method and the substitution method. A variety of other applications require that we use a formula before we can set up and solve the linear system. The first formula that we are going to study is the *distance formula*.

> ### DISTANCE FORMULA
> $$d = r \cdot t, \quad \text{or} \quad \text{distance} = \text{rate} \cdot \text{time}$$

This formula applies to situations in which the *rate*, which we commonly refer to as the *speed*, is constant. Often, the distance formula shows up in problems involving airplanes, cars, and ships. To set up these problems correctly, it is important to understand the relationship between the rate (speed) of the plane or ship and the rate (speed) of the wind or current. We examine the rate in the next example.

Example 4 Finding the rate

Answer each of the following questions.

a. A small plane can fly at a rate of 100 mph in still air (without any wind). Currently, the wind speed is 15 mph. Find the rate of the plane if the wind is a headwind (the plane is flying into the wind, so the wind is slowing the plane down).

b. A boat can travel at the rate of 9 knots in still water. The rate of the current is 4 knots. Find the rate of the boat if the boat is traveling downstream (with the current, so the current is speeding the boat up).

SOLUTION

a. With a headwind, the wind is slowing the plane down. Therefore, we subtract the rate of the wind from the rate of the plane. The rate of the plane with the headwind is $100 - 15 = 85$, or 85 mph.

b. When the boat is traveling downstream, the current is pushing the boat, so its rate is faster. Therefore, we add the rate of the current to the rate of the boat. The rate of the boat traveling downstream is $9 + 4 = 13$, or 13 knots.

PRACTICE PROBLEM FOR EXAMPLE 4

Answer each of the following questions.

a. A passenger jet can fly at a rate of 480 mph in still air. Currently, the wind speed is 25 mph. Find the rate of the plane if the wind is a tailwind (the plane is flying with the wind, so the wind is speeding the plane up).

b. A ship can travel at the rate of 15 mph in still water. The rate of the current is 4 mph. Find the rate of the ship if the boat is traveling upstream (against the current, so the current is slowing the ship down).

> ### Interpreting the Rate Correctly
>
> - Let s = rate of the plane in still air, and let w = rate of the wind. When a plane is flying with a **headwind** (against the wind, or into the wind), its rate is $s - w$. When a plane is flying with a **tailwind** (with the wind), its rate is $s + w$.
>
> - Let b = rate of the ship (boat) in still water and c = rate of the current. When a boat is traveling **downstream** (with the current), the rate of the ship (boat) is $b + c$. When a boat is traveling **upstream** (against the current), the rate of the ship (boat) is $b - c$.

Now we will apply these ideas to some problems.

| Example 5 | Rate of a plane |

A small plane can fly 150 miles with a headwind in 2.5 hours. It makes the return trip (with a tailwind) in 1.5 hours. Find the rate of the plane in still air and the rate of the wind.

SOLUTION

First, write two equations to describe what is happening in this problem. The two situations are the plane flying against a headwind and the plane flying with a tailwind.

Let s = rate of the plane in still air, and let w = rate of the wind.

Headwind: A headwind slows the plane down, so the plane's rate with a headwind is $s - w$. Using the formula $d = r \cdot t$ with the given distance $d = 150$ and time $t = 2.5$ yields

$$150 = (s - w) \cdot 2.5$$

Tailwind: A tailwind speeds the plane up, so the plane's rate with a tailwind is $s + w$. Using the formula $d = r \cdot t$, with the given distance $d = 150$ and time $t = 1.5$ yields

$$150 = (s + w) \cdot 1.5$$

These two equations form a system of equations that we will solve using the substitution method.

$$150 = (s - w) \cdot 2.5$$
$$150 = (s + w) \cdot 1.5$$

Solving the first equation for s may be done by first dividing both sides by 2.5.

$$150 = (s - w) \cdot 2.5$$

$$\frac{150}{2.5} = \frac{(s - w) \cdot 2.5}{2.5} \qquad \text{Divide both sides by 2.5.}$$

$$60 = s - w$$

$$\underline{+w \qquad\quad +w} \qquad \text{Add } w \text{ to both sides to solve for } s.$$

$$60 + w = s$$

or

$$s = 60 + w$$

Substitute $60 + w$ into the s in the second equation to get

$$150 = [(60 + w) + w] \cdot 1.5$$

$$\frac{150}{1.5} = \frac{[(60 + w) + w] \cdot 1.5}{1.5} \qquad \text{Divide both sides by 1.5.}$$

$$100 = 60 + 2w$$

$$\underline{-60 \quad\; -60} \qquad \text{Subtract 60 from both sides.}$$

$$40 = 2w$$

$$\frac{40}{2} = \frac{2w}{2} \qquad \text{Divide both sides by 2 to isolate } w.$$

$$w = 20$$

Vladimir Melnik/Shutterstock.com

■ Connecting the Concepts

How fast is reasonable?

Interpreting whether a solution is *reasonable* to a plane or ship (boat) problem can be difficult if you are not a pilot or a navigator. Small planes typically fly from 75 to 150 miles per hour. Commercial jets often fly at speeds near 500 mph. Usually, only military jets fly at speeds greater than 600 mph. Reasonable wind speeds are 5 to 74 miles per hour. Wind speeds of over 74 miles per hour are hurricane-force winds. Only the most violent tornadoes will have wind speeds of over 200 mph. Boats and ships do not, in general, travel very fast, as the drag of the water is hard to overcome. Boats and ships typically travel at 10 to 25 knots (nautical miles per hour). In these problems, current rates are from 3 to 20 knots. Only the most serious tsunamis travel at 400 to 500 knots. Here, a *boat* refers to a craft of less than 200 feet, and a *ship* refers to a craft over 200 feet.

Substituting $w = 20$ into the first equation yields

$$150 = (s - 20) \cdot 2.5$$

$$\frac{150}{2.5} = \frac{(s - 20) \cdot 2.5}{2.5} \qquad \text{Divide both sides by 2.5.}$$

$$60 = s - 20$$

$$\underline{+20 \qquad +20} \qquad \text{Add 20 to both sides to solve for s.}$$

$$80 = s$$

Check the solution.

Substituting $s = 80$ and $w = 20$ into both equations yields

$150 \overset{?}{=} (80 - 20) \cdot 2.5$	Substitute in $s = 80$ and $w = 20$.	$150 \overset{?}{=} (80 + 20) \cdot 1.5$
$150 \overset{?}{=} 60 \cdot 2.5$	Simplify.	$150 \overset{?}{=} 100 \cdot 1.5$
$150 = 150$	Both equations are true.	$150 = 150$

The rate of the plane in still air is 80 mph, and the rate of the wind is 20 mph.

PRACTICE PROBLEM FOR EXAMPLE 5

A paddleboat travels 20 miles downstream in 6 hours. It takes 8 hours to make the return trip upstream. Find the rate of the paddleboat in still water and the rate of the current.

Another type of problem that we study involves integers. Recall that the integers are the whole numbers and their opposites, which is the set $\{\ldots, -3, -2, -1, 0, 1, 2, 3, \ldots\}$.

Example **6** Finding the numbers

The sum of two numbers is 100. One number is 8 less than 3 times the other number. Find the two numbers.

SOLUTION

The two unknowns are two numbers. Let $x =$ one number, and let $y =$ the other number. The first sentence translates as

$$x + y = 100$$

In Section 1.2, we learned not only that less than means to subtract but also that we subtract in the opposite order in which the sentence is written. Thus, the second sentence translates as

$$x = 3y - 8$$

The system of equations is

$$x + y = 100$$
$$x = 3y - 8$$

Since the second equation has already been solved for x, substitute $3y - 8$ directly into the first equation.

$$(3y - 8) + y = 100 \qquad \text{Substitute } 3y - 8 \text{ in for } x \text{ in the first equation.}$$

$$4y - 8 = 100 \qquad \text{Add 8 to both sides.}$$

$$\underline{+8 \quad +8}$$

$$4y = 108$$

$$\frac{4y}{4} = \frac{108}{4} \qquad \text{Divide both sides by 4 to solve for y.}$$

$$y = 27$$

The first integer is 27. To find the second integer, we substitute 27 for y in one of the equations.

$$x = 3(27) - 8$$

$$x = 73 \qquad \text{Substitute } y = 27 \text{ into the second equation, and evaluate.}$$

To check the work, substitute these values into both equations.

Equation 1		**Equation 2**
$73 + 27 \overset{?}{=} 100$ Substitute in $x = 73$ and $y = 27$.		$73 \overset{?}{=} 3(27) - 8$
$100 = 100$ Both equations are true.		$73 = 73$

The solution checks in both equations.

PRACTICE PROBLEM FOR EXAMPLE 6

The difference of a first integer and a second integer is 54. Three times the first integer is equal to the sum of the second integer and 6. Find the two integers.

Another application that gives rise to systems of linear equations comes from mixture and value problems. These problems often include computing the value of a quantity. For example, if apples are selling at $0.75 per pound and we purchase 3 pounds, the value (worth) is $3 \cdot 0.75 = 2.25$, or $2.25. The amount purchased is 3 pounds, and we say that the unit price (or price per pound) is $0.75.

> ### VALUE FORMULA
>
> The value of a quantity is the monetary worth of that quantity. To compute the value, we use the formula:
>
> $$\text{value} = \text{amount} \cdot \text{unit price}$$

When two different quantities are mixed or blended, for example, as two kinds of ingredients such as almonds and peanuts, the *value of the mix will equal the sum of values of the individual quantities*. The unit price of the mix will be a number in between the unit prices of each quantity.

Example 7   Unit price

Suppose a store has 20 pounds of almonds priced at $5.00 per pound (the unit price). The store also has 30 pounds of peanuts that cost $2.50 per pound (the unit price). The store wants to mix together the almonds and the peanuts.

© altphoto/Fotolia.com

a. Find the value of the almonds and the value of the peanuts.

b. Find the unit price of the mix.

SOLUTION

a. The value of the almonds is $20 \cdot \$5.00 = \$100.00$. The value of the peanuts is $30 \cdot \$2.50 = \$75.00$.

b. The value of the almonds plus the value of the peanuts will equal the value of the mix. Since the unit price of the mix is unknown, we will let $n = $ unit price of the mix. The mix contains 50 pounds of nuts.

$$20 \cdot \$5.00 + 30 \cdot \$2.50 = 50 \cdot n$$

Solving this equation for n yields

$$100 + 75 = 50n$$

$$175 = 50n$$

$$\frac{175}{50} = \frac{50n}{50}$$

$$3.50 = n$$

Therefore, the unit price of the mix is $3.50 per pound. Notice that this price is a number in between the unit price of almonds ($5.00 per pound) and the unit price of peanuts ($2.50 per pound).

PRACTICE PROBLEM FOR EXAMPLE 7

Suppose you have 15 pounds of shelled walnuts priced at $7.49 per pound (the unit price). You also have 20 pounds of hazelnuts that cost $8.49 per pound (the unit price). You want to mix together the almonds and the hazelnuts.

a. Find the value of the walnuts and the value of the hazelnuts.

b. Find the unit price of the mix.

Example 8   Coffee mix

A local coffee shop is making 30 pounds of its house blend of coffee by mixing two types of coffee. The first type is Colombian, and it costs $10.95 per pound. The second type is Guatemalan, and it costs $12.95 per pound. The blend is priced at $11.50 per pound. Find how many pounds of each type of coffee the barista should use in the shop's blend.

© NomenNescio/Big Stock Photo

SOLUTION

Let C = pounds of the Colombian coffee used, and let G = pounds of the Guatemalan coffee used. Since the shop is making 30 pounds of the blend, we have that

$$C + G = 30$$

Compute the value of each individual type of coffee and of the blend. The value of the Colombian coffee is

$$C \cdot 10.95 = 10.95C$$

The value of the Guatemalan coffee is

$$G \cdot 12.95 = 12.95G$$

The value of the blend is the 30 pounds of mix times the unit price for the mix $11.50.

$$30 \cdot 11.50 = 345$$

The sum of the individual values is equal to the value of the blend, so the second equation is

$$10.95C + 12.95G = 345$$

Therefore, the two equations in two unknowns are

$$C + G = 30$$
$$10.95C + 12.95G = 345$$

Solving the first equation for C yields

$$C + G = 30 \qquad \text{Subtract } G \text{ from both sides.}$$
$$\underline{-G \quad -G}$$
$$C = 30 - G$$

Substituting this expression into the second equation gives the following equation to solve for G.

$$10.95(30 - G) + 12.95G = 345 \qquad \text{Substitute in } C = 30 - G.$$
$$328.50 - 10.95G + 12.95G = 345 \qquad \text{Simplify.}$$

$$328.5 + 2.00G = 345$$

$$\underline{-328.5 \qquad\qquad -328.5} \qquad \textit{Subtract 328.5 from both sides.}$$

$$2.00G = 16.50$$

$$\frac{2.00G}{2.00} = \frac{16.50}{2.00} \qquad \textit{Divide both sides by 2.00 to isolate G.}$$

$$G = 8.25$$

The coffee shop needs to use 8.25 pounds of the Guatemalan coffee. To find the amount of Colombian coffee, substitute $G = 8.25$ into the first equation.

$$C + 8.25 = 30 \qquad \textit{Substitute into the first equation to find C.}$$

$$\underline{-8.25 \quad -8.25}$$

$$C = 21.75$$

The coffee shop has to use 21.75 pounds of the Colombian coffee and 8.25 pounds of the Guatemalan coffee to make the 30 pounds of the house blend.

PRACTICE PROBLEM FOR EXAMPLE 8

Organic Foods is making a custom nut blend. The cook is making a 50-pound mix of hazelnuts and almonds. Hazelnuts are priced at \$5.65 a pound, and almonds are priced at \$7.95 a pound. The mix will sell for \$6.50 a pound. Find the amount of hazelnuts and almonds that Organic Foods should include.

4.2 Exercises

For Exercises 1 through 6, solve the equation for the requested variable.

1. Solve $3x + y = -4$ for y.

2. Solve $-5x + y = 7$ for y.

3. Solve $x + 4y = -3$ for x.

4. Solve $x - 3y = -16$ for x.

5. Solve $5x - 10y = 30$ for y.

6. Solve $-3x + 4y = 12$ for x.

For Exercises 7 through 12, select the equation containing a variable with coefficient 1 or -1. Then solve that equation for that variable. Do not solve the system. See Example 2 if you need help getting started.

7. $5x - 6y = 9$
   $x + 3y = 7$

8. $2x - y = 17$
   $5x - 2y = -4$

9. $-3a + 12b = 24$
   $-a + 9b = 6$

10. $\frac{2}{3}a - b = 4$
    $-\frac{1}{2}a + 3b = 5$

11. $-6x + 4y = 7$
    $y = -2x + 1$

12. $y = -5x + 14$
    $3x + 5y = -2$

For Exercises 13 through 22, solve the systems of equations using the substitution method. Check the answer in both of the original equations.

13. $x = 3y - 1$
    $2x + y = 12$

14. $y = 3x - 5$
    $2x + y = 4$

15. $x = -5y + 1$
    $-3x + 2y = 31$

16. $y = -0.5x + 6$
    $2x - y = 8$

17. $2x + y = 10$
    $-6x + y = -5$

18. $x + 3y = 3$
    $3x - y = 6$

19. $y = -6x + 5$

    $y = 4x - 15$

20. $y = \frac{5}{3}x + 4$

    $y = \frac{-2}{3}x - 3$

21. $x = y$
    $2x + y = -6$

22. $y = x$
    $y = -3x + 20$

For Exercises 23 through 36, solve each system using the substitution method.

23. The sum of two numbers is 65. One number is 12 times the other number. Find the two numbers.

    a. Define the variables.
    b. Determine the two equations.
    c. Solve the system.

24. A first number minus a second number is -9. The first number is four times the second number. Find the two numbers.

   a. Define the variables.
   b. Determine the two equations.
   c. Solve the system.

25. The sum of two numbers is 25. One number is four times the other. Find the two numbers.

26. The sum of two numbers is 48. One number is three times the other. Find the two numbers.

27. The sum of two numbers is 12. One number is five times the other. Find the two numbers.

28. The sum of two numbers is 20. One number is nine times the other. Find the two numbers.

29. A first number minus a second number is -7. Four times the first number added to 1 is equal to the second number. Find the two numbers.

30. The sum of two numbers is 22. The first number is equal to twice the second number subtracted from 9. Find the two numbers.

31. The sum of two numbers is 12. One number is equal to the quotient of the other number and 2. Find the two numbers.

32. Twice the first number added to 6 is equal to the second number. The difference between the first number and the second number is 17. Find the two numbers.

33. Ethan is considering two part-time jobs in sales. One job, at a mobile-phone cart, offers him $100 per week plus a 5% commission on his weekly sales. The other job, at a tire store, offers him a weekly base pay of $120 plus a 4% commission on his weekly sales.

   a. Define the variables.
   b. Determine the equations for Ethan's weekly pay for each of the two jobs.
   c. Find the solution to the system. Interpret the solution in terms of Ethan's weekly pay.

34. Maya is considering two part-time jobs in clothing sales. One job, at Value Fashion, offers her $250 per week plus a 3% commission on her weekly sales. The other job, at Amy's Boutique, offers her a weekly base pay of $150 plus a 5% commission on her weekly sales.

   a. Define the variables.
   b. Determine the equations for Maya's weekly pay for each of the two jobs.
   c. Find the solution to the system. Interpret the solution in terms of Maya's weekly pay.

35. Marcus is working two jobs. One job pays him $8.00 an hour, and the other job pays him $9.00 an hour. The total hours he can work each week at both jobs is 20. Marcus would like to earn $176.00 weekly from both jobs.

   a. Define the variables.
   b. Determine the system of equations described in the problem.
   c. Find the solution to the system. Interpret the solution in terms of Marcus's salary and jobs.

36. Amir is working two jobs. The first job pays him $8.00 an hour, and the second job pays him $10.00 an hour. The total number of hours Amir works each week at both jobs is 22. He would like to earn $200 a week working both jobs.

   a. Define the variables.
   b. Determine the system of equations described in the problem.
   c. Find the solution to the system. Interpret the solution in terms of Amir's salary and jobs.

For Exercises 37 through 64, solve the system of equations using the substitution method. Check the answer in both of the original equations. If the system is inconsistent, answer "No solution." If the lines are dependent, answer "Infinitely many solutions."

37. $y = 2x - 1$
    $y = -4x + 5$

38. $y = -x + 9$
    $y = 4x + 6$

39. $y = 4x + 5$
    $y = \dfrac{-1}{2}x - 4$

40. $y = \dfrac{-4}{5}x - 2$
    $y = \dfrac{1}{5}x - 7$

41. $-x + 3y = 1$
    $2x + y = 5$

42. $3x - y = -4$
    $x + 2y = -6$

43. $x + 2y = 3$
    $2x - y = 4$

44. $4x + y = -2$
    $x - 2y = -5$

45. $3x + 2y = 6$
    $y = 2.5x - 4$

46. $-x + 6y = 4$
    $y = -0.5x + 2$

47. $x + 5y = 6$
    $y = 1$

48. $y = 2$
    $3x + 2y = -9$

49. $5x + 2y = -4$
    $-x + y = 5$

50. $x - 2y = 0$
    $-5x + 8y = 8$

51. $-3x + 4y = 12$
    $\dfrac{-3}{4}x + y = -1$

52. $-8x - 2y = 1$
    $4x + y = 2$

53. $5x - 10y = 15$
    $x = 2y + 3$

54. $\dfrac{-1}{4}x + 5y = \dfrac{1}{2}$
    $x - 20y = -2$

55. $x + 3y = 18$
    $2x + 6y = -12$

56. $x - y = 9$
    $y = x - 2$

57. $-x + 3y = 6$
    $3x + y = -5$

58. $\dfrac{3}{7}x - 7y = 35$
    $x = -14$

59. $x + 1 = -9$
$y - 3 = -3$

60. $x - 5 = -12$
$y + 6 = 3.5$

61. $y = 7x + 1$
$14x - 2y = -2$

62. $4x + y = 5$
$y = -4x + 5$

63. $x - \dfrac{1}{4}y = 9$

$2x + y = 1$

64. $6x + 3y = 5$

$y = \dfrac{3}{2}x - \dfrac{4}{3}$

For Exercises 65 through 78, answer each question.

65. The rate of a plane in still air is 120 mph, and the rate of the wind is 15 mph. Find the rate of the plane if the plane is flying into a headwind.

66. The rate of a plane in still air is 550 mph, and the rate of the wind is 25 mph. Find the rate of the plane if the plane is flying with a tailwind.

67. The rate of a plane in still air is 100 miles per hour, and the rate of the wind is 5 mph. Find the rate of the plane if the plane is flying with a tailwind.

68. The rate of a plane in still air is 340 miles per hour, and the rate of the wind is 25 miles per hour. Find the rate of the plane if the plane is flying into a headwind.

69. A boat travels at 7 mph in still water, and the current is flowing at a rate of 1.5 mph. Find the rate of the boat if it is traveling downstream.

70. A boat travels at 11 mph in still water, and the current has a rate of 3.5 mph. Find the rate of the boat if it is traveling downstream.

71. A boat travels at 9 mph in still water, and the current flows at a rate of 2 mph. Find the rate of the boat if it is traveling upstream.

72. A boat travels at 12 mph in still water, and the current has a rate of 1.5 mph. Find the rate of the boat if it is traveling upstream.

73. Oolong tea sells for $7.95 per pound.
   a. Find the value of 5.5 pounds of tea.
   b. Find the value of t pounds of tea.

74. Cashews sell for $4.55 per pound.
   a. Find the value of 26 pounds of cashews.
   b. Find the value of c pounds of cashews.

75. French Roast coffee sells for $11.95 per pound.
   a. Find the value of 26 pounds of coffee.
   b. Find the value of c pounds of coffee.

76. Dried blueberries sell for $13.99 per pound.
   a. Find the value of 2.5 pounds of dried blueberries.
   b. Find the value of b pounds of dried blueberries.

77. The total value of 50 pounds of coffee is $547.50. What is the unit price? Recall that the unit price is the cost per pound.

78. The total value of 5 pounds of Earl Grey tea is $39.75. What is the unit cost? Recall that the unit cost is the cost per pound.

For Exercises 79 through 90, solve each system using the substitution method.

79. A boat travels 50 miles downstream in 2.5 hours. It takes 5 hours to make the return trip upstream. Find the rate of the boat in still water and the rate of the current.
   a. Define the variables.
   b. Determine the two equations.
   c. Solve the system.

80. A plane can fly 600 miles in 4 hours with a tailwind. It makes the return trip (with a headwind) in 6 hours. Find the rate of the plane in still air and the rate of the wind.
   a. Define the variables.
   b. Determine the two equations.
   c. Solve the system.

81. A plane can fly 1275 miles in 3.4 hours with a headwind. It makes the return trip (with a tailwind) in 3 hours. Find the rate of the plane in still air and the rate of the wind.
   a. Define the variables.
   b. Determine the two equations.
   c. Solve the system.

82. A boat travels 30 miles downstream in 3 hours. It takes 5 hours to make the return trip upstream. Find the rate of the boat in still water and the rate of the current.
   a. Define the variables.
   b. Determine the two equations.
   c. Solve the system.

83. Julie wants to make a 50-pound mix of tea by blending two types of tea. The first type is Ceylon, which costs $5.75 per pound, and the second type is black currant tea, which costs $8.75 per pound. Julie wants to price the blend at $7.25 per pound. How many pounds of each type of tea does Julie need to use in her blend?
   a. Define the variables.
   b. Determine the two equations.
   c. Solve the system.

84. Michelle wants to make 10 gallons of punch for sale at her café. She is going to mix sparkling water and lemonade. The sparkling water costs $4.50 a gallon, and the lemonade costs $2.50 a gallon. Michelle would like to price the punch at $3.70 a gallon. Find how many gallons of sparkling water and lemonade Michelle should buy.
   a. Define the variables.
   b. Determine the two equations.
   c. Solve the system.

85. Graciela is making a 25-pound mix of dried papaya and crystallized ginger for her health food store.

The dried papaya costs $9.99 per pound, and the crystallized ginger costs $3.75 per pound. Graciela would like to price the mix at $7.49 per pound. Find how many pounds of dried papaya and crystallized ginger Graciela has to put in the mix.

a. Define the variables.
b. Determine the two equations.
c. Solve the system.

86. Andy is making a 55-pound mix of Costa Rican coffee and Colombian coffee for his cafe. The Costa Rican coffee costs $10.95 per pound, and the Colombian coffee costs $12.95 per pound. Andy would like to price the blend at $12.50 per pound. Find how many pounds of each type of coffee Andy should put in the mix.

a. Define the variables.
b. Determine the two equations.
c. Solve the system.

87. Rita's Auto Detail has the following weekly revenue and cost equations for her business:

$$R = 150n$$

$$C = 100n + 1400$$

where R represents the weekly revenue in dollars and C represents the weekly costs in dollars when she details n cars a week. Find the break-even point for Rita's Auto Detail.

88. Walz Caps has the following weekly revenue and cost equations from selling cycling caps:

$$R = 25h$$

$$C = 9h + 1200$$

where R represents the weekly revenue in dollars and C represents the weekly costs in dollars when the company sells h cycling caps a week. Find the break-even point for Walz Caps.

Courtesy of Walz Caps (www.walzcaps.com)

89. Mobile Style has the following monthly revenue and cost equations from selling mobile phone accessories at a mall kiosk:

$$R = 24.50n$$

$$C = 8.50n + 4300$$

where R represents the monthly revenue in dollars and C represents the monthly costs in dollars when Mobile Style sells n accessories. Find the break-even point for Mobile Style.

90. Tracy's Old Time Foods sells organic canned goods at Renaissance fairs. Tracy has the following revenue and cost equations for her business:

$$R = 8n$$

$$C = 4.5n + 680$$

where R represents the revenue in dollars and C represents the costs in dollars when Tracy sells n jars

of canned goods at a local fair. Find the break-even point for Tracy's Old Time Foods.

For Exercises 91 through 94, answer the following questions.

91. Consider the system of equations:

$$-3x + 5y = 15$$

$$y = \frac{3}{5}x + 3$$

a. Solve this system using the substitution method. How many solutions to this system are there?
b. Graph the two lines on the same axes.
c. Two points on this line are $(0, 3)$ and $(5, 6)$. Are these points solutions to this system?
d. Two points that are not on this line are $(0, 0)$ and $(1, 0)$. Are these points solutions to this system?
e. If there are infinitely many solutions, are the solutions points on the line or points not on the line?

92. Consider the system of equations:

$$4x - 3y = 24$$

$$y = \frac{4}{3}x - 8$$

a. Solve this system using the substitution method. How many solutions to this system are there?
b. Graph the two lines on the same axes.
c. Two points on this line are $(0, -8)$ and $(12, 8)$. Are these points solutions to this system?
d. Two points that are not on this line are $(0, 0)$ and $(2, 4)$. Are these points solutions to this system?
e. If there are infinitely many solutions, are the solutions points on the line or points not on the line?

93. Consider the following system of equations:

$$y = -6x + 8$$

$$18x + 3y = -21$$

a. Solve this system using the substitution method. How many solutions to this system are there?
b. Graph the two lines on the same axes.
c. Two points on the first line, $y = -6x + 8$, are $(0, 8)$ and $(1, 2)$. Are these points solutions to this system?
d. Two points on the second line, $18x + 3y = -21$, are $(0, -7)$ and $(1, -13)$. Are these points solutions to this system?
e. Explain why there are no solutions to this system.

94. Consider the following system of equations:

$$y = -7x + 4$$

$$21x + 3y = -6$$

a. Solve this system using the substitution method. How many solutions to this system are there?
b. Graph the two lines on the same axes.
c. Two points on the first line, $y = -7x + 4$, are $(0, 4)$ and $(1, -3)$. Are these points solutions to this system?

d. Two points on the second line, $21x + 3y = -6$, are $(0, -2)$ and $(-1, 5)$. Are these points solutions to this system?

e. Explain why there are no solutions to this system.

For Exercises 95 through 98, the students were asked to solve the given system using the substitution method. Read over the student's work and find the mistake.

95. $y = 4x - 8$

$2x - y = 6$

Matthew

$y = 4x - 8$

$2x - y = 6$

$2x - (4x - 8) = 6$

$2x - 4x - 8 = 6$

$-2x - 8 = 6$

$\underline{+8 \quad +8}$

$-2x = 14$

$x = -7$

$y = 4(-7) - 8 = -28 - 8 = -36$

The solution is $(-7, -36)$.

---

96. $x = -3y + 4$

$-x + y = 5$

Maya

$x = -3y + 4$

$-x + y = 5$

$-(-3y + 4) + y = 5$

$-3y + 4 + y = 5$

$-2y + 4 = 5$

$\underline{-4 \quad -4}$

$-2y = 1$

$y = \dfrac{-1}{2}$

$x = -3y + 4$

$x = -3\left(\dfrac{-1}{2}\right) + 4$

$x = \dfrac{3}{2} + 4 = \dfrac{3}{2} + \dfrac{8}{2} = \dfrac{11}{2}$

The solution is $\left(\dfrac{11}{2}, \dfrac{-1}{2}\right)$.

---

97. $3x + 4y = 11$

$-5x + 2y = -1$

Zachary

$3x + 4y = 11$

$-5x + 2y = -1$

$3x = -4y + 11$

$-5x + 2y = -1$

$-5(-4y + 11) + 2y = -1$

$20y - 55 + 2y = -1$

$22y = 54$

$y = \dfrac{54}{22} = \dfrac{27}{11}$

$3x = -4\left(\dfrac{27}{11}\right) + 11 = \dfrac{13}{11}$

The solution is $\left(\dfrac{13}{33}, \dfrac{27}{11}\right)$.

---

98. $-2x + 5y = 18$

$-6x - 9y = 6$

Sophia

$-2x + 5y = 18$

$-6x - 9y = 6$

$5y = 2x + 18$

$-6x - 9(2x + 18) = 6$

$-6x - 18x - 162 = 6$

$-24x - 162 = 6$

$-24x = 168$

$x = -7$

$5y = 2(-7) + 18 = -14 + 18 = 4$

The solution is $\left(-7, \dfrac{4}{5}\right)$.

For Exercises 99 through 104, answer each of the following questions.

99. If solving a system of equations using the substitution method results in $0 = 4$, is the system said to be consistent or inconsistent?

100. If solving a system of equations using the substitution method results in $-1 = -1$, is the system said to be consistent or inconsistent?

101. If solving a system of equations by graphing results in two parallel lines, is the system said to be consistent or inconsistent?

102. If solving a system of equations by graphing results in one line, is the system said to be consistent or inconsistent?

103. If solving a system of equations by graphing results in two intersecting lines, is the system said to be consistent or inconsistent?

104. If solving a system of equations using the substitution method results in the solution $(2, 3)$, is the system said to be consistent or inconsistent?

4.3 Solving Systems Using the Elimination Method

LEARNING OBJECTIVES

- Use the elimination method.

- Solve practical applications of systems of linear equations.

- Decide whether to use substitution or elimination.

Using the Elimination Method

There is another algebraic method that is used to solve systems of linear equations. It is called the **elimination** method. This method is the one that computers use to solve linear systems because it is easy to program and is very efficient.

Suppose we want to solve the following linear system:

$$x - y = 10$$
$$x + y = 22$$

Because the two sides of the first equation are equal, we can use the idea of a scale to show that the two sides are in balance.

Recall the addition property of equality, which states that we may add the same quantity to both sides of an equation. For example, we could add 22 to both sides of the first equation.

$$x - y = 10$$
$$\underline{+22 \qquad +22}$$
$$x - y + 22 = 32$$

Adding 22 did not help us to solve the system. However, the second equation tells us that 22 is the same as $x + y$. Therefore, we can add $x + y$ on the left side and 22 on the right side of the first equation.

Algebraically, we follow the same steps. Add the two equations vertically. The second equation, $x + y = 22$, states that $x + y$ is the same amount as 22 because the two sides are equal. Therefore, when the second equation is added to the first equation, we are adding the same quantity to both sides.

■ **Connecting the Concepts**

What is the addition property of equality?

Recall from Chapter 2 that we studied the addition property of equality, which states that the same value can be added to both sides of an equation. This is the property we are using when we add two equations vertically.

$$\begin{array}{r} x - y = 10 \\ \underline{x + y = 22} \\ 2x = 32 \end{array}$$ *The variable y has been eliminated. Solve for x.*

$$\frac{2x}{2} = \frac{32}{2}$$

$$x = 16$$

Now that we know that $x = 16$, we substitute this result into either one of the original equations to solve for y.

$$16 + y = 22$$ *Substitute in x = 16.*

$$\begin{array}{r} 16 + y = 22 \\ \underline{-16 \qquad -16} \\ y = 6 \end{array}$$ *Subtract 16 from both sides to solve for y.*

The solution to the system is the point $(16, 6)$. To check our solution, we substitute the values $x = 16$ and $y = 6$ into both original equations.

Equation 1   **Equation 2**

$16 - 6 \stackrel{?}{=} 10$ *Substitute x = 16, y = 6 into both equations.* $16 + 6 \stackrel{?}{=} 22$

$10 = 10$ *Both statements are true. The solution checks.* $22 = 22$

The whole key to the elimination method is to have the coefficients on one variable (in both equations) that are opposites. This means the coefficients have the same absolute value but different signs. Then when we add the two equations vertically, one variable sums to 0 and is "eliminated."

Steps to Solve a System of Equations Using the Elimination Method

1. Put both lines in general form $(Ax + By = C)$, if necessary.
2. If necessary, multiply both sides of one (or both) equations so that the coefficients on one of the variables are opposites.
3. Add the two equations vertically. At this point in the process, one of the variables should be eliminated.
4. Solve the equation for the remaining variable.
5. Substitute the answer from step 4 into either of the original equations and solve for the other variable. Remember that we are trying to find where two lines intersect, so we must determine the values of *both* variables.
6. Check the solution by substituting into *both* original equations.

■ **Connecting the Concepts**

What is an opposite?

Recall from Chapter R that opposites are two numbers that are the same in absolute value but differ in sign. For example, 6 and -6 are opposites.

Example 1 Putting the elimination method to work

Solve the system using the elimination method. Check the answer.

$$-2x + y = 16$$
$$2x + 3y = 8$$

SOLUTION

The coefficients of x are -2 and 2; that is, the coefficients are opposites. Add the two equations vertically by adding like terms. The x-variable should be eliminated after this step.

$$-2x + y = 16 \qquad \text{Add the two equations vertically.}$$
$$\underline{2x + 3y = 8}$$
$$4y = 24$$

$$\frac{4y}{4} = \frac{24}{4} \qquad \text{Divide both sides by 4 to solve for } y.$$

$$y = 6$$

Now that we know that $y = 6$, substitute this value into either of the original equations to find the value of x. Substituting into the second equation yields

$$2x + 3(6) = 8 \qquad \text{Substitute in } y = 6.$$
$$2x + 18 = 8 \qquad \text{Subtract 18 from both sides.}$$
$$\underline{-18 \;\; -18}$$
$$2x = -10$$

$$\frac{2x}{2} = \frac{-10}{2} \qquad \text{Divide both sides by 2.}$$

$$x = -5$$

Check the solution $(-5, 6)$ by substituting $x = -5$, $y = 6$ into both of the original equations.

Equation 1	Equation 2
$-2(-5) + 6 \overset{?}{=} 16$	$2(-5) + 3(6) \overset{?}{=} 8$
$10 + 6 \overset{?}{=} 16$	$-10 + 18 \overset{?}{=} 8$
$16 = 16$	$8 = 8$

Both equations check, so the solution is $(-5, 6)$.

PRACTICE PROBLEM FOR EXAMPLE 1

Solve the system using the elimination method. Check the answer.

$$x - 2y = 6$$
$$5x + 2y = 18$$

Example 2 Finding opposites to use the elimination method

Solve each system using the elimination method. Check the answer.

a. $2x + y = 11$　　　　**b.** $2x - 3y = 7$
　　$-x + 4y = 8$　　　　　　$-3x + 4y = -10$

SOLUTION

a. First, notice that neither of the coefficients of x or y is an opposite.

$$2x + y = 11 \qquad \text{The original linear system.}$$
$$-x + 4y = 8$$

To eliminate the variable x, multiply both sides of the second equation by 2 so that the coefficients of x are 2 and -2.

$$2x + y = 11 \qquad\qquad\qquad 2x + y = 11$$
$$2(-x + 4y) = 2(8) \qquad\longrightarrow\qquad -2x + 8y = 16$$

Now that the coefficients of x are opposites, add the two equations vertically to eliminate x.

$$2x + y = 11$$
$$\underline{-2x + 8y = 16} \qquad \text{Add the two equations.}$$
$$9y = 27$$

With the variable x eliminated, we can now solve for y.

$$\frac{9y}{9} = \frac{27}{9} \qquad \textit{Divide by 9 and solve for y.}$$

$$y = 3$$

Substitute $y = 3$ into either of the original equations, and solve for x.

$$2x + (3) = 11 \qquad \textit{Substitute y = 3 into the first equation, and solve for x.}$$

$$2x = 8$$

$$\frac{2x}{2} = \frac{8}{2}$$

$$x = 4$$

The solution to this system is the point $(4, 3)$. Check by substituting $x = 4$ and $y = 3$ into both original equations.

Equation 1	Equation 2
$2(4) + 3 \stackrel{?}{=} 11$	$-(4) + 4(3) \stackrel{?}{=} 8$
$8 + 3 \stackrel{?}{=} 11$	$-4 + 12 \stackrel{?}{=} 8$
$11 = 11$	$8 = 8$

Both equations check.

b. $2x - 3y = 7$ $\qquad$ *The original linear system.*

$-3x + 4y = -10$

Considering the coefficients of x, the least common multiple of 2 and 3 is 6. To get coefficients of 6 and -6 for the variable x, multiply the first equation by 3 and the second by 2.

$$3(2x - 3y) = 3(7) \qquad \longrightarrow \qquad 6x - 9y = 21$$

$$2(-3x + 4y) = 2(-10) \qquad\qquad\qquad -6x + 8y = -20$$

Add the two equations to eliminate the variable x.

$$6x - 9y = 21$$

$$\underline{-6x + 8y = -20} \qquad \textit{Add the two equations vertically.}$$

$$-y = 1$$

$$\frac{-y}{-1} = \frac{1}{-1} \qquad \textit{Solve for y.}$$

$$y = -1$$

Substitute $y = -1$ into the first equation and solve for x.

$$2x - 3(-1) = 7$$

$$2x + 3 = 7$$

$$\underline{-3 \quad -3}$$

$$2x = 4$$

$$\frac{2x}{2} = \frac{4}{2}$$

$$x = 2$$

The solution is $(2, -1)$. Check the solution of $(2, -1)$ by substituting $x = 2$ and $y = -1$ back into both original equations.

Equation 1	Equation 2
$2(2) - 3(-1) \stackrel{?}{=} 7$	$-3(2) + 4(-1) \stackrel{?}{=} -10$
$4 + 3 \stackrel{?}{=} 7$	$-6 + -4 \stackrel{?}{=} -10$
$7 = 7$	$-10 = -10$

Because $(2, -1)$ satisfies both original equations, it is the solution to the system.

PRACTICE PROBLEM FOR EXAMPLE 2

Solve each system using the elimination method. Check the answer.

a. $-3x + 5y = 30$
$\quad\; x + 5y = 10$

b. $2x + 3y = 18$
$\quad\; 6x + 9y = -9$

In Example 2, the variable x was eliminated first. The variable y could also have been eliminated in the first step, and the final answer would have been the same. The solution is not affected by which variable is eliminated first.

Example 3   Switching to the general form first

Solve the system using the elimination method. Check your answer.

$$-2x + 3y = 0$$
$$3y = -4x - 18$$

SOLUTION

$$-2x + 3y = 0 \qquad \text{\textit{The original linear system.}}$$
$$3y = -4x - 18$$

The second equation is *not* in general form. Notice that x and y are not on the same side of the equation. The first step is to put the second equation in general form. We do this by moving the x-term on the right side of the equation to the left side of the equation.

$$3y = -4x - 18 \qquad \text{\textit{Add 4x to both sides.}}$$
$$\underline{+4x \qquad +4x}$$
$$4x + 3y = -18$$

The general form of the system is

$$-2x + 3y = 0$$
$$4x + 3y = -18$$

The coefficients of the y variable are both 3. Multiply the first equation by -1 to get the coefficients of the y variables to be opposites (-3 and 3).

$$-1(-2x + 3y) = -1(0) \qquad\longrightarrow\qquad 2x - 3y = 0$$
$$4x + 3y = -18 \qquad\qquad\qquad\qquad 4x + 3y = -18$$

Now that the coefficients of y are opposites, add the two equations vertically to eliminate y.

$$2x - 3y = 0$$
$$\underline{4x + 3y = -18} \qquad \text{\textit{Add the two equations vertically.}}$$
$$6x = -18$$

$$\frac{6x}{6} = \frac{-18}{6} \qquad \text{\textit{Divide both sides by 6 to solve for x.}}$$

$$x = -3$$

Now that we have found the value of x, we also have to find the value of y. Substituting $x = -3$ into the first equation and solving for y yields

$$2(-3) - 3y = 0 \qquad \text{\textit{Substitute in x = -3.}}$$
$$-6 - 3y = 0 \qquad \text{\textit{Add 6 to both sides to isolate y.}}$$
$$\underline{+6 \qquad\quad +6}$$
$$-3y = 6$$

$$\frac{-3y}{-3} = \frac{6}{-3} \qquad \text{\textit{Divide both sides by -3 to solve for y.}}$$

$$y = -2$$

The solution is the point $(-3, -2)$.
Check the solution $(-3, -2)$ by substituting $x = -3$ and $y = -2$ into both original equations.

Equation 1	Equation 2
$2(-3) - 3(-2) \stackrel{?}{=} 0$	$4(-3) + 3(-2) \stackrel{?}{=} -18$
$-6 - (-6) \stackrel{?}{=} 0$	$-12 + (-6) \stackrel{?}{=} -18$
$0 = 0$	$-18 = -18$

Because $(-3, -2)$ satisfies both original equations, it is the solution to the system.

PRACTICE PROBLEM FOR EXAMPLE 3

Solve the system using the elimination method. Check the answer.

$$-2x + y = -3$$
$$4y = -x + 24$$

More Practical Applications of Systems of Linear Equations

The elimination method can be used to solve a variety of applications.

Example 4   Purchasing school supplies

Siria buys two spiral notebooks and one USB drive at the campus bookstore for $25.60. Two days later, Siria buys three more spiral notebooks and two USB drives at the campus bookstore for $48.40. How much does each notebook and USB drive cost individually?

© TEA/Big Stock Photo

SOLUTION

First, define the variables. Let

$$n = \text{cost of each spiral notebook in dollars}$$
$$b = \text{cost of each USB drive in dollars}$$

Siria first purchased two spiral notebooks and one USB drive for $25.60. This purchase translates into the equation

$$2n + b = 25.60$$

On her second trip to the campus bookstore, Siria bought three spiral notebooks and two more USB drives for $48.40. This translates into the equation

$$3n + 2b = 48.40$$

The system of equations to solve is

$$2n + b = 25.60$$
$$3n + 2b = 48.40$$

To eliminate b, multiply the first equation by -2 to get the coefficients of b to be opposites.

$$-2(2n + b) = -2(25.60) \qquad\longrightarrow\qquad -4n - 2b = -51.20$$
$$3n + 2b = 48.40 \qquad\qquad\qquad\qquad 3n + 2b = 48.40$$

$$-4n - 2b = -51.20 \qquad \text{Add the two equations vertically.}$$
$$\underline{3n + 2b = 48.40}$$
$$-1n = -2.80$$
$$-1(-1n) = -1(-2.80) \qquad \text{Multiply both sides by } -1.$$
$$n = 2.80$$

To solve for b, substitute the value for n into the first equation and solve.

$$2n + b = 25.60$$
$$2(2.80) + b = 25.60 \qquad \text{Substitute 2.80 for } n, \text{ and solve for } b.$$
$$5.60 + b = 25.60$$
$$\underline{-5.60 \qquad\quad -5.60}$$
$$b = 20.00$$

Each spiral notebook costs $2.80, and each USB drive costs $20.00.

PRACTICE PROBLEM FOR EXAMPLE 4

Mario is teaching a cake-decorating class at a culinary school. He is buying supplies for his new class. He buys six food-coloring kits and eight cake-decorating kits for $246.00. Later, some more students add his class, and he has to purchase three more food-coloring kits and 3 cake-decorating kits for $99.00. How much does each food-coloring kit and each cake-decorating kit cost individually?

Now we will examine two other types of applications that involve percentages and are commonly encountered. The first type of problem involves simple interest earned on an investment. To calculate simple interest, we use the following formula.

> ### SIMPLE INTEREST FORMULA
>
> $$I = P \cdot r \cdot t$$
>
> where I = interest earned, P = principal (original investment), r = annual interest rate (as a decimal), and t = time (in years).

What's That Mean?

Simple and Compound Interest

Simple interest means interest that is paid only at the end of the time period. For example, if you put $1000 into an account earning 5% interest for 1 year, at the end of the year you will be paid $50.00 in simple interest. *Compound interest* is interest that is paid at set intervals of time, such as daily, monthly, or quarterly, until the end of the time period.

Example 5 Computing simple interest

Compute the simple interest earned on a $2500 investment, earning a 4.5% annual interest rate, over a 2-year time period.

SOLUTION

The principal P is the original investment, so $P = 2500$. The interest rate r has to be converted to decimal form. So

$$r = 4.5\% \qquad \text{Move the decimal point two places}$$
$$r = 0.045 \qquad \text{to the left.}$$

Dmitriy Shironosov/Shutterstock.com

The time t is two years, so $t = 2$. Substituting these values into the formula yields

$$I = P \cdot r \cdot t$$
$$I = (2500)(0.045)(2) \qquad \text{Substitute in the given values and multiply.}$$
$$I = 225.00$$

This account earns $225.00 in interest in 2 years.

Skill Connection

Percents

To convert a percentage to decimal form, move the decimal point two places to the left. Add zeros if necessary. For example,

$$9\% = 0.09.$$

PRACTICE PROBLEM FOR EXAMPLE 5

Compute the simple interest earned on a $15,000 investment, earning a 4% annual interest rate, over a 10-year period.

The simple interest formula appears in systems of equations problems. These problems are often investment problems. When a person has some money to invest, an investment advisor will encourage the person to split the money into several accounts. These accounts include stock accounts, bond accounts, and cash accounts. Stock and bond accounts are not federally insured, meaning that if the company whose stocks or bonds are purchased declares bankruptcy, the investor loses money.

Bank accounts, such as savings and checking accounts, are federally insured. If a bank declares bankruptcy, the U.S. government will pay the account holders back the value of their account up to $250,000.00 (as of this writing).

People invest money in stocks and bonds, even though they are not insured, because stocks and bonds may earn more than the money would in a bank account. In the period 1926–1991, the stock market historically returned about 10% yearly, and many bond accounts returned about 7% yearly. Bonds are considered less risky than stocks. This means that investors are much less likely to lose all their money on bonds than on stocks. However, the more risk an investor takes on, the more the potential return on the investment (the money earned).

Financial advisors will typically advise that money be split between stocks and bonds. The next example investigates how to split investment dollars into two accounts to minimize risk.

What's That Mean?

Stocks versus Bonds

Do you know the difference between a stock and a bond? When you buy *stock* in a company, you are purchasing part ownership in that company. When you buy a *bond* from a company, you are lending that company money, which the company promises to pay back with interest. So think of a bond as lending a company your money and a stock as purchasing part of a company.

Example 6 — Investing in stock and bond funds

Terri receives $20,000.00 from the estate of her great-aunt Mildred. Terri goes to a financial advisor, who tells her to put part of her money in a stock fund that returns 10% interest and part of her money in a bond fund that returns 6.5% interest. How much money should Terri put in each fund if she wants to earn $1500.00 a year in interest?

STAN HONDA/AFP/Getty Images

SOLUTION

We are concerned with two situations in this problem: the amount of money invested in the funds and the amount of interest earned on the funds. Because the question is how much money Terri should invest in each fund, let

$$A = \text{amount of money in dollars Terri invests in the stock fund}$$
$$B = \text{amount of money in dollars Terri invests in the bond fund}$$

Because she has a total of $20,000, we have that

$$A + B = 20,000$$

This equation describes one situation we were concerned with: the amount of money invested in the funds.

The second situation involves the amount of interest earned on the funds. The total interest Terri wants to earn yearly is $1500. Remember that in math, *total* means to *add*. We are going to add the interest she earns on the stock fund to the interest she earns on the bond fund. The total yearly interest of these two funds is $1500.00. The amounts invested, A and B, are the original investments or the principal in each account. Since she wants to earn $1500.00 in one year, $t = 1$.

$$I = P \cdot r \cdot t$$
$$I = A \cdot (0.10) \cdot 1 = 0.10A \qquad I = B \cdot (0.065) \cdot 1 = 0.065B$$

Adding the two interest amounts together to get the total interest, we get the equation

$$0.10A + 0.065B = 1500 \qquad \textit{Total the interest to get \$1500.00.}$$

So the system of equations we have to solve is

$$A + B = 20,000 \qquad \text{The original system.}$$
$$0.10A + 0.065B = 1500$$

Neither the coefficient of A nor the coefficient of B is an opposite. Multiply both sides of the first equation by -0.10 to make the coefficients of A opposites.

$$-0.10(A + B) = -0.10(20,000) \longrightarrow -0.10A - 0.10B = -2000$$
$$0.10A + 0.065B = 1500 \qquad\qquad\qquad 0.10A + 0.065B = 1500$$

$$\begin{array}{ll} -0.10A - 0.10B = -2000 & \text{Add the two equations.} \\ \underline{0.10A + 0.065B = 1500} & \\ \quad -0.035B = -500 & \\ \dfrac{-0.035B}{-0.035} = \dfrac{-500}{-0.035} & \text{Solve for B.} \\ \quad B \approx 14,285.71 & \text{Round to two decimal places.} \end{array}$$

Substitute the value of B into the first equation and solve for A.

$$A + (14,285.71) = 20,000$$
$$A = 5714.29$$

Skill Connection

Rounding

In a problem that involves money, round to two decimal places. This is the cents place.

Notice that the solution is rounded to the hundredths place (cents place) because we are talking about money in dollars. Terri should invest $5714.29 in the stock fund (which is riskier) and $14,285.71 in the bond fund (less risk) to generate $1500.00 in interest annually.

PRACTICE PROBLEM FOR EXAMPLE 6

Russ receives an inheritance of $45,000 from his grandparents. His financial advisor wants him to invest his inheritance in a stock fund that is currently returning 9.5% interest and a bond fund that is currently earning 6.5% interest. Russ wants to earn $4000 a year in interest from his investments. How much should he invest in each account?

The next type of application we are going to look at involves percent mixture problems. These problems are similar to interest problems in that we will multiply a percent (as a decimal) by an amount.

> **Formula for the Amount of a Given Substance in a Solution** To find the amount of a given substance in a solution, use the formula
> $$\text{given substance} = \text{percent} \cdot \text{amount of solution}$$

When using a percent in a problem, always convert it to the decimal form first.

Example 7 Computing a quantity in a solution

Sara is taking a chemistry lab class and has 5 liters of a 45% alcohol solution. How much alcohol is in the solution?

SOLUTION

The amount of solution is 5 liters. The percent must be converted to its decimal form before using it in the formula: $45\% = 0.45$. Therefore,

$$\text{amount of alcohol} = 0.45 \cdot 5 = 2.25$$

There are 2.25 liters of alcohol in the solution.

We now apply this formula to a system of equations.

Example 8 Setting up a mixture problem

James needs to mix a 40% saline solution (a salt and water solution is called *saline*) with a 20% saline solution to make a 25% saline solution. He wants a total of 16 liters in the mix. How many liters of the 40% saline solution and 20% saline solution should he use?

SOLUTION

There are two situations to examine in this problem. The total amount of solution should be 16 liters, and the amount of salt in the mix (solution) should be 25%. Because the question is how many liters of each solution James should include, let

$$A = \text{Amount of the 40\% saline solution (in liters)}$$
$$B = \text{Amount of the 20\% saline solution (in liters)}$$

James wants a total of 16 liters. Remember that *total* means to add. We have our first equation, which is

$$A + B = 16$$

Total (add) the amount of salt in the 40% solution to the amount of salt in the 20% solution to get the total amount of salt in the 25% solution.

$$\text{amount of salt in the 40\% solution} = 0.40 \cdot A = 0.40A$$
$$\text{amount of salt in the 20\% solution} = 0.20 \cdot B = 0.20B$$
$$\text{amount of salt in the final mix of 25\% solution} = 0.25(16) = 4$$

$$0.40A + 0.20B = 4 \qquad \text{Total the two amounts of salt.}$$

So the system of equations is

$$A + B = 16 \qquad \text{The original linear system.}$$
$$0.40A + 0.20B = 4$$

Neither of the coefficients of A or B is an opposite. Multiply both sides of the first equation by -0.20 so that the coefficients of A are opposites.

$$-0.20(A + B) = -0.20(16) \qquad\longrightarrow\qquad -0.20A - 0.20B = -3.2$$
$$0.40A + 0.20B = 4 \qquad\qquad\qquad\quad 0.40A + 0.20B = 4$$

Add the two equations to eliminate B.

$$
\begin{array}{l}
-0.20A - 0.20B = -3.2 \\
\underline{0.40A + 0.20B = 4} \qquad \text{Add the equations vertically.} \\
0.20A = 0.8
\end{array}
$$

$$\frac{0.20A}{0.20} = \frac{0.80}{0.20} \qquad \text{Solve the system for A.}$$

$$A = 4$$

Substitute the value for A back into the first equation to solve for B.

$$4 + B = 16$$
$$B = 12$$

James needs to use 4 liters of the 40% saline solution and 12 liters of the 20% saline solution to make 16 liters of a 25% saline solution.

PRACTICE PROBLEM FOR EXAMPLE 8

A dairy wants to mix whole milk, which has a 4% fat content, with skim milk (a 1% fat content) to make 500 gallons of 2% milk. How many gallons of whole milk and skim milk should be used?

© iStockphoto.com/Chris Elwell

■ Connecting the Concepts

Which method should be used to solve a system?

To solve a linear system algebraically, we can use either the substitution method or the elimination method. When a variable has already been solved for or a variable has a coefficient of ± 1, the substitution method often is used because it can be faster. When the system is given in general form $(Ax + By = C)$ and either a variable has coefficients that are opposites or there is no coefficient that is ± 1, the elimination method is often used.

Substitution or Elimination?

There are many times in an application problem that using one method over the other makes the solving process a bit quicker. In the next example, we will see how using the substitution method might be a bit faster.

Example 9 Comparing angles in a geometry problem

Two angles are supplementary. The measure of the first angle is 3 times as large as the measure of the second angle. Find the degree measures of the two angles.

SOLUTION

Let

$$a = \text{Measure of the first angle in degrees}$$
$$b = \text{Measure of the second angle in degrees}$$

The statement that the two angles are supplementary translates as

$$a + b = 180$$

We are told that the first angle is 3 times as large as the second. This sentence translates as

$$a = 3b$$

The two equations in two unknowns are

$$a + b = 180$$
$$a = 3b$$

Substitution would be the quickest method to solve this system because the second equation has already been solved for a. Substituting the second equation into the first and solving for b yields

$$3b + b = 180 \qquad \text{Substitute } a = 3b \text{ into the first}$$
$$\qquad\qquad\qquad \text{equation, and solve for } b.$$
$$4b = 180$$
$$\frac{4b}{4} = \frac{180}{4}$$
$$b = 45$$

Substitute the value for b into the second equation, and solve for a.

$$a = 3(45)$$
$$a = 135$$

The first angle has measure $135°$, and the second angle has measure $45°$.

PRACTICE PROBLEM FOR EXAMPLE 9

Two angles are complementary. The measure of the second angle is four times the measure of the first angle. Find the degree measure of the two angles.

What's That Mean?

Supplementary and Complementary

In geometry, two angles are said to be *supplementary* if their sum is 180°. Two angles are said to be *complementary* if their sum is 90°.

Skill Connection

Elimination

Solving Example 9 using the elimination method is done below.

$$a + b = 180$$
$$a = 3b$$

$$a + b = 180$$
$$a - 3b = 0$$

$$a + b = 180$$
$$\underline{-a + 3b = 0}$$
$$4b = 180$$
$$\frac{4b}{4} = \frac{180}{4}$$
$$b = 45$$
$$a = 3b = 3(45) = 135$$

To solve using elimination required rewriting the second equation, multiplying the second equation by -1, and then adding the two equations. In this case, the substitution method was more efficient.

Example 10 Choosing substitution or choosing elimination?

Decide whether to solve the system using the substitution method or the elimination method. Do NOT solve the system, but do justify your answer.

a. $y = 6x - 4$ **b.** $x + 2y = 7$ **c.** $-2x + 3y = 5$

    $2x + 3y = 7$ $3x + 4y = -8$ $4x + 5y = -9$

SOLUTION

a. The first equation is $y = 6x - 4$. Because y has already been solved for, this system can be efficiently solved by using the substitution method.

b. The first equation is $x + 2y = 7$. The coefficient of x is 1, so x will be easy to solve for. The system can be solved by using the substitution method. Notice that both equations are in general form, so the system can also be solved using the elimination method. Either method is reasonable.

c. Neither variable in either equation has a coefficient of ± 1. The coefficient of x in the first equation is -2, and the coefficient of x in the second equation is $+4$. If the first equation is multiplied by 2, the coefficients of x will be opposites. This system can be efficiently solved by using the elimination method.

4.3 Exercises

For Exercises 1 through 24, solve the system using the elimination method. Check the solution by substituting into both of the original equations.

1. $2x - y = 16$
   $3x + y = 9$

2. $-3x + y = 9$
   $5x - y = 15$

3. $-x + 6y = -3$
   $x - 2y = -5$

4. $x + 3y = 8$
   $-x + 4y = 6$

5. $-4x + 2y = 12$
   $8x - 2y = -40$

6. $3x + y = -13$
   $3x - y = 1$

7. $4x + 2y = 8$
   $4x - y = -4$

8. $x + 3y = 6$
   $3x + 3y = -18$

9. $4x + 3y = -5$
   $2x - y = 5$

10. $3x + y = 9$
   $-x + 5y = -35$

11. $3x - y = -1$
   $-6x + 2y = 2$

12. $5x - 15y = 45$
   $-x + 3y = -9$

13. $3x - 2y = -14$
   $2x + 3y = 8$

14. $3x + 8y = -7$
   $5x + 3y = -22$

15. $13x + 2y = -40$
   $10x - 3y = 1$

16. $3x - 5y = 16$
   $5x - 4y = 31$

17. $10x + 3y = 22$
   $3x - 2y = 24$

18. $7x - 8y = 12$
   $2x + 5y = -33$

19. $6x + 8y = -8$
   $3x + 4y = 36$

20. $x - y = 7$
   $-3x + 3y = 10$

21. $7x + 2y = -2$
   $-21x - 6y = 6$

22. $2x + 5y = 20$
   $-8x - 20y = -80$

23. $-6x + 2y = -16$
   $3x - y = -2$

24. $4x - 3y = 21$
   $8x - 6y = -3$

For Exercises 25 through 30, solve the system using the elimination method.

25. Two integers sum to 95. The difference of 4 times the first and the second number is 15. Find the two integers.

   a. Define the variables.
   b. Determine the two equations.
   c. Solve the system using the elimination method. Check the solution.

26. A first number minus a second number is 5. The sum of twice the first number and 3 times the second number is 45. Find the two numbers.

   a. Define the variables.
   b. Determine the two equations.
   c. Solve the system using the elimination method. Check the solution.

27. Hunter is the coach of a youth soccer team. Hunter purchases eight T-shirts and six water bottles for $186 to give out at an upcoming youth soccer tournament. Later, she purchases ten more T-shirts and eight water bottles for $237 as additional teams sign up. How much does each individual T-shirt and water bottle cost?

a. Define the variables.
b. Determine the two equations.
c. Solve the system using the elimination method. Check the solution.

28. Gary is organizing a charity dinner and is purchasing door prizes. He buys three coffee mugs and two pen sets for $29.50. As additional attendees sign up for the event, he purchases an additional three coffee mugs and four pen sets for $42.50. How much does each coffee mug and pen set cost individually?

a. Define the variables.
b. Determine the two equations.
c. Solve the system using the elimination method. Check the solution.

29. Martinique, a busy mother of four, purchases three gallons of milk and four loaves of French bread for $23.40. The next week, she purchases two gallons of milk and three loaves of French bread for $16.35. How much does each gallon of milk and loaf of French bread cost individually?

a. Define the variables.
b. Determine the two equations.
c. Solve the system using the elimination method. Check the solution.

30. Jordan is planting his spring garden. He purchases three packages of seeds plus two tomato plants for $11.75. The next week, he purchases an additional four packages of seeds plus one more tomato plant for $11.80. How much does each packet of seeds and each tomato plant cost individually?

a. Define the variables.
b. Determine the two equations.
c. Solve the system using the elimination method. Check the solution.

© iStockphoto.com/fotokostic

For Exercises 31 through 50, solve the system using the elimination method. Check the solution by substituting into both of the original equations.

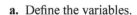

31. $-2x + 5y = 10$
    $2x = 5y + 25$

32. $4x + 5y = -20$
    $5y = -4x + 15$

33. $x + 2y = 18$
    $-3x + 2y = 2$

34. $-2x + 3y = -21$
    $x + 3y = -12$

35. $4x - 3y = -24$
    $x + y = 1$

36. $x + y = 3$
    $6x - 5y = 20$

37. $4x - 5y = -15$
    $2x + y = -11$

38. $11x - 6y = 24$
    $x + 3y = 27$

39. $-14x + 35y = 21$
    $2x - 5y = -3$

40. $12x - 4y = 4$
    $-3x + y = -1$

41. $3x + 5y = 30$
    $y = \dfrac{-3}{5}x + 6$

42. $y = \dfrac{-1}{2}x + 7$
    $x + 2y = 14$

43. $2x - 2y = -14$
    $4x - y = -1$

44. $5x + 4y = 0$
    $-5x + 2y = 30$

45. $y = \dfrac{5}{2}x - 3$
    $5x - 2y = 3$

46. $12x - 2y = 2$
    $-6x + y = 7$

47. $3x - y = 7$
    $-9x + 3y = -21$

48. $\dfrac{3}{4}x + y = -6$
    $-3x - 4y = 24$

49. $2x - 2y = 10$
    $-x + y = 8$

50. $-2x - 3y = 3$
    $2x + 3y = 12$

For Exercises 51 through 58, decide whether to solve the system using the substitution method or elimination method. Do NOT solve the system, but do justify your answer.

51. $3x + 4y = 9$
    $2x - 4y = -3$

52. $2x + 7y = -3$
    $-2x - 3y = 4$

53. $3x - 5y = 7$
    $y = 6x + 1$

54. $-6 + 3y = x$
    $4x + 9y = 8$

55. $y = 2x - 5$
    $y = x + 7$

56. $y = -4x + 5$
    $y = -2x - 3$

57. $x - y = 6$
    $x + y = 3$

58. $2x - 7y = 4$
    $-3x + 7y = 2$

For Exercises 59 through 74, answer each question.

59. Tomas has $500.00 to invest in a simple interest account for 4 years. The interest rate is 4.25%. Find the amount of interest he earns.

60. Tess has $12,500.00 to invest in a simple interest account for 2 years. The interest rate is 4.75%. Find the amount of interest she earns.

61. Steven has $8720.00 to invest in a simple interest account for 3 years. The interest rate is 4.25%. Find the amount of interest he earns.

62. Alejandro has $5000.00 to invest in a simple interest account for 1 year. The interest rate is 3.75%. Find the amount of interest he earns.

63. A simple saline solution is 8.5% sodium. Find the amount of sodium in 10 liters of saline.

64. A mouthwash contains 8% alcohol. Find the amount of alcohol in 16 ounces of mouthwash.

65. Christy is working with an 8% sucrose solution. Find the amount of sucrose in 8 liters of the solution.

66. A juice drink contains 12% real fruit juice. Find the amount of real fruit juice in 8 ounces of the drink.

67. Two angles are complementary. One angle has a measure of 25°. Find the measure of the other angle.

68. Two angles are complementary. One angle has a measure of 64°. Find the measure of the other angle.

69. Two angles are supplementary. One angle has a measure of 110°. Find the measure of the other angle.

70. Two angles are supplementary. One angle has a measure of 125°. Find the measure of the other angle.

71. Teresa has $10,000 to invest. She puts part of her money in a stock account and the rest in a bond account. If Teresa puts n dollars in the stock account, write an expression for the remainder that she puts in the bond account.

72. Nikolai has $4000 to invest. He puts part of his money in a stock account and the rest in a bond account. If Nikolai puts n dollars in the stock account, write an expression for the remainder that he puts in the bond account.

73. Alexis has $3800 to invest. He puts part of his money in a CD and the rest in a money market account. If Alexis puts n dollars in the CD, write an expression for the remainder that he puts in the money market.

74. Lupe has $1500 to invest. She puts part of her money in a certificate of deposit and the rest in a money market account. If Lupe puts n dollars in the CD account, write an expression for the remainder that she puts in the money market account.

For Exercises 75 through 94, set up the system of equations and solve using either the substitution method or elimination method.

75. A small plane flying with the wind travels 375 miles in 3 hours. On the return trip, flying against the wind, the same plane takes 5 hours to travel 375 miles. Find the rate of the plane in still air and the rate of the wind.
   a. Define the variables.
   b. Determine the two equations.
   c. Solve the system. Check the solution.

76. A plane flying with the wind travels 4400 miles in 10 hours. On the return trip, flying against the wind, the same plane takes 11 hours to travel 4400 miles. Find the rate of the plane in still air and the rate of the wind.
   a. Define the variables.
   b. Determine the two equations.
   c. Solve the system. Check the solution.

77. A boat travels with the current 60 miles in 3 hours. It takes the boat 6 hours to travel the same 60 miles against the current on the return trip. Find the rate of the boat in still water and the rate of the current.
   a. Define the variables.
   b. Determine the two equations.
   c. Solve the system. Check the solution.

78. A boat travels with the current 130 miles in 5 hours. Against the current, it takes the boat 13 hours to travel the same 130 miles on its return trip. Find the rate of the boat in still water and the rate of the current.
   a. Define the variables.
   b. Determine the two equations.
   c. Solve the system. Check the solution.

79. To make healthier bread dough, a baker wants to blend whole-wheat and white flour. He has a total of 50 pounds of whole-wheat and white flour in the mix. The whole-wheat flour costs $4.25 per pound, and the white flour costs $3.75 per pound. The mix costs $4.00 per pound. Find the amount of each type of flour that he should include in the mix.
   a. Define the variables.
   b. Determine the two equations.
   c. Solve the system. Check the solution.

80. To make a batch of trail mix, a health food store wants to blend walnuts and yogurt-covered raisins. There is a total of 50 pounds of walnuts and raisins in the mix. The walnuts cost $7.49 per pound, and the yogurt-covered raisins cost $3.49 per pound. The total value of the trail mix is $249.50. Find the amount of walnuts and yogurt-covered raisins that they have to include in the mix.
   a. Define the variables.
   b. Determine the two equations.
   c. Solve the system. Check the solution.

81. Renata is working two jobs. Her first job pays $8.50 an hour, and her second job pays $9.00 an hour. She would like to work a total of 25 hours a week and earn $225.00 a week. Determine how many hours a week Renata should work at each job.
   a. Define the variables.
   b. Determine the two equations.
   c. Solve the system. Check the solution.

82. Gayle is working two jobs. Her first job pays $8.00 an hour, and her second job pays $9.00 an hour. She would like to work a total of 20 hours a week and earn $170.00 a week. Determine how many hours a week Gayle should work at each job.
   a. Define the variables.
   b. Determine the two equations.
   c. Solve the system. Check the solution.

83. Cate has $4000.00 to invest. An investment advisor tells her to put part of her money in a CD earning 4%

interest and the rest in a bond fund earning 5% interest. Cate would like to earn $185.00 in interest every year. How much should she invest in each account?

84. Dianna has $25,000 to invest. An investment advisor tells her to put part of her money in a bond fund at 5% interest and the rest in a stock fund earning 7.5% interest. Dianna would like to earn $1625.00 in interest every year. How much should she invest in each account?

85. Michael has two credit cards. One card is a MasterCard with an annual percentage rate (APR) of 18%, and the other is a store credit card with an APR of 22%. The total Michael owes is $3500.00, and he paid $730.00 this year in interest. How much does Michael owe on each card?

86. Renaldo has two credit cards. One card is a MasterCard with an annual percentage rate (APR) of 15%, and the other is a store credit card with an APR of 20%. The total Renaldo owes is $4500.00, and he paid $750.00 this year in interest. How much does Renaldo owe on each card?

87. Greg needs to mix a 15% hydrochloric acid solution with 20% hydrochloric acid solution to make an 18.75% hydrochloric acid solution. He wants a total of 20 liters in the mix. How many liters of the 15% solution and the 20% solution should he use?

88. Elizabeth wants to mix a 25% saline solution with a 40% saline solution to make a 30% saline solution. She needs a total of 12 ounces in the mix. How many ounces of the 25% saline solution and the 40% saline solution should she use?

89. Christine has to mix a 30% antiseptic alcohol solution with a 50% antiseptic alcohol solution to make a 42% antiseptic alcohol solution. She needs a total of 100 liters in the mix. How many liters of the 30% antiseptic alcohol solution and the 50% antiseptic alcohol solution should she use?

90. Eddie has to mix 5% butterfat milk with 2% butterfat milk to make 3% butterfat milk. He needs a total of 120 gallons in the mix. How many gallons of the 5% butterfat milk and the 2% butterfat milk should he use?

91. Two angles are complementary. The second angle measures 3 degrees more than twice the measure of the first angle. Find the degree measures of both angles.

92. Two angles are complementary. The second angle measures 2 degrees more than three times the measure of the first angle. Find the degree measures of both angles.

93. Two angles are supplementary. The second angle measures 5 less than four times the measure of the first angle. Find the degree measures of both angles.

94. Two angles are supplementary. The second angle measures 4 less than three times the measure of the first angle. Find the degree measures of both angles.

For Exercises 95 through 98, read the student's work carefully and find the error.

95. Solve the system:

$$x + y = 5$$
$$x + 2y = 6$$

> **Micah**
>
> $$x + y = 5$$
> $$\underline{x + 2y = 6}$$
> $$3y = 11$$
> $$y = \frac{11}{3}$$
> $$x + \frac{11}{3} = 5$$
> $$x = 5 - \frac{11}{3} = \frac{15}{3} - \frac{11}{3} = \frac{4}{3}$$
>
> The solution is $\left(\frac{4}{3}, \frac{11}{3}\right)$.

96. Solve the system:

$$3x + y = 6$$
$$2x + y = -1$$

> **Kristine**
>
> $$3x + y = 6$$
> $$\underline{2x + y = -1}$$
> $$5x = 5$$
> $$x = 1$$
>
> $$3(1) + y = 6$$
> $$3 + y = 6$$
> $$y = 3$$
>
> The solution is $(1, 3)$.

97. Solve the system:

$$2x - 3y = 15$$
$$x + 5y = -2$$

> *Aaron*
>
> $$2x - 3y = 15$$
> $$x + 5y = -2$$
>
> $$2x - 3y = 15$$
> $$-2(x + 5y) = -2$$
>
> $$2x - 3y = 15$$
> $$\underline{-2x - 10y = -2}$$
> $$-13y = 13$$
>
> $$y = -1$$
>
> $$x + 5(-1) = -2$$
> $$x - 5 = -2$$
> $$x = 5 + -2 = 3$$
>
> The solution is $(3, -1)$.

98. Solve the system:

$$4x + y = 8$$
$$2x + y = 6$$

> *Angel*
>
> $$4x + y = 8$$
> $$2x + y = 6$$
>
> $$4x + y = 8$$
> $$-1(2x + y) = 6$$
>
> $$4x + y = 8$$
> $$\underline{-2x - y = 6}$$
> $$2x = 14$$
>
> $$x = 7$$
>
> $$2(7) + y = 6$$
> $$14 + y = 6$$
> $$y = -8$$
>
> The solution is $(7, -8)$.

4.4 Solving Linear Inequalities in Two Variables Graphically

LEARNING OBJECTIVES

- Find the solution set for linear inequalities in two variables.

- Graph vertical and horizontal inequalities.

Linear Inequalities in Two Variables

In some situations, we want to come up with a solution to a problem, but the situation has some constraints. For example, a couple may be getting married and would like to know how many people they can invite to their wedding yet stay within their budget. The constraint on this situation is the amount of money the couple has budgeted for guests at their wedding.

DEFINITION

Linear Inequality in Two Variables   A **linear inequality in two variables** is of the form $Ax + By < C$, where A, B, and C are real numbers with neither A nor B as zero. The inequality symbols $>$, $\leq$, and $\geq$ may also be used.

What's That Mean?

Constraint

In general, a *constraint* on a problem is a condition that limits the possible solutions to the problem. Constraints give rise to inequalities.

We will now examine what the solution set to a linear inequality looks like.

Example 1 The wedding planner

Arlene is a wedding consultant. Her clients, Sara and Alex, are getting married and have budgeted $1200 for dinner at the reception. Sara and Alex want to serve their guests a choice of a chicken dinner or a salmon dinner. The catering company that Arlene uses quotes the cost of chicken dinners at $6.50 a plate and the salmon at $8.50 a plate. The total cost of the reception meal is $6.50C + 8.50S$, where C = number of chicken dinners served and S = number of salmon dinners served. Since Sara and Alex want to spend a maximum of $1200 on the reception meal, Arlene wants the total cost to be less than or equal to $1200 or, mathematically,

$$6.50C + 8.50S \leq 1200$$

Given this constraint on their budget, fill in the table below to determine whether the given possible combination of chicken and salmon dinners is within Sara and Alex's budget. Fill in the last two rows with different combinations of your choice.

Number of chicken dinners	Number of salmon dinners	Cost ≤ 1200?
80	75	
29	119	
80	85	

SOLUTION

Number of chicken dinners	Number of salmon dinners	Cost ≤ 1200?
80	75	1157.50
29	119	1200
80	85	1242.50 Not a solution!
75	75	1125
80	80	1200

$6.50(80) + 8.50(75)$
$= 1157.5 \leq 1200$

$6.50(80) + 8.50(85)$
$= 1242.50 \geq 1200$

Notice that the third row in the table does not check because the cost exceeds $1200.00 (our constraint).

From this example, we see there are many solutions to a linear inequality.

DEFINITION

Solution Set to a Linear Inequality in Two Variables The **solution set to a linear inequality in two variables** is the set of all points (x, y) that make the inequality true.

Example 2 Checking solutions

Determine whether the given point is in the solution set of the linear inequality.

$$y > 3x - 5$$

a. $(1, 1)$ **b.** $(0, 0)$

c. $(0, -5)$ **d.** $(2, -6)$

SOLUTION

To see whether a given point is in the solution set, substitute the coordinates of that point into the inequality and see whether it makes the inequality true. If the inequality is true, then the point is in the solution set. If the inequality is false, then the point is NOT in the solution set.

a.
$$(x, y) = (1, 1)$$

$$1 \overset{?}{>} 3(1) - 5 \qquad \text{Substitute in } x = 1, y = 1.$$

$$1 > -2 \qquad \text{This statement is true.}$$

The point $(1, 1)$ is in the solution set.

b.
$$(x, y) = (0, 0)$$

$$0 \overset{?}{>} 3(0) - 5 \qquad \text{Substitute in } x = 0, y = 0.$$

$$0 > -5 \qquad \text{This statement is true.}$$

The point $(0, 0)$ is in the solution set.

c.
$$(x, y) = (0, -5)$$

$$-5 \overset{?}{>} 3(0) - 5 \qquad \text{Substitute in } x = 0, y = -5.$$

$$-5 \overset{?}{>} -5 \qquad \text{This statement is false.}$$

Since -5 is not strictly greater than -5 (it is equal), the point $(0, -5)$ is not in the solution set.

d.
$$(x, y) = (2, -6)$$

$$-6 \overset{?}{>} 3(2) - 5 \qquad \text{Substitute in } x = 2, y = -6.$$

$$-6 \overset{?}{>} 1 \qquad \text{This statement is false.}$$

The point $(2, -6)$ is not in the solution set.

PRACTICE PROBLEM FOR EXAMPLE 2

Determine whether the given point is in the solution set of the linear inequality.

$$y < -x + 7$$

a. $(-2, 1)$ **b.** $(0, 0)$

c. $(0, 7)$ **d.** $(8, 2)$

In this Concept Investigation, we explore how many solutions a linear inequality in two variables can have.

CONCEPT INVESTIGATION

How many solutions are there?

Consider the following linear inequality:

$$y \le -2x + 5$$

1. Check to see whether the following points are in the solution set by substituting the values into the inequality.

$$(0, 5) \quad (2, -1) \quad (4, 4) \quad (0, 2) \quad (3, 0) \quad (-2, 3)$$

2. Plot the points from part 1 that are in the solution set on the following graph. Plot only the points that made the inequality true.

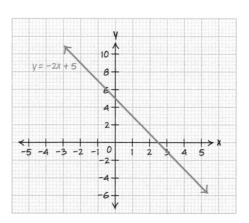

3. List three other points in the solution set. Graph these points on the graph in part 2.

4. Are there other points in the solution set besides the points you have already plotted? How many points do you think there are in the solution set?

From this Concept Investigation, we see that there are a lot of points in the solution set. In fact, the solution set contains infinitely many points. For this particular inequality, all the points below the line are in the solution set. Because we cannot possibly list them all, we shade the graph to indicate that all of those points are solutions to the linear inequality.

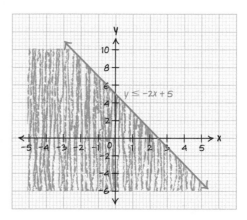

The solution set to a linear inequality in two variables will always consist of all the points on one side of the line. When graphing the solution set, we want to determine which side of the line to shade. Use the following steps to determine which side of the line is the solution set and thus should be shaded.

> **Steps to Find the Solution Set of a Linear Inequality in Two Variables**
>
> 1. Select a test point that is not on the line.
> 2. Substitute the test point into the inequality. Determine whether it makes the inequality true or false.
> 3. Shade in the side of the line that consists of the points that make the inequality true.

■ Connecting the Concepts

Why do we shade part of the graph?

In Chapter 2, we learned how to solve a linear inequality in one variable algebraically, and we examined how to graph the solution on a number line. Remember that the solution consisted of infinitely many values, and we represented the solution set by shading in an interval on a number line. To solve a linear inequality in two variables graphically, we use the xy-plane because we have two variables. Just as in Chapter 2, the solution will consist of infinitely many points, and we will now shade in regions on the xy-plane instead of an interval on a number line.

Example 3   Determine which side should be shaded

Consider the accompanying graph of the line $y = \frac{2}{3}x - 1$. Shade the side of the line that represents the solution set for the inequality $y \geq \frac{2}{3}x - 1$.

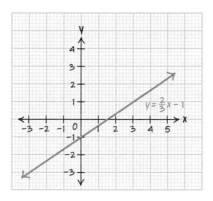

SOLUTION

Pick a test point that is not on the line, say, (3, 0). Substituting (3, 0) into the inequality yields

$$y \geq \frac{2}{3}x - 1 \qquad \text{The test point is } (x, y) = (3, 0).$$

$$0 \overset{?}{\geq} \frac{2}{3}(3) - 1 \qquad \text{Substitute in } x = 3, y = 0.$$

$$0 \overset{?}{\geq} 1 \qquad \text{This statement is false.}$$

The point (3, 0) does not satisfy the inequality. This point lies below the line, so we will not shade below the line. Therefore, we should shade above the line. All points above the line make the inequality true. To confirm this, pick the point (0, 2), which lies above the line. Substituting (0, 2) into the inequality yields

$$y \geq \frac{2}{3}x - 1 \qquad \text{The test point is } (x, y) = (0, 2).$$

$$2 \overset{?}{\geq} \frac{2}{3}(0) - 1 \qquad \text{Substitute in } x = 0, y = 2.$$

$$2 \geq -1 \qquad \text{This statement is true.}$$

The graph of the solution set of the inequality is as follows.

In the next Concept Investigation, we explore how the solution set is different when we use a $<$ or $>$ symbol compared to using a $\leq$ or $\geq$ symbol.

■ CONCEPT INVESTIGATION

Should we include the line?

1. In the table, the first column contains a list of the points on the line $y = -2x + 5$. Test whether these points are in the solution set of the inequalities given in the second and third columns. The first row has been done as an example.

Connecting the Concepts

When is an inequality true?

To determine whether an inequality is true, first simplify both sides of the inequality separately. Then see whether the inequality is a correct statement. If so, the inequality is true.

Points on the line (x, y)	$y \leq -2x + 5$	$y < -2x + 5$
$(0, 5)$	$5 \overset{?}{\leq} -2(0) + 5$ Substitute in $x = 0, y = 5$. $5 \leq 5$ True. This point is in the solution set.	$5 \overset{?}{<} -2(0) + 5$ Substitute in $x = 0, y = 5$. $5 \overset{?}{<} 5$ False. This point is not in the solution set.
$(1, 3)$		
$(2, 1)$		
$(3, -1)$		
$(4, -3)$		

2. All of the points in the first column are on the line. Are these points part of the solution set of $y \leq -2x + 5$? That is, do these points make this inequality true?

3. Should the line $y = -2x + 5$ be included in the graph of the solution set for the inequality $y \leq -2x + 5$?

4. All of the points in the first column are on the line. Are these points part of the solution set of $y < -2x + 5$? That is, do these points make this inequality true?

5. Should the line $y = -2x + 5$ be included in the graph of the solution set for the inequality $y < -2x + 5$?

When the points on the line are included in the solution set, the line itself is part of the solution set and is represented by drawing a solid line. When the points on the line are not included in the solution set, we represent that on the graph with a dashed line.

$$y \leq -2x + 5 \qquad\qquad\qquad y < -2x + 5$$

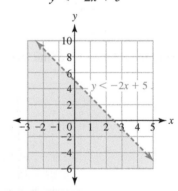

Putting these concepts together yields the following steps for graphing the solution set to a linear inequality in two variables.

> **Steps for Graphing Linear Inequalities in Two Variables**
>
> 1. Graph the line.
> 2. If the inequality is of the form $<$ or $>$, draw in a dashed line. If the inequality is of the form $\leq$ or $\geq$, draw in a solid line.
> 3. The line separates the plane into two regions, above and below the line. Pick a test point in either region (not on the line), and substitute it into the original inequality.
>   a. If the test point makes the inequality true, shade in the region that contains the test point.
>   b. If the test point makes the inequality false, shade in the other region (the one that does not contain the test point).

Example 4   **Graphing inequalities**

Graph the solution set of each inequality.

a. $-3x + 6y \leq 18$ **b.** $-2y > 4x - 9$ **c.** $y \leq 2x$

SOLUTION

a. Graph the line $-3x + 6y = 18$ by finding the intercepts. Be aware that we can graph the line using any technique from Chapter 3. To find the x-intercept, substitute in $y = 0$ and solve for x.

$$-3x + 6(0) = 18 \qquad \text{Substitute in } y = 0.$$

$$-3x = 18 \qquad \text{Solve for } x.$$

$$\frac{-3x}{-3} = \frac{18}{-3} \qquad \begin{array}{l}\text{Divide both sides by } -3 \text{ to}\\ \text{isolate } x.\end{array}$$

$$x = -6$$

The x-intercept is the point $(-6, 0)$. To find the y-intercept, set $x = 0$ and solve for y.

$$-3(0) + 6y = 18 \qquad \text{Substitute in } x = 0.$$

$$6y = 18 \qquad \text{Solve for } y.$$

$$\frac{6y}{6} = \frac{18}{6} \qquad \begin{array}{l}\text{Divide both sides by } 6\\ \text{to isolate } y.\end{array}$$

$$y = 3$$

The y-intercept is the point $(0, 3)$. Since the original inequality symbol was $\leq$, draw in a solid line.

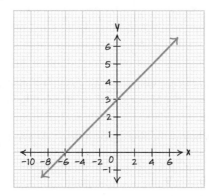

Pick any test point that is not on the line, for example, $(0, 4)$. Substituting $x = 0$, $y = 4$ into the original inequality yields

$$-3(0) + 6(4) \overset{?}{\leq} 18 \qquad \text{Substitute in } x = 0, y = 4.$$

$$0 + 24 \overset{?}{\leq} 18$$

$$24 \overset{?}{\leq} 18 \qquad \text{This is a false statement.}$$

Because this is not true, we do not shade in the region containing the point $(0, 4)$. Shade in the region below the line.

Skill Connection

Graphing Lines

To graph a line, use any of the following techniques from Chapter 3.

1. Generate a table of values. Plot the points and connect with a line.

2. Put the equation of the line in slope-intercept form. Graph using the y-intercept and slope.

3. Find the x- and y-intercepts. Plot the points, and connect with a line.

Connecting the Concepts

Where are the solutions?

All of the points in the shaded region are solutions to the linear inequality. All of these points satisfy the original linear inequality.

b. If we solve the inequality $-2y > 4x - 9$ for y first, it will be easier to determine how to graph the inequality and what region to shade. Solving for y yields

$$-2y > 4x - 9 \qquad \text{The original inequality.}$$

$$\frac{-2y}{-2} < \frac{4x}{-2} - \frac{9}{-2} \qquad \begin{array}{l}\text{Divide both sides by } -2 \text{ to isolate } y.\\ \text{Reverse the inequality symbol.}\end{array}$$

Remember that when we divide by a negative number, we must reverse the inequality.

$$y < -2x + \frac{9}{2}$$

To graph the line $y = -2x + \frac{9}{2}$, plot the y-intercept $\left(0, \frac{9}{2}\right)$ and use the slope $m = \frac{-2}{1} = \frac{\text{rise}}{\text{run}}$ to find another point on the graph. Since this is a strict inequality ($<$), graph a dashed line as below.

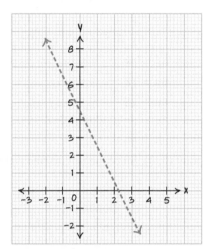

Substitute in a test point to see which region should be shaded. This test point cannot be on the line but should instead be in either of the two regions above the line and below the line.

Select $(0, 0)$, which is below the line. Substitute $(0, 0)$ into the original inequality.

$$-2(0) \overset{?}{>} 4(0) - 9 \qquad \text{Substitute in } x = 0, y = 0.$$

$$0 \overset{?}{>} -9 \qquad \text{Simplify.}$$

$$0 > -9 \qquad \text{This is a true statement.}$$

Since this statement is true, we shaded the region below the line that contains the point $(0, 0)$.

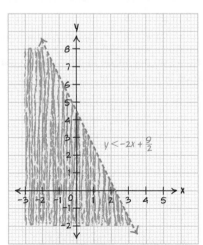

c. $y \leq 2x$ *The original inequality.*

To graph the line $y = 2x$, plot the y-intercept of $(0, 0)$ and use the slope

$m = \dfrac{2}{1} = \dfrac{\text{rise}}{\text{run}}$ to find another point on the graph. Since this is not a strict inequality

($\leq$), graph a solid line as below.

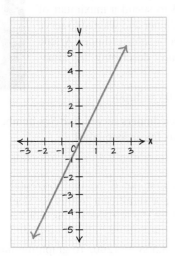

To decide which part of the plane to shade, we have to plug in a test point. This line passes through $(0, 0)$, so we cannot choose it as a test point. Instead, selecting $(2, 2)$ and substituting it into the original inequality yields

$$y \leq 2x$$
$$2 \overset{?}{\leq} 2(2) \qquad \text{Substitute in } x = 2, y = 2.$$
$$2 \leq 4$$

Since this last statement is true, shade the region below the line that contains the point $(2, 2)$.

PRACTICE PROBLEM FOR EXAMPLE 4

Graph the solution set of each inequality.

a. $y < \dfrac{-2}{3}x + 5$

b. $-5x + 4y \geq -20$

c. $y > \dfrac{-4}{3}x$

Example 5 The wedding planner graphed

In Example 1, we discussed the wedding consultant, Arlene. One of her tasks in preparing for Sara and Alex's wedding was planning the reception dinner. Sara and Alex wanted to spend a maximum of $1200.00 on the reception dinner and wanted to serve a choice of a chicken dinner or salmon dinner. Arlene determined that the inequality describing this situation was

$$6.50C + 8.50S \leq 1200$$

Here, C = number of chicken dinners served, and S = number of salmon dinners served. Graph the solution set to this linear inequality.

SOLUTION

To graph the solution set, first put C on the horizontal axis and S on the vertical axis. The choice of axis is not significant in this problem. We could choose to graph C on the vertical axis and S on the horizontal axis, but for now, we will do it the other way.

Graph the line $6.50C + 8.50S = 1200$. To graph the line, graph two points on the line. Two easy points to find are the intercepts.

$$6.50(0) + 8.50S = 1200 \qquad \text{Let } C = 0.$$
$$\frac{8.50S}{8.50} = \frac{1200}{8.50} \qquad \text{Solve for } S.$$
$$S \approx 141.18$$

$$6.50C + 8.50(0) = 1200 \qquad \text{Let } S = 0.$$
$$\frac{6.50C}{6.50} = \frac{1200}{6.50} \qquad \text{Solve for } C.$$
$$C \approx 184.62$$

The graph of the line looks like the following.

All points on the line are part of the solution set, since those points make the cost equal to $1200.00. We are graphing only positive values because negative chicken or salmon dinners does not make sense.

Notice that the solutions we discussed in Example 1 lie below the line. In fact, selecting any point below the line makes the inequality true. To show graphically that all points below the line make the inequality true, shade the half-plane in the first quadrant below the line.

Example 6 Meeting living expenses

Ricardo works two part-time jobs. He has to earn more than $375 a week to pay his bills. His first job pays $7.75 an hour, and his second job pays $8.25 an hour. Write an inequality that expresses this relationship between his total weekly earnings and his goal (minimum) earning per week. Then graph the solution set for this inequality.

SOLUTION

Let a = number of hours per week Ricardo works at the first job, and let b = number of hours per week Ricardo works at the second job. His weekly earnings from both jobs is $7.75a + 8.25b$. He has to earn more than $375 per week to meet his income goals. So his weekly earnings are greater than $375, or

$$7.75a + 8.25b > 375$$

Since the variables a and b represent the number of hours he works in a week, it makes sense that both a and b must be nonnegative numbers. We are looking only for the part of the solution set that lies in the first quadrant. Graph the line $7.75a + 8.25b = 375$ in the first quadrant. Graphing a on the horizontal axis and b on the vertical axis yields the following graph.

Selecting a point that is not on the line, for instance, $(0, 0)$, and substituting it into the original inequality yields

$$7.75(0) + 8.25(0) \overset{?}{>} 375 \qquad \text{Substitute in } a = 0, b = 0.$$

$$0 \overset{?}{>} 375 \qquad \text{This is a false statement.}$$

Therefore, $(0, 0)$ is not in the solution set. Shade in the region above the line.

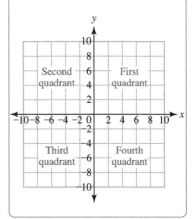

The point (20, 40) lies in the solution set. So if Ricardo works 20 hours a week at his first job and 40 hours a week at his second job, he can earn more than $375.00 a week. Any combination of hours in the shaded region will earn Ricardo more than $375.00 a week.

PRACTICE PROBLEM FOR EXAMPLE 6

Kelli wants to buy two kinds of candy to bring to her daughter's scout troop meeting. She wants to spend no more than $20.00. The first type of candy costs $2.25 a pound, and the second type of candy costs $4.25 a pound. Write an inequality that expresses the relationship between the total cost of the candy and the maximum Kelli wants to spend on candy ($20.00). Then graph the solution set for this inequality.

Graphing Vertical and Horizontal Inequalities

In Chapter 3, we learned how to graph vertical and horizontal lines. Recall that the graph of a horizontal line has the form $y = b$, where b is any real number. The graph of a vertical line has the form $x = c$, where c is any real number. In the next example, we will examine how to graph linear inequalities involving horizontal and vertical lines.

Example 7 Graphing horizontal and vertical inequalities

Graph the solution set of each inequality.

a. $y > -2$ **b.** $x \le 3.5$

SOLUTION

a. First, graph the line $y = -2$. $y = -2$ is of the form $y = b$, so this equation will graph as a horizontal line through $y = -2$. This line should be dashed, since the inequality does not have an "equal to" part. Selecting the test point to be (0, 0) and substituting it into the original inequality, we get

$$0 \overset{?}{>} -2 \qquad \text{Substitute in } y = 0.$$
$$0 > -2 \qquad \text{This is a true statement.}$$

Since this is a true statement, we shade in the region above the line $y = -2$. This shaded region contains the point (0, 0).

b. The graph of $x = 3.5$ is the graph of a vertical line. Select (0, 0) as a test point, since it is not on the line. Substituting it into the original inequality yields

$$0 \overset{?}{\le} 3.5 \qquad \text{Substitute in } x = 0.$$
$$0 \le 3.5 \qquad \text{This is a true statement.}$$

Since this is a true statement, we shade in the part of the plane that contains (0, 0).

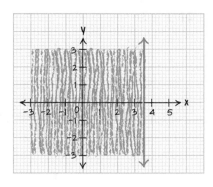

PRACTICE PROBLEM FOR EXAMPLE 7

Graph the solution set of each inequality.

a. $x > 1$ **b.** $y \leq 4$

4.4   Exercises

For Exercises 1 through 10, determine whether the given point is in the solution set of the linear inequality.

1. $y < 2x - 3$

  a. $(5, 0)$
  b. $(6, 0)$

2. $y \geq -\dfrac{1}{4}x - 7$

  a. $(4, 6)$
  b. $(0, 0)$

3. $x \leq -5$

  a. $(-2, 1)$
  b. $(6, 6)$

4. $x > 7.9$

  a. $(8, 1)$
  b. $(-2, 60)$

5. $y > 33$

  a. $(0, 0)$
  b. $(-3, 58)$

6. $y \leq -1.5$

  a. $(3, 0)$
  b. $(-4, -7)$

7. $-4x + y \leq 4$

  a. $(0, 7)$
  b. $(1, -2)$

8. $2x - 3y \geq 2$

  a. $(0, -6)$
  b. $(-1, 5)$

9. $x > -6.5$

  a. $(1, 1)$
  b. $(-8, 10)$

10. $y < 9$

  a. $(-2, 9)$
  b. $(8, 10)$

For Exercises 11 through 18, use the given inequality to answer the following questions: (a) Would you graph the solution using a solid line or a dashed line? (b) Is the given point in the solution set? Note: Do NOT graph the inequality.

11. Inequality: $y < \dfrac{3}{5}x + 8$

  Point: $(0, 8)$

12. Inequality: $y > -6x + 12$

  Point: $(2, 0)$

13. Inequality: $x \leq -5$

  Point: $(-5, 2)$

14. Inequality: $y \geq -6.4$

  Point: $(0, -6.4)$

15. Inequality: $-4x + y \leq 4$

  Point: $(1, 8)$

16. Inequality: $2x - 3y \geq 2$

  Point: $(-2, -2)$

17. Inequality: $x - 6y > 9$

  Point: $(9, 0)$

18. Inequality: $-3x - 5y < 2$

  Point: $(6, -4)$

For Exercises 19 through 28:

a. Select a test point.
b. Substitute it into the inequality.
c. Shade in the correct region to finish the graph of the inequality.

19. $y < 3x - 3$

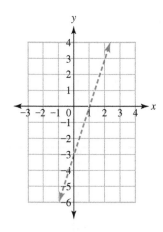

20. $y > -3x + 5$

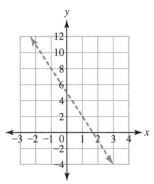

21. $4x - 3y \geq 12$

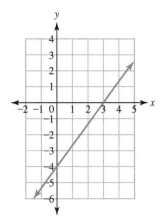

22. $-5x + 4y \leq 20$

23. $-2y < 3x$

24. $x > 3y$

25. $x > 2$

26. $x \leq -1$

27. $y \geq -2$

28. $y < 1$

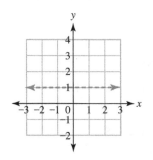

For Exercises 29 through 46, graph the solution set of each linear inequality. Clearly label and scale the axes.

29. $y < -2x + 6$

30. $y > -5x + 8$

31. $y \geq 3x - 7$

32. $y \leq 5x - 6$

33. $y \leq \dfrac{2}{3}x - 4$

34. $y \geq \dfrac{-1}{2}x + 1$

35. $y < \dfrac{-1}{4}x + 3$

36. $y < \dfrac{2}{5}x - 7$

37. $4x + 2y \leq 8$

38. $x + 3y \geq 6$

39. $4x + 3y < -12$

40. $3x + y > 9$

41. $x > -2$

42. $x \leq 5$

43. $y \geq 3.5$

44. $y < -1$

45. $x \geq 0$

46. $y < 0$

For Exercises 47 through 54, use the given information to answer the questions.

47. Jane is asked to bring two kinds of cookies to a Boy Scout meeting. The oatmeal cookies cost $4.00 a box, and the chocolate chip cookies cost $5.50 a box. She wants to spend no more than $25.00 on both kinds of cookies.

   a. Define the variables.

   b. Write an inequality that expresses the relationship between the total cost of both cookies and the maximum Jane wants to spend on cookies ($25.00).

   c. Graph the solution set for this inequality.

48. Joe has been asked to bring chips and salsa to a party. The chips cost $3.99 a bag, and a jar of salsa costs $3.29. He wants to spend no more than $20.00 on both chips and salsa.

   a. Define the variables.

   b. Write an inequality that expresses the relationship between the total cost of both chips and salsa and the maximum that Joe wants to spend ($20.00).

   c. Graph the solution set for this inequality.

49. Shahab works two jobs. The first job pays him $9.00 an hour, and the second job pays him $8.00 an hour. Shahab wants to earn more than $300 a week working both jobs.

   a. Define the variables.

   b. Write an inequality that expresses the relationship between the total hours worked and Shahab's goal of earning more than $300.00 per week.

   c. Graph the solution set for this inequality.

50. Tanya works two jobs. The first job pays her $7.50 an hour, and the second job pays $8.50 an hour. She has to earn more than $500.00 a week working both jobs.

   a. Define the variables.

   b. Write an inequality that expresses the relationship between the total hours Tanya works a week and her goal of earning more than $500.00 a week.

   c. Graph the solution set for this inequality.

51. Paul has split his investment into two accounts. The first account pays 5% simple interest a year, and the second account pays 6% simple interest a year. Paul would like to earn more than $500 a year in interest.

   a. Define the variables.

   b. Write an inequality that expresses the relationship between the total amount invested in both accounts and Paul's goal of earning more than $500 in interest every year.

   c. Graph the solution set for this inequality.

52. LaDonna has split her investment into two accounts. The first account pays 6% simple interest a year, and the second account pays 9% simple interest every year. LaDonna would like to earn more than $1200 a year in interest.

   a. Define the variables.

   b. Write an inequality that expresses the relationship between the total amount invested in both accounts and LaDonna's goal of earning more than $1200.00 a year in interest.

   c. Graph the solution set for this inequality.

53. Francisco is building a fence around a site that will become a rectangular community garden. He has at most 200 feet of fencing material to use. Remember that the perimeter P of a rectangle is given by the formula $P = 2w + 2l$, where w is the width of the rectangle and l is the length.

   a. Define the variables.

   b. Write an inequality that expresses the relationship between the total amount of fencing actually used and the fact that Francisco has at most 200 feet of fencing material available.

   c. Graph the solution set for this inequality.

54. A taxicab charges an $8.25 pickup fee plus $3.25 a mile. Maria has only $40.00 to spend on a cab.

   a. Define the variables.

   b. Write an inequality that expresses the relationship between the cost of the cab and the maximum amount Maria has to spend.

   c. Graph the solution set for this inequality.

For Exercises 55 through 60, match the inequality with the graph.

55.

Graph A

Graph B

1. $y \geq 2$

2. $y > \dfrac{1}{2}x + 2$

 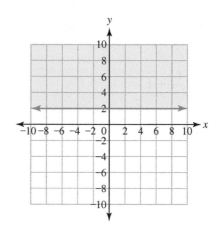

56.

Graph A

Graph B

1. $y \geq x - 4$
2. $x \leq 6$

 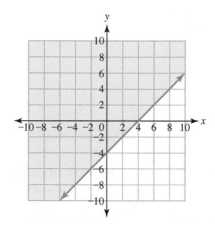

57.

Graph A

Graph B

1. $y < -2x + 2$
2. $y \leq -2x + 2$

58.

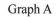

Graph A   Graph B

1. $y < -2x + 4$
2. $y > -2x + 4$

   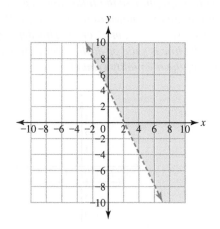

59.

Graph A   Graph B

1. $y \geq 4$
2. $x \geq 4$

   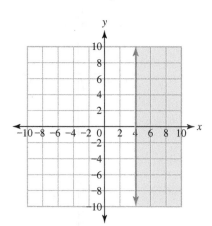

60.

Graph A   Graph B

1. $x \geq 0$
2. $y \geq 0$

   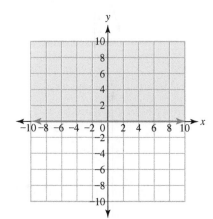

For Exercises 61 through 68, write the linear inequality for the given graph. Use the following steps: (a) Find the equation of the line shown in the graph. (b) Determine whether to use < or >, or ≤ or ≥. This depends on whether the line is solid or dashed. (c) Determine the direction of the inequality symbol.

61.

62.

63.

64.

65.

66.

67.   **68.**

For Exercises 69 through 76, read each problem and determine whether it is an example of an equality or inequality. Do not solve.

69. Pavel wants to earn at least $150.00 in interest a year.

70. Philippa wants to earn $250.00 in interest a year.

71. Naveed wants to work 20 hours a week.

72. Parmida wants to work at most 25 hours a week.

73. Chato wants to study at least 15 hours a week.

74. Zhina wants to earn a 90% on her English essay.

75. Mailin wants to earn at least a 95% on her math test.

76. Sheng wants to earn $14.50 an hour working at his job.

Chapter Summary

4

Section **4.1** Identifying Systems of Linear Equations

- A **system of equations** is a set of two (or more) linear equations.
- A **solution** to a system of equations is an ordered pair, (x, y), that satisfies both linear equations in the system.
- To **check** the solution to a system of equations, substitute the x-value and the y-value into both original equations. If both equations are true, then the solution checks.
- To **solve a system graphically,** first carefully graph both lines, and then look for the intersection point (which is the solution).
- There are **three possibilities** for the solution set to a system of equations:
    1. There is one solution because the two lines intersect at exactly one point.
    2. There is no solution because the two lines are parallel and never intersect.
    3. There are infinitely many solutions consisting of all points on the line because the two lines are in fact the same line.

Example 1 Use the graph to determine the solution to the system of equations.

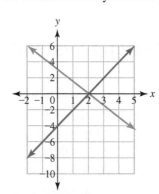

SOLUTION The two lines intersect at the point $(2, 0)$. The solution to the system is the point $(2, 0)$.

Example 2 Graphically determine the solution to the system of equations. Check the solution by substituting into the original system.

$$y = \frac{1}{2}x$$
$$y = -2x + 5$$

SOLUTION   Graphing the two lines on the same axes yields the graph below.

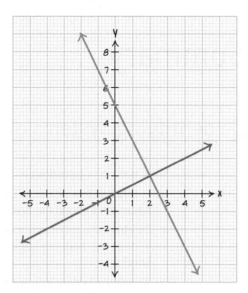

From the graph, we see the two lines intersect at the point $(x, y) = (2, 1)$. Checking the solution yields

Equation 1		Equation 2

$$1 \stackrel{?}{=} \frac{1}{2}(2) \qquad \textit{Substitute in } x = 2, y = 1. \qquad 1 \stackrel{?}{=} -2(2) + 5$$

$$1 \stackrel{?}{=} 1 \qquad\qquad\qquad\qquad\qquad\qquad 1 \stackrel{?}{=} -4 + 5$$

$$1 = 1 \qquad \textit{The point checks in both equations.} \qquad 1 = 1$$

Section 4.2 Solving Systems Using the Substitution Method

● The **substitution method** is an algebraic method of solving a system of equations.

1. Solve one of the two equations for one of the variables.
2. Substitute the expression from the first step for the value of the variable into the other equation.
3. Simplify, and solve for the remaining variable.
4. Substitute the answer from above into either of the original equations, and solve for the remaining variable.
5. Check the solution by substituting into both original equations.

● The **substitution method** can determine whether a system has a single ordered pair for a solution, infinitely many solutions, or no solutions.

● The **distance formula** is $d = r \cdot t$. Here, d refers to the distance, r to the rate (or speed), and t to the time an object has traveled.

● The **value formula** is value = amount · unit price.

Example 3   Solve the system using the substitution method. Check your answer in both of the original equations.

$$2x - 3y = 3$$
$$x - y = 2$$

SOLUTION The original system is

$$2x - 3y = 3$$
$$x - y = 2$$

The second equation has a coefficient of 1 for the x-variable. Solving for x in the second equation yields

$$x - y = 2$$
$$\underline{+y \quad +y}$$
$$x = 2 + y$$

Substituting this into the first equation and simplifying, we get

$2(2 + y) - 3y = 3$	Distribute and simplify.
$4 + 2y - 3y = 3$	
$4 - y = 3$	Subtract 4 from both sides.
$\underline{-4 \qquad -4}$	
$-y = -1$	Multiply both sides by -1.
$y = 1$	

Solve for x.

$x = 2 + y$	Substitute in $y = 1$.
$x = 2 + 1$	
$x = 3$	

The solution is $(x, y) = (3, 1)$.

Checking $(x, y) = (3, 1)$ in both original equations yields

Equation 1		**Equation 2**
$2(3) - 3(1) \overset{?}{=} 3$	Substitute in $x = 3, y = 1$.	$3 - 1 \overset{?}{=} 2$
$6 - 3 \overset{?}{=} 3$		$2 \overset{?}{=} 2$
$3 = 3$		$2 = 2$

The solution checks in both equations.

Example 4 A boat traveled 30 miles downstream in 2 hours. It takes 3 hours to make the return trip upstream. Find the rate of the boat in still water and the rate of the current.

a. Define the variables.

b. Determine the two equations.

c. Solve the system.

SOLUTION a. Let b = rate of the boat in still water and c = rate of the current.

b. The two equations are below.

Recall that $r \cdot t = d$.

$(b + c) \cdot 2 = 30$	Boat traveling with the current.
$(b - c) \cdot 3 = 30$	Boat traveling against the current.

c.

$\dfrac{(b + c) \cdot 2}{2} = \dfrac{30}{2}$	Divide both sides of the first equation by 2.
$b + c = 15$	Solve for b.
$\underline{-c \qquad -c}$	
$b = 15 - c$	

Substituting this value into the second equation and simplifying, we get

$$(b - c) \cdot 3 = 30 \qquad \text{Distribute and simplify.}$$
$$3b - 3c = 30 \qquad \text{Substitute in } b = 15 - c.$$
$$3(15 - c) - 3c = 30 \qquad \text{Distribute and simplify.}$$
$$45 - 3c - 3c = 30$$
$$45 - 6c = 30 \qquad \text{Solve for } c.$$
$$\underline{-45 \qquad\quad -45}$$
$$\frac{-6c}{-6} = \frac{-15}{-6} \qquad \text{Reduce fractions.}$$
$$c = \frac{15}{6}$$
$$c = \frac{5}{2} = 2.5 \qquad \text{Find the value of } b.$$
$$b = 15 - c$$
$$b = 15 - 2.5$$
$$b = 12.5$$

The boat is traveling at 12.5 mph, and the current is 2.5 mph.

Section 4.3 Solving Systems Using the Elimination Method

- The **elimination method** is another algebraic method of solving a system of linear equations.
  1. Put the equations of both lines in standard form.
  2. Multiply both sides of one (or both) equation(s) so that the coefficients of one of the variables are opposites.
  3. Add the two equations vertically.
  4. Solve for the remaining variable.
  5. Substitute the value of the known variable into either original equation, and solve for the value of the other variable.
  6. Check your solution by substituting into both original equations.
- The **elimination method** can determine whether a system has a single ordered pair for a solution, infinitely many solutions, or no solution.
- The **simple interest** formula is

$$I = P \cdot r \cdot t$$

Here, I represents the interest earned, P is the principal, r is the interest rate, and t is the time in years.
- **The amount of a quantity in a solution** formula is

$$\text{given substance} = \text{percent} \cdot \text{amount of solution}$$

Remember to write percents in decimal form when used in a problem.

Example 5 Solve the system using the elimination method. Check the answer by substituting into both of the original equations.

a. $4x - 3y = 21$
  $x + 3y = 9$

b. $4x - 6y = -6$
  $-2x + 3y = -21$

SOLUTION   a. Because the coefficients of y are opposites (3 and -3), add the two equations vertically to eliminate y.

$$4x - 3y = 21$$
$$x + 3y = 9$$
$$\overline{}$$
$$\frac{5x}{5} = \frac{30}{5}$$
$$x = 6$$

Substituting this value into the second equation to find the value of y yields

$$(6) + 3y = 9$$
$$-6 -6$$
$$\overline{}$$
$$\frac{3y}{3} = \frac{3}{3}$$
$$y = 1$$

The solution is the point $(x, y) = (6, 1)$. Check the solution in both original equations.

Equation 1	Equation 2
$4(6) - 3(1) \stackrel{?}{=} 21$	$6 + 3(1) \stackrel{?}{=} 9$
$24 - 3 \stackrel{?}{=} 21$	$6 + 3 \stackrel{?}{=} 9$
$21 = 21$	$9 = 9$

The solution checks.

b. Examining the two equations, we notice that neither variable has coefficients that are opposites. Multiply the second equation by 2 to get the coefficients of x to be opposites.

$$4x - 6y = -6 \qquad\qquad\longrightarrow\qquad\qquad 4x - 6y = -6$$
$$2(-2x + 3y) = 2(-21) \qquad\qquad\qquad\qquad -4x + 6y = -42$$

$$4x - 6y = -6$$
$$-4x + 6y = -42 \qquad \text{Add the two equations.}$$
$$\overline{}$$
$$0 = -48 \qquad \text{This statement is false.}$$

Because $0 \neq -48$, the system has no solution.

Section 4.4   Solving Linear Inequalities in Two Variables Graphically

- A **linear inequality** is an inequality of the form $Ax + By < C$. Here, the symbol $<$ may be any one of the following inequality symbols: $<$, $>$, $\leq$, or $\geq$.

- Many applications involve inequalities. We are often interested in when one quantity is greater than or less than another.

- We **solve linear inequalities** in two variables graphically by the following steps:

  1. Graph the line. Draw a solid line for inequalities of the form $\leq$ or $\geq$ and a dashed line for inequalities of the form $<$ or $>$.

  2. Select a test point that is not on the line, and substitute it into the original inequality. If it makes the inequality true, shade in the region that contains the test point. If not, shade in the region that does not contain the test point.

- The **solution set** is an entire region on the graph, not a single value.

- When multiplying or dividing both sides of an inequality by a negative number, reverse the inequality symbol.

Example 6

Graph the solution set of the linear inequality.

$$x - 4y < 8$$

SOLUTION

First, graph the line $x - 4y = 8$ by plotting the intercepts. Because the inequality involves a $<$ symbol, graph a dashed line to indicate that the points on the line are not part of the solution set. Then pick a test point that is not on the line. Pick $(0, 0)$. Substitute this point into the original inequality, and see whether it makes the inequality true.

$$x - 4y < 8 \qquad \text{Substitute in } (x, y) = (0, 0).$$
$$0 - 4(0) \overset{?}{<} 8$$
$$0 < 8 \qquad \text{This is a true statement.}$$

The point $(0, 0)$ is in the solution set. Shade above the line.

Example 7

Graph the solution set of the linear inequality.

$$x \geq -3$$

SOLUTION

Graph the line $x = -3$. This is a vertical line. Because the inequality involves a $\geq$ symbol, draw a solid line. Pick a test point that is not on the line, for instance, $(0, 0)$. Substitute $(0, 0)$ into the original inequality, and see whether the inequality is true.

$$x \geq -3 \qquad \text{Substitute in } (x, y) = (0, 0).$$
$$0 \geq -3 \qquad \text{This is a true statement.}$$

The point $(0, 0)$ is in the solution set. Shade in the part of the graph to the right of the line.

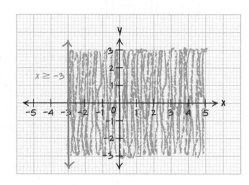

Chapter Review Exercises

1. Use the graph to determine the solution to the system of equations. [4.1]

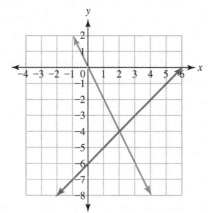

2. Use the graph to determine the solution to the system of equations. [4.1]

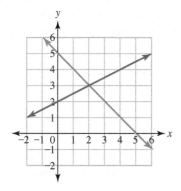

3. Check to determine whether the given point is a solution of the system. [4.1]

$$y = \frac{-4}{3}x$$

$$y = x - 7$$

a. $(6, -8)$ **b.** $(3, -4)$

4. Check to determine whether the given point is a solution of the system. [4.1]

$$y = x + 6$$

$$y = -2x$$

a. $(-2, 4)$ **b.** $(2, -4)$

For Exercises 5 and 6, graphically determine the solution to the system of equations. Clearly label and scale all graphs. Check the solution by substituting into the original system.

5. $y = 5x$

$y = 2x - 3$

6. $y = \frac{-5}{3}x - 3$

$y = x + 5$ [4.1]

For Exercises 7 through 12, solve the system using the substitution method. Check the solution by substituting into the original system.

7. $-3x + y = 1$
$x + y = 13$

8. $2x + y = -4$
$3x + 2y = 7$ [4.2]

9. $y = \frac{-2}{3}x + 1$
$4x - 6y = -6$

10. $x = 4y + 12$
$-2x + 8y = -24$ [4.2]

11. $6x + 2y = 14$
$3x + y = 1$

12. $5y = 2x + 5$
$y = \frac{2}{5}x - 5$ [4.2]

13. A cyclist can ride her bike 48 miles with a tailwind in 2 hours. It takes her 3 hours to make the return trip. Find the rate of the cyclist (with no wind) and the rate of the wind. [4.2]

14. A cyclist can ride his bike 45 miles with a tailwind in 3 hours. It takes him 5 hours to make the return trip. Find the rate of the cyclist (with no wind) and the rate of the wind. [4.2]

15. A small plane can fly with a tailwind 240 miles in 2 hours. It makes the return trip with a headwind in 3 hours. Find the rate of the plane in still air and the rate of the wind. [4.2]

16. A boat travels 28 miles downstream in 2 hours. It takes 4 hours to make the return trip upstream. Find the rate of the boat in still water and the rate of the current. [4.2]

17. The difference of two numbers is 8. Twice the first number added to the second number is 37. Find the two numbers. [4.2]

18. The difference of two numbers is 20. Three times the first number plus the second is 16. Find the two numbers. [4.2]

19. The sum of two numbers is 52. One number is three times the other. Find the two numbers. [4.2]

20. The sum of two numbers is 28. One number is six times the other. Find the two numbers. [4.2]

For Exercises 21 through 28, solve the system using the elimination method. Check the solution by substituting into the original system.

21. $x - 2y = 7$
$3x + 2y = -3$

22. $5x + 7y = 27$
$-5x - y = 9$ [4.3]

23. $3x + 2y = 16$
$10x - 4y = 0$

24. $2x + y = -7$
$-x + 3y = 0$ [4.3]

25. $3x + y = 5$
$3x + y = -8$

26. $6x + y = -5$
$-6x - y = -1$ [4.3]

27. $x + 2y = 3$
$-2x - 4y = -6$

28. $-2x + 3y = 18$
$4x - 6y = -36$ [4.3]

29. Decide whether you would solve the system using the substitution method or elimination method. Do NOT solve the system, but do justify your answer. [4.3]

$$-2x + 5y = -16$$
$$2x - 3y = -12$$

30. Decide whether you would solve the system using the substitution method or elimination method. Do NOT solve the system, but do justify your answer. [4.3]

$$x - 4y = 9$$
$$12x - 7y = -10$$

31. Anne is a professional dog trainer. For her new puppy class, she has purchased four boxes of jerky treats and two leashes for $65.00. Because more students signed up for the class, she later purchased three more boxes of jerky treats and three leashes for $73.50. How much does each box of jerky treats and each leash cost individually? [4.3]

32. Christian is a piano teacher. For his new beginning students, he has purchased three large bags of candy and one metronome for $67.75. Because more students signed up for lessons, he later purchased two more bags of candy and two metronomes for $78.50. How much does each bag of candy and each metronome cost individually? [4.3]

33. Lance has $2000.00 to invest. An investment advisor tells him to put part of his money in a bond fund earning 5% interest and part in a stock fund earning 6% interest. Lance wants to earn $105.00 in simple interest yearly. How much should he invest in each account? [4.3]

34. Ming-Yue has $5000.00 to invest. An investment planner tells her to put part of her money in a bond fund earning 6% interest and part in a stock fund earning 9% interest. Ming-Yue wants to earn $350.00 in simple interest yearly. How much should she invest in each account? [4.3]

35. Two angles are supplementary. One angle is 5 times the measure of the other angle. Find the measures of the two angles. [4.3]

36. Two angles are supplementary. One angle is four times the second angle added to 5. Find the measure of the two angles. [4.3]

37. Two angles are complementary. One angle is 9 times the measure of the other angle. Find the measures of the two angles. [4.3]

38. Two angles are complementary. One angle is twice the second angle. Find the measures of the two angles. [4.3]

39. Tarin wants to mix a 5% saline solution with a 30% saline solution to make a 25% saline solution. He needs a total of 20 ounces in the mix. How many ounces of the 5% saline solution and the 30% saline solution should he use? [4.3]

40. Shelby wants to mix a 6% fruit juice solution with a 12% fruit juice solution to make a 10% fruit juice solution. He needs a total of 20 gallons in the mix. How many gallons of the 6% solution and the 12% solution should he use? Round to the nearest hundredths place if necessary. [4.3]

41. Inna needs to mix raisins and peanuts for a trail mix. She wants to make a total of 10 pounds of the mix. The peanuts cost $2.00 per pound, and the raisins cost $3.60 per pound. The total value of the trail mix is $26.40. Find the amount of peanuts and raisins she needs to include in the mix. [4.3]

42. Lorraine mixes two types of coffee for a blend for her café. The French Roast coffee costs $9.95 per pound, and the Guatemalan coffee costs $12.95 per pound. Lorraine would like to price the blend at $10.95 per pound. If she makes 20 pounds of the blend, how many pounds of each type of coffee does she need to add? [4.3]

43. Determine whether the given point is in the solution set of the linear inequality. [4.4]

$$y < -3x + 5$$

a. $(0, 5)$ **b.** $(-2, -1)$

44. Determine whether the given point is in the solution set of the linear inequality. [4.4]

$$y \geq \frac{2}{3}x - 1$$

a. $(0, -1)$ **b.** $(-3, 3)$

45. Shade in the correct region to graph the solution set of the inequality. [4.4]

$$y > -\frac{2}{3}x + 4$$

46. Shade in the correct region to graph the solution set of the inequality.   [4.4]

$$y < \frac{1}{4}x - 3$$

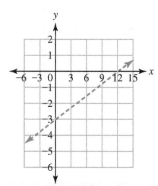

47. Solve the linear inequality graphically.   [4.4]

$$y < -3x + 7$$

48. Solve the linear inequality graphically.   [4.4]

$$y > \frac{1}{2}x - 1$$

49. Solve the linear inequality graphically.   [4.4]

$$2x - y \leq 1$$

50. Solve the linear inequality graphically.   [4.4]

$$x + 2y \geq -4$$

51. Solve the linear inequality graphically.   [4.4]

$$x < -3$$

52. Solve the linear inequality graphically.   [4.4]

$$x \geq 2.5$$

53. Solve the linear inequality graphically.   [4.4]

$$y \leq -2$$

54. Solve the linear inequality graphically.   [4.4]

$$y > 0$$

55. Zita works two jobs. The first job pays her $8.00 an hour, and the second job pays her $9.00 an hour. Zita wants to earn more than $400.00 a week working both jobs.   [4.4]

   a. Define the variables.
   b. Write an inequality that expresses the relationship between the total hours worked and Zita's goal of earning more than $400.00 a week.
   c. Graph the solution set for this inequality.

56. Aaron works two jobs. The first job pays him $8.25 an hour, and the second job pays him $9.00 an hour. Aaron wants to earn more than $300.00 a week working both jobs.   [4.4]

   a. Define the variables.
   b. Write an inequality that expresses the relationship between the total hours worked and Aaron's goal of earning more than $300.00 a week.
   c. Graph the solution set for this inequality.

For Exercises 57 and 58, match the inequality with the graph.   [4.4]

57.

1. $y \leq -\frac{2}{3}x + 4$

2. $y < -\frac{1}{3}x + 6$

Graph A

Graph B

58.

1. $2x - 4y > 12$
2. $6x - 3y < 15$

Graph A

Graph B

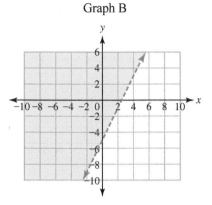

Chapter Test

4

This chapter test should take approximately one hour to complete. Read each question carefully. Show all of your work.

1. Graphically determine the solution to the system of equations. Identify the system as consistent or inconsistent. Clearly label and scale all graphs. Check the solution by substituting into the original system.

$$y = 3x - 1$$
$$y = -2x + 4$$

2. Solve for the variable y: $7x - 3y = -21$.

3. Solve the system of equations using the substitution method. Check the answer in both of the original equations.

$$-2x + y = 1$$
$$2x - 3y = 5$$

4. Solve the system of equations using the elimination method. Check the answer in both of the original equations.

$$4x - 5y = 10$$
$$-2x + 5y = 0$$

5. Solve the system of equations using either the substitution or elimination method. Rami is a personal trainer. As gifts for his clients, he buys three heart rate monitors and five BPA-free water bottles for $159.00. For other clients, he later purchases two more heart rate monitors and four BPA-free water bottles for $114.00. Find how much each heart rate monitor and each BPA-free water bottle costs individually.

6. Solve the system of equations using either the substitution or elimination method. A boat travels

24 miles downstream (with the current) in 2 hours. It takes the boat 3 hours to make the return trip upstream (against the current). Find the rate of the boat in still water and the rate of the current.

7. Solve the system of equations using either the substitution or elimination method. Laurent has $2000.00 to invest. His financial advisor recommends that he put part of his investment in a bond fund that returns 5% simple interest yearly and a stock fund that returns 7% simple interest yearly. Laurent would like to earn $124.00 in interest a year. How much should he invest in each account?

8. Solve the system of equations using the substitution method. Check the answer in both of the original equations.

$$-x + 5y = 15$$
$$2x - 10y = 10$$

9. Solve the system of equations using the elimination method. Check the answer in both of the original equations.

$$-2x - 8y = -8$$
$$x + 4y = 4$$

10. Solve the linear inequality graphically.

$$y < -4x + 7$$

11. Solve the linear inequality graphically.

$$x > 5$$

Chapter 4 Projects

Writing an Infinite, Repeating Decimal as a Fraction

Written Project
One or more people

In this project, you will learn how to convert an infinite, repeating decimal to a fraction.

Example: Consider the infinite, repeating decimal 0.252525….

1. Let $n = 0.252525….$
2. This decimal repeats after the *hundredths* place.
3. Because the decimal repeats after the *hundredths* place, multiply both sides by 100.

$$100n = 25.252525…$$

4. Subtract the equation from step 1 from the equation from step 3.

$$100n = 25.252525…$$
$$-\quad \underline{n = \ \ 0.252525…}$$
$$99n = 25$$
$$\frac{99n}{99} = \frac{25}{99} \qquad \text{Solve for } n.$$
$$n = \frac{25}{99}$$

Problem: Convert the infinite, repeating decimal to fraction form.

$$0.717171…$$

1. Set the decimal equal to n.
2. After what place value does the decimal start to repeat?
3. Multiply both sides of the equation from step 1 by _____ because the decimal repeats after the _____ place.
4. Subtract the equation from step 1 from the equation from step 3.
5. Solve for n.

Which Cell Phone Plan Is Cheaper?

Research Project
One or more people

What you will need
- Prices for basic cell phone plans from two or more cell phone service providers

It will be your job to compare two or more cell phone plans from various cell phone service providers. You should visit, phone, or investigate on the Internet two or more cell phone service providers and find their prices for the most basic service plan they offer. Then you will explore which of these companies is cheaper for a variety of users.

Write up

a. Describe how you collected the information. What companies are you comparing? Give a basic description of the plans you are considering.

b. Create a table of data for each plan that includes several different amounts of minutes used for a month and the cost for those minutes.

c. Draw a graph with all of the plans you are comparing that depicts the monthly cost for different amounts of minutes used. (This might not be a straight line.)

d. Determine when each plan will be the cheapest.

e. Is there a number of minutes when two or more plans cost the same amount? If so, find that amount and describe its significance.

f. Describe what else besides cost you might consider in choosing a cell phone service provider.

g. Which of the cell phone service providers would you choose and why?

Write a Review of a Section for Presentation

Research Project

One or more people

What you will need

- This presentation may be done in class or as an online video.
- If it is done as a video, post it on a Website where it may be easily viewed by the class.
- You might want to use homework or other review problems from the book.
- Make it creative and fun.

Create a five-minute review presentation of one section from Chapter 4. The format of the presentation can be a poster presentation, a blackboard presentation from notes, an online video, or a game format (e.g., Math Jeopardy). The presentation should include the following:

- Any important formulas in the chapter
- Important skills in the chapter, backed up by examples
- Explanation of terms used. For example, what is *modeling*?
- Common mistakes and how to avoid them

Linear Equations

Distributive Property	Use when an equation contains grouping symbols.	$2(x + 4) = 3x - 5$	Section 1.3
Addition and Subtraction Properties of Equality	Use to isolate a term.	$x + 7 = 20$	Section 2.1
Multiplication and Division Properties of Equality	Use to isolate a variable.	$5x = 13$	Section 2.2

Systems of Equations

Substitution Method	Use when a variable is isolated or can be easily isolated.	$y = 6x + 8$ $2x + 4y = 30$	Section 4.2
Elimination Method	Use when the equations are in general form.	$5x - 7y = 42$ $3x + 20y = 103$	Section 4.3

General Solving Techniques

Graphing	Use when you cannot solve the equation algebraically. Graph each side of the equations and find the intersection(s).		All chapters
Numerically	Use when you cannot solve the equation algbraically. Guess a solution and check it. Best used to check solutions.		All chapters

1. Write in exponential form: $\left(\dfrac{-1}{5}\right)\cdot\left(\dfrac{-1}{5}\right)\cdot\left(\dfrac{-1}{5}\right)\cdot\left(\dfrac{-1}{5}\right)$

2. Find the value without a calculator: $(-2)^4$

3. Write using standard notation: 6.103×10^6

4. Underline or circle the terms, and simplify using the order-of-operations agreement:
$$\left|\dfrac{-12}{11-7}\right|+3^3-(-1-8)+18\div3\cdot(9)$$

5. Define the variables: The amount of commission in dollars that a salesperson earns depends on the amount of sales in dollars they make.

6. Translate the phrase into a variable expression: three times the sum of nine and a number.

7. Convert 12 meters to feet. There is 1 foot in 0.3048 meter. Round to the hundredths place.

8. Evaluate the expression for the given value of the variable: $-x^2+3x-1$ for $x=-2$.

9. Simplify: $3(5x-1)-4(3x-7)$

10. Simplify: $-(-(-5x))$

11. Graph the ordered pairs on the same set of axes:

    $(-20,4)\ (15,3)\ (10,-1)\ (-10,-10)\ (25,0)$

12. Are the values of the variables solutions to the equation?

$$4x+3y=-12: x=0\text{ and }y=-4$$

13. Solve: $\dfrac{-3}{4}x=18$.

14. Solve for the indicated variable: $-9x-3y=27$ for y

15. Solve: $3(x-1)-2(x+2)=-3+\dfrac{1}{3}x$

16. Daniel works as an office specialist and makes $13 per hour after taxes. Daniel can calculate his monthly salary using the equation

$$S=13h$$

where S is the monthly salary in dollars that Daniel makes if he works h hours that month.

    a. Find Daniel's monthly salary if he works 110 hours.
    b. How many hours does Daniel have to work a month to make $1820 a month?

17. Solve: $12x+9=5x+26.5$

18. Translate and solve: The sum of eight and three times a number is equal to the difference of twice the number and negative six.

19. Solve: $9y-8=6y+2+3(y+1)-10$

20. Solve the inequality: $-5x+2>37$

21. Complete each part below.

    a. Fill in the table using the given equation.

x	$y=\dfrac{-3}{5}x-7$
-5	
0	
5	
15	
20	

    b. Graph the line by plotting the points in the table. Clearly label and scale the axes.
    c. Is the graph linear or nonlinear?

22. Use the equation $y=\dfrac{-2}{3}x+4$ to create a table of five or more points, and graph them. Clearly label and scale the axes. Connect the points with a smooth curve. Is the graph linear or nonlinear?

23. The average American eats about 4000 calories per day. The amount of calories the average person will eat after d days can be estimated by using the equation $C=4000d$, where C is the total number of calories the average person eats during d days. Create a table of points that make sense in this situation and graph them. Connect the points with a smooth curve.

24. Use the equation $y=x^2-2$ to create a table of nine or more points and graph them. Clearly label and scale the axes. Connect the points with a smooth curve. Is the graph linear or nonlinear?

25. Use the equation $y=-5$ to create a table of five or more points and graph them. Clearly label and scale the axes. Connect the points with a smooth curve. Is the graph linear or nonlinear?

26. Use the equation $x=6$ to create a table of five or more points and graph them. Clearly label and scale the axes. Connect the points with a smooth curve. Is the graph linear or nonlinear?

27. Find the slope of the line given in the graph.

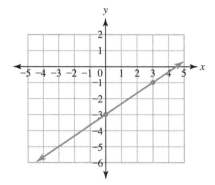

28. Find the slope of the line that goes through points $(-2, 5)$ and $(3, -7)$.

29. Use two points from the table to find the slope of the line that passes through the points.

x	y
−5	11
0	9
5	7
10	5

30. Use two points from the table to find the slope of the line that passes through the points.

x	y
5	−7
7	−7
8	−7
10	−7

31. State which line, the red line or the blue line, has the greater slope. Explain your answer.

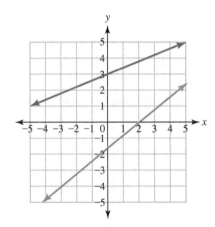

32. Explain whether the line is increasing, decreasing, or neither.

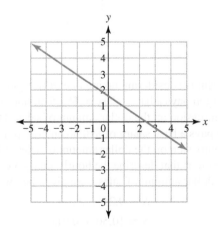

33. Is the line increasing, decreasing, or neither? Explain how you know.

$$y = 3x - 5$$

34. Use the graph to find the x- and y-intercepts. Write the intercepts as ordered pairs (x, y).

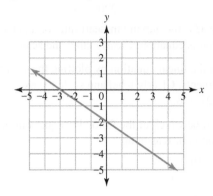

35. Use the following graph to answer the questions.

Source: U.S. Census Bureau, Population Division.

a. Interpret the vertical intercept for the Minnesota line.
b. Interpret the vertical intercept for the Washington line.
c. Find the slope of the Minnesota line. Explain the meaning of the slope in regard to the population of Minnesota.
d. Find the slope of the Washington line. Explain the meaning of the slope in regard to the population of Washington.

36. Find the x-intercept and the y-intercept of the equation $y = -\dfrac{3}{5}x + 15$.

37. Find the slope, x-intercept, and y-intercept of the equation $-4x + 8y = -12$.

38. Graph the equation $y = \dfrac{-3}{2}x + 5$ using the slope and the y-intercept. Graph at least three points. Clearly label and scale the axes.

39. Graph the equation $2x - 4y = 3$ using the slope and the y-intercept. Graph at least three points. Clearly label and scale the axes.

40. The maximum heart rate for a person less than 30 years old can be computed as

$$M = 220 - a$$

where M is the maximum heart rate for a person age a. Graph this equation. Clearly label and scale the axes.

41. Graph the linear equation by plotting the x- and y-intercepts. Clearly label and scale the axes. $3x - 2y = 6$.

42. Determine which of the following equations are linear. Explain your reasoning.

a. $x + 10y = -3$

b. $y = x^2 - 1$

c. $y = |3x - 6|$

d. $y = -2x + 17$

43. Determine whether the two lines are parallel, perpendicular, or neither. Do not graph the lines. The two lines are $y = -5x + 12$ and $10x + 2y = 6$.

44. Determine whether the two lines are parallel, perpendicular, or neither. Do not graph the lines. The two lines are $5x + 2y = 6$ and $y = \frac{2}{5}x + 1$.

45. Use the graph to find the equation of the line. Put the answer in $y = mx + b$ form.

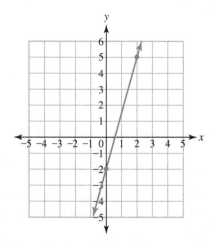

46. Maribel goes on a diet to lose weight. Let the input t represent the week of her diet, and let the output W represent Maribel's weight in pounds. At the start of her diet ($t = 0$), Maribel weighed 155 pounds. After 6 weeks on her diet, she weighed 130 pounds. Find the linear relationship between t and W.

47. Determine the equation of the line that passes through the points $(-5, 11)$ and $(5, 7)$. Put the answer in $y = mx + b$ form.

48. Determine the equation of the line by using point-slope form. The line has slope $m = \frac{2}{3}$ and passes through the point $(-6, 0)$. Put the final answer in $y = mx + b$ form.

49. Determine the equation of the line that passes through the points $(2, -5)$ and $(-3, -5)$. Put the answer in $y = mx + b$ form.

50. Write the equation of the line through the given points. The points are $(3, -5)$ and $(3, 2)$. (*Hint:* Graph the two points if necessary.)

51. Find the equation of the line parallel to $y = -5x + 7$, passing through the point $(-10, 3)$.

52. Find the equation of the line perpendicular to $y = 3x - 11$, passing through the point $(6, -4)$.

53. Solve the system of equations using the table of values.

x	$y = -4x + 2$
-3	14
-2	10
-1	6
0	2
1	-2

x	$y = 3x + 9$
-3	0
-2	3
-1	6
0	9
1	12

54. Determine whether each point is a solution of the system.

$$y = -2x + 3$$
$$y = 4x - 3$$

a. Is $(x, y) = (2, -1)$ a solution of the system?

b. Is $(x, y) = (1, 1)$ a solution of the system?

55. Use the graph to determine the solution to the system.

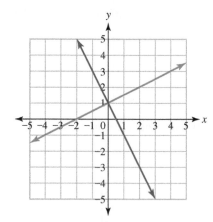

56. Martin is considering taking one of two jobs. The first job pays a base salary of $9.25 an hour plus 2% commission on the dollar amount of sales. The second job pays a base salary of $10.50 an hour plus 1% commission on the dollar amount of sales. The two equations that describe the hourly salary S earned given the dollar amount of sales x are given below.

$$S = 9.25 + 0.02x$$
$$S = 10.50 + 0.01x$$

a. Is $(x, S) = (100, 11.25)$ a solution of the system?

b. Is $(x, S) = (125, 11.75)$ a solution of the system?

57. Graphically determine the solution of the system. Clearly label and scale the axes. Check the solution by substituting it into both original equations.

$$y = -2x + 5$$
$$y = 2x - 3$$

58. Graphically determine the solution of the system. Clearly label and scale the axes. Check the solution by substituting it into both original equations.

$$y = 3x - 4$$
$$y = 2$$

59. Solve the system using the substitution method. Check the solution in both original equations.

$$5x + 4y = 4$$
$$2x + y = -2$$

60. Solve the system using the substitution method. Check the solution in both original equations.

$$-4x + y = 7$$
$$x - y = 8$$

61. Solve the system using the substitution method. Check the solution in both original equations.

$$-2x + 3y = 6$$
$$y = \frac{2}{3}x - 4$$

62. Haleigh is a summer camp coordinator. She purchased fifteen BPA-free water bottles and seven packages of energy bars for $265.00. Later, after more children enrolled in her program, she purchased an additional nine BPA-free water bottles and five more packages of energy bars for $179.00. How much does each water bottle and each package of energy bars cost?

63. The sum of two numbers is 32. The first number is equal to the difference between the second number and 6. Find the two numbers.

64. A plane can fly 450 miles in 3 hours with a tailwind. It makes the return trip (with a headwind) in 4.5 hours. Find the rate of the plane in still air and the rate of the wind.

65. Francis wants to make a 5-pound spice mix by blending two types of spices. The first spice is turmeric, which costs $8.90 per pound. The second spice is ground coriander, which costs $11.20 per pound. Francis wants to price the mix at $9.82 per pound. How many pounds of each type of spice does Francis need to use in his mix?

66. Solve the system using the elimination method. Check the solution in both original equations.

$$3x + y = 7$$
$$2x + y = 3$$

67. Solve the system using the elimination method. Check the solution in both original equations.

$$5x - 2y = 3$$
$$7x + 3y = -19$$

68. Solve the system using the elimination method. Check the solution in both original equations.

$$2x + 3y = 18$$
$$-4x - 6y = -36$$

69. Allyson is organizing PTA gifts for the teachers at her children's elementary school. She buys ten blank large scrapbooks and eight sticker sets for $280.00. Later, she purchases an additional four blank large scrapbooks and six sticker sets for $147.00. How much does each scrapbook and sticker set cost individually?

70. Two angles are supplementary. The second angle measures five times the measure of the first angle. Find the degree measures of both angles.

71. Eric has $12,000.00 to invest. An investment advisor tells him to put part of his money in a CD earning 3% interest and the rest in a bond fund earning 5% interest. Eric would like to earn $440.00 in interest every year. How much should he invest in each account?

72. Determine whether the point $(3, 10)$ is a solution of the linear inequality $3x - y < 7$.

73. Graph the solution set of the linear inequality $-2x + 3y > 6$.

74. Graph the solution set of the linear inequality $3x - 10y \leq 20$.

75. Mai has been asked to bring appetizers to a party. She calls a local restaurant, and they give her the following prices. The spring rolls cost $3.99, and chicken gyoza is $4.25. She wants to spend no more than $20.00 on both appetizers.

    a. Define the variables.
    b. Write an inequality that expresses the relationship between the total cost of both spring rolls and chicken gyoza and the maximum that Mai wants to spend ($20.00).
    c. Graph the solution set for this inequality.

Inequalities and Absolute Values

Andresr/ Shutterstock.com

A target heart rate is a desired range that will allow a person to get the most benefit from an aerobic workout. This range of heart rates can be represented with an inequality. In many aspects of our lives, situations are more realistic when modeled using inequalities. In one of the chapter projects, you will learn how to determine a person's target heart rate and to represent it using inequalities.

9.1 | Absolute Value Equations

LEARNING OBJECTIVES

■ Solve absolute value equations.

■ Solve applications using absolute values.

Absolute Value Equations

The absolute value can be defined in several ways. One way is to use the concept of distance on a number line. The absolute value of a number is defined as the distance from 0 to the number on a real number line. Using distance in the definition may help to see why $|6| = 6$ and $|-6| = 6$. Both 6 and -6 are 6 units from 0 on the real number line.

Since distance is always non-negative, the absolute value will always have a non-negative result.

■ Calculator Details

To take the absolute value of a number or expression on your graphing calculator, you will use the abs function found in the math menu. To get to the abs function, press **MATH** and **〉** to get to the NUM submenu.

The first option on this submenu is abs(. Pressing **1** or **ENTER** will bring abs(into your equation or calculation. Remember to close the parentheses at the end of the expression you are taking the absolute value of.

> ### DEFINITION
>
> **Absolute Value** The absolute value of a real number n, $|n|$, is the distance from zero to n on a real number line.

Using the distance definition of absolute value guides us when solving equations that contain absolute values. The equation $|x| = 8$ is asking what number(s), x, are 8 units from zero on the number line. If we look at the number line, we can see that both 8 and -8 are 8 units from zero.

The absolute value equation becomes two equations, one for the positive side of zero and the other for the negative side of zero.

$$|x| = 8$$
$$x = 8 \quad \text{or} \quad x = -8$$

> ### DEFINITION
>
> **Absolute Value Equation** If n is a positive real number and u is any algebraic expression, then
>
> $$|u| = n$$
> $$u = n \quad \text{or} \quad u = -n$$
>
> If n is negative, then the equation $|u| = n$ has no solution.
>
> If n is zero, $u = 0$.

When solving an equation that contains an absolute value, isolate the expression containing the absolute value. Then write two equations, one with a positive value and one with a negative value.

> **Solving Absolute Value Equations**
> - Isolate the expression containing the absolute value.
> - Rewrite the equation as two equations.
>
> $$|u| = n$$
> $$u = n \quad \text{or} \quad u = -n$$
>
> - Solve each equation.
> - Check the solutions in the original absolute value equation.

Absolute value equations can be solved algebraically using the definition, numerically using a table of values, or graphically using the graphs. The next example explores how to solve absolute value equations using all three methods.

Example 1   Working with absolute value equations

Solve the equation $|x - 2| = 3$ in each of the following ways.

a. Algebraically, by using the definition.

b. Numerically, by using a table of values.

c. Graphically.

SOLUTION

a. Using the definition, we set the input of the absolute value equal to 3 or -3.

$$|x - 2| = 3$$

$x - 2 = 3 \text{ or } x - 2 = -3$ *Set the input of the absolute value equal to 3, -3.*

$$\frac{+2 \ +2}{x = 5} \qquad \frac{+2 \ +2}{x = -1}$$

Check:

$$x = 5 \qquad\qquad x = -1$$
$$|5 - 2| \overset{?}{=} 3 \qquad |-1 - 2| \overset{?}{=} 3$$
$$|3| = 3 \qquad\qquad |-3| = 3 \qquad \textit{Both answers check.}$$

b. To solve the equation numerically, we build a table of values for the expression $|x - 2|$. We are looking for which value of x yields an output of 3.

$$|x - 2| = 3 \quad \begin{array}{l}\textit{Build a table of values to see which}\\\textit{input makes the output equal to 3.}\end{array}$$

Build the table by hand or by using the table feature of a graphing calculator.

x	$|x - 2|$
-2	$|-2 - 2| = |-4| = 4$
-1	$|-1 - 2| = |-3| = 3$
0	$|0 - 2| = |-2| = 2$
1	$|1 - 2| = |-1| = 1$
2	$|2 - 2| = |0| = 0$
3	$|3 - 2| = |1| = 1$
4	$|4 - 2| = |2| = 2$
5	$|5 - 2| = |3| = 3$

X	Y₁	Y₂
-2	4	3
-1	3	3
0	2	3
2	0	3
3	1	3
4	2	3
5	3	3

X=5

From the table, we see the two solutions are $x = -1$ or $x = 5$. The check is the same as above in part a.

■ Skill Connection

Solving Graphically

In Section 4.1, we learned that a system can be solved graphically by graphing both lines on the same axes and looking for the intersection point(s). We can think of the equation $|x - 2| = 3$ as a system, by setting each side equal to y: $y = |x - 2|$ and $y = 3$.

Graphing both of these functions on the same axes can yield the solution. We can use the graphing calculator to graph both functions in the same viewing window to look for the solution(s) quickly.

c. To solve the equation graphically, we enter two equations in the Y= screen on the calculator. Let $Y1 = |x - 2|$ and $Y2 = 3$. Graphing both equations in the same viewing window yields:

Looking carefully at the two graphs, we see that they intersect at the two values $x = -1$ and $x = 5$. The check is the same as in part a.

PRACTICE PROBLEM FOR EXAMPLE 1

Solve the equation $|x - 4| = 6$ in each of the following ways.

a. Algebraically, by using the definition.

b. Numerically, by using a table of values.

c. Graphically.

When we solve absolute value equations using the definition, we are solving the equation *algebraically*. In the next example, we will solve more absolute value equations algebraically.

Example 2   Solving absolute value equations

Solve the following equations algebraically.

a. $|x + 5| = 12$ $\qquad\qquad$ **b.** $2|x - 4| + 3 = 9$

SOLUTION

a. The absolute value is already isolated. Rewrite it as two equations and solve.

$$|x + 5| = 12 \qquad \text{Rewrite into two equations.}$$
$$x + 5 = 12 \quad \text{or} \quad x + 5 = -12$$
$$x = 7 \quad \text{or} \quad x = -17 \quad \text{Solve by subtracting 5 from both sides.}$$

There are two solutions for this equation. Check them both in the original absolute value equation.

$$x = 7 \qquad\qquad\qquad x = -17$$
$$|7 + 5| \stackrel{?}{=} 12 \qquad\qquad |-17 + 5| \stackrel{?}{=} 12$$
$$|12| \stackrel{?}{=} 12 \qquad\qquad |-12| \stackrel{?}{=} 12$$
$$12 = 12 \qquad\qquad\qquad 12 = 12$$

Both solutions work. We can see the two solutions by looking at the graph of both sides of the equation and looking for where the two graphs intersect.

b. First, isolate the absolute value.

$$2|x - 4| + 3 = 9 \qquad \text{Subtract 3 from both sides of}$$
$$\underline{ -3 \quad -3} \qquad \text{the equation.}$$
$$2|x - 4| = 6$$
$$\frac{2|x - 4|}{2} = \frac{6}{2} \qquad \text{Divide both sides of the equation}$$
$$|x - 4| = 3 \qquad \text{by 2.}$$

Rewrite into two equations and solve.

$$|x - 4| = 3$$

$$x - 4 = 3 \qquad \text{or} \qquad x - 4 = -3 \qquad \text{Solve by adding 4 to both}$$
$$x = 7 \qquad \text{or} \qquad x = 1 \qquad \text{sides of the equation.}$$

Check both equations in the original absolute value equation.

$$x = 7 \qquad\qquad\qquad x = 1$$
$$2|7 - 4| + 3 \overset{?}{=} 9 \qquad\qquad 2|1 - 4| + 3 \overset{?}{=} 9$$
$$2|3| + 3 \overset{?}{=} 9 \qquad\qquad 2|-3| + 3 \overset{?}{=} 9$$
$$9 = 9 \qquad\qquad\qquad 9 = 9$$

Both solutions work.

PRACTICE PROBLEM FOR EXAMPLE 2

Solve the following equations.

a. $|x - 2| = 7$ **b.** $-3|w + 1| + 12 = -3$

Some absolute value equations have no solution. An absolute value is a distance and, therefore, is always greater than or equal to zero. If an absolute value expression is set equal to a negative number, there will be no solution. We will explore that idea in the next example.

Example 3 Absolute value equations with no solution

Solve each of the following absolute value equations.

a. $|x + 1| = -2$ **b.** $|h + 3| + 10 = 4$

SOLUTION

a. The absolute value has been isolated on the left side of the equal sign. The right side is -2. An absolute value cannot be negative, so there is no solution to this equation. To observe this visually, graph both sides and look to see where the graphs intersect.

The graphs never intersect, so we see there is no solution to this equation.

b. First, isolate the absolute value.

$$|h + 3| + 10 = 4 \qquad \text{Subtract 10 from both}$$
$$\underline{ -10 \quad -10} \qquad \text{sides of the equation.}$$
$$|h + 3| = -6$$

The absolute value equals a negative number, which is not possible. There is no solution to this equation. A good way to check this result is to graph both sides of the equation and see whether they intersect.

From the graph, we can see the absolute value curve does not intersect the line. This confirms that the result of no solution is correct.

PRACTICE PROBLEM FOR EXAMPLE 3

Solve each of the following absolute value equations.

a. $|x - 4| = -4$ 　　　　　　　　**b.** $|x - 6| + 7 = 3$

Example 4 　An application of absolute value equations

Rebecca is taking a trip across the country and is concerned about gasoline costs. The most efficient mileage expressed as miles per gallon for Rebecca's car can be modeled by the function

$$m(s) = -\frac{1}{3}|s - 60| + 35$$

where m is the gas mileage for Rebecca's car when she is driving at an average speed of s miles per hour, for speeds between 40 and 80 miles per hour. At what speed should Rebecca drive to get gas mileage of 30 miles per gallon during her trip?

SOLUTION

Rebecca wants to get 30 miles per gallon, so $m(s) = 30$. Substitute 30 in for $m(s)$ and solve.

$$m(s) = -\frac{1}{3}|s - 60| + 35$$

$$30 = -\frac{1}{3}|s - 60| + 35$$ 　　Isolate the absolute value by subtracting 35 from both sides.
$$\underline{-35 \qquad\qquad\quad -35}$$

$$-5 = -\frac{1}{3}|s - 60|$$

$$-3(-5) = -3\left(-\frac{1}{3}|s - 60|\right)$$ 　　Multiply both sides by -3 to eliminate the fraction.

$$15 = |s - 60|$$

$s - 60 = 15$ 　or 　$s - 60 = -15$ 　　Rewrite into two equations and solve.

$s = 75$ 　or 　　　$s = 45$

Check these solutions in the original equation, using the table on the calculator.

Rebecca can drive either 75 miles per hour or 45 miles per hour on her trip to get gas mileage of 30 miles per gallon.

PRACTICE PROBLEM FOR EXAMPLE 4

Svetlana is driving from San Antonio to Houston, Texas, on Interstate 10 and will pass through Columbus, Texas, on the way. Svetlana's distance from Columbus can be modeled by the function

$$D(t) = |125 - 65t|$$

where $D(t)$ is Svetlana's distance in miles from Columbus, Texas, after driving for t hours. Find the time when Svetlana will be 25 miles away from Columbus.

9.1 Exercises

For Exercises 1 through 10, solve each of the following absolute value equations using the given method.

1. $|x + 1| = 2$
   a. Algebraically, by using the definition.
   b. Numerically, by using a table of values.
   c. Graphically.

2. $|x + 3| = 4$
   a. Algebraically, by using the definition.
   b. Numerically, by using a table of values.
   c. Graphically.

3. $|x - 3| = 1$
   a. Algebraically, by using the definition.
   b. Numerically, by using a table of values.
   c. Graphically.

4. $|x - 5| = 2$
   a. Algebraically, by using the definition.
   b. Numerically, by using a table of values.
   c. Graphically.

5. $|2x - 4| = 6$
   a. Algebraically, by using the definition.
   b. Numerically, by using a table of values.
   c. Graphically.

6. $|2x - 6| = 2$
   a. Algebraically, by using the definition.
   b. Numerically, by using a table of values.
   c. Graphically.

7. $|3x + 1| = 2$
   a. Algebraically, by using the definition.
   b. Numerically, by using a table of values.
   c. Graphically.

8. $|2x + 5| = 2$
   a. Algebraically, by using the definition.
   b. Numerically, by using a table of values.
   c. Graphically.

9. $|5 - x| = 4$
   a. Algebraically, by using the definition.
   b. Numerically, by using a table of values.
   c. Graphically.

10. $|8 - x| = 9$
   a. Algebraically, by using the definition.
   b. Numerically, by using a table of values.
   c. Graphically.

For Exercises 11 through 38, solve the following equations. Check your answers.

11. $|x| = 12$ **12.** $|x| = 20$

13. $|h + 7| = 15$ **14.** $|m + 9| = 11$

15. $|b - 12| = 8$ **16.** $|w - 8| = 30$

17. $2|r + 11| = 36$ **18.** $8|h - 3| = 4$

19. $3 \ |a + 1| = 9$ **20.** $4|b - 5| = 12$

21. $5|x - 6| = 25$ **22.** $7|x - 2| = 21$

23. $|m - 3| + 2 = 6$ **24.** $|w - 4| + 2 = 5$

25. $|y + 4| - 6 = 7$ **26.** $|x + 3| - 5 = 9$

27. $2|x - 5| + 1 = 11$ **28.** $4|x - 3| + 2 = 18$

29. $-2|x - 5| + 1 = -5$ **30.** $-3|x + 4| + 2 = -4$

31. $-3|x - 12| = -5$ **32.** $-5|y + 14| = -36$

33. $|k + 10| = -3$ **34.** $|s - 4| = -15$

35. $|g - 9| + 12 = 8$ **36.** $|x + 4| + 6 = 1$

37. $-2|d - 8| + 1 = 11$ **38.** $-4|m + 3| + 7 = 3$

39. Ricardo is taking a trip from Arizona to Yosemite National Park in California. The gas mileage in miles per gallon for Ricardo's truck can be modeled by the function

$$m(s) = -\frac{1}{3}|s - 60| + 25$$

where $m(s)$ is the gas mileage for Ricardo's truck when he is driving at an average speed of s miles per hour, for speeds between 40 and 80 miles per hour. At what speed should Ricardo drive to get gas mileage of 20 miles per gallon during his trip?

40. William is driving from Yakima, Washington, to Salt Lake City, Utah. The gas mileage in miles per gallon for William's car can be modeled by the function

$$m(s) = -\frac{1}{2}|s - 55| + 24$$

where $m(s)$ is the gas mileage for William's car when he is driving at an average speed of s miles per hour,

for speeds between 40 and 80 miles per hour. At what speed should William drive to get gas mileage of 22 miles per gallon during his trip?

41. On Ricardo's trip from Arizona to Yosemite National Park, he will pass through Fresno, California, Ricardo's distance from Fresno can be modeled by the function

$$D(t) = |700 - 60t|$$

where $D(t)$ is Ricardo's distance in miles from Fresno after driving for t hours. Find the time when Ricardo will be 50 miles away from Fresno.

42. On William's trip from Yakima, Washington, to Salt Lake City, Utah, he will pass through Boise, Idaho. William's distance from Boise can be modeled by the function

$$D(t) = |365 - 55t|$$

where $D(t)$ is William's distance in miles from Boise after driving for t hours. Find the time when William will be 30 miles away from Boise.

For Exercises 43 to 50, solve the absolute value equations. If there is no solution, answer "no solution."

43. $|x - 8| + 3 = 3$

44. $|y + 5| + 4 = 4$

45. $|p + 4| = -3$

46. $|q - 6| = -1$

47. $|2x + 1| - 10 = -4$

48. $|4x + 6| - 8 = 2$

49. $|x - 7| + 2 = -5$

50. $|y + 8| - 3 = -9$

9.2 Absolute Value Inequalities

LEARNING OBJECTIVES

- Solve absolute value inequalities involving "less than."
- Solve absolute value inequalities involving "greater than."

Absolute Value Inequalities Involving "Less Than" or "Less Than or Equal To"

Inequalities that contain absolute values can also be interpreted by using the distance definition of absolute value. The inequality $|x| < 3$ is asking for all values of x that are less than 3 units from zero on the number line.

If we look at the graph of each side of the inequality, we can see the solution set.

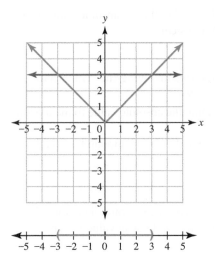

We can see that the red graph of the absolute value is less than 3 when it is below the blue graph of $y = 3$. This happens when x is between -3 and 3.

In solving inequalities with absolute values, it is important to keep in mind what the inequality is asking. The absolute value inequality $|x| < 3$ is asking for x-values that are closer than 3 units away from zero. From the graph, we can see that this interpretation implies that x must be between -3 and 3. Writing this interval with inequalities is similar to the way we rewrote absolute value equations into two equations, but the inequality symbols must be in the correct direction and order.

$$|x| < 3$$
$$-3 < x < 3$$

The last inequality says that x must be between -3 and 3, as seen as the interval on the above graph.

We studied compound inequalities in Section 2.4. In the next example, we will learn how to write a compound inequality given its graph.

Example 1   **Writing an interval using a compound inequality**

Write the given interval using a compound inequality.

a.

b.

SOLUTION

a. This interval has brackets, so the inequalities will include the "equal to" part. The values in the interval are between -5 and 5. The interval written as an inequality is $-5 \le x \le 5$.

b. This interval has parentheses, so the inequalities will not include the "equal to" part. The values in the interval are between -3 and 7. The interval written as an inequality is $-3 < x < 7$.

PRACTICE PROBLEM FOR EXAMPLE 1

Write the given interval using a compound inequality.

When solving absolute value inequalities with a "less than" symbol, write a compound inequality to indicate that the expression must be between the positive number and the opposite of the number. Remember that an absolute value cannot be less than a negative number in the real number system.

> **Solving Absolute Value Inequalities Involving the "Less Than" or "Less Than or Equal To" Symbols**
>
> - Isolate the expression containing the absolute value to the left side of the inequality.
> - Rewrite the absolute value inequality as a compound inequality.
>
> $$|u| < n \qquad\qquad |u| \le n$$
> $$-n < u < n \qquad\qquad -n \le u \le n$$
>
> - Solve the compound inequality. (Isolate the variable in the middle.)
> - Check the solution set in the original absolute value inequality.

Example 2 Solving absolute value inequalities with "less than"

Solve the following inequalities. Give the solution as an inequality and graph the solution set on a number line.

a. $|x| < 4$ **b.** $|x - 2| \le 5$ **c.** $|b + 5| + 15 < 20$

SOLUTION

a. The absolute value is isolated on the left side. Since there is a "less than" symbol, rewrite the absolute value inequality as a compound inequality.

$$|x| < 4$$
$$-4 < x < 4$$

Therefore, x must be between -4 and 4.

The solution set is the interval from -4 to 4. To confirm this solution set, check the endpoints of the interval and pick a number inside the interval to check the direction of the inequalities. Check each of these values in the original absolute value inequality. For the point inside the interval, we can pick any value we want. We will pick $x = 3$.

Left endpoint	Right endpoint	Point inside the interval
$\lvert -4 \rvert \overset{?}{=} 4$	$\lvert 4 \rvert \overset{?}{=} 4$	$\lvert 3 \rvert \overset{?}{<} 4$
$4 = 4$	$4 = 4$	$3 < 4$

The equations and the inequality are true, so the solution set is correct.

b. The absolute value is isolated on the left side. It uses a "less than or equal to" symbol. Rewrite the absolute value inequality as a compound inequality and solve.

$$|x - 2| \le 5$$
$$-5 \le x - 2 \le 5 \qquad \text{Rewrite as a compound inequality.}$$
$$\underline{+2 \qquad\quad +2 \quad +2} \qquad \text{Add 2 to all sides of the inequality.}$$
$$-3 \le x \le 7$$

Therefore, x must be between or equal to -3 and 7.

To confirm the solution set, we will check the endpoints of the interval and pick a number inside the interval to check the direction of the inequality symbols. If we pick $x = 4$ and check all of these values in the original absolute value inequality, we get the following:

Left endpoint	Right endpoint	Point inside the interval
$\|-3 - 2\| \overset{?}{=} 5$	$\|7 - 2\| \overset{?}{=} 5$	$\|4 - 2\| \overset{?}{\leq} 5$
$\|-5\| \overset{?}{=} 5$	$\|5\| \overset{?}{=} 5$	$\|2\| \overset{?}{\leq} 5$
$5 = 5$	$5 = 5$	$2 \leq 5$

The equations for the endpoints and the inequality are true, so the solution set is correct.

c. First, isolate the absolute value. Rewrite it as a compound inequality.

$$\begin{array}{ll} |b + 5| + 15 < 20 & \text{Isolate the absolute value.} \\ \underline{\ -15 \quad -15} & \\ |b + 5| < 5 & \text{Rewrite into a compound} \\ -5 < b + 5 < 5 & \text{inequality and solve.} \\ \underline{-5 \quad\quad -5 \quad -5} & \text{Subtract 5 from all sides.} \\ -10 < b < 0 & \end{array}$$

Therefore, b must be between -10 and 0.

We will confirm the solution set by graphing the left and right sides of the inequality on the calculator and comparing the graphs.

We can see that the absolute value graph is less than 20 when x is between -10 and 0.

PRACTICE PROBLEM FOR EXAMPLE 2

Solve the following inequalities. Give the solution as an inequality, and graph the solution set on a number line.

a. $|x - 8| < 2$ **b.** $|d + 1| - 3 \leq 5$

Example 3   An application of absolute value inequalities with the symbol for "less than"

When a part is made for a machine or other precise application, the accuracy of the size of each part is very important for that part to function properly. The amount the size of a particular part can be larger or smaller than the ideal size is called the tolerance. When a 20-millimeter (mm) bolt is made for an engine, the actual size must be within 0.02 mm of 20 mm. If L is the actual length of the bolt in millimeters, the acceptable lengths of the bolt can be modeled by

$$|L - 20| \leq 0.02$$

Find the acceptable lengths of these bolts.

SOLUTION

Solve the absolute value inequality.

$$|L - 20| \leq 0.02$$
$$-0.02 \leq L - 20 \leq 0.02$$
$$19.98 \leq L \leq 20.02$$

We will confirm this solution set by checking the endpoints of the interval in the original absolute value inequality. We know that the ideal length of 20 mm is inside the interval, so the inequality symbols are correct.

Left endpoint	Right endpoint
$|19.98 - 20| \overset{?}{=} 0.02$	$|20.02 - 20| \overset{?}{=} 0.02$
$|-0.02| \overset{?}{=} 0.02$	$|0.02| \overset{?}{=} 0.02$
$0.02 = 0.02$	$0.02 = 0.02$

The equations are true, so the bolts must be between or equal to 19.98 mm and 20.02 mm long.

PRACTICE PROBLEM FOR EXAMPLE 3

A rod in an engine is supposed to be 4.125 inches long. The tolerance for the rod is 0.0005 inch. The acceptable lengths of the rod can be modeled by

$$|L - 4.125| \leq 0.0005$$

where L is the actual length of the rod in inches. Find the acceptable lengths for this rod.

Absolute Value Inequalities Involving "Greater Than" or "Greater Than or Equal To"

Whereas the "less than" symbol asks for numbers closer to zero, the "greater than" symbol asks for numbers farther away from zero. The inequality $|x| > 5$ is asking for the values of x that are more than 5 units away from zero on the number line.

If we look at the graph of each side of the inequality, we can see the solution set.

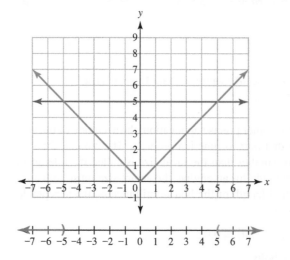

We can see that the red graph of the absolute value is greater than 5 when it is above the blue graph of the line $y = 5$. This occurs when x is less than -5 and when x is greater than 5.

To represent values that are farther away from zero requires an interval on the right and another interval on the left to account for distances in both directions. Therefore, write two inequalities to accommodate the absolute value, with one inequality going left ($<$) and another going right ($>$).

$$|x| > 5$$
$$x < -5 \quad \text{or} \quad x > 5$$

Example 4 Writing an interval using a compound inequality

Write the given interval using a compound inequality.

a.

```
◄┼┼┼┼┼┼┼┼┼)┼┼┼(┼┼┼┼┼┼┼┼►
 -10 -9 -8 -7 -6 -5 -4 -3 -2 -1  0  1  2  3  4  5  6  7  8  9  10
```

b.

```
◄┼┼┼┼┼┼┼┼]┼┼┼┼┼┼[┼┼┼┼┼┼►
 -10 -9 -8 -7 -6 -5 -4 -3 -2 -1  0  1  2  3  4  5  6  7  8  9  10
```

SOLUTION

a. This interval has parentheses, so the inequalities will not include the "equal to" part. The values in the interval are less than -2 or greater than 2. Since a value cannot be in both sides, we use the word "or" between the two inequalities. The interval written as an inequality is $x < -2$ or $x > 2$.

b. This interval has brackets, so the inequalities will include the "equal to" part. The values in the interval are less than -4 or greater than 3. The interval written as an inequality is $x \leq -4$ or $x \geq 3$.

PRACTICE PROBLEM FOR EXAMPLE 4

Write the given interval using a compound inequality.

```
◄┼┼┼┼┼┼┼┼┼┼)┼┼┼(┼┼┼┼┼┼►
 -10 -9 -8 -7 -6 -5 -4 -3 -2 -1  0  1  2  3  4  5  6  7  8  9  10
```

When solving absolute value inequalities with a "greater than" symbol, write a compound inequality to indicate that the expression must be greater than the positive number, or less than the opposite of the number.

Solving Absolute Value Inequalities Involving "Greater Than" or "Greater Than or Equal To"

- Isolate the expression containing the absolute value on the left side of the inequality.
- Rewrite the absolute value inequality into two inequalities, one "less than" and one "greater than."

$$|u| > n \qquad\qquad\qquad |u| \geq n$$
$$u < -n \quad \text{or} \quad u > n \qquad\qquad u \leq -n \quad \text{or} \quad u \geq n$$

- Solve the two inequalities.
- Check the solution set in the original absolute value inequality.

Example 5 Solving absolute value inequalities with "greater than"

Solve the following inequalities. Give the solution as an inequality. Graph the solution set on a number line.

a. $|x| > 2$ **b.** $|p + 4| > 3$ **c.** $|x - 2| + 7 \geq 10$

SOLUTION

a. The absolute value is already isolated. Rewrite the absolute value inequality as two inequalities.

$$|x| > 2$$

$$x < -2 \quad \text{or} \quad x > 2$$

To check this solution, check the endpoints and a point from each of the intervals. We will check -6 for the left interval and 6 for the right interval.

Left interval endpoint	Right interval endpoint	Left interval test point	Right interval test point
$|-2| \stackrel{?}{=} 2$	$|2| \stackrel{?}{=} 2$	$|-6| \stackrel{?}{>} 2$	$|6| \stackrel{?}{>} 2$
$2 = 2$	$2 = 2$	$6 > 2$	$6 > 2$

Each of these points satisfies the original absolute value inequality, so the solution set is correct.

b. The absolute value is already isolated. Rewrite the absolute value inequality as two inequalities and solve.

$$\left| p + 4 \right| > 3$$

Rewrite as two inequalities and solve. Subtract 4 from both sides.

$$p + 4 < -3 \quad \text{or} \quad p + 4 > 3$$

$$p < -7 \quad \text{or} \quad p > -1$$

Check this solution set using the graph of each side on the calculator.

We can see that the absolute value graph is greater than 3 when x is less than -7 or greater than -1.

b. First, isolate the absolute value on the left side of the inequality. Rewrite into two inequalities and solve.

$$|x - 2| + 7 \geq 10$$

Isolate the absolute value.

$$\underline{\;-7 \quad -7}$$

$$|x - 2| \geq 3$$

$$x - 2 \leq -3 \quad \text{or} \quad x - 2 \geq 3$$

Rewrite into two inequalities and solve.

$$x \leq -1 \quad \text{or} \quad x \geq 5$$

Add 2 to both sides.

Check this solution set using the graph of each side of the inequality on the calculator.

We can see that the absolute value graph is greater than 10 when x is less than -1 or greater than 5.

PRACTICE PROBLEM FOR EXAMPLE 5

Solve the following inequalities. Give the solution as an inequality. Graph the solution set on a number line.

a. $|x + 2| > 7$ 　　　　　　　　　**b.** $|g - 3| - 4 \geq 1$

Example 6　An application of absolute value inequalities with "greater than"

A baby's birth weight is considered unusually high or low if it satisfies the inequality

$$|b - 118| > 30$$

where b is a baby's birth weight in ounces. Find the birth weights that would be considered unusually low or high.

SOLUTION

Solve the inequality by rewriting it into two inequalities.

$$|b - 118| > 30$$

$$b - 118 < -30 \quad \text{or} \quad b - 118 > 30$$

$$b < 88 \quad \text{or} \quad b > 148$$

Check this solution set using the endpoints of the intervals and points within each interval.

Left interval endpoint	Right interval endpoint	Left interval test point	Right interval test point
$\lvert 88 - 118 \rvert \overset{?}{=} 30$	$\lvert 148 - 118 \rvert \overset{?}{=} 30$	$\lvert 70 - 118 \rvert \overset{?}{>} 30$	$\lvert 160 - 118 \rvert \overset{?}{>} 30$
$30 = 30$	$30 = 30$	$48 > 30$	$42 > 30$

These checks are true, so the solution set is correct. A baby is considered to have an unusually low birth weight when it weighs less than 88 ounces, and it is considered to have an unusually high birth weight when it weighs more than 148 ounces.

PRACTICE PROBLEM FOR EXAMPLE 6

A recent poll asked people how much TV they watched in an average week. If the number of hours h a person watches TV satisfies the inequality

$$\left| \frac{h - 32}{4.5} \right| > 1.96$$

it would be considered unusual. Find the number of hours that would be considered unusual.

9.2 　Exercises

For Exercises 1 through 10, write the interval shown on the number line using a compound inequality.

1.

2.

3.

4.

5.

6.

7.

8.

9.

10.

For Exercises 11 through 16, write the solution set using inequality notation for the given graph and inequality.

11.

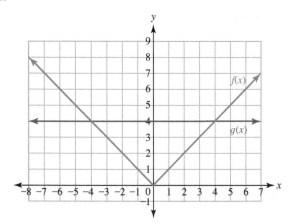

    a. $f(x) < g(x)$ **b.** $f(x) > g(x)$

12.

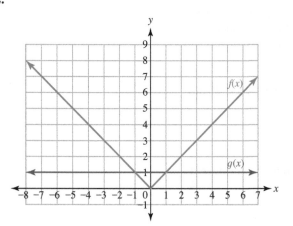

    a. $f(x) < g(x)$ **b.** $f(x) > g(x)$

13.

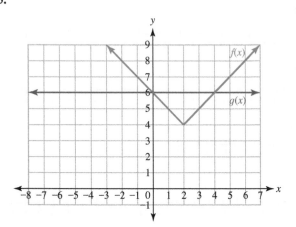

    a. $f(x) \leq g(x)$ **b.** $f(x) \geq g(x)$

14.

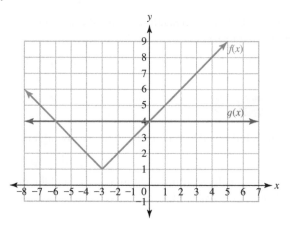

    a. $f(x) \leq g(x)$ **b.** $f(x) \geq g(x)$

15.

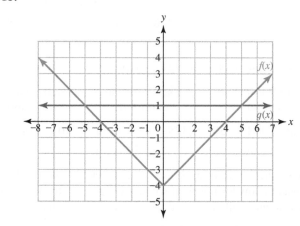

    a. $f(x) < g(x)$ **b.** $f(x) > g(x)$

16.

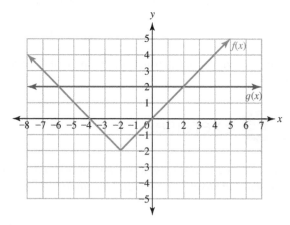

    a. $f(x) \leq g(x)$ **b.** $f(x) \geq g(x)$

For Exercises 17 through 22, solve the inequality algebraically. Give the solution as an inequality. Graph the solution set on a number line. Check your answer, using a graph.

17. $|x| < 5$

18. $|x| < 7$

19. $|h - 3| \leq 4$

20. $|k + 5| \le 2$

21. $|b - 1| < 6$

22. $|p + 3| < 3$

23. A coupling for a satellite fuel line is designed to be 3.00 centimeters long. The tolerance for this part is 0.001 centimeter (cm). The acceptable lengths of the coupler can be modeled by

$$|L - 3.00| \le 0.001$$

where L is the actual length of the coupler in centimeters. Find the acceptable lengths for this part. (The tolerance for a part is how much smaller or larger it can be than the desired size and still be acceptable.)

24. A cylinder for a small engine is designed to be 3.625 inches in diameter. The tolerance for this part is 0.0005 inch. The acceptable diameters of the cylinder can be modeled by

$$|D - 3.625| \le 0.0005$$

where D is the actual diameter of the cylinder in inches. Find the acceptable diameters for this part.

25. A particular pressure sensor measures the pressure in a gas chamber. The accuracy of this sensor is 0.5 pound per square inch (psi). For an experiment, the technician requires the gas chamber to be at a pressure of 20 psi. The acceptable pressures for this experiment will satisfy

$$|P - 20| \le 0.5$$

where P is the measured pressure in pounds per square inch. Find the acceptable pressures for this experiment.

26. A particular thermocouple measures the temperature during a chemical reaction. The accuracy of this thermocouple is 0.05°C. For an experiment, the technician wants to keep the temperature at 22°C. The acceptable temperature readings for this reaction will satisfy

$$|T - 22| \le 0.05$$

where T is the temperature reading in degrees Celsius. Find the acceptable temperature readings for this chemical reaction.

For Exercises 27 through 32, solve the following inequalities algebraically. Give the solution as an inequality. Graph the solution set on a number line. Check your answer, using a graph.

27. $|x| > 3$

28. $|x| > 7$

29. $|p - 4| \ge 2$

30. $|m - 3| \ge 1$

31. $|y + 6| > 3$

32. $|w + 2| > 5$

33. Men's heights have a mean of 69 inches. A height h that satisfies

$$\left|\frac{h - 69}{2.5}\right| > 2$$

is considered unusual. Find the heights that are considered unusual. (The word *mean* is used in statistics for the average value.)

34. Women's heights have a mean of 63.6 inches. A height h that satisfies

$$\left|\frac{h - 63.6}{2.5}\right| > 2$$

is considered unusual. Find the heights that are considered unusual.

35. The normal mean score of the Stanford Binet IQ test is 100. An IQ score S that satisfies

$$\left|\frac{S - 100}{16}\right| > 2$$

is considered unusual.

a. Find the IQ scores that are considered unusual.
b. Albert Einstein was said to have an IQ of 160. Was Einstein's IQ unusual? Explain.

36. Human body temperatures have a mean of 98.20°F. A body temperature that satisfies

$$\left|\frac{T - 98.20}{0.62}\right| > 2$$

is considered unusual.

a. Find the body temperatures that are considered unusual.
b. If a person has a body temperature of 99°F, would it be considered unusual? Explain.

For Exercises 37 through 58, solve the following inequalities algebraically. Give the solution as an inequality. Graph the solution set on a number line. Check your answer.

37. $2\,|r + 6| < 8$

38. $5\,|t + 3| < 20$

39. $4x - 20 > 12$

40. $2x + 6 \le 5x + 9$

41. $|d - 5| + 10 \le 7$

42. $|x + 3| + 15 < 4$

43. $|m + 1| - 2 > 6$

44. $-3|s - 2| + 2 > -4$

45. $\frac{2}{3}x - 8 > \frac{5}{6}x - 4$

46. $\frac{3}{4}m + \frac{2}{3} \ge 5m + \frac{4}{3}$

47. $-6|p - 4| + 3 \le 16$

48. $-4|x + 3| + 9 < 20$

49. $-|x - 4| \ge -2$

50. $-|k + 11| \ge -36$

51. $5 + 2|2x - 4| > 11$

52. $4 - 5|4x + 8| > -6$

53. $12 + 8|3d - 8| \le 10$

54. $20 + 3|5x - 2| \le 11$

55. $1.4x + 3 \ge 4.4x - 1$

56. $|2.5b - 3| - 1.4 \ge -0.6$

57. $\left|\frac{1}{2}x + 3\right| \le 5$

58. $\left|\frac{2}{3}d - 4\right| > 10$

9.3 Nonlinear Inequalities in One Variable

LEARNING OBJECTIVES

▇ Solve nonlinear polynomial inequalities.

▇ Solve rational inequalities.

In Section 2.4, we studied how to solve linear inequalities such as $2x + 3 > 5$, and in Section 9.2, we learned how to solve inequalities involving absolute values. In this section, we investigate how to solve nonlinear polynomial and rational inequalities such as

$$x^2 + 3x - 4 > 0 \quad \text{and} \quad \frac{2x + 5}{x - 3} \leq 0$$

Solving Nonlinear Polynomial Inequalities

Springdale High School is selling candy bars to raise money for their high school band. If they raise the price of each bar, the school can make more money per candy bar but will sell fewer bars in all. They determine that their profit from selling candy bars can be estimated using the model

Mark Herreid/Shutterstock.com

$$P(n) = -500n^2 + 2000n + 4000$$

where $P(n)$ is the profit in dollars from selling candy bars and n is the number of times the price is raised by \$0.50 from the original price of \$0.75. The school wants to make at least \$5500 profit to support the school band, so they want to know how many price increases they should use. We can use inequalities to represent this situation as

$$Pn \geq 5500$$

$$-500n^2 + 2000n + 4000 \geq 5500$$

In this section, we learn how to solve inequalities of this form, and we will solve this inequality in Example 4.

When solving nonlinear inequalities, it is best to set the right side to zero. Having the polynomial expression less than zero means it must be negative, and having it greater than zero means it must be positive. A polynomial may change from positive to negative only on either side of a value that makes the polynomial zero. (Recall that the values that make the polynomial zero are often called *roots* or *zeros* of the polynomial.)

Using this fact, we can determine where a polynomial is positive and negative. We will first find where the polynomial is zero. By plotting the zeros on a number line, we can then determine which intervals of the number line result in the polynomial taking on positive or negative values.

Steps to Solving a Polynomial Inequality

1. Set the right side of the inequality to 0.
2. Factor the left side to find the zeros of the polynomial.
3. Plot the zeros on a number line.
4. Pick a test point from each interval and substitute it into the *original* inequality. Determine whether the inequality is true or false.
5. The solution set is formed by the true regions found in step 4.

Example 1   Solving a quadratic inequality

Solve $x^2 + 3x - 4 > 0$. Write the solution set in three ways:

1. Graphed on a number line.

2. Using interval notation.

3. Using inequality notation.

SOLUTION

The inequality $x^2 + 3x - 4 > 0$ is a quadratic polynomial that is to be greater than zero. To find the intervals that result in this inequality being true, first find the values that make the polynomial equal zero. Set the quadratic equal to zero and solve using factoring.

$$x^2 + 3x - 4 = 0 \qquad \text{Set the quadratic equal to zero.}$$
$$(x + 4)(x - 1) = 0 \qquad \text{Factor.}$$
$$x + 4 = 0 \quad \text{or} \quad x - 1 = 0 \qquad \text{Make two equations and solve.}$$
$$x = -4 \quad \text{or} \qquad x = 1$$

Plot these two values on a number line.

The number line is now separated into three intervals.

> **Skill Connection**
>
> **Writing Intervals Using Different Notation**
>
> In Section 2.4, we learned how to write the solution set to inequalities using both interval notation and inequality notation, as well as how to graph it on a number line.

We now check each of these intervals to determine which make the inequality true. To check, select an x-value from each interval and evaluate the quadratic to see where the inequality is true.

$x = -6$	$x = 0$	$x = 5$
$(-6)^2 + 3(-6) - 4 \overset{?}{>} 0$	$(0)^2 + 3(0) - 4 \overset{?}{>} 0$	$(5)^2 + 3(5) - 4 \overset{?}{>} 0$
$36 - 18 - 4 \overset{?}{>} 0$	$-4 \overset{?}{>} 0$	$25 + 15 - 4 \overset{?}{>} 0$
$14 \overset{?}{>} 0$		$36 \overset{?}{>} 0$
True	False	True

We can see that the intervals on the left and right sides both result in a true inequality statement, so these intervals are the solution set to this inequality. Now graph these intervals on a number line, using parentheses to indicate that the endpoints are not included in the solution set. Then write the solution set using interval notation and inequalities.

$$(-\infty, -4) \quad \text{or} \quad (1, \infty)$$
$$x < -4 \quad \text{or} \quad x > 1$$

PRACTICE PROBLEM FOR EXAMPLE 1

Solve $x^2 + 6x + 8 > 0$. Write the solution set in three ways:

1. Graphed on a number line.

2. Using interval notation.

3. Using inequality notation.

> **Example 2** Solving polynomial inequalities

Solve the given inequalities. Write the solution set in three ways:

1. Graphed on a number line.

2. Using interval notation.

3. Using inequality notation.

a. $x^2 - 2x - 8 \leq 0$ **b.** $x^2 > 25$ **c.** $2x^3 - 12x^2 + 16x < 0$

SOLUTION

a. The quadratic $x^2 - 2x - 8$ is set less than or equal to zero. Solve to find the values of the quadratic that make it zero.

$$x^2 - 2x - 8 = 0$$
$$(x - 4)(x + 2) = 0$$
$$x - 4 = 0 \qquad x + 2 = 0$$
$$x = 4 \qquad x = -2$$

Plot these two values on a number line.

The number line is now separated into three intervals. Check each of these intervals to see where the inequality is true.

$x = -6$	$x = 1$	$x = 7$
$(-6)^2 - 2(-6) - 8 \overset{?}{\leq} 0$	$(1)^2 - 2(1) - 8 \overset{?}{\leq} 0$	$(7)^2 - 2(7) - 8 \overset{?}{\leq} 0$
$36 + 12 - 8 \overset{?}{\leq} 0$	$1 - 2 - 8 \overset{?}{\leq} 0$	$49 - 14 - 8 \overset{?}{\leq} 0$
$40 \overset{?}{\leq} 0$	$-9 \overset{?}{\leq} 0$	$27 \overset{?}{\leq} 0$
False	True	False

The only interval where the quadratic inequality is true is between -2 and 4. Since the inequality is less than or equal to zero, the endpoints are included in the solution set. Now graph the interval on a number line, using square brackets to show that the endpoints are included in the solution set. Then write the solution set using interval notation and inequalities.

$$[-2, 4]$$
$$-2 \leq x \leq 4$$

b. The quadratic inequality, $x^2 > 25$, is not expressed with its right side set to zero. First subtract 25 from both sides to make the expression be greater than zero.

$$x^2 > 25$$
$$x^2 - 25 > 0$$

Now find the zeros by setting the quadratic equal to zero and solving.

$$x^2 - 25 = 0 \quad \text{\textit{Factor as a difference of two squares.}}$$
$$(x + 5)(x - 5) = 0$$
$$x + 5 = 0 \qquad x - 5 = 0$$
$$x = -5 \qquad x = 5$$

Plot these two values on a number line and determine which intervals result in positive values, or where the inequality is true.

$$x = -8 \qquad\qquad x = 0 \qquad\qquad x = 8$$

$$(-8)^2 \overset{?}{>} 25 \qquad (0)^2 \overset{?}{>} 25 \qquad (8)^2 \overset{?}{>} 25$$

$$64 \overset{?}{>} 25 \qquad\qquad 0 \overset{?}{>} 25 \qquad\qquad 64 \overset{?}{>} 25$$

True   False   True

The inequality is true in the two outer intervals. Since the inequality is greater than zero, the endpoints are not included in the solution set. Now, graph the intervals on a number line, and then write using interval notation and inequalities.

$$(-\infty, -5) \quad \text{or} \quad (5, \infty)$$

$$x < -5 \quad \text{or} \quad x > 5$$

c. The polynomial $2x^3 - 12x^2 + 16x < 0$ is set less than zero, so set the polynomial equal to zero and solve.

$$2x^3 - 12x^2 + 16x = 0$$

$$2x(x^2 - 6x + 8) = 0 \qquad \text{Factor out the GCF.}$$

$$2x(x - 4)(x - 2) = 0$$

$$2x = 0 \qquad x - 4 = 0 \qquad x - 2 = 0$$

$$x = 0 \qquad\quad x = 4 \qquad\quad x = 2$$

Plot these three points on a number line and determine which intervals result in a true inequality.

$$x = -4 \qquad\qquad\qquad x = 1$$

$$2(-4)^3 - 12(-4)^2 + 16(-4) \overset{?}{<} 0 \qquad 2(1)^3 - 12(1)^2 + 16(1) \overset{?}{<} 0$$

$$-128 - 192 - 64 \overset{?}{<} 0 \qquad\qquad 2 - 12 + 16 \overset{?}{<} 0$$

$$-384 \overset{?}{<} 0 \qquad\qquad\qquad 6 \overset{?}{<} 0$$

True   False

$$x = 3 \qquad\qquad\qquad x = 7$$

$$2(3)^3 - 12(3)^2 + 16(3) \overset{?}{<} 0 \qquad 2(7)^3 - 12(7)^2 + 16(7) \overset{?}{<} 0$$

$$54 - 108 + 48 \overset{?}{<} 0 \qquad\qquad 686 - 588 + 112 \overset{?}{<} 0$$

$$-6 \overset{?}{<} 0 \qquad\qquad\qquad 210 \overset{?}{<} 0$$

True   False

The inequality is true for values less than zero or between 2 and 4.

$$(-\infty, 0) \quad \text{or} \quad (2, 4)$$

$$x < 0 \quad \text{or} \quad 2 < x < 4$$

PRACTICE PROBLEM FOR EXAMPLE 2

Solve the given inequalities. Write the solution set in three ways:

1. Graphed on a number line.

2. Using interval notation.

3. Using inequality notation.

    a. $x^2 + x - 6 > 0$

    b. $x^2 \leq 49$

    c. $2x^3 - 16x^2 + 30x < 0$

Example 3   Making a profit

The profit $P(d)$ in thousands of dollars when d hundred dolls are sold can be estimated with the model $P(d) = -2d^2 + 20d - 32$. Find when the company will break even or make a profit.

Renata Osinska/Shutterstock.com

SOLUTION

Since we want to know when the company will break even or make a profit, we need to know when $P(d)$ will be greater than or equal to zero. Set the model greater than or equal to zero and find the zeros of the quadratic.

$$-2d^2 + 20d - 32 \geq 0$$
$$-2d^2 + 20d - 32 = 0 \qquad \text{Find the zeros of the quadratic.}$$
$$-2(d^2 - 10d + 16) = 0 \qquad \text{Factor.}$$
$$-2(d - 2)(d - 8) = 0$$
$$d - 2 = 0 \qquad d - 8 = 0$$
$$d = 2 \qquad d = 8$$

Graph the zeros on a number line and check which interval(s) make the inequality true. In this case, it would not make sense to have a negative number of dolls, so negative values for d cannot be part of the solution set. Therefore, our number line begins at zero.

$d = 0$	$d = 5$
$-2(0)^2 + 20(0) - 32 \overset{?}{\geq} 0$	$-2(5)^2 + 20(5) - 32 \overset{?}{\geq} 0$
$0 + 0 - 32 \overset{?}{\geq} 0$	$-50 + 100 - 32 \overset{?}{\geq} 0$
$-32 \overset{?}{\geq} 0$	$18 \overset{?}{\geq} 0$
False	True

$$d = 10$$
$$-2(10)^2 + 20(10) + 32 \overset{?}{\geq} 0$$
$$-200 + 200 + 32 \overset{?}{\geq} 0$$
$$32 \overset{?}{\geq} 0$$

False

The company will break even with sales of 200 or 800 dolls. The company will make a profit for sales between 200 and 800 dolls.

PRACTICE PROBLEM FOR EXAMPLE 3

The height of a rock that has been thrown from the roof of a building can be modeled by the function $h(t) = -16t^2 + 16t + 96$, where $h(t)$ is the rock's height off the ground in feet t seconds after being thrown. Find what times the rock is more than 96 feet off the ground.

Example **4**   **Selling candy bars for the school band**

Recall from the start of the section that a school wants to earn at least $5500 profit from a candy sale to support their band. They found a model for profit of

$$P(n) = -500n^2 + 2000n + 4000$$

where $P(n)$ is the profit in dollars from selling candy bars, and n is the number of times the price is raised by $0.50 from the original price of $0.75. Find the price range they should sell the candy bars for in order to make at least $5500 profit.

SOLUTION

We start by writing the profit model as an inequality to show that we want at least $5500 profit.

$$P(n) \geq 5500$$

$$-500n^2 + 2000n + 4000 \geq 5500$$

To solve this inequality, we get the right side equal to zero and then find the zeros of the remaining quadratic.

$$-500n^2 + 2000n + 4000 \geq 5500$$
$$-500n^2 + 2000n - 1500 \geq 0$$

$$-500n^2 + 2000n - 1500 = 0$$
$$-500(n^2 - 4n + 3) = 0$$
$$-500(n - 1)(n - 3) = 0$$
$$n - 1 = 0 \qquad n - 3 = 0$$
$$n = 1 \qquad\quad n = 3$$

Now we check a value in each interval to find which interval makes the inequality true.

$$n = 0 \qquad\qquad\qquad\qquad n = 2$$

$$-500(0)^2 + 2000(0) + 4000 \overset{?}{\geq} 5500 \qquad -500(2)^2 + 2000(2) + 4000 \overset{?}{\geq} 5500$$
$$0 + 0 + 4000 \overset{?}{\geq} 5500 \qquad\qquad -2000 + 4000 + 4000 \overset{?}{\geq} 5500$$
$$4000 \overset{?}{\geq} 5500 \qquad\qquad\qquad\qquad 6000 \overset{?}{\geq} 5500$$

$$\text{False} \qquad\qquad\qquad\qquad\qquad \text{True}$$

$$n = 5$$
$$-500(5)^2 + 2000(5) + 4000 \overset{?}{\geq} 5500$$
$$-125{,}000 + 10{,}000 + 4000 \overset{?}{\geq} 5500$$
$$-111{,}000 \overset{?}{\geq} 5500$$

$$\text{False}$$

The school can increase the price of a candy bar $0.50 between one and three times. Therefore, the price can be between $1.25 and $2.25 each and the band will earn at least $5500.

Solving Rational Inequalities

When a rational expression is part of an inequality, we will solve it in a similar way as nonlinear polynomial inequalities. As with nonlinear polynomials, find the values where the rational expression is equal to zero. Additionally, find any excluded values that make the rational expression undefined. By plotting both the zeros and excluded values on a number line, we can then determine which intervals of the number line result in positive or negative values.

Steps to Solving a Rational Inequality

1. Set the right side of the inequality to 0.
2. Find any zeros of the inequality by setting the numerator equal to zero.
3. Find any excluded values of the inequality by setting the denominator equal to zero.
4. Plot the zeros and excluded values on a number line.
5. Pick a test point from each interval and substitute it into the original inequality. Determine whether the inequality is true or false.
6. The solution set consists of the true regions. Remember that excluded values can never be part of the solution set.

Example 5 Solving rational inequalities

Solve the rational inequality $\dfrac{x + 5}{x - 4} \leq 0$. Write the solution set in three ways:

1. Graphed on a number line.

2. Using interval notation.

3. Using inequality notation.

SOLUTION
The right side of the inequality is zero. First find when the rational expression equals zero by setting the numerator equal to zero and solving.

$$x + 5 = 0$$
$$x = -5$$

The rational expression equals zero when $x = -5$. Next find the excluded value(s) by setting the denominator equal to zero and solving.

$$x - 4 = 0$$
$$x = 4$$

The rational expression has $x = 4$ as an excluded value. Plot the zero and excluded value on a number line. We will use an open circle for the excluded value since it cannot be part of the solution set.

The number line is now separated into three intervals. Check each of these intervals to see which make the inequality true. To check, choose an x-value from each interval and evaluate the rational expression to see where the inequality is true.

$x = -8$	$x = 0$	$x = 7$
$\dfrac{(-8) + 5}{(-8) - 4} \overset{?}{\leq} 0$	$\dfrac{(0) + 5}{(0) - 4} \overset{?}{\leq} 0$	$\dfrac{(7) + 5}{(7) - 4} \overset{?}{\leq} 0$
$\dfrac{-3}{-12} \overset{?}{\leq} 0$	$\dfrac{5}{-4} \overset{?}{\leq} 0$	$\dfrac{12}{3} \overset{?}{\leq} 0$
$\dfrac{1}{4} \overset{?}{\leq} 0$	$-\dfrac{5}{4} \overset{?}{\leq} 0$	$4 \overset{?}{\leq} 0$
False	True	False

The interval in the middle results in a true inequality statement, so it is the solution set to this inequality. Graph the interval on a number line, and write it using interval notation and using inequalities. The inequality includes an "equal to" part, so we attempt to include the endpoints of the interval. However, the right endpoint is an excluded value, so it cannot be part of the solution set. Therefore, be sure not to include the excluded value $x = 4$.

$$[-5, 4)$$

$$-5 \leq x < 4$$

PRACTICE PROBLEM FOR EXAMPLE 5

Solve the rational inequality $\dfrac{x - 8}{x + 2} \leq 0$. Write the solution set in three ways:

1. Graphed on a number line.   **2.** Using interval notation.

3. Using inequality notation.

Example 6   Solving rational inequalities

Solve the given rational inequalities. Write the solution set in three ways:

1. Graphed on a number line.   **2.** Using interval notation.

3. Using inequality notation.

a. $\dfrac{x - 2}{(x + 3)(x - 7)} > 0$ **b.** $\dfrac{x}{x - 3} \leq 2$ **c.** $\dfrac{x^2 - 16}{x^2 - 3x - 10} < 0$

SOLUTION

a. The rational expression $\dfrac{x - 2}{(x + 3)(x - 7)}$ is set greater than zero. Find when the rational expression equals zero by setting the numerator equal to zero and solving.

$$x - 2 = 0$$
$$x = 2$$

The rational expression equals zero when $x = 2$. Next find the excluded values by setting the denominator equal to zero and solving.

$$(x + 3)(x - 7) = 0$$
$$x + 3 = 0 \qquad x - 7 = 0$$
$$x = -3 \qquad x = 7$$

The rational expression has $x = -3$ and $x = 7$ as excluded values. Now plot the zero and excluded values on a number line. Use open circles to show the excluded values.

The number line is now separated into four intervals. Determine which intervals result in a true inequality.

$$x = -6$$

$$\frac{(-6) - 2}{(-6 + 3)(-6 - 7)} \overset{?}{>} 0$$

$$\frac{-8}{(-3)(-13)} \overset{?}{>} 0$$

$$\frac{-8}{39} \overset{?}{>} 0$$

$$-\frac{8}{39} \overset{?}{>} 0$$

False

$$x = 0$$

$$\frac{(0) - 2}{(0 + 3)(0 - 7)} \overset{?}{>} 0$$

$$\frac{-2}{(3)(-7)} \overset{?}{>} 0$$

$$\frac{-2}{-21} \overset{?}{>} 0$$

$$\frac{2}{21} \overset{?}{>} 0$$

True

$$x = 5$$

$$\frac{(5) - 2}{(5 + 3)(5 - 7)} \overset{?}{>} 0$$

$$\frac{3}{(8)(-2)} \overset{?}{>} 0$$

$$\frac{3}{-16} \overset{?}{>} 0$$

$$-\frac{3}{16} \overset{?}{>} 0$$

False

$$x = 9$$

$$\frac{(9) - 2}{(9 + 3)(9 - 7)} \overset{?}{>} 0$$

$$\frac{7}{(12)(2)} \overset{?}{>} 0$$

$$\frac{7}{24} \overset{?}{>} 0$$

True

Two of the intervals result in a true inequality statement, so they are the solution set to this inequality. Next graph these intervals on a number line, and write them using interval notation and using inequalities. This inequality does not include an "equal to" part, so neither of the endpoints will be part of the solution set.

$$(-3, 2) \quad \text{or} \quad (7, \infty)$$

$$-3 < x < 2 \quad \text{or} \quad x > 7$$

b. The right side of the rational inequality $\dfrac{x}{x - 3} \leq 2$ is not zero. Set the right side to zero and simplify the left side into a single rational expression.

$$\frac{x}{x - 3} \leq 2$$

$$\frac{x}{x - 3} - 2 \leq 0 \qquad \textit{Set right side to zero.}$$

$$\frac{x}{x - 3} - 2 \cdot \left(\frac{x - 3}{x - 3}\right) \leq 0 \qquad \textit{Get a common denominator.}$$

$$\frac{x}{x - 3} + \frac{-2x + 6}{x - 3} \leq 0 \qquad \textit{Combine rational expressions.}$$

$$\frac{-x + 6}{x - 3} \leq 0$$

Find when the rational expression equals zero by setting the numerator equal to zero and solving.

$$-x + 6 = 0$$
$$-x = -6$$
$$x = 6$$

The rational expression equals zero when $x = 6$. Next find the excluded values by setting the denominator equal to zero and solving.

$$x - 3 = 0$$
$$x = 3$$

The rational expression has $x = 3$ as an excluded value. Now plot the zero and excluded value on a number line. Use an open circle to show the excluded value. Determine which intervals result in a true inequality.

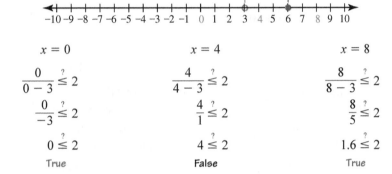

$x = 0$

$$\frac{0}{0-3} \overset{?}{\leq} 2$$
$$\frac{0}{-3} \overset{?}{\leq} 2$$
$$0 \leq 2$$
True

$x = 4$

$$\frac{4}{4-3} \overset{?}{\leq} 2$$
$$\frac{4}{1} \overset{?}{\leq} 2$$
$$4 \overset{?}{\leq} 2$$
False

$x = 8$

$$\frac{8}{8-3} \overset{?}{\leq} 2$$
$$\frac{8}{5} \overset{?}{\leq} 2$$
$$1.6 \overset{?}{\leq} 2$$
True

Two of the intervals result in a true inequality statement, so they are the solution set to this inequality. Now graph these intervals on a number line, and write them using interval notation and using inequalities. This inequality includes an "equal to" part, so the endpoints that are not excluded values will be part of the solution set.

$$(-\infty, 3) \quad \text{or} \quad [6, \infty)$$
$$x < 3 \quad \text{or} \quad x \geq 6$$

c. The right side of the rational inequality $\dfrac{x^2 - 16}{x^2 - 3x - 10} < 0$ is zero. First find when the rational expression equals zero by setting the numerator equal to zero and solving.

$$x^2 - 16 = 0$$
$$(x - 4)(x + 4) = 0 \quad \text{Factor.}$$
$$x - 4 = 0 \qquad x + 4 = 0 \quad \text{Make two equations and solve.}$$
$$x = 4 \qquad\qquad x = -4$$

The rational expression equals zero when $x = 4$ and $x = -4$. Next find the excluded values by setting the denominator equal to zero and solving.

$$x^2 - 3x - 10 = 0$$
$$(x - 5)(x + 2) = 0$$
$$x - 5 = 0 \qquad x + 2 = 0$$
$$x = 5 \qquad\qquad x = -2$$

The rational expression has $x = -2$ and $x = 5$ as excluded values. Now plot the zeros and excluded values on a number line. Use open circles to show the excluded values.

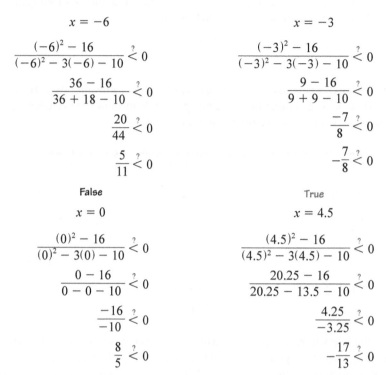

The number line is now separated into five intervals. Determine which intervals result in a true inequality.

$x = -6$

$$\dfrac{(-6)^2 - 16}{(-6)^2 - 3(-6) - 10} \overset{?}{<} 0$$

$$\dfrac{36 - 16}{36 + 18 - 10} \overset{?}{<} 0$$

$$\dfrac{20}{44} \overset{?}{<} 0$$

$$\dfrac{5}{11} \overset{?}{<} 0$$

False

$x = 0$

$$\dfrac{(0)^2 - 16}{(0)^2 - 3(0) - 10} \overset{?}{<} 0$$

$$\dfrac{0 - 16}{0 - 0 - 10} \overset{?}{<} 0$$

$$\dfrac{-16}{-10} \overset{?}{<} 0$$

$$\dfrac{8}{5} \overset{?}{<} 0$$

False

$x = -3$

$$\dfrac{(-3)^2 - 16}{(-3)^2 - 3(-3) - 10} \overset{?}{<} 0$$

$$\dfrac{9 - 16}{9 + 9 - 10} \overset{?}{<} 0$$

$$\dfrac{-7}{8} \overset{?}{<} 0$$

$$-\dfrac{7}{8} \overset{?}{<} 0$$

True

$x = 4.5$

$$\dfrac{(4.5)^2 - 16}{(4.5)^2 - 3(4.5) - 10} \overset{?}{<} 0$$

$$\dfrac{20.25 - 16}{20.25 - 13.5 - 10} \overset{?}{<} 0$$

$$\dfrac{4.25}{-3.25} \overset{?}{<} 0$$

$$-\dfrac{17}{13} \overset{?}{<} 0$$

True

$x = 9$

$$\dfrac{(9)^2 - 16}{(9)^2 - 3(9) - 10} \overset{?}{<} 0$$

$$\dfrac{81 - 16}{81 - 27 - 10} \overset{?}{<} 0$$

$$\dfrac{65}{44} \overset{?}{<} 0$$

False

Two of the intervals result in a true inequality statement, so they are the solution set to this inequality. Graph these intervals on a number line, and write them using interval notation and using inequalities. This inequality does not include an "equal to" part, so none of the endpoints will be part of the solution set.

$$(-4, -2) \quad \text{or} \quad (4, 5)$$
$$-4 < x < -2 \quad \text{or} \quad 4 < x < 5$$

PRACTICE PROBLEM FOR EXAMPLE 6

Solve the given rational inequalities. Write the solution set in three ways:

1. Graphed on a number line. **2.** Using interval notation.

3. Using inequality notation.

a. $\dfrac{x + 4}{(x - 8)(x + 1)} < 0$ **b.** $\dfrac{x}{x + 5} \geq 3$ **c.** $\dfrac{x^2 - 25}{x^2 + 4x - 12} > 0$

9.3 Exercises

For Exercises 1 through 6, write the given interval using inequality notation.

1. $(2, 7)$ **2.** $(4, 9)$

3. $(-\infty, 8)$ **4.** $(-3, \infty)$

5. $(-\infty, 2]$ or $[8, 11]$ **6.** $[-1, 4]$ or $[6, \infty)$

For Exercises 7 through 12, write the given inequality using interval notation.

7. $x > 5$ **8.** $x < 7$

9. $-5 \leq x \leq 8$ **10.** $-3 \leq x \leq 1$

11. $x < 5$ or $x > 9$ **12.** $x < -4$ or $x > -1$

For Exercises 13 through 34, solve the given inequalities. Write the solution set in three ways:
a. Graphed on a number line.
b. Using interval notation.
c. Using inequality notation.

13. $(x + 3)(x - 8) < 0$

14. $(x + 4)(x - 6) < 0$

15. $(x - 5)(x - 9) \geq 0$

16. $(x - 2)(x - 7) \geq 0$

17. $x(x + 5)(x - 6) > 0$

18. $x(x - 3)(x + 1) > 0$

19. $x^2 - 16 \leq 0$

20. $x^2 - 36 \leq 0$

21. $x^2 + 7x + 10 > 0$

22. $x^2 + 12x + 32 > 0$

23. $x^2 - 8x + 20 \geq 5$

24. $x^2 - 7x + 10 \geq 4$

25. $x^2 - 5x - 10 \leq 2x + 8$

26. $x^2 - 3x - 2 \leq 4x + 6$

27. $x^3 + 9x^2 + 18x > 0$

28. $x^3 + 14x^2 + 40x > 0$

29. $2x^3 + 6x^2 - 20x < 0$

30. $3x^3 + 9x^2 - 12x < 0$

31. $2x^2 + 11x + 12 \geq 0$

32. $2x^2 + 15x + 7 \geq 0$

33. $6x^2 + 13x + 5 \leq 0$

34. $4x^2 - 3x - 1 \leq 0$

35. The height of a rock that has been thrown from the roof of a building can be modeled by the function

$$h(t) = -16t^2 + 48t + 64$$

where $h(t)$ is the height off the ground in feet t seconds after being thrown. Find what times the rock is more than 64 feet off the ground.

36. The height of a rock that has been thrown from the roof of a building can be modeled by the function

$$h(t) = -16t^2 + 16t + 96$$

where $h(t)$ is the rock's height off the ground in feet t seconds after being thrown. Find what times the rock is above the ground.

37. A club is raising money for charity. They have found that if they raise the price of each discount card sold, they will make more money per card but will sell fewer in all. The profit $P(n)$ in dollars from selling discount cards, where n is the number of times the price is raised by \$1.5 above the original price of \$8, can be estimated with the model.

$$P(n) = -400n^2 + 3200n + 4800$$

Find the price range the club should sell the discount cards for in order to make at least \$8000 for the charity.

38. A church is raising money for a mission trip. They have found that if they raise the price of each Brazilian burger sold, they will make more money per burger but will sell fewer in all. The profit $P(n)$ in dollars from selling Brazilian burgers, where n is the number of times the price is raised by \$1 above the original price of \$5, can be estimated with the model.

$$P(n) = -300n^2 + 1200n + 2100$$

Find the price range the church should sell the Brazilian burgers for in order to make at least \$3000 for the mission trip.

39. The profit $P(s)$ in hundreds of dollars when s surfboards are sold can be estimated with the model.

$$P(s) = -40s^2 + 880s - 1600$$

Find when the company will break even or make a profit.

40. The profit $P(c)$ in thousands of dollars when c hundred cameras are sold can be estimated with the model.

$$P(c) = -80c^2 + 616c - 120$$

Find when the company will break even or make a profit.

For Exercises 41 through 48, solve the given rational inequalities. Write the solution set in three ways:
a. Graphed on a number line.
b. Using interval notation.
c. Using inequality notation.

41. $\dfrac{x + 5}{x + 2} > 0$

42. $\dfrac{x - 3}{x + 1} > 0$

43. $\dfrac{x - 7}{x - 3} < 0$

44. $\dfrac{x - 2}{x - 8} < 0$

45. $\dfrac{x - 1}{x + 4} \le 0$

46. $\dfrac{x + 8}{x - 3} \le 0$

47. $\dfrac{x - 4}{x - 9} \ge 0$

48. $\dfrac{x - 2}{x - 7} \ge 0$

For Exercises 49 through 52, explain what is wrong with the student's answer. Give the correct answer.

49. $\dfrac{x - 1}{x - 7} \le 0$

> **Henry**
>
> $(-\infty, 1)$ or $(7, \infty)$

50. $\dfrac{x - 4}{x + 6} \ge 0$

> **Danielle**
>
> $(-6, 4]$

51. $\dfrac{x - 5}{x + 3} \le 0$

> **Jennie**
>
> $[-3, 5]$

52. $\dfrac{x + 3}{x + 1} \le 0$

> **Ted**
>
> $[-3, -1]$

For Exercises 53 through 74, solve the given rational inequalities. Write the solution set in three ways:
a. Graphed on a number line.
b. Using interval notation.
c. Using inequality notation.

53. $\dfrac{x - 5}{(x + 3)(x + 7)} > 0$

54. $\dfrac{x - 3}{(x + 2)(x + 6)} > 0$

55. $\dfrac{x + 2}{(x - 4)(x + 5)} < 0$

56. $\dfrac{x + 8}{(x + 3)(x - 2)} < 0$

57. $\dfrac{x - 4}{(x - 2)(x - 8)} \le 0$

58. $\dfrac{x - 1}{(x - 3)(x - 7)} \le 0$

59. $\dfrac{x}{x - 4} \ge 2$

60. $\dfrac{x}{x - 3} \ge 4$

61. $\dfrac{x}{x + 3} < 1$

62. $\dfrac{x}{x + 7} < 1$

63. $\dfrac{x}{x + 3} > 2$

64. $\dfrac{x}{x + 2} > 5$

65. $\dfrac{x + 2}{x^2 + 4x - 45} < 0$

66. $\dfrac{x + 1}{x^2 - 7x + 6} < 0$

67. $\dfrac{x + 5}{x^2 + 12x + 32} > 0$

68. $\dfrac{x - 3}{x^2 + 7x + 10} > 0$

69. $\dfrac{x^2 - 1}{x^2 - 8x + 15} \le 0$

70. $\dfrac{x^2 - 9}{x^2 - 7x - 18} \le 0$

71. $\dfrac{x^2 - 36}{x^2 + 3x + 2} \ge 0$

72. $\dfrac{x^2 - 16}{x^2 - 7x + 10} \ge 0$

73. $\dfrac{x^2 - 49}{x^2 - 14x + 45} < 0$

74. $\dfrac{x^2 - 25}{x^2 - 5x - 24} < 0$

9.4 Solving Systems of Linear Inequalities

LEARNING OBJECTIVES

■ Graph a linear inequality with two variables.

■ Graph a system of linear inequalities.

■ Use a system of linear inequalities to represent an application.

Graphing Linear Inequalities with Two Variables

Many things in life are limited by our circumstances. When we go shopping, we are limited by the amount of money we have as well as by how much of something we need or want. Businesses are often limited by the production in a plant or by the costs associated with production. Dieticians must keep their clients within a certain range of nutrients and, therefore, must balance the types of foods and supplements that they prescribe for a client.

All of these situations can best be looked at as inequalities because a company or person might not need to use the maximum amount of something but may be able to use less. The use of inequalities allows for a set of solutions that will work within the given limitations or constraints. When two or more constraints are considered, a system of inequalities emerges.

Before we consider a system of inequalities, we will investigate an inequality that has two variables and look at its set of solutions. A graph is used to visualize the set of solutions to an inequality with two variables.

CONCEPT INVESTIGATION

What is in the solution set?

Use the inequality and the graph to fill in the table.

$$y \geq 2x - 3$$

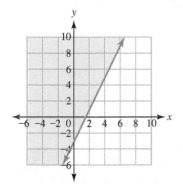

Point	Inequality	Does the point satisfy the inequality?	Is the point in the shaded region?
$(0, 0)$	$0 \overset{?}{\geq} (2(0) - 3)$ $0 \geq -3$	Yes	Yes
$(2, 8)$			
$(-4, -2)$			
$(6, 2)$			
$(0, 6)$			

Do all the points in the shaded region satisfy the inequality?

Which of the points in the table above were in the unshaded region? Did that point satisfy the inequality?

Do you think any of the points in the unshaded region satisfy the inequality?

In your own words, describe the solution set to this inequality.

From this Concept Investigation, we can see that the shaded region represents the solution set to the inequality. The line itself is also a part of this solution set, since the inequality included an "equal to" part. If the inequality does not include an equal to part, the line will only border the solution set but not be part of it. When this occurs, we use a dashed line to indicate that the "equal to" part (line) is not included in the solution set.

> **Graphing a Linear Inequality with Two Variables**
>
> 1. Graph the line as if it were an equation. Use a dashed line if the inequality does not include an "equal to" symbol. Use a solid line if the inequality includes the "equal to" symbol.
> 2. Pick a point on one side of the line and test the inequality.
>   (If not on the line, the point (0, 0) is a very easy point to use as a test point.)
> 3. If the point satisfies the inequality, shade that side of the line.
> 4. If it does not satisfy the inequality, shade the other side of the line.

Example 1   An application of linear inequalities with two variables

A bicycle plant can produce both beach cruisers and mountain bikes. The plant needs 2 hours to build one beach cruiser and 3.5 hours to produce a mountain bike. If the plant operates up to 60 hours per week, what combinations of bikes can they produce in a week?

SOLUTION

First, define the variables.

$$C = \text{number of beach cruisers built in a week}$$

$$M = \text{number of mountain bikes built in a week}$$

Because each cruiser takes 2 hours to build, $2C$ will represent the number of hours it takes the plant to build cruisers that week. It takes 3.5 hours to build a mountain bike, so $3.5M$ represents the number of hours the plant spends building mountain bikes that week. The maximum number of hours the plant operates in a week is 60, so we have the following inequality:

$$2C + 3.5M \le 60$$

This inequality can be graphed. Solve for C to get

$$2C + 3.5M \le 60$$
$$2C \le -3.5M + 60$$
$$C \le -1.75M + 30$$

To graph this inequality, we first graph it as if it were an equation.

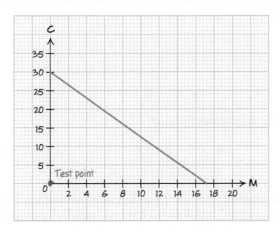

Because this situation requires that the factory work 60 hours or less a week, there will be many possible solutions. To represent all possible solutions, we will shade the side of the line that gives us 60 hours or less each week. To determine which side of the line to shade, test a point on either side of the line to see whether it is a solution to the inequality. If it is a solution, shade the side of the line that the test point is on. If we test the point (0, 0),

$$2(0) + 3.5(0) \overset{?}{\leq} 60$$
$$0 \leq 60$$

it satisfies the inequality, indicating that the lower portion of the graph should be shaded.

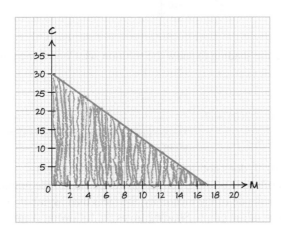

Any point within the shaded region is a solution to this inequality. This means that the plant can build anywhere from no bikes at all to a combination of bikes ranging from no cruisers and 17 mountain bikes to no mountain bikes but 30 cruisers. Any point on the line itself would mean that exactly 60 hours are being used a week. Any point in the shaded region means that fewer than 60 hours are being used. Any point outside the shaded region implies that more than 60 hours would be needed to do the work.

From the example, there is a large set of solutions for this situation. Working with inequalities most often means finding not a single solution, but a set of possible solutions. When graphing an inequality that has two variables, graph the inequality as if it were an equation and then decide which side of the line to shade. Deciding which side of a line to shade can be done by using any point that is not on the line as a test point. If that point is a solution to the inequality, then shade the side that the point is on. If the point is not a solution to the inequality, then test a point on the other side of the line.

In this example, the inequality included things equal to and less than, so the line was drawn as a solid line. If the inequality which is being graphed does not have an "equal to" symbol, then the line is drawn as a dashed line, indicating that it is not a part of the solution set.

> ### Example 2   Graphing linear inequalities with two variables
>
> Graph the following inequalities by hand.
>
> **a.** $y < 2x - 7$ **b.** $y \leq -\dfrac{3}{5}x + 6$ **c.** $-3x - y < -7$

SOLUTION

a. First, graph the inequality $y < 2x - 7$ as if it were an equation. Because the inequality is a "less than" and does not have an "equal to" part, use a dashed line.

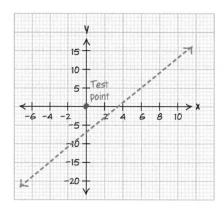

Now, complete the shading to show the solution set. Choose the point $(0, 0)$ as the test point.

$$y < 2x - 7 \qquad \text{Plug in the test point } (0, 0).$$
$$0 \overset{?}{<} 2(0) - 7$$
$$0 \not< -7 \qquad \text{This inequality is not true, so the test point is not a solution.}$$

The test point $(0, 0)$ does not satisfy the inequality because $0 < -7$ is not true. Shade the opposite side of the graph, the lower portion of the graph. When y is isolated on the left side of the inequality, the "less than" symbol implies shading the lower portion of the graph. Shading gives the following graph.

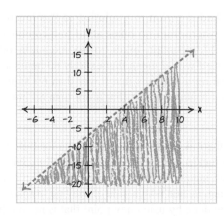

b. Graph the inequality $y \le -\dfrac{3}{5}x + 6$ as if it were an equation. This time, the line will be solid, since the symbol does include an "equal to" part.

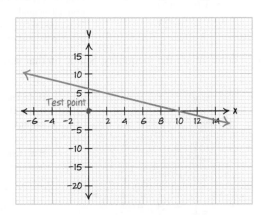

Test the point $(0, 0)$. It satisfies the inequality, so shade the lower portion of the graph.

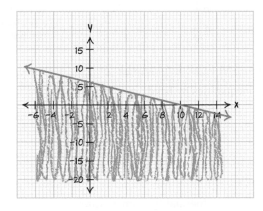

c. Start by putting the inequality $-3x - y < -7$ into slope-intercept form.

$$-3x - y < -7$$
$$-y < 3x - 7$$
$$\frac{-y}{-1} > \frac{3x - 7}{-1}$$
$$y > -3x + 7$$

Remember to reverse the inequality symbol when dividing by a negative number.

This inequality does not have an "equal to" part, so graph the line using dashes to indicate that it is not part of the solution set but only a boundary for it.

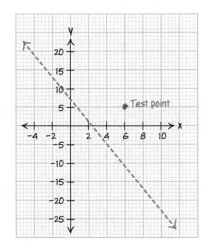

$$y > -3x + 7$$

Test the point (6, 5), which is clearly above the line.

$$-3x - y < -7$$
$$-3(6) - (5) \overset{?}{<} -7$$
$$-23 < -7$$

Plug the test point (6, 5) into the original inequality. This inequality is true, so the test point is a solution.

The test point (6, 5) does satisfy the inequality. Shade on that side of the line.

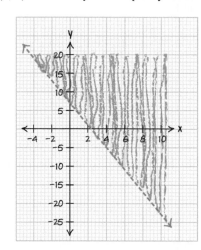

Note that if we pick a point not in the solution set, it will not satisfy the inequality.

If we test the point (0, 0) that is clearly below the line, we get

$$-3x - y < -7$$
$$-3(0) - (0) \overset{?}{<} -7$$
$$0 \overset{<}{\not{}} -7$$

This inequality is not true, so the point (0, 0) is not a solution and therefore is not in the shaded region.

PRACTICE PROBLEM FOR EXAMPLE 2

Graph the following inequalities by hand.

a. $y > 2x - 8$

b. $y \leq -\dfrac{3}{4}x + 5$

Example 3 Finding an inequality from a graph

Find the inequality for the given graph.

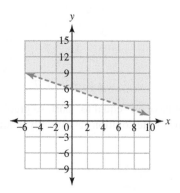

SOLUTION

First, find the equation of the line. From the graph we can see the two points (0, 6) and (6, 3). Using these two points, we can find the slope of the line.

$$m = \frac{3 - 6}{6 - 0} = \frac{-3}{6} = -\frac{1}{2}$$

The point (0, 6) is the y-intercept, so $b = 6$. Therefore, the equation of the line is

$$y = -\frac{1}{2}x + 6$$

Since the line is dashed, the inequality will not have an "equal to" part. The graph is shaded above the line, so we will use the "greater than" symbol.

$$y > -\frac{1}{2}x + 6$$

Check the inequality symbol by checking a point in the shaded region. We will use the point (4, 9).

$$9 \overset{?}{>} -\frac{1}{2}(4) + 6$$

$$9 \overset{?}{>} -2 + 6$$

$$9 > 4$$

The point from the shaded region checks, so the inequality symbol is facing the correct direction.

PRACTICE PROBLEM FOR EXAMPLE 3

Find the inequality for the following graph.

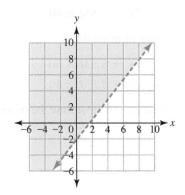

Solving Systems of Linear Inequalities

Now that we can graph an inequality with two variables, we can consider a system of inequalities. Most situations have more than one constraint. The bicycle plant from Example 1 might also have a constraint that they must keep the plant in production at least 40 hours per week. With more than one constraint, the situation calls for a system of inequalities, not just one inequality. When solving a system of inequalities, we will graph each inequality, shading according to the inequality symbol of each line. The area where all the shaded regions overlap will be the solution set to the system of inequalities. If the shaded regions do not overlap, there is no solution to the system.

> **Graphing a System of Linear Inequalities**
>
> 1. Graph both inequalities on the same set of axes, shading according to the inequality symbol of each line.
> 2. The solution set is the *intersection* of the shaded regions of all the inequalities in the system.
> 3. If the shaded regions do not intersect, there is no solution.

Example 4   An application of systems of linear inequalities

Example 1 on page 750 discussed a bicycle plant that had the time constraint that they could not exceed 60 hours of production per week. The same plant must stay in production at least 40 hours per week.

a. Create a system of inequalities to model this situation.

b. Graph the solution set for this system.

c. Can the plant produce ten mountain bikes and five cruisers in a week? Explain.

d. Can the plant produce five mountain bikes and eight cruisers a week? Explain.

SOLUTION

a. First, define the variables as in Example 1.

$$C = \text{number of cruisers built in a week}$$
$$M = \text{number of mountain bikes built in a week}$$

The constraint of not exceeding 60 hours per week results in the inequality from Example 1.

$$2C + 3.5M \leq 60$$

The new constraint of not working less than 40 hours a week results in the inequality

$$2C + 3.5M \geq 40$$

This gives the following system of inequalities:

$$2C + 3.5M \leq 60$$
$$2C + 3.5M \geq 40$$

b. Graph both of these inequalities at the same time, being careful to shade the correct sides of each line.

The *red* area shows the solution set for the first equation.

The *blue* area shows the solution set for the second equation.

The overlapping area is the solution set for the system as a whole.

c. Ten mountain bikes and five cruisers would be the point (10, 5) on the graph. This point is inside the area of the graph where the solution sets of the two inequalities overlap. Therefore, this combination would be a reasonable amount of each type of bike to produce a week.

d. Five mountain bikes and eight cruisers would be the point (5, 8) and would lie outside the overlapping section of this system. Therefore, producing this combination of bikes per week would not meet the constraints.

PRACTICE PROBLEM FOR EXAMPLE 4

A small appliance manufacturer has a plant that produces toaster ovens and electric griddles. The plant must keep its weekly costs below $40,000 and cannot be in operation more than 80 hours a week. It takes 1.25 hours and costs the plant $850 to produce 100 toaster ovens. It takes 2 hours and costs the plant $920 to produce 100 electric griddles.

a. Create a system of inequalities to model this situation. (*Hint:* Define the variable in hundreds.)

b. Graph the solution set for this system.

c. Can the plant produce 1600 toaster ovens and 2000 electric griddles a week? Explain.

d. Can the plant produce 2000 toaster ovens and 3000 electric griddles a week? Explain.

In Example 4, we needed to graph only the area covered by non-negative numbers of bikes being produced. Using only positive values is typical of many real-life situations and actually adds two additional inequalities to the system: $M \geq 0$ and $C \geq 0$. We did not write these inequalities this time, but we could have. Common sense told us that a negative number of bikes could not be produced.

Another type of application that we can consider as a system of inequalities is investment questions like those we did in Section 4.3.

Example 5   **An investment problem using inequalities**

Mary is retiring and has \$500,000 to invest in two accounts. One account pays 5% simple interest, and the other pays 3.5% simple interest. How much should she invest in each account to earn at least \$21,000 in interest each year?

SOLUTION

Define variables as follows:

A = the amount in dollars invested in the account paying 5% annual interest

B = the amount in dollars invested in the account paying 3.5% annual interest

Because Mary can invest up to \$500,000 and must earn at least \$21,000 per year in interest, write the following system of inequalities:

$$A + B \leq 500{,}000$$
$$0.05A + 0.035B \geq 21{,}000$$

If we graph this system, we can find the possible solutions to this situation.

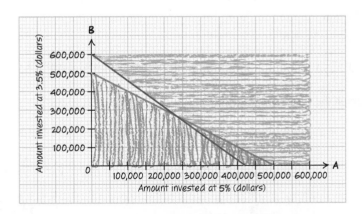

From this graph, we can see that Mary can have many different investment amounts that would earn her the minimum amount of interest she needs and still not use all of her \$500,000. Any combination of investments from the overlapping section of the graph can be used to meet Mary's investment goal. One of the many choices Mary has is:

An investment of $450,000 in the account paying 5% and $50,000 in the account paying 3.5% will satisfy the needs Mary has.

In many systems of equations or inequalities, the points of intersection for the lines of the system are critical values of interest. In the case of Mary's investments, that point of intersection is the investment that meets her needs and invests the total $500,000. This is also the investment with the least amount invested in the more risky account paying 5% and the most money she can invest in the safer account paying 3.5% and still meet her minimum interest needs.

PRACTICE PROBLEM FOR EXAMPLE 5

Don is retiring and has $800,000 to invest in two accounts. One account pays 6.5% annual interest, and the other pays 4.5% annual interest. How much should he invest in each account to earn at least $40,500 in interest each year?

Example 6 Graphing systems of equations

Graph each system of inequalities by hand.

a. $2x + 5y < 15$
$\quad 3x - 2y > 6$

b. $y \geq -1.5x + 5$
$\quad y \leq -1.5x + 2$

SOLUTION

a. Solve these inequalities for y, and then graph them.
Solve the first inequality for y.

$$2x + 5y < 15$$
$$5y < -2x + 15$$
$$y < -\frac{2}{5}x + 3$$

Solve the second inequality for y.

$$3x - 2y > 6$$
$$-2y > -3x + 6$$
$$y < \frac{3}{2}x - 3 \qquad \text{Remember to reverse the inequality symbol when dividing by a negative number.}$$

Now graph the system of inequalities.

$$y < -\frac{2}{5}x + 3$$

$$y < \frac{3}{2}x - 3$$

The section of the graph where the two shadings overlap is the solution set for this system of inequalities.

b. Start by graphing the two inequalities.

$$y \geq -1.5x + 5$$
$$y \leq -1.5x + 2$$

We can see from the graph that the solution sets for these two inequalities give us no intersection, and therefore, there is no solution to the system.

PRACTICE PROBLEM FOR EXAMPLE 6

Graph the following system of inequalities by hand.

$$y \geq x + 2$$
$$y \leq 2x - 3$$

Graphing these systems can also be done using the graphing calculator. See the instructions in the Calculator Details box on this page or in Appendix B.

Example 7   Graphing systems of inequalities on a graphing calculator

Graph the following system of inequalities using a graphing calculator.

$$y < -2x + 5$$
$$y > 3x - 5$$

SOLUTION

Both inequalities have y isolated on the left side. The first inequality has a "less than" symbol, so shade below the line. For the second inequality, shade above the line because it has a "greater than" symbol. Both lines should be dashed because these inequalities do not include any "equal to" parts. The calculator does not show dashed lines when shading. This is something to remember when considering possible solutions.

The two shaded regions intersect on the left side, giving the solution set.

PRACTICE PROBLEM FOR EXAMPLE 7

Graph the following system of inequalities using a graphing calculator.

$$2x - 5y > 12$$
$$4y > 7x - 5$$

Calculator Details

To graph inequalities on your calculator, you can have the calculator shade above or below the line. Use the cursor buttons to go to the left of the Y1 and press Enter until you get the shade above or below symbol you are looking for.

Note that the calculator cannot use shading with dashed lines, so any inequalities without "equal to" in the inequality symbol will graph with a solid line but should be interpreted as a dashed line. Any points on that line should not be considered part of the solution set.

9.4 Exercises

For Exercises 1 through 8, use the following information and graph to answer the questions.

According to the National Institutes of Health, adults are considered underweight or overweight on the basis of a combination of their height and weight. The graph below shows this relationship as a system of inequalities.

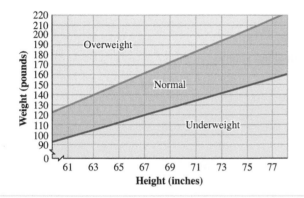

1. What category does a 61″ person weighing 105 pounds fall into?

2. What category does a 75″ person weighing 210 pounds fall into?

3. Above what weight is a 5′9″ person considered overweight?

4. Under what weight is a 6′ person considered underweight?

5. If a 150-pound person is to be considered in the normal weight range, how tall must the person be?

6. If a 130-pound person is to be considered in the normal weight range, how tall must the person be?

7. If a person is 67″ tall, what is the person's normal weight range?

8. If a person is 73″ tall, what is the person's normal weight range?

For Exercises 9 through 12, use the following information and graph to answer the questions.

Bicycles Galore can manufacture up to 500 bikes a month in its Pittsburgh plant. Cruisers cost $75 to manufacture, and mountain bikes cost $135 to manufacture. Bicycles Galore must keep its total monthly costs below $50,000.

9. What is the greatest number of mountain bikes the company can build per month?

10. What is the maximum number of cruisers the company can build per month?

11. Can Bicycles Galore build 400 cruisers and 100 mountain bikes per month? Explain.

12. Can the company build 150 cruisers and 350 mountain bikes per month? Explain.

13. Bicycles Galore can produce up to 500 bikes per month in their Pittsburgh plant. They can make a profit of $65 per cruiser they build and $120 per mountain bike they build. The company's board of directors wants to make a profit of at least $40,000 per month.
    a. Write a system of inequalities to model this problem and graph it by hand.
    b. Can Bicycles Galore meet a demand by the board of directors for $40,000 in profit per month? Explain.
    c. If the company wants to maximize production at 500 bikes, how many of each bike should the plant produce to make the $40,000 profit? Explain.

14. Theresa has started a small business creating jewelry to sell at boutiques. She can make a necklace in about 45 minutes and a bracelet in about 30 minutes. Theresa can work only up to 25 hours a month making the jewelry. She can make $20 profit from a necklace and $18 profit from bracelets. Theresa wants to earn at least $800 profit.
    a. Write a system of inequalities to model this problem and graph it by hand.
    b. Should Theresa make more necklaces or bracelets? Explain.

For Exercises 15 through 26, graph the inequalities by hand.

15. $y > 3x + 2$

16. $y < -4x + 7$

17. $y > \dfrac{5}{4}x - 2$

18. $y < \dfrac{3}{7}x + 1$

19. $y \geq \dfrac{2}{3}x + 6$

20. $y \geq \dfrac{4}{5}x - 5$

21. $y \leq -2x + 6$

22. $y \leq x + 5$

23. $2x + 5y > 10$

24. $3x + 4y < 8$

25. $12x - 4y > 8$

26. $10x - 5y < 20$

For Exercises 27 through 34, write the inequality for the given graph.

27.

28.

29.

30.

31.

32.

33.

34.

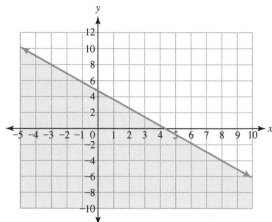

35. Juanita is retiring and has $750,000 to invest in two accounts. One account pays 4.5% simple interest, and the other pays 3.75% simple interest. Juanita wants to know how much she should invest in each account to earn at least $30,000 in interest each year. Write a system of inequalities and graph it by hand to show the possibilities.

36. Casey is retiring and has $2.5 million to invest in stocks and bonds. Casey estimates that the stocks will have an average return of 9.5% and the bonds will pay 7% simple interest. Casey wants $210,000 per year to cover his living and travel expenses each year. Write a system of inequalities and graph it by hand to show the possible amounts he could invest in each account.

37. In preparing meals to eat during an all-day bike race, the team dietician determines that each athlete must consume at least 2000 calories and at least 350 grams of carbohydrates to sustain the energy needed to compete at peak performance. The dietician is providing each athlete with a combination of power bars and sports drinks for the race. Each power bar has 240 calories and 30 grams of carbs. The sports drinks contain 300 calories and 70 grams of carbs.

a. Write a system of inequalities for these dietary needs and graph it by hand.

b. If racers can carry only four drinks, what is the minimum number of power bars they should eat? Explain.

38. The same dietician from Exercise 37 had found that he should increase the calories and carbohydrates for the team to improve their performance. The dietician decides that each athlete must consume at least 2500 calories and at least 420 grams of carbohydrates to sustain the energy needed to compete at peak performance. The dietician is providing each athlete with a combination of power bars and sports drinks for the race. Each power bar has 240 calories and 30 grams of carbs. The sports drinks contain 300 calories and 70 grams of carbs.

a. Write a system of inequalities for these dietary needs and graph it by hand.

b. If racers can carry only four drinks, what is the minimum number of power bars they should eat? Explain.

For Exercises 39 through 50, graph the systems of inequalities by hand or on the calculator.

39. $y > 2x + 4$
$y < -3x + 7$

40. $y < 4x + 5$
$y > -x + 1$

41. $y < \dfrac{2}{5}x - 3$

$y < -\dfrac{3}{4}x + 6$

42. $y \geq \dfrac{1}{3}x + 2$

$y \leq -\dfrac{2}{3}x + 7$

43. $y \leq 2x + 5$
$y \geq 2x + 8$

44. $y < -4x + 10$
$y > -4x + 2$

45. $2x + 4y \leq 5$
$2x - 4y \leq 5$

46. $-4x - 3y \geq 11$
$4x + 3y \geq 5$

47. $5x + 3y > 7$
$4x + 2y < 10$

48. $4x + 5y < 10$
$8x + 10y > 10$

49. $y > \dfrac{2}{3}x - 12$

$6x - 4y > 12$

50. $1.5x + 4.6y \leq 1.8$

$y \geq \dfrac{2}{17}x + 1.2$

Chapter Summary

Section 9.1 Absolute Value Equations

- **Absolute Value:** The absolute value of a real number n, $|n|$, is the distance from zero to n on a real number line.
- **Absolute Value Equation:** If n is a positive real number and u is any algebraic expression,

$$|u| = n$$
$$u = n \quad \text{or} \quad u = -n$$

- If n is negative, then the equation $|u| = n$ has no solution.
- **Solving absolute value equations:**
  1. Isolate the expression containing the absolute value.
  2. Rewrite the equation into two equations.

$$|u| = n$$
$$u = n \quad \text{or} \quad u = -n$$

  3. Solve each equation.
  4. Check the solutions in the original absolute value equation.

Example 1 Solve the equation $|x + 5| = 11$.

SOLUTION
$$|x + 5| = 11$$
$$x + 5 = -11 \quad \text{or} \quad x + 5 = 11$$
$$x = -16 \quad \text{or} \quad x = 6$$

Check these solutions in the original equation.

$$
\begin{array}{cc}
x = -16 & x = 6 \\
|-16 + 5| = 11 & |6 + 5| = 11 \\
11 = 11 & 11 = 11
\end{array}
$$

Section 9.2 Absolute Value Inequalities

- **Solving absolute value inequalities involving "less than" or "less than or equal to":**
  1. Isolate the expression containing the absolute value to the left side of the inequality.
  2. Rewrite the absolute value inequality into a compound inequality.

$$
\begin{array}{cc}
|u| < n & |u| \le n \\
-n < u < n & -n \le u \le n
\end{array}
$$

  3. Solve the compound inequality.
  4. Check the solution set in the original absolute value inequality.

- **Solving absolute value inequalities involving "greater than" or "greater than or equal to":**

  1. Isolate the expression containing the absolute value to the left side of the inequality.

  2. Rewrite the absolute value inequality into two inequalities, one "less than" and one "greater than."

$$|u| > n \qquad\qquad |u| \geq n$$
$$u < -n \quad \text{or} \quad u > n \qquad u \leq -n \quad \text{or} \quad u \geq n$$

  3. Solve the two inequalities.

  4. Check the solution set in the original absolute value inequality.

Example 2

Solve the given inequality. Give the solution as an inequality. Graph the solution set on a number line.

$$|x + 3| \leq 4$$

SOLUTION

$$|x + 3| \leq 4$$
$$-4 \leq x + 3 \leq 4$$
$$-7 \leq x \leq 1$$

Check this solution using a graph.

We can see that the absolute value graph is less than 4 when x is between −7 and 1.

Example 3

Solve the given inequality. Give the solution as an inequality. Graph the solution set on a number line.

$$|x - 2| - 1 > 4$$

SOLUTION

$$|x - 2| - 1 > 4$$
$$|x - 2| > 5$$
$$x - 2 < -5 \quad \text{or} \quad x - 2 > 5$$
$$x < -3 \quad \text{or} \quad x > 7$$

Check this solution using a graph.

We can see that the absolute value graph is greater than 4 when x is less than −3 or greater than 7.

Section **9.3**   Nonlinear Inequalities in One Variable

- **Solving a polynomial inequality:**
  1. Set the right side of the inequality to 0.
  2. Factor the left side to find the zeros of the inequality.
  3. Plot the zeros on a number line.
  4. Pick a test point from each interval and substitute it into the *original* inequality. Determine whether the inequality is true or false.
  5. The solution set is formed by the true regions found in step 4.

- **Solving a rational inequality:**
  1. Set the right side of the inequality to 0.
  2. Find any zeros of the inequality by setting the numerator equal to zero.
  3. Find any excluded values of the inequality by setting the denominator equal to zero.
  4. Plot the zeros and excluded values on a number line.
  5. Pick a test point from each interval and substitute it into the original inequality. Determine whether the inequality is true or false.
  6. The solution set consists of the true regions. Remember that excluded values can never be part of the solution set.

Example 4

Solve $x^2 + 8x - 9 > 0$. Write the solution set in three ways:

1. Graphed on a number line.
2. Using interval notation.
3. Using inequality notation.

SOLUTION The polynomial inequality $x^2 + 8x - 9 > 0$ is greater than zero, so set the polynomial equal to zero and solve.

$$x^2 + 8x - 9 = 0$$

$$(x + 9)(x - 1) = 0 \qquad \text{Factor.}$$

$$x + 9 = 0 \qquad x - 1 = 0$$

$$x = -9 \qquad x = 1$$

Plot these two points on a number line and determine which intervals result in a true inequality.

$x = -10$	$x = -4$
$(-10)^2 + 8(-10) - 9 \overset{?}{>} 0$	$(-4)^2 + 8(-4) - 9 \overset{?}{>} 0$
$100 - 80 - 9 \overset{?}{>} 0$	$16 - 32 - 9 \overset{?}{>} 0$
$11 \overset{?}{>} 0$	$-25 \overset{?}{>} 0$
True	False

$$x = 5$$

$$(5)^2 + 8(5) - 9 \overset{?}{>} 0$$

$$25 + 40 - 9 \overset{?}{>} 0$$

$$56 \overset{?}{>} 0$$

True

The inequality is true for values less than -9 or greater than 1.

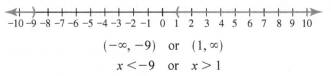

$$(-\infty, -9) \quad \text{or} \quad (1, \infty)$$

$$x < -9 \quad \text{or} \quad x > 1$$

Example 5

Solve the rational inequality $\dfrac{x-5}{x+6} \le 0$. Write the solution set in three ways:

1. Graphed on a number line.
2. Using interval notation.
3. Using inequality notation.

SOLUTION

The right side of the inequality is zero. First find when the rational expression equals zero by setting the numerator equal to zero and solving.

$$x - 5 = 0$$
$$x = 5$$

Next find the excluded value(s) by setting the denominator equal to zero and solving.

$$x + 6 = 0$$
$$x = -6$$

The rational expression has $x = -6$ as an excluded value. Plot the zero and excluded value on a number line. We will use an open circle for the excluded value since it cannot be part of the solution set. Then check each interval to see which make the inequality true.

$x = -8$	$x = 0$	$x = 7$
$\dfrac{(-8)-5}{(-8)+6} \overset{?}{\le} 0$	$\dfrac{(0)-5}{(0)+6} \overset{?}{\le} 0$	$\dfrac{(7)-5}{(7)+6} \overset{?}{\le} 0$
$\dfrac{-13}{-2} \overset{?}{\le} 0$	$\dfrac{-5}{6} \overset{?}{\le} 0$	$\dfrac{2}{13} \overset{?}{\le} 0$
$\dfrac{13}{2} \overset{?}{\le} 0$	$-\dfrac{5}{6} \overset{?}{\le} 0$	
False	**True**	**False**

The inequality includes an "equal to" part, so we attempt to include the endpoints of the interval. However, the left endpoint is an excluded value so it cannot be part of the solution set. Therefore, be sure not to include the excluded value $x = -6$.

$$(-6, 5]$$

$$-6 < x \le 5$$

Section 9.4 Solving Systems of Linear Inequalities

- To **graph a linear inequality with two variables,** graph the line as if it were an equation and shade the side of the line that makes the inequality true. Use a dashed line if the inequality does not include the symbol for "equal to." Use a solid line if the inequality includes the symbol for "equal to."

- To **solve a system of inequalities,** graph all the inequalities on the same set of axes. The region where all the shaded areas overlap is the solution set of the system.

Example **6**   Graph the inequality $y < 3x - 12$.

SOLUTION

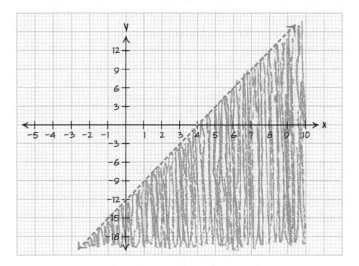

Example **7**   Graph the following system of inequalities by hand.

$$y \geq 2x - 6$$
$$y \leq -3x + 7$$

SOLUTION

Chapter Review Exercises

9

At the end of each exercise, the section number [in brackets] indicates the section where the material is covered.

For Exercises 1 through 16, solve the equations.

1. $|x| = 5$ [9.1]

2. $|y| = 61$ [9.1]

3. $|a + 6| = 7$ [9.1]

4. $|x + 19| = 30$ [9.1]

5. $|x - 7| = 20$ [9.1]

6. $|m - 7.1| = 3.4$ [9.1]

7. $|y - 8| = -16$ [9.1]

8. $|x - 4| = -12$ [9.1]

9. $|2x - 3| = 10$ [9.1]

10. $|5x + 1| = 7$ [9.1]

11. $|2x + 3| - 10 = 40$ [9.1]

12. $|3y - 4| - 8 = 20$ [9.1]

13. $5|x - 7| + 10 = 95$ [9.1]

14. $2|4t - 3| - 7 = 15$ [9.1]

15. Patsy is driving from Des Moines, Iowa, to Milwaukee, Wisconsin. She will pass through Davenport, Iowa, on the way. Patsy's distance from Davenport can be modeled by the function

$$D(t) = |374 - 65t|$$

where $D(t)$ is Patsy's distance from Davenport after driving t hours. Find the time when Patsy will be 60 miles from Davenport. Round to two decimal digits, if necessary. [9.1]

16. Tracy is driving from San Diego, CA, to St. Louis, Missouri. She will pass through Albuquerque, New Mexico, on the way. Tracy's distance from Albuquerque can be modeled by the function

$$D(t) = |1853 - 65t|$$

where $D(t)$ is Tracy's distance from Albuquerque after driving t hours. Find the time when Tracy will be 100 miles from Albuquerque. Round to two decimal digits, if necessary. [9.1]

For Exercises 17 through 20, write the interval shown on the number line using a compound inequality.

17. [9.2]

18. [9.2]

19. [9.2]

20. [9.2]

For Exercises 21 through 32, solve the inequality. Give the solution as an inequality. Graph the solution set on a number line.

21. $|x| < 8.5$ [9.2]

22. $|w| \le 3$ [9.2]

23. $|x| > 6.5$ [9.2]

24. $|y| \ge \dfrac{2}{3}$ [9.2]

25. $|x + 3| \ge 12$ [9.2]

26. $|x - 5| \ge 17$ [9.2]

27. $|x - 7| \le 3$ [9.2]

28. $|w - 5| < 4.9$ [9.2]

29. $2|x + 5| - 4 > 16$ [9.2]

30. $7|t - 2| - 1 \ge 13$ [9.2]

31. $-3|x + 5| + 7 \le 4$ [9.2]

32. $5|a - 3| + 13 \le 8$ [9.2]

For Exercises 33 and 34, write the solution set using inequality notation for the given graph and inequality.

33. [9.2]

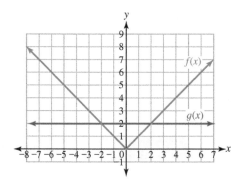

   a. $f(x) < g(x)$

   b. $f(x) > g(x)$

34. [9.2]

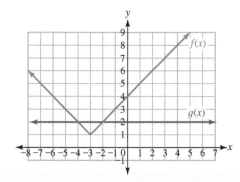

   a. $f(x) < g(x)$

   b. $f(x) > g(x)$

35. Men's heights have a mean of 70 inches. A height h that satisfies $\left|\dfrac{h - 70}{3}\right| > 2$ is considered unusual. Find the range of men's heights that are considered unusual. [9.2]

36. The gestational period (length of pregnancy) for women has a mean of 272 days. A gestational period g that satisfies $\left|\dfrac{g - 272}{9}\right| > 2$ is considered unusual. Find the range of gestational periods that are considered unusual. [9.2]

For Exercises 37 through 39, solve the inequality and write the solution set using inequality notation.

37. $(x + 2)(x + 7) > 0$ [9.3]

38. $x^2 \leq 100$ [9.3]

39. $x^2 + 12x + 32 < 0$ [9.3]

For Exercises 40 through 42, solve the inequality and write the solution set using interval notation.

40. $x^2 + 14x + 48 \geq 0$ [9.3]

41. $-4x^3 + 12x^2 + 40x < 0$ [9.3]

42. $6x^2 + 7x \leq 5$ [9.3]

For Exercises 43 and 44, solve the inequality and graph the solution set on a number line.

43. $x^2 + 13x + 40 < 0$

44. $x^3 + 2x^2 - 24x < 0$

For Exercises 45 through 47, solve the rational inequality and write the solution set using inequality notation.

45. $\dfrac{x + 3}{x - 6} > 0$ [9.3]

46. $\dfrac{x - 7}{x + 2} \leq 0$ [9.3]

47. $\dfrac{x + 5}{x^2 + 4x - 12} \leq 0$ [9.3]

For Exercises 48 and 49, solve the rational inequality and write the solution set using interval notation.

48. $\dfrac{x - 4}{x + 8} \geq 0$ [9.3]

49. $\dfrac{x - 6}{2x^2 + 9x + 4} < 0$ [9.3]

For Exercises 50 and 51, solve the rational inequality and graph the solution set on a number line.

50. $\dfrac{x - 9}{x + 1} < 0$

51. $\dfrac{x + 4}{x^2 - 7x + 6} < 0$

For Exercises 52 through 55, graph the inequality by hand.

52. $y \leq 4x - 10$ [9.4]

53. $y \geq 1.5x - 5$ [9.4]

54. $2x + 5y > 15$ [9.4]

55. $-3x - 4y > 12$ [9.4]

For Exercises 56 through 59, graph the system of inequalities.

56. $y > 2x + 5$
$y < -x + 7$ [9.4]

57. $y > 1.5x + 2$
$4.5x - 3y > 6$ [9.4]

58. $4x + 5y \leq 12$
$2x + 8y \geq 5$ [9.4]

59. $y > \dfrac{2}{3}x - 7$

$y < \dfrac{2}{3}x + 5$ [9.4]

60. A college is selling tickets to a championship basketball game and has up to 12,000 tickets to sell. They can sell both regular admission tickets and student discount tickets. Student tickets cost $9, and regular admission tickets cost $15. The school wants to make at least $140,000 from selling tickets. Write a system of inequalities to determine the combinations of tickets they can sell to make the money they want. [9.4]

Michelle Donahue Hillison / Shutterstock.com

61. Find the inequality for the graph. [9.4]

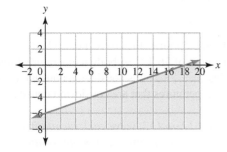

62. Find the inequality for the graph. [9.4]

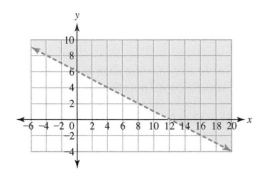

Chapter Test

For Exercises 1 through 5, solve the equation. Check the solution.

1. $|w| = 5$

2. $|x + 7| = 16$

3. $-2|y - 4| = 8$

4. $|x + 5| + 3 = 17$

5. $-3|2x - 1| + 19 = 10$

For Exercise 6, write the interval shown on the number line using a compound inequality.

6.

For Exercises 7 through 10, solve each inequality algebraically. Write the solution set as an inequality. Graph the solution set on a number line.

7. $|t - 8| \geq 7$

8. $|3n + 4| < 12$

9. $2|3n - 7| - 12 > 4$

10. $|x - 4| - 8 < 5.$

11. Black-tailed prairie dogs have a mean body temperature of 36.4°C. A body temperature T that satisfies $\left|\frac{T - 36.4}{0.114}\right| > 2$ is considered unusual. Find the body temperatures that are considered unusual.

For Exercises 12 and 13, solve each inequality. Write the solution set as an inequality. Graph the solution set on a number line.

12. $x^2 + 3x - 10 > 0$

13. $x^2 - 3x - 28 < 0$

For Exercises 14 and 15, solve each inequality. Write the solution set using interval notation.

14. $2x^2 - 5x - 12 \geq 0$

15. $\frac{x + 4}{x - 3} \leq 0$

For Exercises 16 and 17, solve each inequality. Write the solution set using interval notation. Graph the solution set on a number line.

16. $\frac{x - 1}{x^2 - x - 20} \leq 0$

17. $-2x^3 + 6x^2 + 36x > 0$

For Exercise 18, write the inequality for the given graph.

18.

For Exercises 19 through 21, graph the system of inequalities.

19. $x \geq 2$

   $y < -\frac{3}{2}x + 7$

20. $y \geq 2x - 5$

   $y \leq \frac{1}{3}x + 4$

21. $4x - 3y < 6$

   $3x + y > 12$

22. Georgia has up to 20 hours a week to study for her math and history classes. She needs to study at least 12 hours a week to pass her math class. Write a system of inequalities to describe the possible amounts of time she can study for each subject. Graph the system by hand.

Chapter 9 Projects

What Is Your Target Heart Rate?

Written Project

One or more people

When you are exercising, it is recommended that you exercise within your target heart rate zone. Let x = your age, and let y = target heart rate. Doctors use the following formulas to compute the target heart rate zone for adults (age 20 and above).

1. To compute the lower bound, the target heart rate is equal to 50% of 220 minus the age. Write this equation using x and y. Simplify the equation as $y = mx + b$.

2. To compute the upper bound, the target heart rate is equal to 85% of 220 minus the age. Write this equation using x and y. Simplify the equation as $y = mx + b$.

3. Doctors recommend that people exercise with their target heart rate zone found as follows:

   a. The target heart rate should be greater than or equal to 50% of 220 minus the age. Use the equation from step 1 to write this inequality.

   b. The target heart rate should be less than or equal to 85% of 220 minus the age. Use the equation from step 2 to write this inequality.

4. Graph the two inequalities you found in step 3 on the same axes. Put a break in the x-axis to start the ages at 20.

5. Shade in the solution set.

6. What is the target heart rate zone for your age?

Review Presentation

Research Project

One or more people

What you will need

- This presentation may be done in class or as a video.

- If it is done as a video, you might want to post the video on YouTube or another site.

- You might want to use problems from the homework set or review material in this book.

- Be creative, and make the presentation fun for students to watch and learn from.

Create a five-minute presentation or video that reviews a section of Chapter 9. The presentation should include the following.

- Examples of the important skills presented in the section
- Explanation of any important terminology and formulas
- Common mistakes made and how to recognize them

1. Write in exponential form.
$(-3a) \cdot (-3a) \cdot (-3a) \cdot (-3a)$

2. Find the value without a calculator. $\left(-\dfrac{2}{3}\right)^4$

3. Simplify. $-6 \cdot 4 \div 12 + (-4)^2 - (-2 - 5)$

4. Solve for y. $-7x + 3y = 6$

5. Solve. $\dfrac{7n}{2} - \dfrac{7}{4} = n + 2$

For Exercises 6 and 7, solve the given equation for the indicated variable.

6. $abc + b = a$ for c.

7. $P = \dfrac{1}{2}mn^2 + 3$ for m.

8. Gustavo works as a tutor and makes $11 per hour after taxes. He can compute his monthly salary using the equation

$$S = 11h$$

where S is the monthly salary in dollars that Gustavo makes if he works h hours that month.

   a. Find Gustavo's monthly salary if he works 48 hours.
   b. Find Gustavo's monthly salary if he works 32 hours.
   c. How many hours does Gustavo have to work a month if he wants to earn $800 a month?

9. Solve the inequality. $-3(x - 5) > 4$

10. Solve the inequality. $2.5x - 4 < 12.8$

11. Donna is a coordinator for a boys' and girls' club summer program. She would like to take a group of kids to see a 3-D movie. The tickets cost $17.50 each plus an additional fee of $3.00 per person for the 3-D glasses. If she plans on taking 20 children to see a 3-D movie, how much will it cost?

12. Use the equation $y = |x - 3|$ to create a table of nine or more points, and graph them. Connect the points with a smooth curve. Clearly label and scale the axes. Is the graph linear or nonlinear?

13. Find the equation of the line that goes through the two points $(6, 0)$ and $(-3, 6)$. Graph the line, clearly labeling and scaling the axes.

14. Find the x-intercept and the y-intercept of the equation $4x - 5y = 20$. Graph the line using the intercepts. Clearly label and scale the axes.

For Exercises 15 and 16, sketch the graph of the line by hand. Label the vertical and horizontal intercepts.

15. $y = 3x - 4$

16. $y = -\dfrac{1}{3}x + 2$

17. Find the slope and the y-intercept of the line $3x - 5y = 10$.

18. Determine the equation of the line by using point-slope form. The line has slope $m = \dfrac{-1}{5}$ and passes through the point $(-5, 6)$. Put the final answer in $y = mx + b$ form.

19. Write the equation for the line passing through the point $(6, 2)$ and parallel to the line $3x + 4y = 7$. Write the equation in slope-intercept form.

20. Find the equation of the line perpendicular to $y = -4x + 7$, passing through the point $(8, -1)$.

21. Use the table to find the following.

x	y
−6	0
0	4
3	6
15	14
24	20

   a. The slope of the line passing through these points
   b. The y-intercept
   c. The x-intercept
   d. The equation for the line passing through these points. Write the equation in slope-intercept form.

22. Use the graph to find the following.

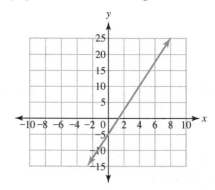

   a. The slope of the line
   b. The vertical intercept
   c. The horizontal intercept
   d. The equation for the line

23. The number of miles Steve plans to run each week can be modeled by

$$R = 1.5w + 5$$

where R is the number of miles run w weeks since he started training.

   a. How many miles does Steve plan to run in week 4?
   b. In what week will Steve run 20 miles?

24. Solve the system, using the substitution method. Check the answer in both original equations.

$$y = \frac{3}{4}x + 5$$

$$5x + 4y = -12$$

25. Solve the system using the elimination method. Check the answer in both original equations.

$$5x - 3y = 9$$
$$x - y = 5$$

26. Solve the system. Check the answer in both original equations.

$$m = 3n - 12$$
$$4m - 12n = 10$$

27. A plane travels 360 miles with the wind in 3 hours. It makes the return trip against the wind in 4 hours. Find the rate of the plane and the rate of the wind.

28. Hamid needs 4 liters of a 12% HCl solution to run an experiment. Hamid has only a 6% HCl solution and a 24% HCl solution to work with. How much of the 6% solution and the 24% solution should he use?

29. Solve the system. Check the answer in both original equations.

$$2x - y = 7$$
$$-6x + 3y = -21$$

30. The perimeter of a rectangle is 28 centimeters. The length is 3 centimeters more than the width. Find the length and the width of the rectangle.

31. Aivy has $8000 to invest. She puts part of the money in a CD earning 3.5% simple interest and part in a bond fund earning 5% simple interest. Aivy would like to earn $325.00 a year in interest. How much money should she put in the CD, and how much money should she put in the bond fund?

32. Graph the solution set of the linear inequality $4x - 5y > -20$.

33. Graph the solution set of the linear inequality.
$$y > -\frac{2}{3}x + 9$$

34. Simplify.

a. $(-3x^4y^3)^3$

b. $-6a^4 \cdot 3ab^5$

c. $(-3xy^2)^3(2x^3y)^2$

35. Simplify.

a. $\dfrac{t^6}{t^2}$

b. $\dfrac{3b^3}{-12b^2}$

c. $\dfrac{-15x^3y^2}{-3x^3y}$

36. Simplify. $\left(\dfrac{-15x^4y^2}{50x^3y}\right)^2$

37. Simplify. Write the final answer using positive exponents only.

a. $\dfrac{-4a^2b}{2a^3b^3}$ b. $(-2x^2y^{-3})^2$ c. $\left(\dfrac{5x}{y}\right)^{-3}$

38. Write the number using scientific notation.

a. 0.000195

b. 52,890,000,000

39. Convert the number in scientific notation to standard notation.

a. 3.004×10^{-5}

b. 9.27×10^8

40. Identify the number of terms, and find the degree of the polynomial.

$$8a^3 - a^2 + 3a$$

41. Find the degree of each term and of the polynomial.

$$5a^3b + 3a^5 - 6b + ab^2$$

42. Add. $(-3b^2 + 2b + 7) + (-b^2 + 5b - 1)$

43. Subtract. $(3x - 6) - (-x + 5)$

44. Multiply and simplify.

a. $(2x + 5)(x - 7)$

b. $(y - 1)(3y^2 + 2y - 1)$

c. $(3x - 4)^2$

d. $3(7a - 2) - 4(-3a + 5)$

45. Divide and simplify. $\dfrac{3x^2 - 6x + 9}{-3x}$

46. Divide using long division. $(3x^2 - 2x - 5) \div (x + 1)$

47. Divide using synthetic division.
$(5x^2 - 22x + 8) \div (x - 4)$

48. Factor.

a. $6x^3y - 18xy + 24x$

b. $5xy + 15x + 2y + 6$

49. Factor the polynomial completely.
$6ab + 36a - 4b - 24$

50. Factor the trinomial.

a. $x^2 - 5x - 14$

b. $-n^2 - 3n + 18$

c. $20y^2 + 11y - 3$

51. Factor the polynomial.

a. $25 - x^2$

b. $9y^2 - 1$

c. $9t^2 - 12t + 4$

d. $x^2 + 16$

e. $3y^2 - 12$

52. Determine whether the following equations are linear, quadratic, or neither. *Do not* solve the equation.

a. $-3(x + 5) - 2x = 9$

b. $x^5 - 2x = 5$

c. $(x + 2)(x - 1) = 0$

53. Solve the quadratic equation by factoring.
  a. $3x^2 - 10x - 8 = 0$
  b. $3x(x + 5) = 0$
  c. $n^2 - 81 = 0$

54. Evaluate the rational expression for the given value of the variable.

$$\frac{2x - 4}{x + 2} \quad \text{for} \quad x = 2$$

55. The parents of a youth soccer team are purchasing a plaque for their championship team. The plaque and the engraving will cost $60.00. The cost per person depends on the number of people who agree to help pay. If n parents agree to pay equal shares, the cost per person in dollars can be found using the equation

$$c = \frac{60}{n}$$

where c is the cost per person in dollars.

  a. Find the cost per person if 10 parents agree to help pay for the plaque.
  b. If there are 15 parents total on the team, what is the lowest possible cost per parent?

56. For each rational expression, find the value(s) of the variable that must be excluded.

  a. $\dfrac{3x + 1}{2x - 7}$

  b. $\dfrac{5t}{(t + 3)(3t - 4)}$

  c. $\dfrac{3y}{6y^2 + 13y - 5}$

57. Simplify each rational expression.

  a. $\dfrac{-6(2x + 5)}{x(2x + 5)}$

  b. $\dfrac{n - 4}{n^2 - 3n - 4}$

  c. $\dfrac{t - 2}{t^2 - 4}$

58. An experienced office specialist can do a week's filing for his corporation in 6 hours. When he works with a new, inexperienced office specialist, the two office specialists can complete the job in time T (in hours).

$$T = \frac{6x}{6 + x}$$

Here, x is the time it takes the inexperienced office specialist to do the job alone.

  a. How long will it take the two office specialists working together if the inexperienced specialist can complete the job alone in 10 hours?
  b. How long will it take the two office specialists working together if the inexperienced specialist can complete the job alone in 8 hours?

59. Simplify each rational expression.

  a. $\dfrac{5n + 7}{2n^2 + 17n + 35}$

  b. $\dfrac{4x^2 - 19x - 5}{(x + 7)(x - 5)}$

  c. $\dfrac{12 - 4x}{x - 3}$

60. Multiply the rational expressions. Simplify.

  a. $\dfrac{-4}{9} \cdot \dfrac{27}{30}$

  b. $\dfrac{-5xy}{15x^2} \cdot \dfrac{45x}{12y^2}$

  c. $\dfrac{x^2 + x - 12}{x^2 + 3x - 10} \cdot \dfrac{(x - 2)}{(x + 4)}$

  d. $\dfrac{y^2 + 5y + 6}{y^2 + y - 20} \cdot \dfrac{y^2 + 4y - 5}{y^2 + 8y + 12}$

61. A 1-pound jar of barbeque sauce is priced at $6.29. Convert this price per pound (lb) to dollars per ounce (oz) so that it can be compared to the price of other containers of barbecue sauce. (Round to two decimal places.)

62. A car is traveling at 35 mph. What is the car's speed in feet per minute?

63. Divide the rational expressions. Simplify.

  a. $\dfrac{-3}{7} \div \dfrac{9}{28}$

  b. $\dfrac{-16x}{5y^2} \div \dfrac{24x^2}{35y}$

  c. $\dfrac{(t + 2)(t - 3)}{(t + 1)(t - 4)} \div \dfrac{(t^2 - 9)}{(t^2 - 1)}$

  d. $\dfrac{a^2 + 4a + 3}{a^2 + 2a - 8} \div \dfrac{a^2 - a - 2}{a^2 - 16}$

64. Simplify each complex fraction.

  a. $\dfrac{\frac{-2x^2}{15y}}{\frac{12x^3}{5y^2}}$
  b. $\dfrac{\frac{b + 2}{2b^2 - 8}}{\frac{b + 5}{b - 2}}$

65. Add or subtract the rational expressions. Simplify.

  a. $\dfrac{6x}{x + 1} + \dfrac{6}{x + 1}$

  b. $\dfrac{6t^2}{t - 5} - \dfrac{30t}{t - 5}$

  c. $\dfrac{y + 6}{(y - 2)(y + 3)} - \dfrac{(y - 2)}{(y - 2)(y + 3)}$

  d. $\dfrac{x - 7}{(x - 1)(x + 5)} + \dfrac{3x}{(x - 1)(x + 5)}$

66. Find the LCD for each set of fractions.

  a. $\dfrac{-4}{5x^2y} \quad \dfrac{1}{10xy}$

b. $\dfrac{-7b}{b-1}$ $\dfrac{6}{b-2}$

c. $\dfrac{15}{4h^2 - 12h}$ $\dfrac{-2}{h-3}$

d. $\dfrac{-2}{a^2 - 8a + 15}$ $\dfrac{5}{a^2 + a - 12}$

67. Find the LCD for each set of fractions. Rewrite each fraction as an equivalent fraction over the LCD.

a. $\dfrac{3}{x-1}$ $\dfrac{-2x}{x+4}$

b. $\dfrac{5k}{k^2 - 36}$ $\dfrac{8}{k^2 - 11k + 30}$

68. Add or subtract the rational expressions. Reduce the final answer.

a. $\dfrac{3x}{2xy} + \dfrac{7x}{xy}$ b. $\dfrac{y}{y-1} - \dfrac{5y-2}{y^2 - 5y + 4}$

69. Simplify each complex fraction.

a. $\dfrac{\dfrac{10}{x} - 5}{\dfrac{6}{x} - 3}$ b. $\dfrac{\dfrac{3}{x} - \dfrac{2}{y}}{\dfrac{1}{x} + \dfrac{4}{y}}$

70. Solve each rational equation. Check the answer in the original problem.

a. $6 + \dfrac{3}{x} = \dfrac{23}{3} - \dfrac{2}{x}$

b. $\dfrac{4}{y-3} + 2 = \dfrac{4}{y-3}$

c. $\dfrac{2}{k-2} + 4 = k + 3$

71. A local business is throwing a retirement party for an employee. The cost of the gift is $100, and the cost of lunch for each person attending is $10.00. The average cost per person for the retirement party and gift can be estimated by the equation

$$C = \dfrac{100 + 10n}{n}$$

where C is the cost per person in dollars when n people attend the retirement lunch.

a. Find the average cost per person if 25 people attend the retirement lunch.

b. How many people must attend for the average cost per person to be $12?

72. Solve each rational equation. Check the answer in the original problem.

a. $\dfrac{6}{a+1} = \dfrac{-3}{a-2}$

b. $\dfrac{3}{5b} - \dfrac{1}{5} = \dfrac{-1}{b}$

c. $\dfrac{3}{x+4} + \dfrac{4}{x-2} = \dfrac{x^2 - 8}{(x+4)(x-2)}$

73. Kenzo can complete his lab assignment in 3 hours. What is his work rate?

74. The Women's Club volunteers can copy the monthly announcements using their new photocopier in about 4 hours. The Club's older photocopier can copy the announcements in 6 hours. How long would it take to copy the announcements using both machines?

75. Write the ratio of 9 to 45 in simplified fraction form.

76. Interpret 400 miles for 16 gallons as a rate in fraction form.

77. Determine the unit rates (round to the nearest cent). Determine which item is the better buy: 36 ounces of coffee beans for $31.00 or 48 ounces of coffee beans for $25.00.

78. A blueprint is drawn to a $\dfrac{1}{16}$-inch scale, so 1 inch on the blueprint equals 16 feet in the building. If the length of a real wall is 40 feet, what will its length be on the blueprint?

79. Solve each proportion. Check the answer in the original problem.

a. $\dfrac{3}{n} = \dfrac{-15}{2}$ b. $\dfrac{x-2}{2} = \dfrac{13x + 10}{14}$

c. $\dfrac{3t - 2}{t+5} = \dfrac{25}{14}$

80. The variable d varies directly with t. Find an equation to represent this relationship if $t = 3$ when $d = 150$. Use the equation to find d when $t = 7.5$.

81. The amount of a weekly paycheck (before taxes), W, varies directly with the amount of time, t, spent working.

a. Find an equation to express this relationship if the amount of the paycheck is $231 for 22 hours of work.

b. Use the equation to find the amount of the weekly paycheck for 32 hours of work.

82. The variable y varies inversely with x. Find an equation to represent this relationship if $x = 12$ when $y = \dfrac{-1}{4}$. Use the equation to find y when $x = 2$.

83. The speed, s, in miles per hour of a car being driven is inversely proportional to the time, t, it has been driven.

a. Find an equation to express this relationship if the speed is 50 mph for 4 hours of driving.

b. Use this equation to find the speed for 6 hours of driving.

84. Evaluate each function for the given value of x.

a. Evaluate $f(x) = -5x + 13$ for $x = -4$.

b. Evaluate $f(x) = -2x^2 + 5$ for $x = -1$.

85. The population of the United States is given in the table.

Year	Population of the United States (in millions)
2003	290
2004	293
2005	296
2006	298
2007	301
2008	304

Source: U.S. Census Bureau.

  a. Find an equation for a model of these data.
  b. Using your model, estimate the population of the United States in 2012.
  c. Give a reasonable domain and range for this model.
  d. What is the vertical intercept for your model? What does it mean in this situation?
  e. Estimate when the U.S. population will reach 325 million.

86. The total revenue for Cisco Systems, Inc. for the past several years is given in the table.

Years Since 2000	Total Revenue (in billions of $)
5	24.8
6	28.5
7	34.9
8	39.5

Source: http://finance.google.com

  a. Find an equation for a model of these data. Write the model using function notation.
  b. What is the vertical intercept for your model? Explain its meaning in regard to revenue.
  c. Give a reasonable domain and range for this model.
  d. Estimate the total revenue for Cisco Systems, Inc. in 2010.
  e. When might the total revenue be 64 billion dollars?
  f. What is the slope of this model? Explain its meaning in regard to revenue.

For Exercises 87 and 88, give the domain for the function.

87. $f(x) = 2x^2 - 6x + 8$

88. $g(x) = \dfrac{3x - 5}{2x^2 - x - 3}$

89. The function $H(d)$ is the number of hours a person sleeps on day d of the month. Explain the meaning of $H(6) = 7$ in this situation.

90. Let $P(d) = -3d + 100$ be the number of people out of 100 remaining on a diet plan d days after starting the diet.
  a. Find $P(14)$ and explain its meaning in terms of the diet.
  b. What is the slope of this function? Explain its meaning in terms of the diet.

91. $f(x) = 9x - 45$
  a. Find $f(3)$.
  b. Find x such that $f(x) = 54$.
  c. Give the domain and range for $f(x)$.

92. $h(x) = -\dfrac{5}{8}x + 11$
  a. Find $h(32)$.
  b. Find x such that $h(x) = \dfrac{13}{8}$.
  c. Give the domain and range for $h(x)$.

93. $g(x) = 7$
  a. Find $g(10)$.
  b. Give the domain and range for $g(x)$.

94. Use the graph to find the following.

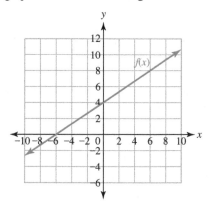

  a. $f(6)$.
  b. Find x such that $f(x) = 0$.
  c. Give the domain and range for $f(x)$.

For Exercises 95 and 96, combine the given functions.

95. $f(x) = 2x - 4$, $g(x) = 3x + 7$
  a. $f(x) + g(x)$
  b. $f(x) - g(x)$
  c. $f(x)g(x)$

96. $f(x) = x + 3$, $g(x) = x^2 + 5$
  a. $f(x) + g(x)$
  b. $f(x) - g(x)$
  c. $f(x)g(x)$

For Exercises 97 and 98, find the composition $(f \circ g)(x) = f(g(x))$.

97. $f(x) = 2x - 4, g(x) = x^2 + 1$

98. $f(x) = x^2 + x, g(x) = 3x + 2$

99. The percentage of Canadian TV subscribers who use cable services can be modeled by

$$C(t) = -2t + 82$$

where $C(t)$ represents the percentage, as a whole number, of Canadian TV subscribers who use cable services t years since 2000. The percentage of Canadian TV subscribers who use satellite services t years since 2000 can be modeled by

$$S(t) = 2t + 17$$

Determine when the percentage of Canadian TV subscribers that use satellite services will be greater than those that use cable services.

Source: Models derived using data from the Canadian Radio−television and Telecommunications Commission.www.crtc.gc.ca.

100. Use the table to find when Y1 < Y2.

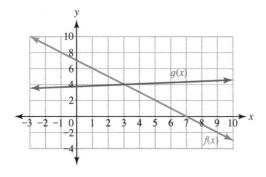

101. Use the graph to find when $f(x) \geq g(x)$.

102. Sandra earns \$400 per week plus 6% commission on all sales she makes. Sandra needs \$565 each week to pay bills. How much in sales does she need to earn at least \$565 per week?

For Exercises 103 through 106, solve the equation. Check your answer.

103. $|x + 2| + 6 = 18$

104. $3|a - 8| - 4 = 44$

105. $|4n + 9| + 20 = 7$

106. $-2|3r + 5| + 15 = 7$

For Exercises 107 through 110, solve the inequality. Give the solution as an inequality. Graph the solution set on a number line.

107. $|x - 2| < 7$

108. $|2x + 3| \leq 15$

109. $|x + 4| \geq 6$

110. $|3x - 7| + 10 > 15$

For Exercises 111 and 112, solve the given inequalities. Write the solution set using interval notation.

111. $x^2 - 7x + 10 > 0$

112. $\dfrac{x + 5}{x - 8} \leq 0$

For Exercises 113 and 114, solve the given inequalities. Write the solution set using inequality notation.

113. $x^2 + 8x - 9 \leq 0$

114. $\dfrac{x - 3}{x^2 + 9x + 14} \geq 0$

For Exercises 115 and 116, sketch a graph by hand of the system of inequalities.

115. $y \geq x - 5$

$y \leq \dfrac{1}{5}x + 2$

116. $3x - 5y < 10$

$x + 2y < 12$

Matrices

APPENDIX TOPICS

- Solve systems of three equations
- Work with matrices
- Matrix row reduction
- Solve a system using matrices
- Finding a quadratic function using matrices

Solving Systems of Three Equations

In Section 4.3, we learned how to solve a system of two equations in two unknowns using the elimination method. We are going to expand this method to solve a system of three equations in three unknowns. Such a system looks like the following.

$$x + y + z = 2$$
$$x - y - z = 1$$
$$3x + 2y + z = 5$$

The three unknowns are the variables x, y, and z. A solution of this system will consist of values of x, y, and z that make all three equations simultaneously true. Be sure to write the point with x, y, and z in the correct order as (x, y, z). Points in the form (x, y, z) are sometimes called *ordered triples*.

> **DEFINITION**
>
> **Solution to a System of Three Equations in Three Unknowns**　A solution is one or more points (x, y, z) that satisfy all three equations.

Example 1　Checking solutions

Consider the following system.

$$x + y + z = 4$$
$$x - y + z = 2$$
$$2x + y - z = 7$$

a. Is $(3, 1, 0)$ a solution of the system?

b. Is $(4, 0, 1)$ a solution of the system?

SOLUTION

a. Substitute in the values $(x, y, z) = (3, 1, 0)$ into all three equations and simplify.

Substitute in $(x, y, z) = (3, 1, 0)$	**Simplify and check**
$x + y + z = 4$	$3 + 1 + 0 = 4$
$x - y + z = 2$	$3 - 1 + 0 = 2$
$2x + y - z = 7$	$2(3) + 1 - 0 = 7$

Since all three equations are true, the point $(x, y, z) = (3, 1, 0)$ is a solution of the system.

b. Substitute in the values $(x, y, z) = (4, 0, 1)$ into all three equations and simplify.

Substitute in $(x, y, z) = (4, 0, 1)$	**Simplify and check**
$x + y + z = 4$	$4 + 0 + 1 = 5 \neq 4$
$x - y + z = 2$	$4 - 0 + 1 = 5 \neq 2$
$2x + y - z = 7$	$2(4) + 0 - 1 = 7$

Because the first two equations are not true, the point $(x, y, z) = (4, 0, 1)$ is not a solution of the system.

To solve a system of three equations in three unknowns, we can use the elimination method that we discussed in Section 4.3. It can help to number the equations.

Example 2 Solving a system of three equations in three unknowns using elimination

Solve the system. Write the solution as a point (x, y, z).

$$x + y + z = 4$$
$$x - y + z = 2$$
$$2x + y - z = 7$$

SOLUTION

First, number the equations. It will help us to keep track of them during the elimination method.

1. $x + y + z = 4$
2. $x - y + z = 2$
3. $2x + y - z = 7$

Add equations 1 and 2 together to eliminate the variable y. Call the result equation 4.

1. $x + y + z = 4$
2. $\underline{x - y + z = 2}$
4. $2x + 2z = 6$

Add equations 2 and 3 together to eliminate the variable y. Call the result equation 5.

2. $x - y + z = 2$
3. $\underline{2x + y - z = 7}$
5. $3x = 9$

From equation 5, we have that

$$3x = 9 \qquad \text{This is equation 5.}$$

$$\frac{3x}{3} = \frac{9}{3} \qquad \text{Divide by 3 to solve for } x.$$

$$x = 3$$

Equation 4 only has two variables, x and z. Substitute this value of x into equation 4 to find the value of z.

$$
\begin{aligned}
2x + 2z &= 6 \qquad \text{\textit{Substitute in x = 3.}} \\
2(3) + 2z &= 6 \\
6 + 2z &= 6 \qquad \text{\textit{Solve for z.}} \\
\underline{-6 \qquad\quad -6} & \\
2z &= 0 \\
z &= 0
\end{aligned}
$$

Now that we have the values of x and z, we find the value of y. Any of the three original equations involves all three variables. Therefore, we can substitute x and z into any of the original equations. Just picking equation 1, we have that

$$
\begin{aligned}
x + y + z &= 4 \qquad \text{\textit{Substitute in x = 3 and z = 0.}} \\
3 + y + 0 &= 4 \qquad \text{\textit{Simplify.}} \\
3 + y &= 4 \qquad \text{\textit{Solve for y.}} \\
\underline{-3 \qquad\quad -3} & \\
y &= 1
\end{aligned}
$$

The solution to this system is the point $(x, y, z) = (3, 1, 0)$. The check was done in Example 1.

As when we solved systems in Chapter 4, sometimes we must multiply one or both equations by a constant before eliminating a variable.

Example 3 Multiplying by a constant first

Solve the system. Write the solution as a point (x, y, z). Check the solution.

$$
\begin{aligned}
x + y + z &= 2 \\
x + 2y - z &= 2 \\
-2x + y + z &= 5
\end{aligned}
$$

SOLUTION

Once again, we number the equations first to keep track of them.

$$
\begin{aligned}
1. \quad & x + y + z = 2 \\
2. \quad & x + 2y - z = 2 \\
3. \quad & -2x + y + z = 5
\end{aligned}
$$

Adding equations 1 and 2 will eliminate the variable z. Call the result equation 4.

$$
\begin{aligned}
1. \quad & x + y + z = 2 \\
2. \quad & \underline{x + 2y - z = 2} \\
4. \quad & 2x + 3y = 4
\end{aligned}
$$

Likewise, adding equations 2 and 3 will eliminate z in those equations. Call this result equation 5.

$$
\begin{aligned}
2. \quad & x + 2y - z = 2 \\
3. \quad & \underline{-2x + y + z = 5} \\
5. \quad & -x + 3y = 7
\end{aligned}
$$

Adding equations 4 and 5 will eliminate neither variable x nor y. If we first multiply equation 5 by 2 and then add it to equation 4, we can eliminate x.

$$
\begin{array}{ll}
5. & -x + 3y = 7 \\
2(5.)\ 2(-x + 3y) = 2(7) & \text{Multiply both sides by 2.} \\
6. & -2x + 6y = 14 \quad \text{Distribute 2 on the left side.}
\end{array}
$$

Now add equation 6 to equation 4.

$$
\begin{array}{ll}
4. & 2x + 3y = 4 \\
6. & -2x + 6y = 14 \\
\hline
& 9y = 18 \\
& \dfrac{9y}{9} = \dfrac{18}{9} \\
& y = 2
\end{array}
$$

Substitute this into equation 5 (or equation 6) to find x.

$$
\begin{array}{ll}
-x + 3y = 7 & \\
-x + 3(2) = 7 & \text{Substitute in } y = 2. \\
-x + 6 = 7 & \text{Isolate } x. \\
\underline{ -6 \quad -6} & \\
-x = 1 & \\
(-1)(-x) = (-1)(1) & \text{Multiply by } -1 \text{ to change} \\
& \text{the signs.} \\
x = -1 &
\end{array}
$$

Substitute the values of x and y into any of the original equations to find z. Using equation 1, we see that

$$
\begin{array}{ll}
(-1) + (2) + z = 2 & \text{Substitute in } x = -1 \text{ and } y = 2. \\
1 + z = 2 & \text{Solve for } z. \\
\underline{-1 -1} & \\
z = 1 &
\end{array}
$$

The solution to this system is the point $(x, y, z) = (-1, 2, 1)$.
To check the solution, substitute the point into all three equations.

Equation	Substitute in $(-1, 2, 1)$	Simplify
1. $\quad x + y + z = 2$	$(-1) + (2) + (1) \stackrel{?}{=} 2$	$2 = 2$
2. $\quad x + 2y - z = 2$	$(-1) + 2(2) - (1) \stackrel{?}{=} 2$	$2 = 2$
3. $-2x + y + z = 5$	$-2(-1) + (2) + (1) \stackrel{?}{=} 5$	$5 = 5$

The solution checks.

Matrices

Using the elimination method requires a lot of manipulation with several equations and can get confusing. To reduce the confusion, we can simplify the work using **matrices.** Using a matrix to solve a system of equations focuses on the coefficients of each term and not on the variables themselves.

Think of a matrix as being like a spreadsheet. When we create a spreadsheet or a table on a computer, we must first specify how many rows and columns it should have. With a matrix, we also specify how many rows and columns it has. The following matrix has two rows and three columns. We write this as 2×3, and say, "2 by 3." The size of a matrix is always given as rows $\times$ columns, in that order.

$$
\begin{bmatrix} 3 & 4 & -1 \\ 0 & 5 & 7 \end{bmatrix}
$$

Matrices are usually written with square brackets around the elements.

We discuss individual elements of a matrix by their position in the matrix. In the matrix $\begin{bmatrix} 3 & 4 & -1 \\ 0 & 5 & 7 \end{bmatrix}$, the number 3 is in row 1, column 1, so we call it the $(1, 1)$ element. The number 7 is in row 2, column 3, so we call it the $(2, 3)$ element.

DEFINITION

Matrix   A **matrix** is a rectangular array of numbers. The *size* of a matrix is given as rows $\times$ columns. An individual element in a matrix is located by its position: (row, column).

$\begin{bmatrix} 4 & 5 \\ -1 & 3 \\ 2 & 0 \end{bmatrix}$ is a 3×2 matrix. The number -1 is in the $(2, 1)$ position.

In Examples 1 and 2, we saw that the elimination method can be used to solve systems of equations. Now we will consider another way to write a system of equations without the variables: using a matrix.

The following system consists of two equations in two unknowns, x and y. To write this system in matrix form, we put the coefficients of x in the first column. The coefficients of y are written in the second column. The right-hand side is put in the third column.

$$\begin{array}{cc} \textbf{System} & \textbf{Matrix form} \\ \begin{aligned} 3x + 2y &= 6 \\ -x + 4y &= 10 \end{aligned} & \begin{bmatrix} 3 & 2 & 6 \\ -1 & 4 & 10 \end{bmatrix} \end{array}$$

Think of the first column as containing the coefficients of x, the second column as containing the coefficients of y, and the third column as containing the right-hand side. The rows correspond to the two equations.

$$\begin{array}{cc} x & y \\ \begin{bmatrix} 3 & 2 & 6 \\ -1 & 4 & 10 \end{bmatrix} \end{array}$$

This type of matrix that represents a system of equations, where the last column contains the right-hand side, has a special name. It is called an *augmented matrix*.

Example 4   Writing an augmented matrix

Write the augmented matrix for each of the following linear systems.

a. $\begin{cases} -3x + 5y = 9 \\ 2x + y = -7 \end{cases}$ **b.** $\begin{cases} x + y + z = 2 \\ -x + 2y + z = 5 \\ x - y = 0 \end{cases}$

SOLUTION

a. The corresponding augmented matrix is

$$\begin{bmatrix} -3 & 5 & 9 \\ 2 & 1 & -7 \end{bmatrix}$$

b. Notice that the third equation does not contain the variable z. If we rewrite the equation so that the missing variable has a coefficient of 0, $x - y = 0$ becomes $x - y + 0z = 0$. The corresponding augmented matrix is

$$\begin{bmatrix} 1 & 1 & 1 & 2 \\ -1 & 2 & 1 & 5 \\ 1 & -1 & 0 & 0 \end{bmatrix}$$

Matrix Row Reduction

Now that we can write a linear system as a matrix, we want to solve the system in matrix form. This is because we won't have to write all of the variables down repeatedly. The coefficients of the variables are stored in the matrix as we saw in Example 3.

We first look at an augmented matrix that is in a special form. This form is called *upper triangular form*. Below are two matrices in upper triangular form.

$$\begin{bmatrix} 1 & 1 & 6 \\ 0 & 2 & -4 \end{bmatrix} \qquad \begin{bmatrix} -1 & 1 & 1 & 1 \\ 0 & -3 & 4 & 3 \\ 0 & 0 & -1 & 4 \end{bmatrix}$$

The *main diagonal* of the matrix runs from the $(1, 1)$ element, through the $(2, 2)$ element, through the $(3, 3)$ element, and so on. It has been drawn on the matrices below.

Main diagonal   **Main diagonal**

$$\begin{bmatrix} 1 & 1 & 6 \\ 0 & 2 & -4 \end{bmatrix} \qquad \begin{bmatrix} -1 & 1 & 1 & 1 \\ 0 & -3 & 4 & 3 \\ 0 & 0 & -1 & 4 \end{bmatrix}$$

The key to recognizing whether a matrix is in upper triangular form is that all the elements below the main diagonal are 0.

When an augmented matrix is in upper triangular form, we can solve the system using a technique called *back-solving*.

Steps to Solving an Augmented Matrix Using Back-Solving

1. Write the last row as an equation in variable form. It will have only one variable. Solve for that variable.
2. Working backwards, write the next to last row as an equation in variable form. It will have only two variables. Substitute in the value of the variable from step 1 to find the value of the unknown variable.
3. If necessary, work backwards once again to write the first row as an equation in variable form. Substitute the values of the variables found in steps 1 and 2 into the equation and solve for the unknown.
4. Write the solution as an ordered pair (x, y) or as an ordered triple (x, y, z).

Note: The matrix must be in upper triangular form.

Example 5   Using back-solving

Solve each augmented matrix using back-solving. Write the solution as an ordered pair or ordered triple.

a. $\begin{bmatrix} 1 & 1 & 6 \\ 0 & 2 & -4 \end{bmatrix}$
b. $\begin{bmatrix} -1 & 1 & 1 & 1 \\ 0 & -3 & 4 & -1 \\ 0 & 0 & -1 & 4 \end{bmatrix}$

SOLUTION

a. $\begin{bmatrix} 1 & 1 & 6 \\ 0 & 2 & -4 \end{bmatrix}$

Rewriting the last row in equation form yields

$$0x + 2y = -4 \qquad \text{or} \qquad 2y = -4$$

Solving this equation for the variable y yields

$$\frac{2y}{2} = \frac{-4}{2}$$

$$y = -2$$

Rewriting the first row in equation form and substituting in $y = -2$ yields

$$x + y = 6 \qquad \text{Rewrite the first row as an equation.}$$
$$x + (-2) = 6 \qquad \text{Substitute in } y = -2.$$
$$\underline{\quad +2 \quad +2 \quad} \qquad \text{Solve for x.}$$
$$x = 8$$

The solution to the system is $(x, y) = (8, -2)$.

b. $\begin{bmatrix} -1 & 1 & 1 & 1 \\ 0 & -3 & 4 & -1 \\ 0 & 0 & -1 & 4 \end{bmatrix}$

Rewriting the last row in equation form yields

$$0x + 0y - 1z = 4 \qquad \text{or} \qquad -z = 4$$

Solving this equation for the variable z yields

$$-1z = 4$$
$$z = -4$$

Working backwards, write the second row in equation form.

$$0x - 3y + 4z = -1$$

Solve this equation for y.

$$-3y + 4z = -1$$
$$-3y + 4(-4) = -1 \qquad \text{Substitute in } z = -4.$$
$$-3y - 16 = -1 \qquad \text{Solve for y.}$$
$$\underline{\qquad +16 \quad +16}$$
$$-3y = 15$$
$$\frac{-3y}{-3} = \frac{15}{-3}$$
$$y = -5$$

Rewrite the first row in equation form. Substitute in $y = -5$ and $z = -4$ and solve for x.

$$-x + y + z = 1 \qquad \text{Rewrite the first row as an equation.}$$
$$-x + (-5) + (-4) = 1 \qquad \text{Substitute in } y = -5 \text{ and } z = -4.$$
$$-x + (-9) = 1 \qquad \text{Solve for x.}$$
$$\underline{\qquad +9 \quad +9}$$
$$-x = 10$$
$$x = -10$$

The solution is the ordered triple $(x, y, z) = (-10, -5, -4)$.

Putting an augmented matrix in upper triangular form is done by using the elementary row operations. There are three operations that are allowable on matrix rows. This means that if we use these three operations, they will not change the solution to the system.

DEFINITION

Elementary Row Operations   The three elementary row operations are as follows:

- Two rows may be interchanged (row swap).
- A row may be multiplied by a nonzero constant.
- A multiple of one row may be added to another row. Use this to overwrite the row we are trying to change.

Let's see how to use these three row operations to put a matrix in upper triangular form. We will work in a systematic fashion, beginning with the first row. We will use the first row and the elementary row operations to put 0's below the $(1, 1)$ element (the first main diagonal element). We will then move on to the second row. Using the $(2, 2)$ element and the elementary row operations, we will put 0's below the $(2, 2)$ element. We will continue on in this fashion until the matrix is in upper triangular form.

Example 6   Putting a matrix in upper triangular form

Put each matrix in upper triangular form.

a. $\begin{bmatrix} 1 & 1 & -1 \\ -2 & 3 & 7 \end{bmatrix}$

b. $\begin{bmatrix} 1 & 1 & 1 & 5 \\ -1 & 2 & 1 & 4 \\ 3 & -1 & -1 & -5 \end{bmatrix}$

SOLUTION

a. $\begin{bmatrix} 1 & 1 & -1 \\ -2 & 3 & 7 \end{bmatrix}$

Begin with the $(1, 1)$ element on the main diagonal. This element is the number 1. We want to put a 0 in the $(2, 1)$ position. This is the first element of the second row. The number -2 is currently in that position. The elementary row operations say that it is okay to add a multiple of one row to another. We multiply row 1 by 2 and add it to row 2. We are trying to change row 2, so we overwrite row 2 with the result.

$$\begin{bmatrix} 1 & 1 & -1 \\ -2 & 3 & 7 \end{bmatrix}$$

$$\rightarrow \begin{bmatrix} 1 & 1 & -1 \\ 2(1) + -2 & 2(1) + 3 & 2(-1) + 7 \end{bmatrix} \quad 2 \cdot \text{row 1} + \text{row 2. Overwrite row 2.}$$

$$\rightarrow \begin{bmatrix} 1 & 1 & -1 \\ 0 & 5 & 5 \end{bmatrix} \quad \text{This matrix is in upper triangular form.}$$

b. $\begin{bmatrix} 1 & 1 & 1 & 5 \\ -1 & 2 & 1 & 4 \\ 3 & -1 & -1 & -5 \end{bmatrix}$

Begin with the $(1, 1)$ element on the main diagonal. This element is the number 1. We want to put a 0 in the $(2, 1)$ position: This is the first element of the second row. The number -1 is currently in that position. The elementary row operations say that it is okay to add a multiple of one row to another. We add rows 1 and 2. We are trying to change row 2, so overwrite row 2 with the result.

$$\begin{bmatrix} 1 & 1 & 1 & 5 \\ -1 & 2 & 1 & 4 \\ 3 & -1 & -1 & -5 \end{bmatrix}$$

$$\rightarrow \begin{bmatrix} 1 & 1 & 1 & 5 \\ 1 + (-1) & 1 + 2 & 1 + 1 & 5 + 4 \\ 3 & -1 & -1 & -5 \end{bmatrix} \quad \text{row 1} + \text{row 2. Overwrite row 2.}$$

$$\rightarrow \begin{bmatrix} 1 & 1 & 1 & 5 \\ 0 & 3 & 2 & 9 \\ 3 & -1 & -1 & -5 \end{bmatrix}$$

We want to next put a 0 in the $(3, 1)$ position. The number 3 is currently in that position. Multiply row 1 by -3, add it to row 3, and overwrite row 3.

$$\begin{bmatrix} 1 & 1 & 1 & 5 \\ 0 & 3 & 2 & 9 \\ 3 & -1 & -1 & -5 \end{bmatrix}$$

$$\rightarrow \begin{bmatrix} 1 & 1 & 1 & 5 \\ 0 & 3 & 2 & 9 \\ -3(1)+3 & -3(1)+(-1) & -3(1)+(-1) & -3(5)+(-5) \end{bmatrix} \quad \begin{array}{l} -3 \cdot \text{row 1} + \\ \text{row 3.} \\ \text{Overwrite row 3.} \end{array}$$

$$\rightarrow \begin{bmatrix} 1 & 1 & 1 & 5 \\ 0 & 3 & 2 & 9 \\ 0 & -4 & -4 & -20 \end{bmatrix}$$

There are 0's in the column below the $(1, 1)$ element on the main diagonal. We move on to the $(2, 2)$ element on the main diagonal. We want to put 0's below this element (in the same column). Looking at the matrix, we see that the $(2, 2)$ element is 3 and the element below it is -4, in the $(3, 2)$ position.

$$\begin{bmatrix} 1 & 1 & 1 & 5 \\ 0 & 3 & 2 & 9 \\ 0 & -4 & -4 & -20 \end{bmatrix}$$

The least common multiple for 3 and -4 is -12. We multiply row 2 by 4 and row 3 by 3.

$$\begin{bmatrix} 1 & 1 & 1 & 5 \\ 4(0) & 4(3) & 4(2) & 4(9) \\ 3(0) & 3(-4) & 3(-4) & 3(-20) \end{bmatrix} \quad \text{Multiply row 2 by 4 and row 3 by 3.}$$

$$\rightarrow \begin{bmatrix} 1 & 1 & 1 & 5 \\ 0 & 12 & 8 & 36 \\ 0 & -12 & -12 & -60 \end{bmatrix}$$

If we now add rows 2 and 3, overwriting row 3, the $(3, 2)$ element will become 0.

$$\begin{bmatrix} 1 & 1 & 1 & 5 \\ 0 & 12 & 8 & 36 \\ 0+0 & 12+(-12) & 8+(-12) & 36+(-60) \end{bmatrix} \quad \begin{array}{l} \text{Add row 2 to row 3,} \\ \text{overwriting row 3.} \end{array}$$

$$\rightarrow \begin{bmatrix} 1 & 1 & 1 & 5 \\ 0 & 12 & 8 & 36 \\ 0 & 0 & -4 & -24 \end{bmatrix} \quad \begin{array}{l} \text{This matrix is in upper} \\ \text{triangular form.} \end{array}$$

Solving Systems with Matrices

We now have the skills to solve a system of equations using augmented matrices. Pulling this all together leads to the following steps.

> **Steps to Solving a System of Equations Using Augmented Matrices**
>
> 1. Write the system as an augmented matrix.
> 2. Using the elementary row operations, put the augmented matrix in upper triangular form.
> 3. Back-solve to find the values of the variables.
> 4. Write the solution as an ordered pair (x, y) or an ordered triple (x, y, z).
> 5. Check the solution in the original equations.

Example **7** Solving a system using augmented matrices

Solve the system using augmented matrices. Write the solution as an ordered pair (x, y) or an ordered triple (x, y, z). Check the solution in the original equation.

a. $\begin{cases} x - 3y = 11 \\ -5x + y = -13 \end{cases}$

b. $\begin{cases} x - y + 2z = 7 \\ 2x + y - z = -7 \\ 3y + z = -3 \end{cases}$

SOLUTION

a. $\begin{cases} x - 3y = 11 \\ -5x + y = -13 \end{cases}$

First, rewrite this system as an augmented matrix.

$$\begin{bmatrix} 1 & -3 & 11 \\ -5 & 1 & -13 \end{bmatrix}$$

Next, we put the matrix in upper triangular form. Using the $(1, 1)$ element to put a 0 below it yields

$$\begin{bmatrix} 1 & -3 & 11 \\ -5 & 1 & -13 \end{bmatrix}$$

$$\rightarrow \begin{bmatrix} 1 & -3 & 11 \\ 5 + -5 & -15 + 1 & 55 + -13 \end{bmatrix} \quad \begin{array}{l} 5 \cdot \text{row 1} + \text{row 2}. \\ \text{Overwrite row 2}. \end{array}$$

$$\rightarrow \begin{bmatrix} 1 & -3 & 11 \\ 0 & -14 & 42 \end{bmatrix}$$

This matrix is now in upper triangular form. Back-solving yields

$$\begin{bmatrix} 1 & -3 & 11 \\ 0 & -14 & 42 \end{bmatrix}$$

$$-14y = 42 \qquad \text{Rewrite row 2 in equation form.}$$

$$\frac{-14y}{-14} = \frac{42}{-14} \qquad \text{Solve for } y.$$

$$y = -3$$

Rewrite row 1 in equation form and substitute in $y = -3$.

$$x - 3y = 11 \qquad \text{Write the first row in equation form.}$$
$$x - 3(-3) = 11 \qquad \text{Substitute in } y = -3.$$
$$x + 9 = 11 \qquad \text{Solve for } x.$$
$$\underline{-9 \quad -9}$$
$$x = 2$$

The solution is the point $(2, -3)$.
Check the solution in both original equations.

First equation	Second equation
$x - 3y = 11$	$-5x + y = -13$
$2 - 3(-3) \stackrel{?}{=} 11$	$-5(2) + (-3) \stackrel{?}{=} -13$
$11 = 11$	$-13 = -13$

b. $\begin{cases} x - y + 2z = 7 \\ 2x + y - z = -7 \\ 3y + z = -3 \end{cases}$

Rewrite the system as an augmented matrix.

$\begin{cases} x - y + 2z = 7 \\ 2x + y - z = -7 \\ 0x + 3y + z = -3 \end{cases}$ *Rewrite equation 3 with a term of 0x.*

$$\begin{bmatrix} 1 & -1 & 2 & 7 \\ 2 & 1 & -1 & -7 \\ 0 & 3 & 1 & -3 \end{bmatrix}$$

To put this augmented matrix in upper triangular form, we use the $(1, 1)$ element to introduce 0's in the column below it.

$$\begin{bmatrix} 1 & -1 & 2 & 7 \\ 2 & 1 & -1 & -7 \\ 0 & 3 & 1 & -3 \end{bmatrix}$$ *$-2 \cdot$ row 1 + row 2. Overwrite row 2.*

$$\rightarrow \begin{bmatrix} 1 & -1 & 2 & 7 \\ -2(1) + 2 & -2(-1) + 1 & -2(2) + -1 & -2(7) + -7 \\ 0 & 3 & 1 & -3 \end{bmatrix}$$

$$\rightarrow \begin{bmatrix} 1 & -1 & 2 & 7 \\ 0 & 3 & -5 & -21 \\ 0 & 3 & 1 & -3 \end{bmatrix}$$ *Use the $(2, 2)$ element to put a 0 below it.*

$$\rightarrow \begin{bmatrix} 1 & -1 & 2 & 7 \\ 0 & 3 & -5 & -21 \\ 0 & 3 & 1 & -3 \end{bmatrix}$$ *$-1 \cdot$ row 2 + row 3. Overwrite row 3.*

$$\rightarrow \begin{bmatrix} 1 & -1 & 2 & 7 \\ 0 & 3 & -5 & -21 \\ 0 & -1(3) + 3 & -1(-5) + 1 & -1(-21) + -3 \end{bmatrix}$$

$$\rightarrow \begin{bmatrix} 1 & -1 & 2 & 7 \\ 0 & 3 & -5 & -21 \\ 0 & 0 & 6 & 18 \end{bmatrix}$$ *This matrix is in upper triangular form.*

Back-solving yields the following.

$$6z = 18$$ *Rewrite row 3 in equation form.*

$$\frac{6z}{6} = \frac{18}{6}$$ *Solve for z.*

$$z = 3$$

Rewrite row 2 in equation form and solve for y.

$$3y - 5z = -21$$ *Rewrite row 2 in equation form.*

$$3y - 5(3) = -21$$ *Substitute in z = 3.*

$$3y - 15 = -21$$ *Solve for y.*

$$\underline{+15 \quad\quad +15}$$

$$3y = -6$$

$$y = -2$$

Substitute $y = -2$ and $z = 3$ into row 1 to solve for x.

$$x - y + 2z = 7 \qquad \text{Rewrite row 1 as an equation.}$$
$$x - (-2) + 2(3) = 7 \qquad \text{Substitute in } y = -2 \text{ and } z = 3.$$
$$x + 2 + 6 = 7 \qquad \text{Solve for x.}$$
$$x + 8 = 7$$
$$\underline{-8 \quad -8}$$
$$x = -1$$

The solution is the point $(-1, -2, 3)$.
To check, substitute the point into all three equations.

First equation	Second equation	Third equation
$x - y + 2z = 7$	$2x + y - z = -7$	$3y + z = -3$
$(-1) - (-2) + 2(3) \stackrel{?}{=} 7$	$2(-1) + (-2) - 3 \stackrel{?}{=} -7$	$3(-2) + (3) \stackrel{?}{=} -3$
$-1 + 2 + 6 \stackrel{?}{=} 7$	$-2 - 2 - 3 \stackrel{?}{=} -7$	$-6 + 3 \stackrel{?}{=} -3$
$7 = 7$	$-7 = -7$	$-3 = -3$

The solution checks.

Solving Systems of Three Equations to Model Quadratics

Matrices can be used to find the equation of a quadratic function in standard form. Recall that a quadratic function in standard form looks like $f(x) = ax^2 + bx + c$. The three unknowns are the coefficients a, b, and c. If we are given three points the function passes through, then we can substitute in those three points and find the values of a, b, and c. To find the quadratic function that passes through three points, use the following steps.

Steps to Find a Quadratic Function Given Three Points

1. Write the function $f(x) = ax^2 + bx + c$ in the form $y = ax^2 + bx + c$.
2. Substitute each of the three given points in for x and y. This will result in three equations with the variables a, b, and c.
3. Write the equations as an augmented matrix.
4. Put the matrix in upper triangular form.
5. Back-solve to find the values of a, b, and c.
6. Write the quadratic function using the values from step 5.

Example 8 Finding a quadratic function using three points

Find the equation of the quadratic function that passes through the points $(1, -18)$, $(2, -14)$, and $(3, -8)$.

SOLUTION

First, substitute in the equation $y = ax^2 + bx + c$ the given points for x and y.

$$y = ax^2 + bx + c$$

Point	Substitute in the point	Simplify
$(1, -18)$	$-18 = a(1)^2 + b(1) + c$	$a + b + c = -18$
$(2, -14)$	$-14 = a(2)^2 + b(2) + c$	$4a + 2b + c = -14$
$(3, -8)$	$-8 = a(3)^2 + b(3) + c$	$9a + 3b + c = -8$

The system is

$$\begin{cases} a + b + c = -18 \\ 4a + 2b + c = -14 \\ 9a + 3b + c = -8 \end{cases}$$

Rewrite the system as an augmented matrix.

$$\begin{bmatrix} 1 & 1 & 1 & -18 \\ 4 & 2 & 1 & -14 \\ 9 & 3 & 1 & -8 \end{bmatrix}$$

Reduce the matrix to upper triangular form.

$$\begin{bmatrix} 1 & 1 & 1 & -18 \\ 4 & 2 & 1 & -14 \\ 9 & 3 & 1 & -8 \end{bmatrix}$$ *Use the (1, 1) element to put 0's below it.*

$$\rightarrow \begin{bmatrix} 1 & 1 & 1 & -18 \\ -4(1)+4 & -4(1)+2 & -4(1)+1 & -4(-18)+-14 \\ 9 & 3 & 1 & -8 \end{bmatrix}$$ *Multiply $-4 \cdot$ row 1, add to row 2, and overwrite row 2.*

$$\rightarrow \begin{bmatrix} 1 & 1 & 1 & -18 \\ 0 & -2 & -3 & 58 \\ 9 & 3 & 1 & -8 \end{bmatrix}$$ *Multiply $-9 \cdot$ row 1, add to row 3, and overwrite row 3.*

$$\rightarrow \begin{bmatrix} 1 & 1 & 1 & -18 \\ 0 & -2 & -3 & 58 \\ -9(1)+9 & -9(1)+3 & -9(1)+1 & -9(-18)+-8 \end{bmatrix}$$

$$\rightarrow \begin{bmatrix} 1 & 1 & 1 & -18 \\ 0 & -2 & -3 & 58 \\ 0 & -6 & -8 & 154 \end{bmatrix}$$ *Use the (2, 2) element to put a 0 below it.*

$$\rightarrow \begin{bmatrix} 1 & 1 & 1 & -18 \\ 0 & -2 & -3 & 58 \\ 0 & -6 & -8 & 154 \end{bmatrix}$$ *Multiply $-3 \cdot$ row 2, add to row 3, and overwrite row 3.*

$$\rightarrow \begin{bmatrix} 1 & 1 & 1 & -18 \\ 0 & -2 & -3 & 58 \\ 0 & -3(-2)+-6 & -3(-3)+-8 & -3(58)+154 \end{bmatrix}$$

$$\rightarrow \begin{bmatrix} 1 & 1 & 1 & -18 \\ 0 & -2 & -3 & 58 \\ 0 & 0 & 1 & -20 \end{bmatrix}$$ *This matrix is in upper triangular form.*

Back-solving yields

$$c = -20$$

Rewrite the second row in equation form and substitute in $c = -20$.

$$-2b - 3c = 58$$
$$-2b - 3(-20) = 58$$
$$-2b + 60 = 58$$
$$\underline{\quad -60 \quad -60 \quad}$$
$$-2b = -2$$
$$b = 1$$

Rewrite the first row in equation form and substitute in $b = 1$ and $c = -20$.

$$a + b + c = -18$$
$$a + (1) + (-20) = -18$$
$$a - 19 = -18$$
$$\underline{+19 \quad +19}$$
$$a = 1$$

The quadratic function that passes through these three points is

$$y = ax^2 + bx + c$$
$$y = (1)x^2 + (1)x + (-20)$$
$$y = x^2 + x - 20$$
$$f(x) = x^2 + x - 20$$

This technique can be used to find a quadratic model from standard form. Substitute in the three data points into standard form, $y = ax^2 + bx + c$, and solve for a, b, and c as above.

A Exercises

For Exercises 1 through 6, check the solution to the system of three equations in three unknowns.

1. $\begin{cases} x + y + z = 2 \\ 2x - y + 4z = -17 \\ x + 3y - z = 18 \end{cases}$

  a. Is $(x, y, z) = (0, 5, 1)$ a solution of the system?
  b. Is $(x, y, z) = (0, 5, -3)$ a solution of the system?

2. $\begin{cases} -x + y + z = 1 \\ x + 2y - z = -7 \\ 3x - y + z = 9 \end{cases}$

  a. Is $(x, y, z) = (1, -2, 4)$ a solution of the system?
  b. Is $(x, y, z) = (0, 0, 4)$ a solution of the system?

3. $\begin{cases} x + y + z = 7 \\ -2x + 3y - 2z = -14 \\ -x - y + 3z = -19 \end{cases}$

  a. Is $(x, y, z) = (-5, 0, 1)$ a solution of the system?
  b. Is $(x, y, z) = (10, 0, -3)$ a solution of the system?

4. $\begin{cases} x + y - z = 4 \\ 2x + 3y + z = 5 \\ x + z = 2 \end{cases}$

  a. Is $(x, y, z) = (4, 1, 0)$ a solution of the system?
  b. Is $(x, y, z) = (3, 0, -1)$ a solution of the system?

5. $\begin{cases} x - y + z = -15 \\ y + z = -1 \\ 3x + 2y = 14 \end{cases}$

  a. Is $x = 16, y = 1, z = 0$ a solution of the system?
  b. Is $x = 0, y = 7, z = -8$ a solution of the system?

6. $\begin{cases} x - y + 2z = 4 \\ 3x + z = -13 \\ 5y - 6z = -30 \end{cases}$

  a. Is $x = 10, y = 6, z = 4$ a solution of the system?
  b. Is $x = -6, y = 0, z = 5$ a solution of the system?

For Exercises 7 through 14, solve the system using the elimination method without using matrices. Check the solution in the original equations.

7. $\begin{cases} x + y - z = 3 \\ x - y + 2z = 6 \\ -x - 2y + 3z = -1 \end{cases}$

8. $\begin{cases} x + 2y - z = -3 \\ -x - y + 4z = 1 \\ x - y + 3z = 3 \end{cases}$

9. $\begin{cases} x + y - 2z = -6 \\ -x + y + z = 7 \\ x - 2y + z = -3 \end{cases}$

10. $\begin{cases} x + y - z = -5 \\ -x + 2y + z = -1 \\ x - 2y + z = 7 \end{cases}$

11. $\begin{cases} x - y + 2z = 6 \\ 2x + y - z = -1 \\ -x - 2y + z = 3 \end{cases}$

12. $\begin{cases} x + y - 2z = -1 \\ -3x + 2z = 8 \\ 2x - 2y + z = -9 \end{cases}$

13. $\begin{cases} 2x + 2y - z = -5 \\ -x - y + z = 4 \\ 3x - y - 2z = -1 \end{cases}$

14. $\begin{cases} 2x + 5y - z = -11 \\ -x + 3y + z = 7 \\ -4x - y + 2z = 26 \end{cases}$

For Exercises 15 through 20, answer the questions about the given matrix.

15. $\begin{bmatrix} 3 & -1 \\ 4 & 7 \end{bmatrix}$

  a. What is the size of this matrix?
  b. What element is in the $(1, 2)$ position?

16. $\begin{bmatrix} 5 & 9 \\ 0 & -3 \end{bmatrix}$

   a. What is the size of this matrix?
   b. What element is in the $(2, 1)$ position?

17. $\begin{bmatrix} 4 & 0 & -2 \\ 3 & -1 & 5 \end{bmatrix}$

   a. What is the size of this matrix?
   b. What element is in the $(1, 3)$ position?

18. $\begin{bmatrix} 9 & -3 & 7 & 1 \\ 0 & -2 & 6 & -3 \\ 1 & 1 & 5 & -4 \end{bmatrix}$

   a. What is the size of this matrix?
   b. What element is in the $(3, 3)$ position?

19. $\begin{bmatrix} 1 & -2 & 6 \\ 0 & -3 & 2 \\ 0 & 1 & 1 \\ -3 & 2 & 5 \end{bmatrix}$

   a. What is the size of this matrix?
   b. What element is in the $(4, 1)$ position?

20. $\begin{bmatrix} 6 & 3 & 2 \\ 1 & 0 & 0 \\ -3 & 0 & 6 \end{bmatrix}$

   a. What is the size of this matrix?
   b. What element is in the $(3, 3)$ position?

For Exercises 21 through 28, write the augmented matrix for the given system. Do not solve the system.

21. $\begin{cases} 2x - y = -5 \\ 4x + 6y = -1 \end{cases}$

22. $\begin{cases} 5x - y = -1 \\ -x + 2y = 0 \end{cases}$

23. $\begin{cases} x - y = 0 \\ -3x + 4y = -1 \end{cases}$

24. $\begin{cases} -x - y = 4 \\ 2x - 7y = -1 \end{cases}$

25. $\begin{cases} -2x + 3y - z = 0 \\ x + y - z = 5 \\ x - y + z = 2 \end{cases}$

26. $\begin{cases} -3x + 5y - 2z = 0 \\ 4x - y - 3z = -7 \\ x - 6y + 3z = 12 \end{cases}$

27. $\begin{cases} -x + y + z = 3 \\ 3y - 2z = 1 \\ -x + 2z = 0 \end{cases}$

28. $\begin{cases} x + 3z = -1 \\ -x - 5y = 6 \\ 2y - z = -3 \end{cases}$

For Exercises 29 through 36, back-solve the given augmented matrix. Assume that the variables are x and y or x, y, and z.

29. $\begin{bmatrix} 3 & 1 & 5 \\ 0 & 2 & -4 \end{bmatrix}$

30. $\begin{bmatrix} 1 & -2 & 0 \\ 0 & 3 & 9 \end{bmatrix}$

31. $\begin{bmatrix} 4 & -3 & 7 \\ 0 & -1 & 5 \end{bmatrix}$

32. $\begin{bmatrix} 5 & -1 & 0 \\ 0 & 2 & 0 \end{bmatrix}$

33. $\begin{bmatrix} 1 & -1 & 0 & 2 \\ 0 & 2 & 1 & 3 \\ 0 & 0 & 1 & -2 \end{bmatrix}$

34. $\begin{bmatrix} 1 & 0 & -3 & 4 \\ 0 & 1 & -1 & 2 \\ 0 & 0 & 1 & 5 \end{bmatrix}$

35. $\begin{bmatrix} 2 & -1 & 1 & 7 \\ 0 & -2 & 1 & -4 \\ 0 & 0 & -3 & 15 \end{bmatrix}$

36. $\begin{bmatrix} 1 & 0 & 5 & -2 \\ 0 & -2 & 1 & -3 \\ 0 & 0 & -4 & 12 \end{bmatrix}$

For Exercises 37 through 44, put the given augmented matrix in upper triangular form.

37. $\begin{bmatrix} 1 & -1 & -5 \\ -2 & 1 & 7 \end{bmatrix}$

38. $\begin{bmatrix} 1 & -1 & 2 \\ -2 & 1 & -5 \end{bmatrix}$

39. $\begin{bmatrix} 4 & 3 & 7 \\ 4 & 11 & 24 \end{bmatrix}$

40. $\begin{bmatrix} 1 & -3 & -5 \\ 3 & -10 & 16 \end{bmatrix}$

41. $\begin{bmatrix} 1 & 1 & 1 & 2 \\ 2 & 3 & 2 & 3 \\ 0 & -2 & 2 & 6 \end{bmatrix}$

42. $\begin{bmatrix} 1 & 2 & 1 & -7 \\ 1 & 3 & 1 & -10 \\ -2 & -3 & 0 & 13 \end{bmatrix}$

43. $\begin{bmatrix} 3 & 0 & 2 & 9 \\ 4 & 1 & 2 & 8 \\ 3 & 2 & 1 & 2 \end{bmatrix}$

44. $\begin{bmatrix} 5 & 2 & 1 & 1 \\ 3 & 0 & 1 & -4 \\ 5 & 1 & 1 & -3 \end{bmatrix}$

For Exercises 45 through 54, solve each system using augmented matrices. Check the solution in the original equations.

45. $\begin{cases} 2x + y = -1 \\ 4x + y = -7 \end{cases}$

46. $\begin{cases} x - 5y = 22 \\ 3x + y = 2 \end{cases}$

47. $\begin{cases} -2x + 3y = 24 \\ 6x + y = -12 \end{cases}$

48. $\begin{cases} 3x + 6y = 21 \\ -2x + 5y = -14 \end{cases}$

49. $\begin{cases} x - 4y + 6z = -3 \\ -x + 5y - 2z = -1 \\ 2x + y - z = 7 \end{cases}$

50. $\begin{cases} -x + 2y + z = -4 \\ 3x - y + 2z = 17 \\ x + 3y + 2z = -3 \end{cases}$

51. $\begin{cases} 4x + y - z = -1 \\ -2x - y + z = -1 \\ -x + 7y - 2z = 7 \end{cases}$

52. $\begin{cases} 2x - y + 3z = 5 \\ -3x + y - 3z = -11 \\ -4x + 3y - z = -3 \end{cases}$

53. $\begin{cases} 2x - y - 2z = 4 \\ -x + 5y = 26 \\ -y + 4z = -10 \end{cases}$

54. $\begin{cases} x - 3y + z = -12 \\ 3x + 4y = -3 \\ 2x - 3z = -16 \end{cases}$

For Exercises 55 through 62, find the equation of the quadratic function in standard form that passes through the given points.

55. The three points are $(-1, -6)$, $(1, 2)$, and $(2, 3)$.

56. The three points are $(-2, -5)$, $(-1, 0)$, and $(0, 3)$.

57. The three points are $(1, 10)$, $(2, 18)$, and $(3, 28)$.

58. The three points are $(-2, -3)$, $(-1, 0)$, and $(1, 12)$.

59. The three points are $(1, 4)$, $(2, 15)$, and $(3, 30)$.

60. The three points are $(-2, -6)$, $(-1, -15)$, and $(1, -21)$.

61. The three points are $(-1, -5)$, $(1, 15)$, and $(2, 16)$.

62. The three points are $(-1, -40)$, $(1, 18)$, and $(2, 35)$.

Using the Graphing Calculator

These instructions are based on the Texas Instruments 83/84 family of calculators. Most of the instructions given here will also work with the TI-82 calculator.

Basic Keys and Calculations

When you are doing basic calculations, a graphing calculator works much the same as a scientific calculator. The home screen is a blank screen where calculations are performed. The following table introduces some of the important keys used for calculations in this text.

Key	What It Does
ENTER	Tells the calculator to do the calculation. Acts like an equals key on most scientific calculators.
÷ × − +	Performs the basic operations of division, multiplication, subtraction, and addition.
(-)	Used for negative numbers. Using the subtraction key for a negative number will result in a syntax error. See the error messages later in this appendix.
x^2	Squares the expression immediately before it. To square more than one thing, parentheses must be used. *Note:* -5^2 is different from $(-5)^2$. $$-5^2$$ [(-)] [5] [x^2] [ENTER] $$(-5)^2$$ [( ] [(-)] [5] [ )] [x^2] [ENTER]
	-5² -25 (-5)² 25
^	Raises the expression immediately before it to the power you choose. To raise more than one thing to a power, parentheses must be used. $$3^7$$ [3] [^] [7] [ENTER]
	3^7 2187
2nd	Acts like a shift key to access things typed above the keys in blue or yellow.
2nd $\sqrt{}$ x^2	Using [2nd] and then [x^2] results in a square root. The calculator will automatically give a left parenthesis. Close with a right parenthesis when you are done entering the radicand. $$\sqrt{25}$$ [2nd] [x^2] [2] [5] [ )] [ENTER]
	√(25) 5

Continued

Key	What It Does
2nd (−) (ANS ?)	Using 2nd and then (−) (ANS ?) results in the answer feature. The answer feature uses the previous result in the next calculation. See the long calculations in the next section.
DEL	Deletes *one piece* of an entry at a time.
CLEAR	Clears (deletes) an *entire* entry at a time. Pressing CLEAR twice on the home screen will clear all previous entries on the screen.
2nd MODE (QUIT)	Using 2nd and then MODE (QUIT) will exit from any screen and return to the home screen where calculations are done.
MATH	Brings up the math menu that can be used for many operations. MATH NUM CPX PRB 1:▶Frac 2:▶Dec 3:³ 4:³√(5:ˣ√ 6:fMin(7↓fMax(
‹ ^ › ▾	These cursor keys move the cursor around the screen.

Additional keys and menus will be introduced throughout this appendix.

Long Calculations

When entering a long expression, use parentheses to force the calculator to correctly use the order of operations. Another option is to do calculations in parts, while using the ANS key to keep values that have already been calculated.

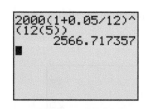

Option 1: All at once.

$$2000 \left(1 + \frac{0.05}{12}\right)^{12(5)}$$

Notice the extra parentheses around the exponent (12(5)). Without the extra set of parentheses, the calculator would raise the base to the 12th power and then multiply the result by 5. This would give an incorrect result. Compare these two calculations: one with parentheses and the other without.

$$2^{5(3)} = 32{,}768$$

Option 2: Using (−) (ANS ?). Here, the (−) (ANS ?) will keep the value of 60 from the first calculation and use it in the second. It will then take the result from the second calculation to multiply by 2000 in the final step.

$$2000 \left(1 + \frac{0.05}{12}\right)^{12(5)}$$

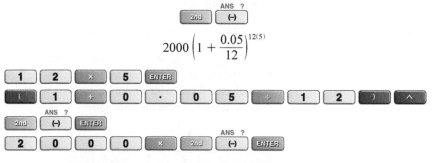

The ANS key recalls the previous numerical answer from the last line.

Converting Decimals to Fractions

To convert a decimal result to a reduced fraction, use the math menu and the first option is ▸Frac.

Without ▸Frac, the result is a decimal approximation.
With ▸Frac, the result is given as a fraction.

$$\frac{1}{5} + \frac{7}{3}$$

Convert 0.2685 to a fraction.

Absolute Values

To use an absolute value in a calculation or equation, use the NUM menu found within the math menu.

Use the cursor to highlight the NUM option in the math menu. **abs(** is the first option, so press ⬚1⬚. Be sure to finish off the parentheses in the calculation.

$$|5 - 24|$$

abs(5-24)
                  19

Complex Number Calculations

In Chapter 10, complex numbers will be introduced. To perform arithmetic with complex numbers, use 2nd ⬚.⬚. The *i* on top of the ⬚.⬚ key represents the imaginary number.

Arithmetic with complex numbers.

$$(2 + 5i) + (8 - 9i)$$

(2+5i)+(8-9i)
               10-4i
(4+3i)(1-7i)
               25-25i

$$(4 + 3i)(1 - 7i)$$

To get a complex number result from taking the square root of a negative number, the calculator must be in complex mode. Change the calculator into complex mode using the mode menu MODE .

Calculations in complex mode.

Go to the mode menu by pressing MODE . Switch to complex mode by moving the cursor down to $a + bi$ and pressing ENTER .

$$\sqrt{-36}$$

Entering an Equation

To enter an equation into the calculator, use the Y= screen. The important keys for doing so are Y= and X,T,O,n .

Y= Gives the Y= screen where equations are entered.

X,T,O,n Enters the variable x into the equation. The other variables listed on this key will not be used in this textbook.

Enter the equation $y = 2x + 5$:

To enter more than one equation, use the ⌄ key to move to the Y₂ = line, and enter the second equation.

Note: The equations must have the y-variable isolated before they are entered into the calculator.

Using the Table Feature

The table feature can be used to evaluate an equation for several x-values. This can be useful to check answers, look for patterns, or solve an equation numerically.

Set up the table feature using 2nd WINDOW .

Option 1: Ask

Have the calculator ask for x-values and give the y-values for the equation entered. Select the following by highlighting them with a black box.

Indpnt: Ask   Depend: Auto

Note: This is the setup the textbook will use most often.

Option 2: Auto

Have the calculator automatically fill up the table with equally spaced x-values and the resulting y-values. Select the following by highlighting them with a black box.

Indpnt: Auto   Depend: Auto

Note: This table will start at $x = 0$ and increase by 1's, giving 0, 1, 2, 3, ...

To start at a different x-value, change TblStart to a different number. To change the increments, change Δ Tbl.

TblStart = 0   ΔTbl = 1   TblStart = 15   ΔTbl = 0.2

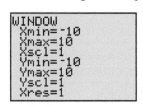

Access the table feature using 2nd GRAPH.

Enter the equation $y = 2x + 5$:

[Y=] [2] [X,T,Θ,n] [+] [5]

TABLE F5
Open the table: 2nd GRAPH

With table set for Ask, enter values for x, and press ENTER.

[6] [ENTER] [8] [ENTER] [2] [2] [ENTER]

Setting the Window

When setting the window, determine what region of the rectangular coordinate system will be displayed. To open the window settings screen, press WINDOW.

```
WINDOW
 Xmin=-10
 Xmax=10
 Xscl=1
 Ymin=-10
 Ymax=10
 Yscl=1
 Xres=1
```

The standard window settings view from −10 to 10 on both the x- and y-axes.

Xmin   Sets the left-hand side (minimum x-value) of the viewing window.

Xmax   Sets the right-hand side (maximum x-value) of the viewing window.

Xscl   Sets the scale (space between tick marks) for the x-axis.

Ymin   Sets the bottom (minimum y-value) of the viewing window.

Ymax   Sets the top (maximum y-value) of the viewing window.

Yscl   Sets the scale (space between tick marks) for the y-axis.

Use the cursor keys to move the cursor to each setting, and type in the new value for that setting.

To set a window for given data, choose values as follows:

Xmin   A slightly smaller value than the smallest input (x-value)

Xmax   A slightly larger value than the largest input (x-value)

Xscl   A scale for the x-axis. One possibility is to use $\text{Xscl} \approx \dfrac{|\text{Xmax} - \text{Xmin}|}{20}$.
The scale can typically be left as 1.

Ymin   A slightly smaller value than the smallest output (y-value)

Ymax   A slightly larger value than the largest output (y-value)

Yscl   A scale for the y-axis. One possibility is to use $\text{Yscl} \approx \dfrac{|\text{Ymax} - \text{Ymin}|}{20}$.
The scale can typically be left as 1.

If you are given an equation and you do not know what window to set, use the table feature to evaluate the equation for several values of x, and use the resulting y-values to set an approximate window. Adjust the window if needed, once you see the portion of the graph shown. The standard window can be set by using the Zoom features of the calculator. These features are discussed later in this appendix.

Graphing a Function

Graphing an equation requires three steps:

1. Enter the equation in the Y= screen: [Y=]

2. Set an appropriate window: [WINDOW]

3. Graph: [GRAPH]

Enter the equation $y = 2x + 5$:

Set an appropriate window [WINDOW]. A standard window should work well for this equation.

Graph the function by pressing [GRAPH].

Tracing a Graph

The TRACE feature, [TRACE], follows the curve and gives the coordinates of points along the curve.

Using TRACE [TRACE]

Graph the equation $y = 3x - 6$:

Press [TRACE], and use [◄] or [►] to move along the curve left or right, respectively.

The values of points along the curve will be displayed at the bottom on the window.

You can also press [TRACE], then enter a value for x, and the calculator will jump to that point on the graph and display the x- and y-values. Entering a value directly works only if the value is between Xmin and Xmax (i.e., can be seen in the window).

Graphing a Scatterplot

To create a scatterplot requires four steps:

1. Enter the data: [STAT]

2. Set an appropriate window: [WINDOW]

3. Turn on the STAT PLOT: [Y=]   ^STAT PLOT F1

4. Graph: [GRAPH]

Since a scatterplot is a statistical plot of data, use the STAT menu to work with data.

Pressing the [STAT] key will give the STAT menu. The features of this menu that will be used most often are as follows:

```
EDIT CALC TESTS
1:Edit…
2:SortA(
3:SortD(
4:ClrList
5:SetUpEditor
```

1: Edit   To input data into lists.

5: SetUpEditor   To restore or bring back any accidentally deleted lists.

Step 1: Enter the data into lists

Open the lists screen by selecting 1: Edit:

To empty old data from a list, use the ⌐ ^ ⌐ to move the cursor onto the title of the list L1 and press ⌐ CLEAR ⌐ ⌐ ENTER ⌐. Repeat this for each list that needs to be emptied of old data. Avoid using ⌐ DEL ⌐ when clearing lists. If you press ⌐ DEL ⌐, the entire list will disappear. The list can be brought back by using SetUpEditor from the main STAT menu.

To enter the given data, move the cursor to the list where the data should be entered, and type the coordinates of the data values one at a time, pressing ⌐ ENTER ⌐ after each one.

x	y
−2	5
4	9
10	−3
17	−15

With the cursor in L1,

Move the cursor over to L2, using ⌐ ▸ ⌐.

Note: Use the ⌐ ↔ ⌐ key, not the subtraction key, for negatives.

It is important that each list have the same number of data entered. If the numbers of data in each list are not equal, an error message will be given when you are creating a scatterplot of the data.

Step 2: Setting the window

Open the window settings screen: ⌐ WINDOW ⌐

Xmin The smallest x-value is −2. Something slightly smaller is $x = -4$.

Xmax The largest x-value is 17. Something slightly larger is $x = 20$.

Xscl 1 seems like a reasonable scale for the x-axis.

Ymin The smallest y-value is −15. Something slightly smaller is $y = -17$.

Ymax The largest y-value is 9. Something slightly larger is $y = 11$.

Yscl 1 seems like a reasonable scale for the y-axis.

```
WINDOW
 Xmin=-4
 Xmax=20
 Xscl=1
 Ymin=-17
 Ymax=11
 Yscl=1
 Xres=1
```

Step 3: Set up and turn on STAT PLOT

Stat plots are set up and turned on by using the STAT PLOT menu: ⌐ 2nd ⌐ ⌐ Y= ⌐.
<small>STAT PLOT F1</small>

Here, you can tell that there are three plots. Any number of these can be turned on at a time, but only one is needed for this scatterplot.

Enter the setup screen for Plot1 by pressing ⌐ 1 ⌐.

To be on, the word "On" must have the black box around it. If it does not have this black box, move the cursor over the word On and press ⌐ ENTER ⌐.

For a scatterplot, be sure that the first option after the word Type is selected with a black box. The Xlist and Ylist should be the same as the lists in which the data were entered.

If these lists are not correct, change them. The default list names are L1 and L2, which can be entered by using [2nd] [1] and [2nd] [2]. The other lists are also available over the numbers 3, 4, 5, and 6.

The Mark setting can be set to any of the three options, but the single dot is harder to see on the screen.

Step 4: Graph the scatterplot

Now that the data have been entered, an appropriate window has been set, and the STAT PLOT has been turned on, simply press [GRAPH].

Graphing an Inequality with Shading

To graph inequalities, the calculator can be set to shade above or below the curve.

Enter the inequality $y \leq x^2 - 5x - 3$:

Move the cursor to the left of the Y1, and press [ENTER] until the shading desired is shown. In this case, shading is below the curve.

Set an appropriate window [WINDOW]. A standard window should be all right for this equation.

Graph the function by pressing [GRAPH].

Error Messages

ERR: INVALID DIM

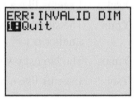

This error occurs when a STAT PLOT is turned on but the stat lists are empty. To fix this error, press [1] to quit. Then either enter data into the lists or turn off the STAT PLOT if you are not graphing a scatterplot.

ERR: DIM MISMATCH

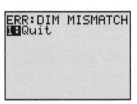

Another error related to stat plots. This error will occur if the lists that are used for a STAT PLOT do not have the same numbers of data in them. To fix this error, press [1] to quit. Then fix the data in the stat lists. Be sure that the STAT PLOT is set up to use the same lists that the data are in.

ERR: WINDOW RANGE

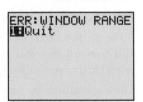

This error occurs when a setting in the window set up is not correct. This usually happens when the Xmin or Ymin is larger than the Xmax or Ymax. To fix this error, press [1] to quit. Then go to the window screen and adjust the settings accordingly. Often, negative numbers get entered incorrectly.

ERR: SYNTAX

This error occurs when you have entered something into the calculator incorrectly. The most common mistake is to use [(-)] instead of [-] or vice versa. Other reasons would be misplacement of commas or parentheses.

To fix syntax errors, press [2] to go to the error. The error will be highlighted with the cursor. In this case, the cursor is flashing on the – because the [(-)] key should have been used instead of [-].

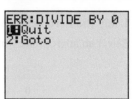

ERR: DIVIDE BY 0

This error occurs whenever a calculation results in division by zero. To fix this error, press [2] to go to the error. The error will be highlighted with the cursor.

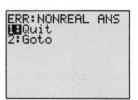

ERR: NONREAL ANS

This error occurs when a calculation results in a nonreal number. This happens most often when the square root of a negative number is taken. To fix this error, press [2] to go to the error. The error will be highlighted with the cursor.

Additional Features (Check with your instructor whether you are allowed to use these in your class.)

Zooming to an Appropriate Window

The ZOOM menu helps find an appropriate window for graphs and scatterplots. [ZOOM]

The main zoom options that are useful in this textbook are as follows:

5: ZSquare   Square window so the graph does not appear stretched.

6: ZStandard   Standard window from −10 to 10 on both axes.

9: ZoomStat   Appropriate window for any stat plot that is turned on.

Using ZoomStat

Enter the data.	Turn on STAT PLOT	ZoomStat
Step 1:	Step 2: STAT PLOT F1	Step 3: (ZoomStat)

The new window	The final graph

Zero, Minimum, Maximum, and Intersect Features

When you are graphing, several features in the CALC menu help you to find special points on the graph.

2: zero   Finds the nearest horizontal intercept (zero) of the curve.

3: minimum   Finds the minimum value of the function within an interval.

4: maximum   Finds the maximum value of the function within an interval.

5: intersect   Finds the intersection point of two curves.

Using the Zero Feature

Select an appropriate window, and graph the equation $y = 0.25x^2 + 0.5x - 6$:

Select 2: zero from the CALC menu.

Left Bound   Right Bound

The calculator will ask for a left bound, so move the cursor to the left of the desired zero, and press **ENTER**. The calculator will ask for a right bound, so move the cursor to the right of the desired zero, and press **ENTER**.

Guess   Zero

The calculator will ask for a guess, so move the cursor close to the desired zero, and press **ENTER**. The zero is shown at the bottom of the screen.

Repeat this process for any other zeros. This will not always work. If a zero only touches the x-axis but does not cross it, the calculator will give back a "no sign change" error message.

Using the Minimum or Maximum Feature

Select an appropriate window, and graph the equation $y = 0.25x^2 + 0.5x - 6$.

Select 3: minimum from the CALC menu.

or

Select 4: maximum from the CALC menu.

The minimum or maximum feature works in the same way as the zero feature. A left bound, right bound, and guess must be provided, as with the process for finding the zeros. The minimum or maximum point will then display at the bottom of the screen. This feature will sometimes result in rounding error. For exact values, use algebraic techniques.

Using the Intersect Feature

Select an appropriate window, and graph the two equations. Enter one in Y1 and the other in Y2.

$$y = 0.25x^2 + 0.5x - 6 \qquad y = 2x - 3$$

Select 5: intersect from the CALC menu:

The calculator will ask for a first curve, so use the up or down cursor to select one of the curves, and press ENTER. The calculator will ask for a second curve, so select the other curve, and press ENTER. The calculator will ask for a guess, so move the cursor close to the intersection, and press ENTER. The intersection point is shown at the bottom of the screen.

Regression

The statistical process for finding a model for data is called *regression*. Regression finds the regression (best fit) curve for a set of data. The calculations that are involved take into account the differences between each point and the regression curve and minimize these differences over all the data. Although these calculations can be tedious and long, the calculator has a regression feature that will quickly calculate the regression curve for data entered into the stat lists.

The regression feature is located in the CALC portion of the STAT menu that we used earlier when creating scatterplots. STAT ▶

The regression features used in this textbook include the following:

   4: LinReg(ax+b)   Finds a linear regression equation.

   5: QuadReg   Finds a quadratic regression equation.

   0: ExpReg   Finds an exponential regression equation.

Calculating a Regression Equation

Enter the data into the STAT lists: STAT 1 (Edit)

Turn on a STAT PLOT: 2nd Y= 1 (Plot1)

Graph the data using ZOOM 9 (ZoomStat).

Decide the type of model that should fit the data. In this case, linear seems appropriate.

Choose the linear regression option in the STAT CALC menu:

STAT ▶ 4 (LinReg(ax+b)).

If the data are in lists L1 and L2, simply press ENTER.

To enter specific lists in which the data are located and to put the equation into the Y= screen so that it can be graphed, enter the list names and the equation name following the LinReg(ax+b):

Graph the equation with the data: GRAPH

The graph of the regression curve fits the points nicely.

Quadratic or exponential regressions both work with the same process.

Answers to Practice Problems

CHAPTER R

Section R.1

*PP for Example 1.

a. Natural numbers (if there are no children enrolled you would not have a kindergarten)

b. Integers

c. Whole numbers

PP for Example 2.

The scale is 3.

PP for Example 3.

PP for Example 4.

a.	-5	$>$	-8
b.	3	$>$	-3
c.	-2	$<$	0

PP for Example 5.

a. 10   **b.** 16

PP for Example 6.

$$-2, |0|, |-4|, |6|, 8$$

PP for Example 7.

a. The opposite of 8. $-(8) = -8$

b. The opposite of -1. $-(-1) = 1$

c. The opposite of 0. $-(0) = 0$

PP for Example 8.

a. -34 **b.** 14

PP for Example 9.

a. -7 **b.** 17

PP for Example 10.

a. 14,494   **b.** -282 **c.** 14,776

*PP = Practice Problem

PP for Example 11.

7

PP for Example 12.

a. -8 **b.** 15

PP for Example 13.

a. -5 **b.** 2   **c.** -9

PP for Example 14.

a. $\boxed{4} - 2 \cdot \boxed{6} + \boxed{8}$

b. $\boxed{3 \cdot 7} \boxed{10 \div 2 \cdot 3} \boxed{5 \cdot 4} + \boxed{1}$

c. $\boxed{-65 \div 5 \cdot 4}$

PP for Example 15.

a. $24 \div 2 \cdot 3 = 36$

b. $9 + 5 \cdot 6 - 8 \div 4 = 37$

c. $6 \div 3 + 4 \cdot 5 - 2 \cdot 2 + 24 \div 8 = 21$

Section R.2

PP for Example 1.

a. $32 = 2 \cdot 2 \cdot 2 \cdot 2 \cdot 2$ **b.** $10 = 2 \cdot 5$

c. $100 = 2 \cdot 2 \cdot 5 \cdot 5$

PP for Example 2.

a. 2   **b.** 32

PP for Example 3.

a. $\dfrac{1}{9}$ **b.** $\dfrac{7}{10}$ **c.** $\dfrac{2}{3}$

PP for Example 4.

a. $\dfrac{6}{11} = \dfrac{18}{33}$ **b.** $\dfrac{3}{8} = \dfrac{21}{56}$

PP for Example 5.

a. The scale is $\dfrac{1}{4}$.

b.

c.

d.

PP for Example 6.

a. $\dfrac{5}{6} + 2\dfrac{4}{6} = 3\dfrac{1}{2}$ **b.** $\dfrac{7}{15} - \dfrac{2}{15} = \dfrac{5}{15} = \dfrac{1}{3}$

PP for Example 7.

$$\dfrac{1}{2}\ \text{gallon}$$

PP for Example 9.

$$\dfrac{57}{8}\ \text{feet} = 7\dfrac{1}{8}\ \text{feet}$$

PP for Example 11.

a. $\dfrac{2}{3} \cdot \dfrac{12}{17} = \dfrac{8}{17}$ **b.** $\dfrac{5}{27} \div \dfrac{20}{9} = \dfrac{1}{12}$

PP for Example 12.

a. $\left(\dfrac{1}{3} \div \dfrac{5}{6}\right) + \left(\dfrac{5}{2}\right) = \dfrac{29}{10}$ **b.** $\left(7\right) - \dfrac{2}{5} \cdot \dfrac{15}{4} + \left(\dfrac{1}{3}\right) = \dfrac{35}{6}$

Section **R.3**

PP for Example 1.

a. The digit in the tenths place is 3.

b. The digit in the ten-thousandths place is 5.

PP for Example 2.

a. $2.46 = 2\dfrac{46}{100} = 2\dfrac{23}{50}$ **b.** $1.025 = 1\dfrac{25}{1000} = 1\dfrac{1}{40}$

c. $10.9 = 10\dfrac{9}{10}$

PP for Example 3.

a. $\dfrac{2}{5} = 0.4$ **b.** $\dfrac{3}{4} = 0.75$ **c.** $\dfrac{1}{9} = 0.\overline{1}$

PP for Example 4.

a. 0.25

b.

c.

d.

e.

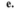

PP for Example 6.

a. 10.99   **b.** 7.16   **c.** $7.32

PP for Example 7.

a. $4.21 \cdot 2.3 = 9.683$ **b.** $3 \cdot 7.99 = \$23.97$

PP for Example 8.

a. $6.24 \div 2.6 = 2.4$ **b.** $30.65 \div 1.6 \approx 19.16$

PP for Example 9.

a. $(3.2) + (4.1 \cdot 2.5) = 13.45$ **b.** $(6 \div 1.5)(-3.1) + (4) = 4.9$

PP for Example 10.

a. $55\% = \dfrac{55}{100} = \dfrac{11}{20}$ **b.** $\dfrac{84}{100} = 84\%$

c. $\dfrac{1}{5} = \dfrac{20}{100} = 20\%$

PP for Example 11.

a. $8.25\% = 0.0825$ **b.** $0.36\% = 0.0036$

c. $0.22 = 22\%$ **d.** $110 = 11{,}000\%$

PP for Example 13.

a. $0.08 \cdot 95 = 7.6$ **b.** $0.30 \cdot 50 = 15$

c. $0.09 \cdot 2500 = 225$

Section **R.4**

PP for Example 1.

a. Integers or rational numbers   **b.** Integers

c. Integers or rational numbers

PP for Example 2.

	Whole Number	Integer	Rational Number	Irrational Number	Real Number
8.3			X		X
$-\dfrac{4}{3}$			X		X
56	X	X	X		X
π				X	X
-15		X	X		X

PP for Example 3.

a. $0.255 = \dfrac{255}{1000} = \dfrac{51}{200}$. Rational.   **b.** $\dfrac{1}{9} = 0.\overline{1}$. Rational.

PP for Example 4.

a. $\sqrt{7} \approx 2.6$ **b.** $\dfrac{2}{7} \approx 0.29$

PP for Example 5.

a. $0.12 per ounce   **b.** $0.21 per ounce

CHAPTER 1

Section 1.1

PP for Example 1.

a. $16^5 = 16 \cdot 16 \cdot 16 \cdot 16 \cdot 16$ **b.** $29 \cdot 29 \cdot 29 \cdot 29 = 29^4$

c. $(-2)^5 = -32$ **d.** $5^6 = 15{,}625$

PP for Example 2.

a. $(-4)^2 = 16$ **b.** $(-5)^3 = -125$

c. $38^0 = 1$ **d.** $-7^2 = -49$

PP for Example 3.

a. $1.02 \times 10^6 = 1{,}020{,}000$

b. $4.51 \times 10^9 = 4{,}510{,}000{,}000$

PP for Example 4.

a. $\boxed{3^4} - \dfrac{\boxed{10}}{2} + \boxed{5 \cdot 4}$ **b.** $\boxed{9^4} - \boxed{16 \cdot 3} + \boxed{9} - \boxed{6}$

PP for Example 5.

a. $6 + 3 \cdot 4 - 2 \div 2 = 17$

b. $8 \div 2 + 6 \cdot 3 - 3 \cdot 3 + 28 \div 4 = 20$

c. $5^2 - 16 + 9 = 18$

PP for Example 6.

a. $16 \div (-8) \cdot 3 - (5 \cdot 3) + 12 \cdot 5 = 39$

b. $(-3 - 4)^2 = 49$

c. $\left|9 - 2 \cdot 3\right| + (-6) \div (-18 \div 3) = 4$

d. $\dfrac{(-2)^2 + 4 \cdot 3}{7 - 2 \cdot 3} - [10 \div 2] = 11$

PP for Example 7.

a. Associative property of addition

b. Commutative property of multiplication

c. Associative property of multiplication

d. Commutative property of addition

PP for Example 9.

a. $5(16 - 7) = 5 \cdot 16 - 5 \cdot 7 = 80 - 35 = 45$

b. $5(16 - 7) = 5 \cdot 9 = 45$

c. Yes

PP for Example 10.

a. $7(2 + 8) - 25 = 45$ **b.** $-(17 - 8) + 5 = -4$

Section 1.2

PP for Example 1.

a. $50 \cdot 4.5 = 225$ miles   **b.** $50 \cdot 7.25 = 362.5$ miles

PP for Example 3.

a. The cost of printing 5 pages is $0.50, the cost of printing 10 pages is $1.00, and the cost of printing 25 pages is $2.50.

b. A home air conditioner uses 14,000 watt-hours when on for 4 hours, 28,000 watt-hours when on for 8 hours, and 84,000 watt-hours when on for 24 hours.

PP for Example 4.

a. $-3(7) + 12 = -9$

b. $-3(-2)^2 + 6(-2) + 1 = -23$

c. $\left|-(5) + 6\right| + 2(5)^2 - 1 = 50$

PP for Example 5.

a. $500 \text{ ft} \cdot \dfrac{1 \text{ m}}{3.28 \text{ ft}} \approx 152.44 \text{ m}$

b. $42 \text{ oz} \cdot \dfrac{28.35 \text{ g}}{1 \text{ oz}} \approx 1190.7 \text{ g}$

c. $156 \text{ lb} \cdot \dfrac{1 \text{ kg}}{2.2 \text{ lb}} \approx 70.91 \text{ kg}$

PP for Example 6.

a. Let t represent the time of day, and let T represent the temperature.

b. Let c represent the number of credits enrolled in, and let T represent the tuition paid.

PP for Example 7.

a. $5n$ **b.** $4n + 9$ **c.** $\dfrac{6}{n}$ **d.** $2n - 16$

PP for Example 8.

a. $x - 29$

b. Let x represent the number of tickets sold. $7x$

c. $150 + 3x$

d. Let m represent the number of minutes over 450. $59.95 + 0.45m$

PP for Example 9.

a. Let m represent the number of miles.
$m \text{ miles} \cdot \dfrac{1.609 \text{ kilometers}}{1 \text{ mile}} = 1.609m \text{ kilometers}$

b. Let t represent the number of teaspoons.
$t \text{ teaspoons} \cdot \dfrac{1 \text{ tablespoon}}{3 \text{ teaspoons}} = \dfrac{t}{3} \text{ tablespoons}$

PP for Example 10.

a. $15 \text{ ft} \cdot 18 \text{ ft} = 270 \text{ ft}^2$ **b.** ft^2, or square feet

c. $270 \cdot 2.38 = \$642.60$

PP for Example 12.

a. Let n represent the number of people who attend the reception. $425 + 22n$

b. To stay within their budget of $3500.00, they can invite 139 people.

Section **1.3**

PP for Example 1.

a. There are four terms. $-5x^2 + \boxed{7c} + 4d^2 + \boxed{8c}$

b. There are three terms. There are no like terms. $45x^2 + 7x - 9$

c. There are four terms. $\boxed{23g^2k} + \boxed{45g^2k^2} \boxed{-16g^2k} + \boxed{57g^2k^2}$

PP for Example 2.

a. $8p + 5p = 13p$

b. $2w + 7 - 9w + 3 = -7w + 10$

c. $3x^2y + 4xy - 7xy + 15x^2y = 18x^2y - 3xy$

d. $8z^2 + 5x - 2z - 20$

PP for Example 3.

a. $-3d + 9c = 9c - 3d$

b. $16 - 2x + 3x^2 = 3x^2 - 2x + 16$

c. $7 - 4b^2 - 2a + 3a^2 = 3a^2 - 2a - 4b^2 + 7$

PP for Example 4.

a. $125h$ **b.** $23h$

c. $125h + 23h = 148h$ **d.** $2b$ **e.** No

PP for Example 6.

a. Multiplication property. $-9(4m^3) = -36m^3$

b. Distributive property. $7(-4x + 6y) = -28x + 42y$

c. Distributive property. $-\dfrac{4}{5}(25c^2 + 5c - 10) = -20c^2 - 4c + 8$

d. Distributive property. $0.4(3x - 6) = 1.2x - 2.4$

PP for Example 7.

a. $5(4x - 9) + 8x + 20 = 28x - 25$

b. $1.5(2w + 7) + 3.5(4w - 6) = 17w - 10.5$

PP for Example 8.

a. $(4x^2 + 5x) - (x^2 - 3x) = 3x^2 + 8x$

b. $4(8t + 9u) - 3(6t - 5u) = 14t + 51u$

Section **1.4**

PP for Example 1.

a. The maximum number of science and engineering degrees was 454,978. They were awarded in 2004.

b. The minimum number of science and engineering degrees was 398,622. They were awarded in 2000.

PP for Example 2.

a. In 1994, the cost of asthma in the United States was about $10 billion.

b. The cost of asthma was projected to be the highest in the year 2000.

PP for Example 4.

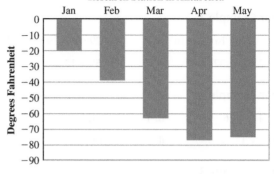

PP for Example 5.

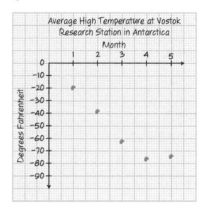

PP for Example 6.

Point	Ordered Pair
A	$(-3, 5)$
B	$(-5, -1)$
C	$(3, -4)$
D	$(5, 4)$
E	$(4, 0)$
F	$(0, 2)$
G	$(-4, 0)$
H	$(0, 0)$

PP for Example 7.

The x-axis has scale 10, and the y-axis has scale 5.

PP for Example 8.

PP for Example 10.

CHAPTER 2

Section 2.1

PP for Example 1.

a. Equation   b. Expression

PP for Example 2.

a. $P = 25n$ Substitute in $P = 4000$ and $n = 120$.

$4000 \stackrel{?}{=} 25(120)$

$4000 \neq 3000$

Because the final results are not equal, $n = 120$ and $P = 4000$ do not give a solution to the equation $P = 25n$. These values state that if 120 batteries are sold, then the profit is $4000. These values do not make the equation true, so they do not make sense in this situation.

b. This is a solution to the equation.

c. This is not a solution of the equation.

PP for Example 3.

a. If Katie takes 11 general education credits this semester, she should take 4 elective credits.

b. If Katie takes 2.5 credits of electives this semester, she should take 12.5 credits of general education.

PP for Example 4.

a. $r = 15$ b. $p = 32.6$

PP for Example 5.

$$P = R - C$$

a. $P = 42,500$. If the company's monthly revenue is $65,000 and its monthly cost is $22,500, its monthly profit is $42,500.

b. $R = 210,000$. If the company's monthly profit is $135,000 and its monthly cost is $75,000, its monthly revenue is $210,000.

PP for Example 6.

$$x = \frac{1}{6}$$

PP for Example 7.

a. $m = 13$ b. $3 = c$

PP for Example 8.

a. $W = e + f$ for e b. $M + N - P = 200$ for N
   $e = W - f$ $N = 200 - M + P$

Section 2.2

PP for Example 1.

$$P = 6s$$

a. $P = 120$. Ann gets paid $120 for 20 subscriptions.

b. $40 = s$. For Ann to make $240, she must sell 40 subscriptions.

PP for Example 2.

a. $d = 13$ b. $m = 6.5$ c. $n = -8.42$

PP for Example 3.

a. $n = \dfrac{-3}{2}$ b. $x = -12$

PP for Example 4.

a. $M = 57$. In the year 2005 ($t = 10$), there were 57 million passenger miles of travel on public transportation.

b. In the year 1999 ($t = 4$), there were 45 million passenger miles of travel on public transportation.

PP for Example 5.

a. $b = 6$ b. $75 = x$ c. $x = 17.5$

PP for Example 6.

a. Half a number minus 13 is equal to 7.

$$\frac{1}{2}n - 13 = 7$$
$$n = 40$$

b. The product of 3 and a number plus 8 is 23.

$$3n + 8 = 23$$
$$n = 5$$

PP for Example 7.

Let t represent time in years, and let V represent the value of the backhoe in dollars. $V = 61,000 - 5000t$.

When the backhoe is 5 years old ($t = 5$), it will be worth $36,000.

PP for Example 8.

a. $\dfrac{V}{lh} = w$ b. $\dfrac{2A}{(b_1 + b_2)} = h$

PP for Example 9.

a. $y = \dfrac{1}{3}x - 3$

b. $\dfrac{-y}{8} + \dfrac{3}{8} = x$

Section **2.3**

PP for Example 1.

a. $x = -20$

b. $x = \dfrac{39}{19}$

c. $-29 = k$

PP for Example 2.

a. $x = -24$

b. $c = \dfrac{-45}{2} = -22.5$

PP for Example 3.

a. No solution

b. $x = 0$

c. All real numbers

PP for Example 4.

a. $\dfrac{2}{3}$ of a number plus 8 equals -2 times the number plus 40.

$$\dfrac{2}{3}x + 8 = -2x + 40$$

$$x = 12$$

b. A number plus twice the difference between the number and 10 is equal to 5 times the number.

$$n + 2(n - 10) = 5n$$

$$n = -10$$

PP for Example 5.

$$x + (x + 25) + (x + 20) = 180$$

The angles measure **45°, 65°, and 70°.**

PP for Example 6.

Let x be the number of people the Clarks invite.

$$5x + 2(0.50)x + 1.5(0.20)x = 500$$

$$x \approx 79$$

If the Clarks spend their entire budget, they can invite 79 people.

Section **2.4**

PP for Example 2.

a. $x < -4$

b. $x \geq -13$

PP for Example 4.

a. $5 + 0.20t \leq 10$

b. $t \leq 25$. Amy can send at most 275 texts a month to stay within her budget of $10.00.

PP for Example 5.

a. $x \geq -7$

b. $x > -8$

PP for Example 6.

a. $(-\infty, 7]$ $x \leq 7$

b. $(-6, \infty)$ $x > -6$

PP for Example 7.

a. $40 \leq h \leq 47$

b. $0 \leq n \leq 2265$

PP for Example 8.

a. $2 < x < 5, (2, 5)$

b. $-16 \leq x < 0$

CHAPTER **3**

Section **3.1**

PP for Example 1.

r = riders	$C = 50r + 4000$
0	4000
50	6500
100	9000
150	11,500
200	14,000
225	15,250
250	16,500

PP for Example 2.

x	$y = -3x + 6$	(x, y)
-2	12	$(-2, 12)$
-1	9	$(-1, 9)$
0	6	$(0, 6)$
1	3	$(1, 3)$
2	0	$(2, 0)$

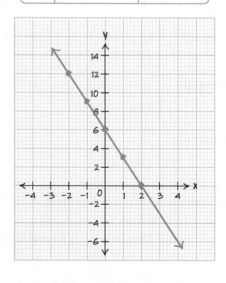

PP for Example 3.

x	$y = 3x - 6$	(x, y)
-2	-12	$(-2, -12)$
-1	-9	$(-1, -9)$
0	-6	$(0, -6)$
1	-3	$(1, -3)$
2	0	$(2, 0)$
3	3	$(3, 3)$

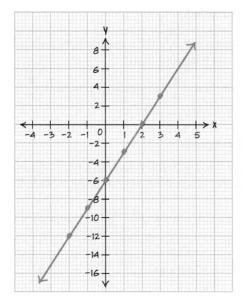

PP for Example 4.

a.

n	$W = 210 - 5n$	(n, W)
0	210	$(0, 210)$
1	205	$(1, 205)$
2	200	$(2, 200)$
4	190	$(4, 190)$
6	180	$(6, 180)$
8	170	$(8, 170)$

b.

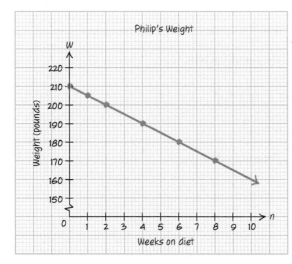

PP for Example 5.

a.

x	$y = x^2 - 5$	(x, y)
-4	11	$(-4, 11)$
-3	4	$(-3, 4)$
-2	-1	$(-2, -1)$
-1	-4	$(-1, -4)$
0	-5	$(0, -5)$
1	-4	$(1, -4)$
2	-1	$(2, -1)$
3	4	$(3, 4)$
4	11	$(4, 11)$

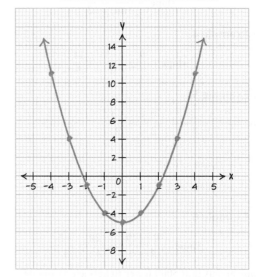

b.

x	$y = |x + 4|$	(x, y)
-7	3	$(-7, 3)$
-6	2	$(-6, 2)$
-5	1	$(-5, 1)$
-4	0	$(-4, 0)$
-3	1	$(-3, 1)$
-2	2	$(-2, 2)$
-1	3	$(-1, 3)$
0	4	$(0, 4)$
1	5	$(1, 5)$

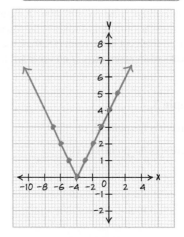

Section 3.2

PP for Example 1.

a. Pay-per-view movies, because the line is higher than the video-on-demand line.

b. The video-on-demand line is steeper, so it is growing at a faster rate.

PP for Example 2.

$$\text{slope} = \frac{\text{rise}}{\text{run}} = \frac{2}{4} = \frac{1}{2}$$

PP for Example 3.

$$\text{slope} = \frac{\text{rise}}{\text{run}} = \frac{-1}{3}$$

PP for Example 4.

$$\text{slope} = \frac{9 - (-5)}{7 - 2} = \frac{14}{5}$$

PP for Example 5.

a. $\text{slope} = \dfrac{23.5 - 24}{2 - 0} = \dfrac{-0.5}{2} = \dfrac{-1}{4}$

b. $\text{slope} = \dfrac{0 - (-3)}{7 - 7} = \dfrac{3}{0}$

The slope is undefined.

PP for Example 6.

$$\text{slope} = \frac{0 - 20}{4 - 0} = \frac{-20}{4} = \frac{-5}{1}$$

The slope means that 5000 fewer tickets are available every hour.

Section 3.3

PP for Example 1.

a. The x-intercept is $(-1.5, 0)$, and the y-intercept is $(0, 3)$.

b. The x-intercepts are $(-2.5, 0)$, $(0, 0)$, and $(5, 0)$. The y-intercept is $(0, 0)$.

PP for Example 2.

a. The vertical intercept is about the point $(0, 1400)$. It means that in the year 2004, the profit for Starbucks was $1,400 million.

b. The vertical intercept is the point $(0, 400)$. It means at the start of summer, there are 400 feet of water in the town's reservoir. The horizontal intercept is the point $(15, 0)$. It means that after 15 weeks of summer, there is no water left in the town's reservoir.

PP for Example 3.

a. The x-intercept is the point $(3, 0)$.

The y-intercept is the point $(0, 21)$.

---

b. The x-intercept is the point $(14, 0)$.

The y-intercept is the point $(0, -8)$.

PP for Example 4.

a. The D-intercept is the point $(0, 60)$. It means that after 0 hours of walking, Deb and Christine have 60 miles to walk.

b. The h-intercept is the point $(20, 0)$. It means that after 20 hours of walking, Deb and Christine will have 0 miles to walk.

c. Yes

PP for Example 5.

a. The slope is $m = \dfrac{-2}{3}$. The x-intercept is the point $(6, 0)$. The y-intercept is the point $(0, 4)$.

b. The slope is $m = \dfrac{1}{4}$. The x-intercept is the point $\left(\dfrac{8}{5}, 0\right)$. The y-intercept is the point $\left(0, \dfrac{-2}{5}\right)$.

PP for Example 6.

a. When $f = 0$, $T = 2$. This means that it takes 2 hours to produce 0 bike frames. The two hours may be the production setup time.

b. The slope is $m = 0.5 = \dfrac{0.5 \text{ hour}}{1 \text{ bike frame}}$. This means that every half hour, a bike frame is produced. This could also be $m = \dfrac{1}{2} = \dfrac{1 \text{ hour}}{2 \text{ bike frames}}$, which means that each hour, 2 bike frames are produced.

PP for Example 7.

a. $y = 3x - 10$

$m = 3$

The y-intercept is $(0, -10)$.

b. $y = 4x + \dfrac{5}{2}$

$m = 4$

The y-intercept is $\left(0, \dfrac{5}{2}\right)$.

c. $y = \dfrac{2}{3}x + 12$

$m = \dfrac{2}{3}$

The y-intercept is $(0, 12)$.

d. $y = \dfrac{-4}{3}x + \dfrac{1}{3}$

$m = \dfrac{-4}{3}$

The y-intercept is $\left(0, \dfrac{1}{3}\right)$.

Section 3.4

PP for Example 1.

a. $y = 3x - 4$

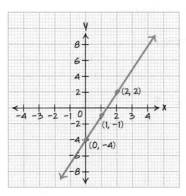

b. $y = -\dfrac{3}{4}x - 3$

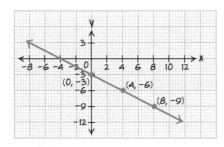

PP for Example 2.

$$y - 8 = \frac{2}{3}(x - 6)$$

$$y = \frac{2}{3}x + 4$$

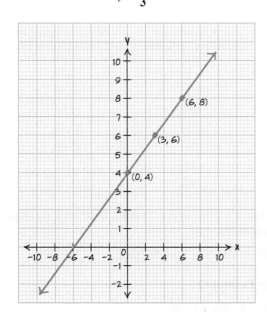

PP for Example 3.

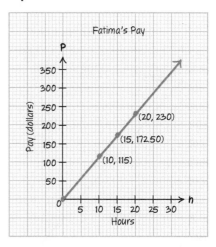

PP for Example 4.

a.

b.

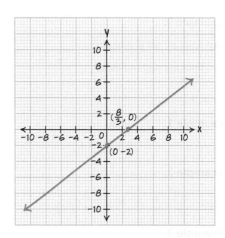

PP for Example 5.

a.

b. If Amanda owes $4500.00 on the credit card that charges 15% interest, then she owes $2300.00 on the credit card that charges 20% interest.

PP for Example 7.

a. Linear. $y = 4x - 7$ b. Not a linear equation

PP for Example 8.

a. The lines are parallel.   b. The lines are not parallel.

PP for Example 9.

a. The two lines are not perpendicular.

b. The two lines are perpendicular.

Section 3.5

PP for Example 1.

$$y = 2x - 4$$

PP for Example 2.

a. $y = -\dfrac{7}{4}x + \dfrac{19}{4}$ b. $y = \dfrac{3}{4}x - \dfrac{7}{2}$

PP for Example 3.

$$d = \dfrac{1}{24}h$$

PP for Example 5.

a. $d = \dfrac{1}{5}s$ or $d = \dfrac{s}{5}$

b. $N = -w + 195$ or $N = 195 - w$

PP for Example 6.

a. The point-slope form is $y - 5 = \dfrac{-1}{2}(x - (-2))$.

The slope-intercept form is $y = \dfrac{-1}{2}x + 4$.

b. The point-slope form is $y - (-1) = \dfrac{1}{6}(x - 6)$.

The slope-intercept form is $y = \dfrac{1}{6}x - 2$.

PP for Example 7.

$$y = \dfrac{-1}{2}x - 2$$

PP for Example 8.

$$y = \dfrac{-7}{3}x + 13$$

CHAPTER 4

Section 4.1

PP for Example 1.

a. $S = 55 + 2.30m$

$I = 50 + 2.50m$

b.

m = number of miles over 15 miles	S = cost of shipping for Ship Quick ($)
0	55.00
5	66.50
10	78.00
15	89.50
20	101.00
25	112.50
30	124.00

m = number of miles over 15 miles	I = cost of shipping for In Town Shipping ($)
0	50.00
5	62.50
10	75.00
15	87.50
20	100.00
25	112.50
30	125.00

c. When $m = 25$ miles over 15 miles, or 40 miles, the shipping costs are the same.

d. She should use In Town Shipping.

PP for Example 2.

a. Yes   b. Yes   c. No

PP for Example 3.

a. About 1960, 1984, and 1987

b. About 1970

PP for Example 4.

The solution is $(2, -3)$.

PP for Example 5.

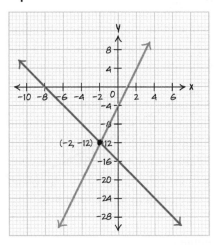

The solution is $(-2, -12)$.

PP for Example 7.

a. The equation for Help-U-Stor is $C = 160m + 10$. The equation for Local Storage Solutions is $C = 150m + 30$.

b.

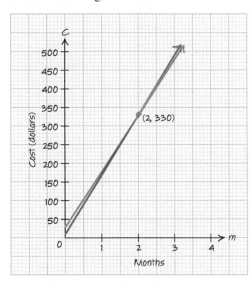

c. The solution is the point $(m, C) = (2, 330)$.

d. You should use Local Storage Solutions.

Section **4.2**

PP for Example 1.

a. The solution is the point $(x, y) = (-11, -9)$.

b. The solution is the point $(x, y) = \left(13, \dfrac{9}{2}\right)$.

PP for Example 2.

The solution is the point $(m, C) = (2, 330)$.

PP for Example 3.

a. The lines are dependent. There are infinitely many solutions to the system.

b. There are no solutions to the system.

PP for Example 4.

a. The speed of the plane with a tailwind is 505 mph.

b. The speed of the ship traveling upstream is 11 mph.

PP for Example 5.

The rate of the boat is $\dfrac{35}{12}$ mph, and the rate of the current is $\dfrac{5}{12}$ mph.

PP for Example 6.

The two integers are -24 and -78.

PP for Example 7.

a. The value of the walnuts is $112.35. The value of the hazelnuts is $169.80.

b. The unit price of the mix is $8.06.

PP for Example 8.

They should include approximately 31.52 pounds of hazelnuts and approximately 18.48 pounds of almonds.

Section **4.3**

PP for Example 1.

The solution is the point $(x, y) = (4, -1)$.

PP for Example 2.

a. The solution is the point $(x, y) = (-5, 3)$.

b. There is no solution to this system.

PP for Example 3.

The solution is the point $(x, y) = (4, 5)$.

PP for Example 4.

Each food coloring kit costs $9.00, and each cake decorating kit costs $24.00.

PP for Example 5.

The simple interest earned is $6000.00.

PP for Example 6.

Russ should invest $35,833.33 in the stock fund and $9166.67 in the bond fund.

PP for Example 8.

The farmer should use 166.67 gallons of the 4% milk and 333.33 gallons of the 1% milk in the mixture.

PP for Example 9.

The measure of the first angle is 18°, and the measure of the second angle is 72°.

Section **4.4**

PP for Example 2.

a. The point is in the solution set.

b. The point is in the solution set.

c. The point is not in the solution set.

d. The point is not in the solution set.

PP for Example 4.

a.

b.

c.

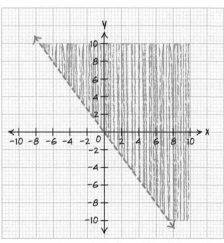

PP for Example 6.

Let f represent the amount in pounds of the first type of candy Kelli purchases, and let s represent the amount in pounds of the second type of candy she purchases. The inequality is $2.25f + 4.25s \le 20$.

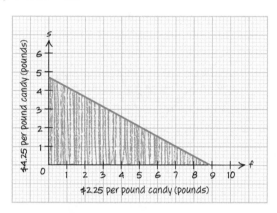

PP for Example 7.

a.

b.

CHAPTER 5

Section 5.1

PP for Example 1.

a. $2^5 = 32$

b. $(-2)^4 = 16$

c. $-2^4 = -16$

d. $(-a)^3 = -a^3$

PP for Example 2.

a. $x^5x^6 = x^{11}$

b. $t^3t = t^4$

c. $7^47^5 = 7^9 = 40{,}353{,}607$

PP for Example 3.

a. $(5x^6y^9)(6x^5y^2) = 30x^{11}y^{11}$

b. $(-9a^4b^3)(4a^2b^6) = -36a^6b^9$

PP for Example 4.

a. $\dfrac{x^9}{x^2} = x^7$

b. $\dfrac{4^9}{4^3} = 4^6 = 4096$

c. $\dfrac{y^3}{y^3} = y^0 = 1$

PP for Example 5.

a. $\dfrac{a^3a^5b^7}{a^2a^4b^2} = a^2b^5$

b. $\dfrac{x^5y^6}{x^2y^4} \cdot \dfrac{x^8y^4}{xy^3} = x^{10}y^3$

PP for Example 6.

a. $(c^4)^6 = c^{24}$

b. $(8^3)^2 = 8^6 = 262{,}144$

PP for Example 7.

a. $(-5a)^4 = 625a^4$

b. $(4ac^4)^3 = 64a^3c^{12}$

c. $\left(\dfrac{a^2}{b^5}\right)^2 = \dfrac{a^4}{b^{10}}$

d. $(-52x^3y^2)^0 = 1$

PP for Example 8.

a. $\left(\dfrac{-3m^7n^5}{m^2n^3}\right)^4 = 81m^{20}n^8$

b. $\dfrac{(5x^3)^2}{(2x^2y^4)^3} = \dfrac{25}{8y^{12}}$

c. $(-2a^5b)^3(6a^3b^5)^2 = -288a^{21}b^{13}$

d. $(4m)^5(4m)^8 = (4m)^{13}$

Section 5.2

PP for Example 1.

a. $b^{-6} = \dfrac{1}{b^6}$

b. $7h^{-2} = \dfrac{7}{h^2}$

c. $4x^{-3} = \dfrac{4}{x^3}$

PP for Example 2.

a. $\dfrac{35x^4}{14x^{10}} = \dfrac{5}{2x^6}$

b. $-12x^{-4}y^3 = \dfrac{-12y^3}{x^4}$

c. $\dfrac{5a^{-5}b^4}{7a^{-2}b^{-1}} = \dfrac{5b^5}{7a^3}$

PP for Example 3.

a. $13{,}000{,}000{,}000 = 1.3 \times 10^{10}$

b. $0.00000002 = 2.0 \times 10^{-8}$

PP for Example 4.

a. $4(1.25 \times 10^8) = 5 \times 10^8$

b. $25(3.4 \times 10^{13}) = 8.5 \times 10^{14}$

c. $\dfrac{7.4 \times 10^8}{1480} = 5 \times 10^5$

PP for Example 5.

$$2.870824 \times 10^9$$

PP for Example 6.

a. $(8.4 \times 10^6)(7.0 \times 10^8) = 5.88 \times 10^{15}$

b. $(1.5 \times 10^{-9})(4.0 \times 10^{-17}) = 6 \times 10^{-26}$

c. $\dfrac{6.4 \times 10^{15}}{2.0 \times 10^4} = 3.2 \times 10^{11}$

PP for Example 7.

The mass of Jupiter is about 317.39 times the mass of the earth.

Section 5.3

PP for Example 1.

a. Binomial. The terms are $5x^2$ and $7x$.

b. Trinomial. The terms are $4a^3b^2$, $-2ab$, and b.

PP for Example 2.

a. The degree is 2. $-x^2 + 4$

b. The degree is 3. $3x^3 + x^2 + x - 4$

c. The degree is 1. $-7x + 5$

PP for Example 3.

a. Working from left to right, the degree of the first term is 5. The degree of the second term is 4. The degree of the third term is 2. The degree of the fourth term is 0. The degree of the polynomial is 5.

b. Working from left to right, the degree of the first term is 6. The degree of the second term is 9. The degree of the third term is 4. The degree of the polynomial is 9.

PP for Example 4.

a. Linear equation in two variables.

b. Linear expression in one variable.

c. Nonlinear equation in two variables.

PP for Example 5.

a. $6x^2 - 6x + 11$

b. $5a^2 + 8ab + 7b^2$

PP for Example 6.

a. $9x^2 + 2x + 10$

b. $3y^2 - 3y + 4$

PP for Example 7.

a. $9c + 25$

b. It will cost \$187 to purchase art projects without the winter projects for the 18 children in her class.

Section **5.4**

PP for Example 1.

a. $6x(4x - 8) = 24x^2 - 48x$

b. $4a(5a^2 - 6a + 8) = 20a^3 - 24a^2 + 32a$

PP for Example 2.

a. $20x^2 - 17x^2 - 53x + 14$

b. $12x^6y^2 + 8x^5y^3 - 20x^4y^4 - 15x^4y - 10x^3y^2 + 25x^2y^3$

PP for Example 3.

$$-24x^3 + 4x^2y + 160xy^2$$

PP for Example 4.

a. $30x^2 + 8x - 6$ \qquad b. $12x^2 - 9xy - 30y^2$

PP for Example 6.

a. $(-0.3t + 17.7)(2.75t + 282) = -0.825t^2 - 35.925t + 4991.40$

b. Substitute in $t = 11$ to find 4496.40 million pounds of canned fruit will be consumed by Americans in the year 2011.

PP for Example 7.

$$(2x + 3)(7x - 4) = 14x^2 + 13x - 12$$

PP for Example 8.

a. $(3x - 8)^2 = 9x^2 - 48x + 64$

b. $(3x^2 + 5y)^2 = 9x^4 + 30x^2y + 25y^2$

c. $\left(\dfrac{t}{4} - 5\right)^2 = \dfrac{t^2}{16} - \dfrac{5t}{2} + 25$

PP for Example 9.

a. This is a product. $(8t)^2 = 64t^2$

b. This is a sum. $(8 + t)^2 = 64 + 16t + t^2$ or $t^2 + 16t + 64$

PP for Example 10.

a. $(2x + 1)(2x - 1) = 4x^2 - 1$

b. $(x + 5y)(x - 5y) = x^2 - 25y^2$

Section **5.5**

PP for Example 1.

a. $\dfrac{30x^2 + 4x}{5x} = 6x + \dfrac{4}{5}$ \qquad b. $\dfrac{24m^4 - 36m}{8m} = 3m^3 - \dfrac{9}{2}$

PP for Example 2.

a. $\dfrac{40x^2 + 12x - 72}{4x} = 10x + 3 - \dfrac{18}{x}$

b. $\dfrac{60m^4n^3 - 51m^3n^2 + 30m^2n}{3m^2n} = 20m^2n^2 - 17mn + 10$

PP for Example 3.

a. $(x^2 + 12x + 32) \div (x + 4) = x + 8$

b. $(20x^2 - 9x - 18) \div (4x + 3) = 5x - 6$

PP for Example 4.

The length is $4x + 2$.

PP for Example 5.

a. $8x + 5 - \dfrac{4}{x - 3}$ \qquad b. $3x^2 - 20x + 33 - \dfrac{62}{x + 3}$

PP for Example 6.

a. $4x^2 - 8x + 13 - \dfrac{19}{x + 2}$ \qquad b. $x^2 + 3x + 9$

PP for Example 7.

a. $-2x^2 - 2x - 15$

b. $3x^4 - 11x^3 + 55x^2 - 274x + 1376 - \dfrac{6280}{x + 5}$

CHAPTER 6

Section **6.1**

PP for Example 1.

a. The GCF is 5. \qquad b. The GCF is $4y$. \qquad c. The GCF is $3xy$.

PP for Example 2.

a. The GCF is 6. \qquad b. The GCF is $8x^2$. \qquad c. The GCF is $25y^2$.

PP for Example 3.

a. The GCF is $3xy$. \qquad b. The GCF is $10pq$.

PP for Example 4.

a. $5x - 35 = 5(x - 7)$

b. $2y^2(y - 3 + 6y^2) = 2y^2(6y^2 + y - 3)$

c. $6x^3 - 2x^2 + 2x = 2x(3x^2 - x + 1)$

PP for Example 5.

a. $-x^2 - 5 = -1(x^2 + 5)$ \qquad b. $-y + 16 = -1(y - 16)$

c. $-16n + 48 = -16(n - 3)$

PP for Example 6.

a. $a(2 - b) - 3(2 - b) = (2 - b)(a - 3)$

b. $x(x + 1) - 5(x + 1) = (x + 1)(x - 5)$

PP for Example 7.

a. $(x + 7)(2x - 5)$ \qquad b. $(2a - b)(3a + b)$

PP for Example 8.

a. $16y^2 - 48y = 16y(y - 3)$

b. $3x^2 + 15x - 3x - 15 = 3(x - 1)(x + 5)$

Section **6.2**

PP for Example 1.

a. $b = 5$ and $c = -6$ **b.** $b = -9$ and $c = -12$

c. $b = -3$ and $c = -5$

PP for Example 2.

a. $x^2 + 11x + 24 = (x + 3)(x + 8)$

b. $-35 + 2x + x^2 = (x + 7)(x - 5)$

c. $x^2 - 13x + 36 = (x - 4)(x - 9)$

PP for Example 3.

a. $a = -3, b = 0, c = -16$ **b.** $a = -1, b = -4, c = 3$

c. $a = -4, b = 8, c = 16$

PP for Example 4.

a. $3x^2 + 23x + 14 = (3x + 2)(x + 7)$

b. $2x^2 + 5x - 42 = (2x - 7)(x + 6)$

c. $3x^2 - 11x + 10 = (3x - 5)(x - 2)$

PP for Example 6.

a. $2(3m - n)(2m + n)$ **b.** $-3(t + 7)(t - 1)$

c. $2(x^2y - x - 5y)$

Section **6.3**

PP for Example 2.

a. This is a difference of squares.

$p^2 - 100 = (p - 10)(p + 10)$

b. This is a difference of squares.

$9x^2 - 64 = (3x - 8)(3x + 8)$

PP for Example 3.

a. This is a perfect square trinomial.

b. This is a perfect square trinomial.

c. This is not a perfect square trinomial.

PP for Example 4.

a. $x^2 + 16x + 64 = (x + 8)^2$ **b.** $9x^2 - 6x + 1 = (3x - 1)^2$

PP for Example 5.

a. $(x + 2)(x^2 - 2x + 4)$

b. $(x - 3y)(x^2 + 3xy + 9y^2)$

c. $2(5a - 2b)(25a^2 + 10ab + 4b^2)$

PP for Example 6.

$(t + 2)(t^2 - 2t + 4)(t - 2)(t^2 + 2t + 4)$

PP for Example 7.

$(3a^5 + 7)(a^5 - 4)$

PP for Example 8.

a. $5(q - 4)(3p + 2)$ **b.** $3(x - 12)(x + 12)$

c. $-3a(2a - 1)(a + 4)$

Section **6.4**

PP for Example 1.

a. Quadratic equation   **b.** Linear equation

PP for Example 2.

a. $x = 6$ **b.** $y = 0, y = 1$

PP for Example 3.

a. $d = \dfrac{-1}{3}, d = \dfrac{-3}{2}$ **b.** $t = \pm 12$

c. $n = 6, n = \dfrac{-1}{2}$

PP for Example 5.

a. $x = \dfrac{1}{4}, x = \dfrac{-2}{5}$ **b.** $x = 0, x = 5, x = -7$

CHAPTER 7
Section **7.1**

PP for Example 1.

a. The cost is $20.00 per student when 20 students go on the trip.

b. The cost is $10.00 per student when 60 students go on the trip.

PP for Example 2.

a. $\dfrac{12}{-4} = -3$ **b.** $\dfrac{2}{126} = \dfrac{1}{63}$

c. $\dfrac{52}{0}$. This is undefined.

PP for Example 3.

a. The excluded value is $x = -3$.

b. The excluded values are $x = 5, x = -2$.

c. There are no excluded values.

PP for Example 4.

a. $\dfrac{a - 4}{a + 6}$ **b.** $\dfrac{1}{x - 5}$

PP for Example 5.

a. $\dfrac{-(x + 5)}{x + 10}$ **b.** $\dfrac{5}{y + 4}$

Section 7.2

PP for Example 1.

a. $\dfrac{14}{13}$ **b.** $\dfrac{x-6}{x-7}$

PP for Example 2.

a. $-\dfrac{(a+8)}{(a+9)(a-3)}$ **b.** $\dfrac{(x-3)(x+6)}{(x-9)(x+3)}$

PP for Example 3.

The cereal is priced at $0.19 per ounce.

PP for Example 4.

The car's speed is 33.528 meters per second.

PP for Example 5.

a. $\dfrac{24 \text{ meters}}{1 \text{ hour}} \cdot \dfrac{1 \text{ mile}}{1609.344 \text{ meters}} = \dfrac{0.01491 \text{ mile}}{1 \text{ hour}}$

b. $\dfrac{0.01491 \text{ mile}}{1 \text{ hour}} \cdot 8 \text{ hours} = 0.1193 \text{ mile}$

PP for Example 6.

a. $\dfrac{9}{4}$ **b.** $\dfrac{5}{3y^2}$ **c.** $\dfrac{y-3}{y-7}$

PP for Example 7.

a. $\dfrac{(b+10)(b-8)}{(b+11)(b+6)}$ **b.** $\dfrac{x+2}{x+5}$

PP for Example 8.

$$\dfrac{x+6}{2(x+4)}$$

Section 7.3

PP for Example 1.

a. $\dfrac{3a+7}{5b^2}$ **b.** $\dfrac{4x+5}{x-3}$ **c.** $\dfrac{2}{m+5}$

PP for Example 2.

a. $\dfrac{7x-5}{3y^2}$ **b.** 3 **c.** $\dfrac{4(x+2)}{(x+3)(x-4)}$

PP for Example 3.

The LCD is $600m^2n$.

PP for Example 4.

a. The LCD is $(k+1)(k-12)(k-3)$.

b. The LCD is $(t-4)(t-5)(t+8)$.

PP for Example 5.

a. The LCD is $150abc^3$.

$$\dfrac{24a^2c}{150abc^3} \quad \text{and} \quad \dfrac{35}{150abc^3}$$

b. The LCD is $(x+6)(x-2)$.

$$\dfrac{8x(x-2)}{(x+6)(x-2)} \quad \text{and} \quad \dfrac{5(x+6)}{(x-2)(x+6)}$$

PP for Example 6.

The LCD is $(t+3)^2(t-4)$.

$$\dfrac{t-5}{t^2+6t+9} = \dfrac{(t-5)(t-4)}{(t+3)^2(t-4)}$$

$$\dfrac{6t}{t^2-t-12} = \dfrac{6t(t+3)}{(t+3)^2(t-4)}$$

PP for Example 7.

a. $\dfrac{3x^2+21x+6}{x+7}$ **b.** $\dfrac{5m^2-37m-28}{(m+4)(m-6)}$

c. $\dfrac{a^2+8a+18}{(a+2)(a+3)(a+5)}$

PP for Example 8.

a. $\dfrac{b+a}{ab}$ **b.** $\dfrac{15+10}{(10)(15)} = \dfrac{25}{150} = \dfrac{1}{6}$

PP for Example 9.

a. $\dfrac{-2z-8}{z-5}$ **b.** $\dfrac{n^2-6}{(n-4)(n+4)(n-1)}$

PP for Example 11.

a. $\dfrac{1}{12}$ **b.** $\dfrac{x}{x+5}$

Section 7.4

PP for Example 1.

a. It will cost $17.25 per person if 40 students go on the trip.

b. A total of 30 students will need to go on the trip for the cost to be $21.00 per person.

PP for Example 2.

a. $t = 4$

b. $x = -3$. It does not check. No solution.

c. $h = -1$

PP for Example 3.

a. $n = 1$ **b.** $x = 6$

PP for Example 5.

a. The two solutions are $x = 4$, $x = -2$. Because $x = 4$ is an excluded value, the only solution is $x = -2$.

b. The two solutions are $h = 6$, $h = -2$. Because $h = 6$ is an excluded value, the only solution is $h = -2$.

PP for Example 6.

Working together, the two painters will take 7.2 hours to paint the house.

Section 7.5

PP for Example 1.

a. $\dfrac{9}{30} = \dfrac{3}{10}$ b. $\dfrac{1}{9}$

PP for Example 2.

a. $\dfrac{6 \text{ pounds}}{1 \text{ month}}$

b. $\dfrac{\$9.29}{8 \text{ ounces}} \approx \$1.16 \text{ per ounce}$

PP for Example 3.

a. $\dfrac{\$2.50}{14 \text{ ounces}} \approx \$0.18 \text{ per ounce}$

b. $\dfrac{\$2.99}{18 \text{ ounces}} \approx \$0.17 \text{ per ounce}$

c. The 18-ounce package is the better buy.

PP for Example 5.

$$\frac{2 \text{ pounds}}{\$0.66} = \frac{7 \text{ pounds}}{x}$$

$$x = \$2.31$$

PP for Example 6.

a. $x = 8$ b. $z = 4$

PP for Example 7.

a. 149.86 centimeters   b. 2.08 ounces

PP for Example 8.

$$1.75 \text{ inches}$$

PP for Example 9.

$$x = 6$$

PP for Example 10.

a. $W = 12.25h$ b. $W = 12.25(35) = \$428.75$

PP for Example 11.

$$y = -6 \quad \text{when} \quad x = -2$$

PP for Example 12.

a. $s = \dfrac{210}{t}$ b. $s = \dfrac{210}{2.5} = 84$

PP for Example 13.

$$y = \frac{5}{9} \quad \text{when} \quad x = 18$$

CHAPTER 8

Section **8.1**

*PP for Example 1.

a. An 8-mile taxi ride costs \$21.30.

b. $m \approx 13.708$. For \$35, you can take a taxi ride of up to 13 miles.

PP for Example 2.

a. $v =$ number of patient visits in a month at this chiropractor's office
   $C =$ monthly cost, in dollars, for v patient visits at this chiropractor's office

$$C = 15v + 8000$$

b. $C = 9500$. This chiropractor's office has a total monthly cost of \$9500 if they have 100 patient visits during the month.

c. $R =$ monthly revenue, in dollars, for this chiropractor's office

$$R = 80v$$

d. $P =$ monthly profit, in dollars, for this chiropractor's office

$$P = 65v - 8000$$

e. $P = 1750$. This chiropractor's office has a profit of \$1750 in a month with 150 patient visits.

f. $200 = v$. For this chiropractor's office to have a monthly profit of \$5000, they would need to have 200 patient visits during the month.

PP for Example 3.

a. $x = 116$

b. $x \approx -3.652$

PP for Example 4.

a. Slope $= -0.07 = \dfrac{-0.07}{1} = \dfrac{-0.07 \text{ psi}}{1 \text{ second}}$. This means that the pressure inside the vacuum chamber is decreasing by 0.07 psi per second.

b. Slope $= 0.55 = \dfrac{0.55}{1} = \dfrac{\$0.55}{1 \text{ taco}}$. Therefore, the cost for making tacos at a local street stand is increasing by \$0.55 (55 cents) per taco made.

PP for Example 5.

a. Slope $= m = -300 = \dfrac{-300}{1} = \dfrac{-300 \text{ stores}}{1 \text{ year}}$. The slope means that the number of sports-cards hobby stores is decreasing by about 300 per year.

b. The vertical intercept is $(0, 4500)$. This intercept means that in 1995, year zero, there were about 4500 sports-cards hobby stores.

c. The horizontal intercept is $(15, 0)$, which implies that there were no more sports-cards hobby stores in 2010. This does not make sense, since there are still sports-cards hobby stores today.

PP for Example 6.

a. C = thousands of cases of chlamydia infection in the United States
t = years since 2000

$$C = 56t + 709.5$$

b. Slope = 56. The number of cases of chlamydia infection in the United States is increasing by about 56 thousand per year.

c. The vertical intercept is $(0, 709.5)$. In 2000, there were 709.5 thousand cases of chlamydia infection in the United States.

Section **8.2**

PP for Example 1.

There are many possible correct answers; only one of these possibilities is given here.

a. t = time in years since 2000
P = population of Arizona (in millions)

b.

	Population of Arizona (millions)
t	
0	5.17
1	5.30
2	5.44
3	5.58
4	5.74
5	5.94
6	6.17

c.

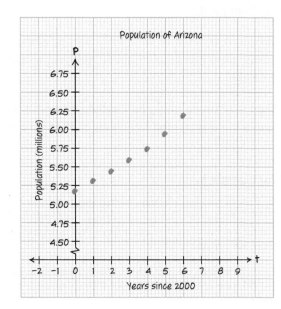

*PP = Practice Problem

PP for Example 2.

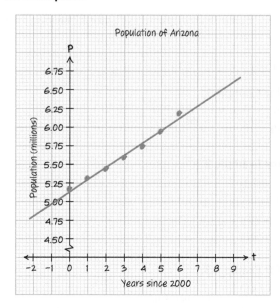

PP for Example 3.

a. y-intercept: $(0, -4)$.

b. x-intercept: $(-7, 0)$.

c. The line has a y-value of -10 when $x = 10$.

d. The line has a y-value of 5 when $x = -15$.

PP for Example 4.

Domain $[-2, 8]$ or $-2 \le t \le 8$, range $[4.76, 6.45]$ or $4.76 \le P \le 6.45$.

Section **8.3**

PP for Example 1.

t = years since 2000.
P = population of Arizona (in thousands)

PP for Example 2.

t = years since 2000.
P = population of Arizona (in thousands)

$$P = 196.14t + 5046.72$$

PP for Example 3.

a. t = years since 2000

P = total prize money given out at professional rodeo events in millions of dollars

$$P = 1.1t + 31.1$$

b. $P = 41$. In 2009, professional rodeos gave out a total of about $41 million in prize money.

c. Slope = 1.1. The total prize money given out at professional rodeo events is increasing by about 1.1 million dollars per year.

d. Domain $[0, 10]$, range $[31.1, 42.1]$.

Section 8.4

PP for Example 1.

a. The table does represent a function, since each input relates to a single output.

b. This table does not represent a function because the name John goes to two separate output values.

c. If we look up the profit for a particular month of a year, the company will have only one amount of profit, so this is a function.

d. California will have one total population each year, so this is a function.

PP for Example 2.

a. This table does represent a function because each input is associated with only one output. It is okay for more than one input to go to the same output, just not the same input to more than one output.

b. This graph passes the vertical line test and thus represents a function.

c. This graph does not pass the vertical line test, since almost every vertical line drawn would hit the graph in more than one place.

d. This equation is a function, since any input value u will result in only one output value C.

e. This equation does not represent a function, since the plus/minus symbol ($\pm$) will give two outputs for almost any input given.

PP for Example 3.

a. 2500 is the value of the input variable, and thus the number of miracle mops produced, and 189 is the cost in hundreds of dollars. Therefore, a good interpretation of this notation is "The cost of producing 2500 miracle mops is $18,900."

b. In 2010, the population of Michigan was 10.4 million people.

PP for Example 5.

a. $f(3) = -7$ **b.** $x = 3$

PP for Example 7.

a. Domain: the set of all real numbers or $(-\infty, \infty)$, range: the set of all real numbers or $(-\infty, \infty)$.

b. Domain: the set of all real numbers or $(-\infty, \infty)$, range is $\{-8\}$.

c. Domain: the set of all real numbers or $(-\infty, \infty)$, range: the set of all real numbers or $(-\infty, \infty)$.

Section 8.5

PP for Example 1.

a. $R(10) = 5988.8$

$P(10) = 2247.2$

Thus, in 2010, the revenue for the California lottery was about $5988.8 million, and the profits were about $2247.2 million.

b. Let $C(t)$ be the costs for the California lottery in millions of dollars t years since 2000. $C(t) = 36.6t^2 - 178.4t + 1865.6$

c. $C(15) = 7424.6$. In 2015, the cost for the California lottery is approximately $7424.6 million.

PP for Example 4.

a. $f(x) + g(x) = 11x - 3$ **b.** $g(x) - f(x) = -3x - 13$

PP for Example 5.

a. $F(t) \cdot I(t) =$ total amount spent on health insurance in dollars for Ford Motor Company employees in year t

b. $F(t) - M(t) =$ number of nonmanagement employees at Ford Motor Company in year t

c. $\dfrac{V(t)}{(F(t) - M(t))} =$ average cost for vacations in dollars per nonmanagement employee at Ford Motor Company in year t

PP for Example 6.

a. $S(45) = 23.7$. At a selling price of $45,000, this car manufacturer is willing to supply 23,700 SUVs.

b. Let $R(p)$ represent the revenue in millions of dollars from selling SUVs at a price of p thousand dollars. $R(p) = 0.008p^3 - 0.5p^2 + 30p$

c. $R(40) = 912$. At a price of $40,000, the car manufacturer can expect a revenue of about $912 million.

PP for Example 7.

a. $f(x)g(x) = 28x^2 - 23x - 15$ **b.** $\dfrac{g(x)}{h(x)} = \dfrac{4x - 5}{9x + 2}$

PP for Example 8.

a. The set of all real numbers.

b. The set of all real numbers.

c. The set of all real numbers.

PP for Example 9.

a. The set of all real numbers except $x = \dfrac{8}{3}$.

b. The set of all real numbers except $x = 7$ and $x = -7$.

PP for Example 10.

a. Domain: the set of all real numbers except zero.

b. Domain: the set of all real numbers except $x = 7$.

c. Δομαιν℧ τηε σετ οφ αλλ ρεαλ νθμβερσ εχψεπτ $x = 5$ or -2.

Section 8.6

PP for Example 2.

a. $P(5) = 9.4$. This urban area had a population of 9.4 million people in 2005.

b. $A(9.4) \approx 41.51$. This urban area had air pollution levels of 41.51 parts per million in 2005.

c. $a(t) = A(P(t)) =$ amount of air pollution in parts per million t years since 2000. $a(t) = A(P(t)) = 18.576t - 51.368$

d. $a(5) \approx 41.5$, $a(7) \approx 78.7$, $a(10) \approx 134.4$. The amount of air pollution in this urban area was 41.5 ppm in 2005, 78.7 ppm in 2007, and 134.4 ppm in 2010.

PP for Example 3.

a. $f(g(x)) = 20x - 27$

b. $(h \circ g)(x) = 50x^2 - 140x + 95$

PP for Example 4.

a. $C(S(h)) = -0.0272h^2 + 0.7548h - 3.8168$

b. $C(S(15)) = 1.3852$. At 3:00 P.M., the CO concentration at Old Faithful was approximately 1.39 parts per million.

CHAPTER 9

Section **9.1**

PP for Example 1.

$$x = 10, x = -2$$

PP for Example 2.

a. $x = 9$ or $x = -5$

b. $x = 4$ or $x = -6$

PP for Example 3.

a. There is no solution for this equation.

b. There is no solution for this equation.

PP for Example 4.

Svetlana will be about 25 miles from Columbus, Texas, after driving 1.5 hours and again after 2.3 hours. The second time is after she has passed Columbus and is 25 miles beyond the town.

Section **9.2**

PP for Example 1.

$$-6 < x < 9$$

PP for Example 2.

a. $6 < x < 10$

b. $-9 \le d \le 7$

PP for Example 3.

$4.1245 \le L \le 4.1255$. The rod's length must be between 4.1245 inches and 4.1255 inches.

PP for Example 4.

$$x < 1 \text{ or } x > 5$$

PP for Example 5.

a. $x < -9$ or $x > 5$

b. $g \le -2$ or $g \ge 8$

PP for Example 6.

$h < 23.18$ or $h > 40.82$. Watching TV less than 23.18 hours a week or more than 40.82 hours a week would be considered unusual.

Section **9.3**

PP for Example 1.

$(-\infty, -4) \text{ or } (-2, \infty)$

$x < -4 \text{ or } x > -2$

PP for Example 2.

a. $(-\infty, -3) \text{ or } (2, \infty)$

$x < -3 \text{ or } x > 2$

b. $[-7, 7]$

$-7 \le x \le 7$

c. $(-\infty, 0) \text{ or } (3, 5)$

$x < 0 \text{ or } 3 < x < 5$

PP for Example 3.

The rock is more than 96 feet off the ground from zero seconds to one second after being thrown from the roof.

PP for Example 5.

$(-2, 8]$

$-2 < x \le 8$

PP for Example 6.

a. $(-\infty, -4) \text{ or } (-1, 8)$

$x < -4 \text{ or } -1 < x < 8$

b. $[-7.5, -5)$

$-7.5 \le x < -5$

c. $(-\infty, -6) \text{ or } (-5, 2) \text{ or } (5, \infty)$

$x < -6 \text{ or } -5 < x < 2 \text{ or } x > 5$

Section 9.4

PP for Example 2.

a.

b.

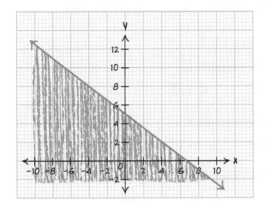

PP for Example 3.

$$y > \frac{5}{4}x - 2$$

PP for Example 4.

a. t = hundreds of toaster ovens produced in a week
g = hundreds of electric griddles produced in a week

$$1.25t + 2g \le 80$$
$$850t + 920g \le 40{,}000$$

b.

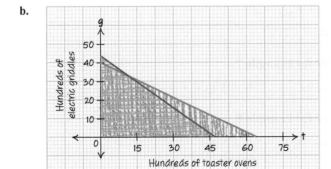

c. The plant can produce 1600 toaster ovens and 2000 electric griddles in a week.

d. Under these constraints, the plant cannot produce 2000 toaster ovens and 3000 electric griddles in a week.

PP for Example 5.

A = amount in the account paying 6.5% annual interest
B = amount in the account paying 4.5% annual interest

$$A + B \le 800{,}000$$
$$0.065A + 0.045B \ge 40{,}500$$

Any combination of investments from the overlapping section of the graph can be used to meet Don's investment goal.

PP for Example 6.

PP for Example 7.

CHAPTER 10

Section 10.1

PP for Example 1.

a. $\sqrt{100} = 10$ **b.** $\sqrt{\dfrac{25}{9}} = \dfrac{5}{3}$ **c.** $\sqrt{0} = 0$

PP for Example 2.

a. Not real   **b.** $-\sqrt{81} = -9$

PP for Example 3.

a. $\sqrt{7} \approx 2.65$ b. $\sqrt{65} \approx 8.06$

PP for Example 4.

a. $\sqrt{(2)^2 + 5} = \sqrt{9} = 3$

b. $\sqrt{3(-2) + 5} = \sqrt{-1}$. Not real.

PP for Example 5.

a. The units represented by s are the speed of the car in miles per hour. The units represented by d are the length of the skid mark in feet.

b. 72.46 feet   c. 58.74 feet

PP for Example 6.

a. The distance is 10.

b. The distance is approximately 13.04.

PP for Example 7.

a. x^7 b. $7x^3$ c. $\dfrac{x}{4}$ d. a^2b^2

PP for Example 8.

a. y^{15} b. $8k^{11}$

PP for Example 9.

a. -5 b. 6   c. 2

PP for Example 10.

a. 10   b. 4

Section 10.2

PP for Example 1.

a. $\sqrt[9]{g^4}$ b. $\sqrt[10]{m^7}$

PP for Example 2.

a. $(7a)^{\frac{1}{2}}$ b. $t^{\frac{3}{4}}$

PP for Example 3.

a. $5\sqrt{3}$ b. $6\sqrt{2}$ c. $\sqrt{30}$

PP for Example 5.

a. $\sqrt{45} \approx 6.71$ b. $\sqrt{45} = 3\sqrt{5}$

PP for Example 6.

a. $y^7\sqrt{y}$ b. $2a\sqrt{3}$ c. $3x^5\sqrt{5x}$

PP for Example 7.

a. x^3y^4 b. $2ab\sqrt{3b}$ c. $3x^5yz\sqrt{5xz}$

PP for Example 8.

a. $3mn^2\sqrt[3]{4m^2}$ b. $x^4y^2z\sqrt[9]{z^2}$

PP for Example 9.

a. $3\sqrt{21}$ b. $-13\sqrt{x}$

c. There are no like terms. $-3\sqrt{b} + 3\sqrt{a}$

PP for Example 10.

a. $7 + \sqrt{11}$ b. $-2\sqrt{a} - 4\sqrt{5}$ c. $19y\sqrt{x} - 8xy$

PP for Example 11.

a. $8\sqrt{7}$ b. $-\sqrt{5}$

PP for Example 12.

a. $-2y\sqrt{3}$ b. $7b\sqrt{2}$ c. $3 + x^2\sqrt{x}$

PP for Example 13.

a. $8\sqrt{2m} + 8\sqrt[3]{7m}$ b. $8\sqrt[5]{x^3y} + 5\sqrt[4]{xy^2}$

Section 10.3

PP for Example 1.

a. $2\sqrt{3}$ b. $4\sqrt{5}$

PP for Example 2.

a. $8x^2$ b. $3a^3\sqrt{7a}$ c. $\sqrt[3]{15abc}$

PP for Example 3.

a. $5y$ b. $15a$ c. $36b$

PP for Example 4.

a. $15y$ b. $-54b^2\sqrt{2}$ c. $28x^4y^6\sqrt[3]{y}$

PP for Example 5.

a. $\sqrt{10y} + 10$ b. $2\sqrt{5} - 8$ c. $-8\sqrt{x} + 2$

PP for Example 6.

a. $\sqrt{15} - 2\sqrt{3} + 9\sqrt{5} - 18$

b. $7 - \sqrt{70} + 4\sqrt{7} - 4\sqrt{10}$

c. $y + \sqrt{y} - 30$

d. $x^2 - 2x\sqrt{5} + 5$

PP for Example 7.

a. $9a$ b. $9 + 6\sqrt{a} + a$

PP for Example 8.

a. -4 b. $x - 4$

PP for Example 9.

a. 5   b. $\dfrac{1}{3}$ c. $3x^2$ d. $\dfrac{2m\sqrt[4]{9}}{n}$

PP for Example 10.

a. $\dfrac{5\sqrt{7}}{7}$ b. $\sqrt{6}$ c. $\dfrac{-2a\sqrt{b}}{5b}$

PP for Example 11.

a. $\dfrac{2\sqrt[3]{25mn}}{5n}$ b. $\dfrac{7x\sqrt[5]{9x^4y^3}}{3y^2}$

PP for Example 12.

a. $\dfrac{-7(1+\sqrt{5})}{4}$ b. $\dfrac{-2(\sqrt{5}-\sqrt{2})}{3}$

Section 10.4

PP for Example 3.

a.   i. $f(20) = 19.544$

    ii. $f(x) = 34$ when $x \approx 105$

b.   i. $h(2) = -6$

    ii. $h(x) = -8$ when $x = 6$

PP for Example 4.

a.   Domain: $x \geq -8$, range: $[0, \infty)$

b.   Domain: $x \leq 3$, range: $[0, \infty)$

c.   Domain: all real numbers, range: all real numbers

PP for Example 5.

a.   Domain: $x \leq -10$, range: $[0, \infty)$

b.   Domain: all real numbers, range: all real numbers

PP for Example 6.

a. $f(x) = \sqrt{x+6}$

b. $f(x) = -\sqrt{5-x}$

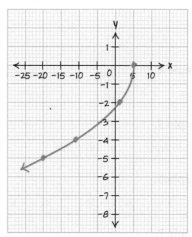

c. $g(x) = -\sqrt[3]{x} - 4$

d. $h(x) = -\sqrt{x+1}$

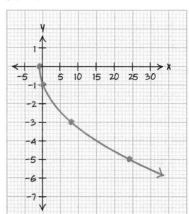

Section 10.5

PP for Example 1.

a.   Yes, it is a solution.   b.   No, it is not a solution.

PP for Example 2.

a.   About 2.74 miles   b.   216 feet

PP for Example 3.

a. $x = 27$ **b.** $y = 169$

c. $x = 16$ **d.** $x = 5$

PP for Example 4.

a. No solution   **b.** $x = 8$

PP for Example 5.

a. About 100.83 feet   **b.** 187.5 feet

PP for Example 6.

a. $x = 5, x = -6$ **b.** $x = 36$ **c.** $x = 6$ $x = 2$

PP for Example 7.

a. $x = 36$ **b.** $x = -246$

Section **10.6**

PP for Example 3.

a. $-1 + 11i$ **b.** $7.6 - 1.6i$

c. $-10 + 2i$ **d.** $-7 - 4i$

PP for Example 4.

a. $-24 + 12i$ **b.** $-29 + 31i$

c. $46 + 22i$ **d.** 29

PP for Example 7.

a. $7 + 4i$ **b.** $-\dfrac{7}{3} - \dfrac{4}{3}i$

c. $-\dfrac{1}{29} + \dfrac{17}{29}i$ **d.** $0.87395 - 1.0672i$

CHAPTER **11**

Section **11.1**

PP for Example 2.

a. This curve increases for $x < 1$ and decreases for $x > 1$.

b. Vertex $= (1, 8)$

c. x-intercept(s): $(-1, 0)$ and $(3, 0)$

d. y-intercept: $(0, 6)$

e. $f(2) = 6$

f. Τηε οθτπθτ οφ τηε φθνψτιον ισ $y = -10$ when the input is about $x = -2$ and $x = 4$.

PP for Example 4.

a.

A quadratic function would be used to model the distribution. The vertex is the minimum point at approximately $(5, -8)$.

b.

A quadratic function would be used to model it. The vertex is the maximum point at $(-2, 4)$.

Section **11.2**

PP for Example 1.

$$f(x) = (x - 4)^2 + 6$$

PP for Example 2.

$$f(x) = -0.5(x + 2)^2 + 4$$

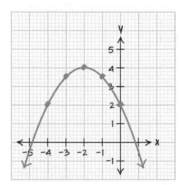

PP for Example 3.

$$f(x) = -x^2 + 8$$

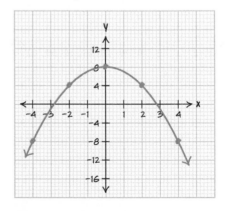

PP for Example 4.

$$C(t) = 833.53\,(t + 1)^2 + 3200$$

a. $C(10) \approx 104{,}057$. There were approximately 104,057 thousand cellular telephone subscribers in 2000. This can also be stated as 104 million cellular telephone subscribers.

b.

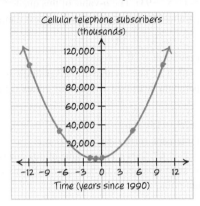

c. The vertex is the lowest point, so the number of cellular telephone subscribers was the least in 1989.

d. $C(-5) \approx 16{,}536$. This answer does not make sense, since there were only 3200 thousand in 1989, so there would not be more than that in 1985.

e. Domain: $[-1, 10]$, range: $[3200, 104{,}057]$.

PP for Example 5.

a. Domain: All real numbers or $(-\infty, \infty)$, range: $y \le 15$ or $(-\infty, 15]$.

b. Domain: All real numbers or $(-\infty, \infty)$, range: $y \ge 4$ or $[4, \infty)$.

c. Domain: All real numbers or $(-\infty, \infty)$, range: $y \le -8.6$ or $(-\infty, -8.6]$.

Section 11.3

PP for Example 1.

a. $C(t) =$ Number of cable television systems in the United States
$t =$ Time in years since 1990

$$C(t) = -33.3(t - 4)^2 + 11250$$

b. The vertex of $(4, 11{,}250)$ represents when the number of cable television systems reached a maximum. Specifically, in 1994, there were the most cable television systems, with a total of 11,250 systems.

c. $C(9) = 10417.5$. In 1999, there were approximately 10,418 cable television systems in the United States.

d. $C(0) = 10717.2$. In 1990, there were approximately 10,717 cable television systems in the United States.

e. In the years 1989 and 1999, there were about 10,500 cable television systems in the United States.

PP for Example 2.

The parabola should be facing downward instead of upward so make the a-value negative. $f(x) = -0.5(x - 3)^2 + 6$

PP for Example 4.

$$f(x) = (x + 2)^2 - 49$$

PP for Example 5.

a. $y = \dfrac{5}{3}x^2 - \dfrac{5}{3}x - 10$

b. $y = -1(x - 2)^2 - 5$

Section 11.4

PP for Example 1.

a. $b = \pm 9$

b. $x = \pm 6$

c. $m = \pm\sqrt{20} = \pm 2\sqrt{5} \approx \pm 4.47$

PP for Example 2.

a. $y = 2, y = -6$

b. $x = 2, x = -1$

c. $a = \dfrac{2 \pm \sqrt{11}}{5}$

$a \approx -0.26, 1.06$

PP for Example 3.

$12.44 \approx t, 1.56 \approx t$. Therefore, in about 1992 and 2002, people were spending an average of 1825 hours per year watching television.

PP for Example 4.

a. $x = \pm 4$

b. $x = 3, \qquad x = \dfrac{1}{2}$

PP for Example 5.

a. $x = \pm 9i$

b. $x = -6 \pm 2i$

PP for Example 6.

a. $b = 12$

b. $c = \sqrt{2} \approx 1.41$

c. $a = \sqrt{160} \approx 12.65$

PP for Example 7.

The length is about 28.45 inches.

PP for Example 8.

a. $d = \sqrt{5} \approx 2.24$

b. $d = \sqrt{145} \approx 12.04$

Section 11.5

PP for Example 1.

a. $x = 2 \pm \sqrt{3}$

$x \approx 3.73, 0.27$

b. $x = -4 \pm \sqrt{5}$

$x \approx -1.76, -6.24$

PP for Example 3.

a. $x = 2$, $\quad x = -10$

b. $x \approx 4.56$, $\quad x \approx 0.44$

c. $x = -2 \pm i\sqrt{26}$

PP for Example 4.

a. $f(x) = 0.25(x + 20)^2 - 103$

b. $h(x) = -3\left(x - \dfrac{2}{3}\right)^2 + \dfrac{34}{3}$

PP for Example 5.

$$f(x) = 2(x + 1)^2 - 32$$

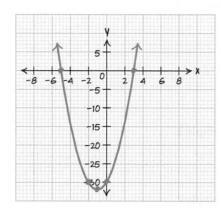

Domain: all real numbers, range: $y \geq -32$ or $[-32, \infty)$.

Section **11.6**

PP for Example 1.

a. $x = \dfrac{-3}{2}$ $\quad x = -5$ $\qquad$ **b.** $x = \dfrac{-1}{3}$ $\quad x = -4$

PP for Example 2.

$t \approx 9.87$, $t \approx 3.66$. In about 1994 and 2000, there were 30,000 people in Hawaii who were unemployed.

PP for Example 3.

a. $x = 0$ $\quad x = -\dfrac{4}{3}$ $\quad x = \dfrac{5}{2}$ $\qquad$ **b.** $x = \pm 4$

PP for Example 5.

$$(-5, -24) \qquad (-13.33, 392.67)$$

PP for Example 6.

a. $w = -3 + 3i$ $\quad w = -3 - 3i$

b. $x = -4 + i\sqrt{2}$ $\quad x = -4 - i\sqrt{2}$

c. $x = 0$ $\quad x = 2 + 3i$ $\quad x = 2 - 3i$

Section **11.7**

PP for Example 1.

a. $f(x) = 4x^2 + 40x + 7$
Vertical intercept $= (0, 7)$.
Vertex $= (-5, -93)$. The a-value of this quadratic is positive, so this parabola faces upward. This vertex is a minimum point.

b. $k(x) = -2(x - 3)^2 + 12$
Vertical intercept $= (0, -6)$.
Vertex $= (3, 12)$. The a-value of this quadratic is negative, so this parabola faces downward. This vertex is a maximum point.

c. $h(t) = -7t^2 - 15t - 6$
Vertical intercept $= (0, -6)$.
Vertex $= (-1.07, 2.04)$. The a-value of this quadratic is negative, so this parabola faces downward. This vertex is a maximum point.

PP for Example 2.

a. $f(x) = 0.25x^2 + 6x - 15$

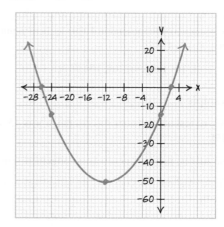

b. $f(x) = 3x^2 + 6x + 7$

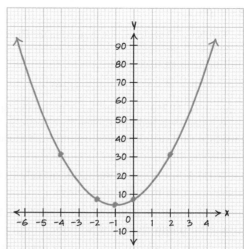

PP for Example 3.

a. $S(15) = 3728.9$. Therefore, Gateway's net sales in 1995 were approximately \$3728.9 million.

b. $t \approx 18.86$, $t \approx -2.99$. Therefore, in 1999, Gateway had net sales of about \$9000 million. At $t = -2.99$, model breakdown occurs because in 1977, Gateway was a new company and could not have made that much in net sales.

c. The vertex is $(7.9, -53.7)$, which represents the lowest net sales for Gateway, Inc. The negative net sales represents model breakdown in this context.

PP for Example 4.

a. $y > 2x^2 - 12x - 8$

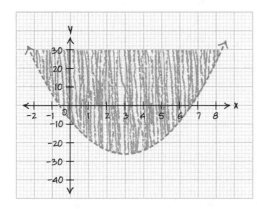

b. $y \leq -0.25x^2 - 3x + 5$

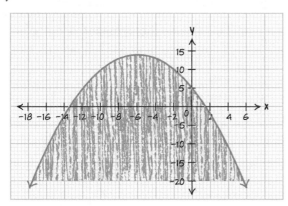

CHAPTER 12

Section 12.1

PP for Example 1.

a. $B(w) =$ Balance on the loan in dollars
   $w =$ Weeks after taking out the loan
$$B(w) = 5000(2)^w$$

b. $B(4) = 80,000$. Thus, if you keep the \$5000 for 4 weeks, you will owe this loan shark \$80,000.

c. After keeping the money for 8 weeks, we would owe the loan shark about 1.28 million dollars.

PP for Example 2.

a. $P(t) =$ World population in billions of people
   $t =$ Time in years after 2000
$$P(t) = 6(2)^{\frac{t}{50}}$$

b. $P(500) = 6144$. This means that if the world population were to grow in ideal circumstances, the population in the year 2500 would be 6144 billion. This seems to be unrealistic and can be considered model breakdown.

c. If this exponential trend continues, the world population will reach 10 billion in the year 2037.

PP for Example 3.

a. $P(d) =$ Percent of a thorium-234 sample remaining
   $d =$ Time in days since the sample was taken
$$P(d) = 100\left(\frac{1}{2}\right)^{\frac{d}{24.5}}$$

b. $P(180) = 0.614$. After 180 days, only 0.614% of the thorium-234 sample will remain.

c. It will take about 32 days for only 40% of the thorium-234 sample to remain.

PP for Example 5.

a. $f(x) = 10(3.1)^x$ **b.** $f(x) = 16(0.9)^{\frac{x}{3}}$

Section 12.2

PP for Example 1.

a. $x = 5$ **b.** $t = 6$ **c.** $x = -2$

PP for Example 2.

a. $x = 3$ **b.** $x = -3$

PP for Example 3.

$w = 5$. If you do not make any payments for 5 weeks, you will owe the loan shark \$160,000.

PP for Example 4.

a. $x = 3$ **b.** $p \approx \pm 3.81$ **c.** $m = 3.4$

PP for Example 5.

a. The equation $5x^8 - 6 = 28$ is a power equation.

b. The equation $3(8^x) - 20 = 40$ is an exponential equation, because the variable is in the exponent.

Section 12.3

PP for Example 1.

a. $f(x) = 8(1.25)^x$. $a = 8$, the vertical intercept is $(0, 8)$, the graph will be above the horizontal axis. The base $b = 1.25$ is > 1, so this graph is increasing, showing exponential growth.

x	$f(x)$
-3	4.1
0	8
3	15.6
6	30.5
9	59.6

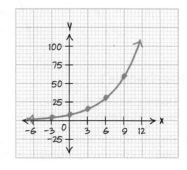

b. $g(x) = 300(0.5)^x$. $a = 300$, the vertical intercept is $(0, 300)$, the graph will be above the horizontal axis. The base $b = 0.5$ is < 1. The graph is decreasing, showing exponential decay.

x	f(x)
−1	600
0	300
1	150
3	37.5
6	4.7

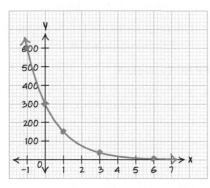

PP for Example 2.

a. $f(x) = -2(2.5)^x$. $a = -2$, the vertical intercept is $(0, -2)$, the graph will be below the horizontal axis. The base $b = 2.5$ is > 1. This graph should show exponential growth, but it has also been reflected over the horizontal axis by the negative a-value.

x	f(x)
−1	−0.8
0	−2
2	−12.5
4	−78.13

b. $h(x) = -145(0.5)^x$. $a = -145$, the vertical intercept is $(0, -145)$, the graph will be below the horizontal axis. The base $b = 0.5$ is < 1. This graph should show exponential decay, but it has also been reflected over the horizontal axis by the negative a-value.

x	f(x)
−2	−580
−1	−290
0	−145
1	−72.5
2	−36.25
3	−18.13

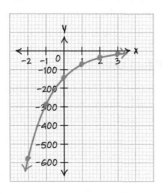

PP for Example 3.

a. Domain: All real numbers or $(-\infty, \infty)$, range: All negative real numbers or $(-\infty, 0)$.

b. Domain: All real numbers or $(-\infty, \infty)$, range: All positive real numbers or $(0, \infty)$.

PP for Example 4.

a. $f(x) = 100(0.2)^x + 20$
Horizontal asymptote $y = 20$.
Domain: All real numbers or $(-\infty, \infty)$,
range: $(20, \infty)$.

x	f(x)
−1	520
0	120
1	40
2	24
3	20.8
4	20.16

b. $g(x) = -4(3)^x - 2$
Horizontal asymptote $y = -2$.
Domain: All real numbers or $(-\infty, \infty)$,
range: $(-\infty, -2)$.

x	g(x)
−2	−2.44
−1	−3.33
0	−6
1	−14
2	−38
3	−110

Section 12.4

PP for Example 1.

a. $y = 8000(0.75)^x$ **b.** $y = 9(4)^x$

PP for Example 2.

$$f(x) = 2.28(1.45)^x$$

PP for Example 4.

$$f(x) = 145(0.795)^x$$

Section 12.5

PP for Example 2.

a. $P(10) \approx 20.5759$. In 2010, the population of Australia would be approximately 20.6 million.

b. $r = 0.008$. The population of Australia is growing at a rate of 0.8% per year.

PP for Example 3.

a. $P(t)$ = Population of Boulder, Colorado
t = Time in years since 2000

$$P(t) = 96,000(1.10)^t$$

b. $P(2) = 116,160$. In 2002, Boulder, Colorado, would have had approximately 116,160 people if the population grew at 10% annually.

PP for Example 4.

a. $P(t)$ = Population of Trinidad and Tobago in millions
t = Time in years since 2008

$$P(t) = 1(0.991)^t$$

b. $P(12) \approx 0.897$. In 2020, Trinidad and Tobago will have approximately 897,000 people if the population decreases by 0.9% annually.

PP for Example 5.

a. $30,000 will grow to $66,589.21 in 10 years if earning 8% annual interest compounded monthly.

b. $30,000 will grow to $66,725.20 in 10 years if the account earns 8% annual interest compounded weekly.

c. $30,000 will grow to $66,760.38 in 10 years if the account earns 8% annual interest compounded daily.

PP for Example 6.

$A \approx 145,769.504$. Therefore, after 12 years, this account will have $145,769.50.

CHAPTER 13
Section 13.1

PP for Example 1.

a. $s(P) = -14.29P + 500$

b. $s(5) = 428.55$. Therefore, it will take about 429 seconds to pump the vacuum chamber down to 5 psi.

c. Domain $0 \leq P \leq 35$, range: $0 \leq s \leq 500$

PP for Example 2.

a. $f^{-1}(x) = -0.25x + 2.25$

b. $g^{-1}(t) = 0.4t + 1.4$

PP for Example 3.

a.

This graph passes the horizontal line test, so $f(t) = \frac{2}{3}t - 7$ is a one-to-one function.

b.

This graph fails the horizontal line test, so $g(w) = 0.5w^3 + 3w^2 - 7$ is not a one-to-one function.

c.

This graph passes the horizontal line test, so $g(x) = -5(0.7)^x$ is a one-to-one function.

PP for Example 4.

$$f \circ f^{-1}(x) = x \qquad f^{-1} \circ f(x) = x$$

Section 13.2

PP for Example 1.

a. $\log 10,000 = 4$

b. $\log_7 49 = 2$

PP for Example 2.

a. $\log_7 7^8 = 8$

b. $\log_4 1 = 0$

PP for Example 4.

a. $\log_3 278 \approx 5.122$

b. $\log_{17} 11 \approx 0.846$

PP for Example 5.

a. $\log_4 65,536 = 8$

b. $6^4 = 1296$

PP for Example 6.

a. $f^{-1}(x) = \dfrac{\log x}{\log 7}$

b. $g^{-1}(t) = 2^t$

c. $h^{-1}(x) = \dfrac{\log\left(\frac{x}{3}\right)}{\log 4}$

PP for Example 7.

a. $x = e^4 \approx 54.598$

b. $x = 12.8$

Section **13.3**

PP for Example 1.

x	$y = \log_5 x$
$\dfrac{1}{125}$	-3
$\dfrac{1}{25}$	-2
$\dfrac{1}{5}$	-1
1	0
5	1
25	2
125	3
625	4

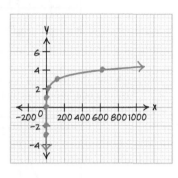

PP for Example 2.

x	$y = \log_{0.25} x$
0.0625	2
1	0
16	-2
64	-3
256	-4

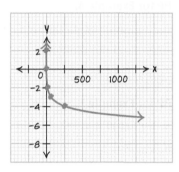

Section **13.4**

PP for Example 1.

a. $\ln 5 + \ln a + \ln b$

b. $\log 7 + \log n - \log m$

PP for Example 2.

a. $\ln\left(\dfrac{18s}{3t}\right) = \ln\left(\dfrac{6s}{t}\right)$

b. $\log_7 (15mn)$

c. $\log (x^2 - 4x - 21)$

PP for Example 3.

a. $\log_4 5 + \log_4 x + 3\log_4 y$

b. $\log 3 + 2\log m - \log 2 - 3\log n$

c. $\dfrac{1}{2}(\ln 2 + \ln x + \ln y)$

PP for Example 4.

a. $\log_5 \dfrac{7m^2 n^3}{p^2}$ b. $\log \dfrac{x\sqrt{y}}{z^3}$ c. $\ln\left(\dfrac{125x^5 y^5 z^3}{32}\right)$

Section **13.5**

PP for Example 3.

a. $x \approx 0.850$

b. $x \approx -0.371$

PP for Example 4.

$t \approx 24.587$. If the population of Boulder, Colorado, continues to grow at a rate of 10% per year, it will reach 1 million people around 2025.

PP for Example 5.

$r \approx 0.0463$. To have $60,000 double in 15 years, the interest rate would need to be about 4.63% compounded monthly.

PP for Example 6.

$t \approx 21.98$. Therefore, it will take about 22 years for $10,000 to triple if it is in an account that pays 5% compounded weekly.

PP for Example 7.

$t \approx 8.664$. It takes about 8.66 years for an investment to double if it is in an account paying 8% compounded continuously.

Section **13.6**

PP for Example 1.

$$x = 9996$$

PP for Example 3.

$10,000 = I$. Therefore, the intensity of a magnitude 8 earthquake would be 10,000 cm.

PP for Example 5.

$0.00501 \approx H^+$. Therefore, a solution with a pH value of 2.3 has a hydrogen ion concentration of 5.01×10^{-3} M.

PP for Example 6.

a. $x \approx 3162.28$ b. $x = 8$

c. $x = \dfrac{e^{-5}}{5} \approx 0.0013$

PP for Example 7.

a. $x \approx 12.91$

b. $x \approx 16.533$

c. $x = -2$

d. $x \approx 4.14$

CHAPTER 14

Section 14.1

PP for Example 1.

a. $x = (y - 2)^2 - 8$

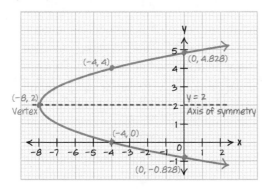

b. $x = -2y^2 + 16y + 5$

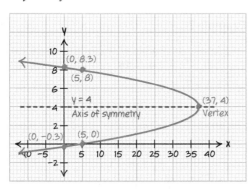

PP for Example 2.

a. $y = \dfrac{x^2}{6}$ Focus: $\left(0, \dfrac{3}{2}\right)$, directrix: $y = -\dfrac{3}{2}$.

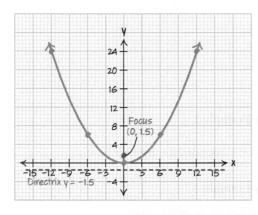

b. $-24x = y^2$ Focus: $(-6, 0)$, directrix: $x = 6$.

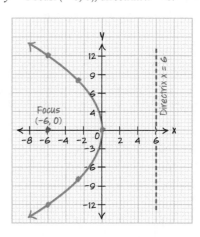

PP for Example 3.

$$y = \frac{x^2}{16} \qquad \text{or} \qquad 16y = x^2$$

PP for Example 4.

The focus should be at the point $(0, 6.25)$, so the receiver should be 6.25 feet above the base of the satellite on the axis of symmetry.

PP for Example 5.

a. $(x - 5)^2 + (y - 7)^2 = 100$ **b.** $(x + 5)^2 + (y + 4)^2 = 81$

PP for Example 6.

a. $x^2 + y^2 = 16$

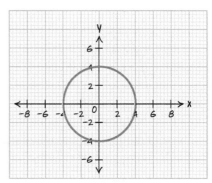

b. $(x - 2)^2 + (y + 3)^2 = 4$

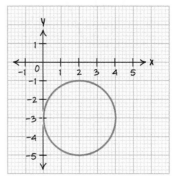

PP for Example 7.

$$(x - 2)^2 + (y + 5)^2 = 9$$

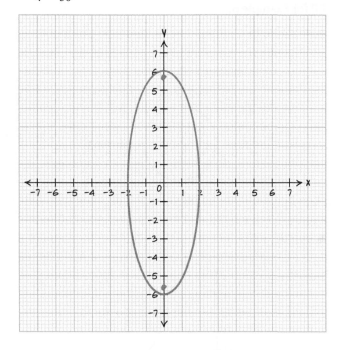

(2, −5)

b. $\dfrac{x^2}{100} + \dfrac{y^2}{16} = 1$

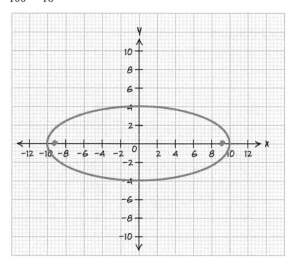

PP for Example 8.

$$(x - 4)^2 + (y - 2)^2 = 16$$

Section **14.2**

PP for Example 1.

a. $\dfrac{x^2}{4} + \dfrac{y^2}{36} = 1$

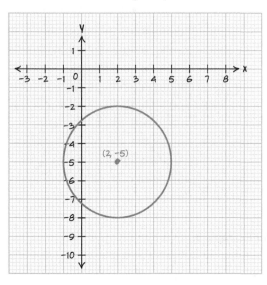

PP for Example 2.

$$\dfrac{x^2}{4} + \dfrac{y^2}{16} = 1$$

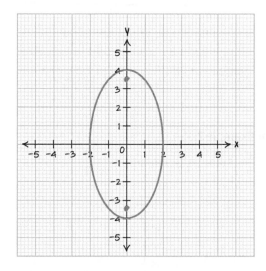

PP for Example 3.

$\dfrac{x^2}{4} + \dfrac{y^2}{9} = 1$. Foci: $(0, 2.24)$ and $(0, -2.24)$.

PP for Example 4.

The equation for the orbit of Mars is

$$\dfrac{x^2}{20{,}022.25} + \dfrac{y^2}{19{,}840} = 1$$

PP for Example 5.

a. $\dfrac{x^2}{36} - \dfrac{y^2}{64} = 1$

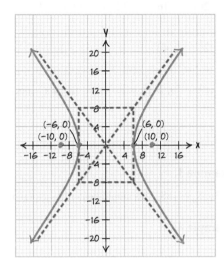

b. $16y^2 - 9x^2 = 144$

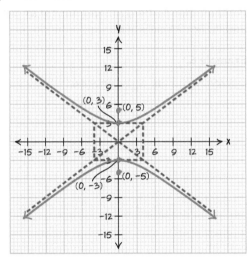

PP for Example 6.

$\dfrac{x^2}{36} - \dfrac{y^2}{9} = 1$. Foci: $(6.71, 0)$ and $(-6.71, 0)$.

PP for Example 7.

a. $9x^2 + 9y^2 + 2x + 7y - 4 = 0$

The coefficients of the two squared terms are the same, so this is the equation of a circle.

b. $16x^2 - 4y^2 - 64 = 0$

The coefficients of the two squared terms are different and have different signs. This is the equation of a hyperbola.

c. $4x^2 + y^2 - 4 = 0$

The coefficients of the two squared terms are different and are both positive. This is the equation of an ellipse.

Section **14.3**

PP for Example 1.

a. 12, 17, 22, 27, and 32.   **b.** $\dfrac{1}{3}, \dfrac{1}{9}, \dfrac{1}{27}$, and $\dfrac{1}{81}$.

PP for Example 2.

a. -11 is the fifth term of the sequence.

b. 204 is the 14th term in the sequence.

PP for Example 3.

a. $a_n = 3 + (n - 1) \cdot 5$

b. $f(n) = (-1)^n$

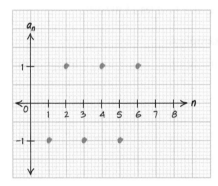

PP for Example 4.

a. The common difference $d = -6$ is constant; therefore, the sequence is arithmetic.

b. The common difference $d = 2$ is constant; therefore, the sequence is arithmetic.

c. The differences are not equal, so the sequence is not arithmetic.

PP for Example 5.

a. Common difference: $d = -2$. General term: $a_n = -2n + 11$.

b. The differences are not equal, so the sequence is not arithmetic.

c. Common difference: $d = \dfrac{1}{3}$. General term: $a_n = \dfrac{1}{3}n - 2$.

PP for Example 6.

a. $a_n = 1200n + 42{,}800$

b. $a_{14} = 59{,}600$. In the 14th year, the salary will be $59,600.

c. $21 = n$. The salary will reach $68,000 in the 21st year.

PP for Example 7.

a. $a_n = \dfrac{2}{5}n - 4$ **b.** $a_n = 3n - 8$

Section **14.4**

PP for Example 1.

a. The sequence is geometric and the common ratio is $r = 0.25$.

b. The sequence is arithmetic.

PP for Example 2.

a. The general term of this geometric sequence is $a_n = 25\left(\dfrac{6}{5}\right)^{(n-1)}$.

b. The general term of this geometric sequence is

$$a_n = 200\left(-\dfrac{2}{5}\right)^{(n-1)}.$$

PP for Example 3.

a. $a_n = 40{,}000(1.02)^{(n-1)}$.

b. $a_5 \approx 43{,}297.29$. In the fifth year, the salary will be $43,297.29.

c. $n \approx 47.27$. The salary will reach $100,000 in the 48th year. We must round n to a whole number, so choosing 48 implies that the salary will be at least $100,000.

PP for Example 4.

a. $a_n = 10(-3)^{(n-1)}$ **b.** $a_n = 320(0.2)^{(n-1)}$

Section **14.5**

PP for Example 2.

a. $\displaystyle\sum_{n=1}^{4}(4n - 20) = -16 + (-12) + (-8) + (-4)$

$\displaystyle\sum_{n=1}^{4}(4n - 20) = -40$

b. $\displaystyle\sum_{n=1}^{5}(2(-3)^n) = -6 + 18 + (-54) + 162 + (-486)$

$\displaystyle\sum_{n=1}^{5}(2(-3)^n) = -366$

PP for Example 3.

$a_n = 10 + 3n$, $S_8 = 188$. This amphitheater has a total of 188 seats.

PP for Example 4.

$S_{44} = 2640$

PP for Example 5.

$S_9 \approx 105{,}152.65$. This family used about 105,152.65 gallons of water during the first 9 months of the year.

PP for Example 6.

a. $S_{12} = 13{,}650$ **b.** $S_{15} \approx 399.9996$

Answers to Selected Exercises

APPENDIX

D

CHAPTER R

Section R.1

1. whole number, integer

3. integer

5. natural number, whole number, integer

7. integer

9. natural number, whole number, integer

11. natural number, whole number, integer

13. natural number, whole number, integer

15. whole number, integer; there could be 0 kittens at the shelter

17. whole number, integer; the employee could have a week off or otherwise work 0 hours in a week

19. integer; the temperature could be positive or negative, so this belongs to the set of integers

21. $\{-5, -4, -3, -2, -1, 0, 1\}$ **23.** $\{1, 2, 3, 4\}$

25. $\{0\}$ **27.** 4   **29.** 0.1

31. ◄—+—+—+—+—+—+—+—+—+—+—+—+—+—+—+—+—+—+—+—►
   −10 −9 −8 −7 −6 −5 −4 −3 −2 −1 0 1 2 3 4 5 6 7 8 9 10

33. ◄—+—+—+—+—+—+—+—+—+—+—+—+—+—+—+—+—+—+—+—►
   −10 −9 −8 −7 −6 −5 −4 −3 −2 −1 0 1 2 3 4 5 6 7 8 9 10

35. ◄—+—+—+—+—+—+—+—+—+—+—+—+—+—+—+—+—+—+—+—►
   −10 −9 −8 −7 −6 −5 −4 −3 −2 −1 0 1 2 3 4 5 6 7 8 9 10

37. $-5 > -15$ **39.** $-3 \le -3$ or $-3 \ge -3$

41. $-4 < -3$ **43.** $0 > -7$ **45.** 3

47. 8   **49.** 16   **51.** 7

53. $\dfrac{-3}{2}, -1, \dfrac{1}{3}, 0.5, 2.95, 3$ **55.** $-5, -2, |-2|, |-5|$

57. $-3.5, \dfrac{2}{3}, |-4|, 4.2, |-5|$

59. The expression translates as "the opposite of five."

   $-(5) = -5$

61. The expression translates as "the opposite of the absolute value of negative 2."

   $-|-2| = -2$

63. The expression translates as "the opposite of negative six."

   $-(-6) = 6$

65. -8 **67.** 9   **69.** -7

71. -16 **73.** 4   **75.** -1

77. $-26°F$ **79.** -50 feet   **81.** 9

83. 8   **85.** 19   **87.** -6

89. -20 **91.** 18   **93.** 3

95. -6 **97.** undefined   **99.** 0

101. 2 terms : $\boxed{-3} + \boxed{5 \cdot 6}$

103. 1 term : $\boxed{-24 \div 3 \cdot 7}$

105. 3 terms: $\boxed{3} + \boxed{22 \div 11} - \boxed{16 \div 4}$

107. 4 terms: $\boxed{92 \cdot (-8)} + \boxed{26 \div 13} - \boxed{1} + \boxed{7(-3)}$

109. 1 term; -6 **111.** 2 terms; 6   **113.** 3 terms; 23

115. 3 terms; -4 **117.** 4 terms; 30

Section R.2

1. $2 \cdot 2 \cdot 2 \cdot 2$ **3.** $17 \cdot 2$ **5.** $7 \cdot 3 \cdot 2$

7. $2 \cdot 2 \cdot 2 \cdot 2 \cdot 2 \cdot 2$ **9.** $7 \cdot 5 \cdot 2$

11. 3   **13.** 15   **15.** 9   **17.** 12

19. 3   **21.** $\dfrac{2}{5}$ **23.** $\dfrac{4}{21}$ **25.** $\dfrac{1}{3}$

27. $\dfrac{-1}{12}$ **29.** $-5\dfrac{2}{7}$ **31.** $\dfrac{10}{15}$ **33.** $\dfrac{40}{56}$

35. $\dfrac{-10}{32}$ **37.** $4\dfrac{10}{45}$ **39.** $\dfrac{15}{3}$

41. ◄—+—+—+—+—+—+—+—+—+—+—+—+—+—+—+—+—+—+—+—►
   −10 −9 −8 −7 −6 −5 −4 −3 −2 −1 0 1 2 3 4 5 6 7 8 9 10

43. ◄—+—+—+—+—+—+—+—+—+—+—+—+—+—+—+—+—+—+—+—►
   −10 −9 −8 −7 −6 −5 −4 −3 −2 −1 0 1 2 3 4 5 6 7 8 9 10

45. ◄—+—+—+—+—+—+—+—+—+—+—+—+—+—+—+—+—+—+—+—►
   −10 −9 −8 −7 −6 −5 −4 −3 −2 −1 0 1 2 3 4 5 6 7 8 9 10

47. ◄—+—+—+—+—+—+—+—+—+—+—+—+—+—+—+—+—+—+—+—►
   −10 −9 −8 −7 −6 −5 −4 −3 −2 −1 0 1 2 3 4 5 6 7 8 9 10

49. ◄—+—+—+—+—+—+—+—+—+—+—+—+—+—+—+—+—+—+—+—►
   −10 −9 −8 −7 −6 −5 −4 −3 −2 −1 0 1 2 3 4 5 6 7 8 9 10

51. 2   **53.** $\dfrac{3}{5}$ **55.** $\dfrac{3}{5}$

57. 5   **59.** $3\dfrac{1}{3}$ **61.** $1\dfrac{1}{2}$ or $\dfrac{3}{2}$

63. $\dfrac{-1}{6}$ **65.** $-1\dfrac{5}{12}$ or $\dfrac{-17}{12}$ **67.** $4\dfrac{5}{6}$

69. $-5\dfrac{3}{4}$ **71.** $3\dfrac{1}{2}$ gallons   **73.** $\dfrac{3}{4}$ teaspoon

75. $9\dfrac{5}{8}$ feet   **77.** $\dfrac{-1}{3}$ **79.** $\dfrac{3}{5}$

81. 9   **83.** $\dfrac{1}{8}$ **85.** does not exist

87. 2   **89.** $\dfrac{5}{12}$ **91.** $\dfrac{9}{7}$ or $1\dfrac{2}{7}$

93. 5   **95.** $\dfrac{-3}{2}$ or $-1\dfrac{1}{2}$ **97.** $\dfrac{1}{54}$

99. 2 terms; $\dfrac{-29}{2}$ or $-14\dfrac{1}{2}$　　**101.** 2 terms; $\dfrac{13}{5}$ or $2\dfrac{3}{5}$

103. 3 terms; $\dfrac{-1}{5}$　　**105.** 3 terms; $\dfrac{35}{12}$ or $2\dfrac{11}{12}$

107. 1 term; $\dfrac{12}{5}$ or $2\dfrac{2}{5}$

Section **R.3**

1. 4　　　**3.** 4　　　**5.** 7　　　**7.** 8

9. 0　　**11.** $2\dfrac{9}{10}$　　**13.** $\dfrac{21}{25}$　　**15.** $7\dfrac{71}{100}$

17. $1\dfrac{1}{125}$　　**19.** $1\dfrac{33}{100}$　　**21.** 0.6　　**23.** 1.25

25. $0.41\overline{6}$　　**27.** $3.1\overline{6}$　　**29.** 0.875

31.

33.

35.

37.

39.

41. 8.3　　**43.** 9.21　　**45.** 210　　**47.** 0.1

49. 1　　**51.** 4.326　　**53.** 6.5176　　**55.** 5.76

57. 7.29　　**59.** 96.5985　　**61.** 5.33　　**63.** 6.749

65. $274.90　　**67.** $9.50　　**69.** 5.418　　**71.** 21.245

73. 0.112　　**75.** $2.97　　**77.** $1.95　　**79.** 820

81. 0.06　　**83.** 8.4　　**85.** 0.037

87. 2 terms; 13.35　　　**89.** 2 terms; 19.57

91. 3 terms; 214.3　　　**93.** 3 terms; 47.42

95. 1 term; 134.4

97. a. $1.25 + 0.99 + 2(0.59)$　**b.** addition and multiplication

　　c. 3 terms　　　　　**d.** multiplication; addition

　　e. $3.42

99. a. $2(1.59) + 2(3.99)$　**b.** addition and multiplication

　　c. 2 terms　　　　　**d.** multiplication; addition

　　e. $11.16

101. 0.34　　**103.** 47%　　**105.** 1.7%　　**107.** 36%

109.

Percent	Decimal	Fraction
16%	0.16	$\dfrac{4}{25}$

111.

Percent	Decimal	Fraction
28.5%	0.285	$\dfrac{57}{200}$

113.

Percent	Decimal	Fraction
0.12%	0.0012	$\dfrac{3}{2500}$

115. 10.24　　**117.** 0.56　　**119.** 10 dogs　　**121.** 6 diners

123. 12 g　　**125.** 600 mg　　**127.** $1.50　　**129.** $36.48

Section **R.4**

1.

	Whole Number	Integer	Rational Number	Irrational Number	Real Number
1.47			X		X
$\dfrac{16}{49}$			X		X
-7		X	X		X
$\sqrt{5}$				X	X
9	X	X	X		X

3. rational number　　**5.** rational number　　**7.** both

9. rational number　　**11.** both　　**13.** both

15. $-3, 0, \dfrac{5}{2}$　　**17.** $\pi, \sqrt{2}$　　**19.** 16, 0, 2

21. 3, 111　　　　**23.** 56

25. 0.625; rational; the number $\dfrac{5}{8}$ is rational because it is a fraction, a ratio of integers.

27. $1\dfrac{17}{50}$; rational; the number 1.34 is rational because it is a finite decimal.

29. $0.\overline{09}$; rational; the number $\dfrac{1}{11}$ is rational because it is a fraction, a ratio of integers.

31. $\dfrac{133}{10000}$; rational; the number 0.0133 is rational because it is a finite decimal.

33. 0.273; rational; the number $\dfrac{3}{11}$ is rational because it is a fraction, a ratio of integers.

35. 3.3166; irrational; $\sqrt{11}$ is irrational because it can be expressed as an infinite, nonrepeating decimal and it cannot be expressed as a ratio of integers.

37. 3.141593; irrational; π is irrational because it can be expressed as an infinite, nonrepeating decimal and it cannot be expressed as a ratio of integers.

39. $0.48 per ounce　　　**41.** $0.06 per ounce

43. $0.11 per ounce　　　**45.** 2 terms; $\dfrac{3}{5}$

47. 3 terms; 11.4　　　**49.** 2 terms; $5\dfrac{1}{10}$ or $\dfrac{51}{10}$ or 5.1

51. 2 terms; $4\dfrac{9}{50}$ or $\dfrac{209}{50}$ or 4.18

53. 3 terms; $-1\dfrac{7}{12}$ or $\dfrac{-19}{12}$ or $-1.58\overline{3}$

55. 3 terms; $\dfrac{-153}{28}$ or $-5\dfrac{13}{28}$

Chapter R Review Exercises

1. **a.** integer
   b. whole number, integer
   c. natural number, whole number, integer

2. **a.** natural number, whole number, integer
   b. integer
   c. whole number, integer

3. whole number, integer; there could be 0 students in the chemistry lab

4. whole number, integer; there could be 0 trees in the park

5. $\{0, 1, 2, 3, 4\}$ 6. $\{-6, -5, -4, -3\}$ 7. 2   8. 15

9.

10.

11. $-3 > -5$ 12. $-9 < -2$ 13. 9   14. 6.7

15. $-2, \frac{2}{5}, 3, |-7|$ 16. $-4, -0.1, \left|\frac{-2}{3}\right|, 1.8$

17. the opposite of negative 8; 8

18. the opposite of negative 1; 1

19. **a.** -67 **b.** -26 **c.** -10 **d.** -5
20. **a.** -18 **b.** 68   **c.** -14 **d.** -7
21. **a.** -150 **b.** 8   **c.** -16 **d.** 5
22. **a.** 30   **b.** -18 **c.** -3 **d.** 8

23. 3 terms   24. 3 terms   25. 3 terms; 25
26. 3 terms; -7 27. $3 \cdot 3 \cdot 3$ 28. $5 \cdot 3 \cdot 3$

29. 4   30. 15   31. $\frac{5}{11}$

32. $\frac{2}{5}$ 33. $\frac{35}{56}$ 34. $\frac{18}{42}$

35. **a.** rational number   **b.** both   **c.** rational number
36. **a.** rational number   **b.** rational number   **c.** both

37. **a.** $\frac{2}{3}$ **b.** $\frac{5}{12}$ **c.** $\frac{-1}{6}$ **d.** $2\frac{1}{6}$

38. **a.** $\frac{1}{2}$ **b.** $\frac{4}{15}$ **c.** $\frac{-3}{20}$ **d.** $\frac{7}{10}$

39. **a.** $\frac{1}{6}$ **b.** 4

40. **a.** $\frac{-1}{5}$ **b.** $\frac{2}{3}$

41. **a.** $\frac{2}{11}$ **b.** $\frac{1}{45}$ **c.** $\frac{2}{3}$

42. **a.** $\frac{3}{7}$ **b.** $\frac{3}{14}$ **c.** $\frac{3}{4}$

43. 2 terms; $-5\frac{1}{2}$ or $\frac{-11}{2}$ 44. 2 terms; $\frac{1}{3}$

45. hundredths   46. thousandths

47. $2\frac{3}{4}$ 48. $4\frac{17}{25}$ 49. $0.\overline{4}$ 50. 0.625

51. **a.** 10.644   **b.** 0.074

52. **a.** 21.071   **b.** 1.246
53. **a.** 4.841   **b.** 2.7
54. **a.** 34.96   **b.** 9.5
55. 3 terms; 4.1   56. 3 terms; -7.65 57. 0.02
58. 5.4   59. 0.0875   60. 0.0545
61. $\frac{7}{25}$ 62. $\frac{9}{20}$ 63. 4.56%
64. 7.75%   65. 190.5%   66. 201%
67. 80%   68. 6%   69. 120%
70. $333\frac{1}{3}\%$ 71. 3.7125   72. 0.3105
73. 1.1   74. 1.632   75. $19.98
76. $\frac{4}{3}, -16.9, 0$ 77. $-7.5, 2, \frac{5}{4}$ 78. $\sqrt{5}$
79. π 80. 0.43   81. 4.583
82. $-2\frac{3}{5}$ or $\frac{-13}{5}$ or -2.6 83. $12\frac{71}{100}$ or $\frac{1271}{100}$ or 12.71
84. $3\frac{1}{6}$ or $\frac{19}{6}$ 85. $\frac{-2}{3}$
86. $\frac{19}{50}$ or 0.38   87. $1\frac{6}{25}$ or $\frac{31}{25}$ or 1.24
88. $55\frac{3}{5}$ or $\frac{278}{5}$ or 55.6   89. 39.53
90. $\frac{2}{3}$ 91. $\frac{11}{5}$ or $2\frac{1}{5}$

Chapter R Test

1.

	Whole Number	Integer	Rational Number	Irrational Number	Real Number
2.25			X		X
$\frac{2}{3}$			X		X
-6		X	X		X
$\sqrt{2}$				X	X
10	X	X	X		X

2. 5

3.

4. $-4, \frac{13}{5}, -(-6.8), |-11|$

5. **a.** $-9 > -11$ **b.** $\frac{1}{3} > 0.3$

6. **a.** -3 **b.** 6

7. $2 \cdot 2 \cdot 3 \cdot 3$

8. **a.** 4   **b.** -1.05 **c.** -4

9. **a.** -48 **b.** 9   **c.** 9.2

10. 4 terms; 7   11. 3 terms; 35   12. 2 terms; -29

13. 3 terms; 127   **14.** 3 terms; $10\frac{2}{3}$ or $\frac{32}{3}$

15. 3 terms; 4.8   **16.** $2 \cdot 5 \cdot 5$

17. 18   **18.** $\frac{6}{7}$ **19.** $\frac{18}{63}$

20. 3   **21.** $\frac{21}{20}$ or $1\frac{1}{20}$

22. a. $\frac{-3}{2}$ or $-1\frac{1}{2}$ **b.** $\frac{-4}{3}$ or $-1\frac{1}{3}$

23. thousandths

24. 5.023

25.

Percent	Decimal	Fraction
1.05%	0.0105	$\frac{21}{2000}$

26. 18.54

CHAPTER 1
Section 1.1

1. 7^5 **3.** $5 \cdot 5 \cdot 5$ **5.** $(-7) \cdot (-7) \cdot (-7)$

7. $(-3)^5$ **9.** $\left(\frac{2}{3}\right)^3$ **11.** $\frac{5}{8} \cdot \frac{5}{8} \cdot \frac{5}{8}$

13. 8   **15.** 16   **17.** -25

19. 1   **21.** 2187   **23.** 25

25. -2401 **27.** -1 **29.** $\frac{27}{64}$

31. 0.1225   **33.** -216 **35.** 1,034,000

37. 93,000,000   **39.** 4,001,000,000   **41.** $-54,870$

43. Three terms: $(4 \div 2) + (3 \cdot 27) - (|-27|)$

45. Two terms: $(8 \cdot 9) - (4 \cdot 16^2)$

47. Two terms: $\left(\frac{3}{7}\right) - \left(\frac{1}{2} \div 8\right)$

49. One term: $\left((-4)^5 \cdot 2 \div 32\right)$

51. One term: $\left((-64) \div 4 \div 2\right)$

53. 20   **55.** $\frac{-2}{5}$ **57.** 33

59. $1\frac{4}{25}$ or $\frac{29}{25}$ **61.** -32 **63.** -17

65. -35 **67.** 17   **69.** 8

71. 3   **73.** 1728   **75.** $-4\frac{2}{5}$ or -4.4

77. -14 **79.** 91

81. Associative property of addition

83. Commutative property of multiplication

85. Distributive property

87. Commutative property of addition

89. Distributive property

91. Associative property of multiplication

93.

Operation	Commutative Property	Associative Property
Addition	X	X
Subtraction		
Multiplication	X	X
Division		

95. $2 \cdot 5 + 2 \cdot 9$ **97.** $16 \cdot 9 - 16 \cdot 5$

99. $-2 \cdot 8 + (-2) \cdot 7$ **101.** $-2 \cdot 7 - (-2) \cdot 16$

103. $\frac{7}{9} \cdot 11 + \frac{7}{9} \cdot 15$ **105.** 120

107. -165 **109.** -42

111. 12   **113.** -6

Section 1.2

1. If Sarah worked 15 hours in a week, her weekly pay would be $168.75.

3. If Thomas sold 53 rolls of wrapping paper, he would earn $265.00 in revenue.

5. If Marcus sells $1045.00 worth of merchandise in a week, his commission would be $73.15.

7. If Vinny runs for 2.5 hours at a pace of 7.5 miles per hour, he will run 18.75 miles.

9. If Judy is currently listing 5 houses, she estimates spending $1,250.00 on advertising.

11. If Fusako drives for 6.5 hours at an average speed of 75 miles per hour, she will drive 487.5 miles.

13. -15 **15.** 3   **17.** 14

19. -9 **21.** $\frac{3}{2}$ or $1\frac{1}{2}$ **23.** 916

25. -140 **27.** $\frac{-7}{5}$ or $-1\frac{2}{5}$ **29.** 105

31. 5   **33.** $7\frac{1}{3}$ yd or $7.\overline{3}$ yd   **35.** ≈ 0.2 mi

37. ≈ 77.44 m   **39.** 17.358 lb   **41.** 56.775 l

43. $0.\overline{50}$ acre   **45.** 601,000 thousand

47. 5.397 billion   **49.** 9000 billion

For Exercises 51 through 96, the letters chosen to represent the variables can vary.

51. Let E = the amount owed in dollars on a monthly electric bill and k = the number of kilowatt-hours of electricity used during that month.

53. Let T = the amount you pay yearly (in dollars) in federal taxes and d = your income (in dollars) for that year.

55. Let F = the temperature outdoors in degrees Fahrenheit and t = the time of day.

57. Let p = the amount of first-class postage you owe (in dollars) for a package and w = the weight of the package you are shipping (in pounds).

59. Let c = the cost in dollars of attending a community college and u = the number of credits a student enrolls in per semester.

Let x = an unknown number.

61. $x + 62$ or $62 + x$

63. $2x + 9$ or $9 + 2x$

65. $\dfrac{16}{x}$

67. $\dfrac{1}{3}x - 7$

69. $8x - 12$

71. $-5x^2$

73. $16 + \dfrac{x}{4}$ or $\dfrac{x}{4} + 16$

75. $\dfrac{6}{x - 2}$

77. $\dfrac{1}{2}x + 6$ or $6 + \dfrac{1}{2}x$

79. $7 - 2x$

81. Let c = the number of credit hours a part-time resident student is enrolled in for one semester. $132c + 7c + 7c + 4$

83. Let L = the number of hours the house-painting company charges for labor. $175 + 17L$

85. Let x = the number of ounces a piece of first-class mail weighs in excess of 1 ounce.

$$0.44 + 0.17x$$

or

Let z = the number of ounces a piece of first-class mail weighs. $0.44 + 0.17(z - 1)$

87. Let n = the number of pounds. $\dfrac{n}{2.2}$ kg

89. Let n = the number of miles. $5280n$ ft

91. Let n = the number of liters. $\dfrac{n}{3.785}$ gal

93. Let n = the number of acres. $43{,}560n$ ft^2

95. Let n = the number of seconds. $\dfrac{n}{60}$ min

97. a. The area of Bill's living room is 300 ft^2. The units are in square feet.

  b. 300 ft$^2 \approx 34$ yd^2 rounded up to the nearest full square yard.

  c. The Berber carpet Bill wants will cost $658.92.

  d. It will cost $59.50 to ship Bill's carpet.

  e. The total cost of Bill's carpet and shipping will be $718.42.

99. a. The total weight of the luggage is 72 lb.

  b. The total weight of the luggage is 74.2 lb.

101. $4.5 - t$

Time to Drive from San Diego to Los Angeles	Time to Drive from Los Angeles to San Diego
1	$4.5 - 1 = 3.5$
2	$4.5 - 2 = 2.5$
2.5	$4.5 - 2.5 = 2$
3	$4.5 - 3 = 1.5$
t	$4.5 - t$

103. $2500 - d$

Amount Invested in the 3.5% Account	Amount Invested in the 7% Account
0	$2500 - 0 = 2500$
500	$2500 - 500 = 2000$
100	$2500 - 100 = 2400$
1500	$2500 - 1500 = 1000$
d	$2500 - d$

105. $65 - c$

Pounds of Colombian Coffee	Pounds of Kenyan Coffee
0	$65 - 0 = 65$
10	$65 - 10 = 55$
20	$65 - 20 = 45$
50	$65 - 50 = 15$
c	$65 - c$

For Exercises 107 through 110, the letters chosen to represent the variables can vary.

107. a. $12p$ (when p represents the number of people invited to the party)

  b. Sandy can invite approximately 41 people to the party.

109. a. $18a + 15a$ (when a represents the number of people attending the reception)

  b. Approximately 51 people can attend the conference reception, and Tricia will stay within the budget.

Section 1.3

1. Three terms; $2x$ and $7x$ are like terms

3. Four terms; 3 and -5 are like terms; $2h$ and $7h$ are like terms

5. Four terms; $3x^2$ and $7x^2$ are like terms; $5x$ and $3x$ are like terms

7. Three terms; no like terms

9. Four terms; $7xy$ and $-2xy$ are like terms

11. $20x$

13. $-6p$

15. $-2x + 4y$

17. $-11n - 8$

19. $-x^2 + 11x - 6$

21. $3x - 8y$

23. $-8m + 7n + 12$

25. $7x^2 - x + 5$

27. $-7x^5 - 3x^2 + 5x + 8$

29. $\dfrac{-1}{2}a^6 + 3a^2 + a - \dfrac{7}{5}b$

31. a. $4.19k$ **b.** $1.39k$
  c. $4.19k + 1.39k$ **d.** $5.58k$

33. a. $8.79k$ **b.** $1.19k$
  c. $1.39k$ **d.** $11.37k$

35. a. $0.15I$ **b.** $0.08I$ **c.** $0.23I$

37. $8x + 7$

39. $4t + 14$

41. $7x^2 + 9x$

43. $4k^2 + 5k - 9$

45. $5x - xy + 7y$

47. $5a^2b^3 + 8a^2b^2 + 6ab^2$

49. $7s^5t^3 + 4s^3t^5 + 9s^2t$

51. Distributive property; $6x + 14$

53. Multiplication property; $10xy$

55. Distributive property; $-28x^2 - 36x + 24$

57. Multiplication property; $-20a^2bc$

59. Distributive property; $6xy - 14y$

61. Incorrect; $6xy$ **63.** Incorrect; $6k - 12$

65. Incorrect; $21mn$ **67.** Correct

69. Incorrect; $4x + 6$ **71.** $23x + 30$

73. $-10g - 12$ **75.** $-3x + 12$

77. $-2k^2 - 15k + 5$ **79.** $5x + 8xy + 14$

81. $-4x^2 - 3x$ **83.** $26w^2 + 36w - 9$

85. $7r^2 + 3r + 9$ **87.** $8.9t + 15.8$

89. $3h + 43$ **91.** $9x - 7$ **93.** $11a - 16$

95. $5b$ **97.** $2l + 2w$ **99.** $3x + 5y$

101. $6x + 16y - 12$ **103.** $12x + 9$ **105.** $12a$

Section **1.4**

1. a. The maximum percentage of violent crime reported to the police was 48.7%. This happened during the years 2004–2005.

   b. The minimum percentage of property crime reported to the police was 33.4%. This happened during the years 1992–1993 and 1994–1995.

3. a. The fastest marathon time is 2h03:59. This happened in the year 2008.

   b. Most of the top 10 runners come from Kenya.

5. a. The percentage of obese adults was highest during the year 2004. Approximately 23% of the adult population was obese that year.

   b. The percentage of obese adults was lowest during the year 1998. Approximately 18% of the adult population was obese that year.

7. a. New home sales were at their lowest point during the year 2009. There were approximately 400,000 sales made.

   b. New home sales were at their highest point during the year 2005. There were approximately 1,300,000 sales made.

9.

11.

13.

15.

17.

19.

21. A: $(5, 4)$ B: $(-8, 7)$ C: $(-4, -6)$ D: $(2, -3)$

23. A: $(2, 0)$ B: $(0, 3)$ C: $(-5, 0)$ D: $(0, -4)$

25. x-axis: The scale is 5 y-axis: The scale is 1

27. x-axis: The scale is 0.5 y-axis: The scale is 0.1

29. A: $(24, 6)$ B: $(0, 21)$ C: $(-16, 12)$ D: $(12, 0)$
E: $(-28, -9)$

31.

33.

35.

37.

39.

41.

43.

45. The student transposed the *x*- and *y*-coordinates, graphing the point $(4, 3)$ instead of $(3, 4)$.

47. The student is confusing the *x*- and *y*-coordinates and has transposed the coordinates for each point.

49. The student was inconsistent with the scale of the *y*-axis, with a scale of 10 for positive values and a scale of 1 for negative values.

Chapter 1 Review Exercises

1. 6^5

2. 8^4

3. $\left(\dfrac{3}{8}\right)^3$

4. $\left(\dfrac{-4}{5}\right)^5$

5. $5 \cdot 5 \cdot 5 \cdot 5 \cdot 5 \cdot 5$

6. $(-2) \cdot (-2) \cdot (-2)$

7. $\left(\dfrac{-2}{5}\right) \cdot \left(\dfrac{-2}{5}\right) \cdot \left(\dfrac{-2}{5}\right) \cdot \left(\dfrac{-2}{5}\right)$

8. $\left(\dfrac{1}{11}\right) \cdot \left(\dfrac{1}{11}\right) \cdot \left(\dfrac{1}{11}\right)$

9. -27

10. 36

11. $\dfrac{16}{81}$

12. $\dfrac{-8}{27}$

13. $207{,}000$

14. $5{,}670{,}000$

15. $\boxed{-3} + \boxed{4 \cdot (-2)} + \boxed{24 \div 8} \boxed{-3^2} + \boxed{(-2)}; -19$

16. $\boxed{27 \div 3} \boxed{-5^2} + \boxed{(-10)} + \boxed{20} \boxed{-3 \cdot (-5)}; 9$

17. $\boxed{5 \div \dfrac{15}{7}} + \boxed{\dfrac{2}{3}} \boxed{-1}; 2$

18. $\boxed{-4} \boxed{-\dfrac{1}{5}} + \boxed{\dfrac{3}{2} \cdot \dfrac{4}{15}}; -3\dfrac{4}{5}$ or $\dfrac{-19}{5}$

19. -6

20. -36

21. $-3\dfrac{2}{3}$ or $\dfrac{-11}{3}$

22. $\dfrac{-2}{5}$

23. 21

24. $5\dfrac{1}{2}$ or $\dfrac{11}{2}$

25. -48 **26.** 60 **27.** 3

28. 3 **29.** 63 **30.** 29

31. Commutative property of multiplication

32. Commutative property of addition

33. Distributive property

34. Distributive property

35. Associative property of addition

36. Associative property of multiplication

37. Commutative property of addition

38. Commutative property of multiplication

For Exercises 39–44, the letters chosen to represent the variables can vary.

---

39. Let D = the amount of money (in dollars) you earn in a month and h = the number of hours you work in a month.

40. Let R = the amount of money (revenue in dollars) a local playhouse earns for a night and t = the number of tickets sold for that night.

Let n = an unknown number.

---

41. $3n - 6$ **42.** $5n + 8$ **43.** $\frac{1}{2}(n - 4)$

44. $\dfrac{n + 12}{16}$ **45.** 22.86 cm   **46.** ≈ 34.18 miles

47. $84.\overline{09}$ kg   **48.** 220 lb   **49.** ≈ 1.94 oz

50. 141.75 g   **51.** $9\dfrac{5}{6}$ **52.** -28

53. -5 **54.** -23 **55.** -25

56. -9 **57.** 8.25 **58.** 29

59. -86 **60.** 12

61. $4500 - d$

Amount Invested in the First Account	Amount Invested in the Second Account
0	$4500 - 0 = 4500$
1000	$4500 - 1000 = 3500$
2000	$4500 - 2000 = 2500$
3500	$4500 - 3500 = 1000$
d	$4500 - d$

62. $20 - d$

First Piece	Second Piece
0	$20 - 0 = 20$
4	$20 - 4 = 16$
8	$20 - 8 = 12$
16	$20 - 16 = 4$
d	$20 - d$

63. 800,000 thousand

64. 700,000 million

65.

66.

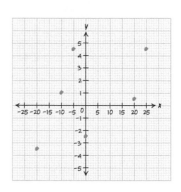

67. Four terms; $-6p$ and $7p$ are like terms; 4 and -9 are like terms

68. Four terms; $5x$ and $-\frac{2}{3}x$ are like terms; 16 and 12 are like terms

69. Four terms; $-3x^2$ and $-4x^2$ are like terms

70. Four terms; $-\frac{2}{5}y$ and $-6y$ are like terms

71. a. $3.25s$ **b.** $1.25s$
   c. $3.25s + 1.25s$ **d.** $4.5s$

72. a. $d - 500$ **b.** $4(85)$
   c. $d - 500 - 4(85)$ **d.** $d - 840$

73. $4y^3 + 4y^2$ **74.** $4a^2b - 13ab$ **75.** $-x - 5$

76. $x - 12$ **77.** $-6.25a + 2.1b$ **78.** $-0.3x + 1.9y$

79. $2x^2 + x + 12$ **80.** $5y^2 - 7y + 19$

81. a. Multiplication property   **b.** $-48ab^2$

82. a. Multiplication property   **b.** $-12xy$

83. a. Distributive property   **b.** $-15x + 30y$

84. a. Distributive property   **b.** $6a - 16b$

85. a. Multiplication property   **b.** $13x$

86. a. Distributive property   **b.** $-5y + 7$

87. $-6x + 27$ **88.** $x + 7$ **89.** $2x - 3$

90. $-9y + 5$ **91.** $-6a + 8b$ **92.** $7x - 18y$

93. $11x - 9$ **94.** $4h - 6k$ **95.** 0

96. $0.5x + 8.3y$ **97.** $6x + 8y + 6$ **98.** $8m + 2w$

99. $(6, 1), (4, 5), (-1, 6), (-2, 0), (-5, -2), (3, -4)$

100. $(5, 0), (6, 3), (0, 6), (-4, 3), (-3, -5), (2, -1)$

101. x-axis: The scale is 30

 y-axis: The scale is 7

102. x-axis: The scale is 10

 y-axis: the scale is 200

103.

104.

105.

106.

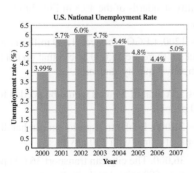

Chapter 1 Test

1. 3^6

2. $\left(\dfrac{-5}{8}\right) \cdot \left(\dfrac{-5}{8}\right) \cdot \left(\dfrac{-5}{8}\right)$

3. -8

4. $42{,}990{,}000$

5. Four terms; 7

6. Three terms; 41

7. Two terms; 5

8. Four terms; 34

9. Associative property of addition

10. Distributive property

11. Commutative property of multiplication

12. Lucas's weekly salary would be \$330.00 if he worked 24 hours in a week.

13. Let L = the number of hours charged for labor;

 $20 + 65L$

14. ≈ 91.74 m **15.** 2 **16.** $6x^2 - 15x + 3$

17. $7h - 3hk + 3k^2 + 22$

18. $3x + 2y$

19. a. The index was at its highest approximately during the third quarter of 2003.

 b. The index was at its lowest approximately during the third quarter of 2006.

 c. The scale on the vertical axis is 5.

 d. The scale on the horizontal axis is 1.

20. x-axis: The scale is 12

 y-axis: The scale is 5

21.

22. $(4, 50), (-4, 50), (-10, 0), (0, -50), (4, -10)$

CHAPTER 2

Section 2.1

1. Expression **3.** Equation

5. Expression **7.** Equation

9. Equation **11.** Expression

13. a. $S = 190$. If Joe works 20 hours in a week, his salary will be $190.00.

b. Yes, $S = 332.50$ when $h = 35$ is a solution to the equation $S = 9.5h$. These values represent that if Joe works 35 hours in a week, his salary will be $332.50.

c. No, $S = 240$ when $h = 25$ is not a solution to the equation $S = 9.5h$. These values represent Joe's salary and the hours worked. If Joe works 25 hours in a week, his salary would be $237.50, not $240.00.

d. Yes, $S = 380$ when $h = 40$ is a solution to the equation $S = 9.5h$. These values represent that if Joe works 40 hours in a week, his salary will be $380.00.

15. a. Yes, $D = 240$ when $t = 4$ is a solution to the equation $D = 60t$.

b. These values represent that 240 miles is the distance traveled when driving for 4 hours.

17. a. Yes, $C = 37.7$ when $r = 6$ is a solution to the equation $C = 2\pi r$.

b. These values represent that a circle with a radius of 6 has a circumference of 37.7 (rounded to one decimal place).

19. a. Yes, $F = 4500$ when $L = 300$ is a solution to the equation $F = 15L$.

b. These values represent that a loan of $300,000.00 would have an origination fee of $4500.00.

21. a. No, $F = 2000$ when $L = 225$ is not a solution to the equation $F = 10L$.

b. These values represent that a loan of $225,000.00 would have an origination fee of $2000.00, but a loan of that value would have an origination fee of $2250.00.

23. a. Yes, $S = 155.6$ when $f = 2$ is a solution to the equation $S = 77.8f$.

b. These values represent that it would require 155.6 cubic yards of sand to fill a volleyball court 2 feet deep.

25. Yes, $x = 11$ is a solution to the equation.

27. No, $m = 8$ is not a solution to the equation.

29. Yes, $x = 28$ is a solution to the equation.

31. Yes, $x = 5$ is a solution to the equation.

33. Yes, $x = 1$ is a solution to the equation.

35. No, $t = 3$ is not a solution to the equation.

37. Yes, $x = 5$ and $y = 1$ are solutions to the equation.

39. Yes, $x = -4$ and $y = 0$ are solutions to the equation.

41. Yes, $m = 3$ and $n = 5$ are solutions to the equation.

43. No, $x = 0$ and $y = 5$ are not solutions to the equation.

45. a. An additional 45 lb of other cargo could be stored on the roof of the car.

b. An additional 85 lb of luggage could be stored on the roof of the car.

47. The company's profit is $8000.

49. The company's profit is −$3000.00; therefore, the company is operating at a loss.

51. The company must generate $29,000 in revenue.

53. $x = 25$ **55.** $x = 24.5$ **57.** $m = 19$

59. $p = 27$ **61.** $k = -15$ **63.** $x = 8$

65. $a = 2.5$ **67.** $x = 1$ **69.** $m = \dfrac{5}{3}$

71. $m = \dfrac{1}{9}$ **73.** $x = 9$ **75.** $d = 8.25$

77. $x = -3.4$ **79.** $x = \dfrac{1}{35}$ **81.** $y = \dfrac{-1}{2}$

83. $R = C + P$ **85.** $l = 220 - s - c$

87. $A = 90 - B$ **89.** $M = T - 45$

91. $y = -x - 4$ **93.** $G = D - 3F + 30$

95. $w = t + 3u$ **97.** $b = P - a - c$

99. $x = 3y + 5$

101. Equation; $x = 14$

103. Expression; $2x + 7$

105. Expression; $17a^2 + 6a + 10$

107. Equation; $c = 4$

109. Equation; $p = 34$

Section **2.2**

1. $x = -27$ **3.** $y = 5\dfrac{1}{2}$ **5.** $g = 13$

7. $x = 9$ **9.** $x = 15$ **11.** $n = 2.5$

13. $c = -7$ **15.** $t = 70$ **17.** $x = -15$

19. $n = \dfrac{-14}{25}$ **21.** $k = 14$

23. a. $S = 1360$. If Victoria works 80 hours, her salary will be $1360.

b. $h = 120$. Victoria has to work 120 hours to make $2040 a month.

c. $h \approx 41.18$. Victoria has to work approximately 41.18 hours to earn $700.

25. a. $F = 2700$. The loan fees will be $2700 for a loan of $180,000.

b. $L = 133,333.\overline{3}$. Pablo can suggest a maximum loan amount of approximately $133,333.33 to keep the fees down to only $2000.

27. a. $D = 9000$. There will be 9000 bricks that do not meet the quality standards if 500 million bricks are produced.

b. $D = 734.4$. Approximately 734 bricks will not meet the quality standards of the 40.8 million bricks produced in a day.

c. $b = 1200$. LEGO produced 1200 million (or 1.2 billion) bricks if there are 21,600 bricks that do not meet the company's quality standards.

29. a. $B = 5$. A total of 5 buses would be needed to transport 300 people.

b. $P = 21,000$. Public transportation can handle 21,000 people at a time with 350 city buses.

c. $P = 36,000$. The city can transport 36,000 people at a time with 600 school and city buses.

31. a. $M = 2374$. The total amount of money taken out in 2006 for single- and multi-family homes in the United States is $2374 billion.

b. $t = 8$. In the year 2008, the total amount of money in mortgages for single-family and multi-family homes in the United States was only $1900 billion.

33. a. $f = 172.5$. The fee will be $172.50 if the final price of a tractor was $15,250.

b. $p = 10,400$. The final price of the log splitter was $10,400 if the total fee charged for selling the item was $124.

c. $p = 25,000$. The final price of the tractor was $25,000 if the total fee charged for selling the item was $270.

35. a. $F = 2.75$. The fee for a $100 transaction is $2.75.

b. $p = 360$. The total transaction was $360 if the fee charged was $9.25.

c. $p = 1500$. The total transaction was $1500 if the fee charged was $37.75.

37. $x = 8$ **39.** $p = 45$ **41.** $c = 8$

43. $t = -3$ **45.** $m = 6\frac{1}{2}$ **47.** $h = 31$

49. $x = 25$ **51.** $n \approx -0.53$ **53.** $m = 3.4$

55. $z = -3\frac{1}{5}$ **57.** $x = 12$ **59.** $w = 24.8$

61. $x = 40$ **63.** $x = \frac{9}{10}$

65. a. Let C = the total cost in dollars to ship n number of items.
$$C = 6.99 + 1.99n$$

b. $C = 16.94$. It costs $16.94 to ship 5 items UPS Ground.

c. $n = 3$. A total of 3 items can be shipped UPS Ground for $12.96.

67. a. Let T = the total time in minutes it will take the machine shop to produce c cranks.
$$T = 360 + 5c$$

b. $T = 610$. It will take 610 minutes, or 10 hours and 10 minutes, to produce 50 cranks.

c. $c = 163$. The machine shop made 163 cranks if it took 1175 minutes to produce the cranks.

69. Let "a number" = x.

$3x = 45$

$x = 15$

71. Let l = the length of the garden.

$56 = 2l + 2 \cdot 8$

$l = 20$

The length of the garden is 20 feet.

73. Let h = the height of the triangle, using the formula $A = \frac{1}{2}bh$ to find the area of a triangle where A = area and b = base.

$$40 = \frac{1}{2} \cdot 8h$$

$$h = 10$$

The height of the triangle is 10 inches.

75. Let "a number" = x.

$\dfrac{x}{7} = 13$

$x = 91$

77. Let "a number" = x.

$6 + 7x = 62$

$x = 8$

79. Let "a number" = x.

$\dfrac{1}{3}x - 8 = 28$

$x = 108$

81. Let "a number" = x.

$2x - 15 = 40$

$x = 27.5$

83. Let "an unknown number" = x.

$8 - x = 19$

$x = -11$

85. Let "a number" = x.

$2x - 7 = 11$

$x = 9$

87. $l = \dfrac{P - 2w}{2}$ or $l = \dfrac{P}{2} - w$ **89.** $h = \dfrac{V}{\pi r^2}$

91. $b = \dfrac{2A}{h}$ **93.** $t = \dfrac{W + 20}{3}$

95. $B = \dfrac{P - 2b}{2}$ or $B = \dfrac{P}{2} - b$ **97.** $y = \dfrac{5}{3}x + 5$

99. $y = \dfrac{x - 9}{5}$ or $y = \dfrac{1}{5}x - \dfrac{9}{5}$ **101.** $x = \dfrac{y - 23}{3}$

103. $x = \dfrac{y - 5}{9}$ **105.** $r = \dfrac{I}{Pt}$

107. Expression; $5a^2 + 18a - 5$

109. Equation; $x = 7$

111. Equation; $r = 20$

113. Expression; $20m - 3n + 11$

115. Equation; $y = 5.6$

Section 2.3

1. Let "a number" = x.

$4x = x + 33$

$x = 11$

3. Let "a number" = x.

$5x + 8 = 3x - 4$

$x = -6$

5. Let "a number" = x.

$2x = 5(x + 6)$

$x = -10$

7. Let "a number" = x.

$20 - 3x = 4x - 22$

$x = 6$

9. Let "a number" $= x$.

$\dfrac{1}{2}x = x + 5$

$x = -10$

11. Let "a number" $= x$.

$5 + \dfrac{x}{2} = x - 7$

$x = 24$

13. Let "a number" $= x$.

$x - 8 = 5x + 4$

$x = -3$

15. Let "a number" $= x$.

$\dfrac{1}{4}x - 8 = 2x - 29$

$x = 12$

17. $x = 10$ **19.** $t = 8$ **21.** $b = -6$

23. No solution   **25.** All real numbers   **27.** $h = -8$

29. $x = 7$ **31.** $h = -5$ **33.** $x = 6$

35. No solution   **37.** $d = -6$ **39.** $x = 20$

41. $x = 12$ **43.** $y = 1.4$ **45.** $t = -0.01$

47. $x = 22.5$. The measures of the 3 angles are 22.5°, 45°, and 112.5°.

49. $x = 4$. The length and width of the yard measure 13 ft and 20 ft.

51. $x = 7\dfrac{7}{12}$. The length of each side of the yard measures $20\dfrac{3}{4}$ ft.

53. $x = 11$. The length and width of the lawn measure 6 ft and 44 ft.

55. $x = 36$. The measures of the 3 angles are 36°, 72°, and 72°.

57. All real numbers   **59.** No solution

61. $r = 0$ **63.** All real numbers

65. $g = 25$ **67.** $x = 20$

69. No solution

71. $x = 55$. The measures of the 3 angles of the triangle are 75°, 55°, and 50°.

73. $x = 63$. The measures of the 3 angles of the triangle are 63°, 68°, and 49°.

75. $x = 100$. The measures of the 4 angles of the quadrilateral are 100°, 75°, 65°, and 120°.

77. $p = 80$. The lengths of the sides are 77 ft, 100 ft, 80 ft, and 85 ft.

79. $s = 60$. The lengths of the sides are 60 ft, 120 ft, 55 ft, and 110 ft.

81. Carlotta can supply 14 students for the bike tour.

83. a. Let $S =$ the total amount in dollars needed for supplies.

$S = 9.7 + 0.45k + 0.825k + 0.05k$ or $S = 9.7 + 1.325k$

   b. $S = 109.075$. If 75 kids came to build the project, the cost would be $109.08.

   c. $k = 226.64$. The manager can buy supplies for 226 projects.

85. Expression; $6a^2 - 4a + 17ab + 3$

87. Equation; $x = -7.\overline{3}$

89. Equation; no solution

91. Expression; $-2x + 19$

93. Equation; $x = 15\dfrac{3}{7}$

Section **2.4**

1. $x \geq 7$ **3.** $d < 7.5$ **5.** $x \leq -12$

7. $a > 61$ **9.** $g \leq 15$ **11.** $m > 9\dfrac{1}{5}$

13. $x \geq -8$ **15.** $x < 2$ **17.** $x \leq -2$

19. $k < 11$ **21.** $x < -7$

23. a. $11h \geq 275$

   b. $h \geq 25$. Kati needs to work at least 25 hours this week so she can pay her rent.

   c. $11h \geq 400$

   $h \geq 36.\overline{36}$. Kati must work at least 36.36 hours to earn at least $400 a week.

25. a. $30 + 0.5m \leq 45$

   b. $m \leq 30$. To stay within his budget, Kevin can use no more than 30 minutes over his allowed 200 minutes.

   c. $30 + 0.5m \leq 40$

   $m \leq 20$. If Kevin needs to keep his bill to at most $40, he can use no more than 20 minutes over his allowed 200 minutes.

27. a. $9 + 0.1t \leq 18$

   b. $t \leq 90$. To stay within his budget, Warren can send no more than 90 texts over his 200 texts allowed.

   c. $9 + 0.1t \leq 15$

   $t \leq 60$. If Warren needs to keep his bill to at most $15, he can send no more than 60 texts over his 200 texts allowed.

29. a. $75 + 3m \leq 115$

   b. $m \leq 13\dfrac{1}{3}$. Alicia can have her car towed up to 23 miles in order to spend no more than $115 for the tow.

31. $t \geq 16.5$. The population of Arkansas is projected to be 3 million or more after the year 2016.

33. $t \geq 5.69$. The population of Florida is projected to be 18 million or more after the year 2005.

35. $x < 4$ **37.** $n > -9$ **39.** $t \leq 0$

41. $2x < 6$

   $x < 3$

43. $2x + 1 \geq 5$

   $x \geq 2$

45. $x > 5$

   $(5, \infty)$

47. $m < -6$

$(-\infty, -6)$

49. $x \le -4$

$(-\infty, -4]$

51. $x > \dfrac{1}{4}$

$\left(\dfrac{1}{4}, \infty\right)$

53. $a \ge 12$

$[12, \infty)$

55. $k \le 3$

$(-\infty, 3]$

57. $z \le 12$

$(-\infty, 12]$

59. $c \ge -2.5$

$[-2.5, \infty)$

61. $w \le 7.6$

$(-\infty, 7.6]$

63.

$x \ge -1$

65.

$x < 9$

67.

$x > 69$

69.

$x \le -16$

71. Let s = the number of students enrolled in the beginning algebra class.

$16 \le s \le 38$

73. Let s = the number of students that can ride on the bus.

$0 \le s \le 71$

75. Let p = the number of people the camp can accommodate.

$200 \le p \le 450$

77. Let h = the height requirements in inches for children to ride on some attractions with an adult.

$42 \le h \le 52$

79. Let r = the average adult's resting heart rate in beats per minute.

$66 \le r \le 100$

81. $3 < x < 4$

$(3, 4)$

83. $-6 < y < -2$

$(-6, -2)$

85. $3 < x < 6$

$(3, 6)$

87. $6 < k < 10$

$(6, 10)$

89. $6 \le x \le 10$

$[6, 10]$

91. $-9 \le m \le -3$

$[-9, -3]$

93. $-20 \le x \le 4$

$[-20, 4]$

95. $8 < x < 60$

$(8, 60)$

97. $-\dfrac{28}{3} < x < -\dfrac{4}{3}$

$\left(-\dfrac{28}{3}, -\dfrac{4}{3}\right)$

99. $2.75 \le x \le 5.25$

$[2.75, 5.25]$

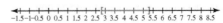

101. $-5 \le v < -1$

$[-5, -1)$

103. $\dfrac{3}{5} < a \le \dfrac{33}{5}$

$\left(\dfrac{3}{5}, \dfrac{33}{5}\right]$

105. Inequality

$x > 17$

$(17, \infty)$

107. Expression

$-8x + 7$

109. Equation

$h = -14$

111. Inequality

$a \le 6$

$(-\infty, 6]$

113. Equation

$x = 17$

115. Inequality

$-5.5 < a < 2.5$

$(-5.5, 2.5)$

117. Expression

$\dfrac{10}{9}b + 3$

119. Inequality

$-14 \le g < -8$

$[-14, -8)$

Chapter 2 Review Exercises

1. a. Yes, $D = 262.5$ when $t = 3.5$ is a solution to the equation $D = 75t$.

  b. These values represent that 262.5 miles is the distance traveled when driving for 3.5 hours.

2. a. Yes, $F = 6900$ when $L = 600$ is a solution to the equation $F = 11.5L$.

  b. These values represent that a loan of $600,000 would have an origination fee of $6900.

3. No, the values $x = -2$ and $y = 3$ are not solutions to the equation $-2x + 4y = -8$.

4. Yes, the values $x = -3$ and $y = 14$ are solutions to the equation $y = -3x + 5$.

5. $P = 23,000$. The company has a profit of $23,000.

6. $P = 39,000$. The company has a profit of $39,000.

7. $x = -6$ **8.** $p = 7$ **9.** $a = -17$

10. $b = -23$ **11.** $k = 2$ **12.** $x = \dfrac{6}{5}$

13. $y = 14.4$ **14.** $h = 1.02$ **15.** $q = -2p + 9$

16. $x = y + 2$ **17.** $y = \dfrac{1}{3}x - 2$ **18.** $p = \dfrac{5}{3}q - 10$

19. $y = 12$ **20.** $x = -16$ **21.** $a = -7$

22. $x = 8$ **23.** $b = 11$ **24.** $y = -7$

25. $x = -24$ **26.** $n = 12$ **27.** $t \approx -1.35$

28. $k = 33$

29. a. $J \approx 4.13$. To transport 520 people, 5 airplanes would be needed.

  b. $P = 1890$. If the airline carrier has 15 planes, they can transport 1890 people at a time.

30. a. $S = 1960$. Devora's monthly salary will be $1960 if she works 140 hours.

  b. $h = 150$. Devora has to work 150 hours a month to make $2100 a month.

  c. $h = 95$. Devora has to work 95 hours a month to earn $1330 a month.

31. $x = -9$ **32.** $y = 10$ **33.** $a = 7$

34. $k = -3$ **35.** $x = -20$ **36.** $x = 18$

37. $x = -16$ **38.** $y = -24$

39. Let "a number" $= x$.

  $9x = 76$

  $x = 8\dfrac{4}{9}$

40. Let "a number" $= x$.

  $12 = -2x$

  $x = -6$

41. Let "a number" $= x$.

  $2x + 16 = -44$

  $x = -30$

42. Let "a number" $= x$.

  $\dfrac{1}{2}x + 4 = -18$

  $x = -44$

43. Let "a number" $= x$.

  $\dfrac{x}{4} = 0.25$

  $x = 1$

44. Let "a number" $= x$.

  $-\dfrac{x}{3} = 0.75$

  $x = -2.25$

45. Let "a number" $= x$.

  $8 - 3x = 17$

  $x = -3$

46. Let "a number" $= x$.

  $2x - 9 = 7$

  $x = 8$

47. $m = \dfrac{D}{ca}$ **48.** $h = \dfrac{V}{lw}$ **49.** $d = \dfrac{C}{\pi}$

50. $h = \dfrac{2A}{b}$ **51.** $y = 3x + 4$ **52.** $y = 2x - 6$

53. Let "a number" = x.

$2x + 1 = 3x - 4$

$x = 5$

54. Let "a number" = x.

$\dfrac{1}{2}x + 10 = x - 4$

$x = 28$

55. $x = 4$ **56.** $y = -3$ **57.** $a = 5\dfrac{3}{7}$

58. $x = -10$ **59.** No solution   **60.** No solution

61. All real numbers   **62.** All real numbers

63. $x = 62$. The measures of the 3 angles are $62°$, $68°$, and $50°$.

64. $x = 34$. The measures of the 3 angles are $102°$, $54°$, and $24°$.

65. $x > 12$

$(12, \infty)$

66. $x \le 7$

$(-\infty, 7]$

67. $x \ge -7$

$[-7, \infty)$

68. $y \le -3$

$(-\infty, -3]$

69. $y \le \dfrac{17}{5}$

$\left(-\infty, \dfrac{17}{5}\right]$

70. $x > -\dfrac{2}{3}$

$\left(-\dfrac{2}{3}, \infty\right)$

71. $y \ge 20$

$[20, \infty)$

72. $t < 30$

$(-\infty, 30)$

73. $x > -12$

$(-12, \infty)$

74. $y < -2$

$(-\infty, -2)$

75. $-3 < x < 4$

$(-3, 4)$

76. $1 < x < 6$

$(1, 6)$

77. $-6 < x < 27$

$(-6, 27)$

78. $-38 < y < -32$

$(-38, -32)$

79. $x \ge -3$

80. $x > 5$

81. $x < 6$

82. $x \le -12$

83. $x < -6$ **84.** $y \ge 0$

85. $n > 30$. Kiano must sell more than 30 stained-glass windows to make a profit.

86. $d \le 3$. Jessie can rent a car for 3 days or less if she wants to spend only \$119.12 or less.

87. a. $7.5 + 0.1t \le 10$

   b. $t \le 25$. To stay within her budget, Karyn can send no more than 25 texts over her 200 texts allowed.

88. a. $50 + 1.5m \le 65$

   b. $m \le 10$. Trey can have the TV delivered and stay within his budget for the delivery charge if he lives 10 miles or less from the store.

Chapter 2 Test

1. No, $b = -2$ is not a solution of $5b + 8 = 2$.

2. Yes $t = 4.2$ and $D = 294$ are solutions to the equation $D = 70t$.

3. $x = -12$ **4.** $c = P - a - b$

5. $P = 162{,}000$. The company has a profit of $162,000.

6. $w = -90$ **7.** $p = 36$ **8.** $x = -36$

9. All real numbers   **10.** No solution

11. Let $l =$ the length of the building lot.

$330 = 2l + 2 \cdot 40$

$l = 125$. The length of the building lot is 125 feet.

12. $x = \dfrac{y - b}{m}$

13. Let "a number" $= x$.

$4x + 7 = -17$

$x = -6$

14. $x = 2$ **15.** All real numbers

16. $x = 10$. The measures of the 3 angles are 10°, 110°, and 60°.

17. $x \geq -16$

18. $x < 2$

19. $6 \leq x \leq 11$

20. a. $10.25h > 287$

b. $h > 28$. To earn more than $287.00 a week to meet his expenses, Aiden must work more than 28 hours.

Cumulative Review for Chapters 1–2

1. $\left(\dfrac{9}{4}\right)^6$ **2.** $(-4) \cdot (-4) \cdot (-4)$

3. -1 **4.** $304{,}500{,}000$

5. $\dfrac{\left(\dfrac{84}{10 - 6} \cdot 3\right)\left(2^2\right) + (-5) + \left(20 \div 4 \cdot (-3)\right)}{49}$

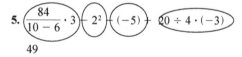

6. 20

7. Commutative property of addition

8. Let $R =$ the amount of revenue in dollars the soccer club makes, and let $c =$ the number of candy bars sold.

9. Let "a number" $= x$.

$8x - 7$

10. 28.956 meters

11. -40

12. $50 - n$

Number of Biscuits for Scout	Number of Biscuits for Shadow
0	$50 - 0 = 50$
5	$50 - 5 = 45$
10	$50 - 10 = 40$
15	$50 - 15 = 35$
n	$50 - n$

13. $-12x^2 + 5x + 15xy$

14. $3x + 13$

15. $4b - 8c$

16. $(4, 0), (1, 2), (-3, 4), (-3, -5), (0, -3), (6, -2)$

17.

18.

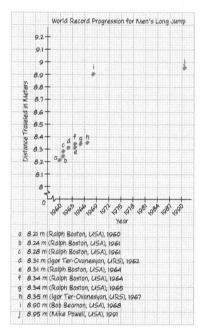

19. Yes, $x = -1.5$ and $y = 0$ are solutions to the equation $4x - 7y = -6$.

20. $y = -5$ **21.** $x = \dfrac{7}{6}$ or $x = 1\dfrac{1}{6}$

22. $n = 4.057$ **23.** $y = \dfrac{3}{5}x + 6$

24. $x = 3$ **25.** $n = -12$

26. $z = -1.59$

27. a. $S = 1440$. If Corinthia works 120 hours in a month, her monthly salary would be $1440.

b. $h = 140$. Corinthia would need to work 140 hours in a month to make $1680 a month.

c. $h = 100$. Corinthia would need to work 100 hours in a month if she wants to earn only $1200 a month.

28. $y = 4$ **29.** $x = 65$ **30.** $x = 4.5$

31. Let "a number" $= x$.

$2x + 20 = 6$

$x = -7$

32. $m = \dfrac{P}{rg}$ **33.** $y = 2x + 10$

34. Let "a number" $= x$.

$2x + 8 = 4x - 18$

$x = 13$

35. $y = -4$ **36.** $n = -16$ **37.** $w = 2$

38. $x = 55$. The measures of the 3 angles are 55°, 73°, and 52°.

39. $x > 8$ **40.** $r \geq -28$

41. $3 < x < 7$ **42.** $t < \dfrac{112}{3}$ or $t < 37\dfrac{1}{3}$

43. Let $s =$ the number of students enrolled in the class.

$15 \leq s \leq 25$

44. Let $n =$ the course number.

$200 \leq n < 400$

CHAPTER 3
Section 3.1

1.

$s =$ Sales (dollars)	$P =$ Monthly pay (dollars)
0	300
1000	350
8000	700
30,000	1800
50,000	2800

3.

$h =$ Hours since opening	$C =$ Number of customers for the day
0	2
1	10
3	26
6	50
10	82

5.

$n =$ Number of studs purchased	$C =$ Cost (dollars)
4	14
6	21
8	28
11	38.50
18	63

7.

$h =$ Hours of bowling	$C =$ Calories burned
1	259
2	518
3	777
5	1295
6	1554

9.

11.

13.

15.

17.

t	$P = -8t + 17$
-4	49
-2	33
0	17
2	1
4	-15

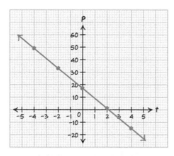

The graph is linear.

19.

x	$y = \lvert x - 2 \rvert$
-6	8
-3	5
0	2
2	0
3	1
6	4

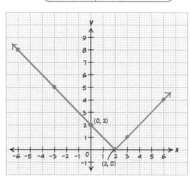

The graph is nonlinear.

21.

s	$R = s^2 + 7$
-2	11
-1	8
0	7
1	8
2	11

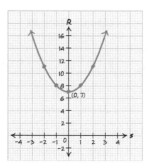

The graph is nonlinear.

23.

x	$y = -2x^2 + 3$
-2	-5
-1	1
0	3
1	1
2	-5

The graph is nonlinear.

25.

x	$y = 2x - 8$
-1	-10
0	-8
2	-4
4	0
7	6

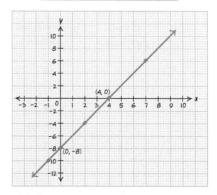

The graph is linear.

27.

x	y = 0.5x + 3
−8	−1
−4	1
0	3
4	5
8	7

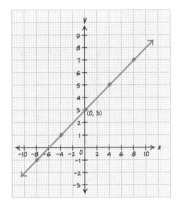

The graph is linear.

29.

x	y = −2x + 10
−2	14
0	10
2	6
4	2
7	−4

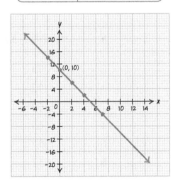

The graph is linear.

31.

x	y = −0.4x + 2
−10	6
−5	4
0	2
5	0
10	−2

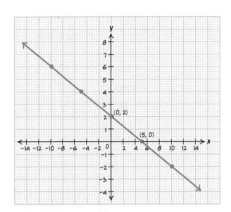

The graph is linear.

33.

x	y = 3x
−3	−9
−1	−3
0	0
1	3
3	9

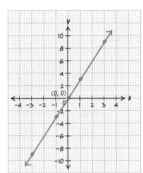

The graph is linear.

35.

x	y = −3x
−3	9
−1	3
0	0
1	−3
3	−9

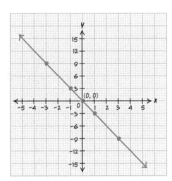

The graph is linear.

37.

x	$y = \frac{1}{2}x + 3$
−10	−2
−6	0
0	3
6	6
10	8

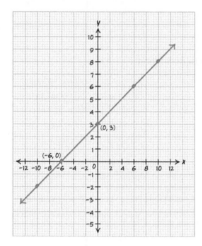

The graph is linear.

39.

x	$y = \frac{2}{3}x - 5$
−6	−9
0	−5
3	−3
6	−1
9	1

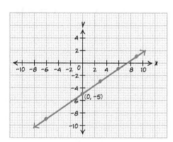

The graph is linear.

41.

x	$y = -\frac{1}{5}x - 2$
−10	0
−5	−1
0	−2
5	−3
10	−4

The graph is linear.

43.

d	$T = 5d$
0	0
1	5
2	10
5	25
7	35

45.

h	$T = 75 - 3h$
0	75
1	72
2	69
4	63
6	57
8	51

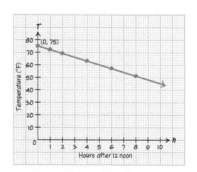

47.

m	g = 24,000 − 100m
0	24,000
50	19,000
100	14,000
175	6500
240	0

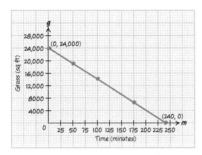

49.

x	y = x² + 1
−5	26
−3	10
−2	5
−1	2
0	1
1	2
2	5
3	10
5	26

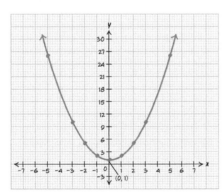

The graph is nonlinear.

51.

x	y = x² − 4
−5	21
−3	5
−2	0
−1	−3
0	−4
1	−3
2	0
3	5
5	21

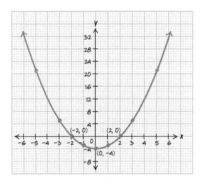

The graph is nonlinear.

53.

x	y = (x + 3)²
−7	16
−6	9
−5	4
−4	1
−3	0
−2	1
−1	4
0	9
1	16

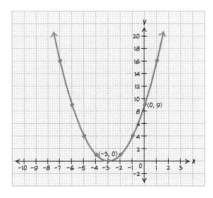

The graph is nonlinear.

55.

x	$y = (x - 2)^2$
-2	16
-1	9
0	4
1	1
2	0
3	1
4	4
5	9
6	16

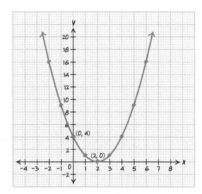

The graph is nonlinear.

57.

x	$y = |x| + 2$
-8	10
-6	8
-4	6
-2	4
0	2
2	4
4	6
6	8
8	10

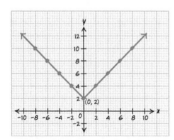

The graph is nonlinear.

59.

x	$y = |x + 2|$
-9	7
-7	5
-5	3
-3	1
-2	0
-1	1
1	3
3	5
5	7

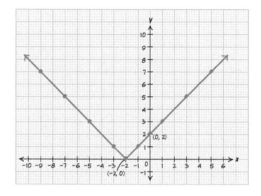

The graph is nonlinear.

61.

x	$y = |x - 3|$
-3	6
-1	4
0	3
2	1
3	0
4	1
6	3
7	4
9	6

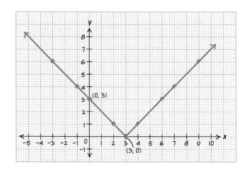

The graph is nonlinear.

63.

x	y = 6
−9	6
−5	6
0	6
5	6
9	6

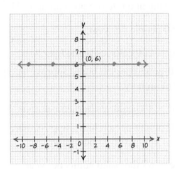

The graph is linear.

65.

x = 7	y
7	−9
7	−5
7	0
7	5
7	9

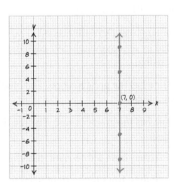

The graph is linear.

67.

x	y = −3.5
−9	−3.5
−5	−3.5
0	−3.5
5	−3.5
9	−3.5

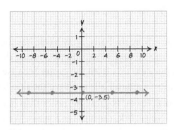

The graph is linear.

69.

x = −1.5	y
−1.5	−9
−1.5	−5
−1.5	0
−1.5	5
−1.5	9

The graph is linear.

71.

x = 0	y
0	−9
0	−5
0	0
0	5
0	9

The graph is linear.

Section **3.2**

1. a. Buffalo–Niagara Falls, New York, has the larger population than El Paso, Texas, during these years. We can conclude this from the graph because the line for Buffalo–Niagara Falls is above the line for El Paso.

   b. El Paso, Texas, is growing faster than Buffalo–Niagara Falls, New York, during these years. We can conclude this from the graph because the line for El Paso is rising at a steeper rate than the line for Buffalo–Niagara Falls, which is actually going down.

3. Archery burns more calories per hour than billiards does. We can conclude this from the graph because the line for archery is steeper than the line for billiards.

5. a. California has more adults who have diagnosed diabetes. We can conclude this from the graph because the line for California is above the line for Florida.

   b. The number of adults with diagnosed diabetes is growing more slowly in Florida than in California. We can conclude this from the graph because the line for California is rising at a steeper rate than the line for Florida.

7. a. The Rock-On Live Tour had more tickets available at the start of sales. We can conclude this from the graph because the line for the Rock-On Live Tour at the start of sales is above the line for the Classics Rule Tour.

   b. The Rock-On Live Tour sold out first. We can conclude this from the graph because the line reaches zero on the graph before the line for the Classics Rule Tour.

   c. The available tickets for the Rock-On Live Tour decreased faster than the available tickets for the Classics Rule Tour. We can conclude this from the graph because the line for Rock-On Live Tour is decreasing at a steeper rate than the line for Classics Rule Tour.

9. Slope = 2

11. Slope = $\dfrac{3}{2}$

13. Slope = 0

15. Slope = $\dfrac{1}{4}$

17. Slope is undefined.

19. Slope = $-\dfrac{1}{2}$

21. Slope = -3

23. Slope = 2

25. Slope = $\dfrac{1}{4}$

27. Slope = 3

29. Slope = 0

31. Slope = $\dfrac{1}{2}$

33. Slope is undefined.

35. Slope = -4

37. The blue line has a slope that is closer to zero than that of the red line. The blue line is closer to horizontal than the red line.

39. The blue line has a slope that is closer to being undefined than that of the red line. The blue line is closer to vertical than the red line.

41. Slope = 3

43. Slope = $\dfrac{3}{2}$

45. Slope is undefined.

47. Slope = $\dfrac{1}{3}$

49. Slope = -4

51. Slope = 0

53. Slope = $-\dfrac{1}{2}$

55. a. Slope = $-5\dfrac{1}{6}$ thousand people per year

   b. The population of Buffalo–Niagara Falls, New York, is declining at a rate of approximately $5\dfrac{1}{6}$ thousand, or 5167 people per year.

57. a. Slope = $11\dfrac{3}{4}$ thousand people per year

   b. The population of Oklahoma City, Oklahoma, is increasing at a rate of approximately $11\dfrac{3}{4}$ thousand, or 11,750 people per year.

59. a. Slope ≈ 200 calories burned per hour

   b. A 130-pound person burns approximately 200 calories per hour of archery.

61. a. Slope ≈ 400 calories burned per hour

   b. A 130-pound person burns approximately 400 calories per hour of competitive badminton.

63. a. Slope ≈ 83 thousand adults per year

   b. The number of adults with diagnosed diabetes in California is increasing by approximately 83 thousand, or 83,000 people per year.

65. a. Slope ≈ 18 thousand adults per year

   b. The number of adults with diagnosed diabetes in South Carolina is increasing by approximately 18 thousand, or 18,000 people per year.

67. a. Slope = $-178\dfrac{4}{7}$ tickets per hour

   b. The number of available tickets for the Rock-On Live Tour declined by approximately 179 tickets per hour.

69. a. Slope ≈ $-91\dfrac{41}{49}$ dollars per day

   b. The amount that Deb still needed to raise for breast cancer declined by approximately $92 each day after she began fund-raising.

71. The blue line has the greater slope. The blue line is steeper than the red line.

73. The red line has the greater slope. The red line is steeper than the blue line.

75. The line is rising from left to right; therefore, it is increasing.

77. The line is falling from left to right; therefore, it is decreasing.

79. The line is horizontal; therefore, it is neither increasing nor decreasing.

81. When graphed, the line is falling from left to right; therefore, it is decreasing. The slope is negative.

83. The equation has no x-value, only a y-value. For any value of x, the y-value would remain the same; therefore, the line is horizontal and is neither increasing nor decreasing.

85. When graphed, the line is rising from left to right; therefore, it is increasing. The slope is positive.

87. The output value is increasing.

89. The output value is decreasing.

91. The output value is decreasing.

93. The output value is increasing.

95. a. The red line appears to be decreasing more rapidly.

b. Red line slope $= -1$

Blue line slope $= -\dfrac{1}{2}$

c. The line that is decreasing more rapidly has a slope that is less (has a greater negative value) than the other line.

Section **3.3**

1. x-intercept is the point $(2, 0)$.

y-intercept is the point $(0, -1)$.

3. x-intercept is the point $(3, 0)$.

y-intercept is the point $(0, 2)$.

5. x-intercept is the point $(2, 0)$.

y-intercept is the point $(0, 10)$.

7. x-intercepts are the points $(0, 0)$ and $(-6, 0)$.

y-intercept is the point $(0, 0)$.

9. x-intercepts are the points $(-4, 0)$, $(-2, 0)$, and $(4, 0)$.

y-intercept is the point $(0, -50)$.

11. a. The vertical intercept is the point $(0, 1169)$, meaning that the population of Buffalo–Niagara Falls, New York, was about 1169 thousand, or 1,169,000 people in the year 2000.

b. The vertical intercept is the point $(0, 682)$, meaning that the population of El Paso, Texas, was about 682 thousand, or 682,000 people in the year 2000.

13. The intercept for these lines is the point $(0, 0)$, meaning that zero calories are burned during zero hours of exercise.

15. a. The vertical intercept is the point $(0, 741)$, meaning that there were 741 thousand, or 741,000, adults in California with diagnosed diabetes in the year 1990.

b. The vertical intercept is the point $(0, 262)$, meaning that there were 262 thousand, or 262,000, adults in Florida with diagnosed diabetes in the year 1990.

17. a. The vertical intercept for the Rock-On Live Tour line is the point $(0, 2500)$, meaning that there were 2500 tickets available at the start of ticket sales. The horizontal intercept is the point $(14, 0)$, meaning that 14 hours after going on sale, the tickets were sold out.

b. The vertical intercept for the Classics Rule Tour line is the point $(0, 2000)$, meaning that there were 2000 tickets available at the start of ticket sales. The horizontal intercept is the point $(18, 0)$, meaning that 18 hours after going on sale, the tickets were sold out.

19. x-intercept is the point $(-4, 0)$.

y-intercept is the point $(0, 20)$.

21. x-intercept is the point $(9, 0)$.

y-intercept is the point $(0, -36)$.

23. x-intercept is the point $(-6, 0)$.

y-intercept is the point $(0, 3)$.

25. x-intercept is the point $(-9, 0)$.

y-intercept is the point $(0, 6)$.

27. x-intercept is the point $(-15, 0)$.

y-intercept is the point $(0, 3.75)$.

29. x-intercept is the point $(0, 0)$.

y-intercept is the point $(0, 0)$.

31. x-intercept is the point $(15, 0)$.

y-intercept is the point $(0, 3)$.

33. x-intercept is the point $\left(2\dfrac{1}{2}, 0\right)$.

y-intercept is the point $(0, -5)$.

35. x-intercept is the point $\left(7\dfrac{1}{2}, 0\right)$.

y-intercept is the point $(0, 10)$.

37. There is no x-intercept.

y-intercept is the point $(0, 6)$.

39. x-intercept is the point $(-5, 0)$.

There is no y-intercept.

41. a. The P-intercept is the point $(0, 2674)$, meaning that there were 2674 thousand, or 2,674,000, American Indians and Alaska Natives in the United States in the year 2000.

b. The t-intercept is the point $\left(-70\dfrac{7}{19}, 0\right)$, meaning that there were no American Indians and Alaska Natives in the United States in the year 1929.

c. The t-intercept does not make sense because there were more than 0 American Indians and Alaska Natives in the United States in the year 1929. The P-intercept makes sense in this situation, as it is reasonable that there were 2,674,000 American Indians and Alaska Natives in the United States in the year 2000.

43. a. The P-intercept is the point $(0, 0.65)$, meaning that the price of navel oranges was \$0.65 per pound in the year 2000.

b. The t-intercept is the point $(-13, 0)$, meaning that there was no charge for navel oranges in the year 1987.

c. The t-intercept does not make sense because navel oranges would not have been offered free of charge in 1987. The P-intercept makes sense in this situation, as it is reasonable that navel oranges cost \$0.65 per pound in the year 2000.

45. a. The C-intercept is the point $(0, 25)$, meaning that there were 25 cars sold during week 0 of the year.

b. The w-intercept is the point $\left(12\dfrac{1}{2}, 0\right)$, meaning that no cars were sold during week 13, of the year.

c. The C-intercept could mean that the last week of the previous year the car lot sold 25 cars. The w-intercept could make sense if there were no cars sold during a given week.

47. a. The D-intercept is the point $(0, 12{,}500)$, meaning that José had \$12,500 in credit card debt before he began to pay his cards off.

b. The m-intercept is the point $(50, 0)$, meaning that José had no credit card debt 50 months after starting to pay his cards off.

c. The D-intercept makes sense because it is reasonable to have \$12,500 in credit card debt. The m-intercept makes sense in this situation, as it is reasonable that it would take José 50 months to pay off the credit cards and have no debt.

49. Slope $= -3$

x-intercept is the point $(9, 0)$.

y-intercept is the point $(0, 27)$.

51. Slope $= 8$

x-intercept is the point $(2, 0)$.

y-intercept is the point $(0, -16)$.

53. Slope $= \dfrac{1}{2}$

x-intercept is the point $(-12, 0)$.

y-intercept is the point $(0, 6)$.

55. Slope $= -\dfrac{1}{3}$

x-intercept is the point $(15, 0)$.

y-intercept is the point $(0, 5)$.

57. Slope $= \dfrac{2}{3}$

x-intercept is the point $(6, 0)$.

y-intercept is the point $(0, -4)$.

59. Slope $= 1.5$

x-intercept is the point $(2, 0)$.

y-intercept is the point $(0, -3)$.

61. Slope $= 0$

There is no x-intercept.

y-intercept is the point $(0, -5)$.

63. Slope is undefined.

x-intercept is the point $(6, 0)$.

There is no y-intercept.

65. The slope is 38, which represents that there are 38 thousand, or 38,000, more American Indians and Alaska Natives in the United States for each year.

67. The slope is 0.05, which represents that the price for navel oranges increases by about $0.05 each year.

69. The slope is -2, which represents that during each successive week of the year, Big Jim's Car Lot sells 2 fewer cars than the week before.

71. a. The R-intercept is the point $(0, 29.4)$, which represents that the total revenue earned by Cisco Systems, Inc. during the year 2005 was $29.4 billion.

   b. The slope is 5, which represents an additional $5 billion in revenue each year.

73. Slope $= -3$

y-intercept is the point $(0, 18)$.

75. Slope $= -\dfrac{3}{2}$

y-intercept is the point $(0, 3)$.

77. Slope $= \dfrac{2}{7}$

y-intercept is the point $(0, -3)$.

79. Slope $= \dfrac{1}{2}$

y-intercept is the point $\left(0, \dfrac{7}{2}\right)$.

81. Slope $= 2$

y-intercept is the point $(0, -13)$.

83. Slope $= \dfrac{1}{2}$

y-intercept is the point $(0, 12)$.

85. Slope $= 0$

y-intercept is the point $(0, 7)$.

Section **3.4**

1. $y = 2x + 3$ Graph A

$y = -2x + 3$ Graph C

$y = 2x - 3$ Graph B

3. $y = \dfrac{1}{2}x + 2$ Graph C

$y = \dfrac{1}{2}x - 3$ Graph A

$y = \dfrac{1}{2}x + 5$ Graph B

5.

7.

9.

11.

13.

15.

17.

19.

21.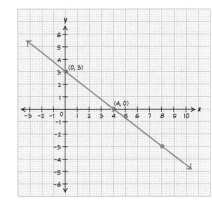

23. Jill graphed a slope of $-\dfrac{1}{2}$ instead of the slope of $\dfrac{1}{2}$.

25. Kwong graphed a slope of 2 instead of the slope of -2.

27. Marybeth graphed a slope of $\dfrac{1}{2}$ instead of the slope of 2.

29. José graphed a y-intercept of $(0, -1)$ instead of the correct y-intercept of $(0, 2)$.

31.

33.

35.

37.

39.

41.

43.

45.

47.

49.

51. a.

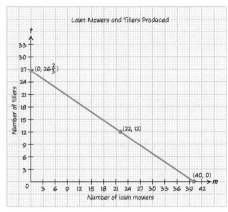

b. The factory can produce 22 lawn mowers if the workers make 12 tillers that week.

53. a.

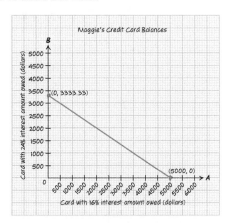

b. The A-intercept represents one possible distribution of credit card balances: if the card with 16% interest had a balance of $5000, the card with 24% interest had a balance of $0.

55. Linear $y = \frac{3}{2}x + 7$

57. Nonlinear

59. Nonlinear

61. Linear $y = \frac{1}{2}x - 7\frac{1}{4}$

63. Nonlinear

65. Nonlinear

67. Linear $y = \frac{3}{4}x + 4\frac{1}{4}$

69. Nonlinear

71. Slope and y-intercept

73. x- and y-intercepts

75. Table of points

77. Slope and y-intercept, or x- and y-intercepts

79. x- and y-intercepts

81. Table of points

83. Parallel

85. Perpendicular

87. Neither parallel nor perpendicular

89. Perpendicular

91. Parallel

93. Neither parallel nor perpendicular

Section 3.5

1. $y = \frac{1}{6}x + 1$ **3.** $y = -\frac{5}{2}x$ **5.** $y = 4$

7. $y = \frac{110}{3}x - 86\frac{2}{3}$ **9.** $y = -\frac{5}{36}x + 4\frac{11}{12}$

11. The equation of the line that describes this relationship is
$c = \frac{1}{100}y.$

13. The equation of the line that describes this relationship is
$F = -2t + 77.$

15. The equation of the line that describes this relationship is
$W = -2t + 165.$

17. The slope is $\frac{1}{100}$, which represents that there is 1 century per 100 years.

19. The slope is -2, which represents that the temperature drops by 2 degrees per hour after 1:00 P.M.

21. The slope is -2, which represents that Irina is losing 2 pounds per week.

23. The y- and c-intercepts are both the point $(0, 0)$. This represents that for 0 years, there are 0 centuries.

25. The t-intercept is the point $(38.5, 0)$. This represents that 38.5 hours after noon the temperature would be 0 degrees Fahrenheit. This value does not make sense in the given situation.

The F-intercept is the point $(0, 77)$. This represents that when $t = 0$, presumably 12:00 noon, the temperature would be 77 degrees Fahrenheit.

27. The t-intercept is the point $(82.5, 0)$. This represents that 82.5 weeks after starting her diet, Irina will weigh 0 pounds. This value does not make sense in the given situation.

The W-intercept is the point $(0, 165)$. This represents that at the start of her diet (0 weeks into her diet), Irina weighs 165 pounds.

29. a. The equation of the line that describes this relationship is
$d = 45g.$

b. The slope of 45 represents that for 45 highway miles driven, the Prius uses 1 gallon of gas, or the Prius gets 45 mpg.

c. The g- and d-intercepts are both the point $(0, 0)$. This represents that for 0 miles driven, there are 0 gallons of gas used.

31. a. The equation of the line that describes this relationship is
$c = 45m + 125$.

   b. The slope of 45 represents that the cost increases by $45
for every month of membership.

   c. The m-intercept is the point $\left(-2\frac{7}{9}, 0\right)$. This represents

   that $2\frac{7}{9}$ months before beginning a membership, the

   cost would be $0. This value does not make sense in the
   problem situation.

   The c-intercept is the point $(0, 125)$. This represents that
   for 0 months of membership, the cost is $125.

33. $y = x - 9$ **35.** $y = \frac{2}{3}x + 1$ **37.** $y = -4x - 2$

39. $y = 5$ **41.** $y = 3x - 15$ **43.** $y = -2x - 7$

45. $y = 6x - 9$ **47.** $y = \frac{2}{3}x$ **49.** $y = 5$

51. $y = 3x + 2$ **53.** $y = -3x + 4$ **55.** $y = \frac{1}{2}x + 1$

57. $y = -6$ **59.** $2x + 3y = 21$ **61.** $y = \frac{3}{4}x - 6$

63. $y = -6x - 63$ **65.** $-7x + y = 9$ **67.** $x = 5$

69. $x = 0$ **71.** $y = 6x + 42$ **73.** $y = \frac{1}{5}x + 4$

75. $y = -\frac{8}{3}x - 28$ **77.** $y = -\frac{4}{5}x - 3$ **79.** $y = 6$

81. $y = 5$ **83.** $x = 1$ **85.** $x = 5$

Chapter 3 Review Exercises

1.

h = Hours of walking	C = Calories burned
1	87
2	174
3	261
4	348
6	522

2.

n = Number of plants purchased	C = Cost (dollars)
2	10.50
4	21.00
8	42.00
14	73.50
20	105.00

3.

4.

5.

x	$y = -3x + 8$
-1	11
0	8
1	5
3	-1
5	-7

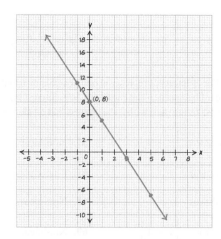

6.

x	y = −5x − 3
−2	7
−1	2
0	−3
1	−8
2	−13

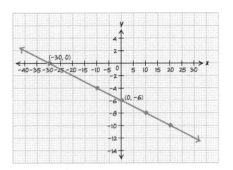

7.

x	$y = \dfrac{3}{4}x + 1$
−8	−5
−4	−2
0	1
4	4
8	7

9.

x	y = 5
−9	5
−5	5
0	5
5	5
9	5

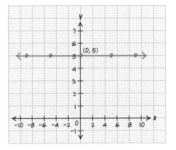

10.

x	y = −4
−9	−4
−5	−4
0	−4
5	−4
9	−4

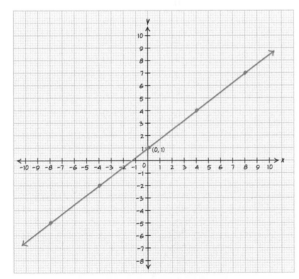

8.

x	$y = \dfrac{-1}{5}x - 6$
−30	0
−10	−4
0	−6
10	−8
20	−10

11.

x = −3	y
−3	−9
−3	−5
−3	0
−3	5
−3	9

14.

x	$y = -x^2 + 5$
-4	-11
-3	-4
-2	1
-1	4
0	5
1	4
2	1
3	-4
4	-11

12.

$x = 5$	y
5	-9
5	-5
5	0
5	5
5	9

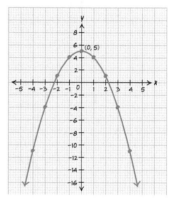

13.

x	$y = x^2 + 2$
-4	18
-3	11
-2	6
-1	3
0	2
1	3
2	6
3	11
4	18

15.

x	$y = \lvert 9 - 3x \rvert$
-1	12
0	9
1	6
2	3
3	0
4	3
5	6
6	9
7	12

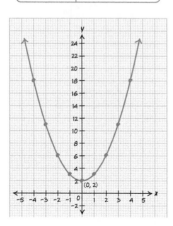

16.

x	$y = \lvert x + 2 \rvert$
-5	3
-4	2
-3	1
-2	0
-1	1
0	2
1	3
2	4
3	5

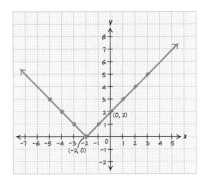

17. **a.** Bakersfield, California, has a larger population than Wichita, Kansas, during these years. We can conclude this from the graph because the line for Bakersfield is above the line for Wichita.

   b. Bakersfield, California, is growing faster than Wichita, Kansas, during these years. We can conclude this from the graph because the line for Bakersfield is rising at a steeper rate than the line for Wichita.

18. **a.** St. Louis, Missouri–Illinois, has a larger population than San Antonio, Texas, during these years. We can conclude this from the graph because the line for St. Louis is above the line for San Antonio.

   b. San Antonio, Texas, is growing faster than St. Louis, Missouri–Illinois, during these years. We can conclude this from the graph because the line for San Antonio is rising at a steeper rate than the line for St. Louis.

19. Slope $= \dfrac{1}{2}$ **20.** Slope $= -\dfrac{1}{4}$ **21.** Slope $= -\dfrac{3}{4}$

22. Slope $= \dfrac{3}{8}$ **23.** Slope $= \dfrac{2}{5}$ **24.** Slope $= \dfrac{1}{3}$

25. The slope for Bakersfield, California, is $19\dfrac{1}{3}$ thousand, or 19,333 people per year. This means that the population of Bakersfield is increasing at a rate of approximately 19,333 people per year.

26. The slope for San Antonio, Texas, is $38\dfrac{1}{2}$ thousand, or 38,500 people per year. This means that the population of San Antonio is increasing at a rate of approximately 38,500 people per year.

27. x-intercept is the point $(-3, 0)$.
   y-intercept is the point $(0, -1)$.

28. x-intercepts are the points $(-2, 0)$, $(0, 0)$ $(3, 0)$, and $(4, 0)$.
   y-intercept is the point $(0, 0)$.

29. **a.** The vertical intercept for the Bakersfield line is $(0, 664)$. This means that the population of Bakersfield was approximately 664 thousand, or 664,000, people in the year 2000.

   b. The vertical intercept for the Wichita line is $(0, 572)$. This means that the population of Wichita was approximately 572 thousand, or 572,000, people in the year 2000.

30. **a.** The vertical intercept is $(0, 2000)$. This means that the balance of the credit card debt is $2000 at the beginning of the year.

   b. The horizontal intercept is $(16, 0)$. This means that the balance of the credit card debt was paid down to zero 16 weeks since the beginning of the year.

31. x-intercept is the point $(4, 0)$.
   y-intercept is the point $(0, 3)$.

32. x-intercept is the point $(3, 0)$.
   y-intercept is the point $(0, -6)$.

33. **a.** The T-intercept is $(0, 1)$. This means that it would take 1 hour to paint 0 dolls. In this problem situation, it means that in addition to the time it takes to paint each doll, there is an additional hour of work to do.

   b. The d-intercept is $\left(-\dfrac{2}{3}, 0\right)$. This means that it would take 0 hours to paint $-\dfrac{2}{3}$ dolls. This does not make sense in terms of the problem situation.

34. **a.** The C-intercept is $(0, 10)$. This means that there is a base cost of $10 to produce the dolls regardless of how many dolls are painted.

   b. The d-intercept is $\left(-\dfrac{2}{5}, 0\right)$. This means that it would cost nothing to paint $-\dfrac{2}{5}$ dolls. This does not make sense in terms of the problem situation.

35. x-intercept is the point $(3, 0)$.
   y-intercept is the point $(0, 9)$.
   Slope $= -3$

36. x-intercept is the point $(-6, 0)$.
   y-intercept is the point $(0, 12)$.
   Slope $= 2$

37. x-intercept is the point $(7.077, 0)$.
   y-intercept is the point $(0, -7.112)$.
   Slope $= 1.005$

38. x-intercept is the point $(39, 0)$.
   y-intercept is the point $(0, 9.75)$.
   Slope $= -0.25$

39. x-intercept is the point $(-4, 0)$.
   y-intercept is the point $(0, -2)$.
   Slope $= -\dfrac{1}{2}$

40. x-intercept is the point $(-12, 0)$.

y-intercept is the point $(0, -4)$.

Slope $= -\dfrac{1}{3}$

41. x-intercept is the point $(-5, 0)$.

y-intercept is the point $(0, 4)$.

Slope $= \dfrac{4}{5}$

42. x-intercept is the point $(-10, 0)$.

y-intercept is the point $(0, 2)$.

Slope $= \dfrac{1}{5}$

43. a. The slope is 7.4 thousand, or 7,400, people per year. This means that the population of Alaska is increasing at a rate of approximately 7,400 people per year.

   b. The P-intercept is $(0, 626)$. This means that the population of Alaska was approximately 626 thousand, or 626,000, people in the year 2000.

44. a. The slope is 2.5. This means that the cost increases by $2.50 for every set of clamps produced.

   b. The C-intercept is $(0, 200)$. This means that there is a base cost of $200 regardless of how many sets of clamps are produced.

45.

46.

47.

48.

49.

50.

51.

52.

53.

54.

55.

56.

57.

58.

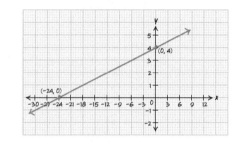

59. $y = -4x + 3$

60. $y = \dfrac{2}{3}x - 6$

61. Let $C =$ the number of calories burned, and let $t =$ the time in hours spent running. The equation of the line that describes this relationship is $C = 852t$.

62. Let $C =$ the number of calories burned, and let $t =$ the time in hours spent golfing using a handcart. The equation of the line that describes this relationship is $C = 264t$.

63. The slope of 852 means that a 160- to 170-pound person will burn 852 calories per hour while running at a pace of 8 mph.

64. The slope of 264 means that a 160- to 170-pound person will burn 264 calories per hour while golfing using a handcart.

65. $y = -x + 8$ **66.** $y = -\dfrac{2}{3}x + 5$ **67.** $y = \dfrac{1}{10}x + 5$

68. $y = \dfrac{1}{2}x - 7$ **69.** $y = -11$ **70.** $y = 12$

71. $x = 1$ **72.** $x = -4$ **73.** $y = \dfrac{1}{2}x + 6$

74. $y = -\dfrac{1}{3}x + 2$ **75.** $y = -\dfrac{3}{4}x + 2$ **76.** $y = -\dfrac{1}{6}x + 3$

77. Parallel   **78.** Parallel   **79.** Perpendicular

80. Perpendicular

81. $y = \dfrac{1}{8}x + 4$ **82.** $y = \dfrac{5}{2}x - 26$ **83.** $y = \dfrac{3}{4}x - 14$

84. $y = 2x - 1$ **85.** $5x + 6y = 42$ **86.** $4x + 5y = -45$

87. $y = \dfrac{6}{5}x - 6$ **88.** $y = \dfrac{1}{2}x + 10$ **89.** $2x + y = -7$

90. $7x + y = 32$ **91.** $y = \dfrac{2}{3}x - 8$ **92.** $y = -\dfrac{5}{7}x - 3$

Chapter 3 Test

1.

x	$y = -5x + 2$
-2	12
-1	7
0	2
1	-3
2	-8

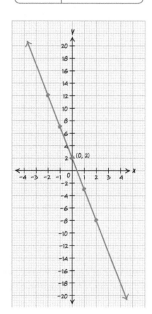

2.

x	$y = x^2 - 1$
-4	15
-3	8
-2	3
-1	0
0	-1
1	0
2	3
3	8
4	15

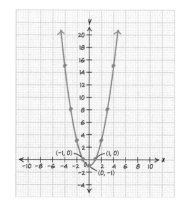

3. Slope $= 1$

4. The slope is 18,744.75. This means that during the years 1999–2003, there were approximately 18,745 more children diagnosed with autism each year.

5. x-intercept is the point $(3, 0)$.

y-intercept is the point $(0, -2)$.

6. a. The vertical intercept is $(0, 5.6)$, which represents that 5.6 billion kilowatt-hours of electricity were generated by wind in the year 2000.

b. The vertical intercept is $(0, 14)$, which represents that 14 billion kilowatt-hours of electricity were generated by geothermal in the year 2000.

7. Slope $= \dfrac{3}{5}$

x-intercept is the point $\left(\dfrac{2}{3}, 0\right)$.

y-intercept is the point $\left(0, -\dfrac{2}{5}\right)$.

8.

9.

10.

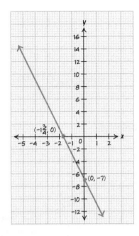

11. a. Nonlinear

    b. Linear

    $y = 3x + 14$

12. $y = 5x - 7$ **13.** $y = \dfrac{1}{4}x + 2\dfrac{1}{2}$

14. $W = -5t + 235$

15. The slope is -5, which represents that Paul is losing weight at a rate of 5 pounds per week.

16. $y = \dfrac{3}{4}x - 5$ **17.** Perpendicular

18. $y = \dfrac{2}{5}x - 1$

CHAPTER 4

Section 4.1

1. $(-5, 6)$ **3.** $(2, 6)$

5. $(0, 3)$ **7.** $(9, 1)$

9. a. No.   **b.** Yes.

11. a. No.   **b.** No.

13. a. Yes.   **b.** Yes.

15. a. No.   **b.** No.

17. a. No.   **b.** Yes.

19. a. Yes.   **b.** Yes.

21. About 125 mg/dL.

23. a. Let t = number of tracks,

       let C = monthly cost in dollars.

       Music OnLine: $C = 0.80t + 10$

       GotTunes: $C = 1t + 8$

b.

Music OnLine		GotTunes	
t	C	t	C
0	10.00	0	8.00
2	11.60	2	10.00
4	13.20	4	12.00
6	14.80	6	14.00
8	16.40	8	16.00
10	18.00	10	18.00
12	19.60	12	20.00

    c. 10 tracks cost \$18.00.

    d. GotTunes.

25. a. Let m = number of months;

       let C = cost in dollars.

       Fitness Plus: $C = 15m + 100$

       Rock's Gym: $C = 20m + 80$

b.

Fitness Plus		Rock's Gym	
m	C	m	C
0	100	0	80
1	115	1	100
2	130	2	120
3	145	3	140
4	160	4	160
5	175	5	180
6	190	6	200

    c. Four months costs \$160.

    d. Fitness Plus.

27. $(1, 1)$ **29.** $(100, -4)$ **31.** $(-3, 2)$ **33.** No solution.

35. a. Yes.   **b.** No.

37. a. No.   **b.** Yes.

39.

$(1, -3)$, consistent.

41.

$(5, 0)$, consistent.

43.

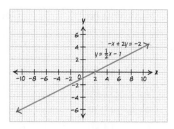

Infinitely many solutions, consistent.

45.

No solution, inconsistent.

47.

$(-1, 2)$, consistent.

49.

$(-1, -3)$, consistent.

51.

$(-4, 5)$, consistent.

53.

$(-9, -2.5)$, consistent.

55.

No solution, inconsistent.

57.

No solution, inconsistent.

59.

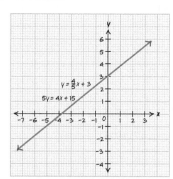

Infinitely many solutions, consistent.

61.

$(6, 7)$, consistent.

63. 12 hours, $900

65. 115 products, $690

67. a. Let h = number of hours; let C = cost in dollars.

$$C = 60h + 10$$

b. $C = 55h + 15$

c.

$(1, 70)$

69. The oven costs $640, and the microwave costs $320.

71. The length is 9 cm, and the width is 3 cm.

73. a. Let p = number of people; let C = cost in dollars;

$$C = 5.75p + 255$$

b. Let R = revenue; $R = 10.00p$

c.

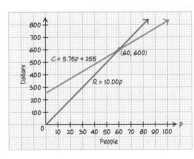

$(60, 600)$

d. They have to sell 60 tickets.

75. Parallel.   **77.** Neither.

79. Perpendicular.   **81.** Parallel.

83. Parallel.   **85.** One solution.

87. No solutions.   **89.** Infinitely many solutions.

Section 4.2

1. $y = -3x - 4$ **3.** $x = -4y - 3$

5. $y = \dfrac{1}{2}x - 3$ **7.** $x + 3y = 7$
$x = -3y + 7$

9. $-a + 9b = 6$ **11.** $y = -2x + 1$
$a = 9b - 6$

13. $(5, 2)$ **15.** $(-9, 2)$

17. $\left(\dfrac{15}{8}, \dfrac{25}{4}\right)$ **19.** $(2, -7)$

21. $(-2, -2)$

23. a. Let x = the first number; let y = the second number.

b. $x + y = 65$
$x = 12y$

c. $x = 60, y = 5$

25. The numbers are 5 and 20.

27. The numbers are 2 and 10.

29. The numbers are 2 and 9.

31. The numbers are 4 and 8.

33. a. Let w = weekly sales; let P = pay in dollars.

b. $P = 100 + 0.05w$
$P = 120 + 0.04w$

c. $(2000, 200)$. If Ethan makes $2000 in weekly sales, he will earn $200 in either job.

35. a. Let f = number of hours of the first job; let s = number of hours of the second job.

b. $f + s = 20$
$8f + 9s = 176$

c. $f = 4, s = 16$

Marcus should work 4 hours at the first job and 16 hours at the second job.

37. $(1, 1)$ **39.** $(-2, -3)$

41. $(2, 1)$ **43.** $\left(\dfrac{11}{5}, \dfrac{2}{5}\right)$

45. $\left(\dfrac{7}{4}, \dfrac{3}{8}\right)$ **47.** $(1, 1)$

49. $(-2, 3)$ **51.** No solution.

53. Infinitely many solutions.

55. No solution.   **57.** $(-2.1, 1.3)$ **59.** $(-10, 0)$

61. Infinitely many solutions.

63. $\left(\dfrac{37}{6}, \dfrac{-34}{3}\right)$ **65.** 105 mph.   **67.** 105 mph.

69. 8.5 mph.   **71.** 7 mph.

73. a. \$43.73.   **b.** \$7.95t

75. a. \$310.70.   **b.** \$11.95c

77. \$10.95/lb.

79. a. Let s = rate of the boat in miles per hour; let c = rate of the current in miles per hour.

    b. $2.5(s + c) = 50$

       $5(s - c) = 50$

    c. $s = 15$ mph, $c = 5$ mph

81. a. Let p = rate of the plane in miles per hour; let w = rate of the wind in miles per hour.

    b. $3.4(p - w) = 1275$

       $3(p + w) = 1275$

    c. $p = 400$ mph, $w = 25$ mph

83. a. Let c = amount of Ceylon tea in pounds; let b = amount of black currant tea in pounds.

    b. $c + b = 50$

       $5.75c + 8.75b = 362.50$

    c. 25 lb of each.

85. a. Let p = amount of papaya in pounds; let g = amount of ginger in pounds.

    b. $p + g = 25$

       $9.99p + 3.75g = 187.25$

    c. 14.98 lb of papaya, 10.02 lb of ginger.

87. 28 cars, \$4200.   **89.** About 269 accessories, \$6588.50

91. a. Infinitely many solutions.

    b.

    c. Yes.

    d. No.

    e. Points on the line.

93. a. No solutions.

    b.

    c. No.

    d. No.

    e. A solution is a point on both lines at the same time. These lines do not intersect.

95. $2x - 4x - 8 = 6$ should have been written

$$2x - 4x + 8 = 6$$

97. $-5(-4y + 11) + 2y = -1$ should have been written

$$-5\left(\dfrac{-4}{3}y + \dfrac{11}{3}\right) + 2y = -1$$

99. Inconsistent.   **101.** Inconsistent.   **103.** Consistent.

Section **4.3**

1. $(5, -6)$ **3.** $(-9, -2)$ **5.** $(-7, -8)$

7. $(0, 4)$ **9.** $(1, -3)$

11. Infinitely many solutions.

13. $(-2, 4)$ **15.** $(-2, -7)$ **17.** $(4, -6)$

19. No solution.

21. Infinitely many solutions.

23. No solution.

25. a. Let f = the first integer, let s = the second integer.

    b. $f + s = 95$

       $4f - s = 15$

    c. $f = 22, s = 73$

27. a. Let t = cost of the T-shirt in dollars; let w = cost of the water bottle in dollars.

    b. $8t + 6w = 186$

       $10t + 8w = 237$

    c. $t = 16.5, w = 9$

29. a. Let m = price of the milk in dollars; let b = price of a bread loaf in dollars.

    b. $3m + 4b = 23.40$

       $2m + 3b = 16.35$

    c. $m = \$4.80, b = \$2.25$

31. No solution.   **33.** $(4, 7)$

35. $(-3, 4)$ **37.** $(-5, -1)$

39. Infinitely many solutions.

41. Infinitely many solutions.

43. $(2, 9)$ **45.** No solution.

47. Infinitely many solutions.

49. No solution.

51. Elimination because $4y - 4y = 0$.

53. Substitution because one equation is already solved for y.

55. Substitution because one equation is already solved for y.

57. Elimination because the coefficients of y are opposites.

59. $85.   **61.** $1111.80.

63. 0.85 liter.   **65.** 0.64 liter.

67. 65°.   **69.** 70°.

71. $10{,}000 - n$ **73.** $3800 - n$

75. a. Let p = rate of the plane in miles per hour; let w = rate of the wind in miles per hour.

    b. $3(p + w) = 375$

        $5(p - w) = 375$

    c. $p = 100$ mph, $w = 25$ mph

77. a. Let b = rate of the boat in miles per hour; let c = rate of the current in miles per hour.

    b. $3(b + c) = 60$

        $6(b - c) = 60$

    c. $b = 15$ mph, $c = 5$ mph

79. a. Let w = amount of whole wheat flour in pounds; let f = amount of white flour in pounds.

    b. $w + f = 50$

        $4.25w + 3.75f = 200$

    c. $w = 25$ lb, $f = 25$ lb

81. a. Let f = number of hours of first job; let s = number of hours of second job.

    b. $f + s = 25$

        $8.50f + 9.00s = 225$

    c. $f = 0$ hours, $s = 25$ hours

83. $1500 in the CD, $2500 in the bond.

85. $1000 on the MasterCard; $2500 on the store credit card.

87. 5 liters of 15% solution; 15 liters of 20% solution.

89. 40 liters of 30% solution; 60 liters of 50% solution.

91. One angle is 29°, and the other angle is 61°.

93. One angle is 37°, and the other angle is 143°.

95. The coefficients of x are not opposites, so they do not eliminate when added.

97. $-2(x + 5y) = -2$ should have been written $-2(x + 5y) = \mathbf{4}$.

Section **4.4**

1. a. Yes.   **b.** Yes.

3. a. No.   **b.** No.

5. a. No.   **b.** Yes.

7. a. No.   **b.** Yes.

9. a. Yes.   **b.** No.

11. a. Dashed.   **b.** No.

13. a. Solid.   **b.** Yes.

15. a. Solid.   **b.** Yes.

17. a. Dashed.   **b.** No.

19. a. $(0, 0)$

    b. $0 < -3$, No.

    c.

21. a. $(0, 0)$

    b. $0 \geq 12$, No.

    c.

23. a. $(1, 1)$

    b. $-2 < 3$, Yes.

    c.

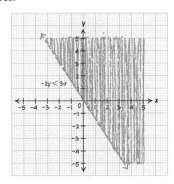

25. a. $(0, 0)$

    b. $0 > 2$, No.

    c.

27. a. $(0, 0)$

    b. $0 \geq -2$, Yes.

    c.

29.

31.

33.

35.

37.

39.

41.

43.

45.

47. a. Let m = number of oatmeal cookies; let c = number of chocolate chip cookies.

b. $4.00m + 5.50c \leq 25.00$

c.

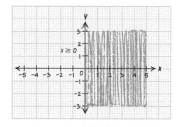

49. a. Let f = number of hours of the first job; let s = number of hours of the second job.

b. $9f + 8s > 300$

c.

51. a. Let f = amount in first account in dollars; let s = amount in second account in dollars.

b. $0.05f + 0.06s > 500$

c.

53. a. Let w = width, let l = length.

    b. $2w + 2l \leq 200$

    c.

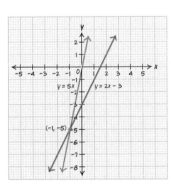

55. (1) Graph B, (2) Graph A

57. (1) Graph A, (2) Graph B

59. (1) Graph A, (2) Graph B

61. a. $y = -1$ **b.** $\geq$ or $\leq$ **c.** $y \geq -1$

63. a. $y = 3x$ **b.** $>$ or $<$ **c.** $y > 3x$

65. a. $y = -2x$ **b.** $\geq$ or $\leq$ **c.** $y \geq -2x$

67. a. $x = 2$ **b.** $>$ or $<$ **c.** $x < 2$

69. Inequality.   **71.** Equality.

73. Inequality.   **75.** Inequality.

Chapter 4 Review Exercises

1. $(2, -4)$

2. $(2, 3)$

3. a. No.   **b.** Yes.

4. a. Yes.   **b.** No.

5.

$(-1, -5)$

6.

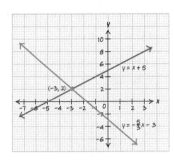

$(-3, 2)$

7. $(3, 10)$ **8.** $(-15, 26)$ **9.** $(0, 1)$

10. Infinitely many solutions.

11. No solution.   **12.** No solution.

13. The cyclist's rate is 20 mph, and the wind's rate is 4 mph.

14. The cyclist's rate is 12 mph, and the wind's rate is 3 mph.

15. The plane's rate is 100 mph, and the wind's rate is 20 mph.

16. The boat's rate is 10.5 mph, and the current's rate is 3.5 mph.

17. The first number is 15, and the second number is 7.

18. The first number is 9, and the second number is -11.

19. The first number is 39, and the second number is 13.

20. The first number is 24, and the second number is 4.

21. $(1, -3)$ **22.** $(-3, 6)$ **23.** $(2, 5)$

24. $(-3, -1)$

25. No solution.

26. No solution.

27. Infinitely many solutions.

28. Infinitely many solutions.

29. Elimination because $-2x + 2x = 0$.

30. Substitution because it is easy to solve for x in $x - 4y = 9$.

31. The jerky treats cost $8.00, and the leash costs $16.50.

32. The candy costs $14.25, and the metronome costs $25.00.

33. Lance should invest $1500 in bonds and $500 in stocks.

34. Ming-Yue should invest $3333.33 in bonds and $1666.67 in stocks.

35. One angle is 150°, and the other angle is 30°.

36. One angle is 145°, and the other angle is 35°.

37. One angle is 81°, and the other angle is 9°.

38. One angle is 60°, and the other angle is 30°.

39. Tarin should use 4 ounces of the 5% solution and 16 ounces of the 30% solution.

40. Shelby should use 6.67 gallons of the 6% juice and 13.33 gallons of the 12% juice.

41. Inna should use 6 pounds of peanuts and 4 pounds of raisins.

42. Lorraine should use $13\frac{1}{3}$ pounds of French Roast and $6\frac{2}{3}$ pounds of Guatemalan coffee.

43. a. No. **b.** Yes.

44. a. Yes. **b.** Yes.

45.

46.

47.

48.

49.

50.

51.

52.

53.

54.

55. a. Let f = number of hours of the first job, let s = number of hours of the second job.

b. $8f + 9s > 400$

c.

56. a. Let f = number of hours of the first job, let s = number of hours of the second job.

b. $8.25f + 9.00s > 300$

c.

57. (1) Graph B, (2) Graph A

58. (1) Graph A, (2) Graph B

Chapter 4 Test

1.

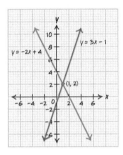

Consistent, (1, 2).

2. $y = \dfrac{7}{3}x + 7$ **3.** $(-2, -3)$ **4.** $(5, 2)$

5. The monitor costs $33, and the water bottle costs $12.

6. The boat's rate is 10 mph, and the current's rate is 2 mph.

7. Laurent should invest $800 in the bond fund and $1200 in the stock fund.

8. No solution.

9. Infinitely many solutions.

10.

11.

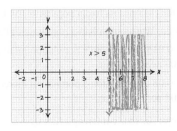

Cumulative Review for Chapters 1–4

1. $\left(\dfrac{-1}{5}\right)^4$ **2.** 16   **3.** 6,103,000

4. 93

5. Let c = the amount of the commission in dollars; let n = the amount of sales in dollars.

6. $3(9 + x)$ **7.** 39.37 feet.   **8.** -11

9. $3x + 25$ **10.** $-5x$

11.

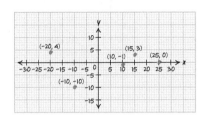

12. Yes   **13.** $x = -24$ **14.** $y = -3x - 9$

15. $x = 6$

16. a. $1430.   **b.** 140 hours.

17. $x = 2.5$

18. $8 + 3n = 2n - (-6), n = -2$

19. No solution.

20. $x < -7$

21. a.

x	$y = \dfrac{-3}{5}x - 7$
-5	-4
0	-7
5	-10
15	-16
20	-19

b.

c. Linear.

22.

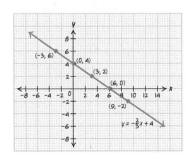

Linear.

23.

d	C
1	4000
2	8000
3	12,000
4	16,000

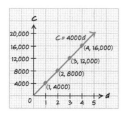

24.

x	y
−4	14
−3	7
−2	2
−1	−1
0	−2
1	−1
2	2
3	7
4	14

Nonlinear.

25.

x	y
−2	−5
−1	−5
0	−5
1	−5
2	−5
3	−5

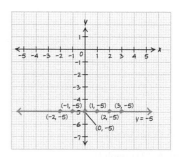

Linear.

26.

x	y
6	0
6	1
6	2
6	3
6	4

Linear.

27. $m = \dfrac{2}{3}$ **28.** $m = \dfrac{-12}{5}$ **29.** $m = \dfrac{-2}{5}$

30. $m = 0$

31. The red line because it rises faster when the *x*-values are increasing than the blue line.

32. Decreasing because the *y*-values get smaller as the *x*-values get bigger.

33. Increasing because $m > 0$.

34. $(−3, 0)$ and $(0, −2)$

35. **a.** In 2000, Minnesota had a population of 4.94 million.

　　b. In 2000, Washington had a population of 5.89 million.

　　c. $m = 0.035$. Minnesota's population increases by about 35,000 people a year.

　　d. $m = 0.08$. Washington's population increases by about 80,000 people a year.

36. *y*-intercept: $(0, 15)$; *x*-intercept: $(25, 0)$

37. $m = \dfrac{1}{2}$; *y*-intercept: $\left(0, \dfrac{-3}{2}\right)$; *x*-intercept: $(3, 0)$

38.

39.

40.

41.

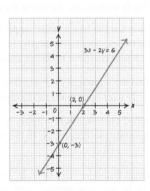

42. a. Linear because the exponents on the variables are all 1.

   b. Not linear because the exponent on the variable is not 1.

   c. Not linear because there is an absolute value that involves the variable.

   d. Linear because the exponents on the variables are all 1.

43. Parallel.   **44.** Perpendicular.

45. $y = \dfrac{7}{2}x - 2$ **46.** $W = \dfrac{-25}{6}t + 155$

47. $y = \dfrac{-2}{5}x + 9$ **48.** $y = \dfrac{2}{3}x + 4$ **49.** $y = -5$

50. $x = 3$ **51.** $y = -5x - 47$ **52.** $y = \dfrac{-1}{3}x - 2$

53. $(-1, 6)$

54. a. No.   **b.** Yes.

55. $(0, 1)$

56. a. No.   **b.** Yes.

57.

58.

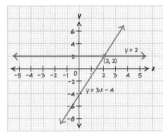

59. $(-4, 6)$ **60.** $(-5, -13)$

61. No solution.

62. The bottles cost $6, and the packages cost $25.

63. One number is 13, and the other number is 19.

64. The plane's rate is 125 mph, and the wind's rate is 25 mph.

65. Francis needs to use 3 pounds of turmeric and 2 pounds of ground coriander.

66. $(4, -5)$ **67.** $(-1, -4)$

68. Infinitely many solutions.

69. The scrapbooks cost $18.00, and the stickers cost $12.50.

70. One angle is 30°, and the other angle is 150°.

71. Eric should invest $8000 in the CD and $4000 in the bond fund.

72. Yes.

73.

74.

75. a. Let r = the number of spring rolls, let g = the number of gyozas.

b. $3.99r + 4.25g \leq 20$

c.

CHAPTER 5

Section **5.1**

1. add

3. multiply

5. addition, subtraction

7. 4

9. -8

11. -25

13. -1

15. x^9; product rule for exponents

17. 5,764,801; product rule for exponents

19. $15w^{12}$; product rule for exponents

21. $40x^6y^5$; product rule for exponents

23. $-15m^{10}n^7$; product rule for exponents

25. $-18x^6y^4$; power rule and product rule for exponents

27. $1,679,616x^8$; power rule and product rule for exponents

29. $117,649b^6$; power rule and product rule for exponents

31. $-1024m^5$; power rule and product rule for exponents

33. x^7; quotient rule for exponents

35. $5k^{14}$; quotient rule for exponents

37. x^{10}; power rule for exponents

39. $a^{10}b^{30}$; powers of products rule for exponents

41. Elizabeth simplified the expression incorrectly. The student multiplied exponents instead of adding.

43. Elba simplified the expression incorrectly. The student subtracted coefficients instead of dividing.

45. Luis simplified the expression incorrectly. The student multiplied the coefficient by the exponent instead of multiplying the coefficient by itself.

47. Yomaira simplified the expression incorrectly. The student did not apply the exponent to the negative sign.

49. Andrew simplified the expression incorrectly. The student did not apply the exponents before dividing, or the student ignored the exponents altogether.

51. x^3y^3; product and quotient rules for exponents

53. m^4n; product and quotient rules for exponents

55. $\dfrac{b}{2}$; quotient rule for exponents

57. $\dfrac{15x^4}{7}$; product and quotient rules for exponents

59. $\dfrac{x^2}{5}$; quotient rule for exponents

61. b^3; product and quotient rules for exponents

63. $\dfrac{a^3b^3}{3}$; product and quotient rules for exponents

65. $9c^4d^{10}$; power rule for exponents and powers of products

67. $25a^{14}b^{10}$; power rule for exponents and powers of products

69. 1; zero exponent

71. $36x^6y^6$; power rule for exponents and powers of products and quotients

73. $\dfrac{169x^4y^8}{9}$; power rule for exponents and powers of products and quotients

75. 1; zero exponent

77. $45x^5y^{11}$; power rule for exponents and powers of products

79. $432m^{11}n^{21}$; power rule for exponents and powers of products

81. $648a^{11}b^9$; power rule for exponents and powers of products

83. $\dfrac{16x^{10}}{25}$; power rule for exponents and powers of products and quotients

85. $2x^4y^3$; power rule for exponents and powers of products and quotients

87. Elias mistakenly applied the power to the negative sign.

89. Beverly multiplied the bases before applying the exponent and included the exponent incorrectly. In the order of operations, exponents come before multiplication.

91. Alexis applied the exponent over addition, but exponents can be applied only over operations of multiplication or division.

93. Victoria divided the bases before applying the exponent and included the exponent incorrectly. In the order of operations, exponents come before division.

95. a. Yes, the expression $(x + 3)^2(x + 3)^5$ can be simplified to $(x + 3)^7$ by using the product rule for exponents. In this case, $(x + 3)$ is the base, and the exponents are added.

b. No, the exponent 7 in the expression $(x + 3)^7$ cannot be applied to x and 3 to get $x^7 + 3^7$. This would be applying the power rule to a sum, but the power rule applies only to products and quotients.

97. No, $x^2 + x^3$ cannot be simplified. These are not like terms because they do not have the same exponent and therefore cannot be combined using addition.

99. $A = 49x^2$

101. $V = 125x^3$

103. $A = 4\pi x^2$

105. $A = 6x^2$

Section **5.2**

1. $\dfrac{1}{x^3}$

3. $\dfrac{1}{9}$

5. $\dfrac{1}{32}$

7. $\dfrac{4}{d^6}$ **9.** $\dfrac{-5}{a^4}$ **11.** $\dfrac{5x^2y^3}{2}$

13. $\dfrac{x^4}{5}$ **15.** $\dfrac{1}{2a^3}$ **17.** $\dfrac{1}{9x}$

19. $\dfrac{y^3}{x^2}$

21. Julia treated the negative sign as though it were a negative exponent. The expression is already in simplest form.

$$\dfrac{-2x}{y}$$

23. Frida applied the negative exponent to the coefficient, but it applies only to the variable.

$$\dfrac{42}{a}$$

25. Christopher applied the negative exponent only to the variable, but it applies to the whole term.

$$\dfrac{1}{25x^2}$$

27. Madalyn applied a positive exponent to the coefficient and applied the negative exponent only to the variable, but the negative exponent applies to the whole term.

$$\dfrac{1}{9x^2}$$

29. $\dfrac{1}{x^4}$ **31.** $\dfrac{1}{m^3n}$ **33.** $\dfrac{5y^5}{3x^6}$

35. $\dfrac{4}{x^2y^8}$ **37.** $\dfrac{12n^8}{5m^5}$ **39.** $\dfrac{-5x}{2y^7}$

41. $\dfrac{8}{x^6}$ **43.** $\dfrac{25}{x^6}$ **45.** $\dfrac{-54}{a^5b^3}$

47. $\dfrac{4y^8}{9x^4}$ **49.** $\dfrac{b^6}{a^2}$

51. Joseph subtracted 5 for the exponent in the denominator rather than subtracting -5.

$$x^8$$

53. Mackenzie did not retain the negative sign for the coefficient and incorrectly moved the coefficient in the denominator to the numerator.

$$\dfrac{-1}{8x^7}$$

55. Tristan did not apply the power of products rule correctly, missing the first variable.

$$\dfrac{1}{x^6y^2}$$

57. 623,000,000

59. The mass of the earth: 5,980,000,000,000,000,000,000,000 kg.

61. 0.000000003745

63. An electron's mass: 0.00000000000000000000000000000167 kg.

65. 6.2×10^{10} **67.** 4.3×10^{-6}

69. The 2008 fourth-quarter revenue for Google, Inc.: 5.7×10^9.

71. The 2008 U.S. GDP: 1.43×10^{13}.

73. The average width of a human hair: 7.0×10^{-5} meter.

75. The width of pits where data on compact discs are stored: 5.0×10^{-7} meter.

77. 8.4×10^{11} **79.** 7.5×10^{-12}

81. 2.52×10^{14} **83.** 3.6×10^{-6}

85. 5.0×10^7 **87.** 2.0×10^{14}

89. 1.5×10^{25} **91.** 3.6×10^{-22}

93. 6.0×10^{27} **95.** 2.4×10^{-17}

97. -1.35×10^{12} **99.** -1.8×10^{24}

101. The mass of Saturn is approximately 5.681×10^{26} kg.

103. The mass of Mercury is approximately 3.289×10^{23} kg.

105. The average distance from Pluto to the sun is approximately 5.9092×10^9 km.

107. The average distance from Mars to the sun is approximately 2.244×10^8 km.

109. The diameter of Mars is approximately 6.4×10^3 km.

111. The electric charge of 200 protons is 3.204×10^{-17} coulomb.

113. The mass of 500 electrons is 8.35×10^{-25} kg.

115. The mass of 3 million electrons is 5.01×10^{-21} kg.

117. 8.4×10^{24} **119.** 3.75×10^5

121. 3.78×10^{34} **123.** 2.13×10^{-14}

125. 2.0×10^4 **127.** 9.0×10^{-14}

129. 4.8×10^{19}

131. The mass of Venus is 0.81 times as large as the mass of the earth.

133. The diameter of Jupiter is 11.156 times larger than the diameter of the earth.

135. Each person's share of the U.S. national debt in January 2009 was approximately $34,641.

Section 5.3

1. Terms: x^2, $2x$, and 5.
This is a trinomial.

3. Terms: $4x$ and 8.
This is a binomial.

5. Term: $8x^3y$.
This is a monomial.

7. Terms: $7m^2$ and -9.
This is a binomial.

9. Terms: $14x^3y$, $7x^2y^2$, and $-9xy$.
This is a trinomial.

11. Terms: $2m^7n^3$ and $-4m^2n^5$.
    This is a binomial.

13. Terms: $-45mn^2$ and 56.
    This is a binomial.

15. Two terms
    Descending order: $\frac{3}{2}x - 12$
    Degree is 1.

17. Three terms
    Descending order: $-6x^2 + 3x - 9$
    Degree is 2.

19. One term
    Descending order: -45
    Degree is 0.

21. Four terms
    Descending order: $-y^3 + 9y^2 + 4y + 7$
    Degree is 3.

23. Three terms
    Descending order: $-3b^8 + 2b^7 + 9b$
    Degree is 8.

25. Degree of the term $-6xy^2$ is 3.
    Degree of the polynomial is 3.

27. Degree of the term $3a$ is 1.
    Degree of the term $2ab$ is 2.
    Degree of the term $-6b^2$ is 2.
    Degree of the polynomial is 2.

29. Degree of the term 1 is 0.
    Degree of the term $-x^3y^3$ is 6.
    Degree of the polynomial is 6.

31. Degree of the term $-24x^2yz^3$ is 6.
    Degree of the term $6z$ is 1.
    Degree of the term $-7y$ is 1.
    Degree of the term 5 is 0.
    Degree of the polynomial is 6.

33. Degree of the term -29 is 0.
    Degree of the polynomial is 0.

35. $x^2 + 2x + 5$ is an expression that has a second-degree
    term, so it is not linear. There is no equal sign, so it is an
    expression, not an equation.

37. $4x + 8$ is a polynomial in 1 variable with degree 1, so it is a
    linear expression in one variable. There is no equal sign, so it
    is an expression, not an equation.

39. $y = 4x + 3$ is an equation in two variables that has degree
    1, so it is a linear equation in two variables. It is an equation
    because there is an equal sign.

41. $5x - (2x + 8) = 4x$ is a linear equation in one variable that
    has degree 1. It is an equation because there is an equal sign.

43. $4xy + 7x - 9xy$ is a polynomial in two variables that has
    degree-2 terms. It is not linear because is it not of degree 1.
    There is no equal sign, so it is an expression, not an equation.

45. $y = 2x^2 + 3x - 20$ is an equation in two variables that has
    a second-degree term, so it is not linear. It is an equation
    because there is an equal sign.

47. $2x + 7y = 68$ is an equation in two variables that has degree
    1, so it is a linear equation in two variables. It is an equation
    because there is an equal sign.

49. $7x + 14$

51. $5t^2 + 8t - 5$

53. $-9m^2 + 13m - 9$

55. $2x + 6$

57. $13n - 9$

59. $2h^2 - 2h + 4$

61. Reina treated this as a product, adding exponents, rather than
    a sum and should have added coefficients.
    Correctly simplified, it is $3x$.

63. Fari did not subtract the entire quantity of $(4x + 5)$,
    subtracting only the first term and not the second term.
    Correctly simplified, it is $-x - 7$.

65. Anya did not subtract the entire quantity of $(2x^2 - 5x)$,
    subtracting only the first term and not the second term.
    (Subtracting a negative changes it to adding the term.)
    Correctly simplified, it is $-x^2 + 9x - 8$.

67. a. The total cost for a class to see the life of a pumpkin demo
       and visit the petting zoo is $3.5k + 15$.
    b. The cost for 33 students to see the life of a pumpkin demo
       and visit the petting zoo is $130.50.

69. a. The total cost for a class to see the life of a pumpkin
       demo, take a tractor ride, and take home a pumpkin is
       $7.25k + 10$.
    b. The cost for 60 students to see the life of a pumpkin
       demo, take a tractor ride, and take home a pumpkin is
       $445.

71. a. The total cost for the Grizzlies to purchase all the gear is
       $26m + 95$.
    b. The cost for 15 members to purchase all the gear is $485.

73. a. The total cost for the Grizzlies to purchase T-shirts and go
       on the Dos Picos campout is $37.5m + 155$.
    b. The cost for 12 members to purchase T-shirts and go on
       the Dos Picos campout is $605.

75. a. The total cost for a 5-day trip is $150m + 350$.
    b. The cost for 30 ski club members to go on the 5-day trip
       is $4850.

77. $3x^2 + 2x + 20$

79. $P = 12x + 26$

81. $7x^2 + 26x$

83. $5a^2 - 4ab - 2b$

85. $-10t^2 + 6t - 20$

87. $-12a + 6b$

89. $-6m^2 + 13mn - 4n$

91. $45a^2 + 9a - 24$

93. $-x^2 + 15x - 3$

95. $2m^3 - 3m^2 + 20m - 6$

Section 5.4

1. $10x + 35$

3. $14x^2 + 12x$

5. $-12x - 6$

7. $12x^2 + 18x - 30$

9. $-7x^2 - 28x + 21$

11. $15x^3 - 9x^2 + 12x$

13. The number of screws needed to hold down a lid after an
    accident can be represented by the expression $6P$.

15. $x^3 + 7x^2 + 7x - 15$

17. $5x^3 - 13x^2 - 2x + 16$

19. $8x^3 + 16x^2 - 36x + 21$

21. $16x^3 - 36x^2 + 6x + 9$

23. $2x^4 + 3x^3 + 2x^2 + 9x - 12$

25. $x^2 + 8x + 15$

27. $x^2 + 4x - 12$

29. $a^2 + 7a + 10$

31. $2m^2 + 3mn + n^2$

33. $5x^3 - 4x^2 + 15x - 12$

35. a. The total amount of high-fructose corn syrup consumed by people in the United States is represented by the expression $-1.925t^2 - 25.25t + 17,653.2$ million pounds.
  b. The total amount of high-fructose corn syrup consumed by Americans in 2010 is approximately 17,208.2 million pounds, or 17,208,200,000 pounds.

37. a. The average income of a family in the United States in 2010 is estimated at $65,000.
  b. The number of families in the United States in 2010 is estimated at 86,000,000.
  c. The total income in billions of dollars of all families in the United States can be represented by the expression $4.25t^2 + 223.7t + 2928$.
  d. The total income of all families in the United States in 2012 is estimated at $6,224,400,000,000.

39. $A = 15x^2 - 4x - 32$

41. $x^2 + 12x + 36$

43. $x^2 - 6x + 9$

45. $9x^2 + 30x + 25$

47. $25x^2 - 30x + 9$

49. $4a^2 + 28ab + 49b^2$

51. $9x^4 + 30x^2 + 25$

53. $16d^6 - 40cd^3 + 25c^2$

55. $x^2 - 25$

57. $4a^2 - 25$

59. $\dfrac{x^2}{4} - 1$

61. $\dfrac{16}{25}x^2 - \dfrac{24}{5}x + 9$

63. $9a^2 - 4b^2$

65. $x^4 - 25$

67. $4a^{10} - 9b^2$

69. Product
$4x^2$

71. Sum
$y^2 + 12y + 36$

73. Sum
$x^2 + 2xy + y^2$

75. Product
$\dfrac{1}{4}n^2$

77. Product
$\dfrac{1}{25}a^2$

79. Tristan left out the exponent when multiplying the first terms, which should be x^2.
$x^2 + x - 12$

81. Dolores left out the middle step when squaring a binomial, adding twice the product of the two terms.
$x^2 + 8x + 16$

83. Tyler did not square the coefficient of the first term and left out the middle step when squaring a binomial, adding twice the product of the two terms.
$\dfrac{4}{9}a^2 - \dfrac{4}{3}a + 1$

85. $5x^3 + 50x^2 + 105x$

87. $24x^3 - 10x^2 - 56x$

89. $7a^3 - 28a$

91. $7h^3 + 70h^2 + 175h$

93. $200x^4 - 320x^3 + 128x^2$

95. $x^2 - 2x - 16$

97. $3x^2 - 12$

99. $x^2 - 3x + 7$

101. $14x + 7$

103. $7x^2 + 6x - 33$

105. $-22t^2 - t - 15$

Section **5.5**

1. Monomial

3. Monomial

5. Polynomial of more than one term

7. Polynomial of more than one term

9. Polynomial of more than one term

11. $6x^2 + 8x - 4$

13. $5m^2 - 4m + 12$

15. $\dfrac{1}{2}x^4 + \dfrac{7}{4}x^2 - \dfrac{15}{4}x + \dfrac{3}{2}$

17. $3h^3 + \dfrac{12}{7}h - \dfrac{2}{7}$

19. $5x + 6 - \dfrac{1}{x}$

21. $\dfrac{12}{7}d^3 - \dfrac{3}{2}d + \dfrac{1}{d}$

23. $\dfrac{4x}{y} - 2 + \dfrac{3y}{x}$

25. $3m^3n - \dfrac{10}{3}m + \dfrac{5}{2n}$

27. Correct. $3(x - 2) = 3x - 6$

29. Correct. $(x + 3)(x - 2) = x^2 + x - 6$

31. Correct. $(x^2 + x + 1)(x - 1) = x^3 - 1$

33. $x + 9$

35. $x - 7$

37. $m - 4$

39. $2x + 5$

41. $5d - 7$

43. Length $= x + 7$

45. Length $= 7a - 8$

47. $x + 9 + \dfrac{7}{x - 4}$

49. $b - 7 - \dfrac{8}{b - 3}$

51. $x + 4 - \dfrac{11}{2x + 5}$

53. $3a - 2 + \dfrac{5}{4a + 7}$

55. $3x - 7 - \dfrac{6}{5x - 2}$

57. $x^2 + 5x + 7$

59. $2a^2 + 4a - 5$

61. $5x^2 + 15x + 47 + \dfrac{153}{x - 3}$

63. $a^2 - 2a + 4$

65. $4x^2 + 6x + 9$

67. $x + 4$

69. $2m + 7$

71. $4x + 5$

73. $3x + 5 + \dfrac{5}{x + 4}$

75. $2x^2 + 3x + 5$

77. $t^2 - 12 + \dfrac{52}{t + 3}$

79. $t^2 + 6t + 12$

81. $4a^2 - 8a + 18 + \dfrac{4}{a + 2}$

Chapter 5 Review Exercises

1. $28x^8$

2. $-24y^5$

3. $24x^9y^5$

4. $-28x^3y^{10}$

5. $\dfrac{-xy^2}{4}$

6. $\dfrac{-x^6}{2}$

7. $c^{11}d^4$

8. $\dfrac{1}{2ab^2}$

9. $125a^6b^{15}$

10. $4x^4y^6$

11. $\dfrac{-a^3b^9}{8}$

12. $\dfrac{10{,}000m^{12}n^8}{2401}$

13. $-3087x^{12}y^{17}$

14. $22{,}500x^{18}y^8$

15. 1

16. 1

17. $\dfrac{-5y^4}{2x^5}$

18. $\dfrac{a^3}{3b^2}$

19. $\dfrac{-9}{x^4y^{13}}$

20. $\dfrac{-12m^4}{n^{10}}$

21. $\dfrac{c^6}{d^8}$

22. y^4z^{13}

23. 5.26×10^{10}

24. 6.512×10^7

25. The average distance from Neptune to the sun is about 4.55×10^9 km.

26. The width of one helix of the DNA molecule is 2.0×10^{-9} meter.

27. 0.000006024

28. $43{,}000{,}000$

29. The width of a flu virus is 0.0000003 meter.

30. The approximate width of a carbon nanotube shaft of one of the first nanomotors created is 0.0000000075 meter.

31. 1.4×10^{20}

32. -1.71×10^{-6}

33. 5.0×10^{-21}

34. 3.1×10^{16}

35. 1.5×10^{19}

36. 1.44×10^{-16}

37. Three terms
Degree is 2

38. Two terms
Degree is 1

39. Degree of the term $-5a^3b$ is 4.
Degree of the term $6a^5$ is 5.
Degree of the term $-7b^2$ is 2.
Degree of the term 8 is 0.
Degree of the poynomial is 5.

40. Degree of the term $20a^2b^3c$ is 6.
Degree of the term $18ab^2c^2$ is 5.
Degree of the term $-9bc^8$ is 9.
Degree of the polynomial is 9.

41. $7x - 16y = -23$ is linear because it has degree 1.

42. $y = 3x - 8$ is linear because it has degree 1.

43. $y = 3x^2 + 10$ is not linear because it has a second-degree term.

44. $y = 25 - x^2$ is not linear because it has a second-degree term.

45. $P = 11x + 19$

46. $P = 6x + 8$

47. There are $17 - 0.1w$ more students that attend the math class than the English class.

48. **a.** The cost for one student to go on the trip for 5 days is $850.

b. The cost for n students to go on the trip for 5 days is $850n$.

49. $8a^2 - 4a - 7$

50. $10x^2 - 5x + 12$

51. $3x^2 - 8x + 10$

52. $-7n^2 - 3n - 5$

53. $A = 36x^2 - 43x - 35$

54. The cost for gasoline used by Vista Unified School District during week w of the year can be represented by the expression $0.2w^2 + 16.75w + 322.5$.

55. $35x^2 + 40x$

56. $-56x^3 - 16x^2 + 32x$

57. $6x^2 + 3x - 30$

58. $8x^2 - 26x + 21$

59. $9x^2 - 49$

60. $16a^2 - 25b^2$

61. $x^3 - x^2 + x + 14$

62. $x^3 + x^2 - 23x + 12$

63. $9x^2 + 42x + 49$

64. $36x^2 - 108x + 81$

65. $15m^3 + 20m^2 - 160m$

66. $-30a^3 - 2a^2 + 80a$

67. Length $= 2x - 7$

68. Length $= 7x - 3$

69. $10x + 3 - \dfrac{4}{x}$

70. $5ab^2 - 6b + \dfrac{3}{a}$

71. $x + 7$

72. $3a + 7$

73. $m - 5 + \dfrac{5}{m - 3}$

74. $4p^2 - 10p + 25$

75. $2t + 5$

76. $5r - 3 + \dfrac{2}{r + 4}$

77. $4x^2 + 7x - 2$

78. $5y^2 + 15y + 25$

Chapter 5 Test

1. $20x^{10}y^7$

2. m^2n

3. $\dfrac{8b^9}{a^{12}}$

4. $\dfrac{10y^7}{7x^8}$

5. 1

6. 1

7. The diameter of an average red blood cell is 7.0×10^{-6} meter.

8. The average distance from the sun to Pluto is roughly 5,900,000,000 km.

9. 3.65×10^{10}

10. 1.35×10^{12}

11. 1.3×10^{-14}

12. $5x^2 + 5x - 4$

13. $3a^2 - 13a + 13$

14. $14x^3 + 21x^2 - 49x$

15. $4x^2 - 25$

16. $12x^3 - 10x^2 + 7x - 20$

17. $36x^2 - 84x + 49$

18. $2m + 3 - \dfrac{4}{m}$

19. $2d - 3$

20. $3x^2 + x - 2 - \dfrac{14}{x + 2}$

21. $A = 40x^2 - 17x - 12$

22. $P = 26x - 2$

23. $x^3 + 3x + 4$

CHAPTER 6
Section 6.1

1. 3

3. 8

5. $3a$

7. $27y^2$

9. xy

11. 3

13. $5a$

15. $-3x$

17. $-2ab$

19. $3x$

21. $5(2x + 11)$

23. $2(3x + 1)$

25. $-5y(3 + 4y)$

27. $16a^2(3a^2 - 1)$

29. $-6(x + y)$

31. $3p(4p^5 - 2p^2 + 1)$

33. $16a^2b^2(3a^2 - b^2)$

35. $(x + 4)(2 + y)$

37. $(x - 2)(9x + 5)$

39. $(x + 8)(2x - 1)$

41. $(y + 5)(3 - 2y)$

43. $(5y + 7)(-3x + 2)$

45. Commutative property of multiplication.

47. Commutative property of addition.

49. Distributive property, $-6(x + 2)$ **51.** $-9(x - 3)$

53. $-(y + 2)$

55. $-(-5 + x)$ or $-(x - 5)$

57. $-(x^2 - 7)$

59. $(x + 5)(x + 4)$

61. $(x + 7)(x + 11)$

63. $(x - 2)(x + 6)$

65. $(x + 8)(x - 3)$

67. $(xy + 8)(x - 3)$

69. $(n - 1)(2m - 5)$

71. $(3b - 2)(a - 3)$

73. $(2x - 1)(y + 3)$

75. $(a - 3b)(2a + b)$

77. Javier: no, Joey: yes

79. Abi: yes, Noah: no

81. Kyla: yes, Lucia: no

83. $6b^2(ab - 2a^2 + 3)$

85. $-3x(2x - 1)$

87. $-17(p - 2q)$

89. $27x(3x^2 - 1)$

91. $2(p + 3)(p + 2)$

93. $6(n - 2)(n - 1)$

95. Didn't factor; multiplied.

97. Forgot $+1$ in the parentheses: $2x(3x - 4y + 1)$

99. Didn't multiply; factored.

Section 6.2

1. 2

3. 1

5. factors

7. sum

9. Rewrite the polynomial as a product.

11. Commutative property of addition.

13. $a = 1, b = -6, c = 5$ **15.** $a = 1, b = -6, c = -1$

17. $a = 1, b = 0, c = -7$ **19.** $a = 1, b = -2, c = 0$

21. $a = 2, b = 6, c = -8$ **23.** $a = -1, b = -6, c = 7$

25. $a = -6, b = -3, c = 5$ **27.** $a = 1, b = -2, c = 16$

29. $(x + 1)(x + 5)$ **31.** $(x + 6)(x - 3)$

33. $(x - 8)(x + 5)$ **35.** $(x - 8)(x - 7)$

37. Prime.   **39.** $(2x + 3)(x + 2)$

41. Prime.   **43.** $(7x - 1)(x + 6)$

45. $(3x - 1)(x - 6)$ **47.** $(x - 3)(4x - 5)$

49. $-(x - 3)(x + 2)$ **51.** Prime.

53. $4y(x - 2y)$ **55.** $2b(3a^2 - 6a + 1)$

57. $3(x + 4)(x - 6)$ **59.** $5(3a + b)(a - b)$

61. $3(4x - 1)(x + 2)$ **63.** $t(t - 6)(t + 5)$

65. $2a(a - 4)(a - 5)$ **67.** $4c(2c + 5)(3c - 8)$

69. $y(x - 9)(x - 7)$ **71.** $(5m + 9n)(2m - 3n)$

Section 6.3

1. 2

3. 1

5. 4

7. Yes.

9. No.

11. Yes.

13. $(x + 12)(x - 12)$ **15.** $(1 + y)(1 - y)$

17. Prime.   **19.** $(10x + 7)(10x - 7)$

21. Prime.   **23.** $(9 - a)(9 + a)$

25. $(4x - 7)(4x + 7)$ **27.** $(3t - 2)(3t + 2)$

29. Yes.   **31.** Yes.

33. No.   **35.** Yes.

37. $(x + 1)^2$ **39.** $(y - 4)^2$

41. $(3p - 1)^2$ **43.** $(t + 3)(t + 2)$

45. $(2x + 5)(3x - 4)$ **47.** $(2x + 5y)^2$

49. $(3x + 4y)^2$ **51.** $-(t - 3)^2$

53. Prime.   **55.** $(m - 4)(m^2 + 4m + 16)$

57. $(x + 5)(x^2 - 5x + 25)$ **59.** $3(g - 2)(g^2 + 2g + 4)$

61. Prime. The sum of two squares does not factor.

63. Prime. The polynomial is not a perfect square trinomial.

65. $3(x + 5)(x - 5)$ **67.** $17x(y - 2x)$

69. $5(x + 5)(x - 5)$ **71.** $2(2p - 1)(r + 3)$

73. $3(2x + 1)(x - 5)$ **75.** $-2(3a + 1)^2$

77. $5(x^2 + 4)$; The polynomial $x^2 + 4$ is prime.

79. $3(t + 1)^2$ **81.** $5x(y + 4)^2$

83. $5(x - 7)(x + 3)$ **85.** $-2(2x - 3)(5x - 4)$

87. $a(3a - 5)(a + 4)$

89. $(r + 2)(r - 2)(r^2 - 2r + 4)(r^2 + 2r + 4)$

91. $(4b^2 + 25c^2)(2b + 5c)(2b - 5c)$

93. $(h^2 + 5)(h^2 - 2)$ **95.** $(g^4 + 3)^2$

97. $(2t^6 + 3)(t^6 + 5)$ **99.** $2(4x^8 + 6x^4 + 9)$

101. $7(g^2 + 9h^2)(g + 3h)(g - 3h)$

103. $(x - 1)(x + 1)(x^2 + 1)(x^4 + 1)(x^8 + 1)$

Section **6.4**

1. Linear.   **3.** Neither.

5. Quadratic.   **7.** Quadratic.

9. Linear.   **11.** Linear.

13. Quadratic.   **15.** $x = -3$

17. $n = \dfrac{5}{2}$ **19.** $a = 0, a = 8$

21. $y = 0, y = \dfrac{-7}{2}$ **23.** $t = 0, t = \dfrac{-5}{2}$

25. $x = -5, x = 6$ **27.** $p = 0, p = \dfrac{-3}{2}, p = 9$

29. $x = -2, x = -3$ **31.** $a = -3, a = -4$

33. $x = -3, x = 1$ **35.** $t = 3, t = 4$

37. $x = -2, x = -1$ **39.** $x = \dfrac{1}{2}, x = -5$

41. $x = \dfrac{-2}{3}, x = 4$ **43.** $x = \dfrac{-5}{2}, x = \dfrac{-4}{3}$

45. $a = \dfrac{-2}{3}, a = \dfrac{-3}{8}$

47. a. $P = 256$. If the company sells 4 appliances in an order, the average profit per appliance will be $256.

   b. To make an average profit of $300 per appliance, the company needs to sell either 5 or 15 appliances in a single order.

49. a. $P = 39$. If the company sells 3 planes to an airline, they will earn an average profit of $39 million per plane.

   b. An order of 6 or 10 planes will result in an average profit per plane of $60 million.

51. Width = 2 feet, length = 12 feet

53. Width = 9 cm, length = 16 cm

55. Base = 10 inches, height = 6 inches

57. The ball will hit the ground after 3 seconds.

59. The ball at a height of 128 ft at 1 second and 3 seconds.

61. $x = -1, x = -3$ **63.** $a = \dfrac{3}{2}, a = 3$

65. $x = -2, x = 7$ **67.** $n = -5, n = -4$

69. $x = -4, x = 3$ **71.** $y = -8, y = 2$

73. $t = -5, t = 5$ **75.** $g = -10, g = 10$

77. $x = \dfrac{20}{3}, x = -3$ **79.** $t = 0, t = -3, t = 3$

81. $x = 0, x = -3, x = -4$ **83.** $t = 0, t = 3, t = 5$

85. $(x + 8)^2$ **87.** $n = \dfrac{5}{2}, n = -\dfrac{5}{2}$

89. $(a + 7)(a + 1)$ **91.** $x = 0, x = -3, x = 2$

93. $m = -\dfrac{1}{2}, m = \dfrac{3}{2}$ **95.** $(4b + 5)(10b - 3)$

97. $m = 5, m = -5$ **99.** Prime.

Chapter 6 Review Exercises

1. $2x^2(6x^3 + 5x - 3)$ **2.** $3b^2(a^3 + 2a - 3)$

3. $(3a + 5)(2a - 7)$ **4.** $(x + 3)(2y - 5)$

5. $(4x + 3)(x + 2)$ **6.** $(2t + 7)(t - 6)$

7. $(5m - 7)(m + 2n)$ **8.** $(2x - 1)(3y + 5)$

9. $(a + 4)(a + 6)$ **10.** $(m + 8)^2$

11. $(x - 4)(x - 5)$ **12.** $(h - 9)(h - 4)$

13. $(x - 7)(x + 3)$ **14.** $(y - 9)(y + 2)$

15. $(2x + 3)(x + 5)$ **16.** $(3a + 1)(a + 6)$

17. $(5x - 2)(x + 3)$ **18.** $(3b - 4)(b + 7)$

19. $(4x + 5)(x - 8)$ **20.** $(3y - 4)^2$

21. $-(5b - 2)(2b - 3)$ **22.** $-(2t - 5)(t - 5)$

23. $g(g - 3)(g - 5)$ **24.** $(3x - 4y)(2x + 5y)$

25. $(n - 9)(n + 9)$ **26.** $(t + 8)(t - 8)$

27. $(3a + 10)(3a - 10)$ **28.** $(2x - 7)(2x + 7)$

29. Prime.   **30.** Prime.

31. $(3x - 7)(x - 9)$ **32.** $(4y - 5)(x^2 + 2)$

33. $3c(2a + 1)(b - 4)$ **34.** $2z(x - 6)(2y + 1)$

35. $(3x - 1)(9x^2 + 3x + 1)$

36. $(5w + 2x)(25w^2 - 10wx + 4x^2)$

37. $(t + 2)(t - 2)(t^2 - 2t + 4)(t^2 + 2t + 4)$

38. $(5m^3 - 7)(2m^3 - 3)$ **39.** $5(4h + 5)(4h - 5)$

40. $2b(3a + 7)^2$

41. $3(r^2 + 4)(r + 2)(r - 2)$

42. $x = -7, \dfrac{5}{3}$ **43.** $x = 3, \dfrac{9}{2}$

44. $y = 0, \dfrac{3}{2}$ **45.** $x = 0, \dfrac{1}{3}$

46. $x = 4, -7$ **47.** $x = 9, -6$

48. $x = -7, \dfrac{5}{2}$ **49.** $y = -4, \dfrac{1}{3}$

50. $m = 4, -8$ **51.** $n = -7, 5$

52. $a = 9, -9$ **53.** $x = 7, -7$

54. $y = 2, -2$ **55.** $a = 3, -3$

56. $t = 0, 5, -6$ **57.** $x = 0, \dfrac{-3}{2}, 5$

58. $x = 4, -9$ **59.** $x = \dfrac{1}{3}, -1$

60. The length is 9 cm, and the width is 4 cm.

61. a. If RC Toys, Inc. sells 8000 toy cars, they will earn a profit of $144 thousand.

  b. To earn $120 thousand profit, RC Toys, Inc. needs to sell either 5000 or 12,000 toy cars.

Chapter Test

1. $(x + 6)(x - 4)$ **2.** $(a - 6)(a - 8)$

3. $(x + 10)(x - 10)$ **4.** $(5m + 1)(5m - 1)$

5. $(3x - 1)(2x + 3)$ **6.** $(2y + 5)^2$

7. $t(4t - 7)(t + 3)$ **8.** $2x(x - 4)(x + 1)$

9. $(5a + 2)(b - 2)$ **10.** $(2m - 3)(n + 8)$

11. $(t - 10)^2$ **12.** $7x(x + 2)(x - 2)$

13. $(2m + 5n)(4m^2 - 10mn + 25n^2)$

14. Prime.

15. $(3m^4 - 4)(2m^4 - 7)$

16. $(a - 5b)(a^2 + 5ab + 25b^2)$

17. $t = -3, -10$

18. $w = 2, -2$

19. $x = 0, 6, -8$

Cumulative Review for Chapters 1–6

1. $(2x)^5$ **2.** $\dfrac{-1}{8}$

3. -18 **4.** 11

5. $-15a + b$ **6.** $4x + 6$

7. $y = \dfrac{6}{5}x - 7$ **8.** $y = -20$

9. $b = P - a - c$ **10.** $n = \dfrac{2}{3}$

11. a. 422.5 miles.   **b.** 7 hours.

12. $x = \dfrac{-32}{11}$ **13.** $x > 10$

14. a.

x	$y = \dfrac{2}{3}x - 4$
-6	-8
-3	-6
0	-4
3	-2
6	0

  b.

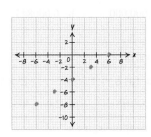

  c. Linear.

15.

m	$C = 124m$
0	0
1	124
2	248
3	372
4	496

16.

x	$y = x^2 + 3$
-4	19
-3	12
-2	7
-1	4
0	3
1	4
2	7
3	12
4	19

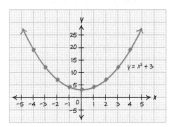

  Nonlinear.

17. $m = -2$

18. x-intercept: $(8, 0)$, y-intercept: $(0, -3)$.

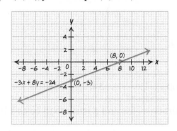

19. $m = \dfrac{-2}{7}$, $(7, 0)$, $(0, 2)$

20.

21.

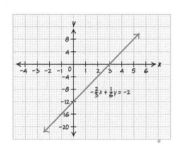

22. Parallel.

23. $y = \dfrac{2}{3}x + 3$

24. $C = 600h$

25. $y = \dfrac{-5}{2}x + 6$

26. $y = 4$

27. $y = \dfrac{-7}{2}x + 3$

28. $y = \dfrac{1}{2}x - 3$

29. $y = \dfrac{-5}{3}x + 2$

30. $(-5, 3)$

31. a. No.   **b.** Yes.

32. $(1, -4)$

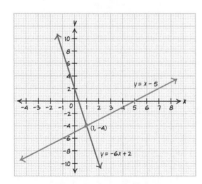

33. No solution.   **34.** $(-7, 16)$

35. Each T-shirt costs $9, and a basketball costs $16.

36. The boat's rate is 9 mph, and the current rate is 1 mph.

37. Emma should put 25 lb of papaya and 15 lb of pineapple in the mix to make 40 lb of $9.49 per pound mix.

38. $(6, -5)$ **39.** No solution.

40. The first angle is 35°, and the second angle is 55°.

41. Seamus should invest $2000 in the CD and $8000 in the bonds.

42. No.

43.

44. 9   **45.** -9

46. a. x^8 **b.** $12a^5$ **c.** $15a^5b^4$

47. a. n^6 **b.** $35t^5$ **c.** $-27x^3y^7$

48. a. $27x^{12}$ **b.** $-8x^6$ **c.** $4x^6y^8$

49. a. $25y^8$ **b.** $-243y^{10}$ **c.** $64a^{15}b^6$

50. a. $-63x^5$ **b.** $-72x^2y^{11}$

51. a. $-64n^{19}$ **b.** $-25x^9y^{22}$

52. a. x^6 **b.** $\dfrac{-1}{2}a^4$ **c.** x^2y^2

53. a. y^2 **b.** $-5y$ **c.** a^2b^4

54. $\dfrac{9}{100}x^2y^2$ **55.** $-343n^9m^3$

56. $A = 16x^2$ **57.** $A = 9\pi n^2$

58. a. $\dfrac{5}{t^2}$ **b.** $-2x^3$

59. a. $\dfrac{6}{n^5}$ **b.** $-7y^4$

60. a. $\dfrac{x^2}{y}$ **b.** $\dfrac{-y}{3x^4}$ **c.** $\dfrac{9}{n^6}$ **d.** $\dfrac{y^2}{x^4}$

61. a. $\dfrac{t^4}{r}$ **b.** $\dfrac{-2m^2}{3n}$ **c.** $\dfrac{-64}{m^6}$ **d.** $\dfrac{y^{12}}{x^3}$

62. a. 8.951×10^{11} **b.** 4.13×10^{-4}

63. a. 6.487×10^8 **b.** 6.92×10^{-6}

64. a. 67,500,000   **b.** 0.0000358

65. a. 401,000,000   **b.** 0.000843

66. 1×10^9

67. 0.0000000025

68. a. 2.88×10^9 **b.** 1.7×10^{12} **c.** 8.5×10^{-8}

   d. 2.666×10^{22} **e.** 2.0×10^8

69. Four terms, third-degree

70. Two terms, second-degree

71. $4xy^2$: degree = 3
   $-xy$: degree = 2
   $2y^4$: degree = 4
   $9x$: degree = 1
   Degree of polynomial is 4.

72. $8a^5b$: degree = 6
   $3a^3$: degree = 3
   $-6b^5$: degree = 5
   5: degree = 0
   Degree of polynomial is 6.

73. $-x^2 - 4x - 3$ **74.** $2y^2 + 6y - 12$

75. $-6x^2 + 5x - 16$ **76.** $-7a^2 - 2a + 40$

77. $-10n + 18$ **78.** $6n - 3$

79. a. $x^2 + 3x - 28$ **b.** $6x^2 - 13x - 5$

   c. $x^3 - x^2 - 2x + 8$ **d.** $n^2 + 8n + 16$

   e. $4x^2 - 1$

80. a. $y^2 + 6y - 27$ **b.** $-8x^2 - 10x + 7$

   c. $x^3 + 3x^2 - 6x + 2$ **d.** $n^2 - 6n + 9$

   e. $9x^2 - 25$

81. $-7x - 20$ **82.** $-10y + 22$

83. $-2n + 4 - \dfrac{5}{n}$ **84.** $-y + 2 - \dfrac{4}{y}$

85. $2x - 1$ **86.** $3x + 1$

87. $3x^2 + 16x - 12$ **88.** $4x^2 + 27x + 35 + \dfrac{19}{x - 3}$

89. a. $-3ab(4a - b + 10)$ **b.** $(n + 3)(2n - 1)$

90. a. $16x^2y^2(xy + 3)$ **b.** $(m - 4)(-3m + 2)$

91. $(3a + 1)(b - 4)$ **92.** $(2x - 5)(y + 6)$

93. $3(x + 1)(x - 5)$ **94.** $2(y - 7)(y - 2)$

95. a. $(x + 6)(x - 5)$ **b.** $-(x + 3)(x - 2)$

   c. $(2x + 3)(2x - 1)$

96. a. $(x - 9)(x + 4)$ **b.** $-(x - 5)(x + 4)$

   c. Prime.

97. a. $2n(n - 5)(n + 2)$ **b.** $5(x + 3y)(2x + y)$

98. a. $3t(t - 9)(t - 6)$ **b.** $3(x - 7y)(2x + y)$

99. a. $(t - 7)(t + 7)$ **b.** $(3 - 2y)(3 + 2y)$

   c. $(2x + 5)^2$ **d.** Prime.

   e. $5(x + 3)(x - 3)$

100. a. $(y + 6)(y - 6)$ **b.** $(1 - 5n)(1 + 5n)$

   c. $(3y - 2)^2$ **d.** Prime.

   e. $3(y + 4)(y - 4)$

101. a. $(5x - 4)(25x^2 + 20x + 16)$

   b. $(2m + 5)(4m^2 - 10m + 25)$

102. a. $(5x^2 - 3)(4x^2 + 7)$

   b. $(a + 3b)(a - 3b)(a^2 + 3ab + 9b^2)(a^2 - 3ab + 9b^2)$

103. a. Quadratic.   **b.** Neither.   **c.** Linear.

104. a. Linear.   **b.** Quadratic.   **c.** Neither.

105. a. $x = -4, -8$ **b.** $x = \dfrac{3}{2}, -5$

   c. $x = 7, -5$ **d.** $x = 7, -7$

106. a. $x = -3, -7$ **b.** $x = \dfrac{-1}{4}, 6$

   c. $x = 3, -2$ **d.** $n = 5, -5$

CHAPTER 7
Section **7.1**

1. 2   **3.** $\dfrac{25}{34}$ **5.** $\dfrac{1}{10}$

7. Undefined.   **9.** 0

11. a. $c = 25$. The cost per person is $25 if 10 people agree to help pay for the gift.

   b. $c = 5$. The lowest possible cost per person is $5 if there are 50 employees in the company.

13. a. $c = 75$. The cost per person is $75 if 8 people go on the trip.

   b. $c = 41$. The lowest possible cost per person is $41 if the trip is limited to 25 people.

15. a. $c = 200$. The cost of each surfboard is $200 if 8 surfboards are made in a week.

   b. $c = 180$. The lowest cost per surfboard for a week is $180 if 10 surfboards can be made in a week.

17. $s = 3108.33$. Spending per person in 2010 by the state of Texas is estimated at $3108.33.

19. $x = 0$ is excluded.

21. $x = 3$ is excluded.

23. $a = \dfrac{-4}{3}$ is excluded.

25. No excluded values for this expression.

27. $x = 3, -2$ are excluded.

29. $h = -4, 8$ are excluded.

31. $r = 3, 2$ are excluded.

33. $n = -2$ is excluded.

35. $b = -2$ is excluded.

37. $\dfrac{4}{x}$ **39.** $7n$ **41.** $\dfrac{1}{a + 5}$

43. $\dfrac{4x}{x - 3}$ **45.** $\dfrac{h + 6}{h + 4}$ **47.** $\dfrac{1}{r + 3}$

49. a. $T = 2.4$. The two landscapers working together can complete the job in 2.4 hours, or 2 hours and 24 minutes, if it takes the assistant 6 hours to complete the job alone.

   b. $T \approx 2.32$. The two landscapers working together can complete the job in 2.32 hours, or 2 hours and 19 minutes, if it takes the assistant 5.5 hours to complete the job alone.

51. a. $T = \dfrac{40}{13} \approx 3.08$. The two staff members working together can complete the job in 3.08 hours, or 3 hours and 5 minutes, if it takes the office specialist 8 hours to complete the job alone.

b. $T = \dfrac{65}{23} \approx 2.83$. The two staff members working together can complete the job in 2.83 hours, or 2 hours and 50 minutes, if it takes the assistant 5.5 hours to complete the job alone.

53. a. $y = 52.5$. Jack's speed on his return trip is 52.5 mph if he drives at 70 mph to the city.

b. $y = 66$. Jack's speed on his return trip is 66 mph if he drives at 55 mph to the city.

55. a. $y = \dfrac{4500}{11} \approx 409.09$. The pilot's speed on her return trip is 409.09 mph if she flies at 500 mph to the city.

b. $y = \dfrac{3825}{8} \approx 478.13$. The pilot's speed on her return trip is 478.13 mph if she flies at 425 mph to the city.

57. The student divided out common terms, but only common factors can be divided. Correctly simplified: $\dfrac{x + 2}{x + 4}$

59. The student divided out common terms, but only common factors can be divided. Correctly simplified: $\dfrac{x}{x + 7}$

61. The student divided out common terms, but only common factors can be divided. Correctly simplified:
$$\dfrac{(x + 2)\cancel{(x - 2)}}{\cancel{(x - 2)}} = x + 2$$

63. $\dfrac{1}{n + 2}$ **65.** $\dfrac{2}{b + 5}$ **67.** $\dfrac{x + 15}{(x + 2)(x + 7)}$

69. $\dfrac{1}{a - 3}$ **71.** $\dfrac{r - 9}{r - 7}$

73. $\dfrac{y + 12}{y - 11}$ **75.** $-(x - 1)$

77. $-(y - 4)$ **79.** $-(3x^2 + 2x - 5)$

81. $-(2x^2 - 3x + 8)$ **83.** $-(8x^2 - 4)$

85. -3 **87.** -1

89. $\dfrac{4}{3}$ **91.** $\dfrac{-w - 7}{w + 3}$ or $-\dfrac{w + 7}{w + 3}$

93. $\dfrac{1}{a + 4}$ **95.** $\dfrac{-1}{x - 5}$

97. $\dfrac{m - 1}{3}$ **99.** $\dfrac{-3}{t - 6}$

Section 7.2

1. $\dfrac{32}{15}$ **3.** $\dfrac{-18}{115}$ **5.** $\dfrac{3}{10y}$

7. $\dfrac{-2n}{5}$ **9.** $\dfrac{x + 5}{x + 2}$ **11.** $\dfrac{(a + 7)(a + 3)}{(a + 2)(a - 5)}$

13. $\dfrac{x + 2}{x - 4}$ **15.** $\dfrac{m - 5}{m + 9}$ **17.** $\dfrac{h + 3}{h + 2}$

19. $\dfrac{1}{(b + 3)(b - 6)}$ **21.** $\dfrac{k - 5}{k + 3}$ **23.** $\dfrac{h + 4}{h - 3}$

25. $\dfrac{x + 6}{x + 1}$ **27.** $\dfrac{t - 4}{t - 6}$ **29.** $\dfrac{1}{4x + 8}$ or $\dfrac{1}{4(x + 2)}$

31. $\dfrac{-4}{(x - 1)(x + 2)}$ **33.** $\dfrac{3(x - 7)}{x(x + 4)}$

35. The child's drug dosage is 13.6 mg/lb.

37. The adult's drug dosage is 20.5 mg/lb.

39. The price for the 5-pound bag of rice is $0.10 per ounce.

41. The price for the 1-pound jar of peanut butter is $0.24 per ounce.

43. The car's speed is 96.6 kilometers per hour.

45. The car's speed is 4400 feet per minute.

47. The car's speed is 22.4 meters per second.

49. a. The dosage is 9 mg per hour.

b. The patient will receive 216 mg of dopamine in a 24-hour period.

51. a. The cyclist's rate is 24.85 miles per hour.

b. The cyclist can ride 149.1 miles during a 6-hour ride.

53. The Solartaxi will use about 64.36 kWh when traveling 500 miles.

55. $\dfrac{18}{25}$ **57.** $\dfrac{85}{12}$ **59.** $\dfrac{4}{11x^2}$

61. $\dfrac{-5m^2n}{3}$ **63.** $\dfrac{x + 4}{x - 3}$ **65.** $\dfrac{(a + 3)^2}{(a + 4)(a + 1)}$

67. $\dfrac{x - 7}{x + 5}$ **69.** $\dfrac{n - 5}{n + 3}$ **71.** $\dfrac{(h + 9)^2}{(h + 7)(h + 2)}$

73. $\dfrac{(b + 7)^2}{(b + 5)(b + 4)}$ **75.** $\dfrac{(k + 9)(k + 2)}{(k - 7)(k + 6)}$

77. $\dfrac{-2}{xy}$ **79.** 5

81. $\dfrac{1}{5x - 15}$ or $\dfrac{1}{5(x - 3)}$ **83.** $\dfrac{-15m^2n^2}{2}$

85. $\dfrac{x + 7}{2x - 16}$ or $\dfrac{x + 7}{2(x - 8)}$ **87.** $-\dfrac{7x + 21}{3}$ or $\dfrac{-7(x - 3)}{3}$

89. $\dfrac{-12b}{7a}$ **91.** $\dfrac{z + 2}{z + 5}$

93. 30   **95.** $a + 2$

97. $\dfrac{(a + 3)^2}{(a - 3)(a + 8)}$ **99.** $\dfrac{(b + 5)(b - 4)}{(b + 4)(b - 5)}$

Section 7.3

1. $\dfrac{10}{7c^2}$ **3.** $\dfrac{3}{a^2}$ **5.** $\dfrac{2x + 3}{x + 5}$

7. $\dfrac{4h - 3}{h - 9}$ **9.** 5   **11.** $2a$

13. $\dfrac{1}{h + 4}$ **15.** $\dfrac{1}{z - 3}$ **17.** $\dfrac{1}{x + 2}$

19. $\dfrac{2a + 4}{(2a + 3)(a - 4)}$ **21.** 150   **23.** $7xy^3z^2$

25. $(h - 9)(h - 6)$ **27.** $2a - 6$ or $2(a - 3)$

29. $(h + 4)(h + 7)(h + 2)$ **31.** $(z + 2)(z - 3)(z - 5)$

33. $(m + 10)(m - 2)(m + 5)$ **35.** $\dfrac{9}{168}$ $\dfrac{32}{168}$

37. $\dfrac{63n^3}{180m^3n^2}$ $\dfrac{50m^2}{180m^3n^2}$

39. $\dfrac{10x + 20}{(x + 4)(x + 2)}$ $\dfrac{5x^2 + 20x}{(x + 4)(x + 2)}$

41. $\dfrac{5}{7(a - 2)}$ $\dfrac{63}{7(a - 2)}$

43. $\dfrac{z^2 - 4z - 32}{(z + 5)(z - 8)(z - 2)}$ $\dfrac{z^2 + 6z + 5}{(z + 5)(z - 8)(z - 2)}$

45. $\dfrac{2x^2 + 4x}{(x + 3)(x - 3)(x + 2)}$ $\dfrac{x^2 - 3x}{(x + 3)(x - 3)(x + 2)}$

47. $\dfrac{15m - 15}{(m + 8)(m - 2)(m - 1)}$ $\dfrac{3m - 6}{(m + 8)(m - 2)(m - 1)}$

49. $\dfrac{26}{45}$ **51.** $\dfrac{48x + 5z^2}{6xyz^2}$ **53.** $\dfrac{-3m^2 + 4n^3}{9m^3n^2}$

55. $\dfrac{4h^2 - 21h - 27}{(h - 9)(h - 6)}$ **57.** 4   **59.** $\dfrac{3b - 7}{b - 7}$

61. $\dfrac{17}{4(a - 2)}$ **63.** $\dfrac{x^2 + 4x + 3}{(x + 5)(x + 4)}$

65. $\dfrac{m^2 + 8m + 15}{(m + 10)(m + 2)}$ **67.** $\dfrac{3x^2 + x}{(x + 3)(x - 3)(x + 2)}$

69. $\dfrac{8m + 55}{(m + 10)(m + 5)(m - 2)}$

71. a. $\dfrac{a + b}{ab}$

   b. The two brothers working together can mow $\dfrac{5}{6}$ of the lawn in one hour.

73. a. $\dfrac{m + n}{mn}$

   b. The two employees working together can file $\dfrac{9}{20}$ of the fall applications in one day.

75. $\dfrac{11x + 21}{(x + 3)(x + 1)}$ **77.** $\dfrac{32x}{(x + 3)(x + 2)}$

79. $\dfrac{n + 5}{2(n + 3)}$ **81.** $\dfrac{8h^2 - 26h - 42}{(h - 7)(h - 4)}$ **83.** 7

85. $\dfrac{(c + 1)(5c + 3)}{c - 1}$ **87.** $\dfrac{3}{2}$ **89.** $\dfrac{7b}{3(a - 2)}$

91. $\dfrac{7}{5}$ **93.** $\dfrac{-4a + 3}{7a + 5}$ **95.** $\dfrac{4x^2 - x}{3x^2 - 2}$

97. 1   **99.** $\dfrac{5x + 4y}{-7x + 6y}$

101. a. The average cost for food is $63.64 if 20 players go on the trip.

   b. The average cost for transportation and lodging is $90.91 if 20 players go on the trip.

   c. $\dfrac{125n + 900}{n + 2}$

   d. The average cost for all expenses is $149.07 if 25 players go on the trip.

Section 7.4

1. $x = 3$ **3.** $n = 8$ **5.** $x = 2$

7. $x = 1$ **9.** $x = 1$ **11.** $x = -6$

13. $r = 0$ **15.** $n = 3, -9$

17. $k = -5, -6$

19. a. The cost per person is $25 if 100 people attend the banquet.

   b. There must be 400 people attending the banquet for the cost per person to be $6.25.

21. a. The cost per person is $15 if 10 people agree to help pay for the gift.

   b. There must be 30 people who agree to help pay for the gift for the cost per person to be $5.

23. a. The cost per person is $87.50 if 8 people go on the trip.

   b. If they want the cost per person to be $75, they should recruit 10 people to go on the trip.

25. a. The cost for each large shutter is $550 if 4 large shutters are made in a week.

   b. For the cost per shutter to be $400, there must be 8 large shutters made in a week.

27. $r = -4$ **29.** $g = \dfrac{10}{99}$ **31.** $x = -12$

33. No solution.   **35.** $x = 10$ **37.** $p = -3$

39. $t = 43$ **41.** No solution.   **43.** No solution.

45. $n = 5$ **47.** $k = -3$ **49.** $x = 3$

51. $m = 4$ **53.** $a = 2, 12$ **55.** $b = 3$

57. $x = 5$ **59.** $n = -1$ **61.** $h = -10$

63. Brittany's work rate is 1 per 30 minutes or 2 per hour.

65. The pump's work rate is $\dfrac{1}{12}$ per hour.

67. Kasim's work rate is $\dfrac{1}{2}$ per hour.

69. Sherri and Jen can scan the file box of medical records in $\dfrac{15}{19}$ of an hour, or about 47 minutes, if they work together.

71. Martin and Bill can mow the lawn in $3\dfrac{1}{5}$ hours, or 3 hours and 12 minutes, if they work together.

73. Using both copy machines, the bulletins can be copied in $4\dfrac{4}{9}$ hours, or about 4 hours and 27 minutes.

75. a. Expression.   **b.** $\dfrac{x + 3}{x + 1}$

77. a. Equation.   **b.** $x = \dfrac{2}{7}$

79. a. Expression.   **b.** $\dfrac{-x - 36}{(x + 8)(x + 1)}$

81. a. Expression.   **b.** $5x$

83. a. Equation.   **b.** $x = 2$

85. a. Expression.   **b.** $\dfrac{x^2 + 3x + 2}{(x - 2)^2}$

Section 7.5

1. $\dfrac{4}{15}$ **3.** $\dfrac{3}{10}$ **5.** $\dfrac{5}{12}$

7. $\dfrac{3}{8}$ 9. $\dfrac{3}{40}$

11. $3.89 per ounce.

13. $900 per ounce.

15. 7.5 miles per hour.

17. $1\dfrac{1}{3}$ feet per minute.

19. 24 Duracell AA batteries for $14.49 cost $0.60 for each battery.

   16 Duracell AA batteries for $10.99 cost $0.69 for each battery.

   24 Duracell AA batteries for $14.49 are the better buy.

21. An 11-oz bag of Lay's Classic potato chips for $3.29 costs $0.30 per ounce.

   A 14-oz bag of Lay's Classic potato chips for $4.49 costs $0.32 per ounce.

   An 11-oz bag of Lay's Classic potato chips for $3.29 is the better buy.

23. A 16-oz bottle of Herdez salsa casera for $2.50 costs $0.16 per ounce.

   A 24-oz bottle of Herdez salsa casera for $4.19 costs $0.17 per ounce.

   A 16-oz bottle of Herdez salsa casera for $2.50 is the better buy.

25. The toy couch will be $3\dfrac{1}{3}$ inches tall.

27. The length of a 12-foot wall will be 3 inches on the blueprint.

29. The length of the window in the stadium will be 20 feet.

31. The cost of 304 feet of vinyl fencing is $5776.

33. The cost of 3900 square feet of shingles is $1550.

35. **a.** The total fat in a medium order of french fries is about 18.17 grams.

   b. The amount of saturated fat in a medium order of french fries is about 1.65 grams.

37. $x = 15$ 39. $b = 12$ 41. $y = -1$

43. $x = 0$ 45. $y = 6$ 47. $x = -11$

49. 25 miles is approximately equal to 40.23 km.

51. 165 pounds is equal to 75 kilograms.

53. 45 inches is equal to 114.3 centimeters.

55. 60 acres is equal to 2,613,600 square feet.

57. The width of the enlarged photo will be 12.5 inches.

59. $x = 7.5$ 61. $x = 6\dfrac{2}{3}$

63. The Victory Obelisk is 141.8 meters tall.

65. The amount of unsalted butter needed to make 16 servings is $\dfrac{4}{5}$ cup.

67. The amount of chicken broth needed to make 12 servings is $3\dfrac{3}{5}$ cups.

69. The amount of milk needed to make 16 servings is 16 cups.

71. The amount of maple syrup needed to make 12 servings is $2\dfrac{1}{4}$ cups.

73. $y = \dfrac{10}{3}x; y = 50$ when $x = 15$

75. $d = 3t; d = 30$ when $t = 10$

77. $y = \dfrac{5}{8}x; y = 10.625$ when $x = 17$

79. **a.** $C = 576h$

   b. $C = 2016$. A 150-pound person burns 2016 calories during 3.5 hours of mountain biking.

81. **a.** $D = 65t$

   b. $D = 357.5$. 357.5 miles are traveled in 5.5 hours.

83. **a.** $T = 32c$

   b. $T = 480$. A student who enrolls in 15 credits will owe $480 for tuition.

85. **a.** $F = \dfrac{6}{5}x$

   b. $x = 8\dfrac{1}{3}$. A force of 10 pounds will stretch the spring $8\dfrac{1}{3}$ inches.

87. **a.** $W = 14.5t$

   b. $W = 362.5$. The amount of the paycheck would be $362.50 for 25 hours of work.

89. $y = \dfrac{15}{x}; y \approx 2.73$ when $x = 5.5$.

91. $P = \dfrac{1000}{n}; P = 20$ when $n = 50$.

93. $C = \dfrac{180}{h}; C = 60$ when $h = 3$.

95. **a.** $k = 30$

   b. $P = 6$. The inside air pressure of the balloon is 6 psi when the volume of the balloon is 5 in³.

97. **a.** $s = \dfrac{275}{t}$

   b. $s \approx 78.57$. The speed is approximately 78.57 mph for 3.5 hours of driving.

99. **a.** $I = \dfrac{900}{d^2}$

   b. $I = 9$. The illumination is 9 foot-candles at a distance of 10 feet from the light.

Chapter 7 Review Exercises

1. $\dfrac{9}{2}$

2. Undefined.

3. The cost per person is $72 when 50 members go to the competition.

4. The average spending per person by the state of Washington in 2010 is \$4316.44.

5. $x = -7$ is excluded.

6. $n = -2, 6$ are excluded.

7. $b = -3, -1$ are excluded.

8. $t = \pm5$ is excluded.

9. $\dfrac{-1}{8x}$

10. $\dfrac{-1}{x+1}$

11. $\dfrac{y-8}{y+3}$

12. $\dfrac{1}{g+8}$

13. $\dfrac{-1}{h+3}$

14. $\dfrac{4}{n-2}$

15. A 130-pound rower will burn approximately 70.8 calories during a 6-minute event.

16. The runner's speed is 880 feet per minute.

17. $\dfrac{-1}{10k}$

18. $\dfrac{-x^2}{3}$

19. $\dfrac{-2mn}{21}$

20. $\dfrac{-9q}{8p^2}$

21. $\dfrac{x+2}{x+3}$

22. $\dfrac{1}{d+6}$

23. $\dfrac{k-2}{k+3}$

24. $\dfrac{p-3}{p+2}$

25. $\dfrac{z^2+7z+10}{(z-5)(z-3)}$

26. 1

27. $\dfrac{7x+7}{x+2}$

28. $\dfrac{7n+3}{5n+1}$

29. $\dfrac{3}{x+4}$

30. $\dfrac{5}{h-5}$

31. $\dfrac{6x-5}{x+6}$

32. $\dfrac{2y+5}{y-3}$

33. $\dfrac{6}{n-4}$

34. $\dfrac{2x+5}{(x+3)(x+5)}$

35. $\dfrac{24b^2c}{18a^2b^3c} \quad \dfrac{11a^2}{18a^2b^3c}$

36. $\dfrac{-9x^2}{8x^3y^3} \quad \dfrac{14y}{8x^3y^3}$

37. $\dfrac{7}{2(v+4)} \quad \dfrac{22}{2(v+4)}$

38. $\dfrac{-1}{y-3} \quad \dfrac{11}{y-3}$

39. $\dfrac{5p-40}{(p+2)(p-3)(p-8)} \quad \dfrac{3p^2-9p}{(p+2)(p-3)(p-8)}$

40. $\dfrac{-x+2}{(3x-1)(x+4)(x-2)} \quad \dfrac{3x^2+12x}{(3x-1)(x+4)(x-2)}$

41. $\dfrac{z^2-12z+35}{(z+7)(z+2)(z-7)} \quad \dfrac{4z+8}{(z+7)(z+2)(z-7)}$

42. $\dfrac{x^2-13x+36}{(x+9)(x-9)(x+5)} \quad \dfrac{-3x-15}{(x+9)(x-9)(x+5)}$

43. $\dfrac{-8a^2+35bc}{50a^3b^2}$

44. $\dfrac{xy+6}{3xy^2}$

45. $\dfrac{13y-19}{(y+2)(y-7)}$

46. $\dfrac{-t+39}{(t+6)(t-3)}$

47. $\dfrac{k^2+2k-1}{(k+2)(k+1)}$

48. $\dfrac{w-1}{w-4}$

49. $\dfrac{x^2-5}{(x-5)(x+2)}$

50. $\dfrac{y-2}{y+6}$

51. $m = 22$. There must be 22 members of the band who travel to the competition in order for the cost per person to be \$100.

52. $t \approx 8$. In the year 2008, the state of Washington spent \$4241 per resident.

53. $h = -4$

54. $f = -1$

55. $r = \dfrac{25}{62}$

56. $x = \dfrac{4}{39}$

57. $w = \dfrac{-13}{5}$

58. $b = \dfrac{1}{2}$

59. $n = 8$

60. $x = 4$

61. $a = 3$

62. $d = -9$

63. $\dfrac{6x+2}{8x-3}$

64. $\dfrac{4x+5}{2x-3}$

65. $\dfrac{3n}{3n+1}$

66. $\dfrac{n-4}{n}$

67. $t = 5\dfrac{5}{11}$. Working together, Amin and Danya can typeset a chapter in $5\dfrac{5}{11}$ hours, or about 5 hours and 27 minutes.

68. $t = 10\dfrac{4}{5}$. Working together, Mike and his assistant can paint the house in $10\dfrac{4}{5}$ hours, or 10 hours and 48 minutes.

69. $\dfrac{7}{12}$

70. $\dfrac{3}{8}$

71. \$0.75 per pound

72. 21 miles per hour

73. 946 milliliters of Concrobium Mold Control for \$9.49 costs \$0.010 per milliliter.

3784 milliliters of Concrobium Mold Control for \$35.49 costs \$0.009 per milliliter.

3784 milliliters of Concrobium Mold Control for \$35.49 is the better buy.

74. 12 extra large grade AA eggs for \$2.59 cost \$0.22 per egg.

18 extra large grade AA eggs for \$4.49 cost \$0.25 per egg.

The package of 12 extra-large grade AA eggs for \$2.59 is the better buy.

75. There are approximately 93 milligrams of sodium in a 32 fl. oz. serving of Pepsi.

76. There are approximately 109 grams of sugar in a 32 fl. oz. serving of Pepsi.

77. $x = -1$

78. $x = 13$

79. $x = 8$

80. $x = -5$

81. $x = 30$

82. $h \approx 146.41$. The original height of the Great Pyramid of Giza is approximately 146.41 meters.

83. $y = \dfrac{1}{3}x; y = \dfrac{10}{3}$ when $x = 10$

84. $y = 18x; y = 108$ when $x = 6$

85. $y = \dfrac{-4}{x}; y = 2$ when $x = -2$

86. $y = \dfrac{-7}{x}; y = \dfrac{-1}{3}$ when $x = 21$

Chapter 7 Test

1. $\dfrac{b+2}{b-4}$

2. $\dfrac{c-7}{c+2}$

3. $x = -7$ is excluded.

4. $x = 8, -3$ are excluded.

5. The rocket is traveling at 220 feet per second.

6. $\dfrac{d + 2}{d + 7}$

7. $\dfrac{p + 3}{(p - 6)(p + 4)}$

8. $\dfrac{k - 3}{2}$

9. $(x + 3)(x + 7)$

10. $\dfrac{5x + 7}{x + 3}$

11. $\dfrac{6n - 44}{(n - 7)(n - 8)}$

12. $\dfrac{a - 2}{a - 4}$

13. $\dfrac{g + 17}{(g - 3)(g + 2)}$

14. $\dfrac{-2t + 2}{(t - 3)(t + 1)}$

15. $\dfrac{-2x^2}{(x + 6)(x^2 + 4)}$

16. a. $c = 35$. The average cost per foot is \$35 when 10 feet of mow curb are installed.

  b. $m = 30$. There must be 30 feet of mow curb installed for the average cost to be \$25 per foot.

17. $m = 4$

18. $r = -4$

19. $z = 38$

20. $h = -2$

21. It would take $7\frac{1}{7}$ minutes, or about 7 minutes and 9 seconds, to fill the truck if both pumps were used.

22. a. 5 feet of lights for \$1.35 cost \$0.27 per foot.

  b. 8 feet of lights for \$2.24 cost \$0.28 per foot.
     5 feet of lights for \$1.35 is cheaper.

23. $x = 15$

24. It takes 52 seconds to download a 5.2-megabyte song.

25. $y = \dfrac{10}{x}$; $y = \dfrac{1}{4}$ when $x = 40$

Cumulative Review for Chapters 1–7

1. $(-3a)^4$

2. -36

3. 43

4. 223.04 ft

5. 3

6. $2n + 16$

7. $-7t + 4$

8. $y = \dfrac{2}{5}x + 2$

9. $n = \dfrac{-7}{9}$

10. 17t

11. $C = R - P$

12. $t = 1.32$

13. Let l represent the length.
     $2l + 2(22) = 102$
     $l = 29$ ft

14. $a = 2$

15. $x < \dfrac{-1}{8}$

16. a.

x	$y = |x + 5|$
-8	3
-5	0
-2	3
0	5
2	7

b.

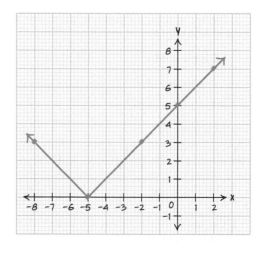

c. Non-linear.

17.

h	$C = 508h$
0	0
0.5	254
1	508
1.5	762
2	1016

Calories burned by a 160lb man while free-style lap swimming

18. a. Let T represent the tuition paid for taking c credit hours.
     $T = 20 + 36c$

  b. The slope is $36 = \dfrac{\$36}{1 \text{ credit}}$.

  c. The tuition is increasing at the rate of \$36.00 per credit hour.

19. $m = \dfrac{-4}{7}$

20. The x-intercept is $\left(\dfrac{9}{2}, 0\right)$ and the y-intercept is $(0, -3)$.

21.

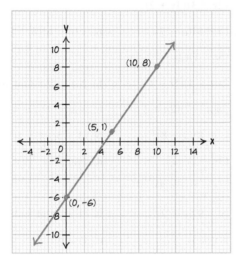

22. Perpendicular.

23. $y = \dfrac{3}{8}x + 7$

24. $y = 5$

25. $y = \dfrac{-3}{2}x + 4$

26. $y = -5x - 10$

27. $(-2, 7)$

28. a. No.

  b. Yes.

29.

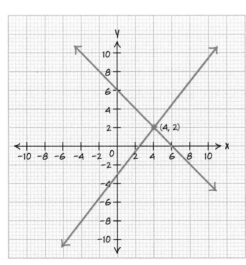

30. $(x, y) = (4, 5)$

31. No solution.

32. Each package of glue sticks costs \$6.00 and each package of whiteboard markers costs \$7.50.

33. The rate of the plane in still air is 130 mph and the rate of the wind is 20 mph.

34. She needs to put in 4.5 pounds of white tea and 5.5 pounds of blueberry herbal tea in the mix.

35. $(x, y) = (-4, -6)$

36. There are infinitely many solutions.

37. The two angles measure 45° and 135°.

38. Conrad should invest \$3500 in the CD and \$1500 in the money market fund.

39. No.

40.

41.

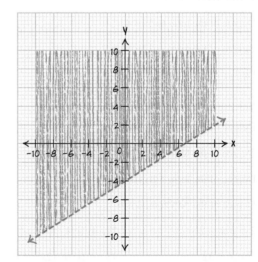

42. 1

43. -1

44. a. a^9

  b. $-15b^9$

  c. $4x^4y^3$

45. a. $9t^5$ **b.** $-48n^4$ **c.** $-10a^5b^5$ **c.** $25y^2 + 20y + 4$ **d.** $n^2 - 36$

46. a. $64t^6$ **b.** $25n^{10}$ **c.** $36a^2b^{14}$ **76.** $-13a + 25$ **77.** $-20t + 37$

47. a. $27a^{21}$ **b.** $81b^{12}$ **c.** $-8x^9y^{12}$ **78. a.** $-2x - 3 + \dfrac{1}{x}$ **b.** $n^2 - 2n + \dfrac{3}{n}$

48. a. $75x^7y^4$ **b.** $392a^7b^{18}$ **79. a.** $4x + 1$ **b.** $x - 4$

49. a. $-192p^8q^{12}$ **b.** $225g^5h^{12}$ **80. a.** $3x - 2$ **b.** $5x + 2$

50. a. a^3 **b.** $\dfrac{-b}{4}$ **c.** $\dfrac{3a^3}{16}$ **81. a.** $5x^2(-2x^3 + 4x + 1)$ **b.** $(b - 5)(3a - 2)$

51. a. n^3 **b.** $\dfrac{-a}{3}$ **c.** r **82. a.** $25ab^3(-a^2b + 3)$ **b.** $(h + 2)(-7g + 3)$

52. $\dfrac{a^4b^6}{9}$ **53.** $16x^6y^4$ **83.** $(y + 4)(x - 2)$ **84.** $(a - 5)(b + 2)$

54. $A = 12x^2$ **55.** $A = 36\pi x^2$ **85.** $2(a - 5)(b + 6)$ **86.** $3(x + 4)(y - 2)$

56. a. $\dfrac{-6}{y^3}$ **b.** $-a^2$ **87. a.** $(a - 7)(a + 4)$ **b.** $-(y - 6)(y - 3)$

57. a. $\dfrac{-7}{t}$ **b.** $-5r^3$ **c.** $(2x - 3)(3x + 2)$

58. a. $\dfrac{b^3}{a^3}$ **b.** $\dfrac{-2t^{12}}{5r^3}$ **88. a.** $(a - 3)(a - 7)$ **b.** $-(b - 6)(b - 7)$

c. $\dfrac{16}{x^8}$ **d.** $\dfrac{b^2}{a^4}$ **c.** $(5t - 1)(2t + 7)$

59. a. $\dfrac{y}{x^2}$ **b.** $\dfrac{-2q^5}{3p^8}$ **89. a.** $2t(t + 3)(5t - 1)$ **b.** $2(a - 2b)(3a + b)$

c. $\dfrac{9}{x^{10}}$ **d.** $\dfrac{y^{12}}{x^9}$ **90. a.** $3n(n - 7)(2n + 5)$ **b.** $3(2r - 1)(t + 4)$

60. a. 6.213×10^9 **b.** 4.68×10^{-5} **91. a.** $(x - 8)(x + 8)$ **b.** $(4 - 5t)(4 + 5t)$

c. $(3x - 1)^2$ **d.** Prime.

61. a. 7.291×10^{10} **b.** 2.73×10^{-3} **e.** $3(t - 3)(t + 3)$

62. a. $106{,}000$ **b.** 0.0005071 **92. a.** $(y - 9)(y + 9)$ **b.** $(1 - 2a)(1 + 2a)$

63. a. $31{,}570{,}000$ **b.** 0.00005163 **c.** $2(x + 3)^2$ **d.** Prime.

64. 1×10^{-4} **65.** 5.913×10^9 **e.** $(2n - 5)(n + 5)$

66. 4 terms. Degree is 5.   **93. a.** Linear.   **b.** Quadratic.

67. 1 term. Degree is 9.   **c.** Linear.

68. Degree of the term $6ab^3$ is 4.   **94. a.** $a = 5, a = -7$ **b.** $x = 6, x = \dfrac{-1}{5}$

Degree of the term $-12a^5b^2$ is 7.   **c.** $x = 8, x = 3$ **d.** $b = 1, b = -1$

Degree of the term $16b^6$ is 6.   **95. a.** $b = -6, b = -8$ **b.** $x = \dfrac{4}{5}, x = -2$

Degree of the polynomial is 7.   **c.** $x = 8, x = 7$ **d.** $r = 10, r = -10$

69. Degree of the term $-17x^4y^2$ is 6.   **96.** $\dfrac{1}{22}$

Degree of the term $2xy^3$ is 4.   **97. a.** $x = \dfrac{-7}{5}$ is excluded.

Degree of the term -8 is 0.   **b.** $x = 3, x = -6$ are excluded.

Degree of the polynomial is 6.   **98. a.** $y = 2$ is excluded.

70. $2x^2 + x - 2$ **71.** $4y + 4$ **b.** $x = \dfrac{1}{2}, x = -5$ are excluded.

72. $-12x + 32$ **73.** $-2x^3 + 12x^2 - 4x$ **99. a.** $\dfrac{1}{t + 1}$ **b.** $\dfrac{1}{x - 2}$

74. a. $5a^2 + 9a - 2$ **b.** $y^3 - y^2 - 10y + 12$ **c.** -1

c. $9x^2 - 6x + 1$ **d.** $25x^2 - 4$ **100. a.** $\dfrac{1}{n + 2}$ **b.** $\dfrac{1}{4(x - 1)}$

75. a. $3x^2 + 20x - 7$ **b.** $3t^3 + 5t^2 + 6t + 16$ **c.** -1

101. a. $T = \dfrac{15}{8} = 1.875$ hours   **b.** $T = \dfrac{12}{7} \approx 1.71$ hours

102. a. $\dfrac{1}{(n-5)(n+3)}$ **b.** $\dfrac{1}{(x-2)(x-3)}$

103. a. $\dfrac{1}{(x+5)(2x+9)}$ **b.** $\dfrac{2}{(t-3)(t-5)}$

104. 22 feet per second.

105. ≈ 19.09 milligrams per pound

106. a. $\dfrac{1}{3(a+5)}$ **b.** $\dfrac{z+2}{(z-6)(z+5)}$

107. a. $\dfrac{1}{5(x-1)}$ **b.** $\dfrac{n-1}{5(n+4)}$

108. a. $\dfrac{-20}{h^2 k}$ **b.** $\dfrac{15}{y}$

109. a. $\dfrac{70x}{y^2}$ **b.** $\dfrac{3y}{4}$

110. a. 4   **b.** $\dfrac{3}{x+2}$

111. a. 3   **b.** 2

112. The LCD is $(x-2)(x+1)$

a. $\dfrac{4x+4}{(x-2)(x+1)}$ $\dfrac{3x-6}{(x+1)(x-2)}$

The LCD is $3(t+7)$

b. $\dfrac{18t}{3(t+7)}$ $\dfrac{-5}{3(t+7)}$

The LCD is $(x+1)(x-3)(x+5)$

c. $\dfrac{-2x-10}{(x+1)(x-3)(x+5)}$ $\dfrac{6x+6}{(x+1)(x-3)(x+5)}$

113. The LCD is $(n-6)(n+4)$

a. $\dfrac{-9n-36}{(n-6)(n+4)}$ $\dfrac{12n-72}{(n-6)(n+4)}$

The LCD is $6(y-3)$

b. $\dfrac{42y}{6(y-3)}$ $\dfrac{-3y}{6(y-3)}$

The LCD is $(x-2)(x+1)(x-4)$

c. $\dfrac{5x-20}{(x-2)(x+1)(x-4)}$ $\dfrac{-7x-7}{(x-2)(x+1)(x-4)}$

114. a. $\dfrac{18+a}{3(b-5)}$ **b.** $\dfrac{-2x-1}{x-2}$

c. $\dfrac{6m-26}{(m+1)(m-4)}$

115. a. $\dfrac{5}{2(5x-3)}$ **b.** $\dfrac{2y-3}{y-7}$

c. $\dfrac{10x-43}{(x+4)(x-6)}$

116. $\dfrac{4-2x}{3+x}$ **117.** $\dfrac{5t}{(t+6)(3-2t)}$

118. a. The average cost is $16.25 per person when 12 people attend.

b. 15 people must attend for the average cost per person to be $15.00.

119. a. $x = -2$ **b.** No solution.

c. $t = 0, t = 5$ **d.** $x = -8$

120. a. $n = \dfrac{11}{2} = 5.5$ **b.** No solution.

c. $x = 0, x = -6$ **d.** $x = -8$

121. a. $w = \dfrac{8{,}500{,}000}{15} \approx \$566{,}666.67$

b. 20 people should pitch in to buy tickets.

122. About 8.57 minutes.   **123.** $\dfrac{3}{4}$

124. $\dfrac{\$4.59}{1 \text{ gal}}$

125. 115 square yards of carpet costs $3904.25

126. a. $a = -5$ **b.** $a = -7$

127. a. $b = -8$ **b.** $n = -2$

128. $x = 8$ **129.** $x = 3.75$

130. $y = -6x$

$y = -6(-4) = 24$

131. $y = \dfrac{12}{x}$

$y = \dfrac{12}{6} = 2$

CHAPTER 8

Section **8.1**

1. a. After 1 hour of training, a new employee can produce 30 candies per hour.

b. After 4 hours of training, a new employee can produce 60 candies per hour.

c. A new employee can produce 150 candies per hour after 13 hours of training.

3. a. In 1992 there were approximately 4178 homicides of 15- to 19-year-olds in the United States.

b. In 2002 there were approximately 1019 homicides of 15- to 19-year-olds in the United States.

c. In 1982 there were approximately 7337 homicides of 15- to 19-year olds in the United States.

5. a. If you sell 100 printed T-shirts you will lose $150.

b. If you sell 400 printed T-shirts you will make $300 profit.

c. To make $1000 profit you must sell 867 printed T-shirts.

7. a. It costs $52.50 to take a 25-mile taxi ride in NYC.

b. For $100 you can take about a 48-mile taxi ride in NYC.

9. $P = 4200$ looks correct. This would mean that 4,200,000 people live in Kentucky. $P = 3.5$ is too small and $P = -210$ is not possible.

11. $T = -50$ looks correct. This would mean that the temperature at the South Pole is -50 degrees Fahrenheit. Both $T = 75$ and $T = 82$ are too warm.

13. a. On sales of $2000 you will make $80 in commissions.

   b. On sales of $50,000 you will make $3920 in commissions.

   c. To make $500 per week, you will need $7250 in sales each week.

15. a. $B = 29.95 + 0.55m$

   b. If you drive the 10-foot truck 75 miles it will cost you $71.20.

   c. For a total of $100 you can rent the 10-foot truck from Budget and drive it 127 miles.

17. a. $P = 250 + 0.07s$

   b. If you have sales of $2000 in a week, your pay will be $390.

   c. To earn $650 per week, you must have $5714.29 in sales each week.

19. a. Let C be the total cost (in dollars) for a trip to Las Vegas, and let d be the number of days you stay. $C = 125 + 100d$.

   b. A 3-day trip to Las Vegas will cost $425.

   c. If you have $700 and gamble half of it, you can stay in Las Vegas for only 2 days.

21. a. Let C be the total cost (in dollars) for shooting a wedding and let p be the number of proofs edited and printed. Then $C = 5.29p + 400$.

   b. If the photographer edits and prints 100 proofs the cost will be $929.

   c. With a budget of $1250, the photographer can edit and print 160 proofs.

23. a. Let C be the total cost (in dollars) for selling s snow cones for a month: $C = 7000 + 0.45s$.

   b. The monthly cost for selling 3000 snow cones is $8350.

   c. For a $10,600 budget the vendor can sell up to 8000 snow cones.

25. a. Let C be the total cost (in dollars), for the Squeaky Clean Window Company to clean windows for a day, when w windows are cleaned.

$$C = 1.5w + 230$$

   b. If the Squeaky Clean Window Company cleans 60 windows in a day it will cost the company $320.

   c. To stay within a budget of $450 the Squeaky Clean Window Company can clean up to 146 windows.

27. Maria's work is correct. Javier needs a decimal to correctly represent 55 cents per bottle in terms of dollars per bottle.

29. a. Let C be the total cost (in dollars) for pest management from Enviro-Safe Pest Management when m monthly treatments are done,

$$C = 150 + 38m$$

   b. If your house is treated for 18 months after the initial treatment it will cost $834.

31. a. Let C be the total monthly cost (in dollars) for a manufacturer to produce g sets of golf clubs.

$$C = 23,250 + 145g$$

   b. It costs the manufacturer $37,750 to produce 100 sets of golf clubs.

   c. $g \approx -22.4$. This does not make sense. Their costs can never be lower than their fixed costs of $23,250.

   d. To break even selling 100 sets of golf clubs per month the manufacturer must sell each set for $377.50.

33. a. $C = 1500 + 1.5n$ for $n \le 500$.

   b. It costs Rockon $1875 to make 250 CDs.

   c. With a budget of $2000, Rockon can order 333 CDs.

   d. With a budget of $3000, Rockon can order 1000 CDs. This does not make sense. They can only order up to 500 CDs.

35. $x = 10$ **37.** $d = 20$ **39.** $m = 8$

41. $x = -\dfrac{20}{11}$ **43.** $d = \dfrac{301}{10}$ **45.** $d \approx -0.45$

47. $c = \dfrac{113}{3}$ **49.** $d \approx -7.27$ **51.** $z = \dfrac{17}{6}$

53. $v = \dfrac{42}{31}$ **55.** $t = \dfrac{34}{15}$

57. Yes, rounding the outside temperature to 73 degrees Fahrenheit is appropriate because a difference of 0.4 degree Fahrenheit would not be noticed.

59. The discounted price should be rounded to $236.57 because our monetary units extend to the hundredth place value.

61. The number of cars should be rounded to 313. To make the profit of $400 the company needs to wash just slightly more than 312 cars. Therefore, the next possible whole number greater than that is 313.

63. a. Slope $= 75.8$. The population of Washington state increases 75.8 thousand each year.

   b. The vertical intercept is $(0, 5906.2)$. In 2000 the population of Washington state was 5906.2 thousand.

   c. The horizontal intercept is $(-77.9, 0)$. In 1922, the population of Washington state was 0. This does not make sense.

65. a. Slope $= 4.02$. The annual amount of public expenditure on medical research in the United States increases $4.02 billion each year.

   b. The vertical intercept is $(0, 25.8)$. The annual amount of public expenditure on medical research in the United States in 2000 was $25.8 billion.

   c. The horizontal intercept is $(-6.42, 0)$. The annual amount of public expenditure on medical research in the United States was $0 in 1994. This is model breakdown.

67. a. Slope $= 500$. The monthly profit for a small used car lot increases by $500 for every car that is sold.

   b. The vertical intercept is $(0, -6000)$. If the small used car lot sells 0 cars, it will lose $6000.

c. The horizontal intercept is (12, 0). The small used car lot will need to sell 12 cars in order to break even in their monthly profit.

69. a. Let P the total profit in dollars Dan earns teaching surfing lessons and let s be the number of 1-hour surf lessons Dan gives. This can be represented by the equation

$$P = 30s - 700.$$

b. Slope = 30. Dan earns $30 for every 1-hour surf lesson he gives.

c. The vertical intercept is (0, −700). If Dan doesn't give any surf lessons, he will lose $700 in profit.

d. The horizontal intercept is (23.33, 0). Dan will need to give 24 one-hour surf lessons in order to break even in profit.

71. a. Let T be the total amount of money raised by the PTA for a new track at Mission Meadows Elementary School in dollars and let a be the total pounds of aluminum cans the PTA recycles. $T = 1.24a + 2000$

b. Slope = 1.24. The PTA at Mission Meadows Elementary School earns $1.24 for every pound of aluminum cans they recycle.

c. The vertical intercept is (0, 2000). The PTA at Mission Meadows Elementary School will have $2000 to put toward a new track if they recycle 0 pounds of aluminum cans.

d. The horizontal intercept is (−1612.9, 0). The PTA at Mission Meadows Elementary School will need to recycle −1612.9 pounds of aluminum cans in order to earn $0 for a new track. This does not make sense.

73. a. Let P be the total percentage of Americans who have been diagnosed with diabetes and let t be time in years since 2000.

$$P = 0.15t + 4.5$$

b. When $t = 10$, then $P = 6$. This implies 6% of Americans will be diagnosed with diabetes in 2010.

c. Slope = 0.15. The percentage of Americans diagnosed with diabetes increases 0.15 percentage points each year.

75. a. Let C be the cost in dollars and n be the number of shirts.

$$C = \frac{17}{2n} + 25$$

b. When $n = 50$ then $C = 450$. It will cost $450 for 50 shirts.

c. Slope = 8.5. The cost of the shirts increases by $8.50 per shirt.

d. The vertical intercept is (0, 25). It costs $25 if 0 shirts are purchased. This is model breakdown.

e. The horizontal intercept is (−2.94, 0). To pay $0, you would have to purchase −3 shirts. This is model breakdown.

77. a. Let P be the population of Washington state t years since 2000. $P = 104.5t + 5383.5$

b. If $t = 30$ then $P = 8518.5$. In 2030, the population of Washington state will be about 8518.5 thousand.

c. Slope = 104.5. The population of Washington state increases 104.5 thousand each year.

d. The vertical intercept is (0, 5383.5). In 2000 the population of Washington state was 5383.5 thousand.

e. The horizontal intercept is (−51.52, 0). In 1949, the population of Washington state was 0. This does not make sense.

79. a. $W = 5h + 100$ where W is the optimal weight of a woman in pounds and h is the number of inches past 5 feet.

b. If $h = 12$ then $W = 160$. The optimal weight of a woman who is 6 feet tall is 160 pounds.

c. Slope = 5. For every inch taller than 4 feet, a woman's optimal weight increases 5 pounds.

d. The vertical intercept is (0, 100). A woman's optimal weight at 5 feet tall is 100 pounds.

e. The horizontal intercept is (−20, 0). At 3 feet 4 inches, a woman's optimal weight is 0 pounds. This does not make sense.

81. Let G be the number of gastric bypasses performed and t be the number of years past 2000.

$$G = 181.5t + 226.5$$

a. If $t = 5$ then $G = 1134$. The number of teenagers who had gastric bypass surgery in 2005 was 1134.

b. Slope = 181.5. The number of teenagers who undergo gastric bypass surgery increases by about 182 each year.

c. The vertical intercept is (0, 226.5). In 2000, 227 teenagers underwent gastric bypass surgery.

d. The horizontal intercept is (−1.25, 0). In 1998, 0 teenagers underwent gastric bypass surgery. This does not make sense.

Section **8.2**

1. a. The total prize money at Wimbledon in 2002 was 8.5 million British pounds.

b. In 2003 the total prize money at Wimbledon was 8.5 million British pounds.

c. (0, 7) In the year 2000 the winnings were 7 million British pounds

d. Domain: [2, 11]; Range: [8.5, 14]

3. (A) and (E) **5.** (C) and (F)

7. 50   **9.** 0.01

11. 50   **13.** 10,000

15. a. (0, 2)   **b.** (−3, 0)   **c.** $x = 3$ **d.** $y = 2.6$

17. a. (0, 5)   **b.** (4, 0)   **c.** Input value = −10
d. Input value = 15   **e.** Output value = −8

19. a. (0, −8)   **b.** (30, 0)   **c.** $x = 11$
d. $x = -9$ **e.** $y = -3$

21. a. False, (0, −2)   **b.** True
c. False, $x = -4.5$ **d.** False, $x = -1.5$
e. True

23. a. (−15, 0)   **b.** (0, −10)   **c.** $x = 15$ **d.** $x = 7.5$
e. $y = -3$

25. a. (0, 1)   **b.** (−2, 0)   **c.** Input value = 1
d. Input value = −4   **e.** Output value = 2.5

27. a. Dependent variable: C = cost in dollars for producing chocolate-dipped key lime pie bars.

Independent variable: b = the number of bars produced.

b. Graphic title: Cost of Key Lime Bars on a Stick

c. When b = 200 then C = \$485.

The cost of producing 200 key lime bars on a stick is about \$485.

d. Domain $0 \le b \le 200$;   Range $240 \le C \le 485$

29. a. Dependent variable: G = gross profit for Quiksilver, Inc. in millions of dollars.

Independent variable: t = years since 2000.

b.

c. When t = 10 then G = 1850. The gross profit for Quiksilver, Inc. in 2010 will be \$1850 million.

d. Domain: $1 \le t \le 10$;   Range: $50 \le G \le 1850$

31. Maria's model fits the data better. There is a smaller variance between the data points and the "Line of Best Fit."

33. $0 \le t \le 10$ is not a reasonable domain because the model predicts a negative value of cases per 100,000 population for t values of about 8.2. Domain: $[0, 7]$; Range: $[0.6, 4.1]$

35. a. Dependent variable: P = population of the United States in millions

Independent variable: t = years since 1995

b.

c. When t = 14 then $P \approx 308$. The population of the United States in 2009 will be around 308 million people.

d. Domain: $[0, 14]$;   Range: $[266, 308]$

e. $(0, 266)$

f. In 1995 there were approximately 266 million people in the United States.

37. a. W = number of deaths of women induced by illegal drugs in the United States

t = years since 2000.

b. When t = 7 then $W \approx 15,000$. The number of drug-induced deaths of females in the United States in 2007 was around 15,000.

c. The number of drug-induced deaths of females in the United States reached 4000 in 1998.

d. Domain: $-1 \le t \le 7$;   Range: $8200 \le W \le 15,000$.

39. a. T = The number of years someone will live. a = Age in years

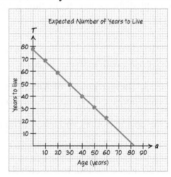

b. When a = 45 then T = 35.
A 45-year-old person would live around 35 years.

c. Domain: $[0, 80]$;   Range: $[3, 77]$

d. The graphical model predicts a 90-year-old person to live negative years. This is model breakdown.

e. The vertical intercept is $(0, 77)$.

f. At birth, a person will live about 77 years.

Section 8.3

1. b   **3.** c   **5.** c

7. a   **9.** x-scl = 1 y-scl = 5

11. x-scl = 1 y-scl = 0.1

13. x-min = -45 x-max = -5 x-scl = 5
y-min = -20 y-max = 35 y-scl = 5

15. a. R = revenue in thousands of dollars for Quick Tire Repair Inc., t = years from 2000. $R = 4t + 584$

b. Domain: [2, 14];   Range: [592, 640]

c. Quick Tire Repair Inc. will have $700 thousand revenue in 2029.

d. Slope = 4. Quick Tire Repair Inc's. revenue is increasing about $4 thousand per year.

17. $y = 2.5x + 8$ **19.** $y = -0.75x + 20$

21. a. Let M = millions of metric tons of beef and pork, t = years since 2000. $M = 2.3t + 132.1$

b. In 2006 there were about 145.9 million metric tons of beef and pork produced worldwide.

c. In 2019 the worldwide production of beef and pork will be about 175 million metric tons.

d. Domain: [−3, 10];   Range: [125.2, 155.1]

e. Slope = 2.3. There is an increase of 2.3 million metric tons per year in the production of beef and pork worldwide.

23. The slope is incorrect; the numerator and denominator are reversed. The slope should be

$$m = \frac{365 - 265}{100 - 20} = 1.25 \quad \$1.25 \text{ per bar}$$

25. The slope is incorrect. The order of subtraction is reversed in the numerator. The slope should be

$$m = \frac{1105 - 90}{3000 - 100} = 0.35 \quad \$0.35 \text{ per pen}$$

27. a. Let C be the number of reported chlamydia cases in thousands, and t the number of years since 2000. $C = 58.3t + 702$

b. Slope = 58.3. The reported number of chlamydia cases increases by 58.3 thousand cases per year.

c. There were 1,051,800 estimated cases of chlamydia in 2006.

29. a. Let E be the total egg production in the United States (in billions), t the years since 2000. $E = 1.1t + 84.7$

b. In 2008 the total egg production in the United States was 93.5 billion.

c. Domain: [−4, 10];   Range: [80.3, 95.7]

d. Slope = 1.1 billion/year. The egg production is increasing by 1.1 billion eggs per year in the United States.

31. Let U, S, and F be the number of Internet users in the United Kingdom, Spain, and Finland in millions, respectively, and let t be time in years since 1990.

$$U = 5.5t - 37$$
$$S = 2.27t - 17.6$$
$$F = 0.25t - 0.6$$

33. The United Kingdom has the greatest growth. United Kingdom (5.5) > Spain (2.27) > Finland (0.25).

35. a. Let R be total revenue for FedEx in millions of dollars and let t be time in years since 2000.

$$R = 2433.5t + 17,195.5$$

b. Domain: [−3, 10]; Range: [9895, 41,531]

c. Slope = 2433.5. The total revenue for FedEx increases $2433.5 million each year.

d. If $t = 10$ then $R = 41,530.5$. In 2010, the total revenue for FedEx will be $41,530.5 million.

37. a. Let M be the total consumption of milk in the United States in millions of gallons, and let t be time in years since 2000.

$$M = -36.5t + 9301.5$$

b. Domain: [−3, 10];   Range: [8936.5, 9411]

c. The vertical intercept is (0, 9301.5). In 2000, the total consumption of milk in the United States was 9301.5 million gallons of milk.

d. In 2008, Americans consumed approximately 9000 million gallons of milk.

e. The horizontal intercept is (254.8, 0). In 2255, Americans will consume 0 gallons of milk. This is model breakdown.

39. a. Let H be the total amount spent by individuals on health care in the United States in billions of dollars, and let t be time in years since 2000.

$$H = 17t + 147$$

b. Domain: [3, 14];   Range: [198, 385]

c. Slope = 17. The amount of money Americans spend on health care increases $17 billion each year.

d. If $t = 15$ then $H = 402$. In 2015, Americans will spend $402 billion on health care.

e. The amount that Americans will spend on health care will reach $500 billion in 2021.

41. $y = 6x - 20$ **43.** $y = -3x + 8$

45. $y = \frac{1}{3}x - 5$ **47.** $y = -0.19x + 2.66$

49. $y = 15x + 342$ **51.** $y = -41x - 3468$

Section **8.4**

1. This is not a function because two children the same age may not be in the same grade.

Input: a = years old.

Output: G = grade level of student.

3. This is not a function because two children the same age may not be the same height.

Input: a = years old.

Output: H = heights in inches of children attending Mission Meadows Elementary School.

5. This is a function.

Input: t = years after starting the investment.

Output: I = interest earned from an investment in dollars.

7. This is not a function because each year there will be several songs at the top of the pop charts.

Input: y = year.

Output: S = song at the top of the pop charts.

9. This is a function.

 Input: t = year.

 Output: T = amount of taxes you paid in dollars.

11. This is a function.

13. This is not a function, because the input of 1 hour of poker play is related to two different amounts of winnings.

15. This is a function.

17. This is not a function, because the input of Monday is related to two different amounts of money spent on lunch.

19. Domain = {Jan., Feb., May, June}

 Range = {5689.35, 7856.12, 2689.15, 1005.36}

21. Domain = {1, 2, 3, 4, 5}

 Range = {−650, −100, −150, 60, 125, 200, 300}

23. The death rate from HIV for 20-year-olds is 0.5 per 100,000.

25. In 2002 there were 14,304 small business loans made to minority-owned small businesses.

27. The amount spent on lunch on Tuesday was $5.95 and $6.33.

29. Yes, this is a function. Each input has one output.

31. No, this is not a function. The y^2 means some inputs will have more than one output.

33. Yes, this is a function. Each input has one output.

35. Yes, this is a function. Passes the Vertical Line Test.

37. Yes, this is a function. Passes the Vertical Line Test.

39. No, this is not a function. Fails the Vertical Line Test.

41. **a.** On the first day of starting a diet, a person's weight will be 86.5 kg.

 b. 10 days after starting a diet, a person's weight will be 82 kg.

 c. 30 days after starting a diet, a person's weight will be 75 kg.

 d. 100 days after starting a diet, a person's weight will be 88 kg.

43. **a.** Eight ounces of chocolate were consumed in the Clark household on the 5th day of the month.

 b. Twenty ounces of chocolate were consumed in the Clark household on the 15th day of the month.

 c. Twenty-eight ounces of chocolate were consumed in the Clark household on the 30th day of the month.

45. **a.** $P(\text{Ohio}) = 11.48$

 b. $P(\text{Texas}) = 23.507783$

 c. $P(\text{Wyoming}) = 0.515004$

47. **a.** $B(t) = 38t + 748$

 b. $B(9) = 1090$. In 2009 the average Social Security benefit for retired workers was $1090.

 c. $t = 33$. The average monthly Social Security benefit will be $2000 in 2033.

 d. Domain: [−1, 10]; Range: [710, 1128]

 e. (0, 748). In 2000 the average monthly Social Security benefit was $748.

49. **a.** $M(t) = 0.67t + 39.16$

 b. Domain: [−3, 10]; Range: [37.15, 45.86]

 c. (0, 39.16). In 2000 there were 39.16 million people enrolled in Medicare.

 d. $M(10) = 45.86$. In 2010 there were 45.86 million people enrolled in Medicare.

 e. $t \approx 16.18$. In 2016 there will be 50 million people enrolled in Medicare.

51. **a.** $f(5) = 3$ **b.** $f(-10) = -27$ **c.** $x = 3$

 d. Domain: The set of all real numbers

 Range: The set of all real numbers

53. **a.** $h(15) = \dfrac{31}{3}$ **b.** $h(-9) = -\dfrac{17}{3}$ **c.** $x = \dfrac{11}{2}$

 d. Domain: The set of all real numbers

 Range: The set of all real numbers

55. **a.** $g(2) = -18$ **b.** $g(-11) = -18$

 c. Domain: The set of all real numbers

 Range: {−18}

57. Ashlyn set $x = 20$ and solved for $f(20)$. The correct solution is $x = 3$.

59. Alicyn should not have restricted the domain and range. The correct solution is:

 Domain: The set of all real numbers

 Range: The set of all real numbers

61. **a.** $f(2) = 1.6$

 b. $f(-14) = -49.6$

 c. $x = -1.625$

 d. Domain: The set of all real numbers

 Range: The set of all real numbers

63. **a.** $h(105) = 1970$

 b. $x = -\dfrac{320}{7}$

 c. Domain: The set of all real numbers

 Range: The set of all real numbers

65. **a.** $f(3) = 2$

 b. $f(-2) = -8$

 c. $x = -1$

 d. Domain: The set of all real numbers

 Range: The set of all real numbers

 e. Vertical intercept (0, −4)

 Horizontal intercept (2, 0)

67. **a.** $f(25) = 50$

 b. $f(100) = 275$

 c. $x = 75$

d. Domain: The set of all real numbers

Range: The set of all real numbers

e. Vertical intercept $(0, -25)$

Horizontal intercept $(8, 0)$

69. a. $h(2) = 3$

b. $h(5) = -4$

c. $x = -0.2$ and $x = 4.2$

d. Domain: The set of all real numbers

Range: $(-\infty, 3]$

e. Vertical intercept $(0, 0)$

Horizontal intercepts $(0, 0)$ and $(4, 0)$

Section 8.5

1. a. $T(0) = 712.3$, so in 2000, the average American ate 712.3 pounds of fruits and vegetables.

b. $F(0) = 289.6$, so in 2000, the average American ate 289.6 pounds of fruit.

c. $T(0) - F(0) = 422.7$, so in 2000, the average American ate 422.7 pounds of vegetables.

d. Let $V(y)$ be the average number of pounds of vegetables each American eats per year.

$$V(y) = -y + 422.7$$

e. $V(0) = 422.7$, so in 2000, the average American ate 422.7 pounds of vegetables.

f. $V(10) = 412.7$, so in 2010, the average American will eat approximately 412.7 pounds of vegetables. $V(15) = 407.7$, so in 2015, the average American will eat approximately 407.7 pounds of vegetables. $V(20) = 402.7$, so in 2020, the average American will eat approximately 402.7 pounds of vegetables.

3. a. Let $O(t)$ be the per capita consumption of milk products in gallons per person other than whole milk in the United States t years since 2000.

$$O(t) = -0.08t + 14.33$$

b. $W(5) = 7.04$, so 7.04 gallons of whole milk were consumed per person in the United States in 2005.

c. $O(5) = 13.93$, so 13.93 gallons of milk products other than whole milk were consumed per person in the United States in 2005. $O(10) = 13.53$, so 13.53 gallons of milk products other than whole milk were consumed per person in the United States in 2010.

d. Slope $= -0.21$. The amount of whole milk consumed per person in the United States is decreasing by approximately 0.21 gallon per year.

e. M-intercept: $(0, 22.42)$. In 2000, 22.42 gallons of milk products were consumed per person in the United States.

5. $U(t) - M(t)$ is the number of women in millions the United States t years since 1900.

7. $S(d) \cdot T(d)$ is the miles driven on day d of a cross-country trip.

9. $\dfrac{D}{U}(t)$ is the average amount of national debt per person in the United States in dollars t years since 1900.

11. $U(t) \cdot D(t)$ is the total amount of personal debt in the United States t years since 1900.

13. a. $M(t) + F(t) = 100$ because the percentage must add up to 100.

b. $F(t) = 0.24t + 11.36$

c. $F(5) = 12.56$. In 2005, approximately 12.56% of jail inmates in United States federal and state prisons were female.

d. Slope $= 0.24$. The percentage of jail inmates who are female in U.S. federal and state prisons is increasing by approximately 0.24 percentage point per year.

e. M-intercept $= (0, 88.64)$. The percentage of jail inmates who are male in U.S. federal and state prisons was 88.64% in 2000.

15. a. $O(t) = 0.433t + 62.67$

b. $R(t) = -0.433t + 37.33$

c. $R(20) = 28.67$. In 2010, approximately 28.67% of occupied housing units should be renter occupied.

d. Slope $= -0.433$. The number of housing units that are renter occupied is decreasing by 0.433 percentage point each year.

17. a. Let $N(w)$ be the total area in square inches of a Norman window with a height of 75 inches for the rectangle part and a width of w inches.

$$N(w) = \frac{\pi}{8}w^2 + 75w$$

b. $N(36) = 3208.94$. A Norman window with a height of 75 inches for the rectangular part and a width of 36 inches will have a total area of 3208.94 square inches.

19. a. $-3x + 17$ **b.** $9x - 1$

c. $-18x^2 - 21x + 72$ **d.** $\dfrac{3x + 8}{-6x + 9}$

21. a. $\dfrac{5}{2}x - \dfrac{2}{5}$ **b.** $\dfrac{3}{2}x - \dfrac{4}{5}$

c. $x^2 + \dfrac{1}{10}x - \dfrac{3}{25}$ **d.** $\dfrac{\frac{1}{2}x + \frac{1}{5}}{2x - \frac{3}{5}}$

23. a. $x^2 + 7x + 15$ **b.** $x^2 + x + 5$

c. $3x^3 + 17x^2 + 50x + 50$ **d.** $\dfrac{3x + 5}{x^2 + 4x + 10}$

25. $f(x) + g(x) = 10x - 2$. Jose set the expression equal to zero and solved for x.

27. a. $R(10) = 153.9$. In 2010, IBM had revenue of $153.9 billion for goods sold. $C(10) = 97.1$. In 2010, IBM had a cost of $97.1 billion for selling goods.

b. Let $P(t)$ be the profit of IBM in billions of dollars t years since 2000.

$$P(t) = 0.6t^2 - 4.8t + 44.8$$

c. $P(10) = 56.8$. According to the model, IBM's profit in 2010 was approximately $56.8 billion.

29. a. $R(11) = 11,343.2$. The revenue earned by Pearson Publishing Co. in 2011 is approximately 11,343.2 million British pounds. $P(11) = 6160.8$. The profit earned by Pearson Publishing Co. in 2011 is approximately 6160.8 million British pounds.

 b. Let $C(t)$ be the publishing costs at Pearson Publishing Co. in millions of British pounds t years since 2000.

$$C(t) = 76.2t^2 - 645t + 3057.2$$

 c. $C(11) = 5182.4$. The costs at Pearson Publishing Co. for 2011 are approximately 5182.4 million British pounds.

31. a. $S(100) = 60$. Car stereo producers are willing to supply 60 thousand car stereos if the price is set at $100.

 b. Let $R(p)$ be the revenue in thousands of dollars from selling the supplied car stereos at a price of p dollars.

$$R(p) = 0.009p^3 - 0.5p^2 + 20p$$

 c. If car stereos are sold for $90 each, the projected revenue will be about $4,311,000.00.

33. a. $S(25) = 33.75$. Car manufacturers are willing to supply about 33,750 minivans if they can be sold for $25,000 each.

 b. Let $R(p)$ be the revenue in millions of dollars from selling minivans at a price of p thousand dollars.

$$R(p) = 0.11p^3 - 3.2p^2 + 45p$$

 c. $R(31) = 1596.81$. If minivans sell for $31,000 each, the projected revenue will be about $1.6 billion.

35. a. $I(5) = 114,111$. There were about 114,111 immigrants admitted to the United States as permanent residents under refugee acts in 1995.

 b. $E(5) = 47,414$. There were about 47,414 European immigrants admitted to the United States as permanent residents under refugee acts in 1995.

 c. Let $N(t)$ be the number of non-European immigrants admitted to the United States as permanent residents under refugee acts t years since 1990.

$$N(t) = -11,422t^2 + 138,443t - 339,968$$

 d. $N(8) = 36,568$. There were about 36,568 non-European immigrants admitted to the United States as permanent residents under refugee acts in 1998.

37. a. Let $U(t)$ be the number of U.S. residents in millions who are Caucasian and under 18 years old t years since 1990.

$$U(t) = -0.014t^2 + 0.524t + 51.579$$

 b. $U(12) = 55.851$. In 2002, there were approximately 56 million Caucasian U.S. residents who were under 18 years old.

39. a. 2   **b.** 44

 c. -483 **d.** $-\dfrac{23}{21}$

41. a. $\dfrac{23}{5} = 4.6$ **b.** $\dfrac{11}{5} = 2.2$

 c. $\dfrac{102}{25} = 4.08$ **d.** $\dfrac{6}{17} \approx 0.35$

43. a. 75   **b.** 35

 c. 1100   **d.** $\dfrac{4}{11}$

45. c

47. a

49. a. $9x + 8$ **b.** 26

 c. $20x^2 + 33x + 7$ **d.** 1551

51. a. $4x^2 - 1$ **b.** 15

 c. $4x^3 + 9x^2 + 3x + 2$ **d.** 76

53. a. Domain: The set of all real numbers.

 b. Domain: The set of all real numbers.

 c. Domain: The set of all real numbers.

55. a. Domain: The set of all real numbers.

 b. Domain: The set of all real numbers.

 c. Domain: The set of all real numbers.

57. a. Domain: The set of all real numbers.

 b. Domain: The set of all real numbers.

 c. Domain: The set of all real numbers.

59. Domain: The set of all real numbers except $x = 0$.

61. Domain: The set of all real numbers except $x = 3$.

63. Domain: The set of all real numbers except $b = -11$.

65. Domain: The set of all real numbers except $t = -\dfrac{5}{4}$.

67. Domain: The set of all real numbers except $a = -\dfrac{7}{2}$, $a = 3$.

69. Domain: The set of all real numbers except $n = -4, n = -10$.

71. Domain: The set of all real numbers except $m = -3$ and $m = -4$.

73. Domain: The set of all real numbers.

75. Domain: The set of all real numbers except $t = -7$ and $t = 7$.

77. Domain: The set of all real numbers except $r = -3$ and $r = -2$.

79. Domain: The set of all real numbers except $t = 5$ and $t = 2$.

81. Domain: The set of all real numbers.

83. a. Domain: The set of all real numbers except $x = -5$ and $x = 7$.

 b. $f(0) = 0$

 c. $f(x) = 5$ when $x \approx -4.5$ and $x \approx 7.5$

85. a. Domain: The set of all real numbers except $x = -3$ and $x = 4$.

 b. $h(1) \approx -1$

 c. $h(-4) \approx 1.9$

 d. $h(x) = -2$ when $x \approx -1.9$ and $x \approx 2.8$

87. Domain: The set of all real numbers except $x = -3$. The value represents a vertical asymptote because the factor $(x + 3)$ does not simplify with the numerator.

89. Domain: The set of all real numbers except $x = -3$ and $x = -1$. The values represent vertical asymptotes because the factors $(x + 3)$ and $(x + 1)$ do not simplify with the numerator.

91. Domain: The set of all real numbers except $x = -5$ and $x = -2$. The value $x = -5$ represents a vertical asymptote because the factor $(x + 5)$ does not simplify with the numerator. The value $x = -2$ represents a hole because the factor $(x + 2)$ simplifies with the numerator.

93. Domain: The set of all real numbers except $x = \frac{4}{3}$ and $x = -\frac{5}{2}$. The values represent vertical asymptotes because the factors $(3x - 4)$ and $(2x + 5)$ do not simplify with the numerator.

95. Domain: The set of all real numbers except $x = -1$ and $x = -2$. The value $x = -1$ represents a vertical asymptote because the factor $(x + 1)$ does not simplify with the numerator. The value $x = -2$ represents a hole because the factor $(x + 2)$ simplifies with the numerator.

97. Domain: The set of all real numbers except $x = 0$, $x = -2$, and $x = 4$. The values $x = -2$ and $x = 4$ represent vertical asymptotes because the factors $(x + 2)$ and $(x - 4)$ do not simplify with the numerator. The value $x = 0$ represents a hole because the factor (x) simplifies with the numerator.

99. Domain: The set of all real numbers except $x = 4$ and $x = -4$. The value $x = 4$ represents a vertical asymptote because the factor $(x - 4)$ does not simplify with the numerator. The value $x = -4$ represents a hole because the factor $(x + 4)$ simplifies with the numerator.

101. Domain: The set of all real numbers. There are no vertical asymptotes or holes.

Section **8.6**

1. a. $f(g(x)) = 12x + 22$ **b.** $g(f(x)) = 12x + 33$

3. a. $f \circ g(x) = -18x + 35$ **b.** $g \circ f(x) = -18x - 39$

5. a. $8x + 29$ **b.** $8x + 16$

7. a. $-56x + 116$ **b.** $-56x - 73$

9. a. Let $K(w)$ be the total weekly cost in dollars for week w of production.

$$K(w) = C(T(w)) = 875w + 10,250$$

b. $T(5) = 5500$. There were 5500 toys produced during week 5.

c. $C(5000) = 13,750$. The total weekly cost from production of 5000 toys per week is $13,750.

d. $K(7) = 16,375$. The total weekly cost of production for week 7 was $16,375.

e. $K(w) = 18,500$ when $w \approx 9.4$. The weekly cost will reach and surpass $18,500 in week 10 of production.

11. a. $V(10) = 4$. A West Tech employee will get 4 weeks of vacation per year after working with the company for 10 years.

b. $C(4) = 6575$. West Tech's cost for a 10-year employee's vacation is $6575.

c. Let $K(y)$ be the cost for vacation taken by an employee who has been with the company for y years.

$$K(y) = C(V(y)) = 375y + 2825$$

d. $K(20) = 10,325$. West Tech's cost for a 20-year employee's vacation is $10,325.

e. $K(30) = 14,075$. West Tech's cost for a 30-year employee's vacation is $14,075.

13. a. $A(4) = 6600$. On the fourth day of the Renaissance fair, there were 6600 people in attendance.

b. $P(6600) = 10700$. On the fourth day of the Renaissance fair, a profit of $10,700 was made.

c. Let $T(d)$ be the profit in dollars made at the Renaissance fair d days after the fair opens.

$$T(d) = P(A(d)) = -800d^2 + 7000d - 4500$$

d. $T(3) = 9300$. The Renaissance fair made $9300 profit on the third day of the fair.

e. $T(1) + T(2) + T(3) + T(4) + T(5) + T(6) + T(7) = 52,500$. If the Renaissance fair lasts a total of 7 days, the total profit would be $52,500.

15. $P(B(t)) = $ profit in thousands of dollars for Pride Bike Co. in year t.

17. $H(T(d)) = $ number of homeless people who seek space at the homeless shelter on day d of the week.

19. a. $x - \frac{1}{10}$ **b.** $x - \frac{1}{5}$

21. a. $2.4276x + 6.7732$ **b.** $2.4276x + 14.9152$

23. a. $x^2 + 6$ **b.** $x^2 + 2x + 6$

25. a. $x^2 + 5$ **b.** $x^2 - 2x + 7$

27. a. $3x^2 + 12x + 35$ **b.** $9x^2 + 42x + 55$

29. a. $4x^2 + x + 3$ **b.** $4x^2 + 17x + 19$

31. $f(g(x)) = 21x + 14$. Lilybell did $f(x)g(x)$.

33. $f(g(x)) = 21x + 14$. Colter did $g(f(x))$.

35. a. -55 **b.** -129

37. a. $\frac{19}{10} = 1.9$ **b.** $\frac{9}{5} = 1.8$

39. a. -0.5096 **b.** 7.6324

41. a. 31 **b.** 41

43. a. 14 **b.** 10

45. a. 170 **b.** 490

47. a. 21 **b.** 69

49. $N(t) = T(t) - K(t) = $ number of people over 12 years old who go on the tour in year t.

51. $A(T(t) - K(t)) = $ cost for all people over 12 years old who traveled on the tour in year t.

53. $C(K(t)) - A(T(t) - K(t)) = $ difference between the cost for all children under 12 years old and the cost for all people over 12 years old who traveled on the tour in year t.

55. a. $f(x)g(x) = 27x^2 + 69x + 14$

b. $f(x) + g(x) = 12x + 9$

c. $f(g(x)) = 27x + 65$

57. a. $f(3) + g(3) = -15$

   b. $f(4)g(4) = -420$

   c. $f(g(7)) = -134$

59. a. $f(g(x)) = \dfrac{1}{6}x + \dfrac{5}{6}$

   b. $f(42)g(42) = 318.75$

   c. $f(x) + g(x) = \dfrac{11}{12}x + \dfrac{13}{12}$

61. a. $f(g(x)) = 5.25x + 18$

   b. $g(f(6)) = 56.25$

   c. $g(x) - f(x) = 2x + 4.5$

Chapter 8 Review Exercises

1. a. $h = 9.75$ in. The height after 1 week (7days) is 9.75 inches.

   b. 10 days. The course grass attendants should cut the grass in the rough 10 days before the tournament.

2. Let C be the cost in dollars of the satellite phone service and m be the number of minutes used.

   a. $C = 10m + 10$

   b. $C = 40$. A 3-minute call cost $40.

   c. $m = 29$. The satellite call can last 29 minutes for $300.

3. Let C be the cost in dollars of renting a Bobcat for h hours.

   a. $C = 40h + 15$

   b. $C = 95$. Renting a Bobcat for 2 hours will cost $95.

   c. $C = 975$. A three-day rental of a Bobcat will cost $975.

4. $C =$ the cost to produce putters, n is the number of putters.

   a. $C = 24.44n + 477.80$

   b. Vertical intercept is (0, 477.80). It cost $477.80 to produce 0 putters.

   c. $C = \$2921.80$. The cost to produce 100 putters is $2921.80.

   d. Domain: [0, 100];   Range: [477.80, 2921.80]

   e. Slope = 24.44. For every putter produced the cost increases by $24.44.

5. $P =$ profit for Costco Wholesale Corporation in millions of dollars, t the years since 2000.

   a. $P = 634.2t + 3510.6$

   b. 2008. The gross profit for Costco Wholesale will be 9 billion dollars in 2008.

   c. 9218.4 million. The gross profit for Costco Wholesale in 2009 will be 9.2184 billion dollars.

   d. Domain: [0, 9];   Range: [3510.6, 9218.4]

   e. Slope 634.2 million per year. The gross profit increases by 634.2 million for each year of operation.

6. a. Let P be the percent of full-time workers in private industry who filed an injury case t years since 2000.

$$P(t) = -0.167t + 5.2$$

   b. Slope $= -0.167$. The percent of full-time workers in private industry who filed an injury case is decreasing by about 0.167 percentage point per year.

   c. $P(3) = 4.699$. In 2003 about 4.7 percent of full-time workers in private industry filed an injury case.

   d. Vertical intercept (0, 5.2). In 2000 about 5.2% of full-time workers in private industry filed an injury case.

   e. Horizontal intercept (31.14, 0). In about 2031 there will be no injury cases filed by full-time workers in private industry. This is probably model breakdown since there will most likely always be some injury cases.

7. a. Let S be the number of kindergarten through twelfth grade students in millions in Texas public schools t years since 2000.

$$S(t) = 0.08t + 4$$

   b. Slope = 0.08. The number of kindergarten through twelfth grade students in Texas public schools is increasing by about 0.08 million (80 thousand) per year.

   c. $S(11) = 4.88$. In 2011 Texas can expect to have about 4.88 million kindergarten through twelfth grade students in public schools.

8. a. 7.1 million candles will be produced in 2015.

   b. 5.98 million candles will be produced in 2013.

   c. 10 million candles will be produced in 2020.

9. a. (0, 4)   **b.** (1.3, 0)

   c. Slope $= -3$ **d.** $f(4) = -8$

   e. $f(x) = 16$ when $x = -4$

   f. $f(x) = -3x + 4$

10. a. $(0, -5)$ **b.** (3.3, 0)   **c.** Slope $= \dfrac{3}{2}$

   d. $h(-2) = -8$ **e.** $h(x) = -2$ when $x = 2$

   f. $h(x) = \dfrac{3}{2}x - 5$

11. The electricity cost for using holiday lights 6 hours a day is $13.

12. a. $P(10) = 10{,}279$. In 2010 the population of Michigan will be about 10,279 thousand.

   b. The population of Michigan will reach 11,000 thousand in about 2034. This may be model breakdown if the current population growth does not continue.

13. a. $f(10) = 12$ **b.** $x = 4$

   c. Domain: The set of all real numbers

   Range: The set of all real numbers

14. a. $h(12) = 6$ **b.** $x = 33$

   c. Domain: The set of all real numbers

   Range: The set of all real numbers

15. a. $g(3) = 12$ **b.** $g(-20) = 12$

c. Domain: The set of real numbers

Range: $\{12\}$

16. a. $f(5) = 10.75$ **b.** $x = -10.4$

c. Domain: The set of all real numbers;   Range: The set of all real numbers

17. Let $P(t)$ be the monthly profit in dollars for Hope's Pottery when v vases are produced and sold in the month.

$$P(t) = 90v - 5000$$

18. a. Let $P(t)$ be the total prescription drug sales in the United States in billions of dollars t years since 2000.

$$P(t) = 17t + 149.4$$

b. Let $M(t)$ be the amount of mail-order prescription drug sales in the United States in billions of dollars t years since 2000.

$$M(t) = 4.75t + 21.7$$

c. $P(10) = 319.4$. In 2010, the total prescription drug sales in the United States were about \$319.4 billion.

d. $M(10) = 69.2$. In 2010, the mail-order prescription drug sales in the United States were about \$69.2 billion.

e. Let $N(t)$ be the non-mail-order prescription drug sales in the United States in billions of dollars t years since 2000.

$$N(t) = 12.25t + 127.7$$

f. $N(9) = 237.95$. In 2009, the non-mail-order prescription drug sales in the United States were about \$237.95 billion.

$N(15) = 311.45$. In 2015, the non-mail-order prescription drug sales in the United States will be about \$311.45 billion.

19. a. $J(9) = 778.31$. In 1999, the federal funding for research and development at Johns Hopkins University was about \$778.31 million.

$W(t) = 382.79$. In 1999, the federal funding for research and development at the University of Washington was about \$382.79 million.

b. Let $D(t)$ be the difference between the federal funding at Johns Hopkins University and the University of Washington in millions of dollars t years since 1990.

$$D(t) = 13.38t^3 - 267.06t^2 + 1749.66t - 3473.58$$

c. $D(10) = 697.02$. In 2000, Johns Hopkins University had about \$697.02 million more federal funding for research and development than the University of Washington.

20. $U(t) - C(t)$. The number of adults 20 years old or older in the United States t years since 1900.

21. $(R - C)(l)$. The profit in thousands of dollars for Luxury Limousines, Inc. to produce and sell l limousines per year.

22. $ES(t)$. The total number of sick days taken by Disneyland employees in year t.

23. $W(E(t))$. The annual workers compensation insurance costs in dollars at Disneyland in year t.

24. $(M + R)(t)$. The total amount spent on cancer treatments and research in the United States in year t.

25. a. $2x + 11$ **b.** $10x - 5$

c. $-24x^2 + 36x + 24$

26. a. $-2x + 68$

Domain: The set of all real numbers.

b. $-32x$

Domain: The set of all real numbers.

c. $-255x^2 - 68x + 1156$

Domain: The set of all real numbers.

d. $\dfrac{15x + 34}{-17x + 34}$

Domain: The set of all real numbers. except $x = 2$.

27. a. $4.4x - 6.4$

Domain: The set of all real numbers.

b. $-3.6x + 7.6$

Domain: The set of all real numbers.

c. $1.6x^2 - 0.4x - 4.2$

Domain: The set of all real numbers.

28. a. $\dfrac{16}{7}$ **b.** $\dfrac{2}{7}$ **c.** $\dfrac{9}{7}$

29. a. Let $L(t)$ be the number of people in California's labor force in millions t years since 1990.

$$L(t) = 0.37t + 13.2$$

b. Let $U(t)$ be the number of people in California who are considered unemployed in millions t years since 1990.

$$U(t) = -0.07t + 1.56$$

c. In 2005, there were about 18.75 million people in California's labor force.

d. In 2005, there were about 510,000 people in California who are considered unemployed. This might be too low and might be model breakdown.

e. Let $P(t)$ be the percentage as a decimal of California's labor force that is considered unemployed t years since 1990.

$$P(t) = \frac{U(t)}{L(t)} = \frac{-0.07t + 1.56}{0.37t + 13.2}$$

f. In 1998, 6.2% of California's labor force was considered unemployed.

In 1999, 5.6% of California's labor force was considered unemployed.

In 2000, 5.1% of California's labor force was considered unemployed.

In 2005, 2.7% of California's labor force was considered unemployed. This might be too low and might be model breakdown.

30. Domain: The set of all real numbers except $x = 9$

31. Domain: The set of all real numbers except $x = -5$ and $x = 3$

32. Domain: The set of all real numbers except $x = -\dfrac{3}{2}$ and $x = 5$

33. Domain: The set of all real numbers

34. Domain: The set of all real numbers except $x = -6$ and $x = 4$

35. Domain: The set of all real numbers except $x = -3$ and $x = 6$

36. a. $-24x + 51$ **b.** $-24x - 4$

37. a. $-255x + 544$ **b.** $-255x - 544$

38. a. $\dfrac{8}{5}x - \dfrac{11}{5}$ **b.** $\dfrac{8}{5}x - \dfrac{23}{5}$

39. a. $\dfrac{6}{7}$ **b.** $\dfrac{-31}{7}$

40. a. -6.1 **b.** -7.5

     c. -4.76 **d.** -1.58

     e. 6.15

41. a. -3.58 **b.** 0.58

     c. 3.12 **d.** -3.305

Chapter 8 Test

1. a. Let C be the number of work-related injury cases in thousands in the U.S. private industry t years since 2000.

$$C(t) = -79.3t + 4333$$

     b. $C(9) = 3619.3$. In 2009 there were about 3619.3 thousand work-related injury cases in the U.S. private industry.

     c. Slope $= -79.3$ The number of work-related injury cases in the U.S. private industry is decreasing about 79.3 thousand cases per year.

     d. Domain: $[0, 8]$

     Range: $[3698.6, 4333]$

     e. In 1992 there were about 5 million work-related injury cases in the U.S. private industry.

2. a. Six months after starting to sell paintings John Clark will sell approximately 42 paintings.

     b. John Clark will sell 50 painting during the 10th month after starting to sell paintings.

3. a. Let R be the total revenue in millions of dollars for Apple Inc. t years since 2000.

$$R(t) = 5518t - 13793$$

     b. Vertical intercept $(0, -13793)$. In 2000 Apple Inc. had total revenue of $-\$13,793$ million. This is model breakdown since Apple could not have a negative revenue.

     c. Domain: $[3, 9]$;   Range: $[2761, 35869]$

     d. $R(10) = 41387$. In 2010 Apple Inc. had a total revenue of about $\$41,387$ million.

     e. Apple Inc.'s total revenue was about $\$30$ billion in 2008.

     f. Slope $= 5518$. Apple Inc.'s total revenue increases about $\$5518$ million dollars per year.

4. Domain: The set of all real numbers

     Range: The set of all real numbers

5. In 2010 the population of New York will be about 19.4 million.

6. a. To earn a 70% on the exam you need to study about 19 hours.

b. To earn a 100% on this exam, you need to study about 25 hours.

7. Domain: The set of all real numbers

8. a. $h(35) = 26$

     b. $x = -\dfrac{7}{2}$

     c. Domain: The set of all real numbers

     Range: The set of all real numbers

9. a. $g(6) = -9$

     b. Domain: The set of all real numbers

     Range: $\{-9\}$

10. A relation may not be a function if the input value was paired with more than one output value.

11. a. $T(9) = 16.74$. In 1999, New Zealand spent about 16.74 million New Zealand dollars on the treatment of diabetes.

     b. $R(t) = 10$ when $t \approx 7.3$. New Zealand spent about 10 million New Zealand dollars on diabetes research in 1997.

     c. Let $D(t)$ be the total New Zealand spent on diabetes research and treatment in millions of New Zealand dollars t years since 1990.

$$D(t) = R(t) + T(t) = 2.4t + 7.36$$

     d. $D(10) = 31.36$. New Zealand spent about 31.36 million New Zealand dollars on research and treatment of diabetes in 2000.

12. a. $f(x) - g(x) = 2x + 24$

     b. $f(x)g(x) = 8x^2 + 6x - 119$

     c. $f(g(x)) = 8x - 11$

13. a. $(f + g)(4) = 14.15$

     b. $fg(-2) = 36.075$

     c. $f \circ g(6) = 20.485$

     d. $g(f(0)) = -2.82$

14. a. $S(10) = 544.6$. In 2000, there were approximately 544.6 thousand science/engineering graduate students in doctoral programs.

     b. Let $M(t)$ be the number of male science/engineering graduate students in doctoral programs in thousands t years since 2000.

$$M(t) = 0.8t^2 + 0.7t + 225.7$$

     c. $M(10) = 312.7$. In 2010, there were approximately 312.7 thousand male science/engineering graduate students in doctoral programs.

15. a. $P(6) = 51.8$. In 2006 about 51.8% of murders were committed by using a handgun.

     b. Let $H(t)$ be the number of murders in thousands that were committed by using a handgun t years since 2000.

$$H(t) = M(t)\frac{P(t)}{100} = -0.00006t^3 - 0.0013t^5 + 0.0095t^4$$
$$- 0.075t^3 + 0.58t^2 - 1.43t + 6.78$$

  c. $H(7) = 7.6$. In 2007, about 7.6 thousand murders were committed by using a handgun.

16. $(T - B)(t)$ is the number of girls attending the tennis camp in year t.

17. $M(B(t))$ is the number of boys' matches at the camp in year t.

18. $C(T(t))$ is the total cost for the camp in year t.

19. $A(t) \cdot M(T(t))$ is the time in minutes it takes for all the matches to be played in year t.

20. **a.** Domain: The set of all real numbers except
     $x = -9$ and $x = 3$.

  b. Domain: The set of all real numbers except
     $x = -2$ and $x = 4$.

CHAPTER 9

Section **9.1**

1. $x = 1, x = -3$ **3.** $x = 4, x = 2$

5. $x = 5, x = -1$ **7.** $x = \frac{1}{3}, x = -1$

9. $x = 1, x = 9$ **11.** $x = \pm 12$

13. $h = 8$ or $h = -22$ **15.** $b = 20$ or $b = 4$

17. $r = 7$ or $r = -29$ **19.** $a = 2, a = -4$

21. $x = 11, x = 1$ **23.** $m = 7, m = -1$

25. $y = 9, y = -17$ **27.** $x = 10, x = 0$

29. $x = 8, x = 2$ **31.** $x = \frac{41}{3}$ or $x = \frac{31}{3}$

33. No solution.   **35.** No solution.

37. No solution.

39. Ricardo should travel at an average speed of 45 mph or 75 mph.

41. Ricardo will be 50 miles away from Fresno after about 10.83 hours and again after about 12.5 hours.

43. $x = 8$ **45.** No solution

47. $x = \frac{5}{2}, x = \frac{-7}{2}$ **49.** No solution

Section **9.2**

1. $-6 < x < 6$ **3.** $x \leq -3$ or $x \geq 3$

5. $x < -5$ or $x > -2$ **7.** $-3 \leq x \leq 8$

9. $x < -6$ or $x > 5$

11. **a.** $-4 < x < 4$
    b. $x < -4$ or $x > 4$

13. **a.** $0 \leq x \leq 4$
    b. $x \leq 0$ or $x \geq 4$

15. **a.** $-5 < x < 5$
    b. $x < -5$ or $x > 5$

17. $-5 < x < 5$

19. $-1 \leq h \leq 7$

21. $-5 < b < 7$

23. The acceptable lengths of this coupler are $2.999 \leq L \leq 3.001$ centimeters.

25. The acceptable pressures for this experiment are $19.5 \leq P \leq 20.5$ psi.

27. $-3 < x$ or $x > 3$

29. $p \leq 2$ or $p \geq 6$

31. $y < -9$ or $y > -3$

33. $h < 64$ or $h > 74$. Men's heights that are less than 64 inches or greater than 74 inches are considered unusual.

35. **a.** IQ scores that are below 68 or above 132 would be considered unusual.

  b. Yes. Albert Einstein's IQ was unusual. His IQ was greater than 132.

37. $-10 < r < -2$

39. $x > 8$

41. No solution.

43. $m < -9$ or $m > 7$

45. $x < -24$

47. All real numbers.

49. $2 \leq x \leq 6$

51. $x < \frac{1}{2}$ or $x > \frac{7}{2}$

53. No solution.

55. $x \leq \dfrac{4}{3}$

57. $-16 \leq x \leq 4$

Section **9.3**

1. $2 < x < 7$

3. $x < 8$

5. $x \leq 2$ or $8 \leq x \leq 11$

7. $(5, \infty)$

9. $[-5, 8]$

11. $(-\infty, 5)$ or $(9, \infty)$

13. a.

b. $(-3, 8)$

c. $-3 < x < 8$

15. a.

b. $(-\infty, 5]$ or $[9, \infty)$

c. $x \leq -5$ or $x \geq 9$

17. a.

b. $(-5, 0)$ or $(6, \infty)$

c. $-5 < x < 0$ or $x > 6$

19. a.

b. $[-4, 4]$

c. $-4 \leq x \leq 4$

21. a.

b. $(-\infty, -5)$ or $(-2, \infty)$

c. $x < -5$ or $x > -2$

23. a.

b. $(-\infty, 3]$ or $[5, \infty)$

c. $x \leq 3$ or $x \geq 5$

25. a.

b. $[-2, 9]$

c. $-2 \leq x \leq 9$

27. a.

b. $(-6, -3)$ or $(0, \infty)$

c. $-6 < x < -3$ or $x > 0$

29. a.

b. $(-\infty, -5)$ or $(0, 2)$

c. $x < -5$ or $0 < x < 2$

31. a.

b. $(-\infty, -4]$ or $\left[-\dfrac{3}{2}, \infty\right)$

c. $x \leq -4$ or $x \geq -\dfrac{3}{2}$

33. a.

b. $\left[-\dfrac{5}{3}, -\dfrac{1}{2}\right]$

c. $-\dfrac{5}{3} \leq x \leq -\dfrac{1}{2}$

35. The rock is more than 64 feet off the ground between zero and 3 seconds after being thrown.

37. To make at least \$8000 for the charity the club should sell the discount cards for a price of \$11.00 up to \$17.00.

39. When 2 to 20 surf boards are sold the company will break even or make a profit.

41. a.

b. $(-\infty, -5)$ or $(-2, \infty)$

c. $x < -5$ or $x > -2$

43. a.

b. $(3, 7)$

c. $3 < x < 7$

45. a.

b. $(-4, 1]$

c. $-4 < x \leq 1$

47. a.

b. $(-\infty, 4]$ or $(9, \infty)$

c. $x \le 4$ or $x > 9$

49. Henry chose the wrong interval and should have included the 1 in the solution set. $[1, 7)$

51. Jennie should not have included the -3 in the solution set. $(-3, 5]$

53. a.

b. $(-7, -3)$ or $(5, \infty)$

c. $-7 < x < -3$ or $x > 5$

55. a.

b. $(-\infty, -5)$ or $(-2, 4)$

c. $x < -5$ or $-2 < x < 4$

57. a.

b. $(-\infty, 2)$ or $[4, 8)$

c. $x < 2$ or $4 \le x < 8$

59. a.

b. $(4, 8]$

c. $4 < x \le 8$

61. a.

b. $(-3, \infty)$

c. $x > -3$

63. a.

b. $(-6, -3)$

c. $-6 < x < -3$

65. a.

b. $(-\infty, -9)$ or $(-2, 5)$

c. $x < -9$ or $-2 < x < 5$

67. a.

b. $(-8, -5)$ or $(-4, \infty)$

c. $-8 < x < -5$ or $x > -4$

69. a.

b. $[-1, 1]$ or $(3, 5)$

c. $-1 \le x \le 1$ or $3 < x < 5$

71. a.

b. $(-\infty, -6]$ or $(-2, -1)$ or $[6, \infty)$

c. $x \le -6$ or $-2 < x < -1$ or $x \ge 6$

73. a.

b. $(-7, 5)$ or $(7, 9)$

c. $-7 < x < 5$ or $7 < x < 9$

Section **9.4**

1. A 61″ tall person weighing 105 pounds falls into the normal range.

3. A 5′9″ (69″) tall person is considered overweight if the person weighs above 172 pounds.

5. A person who weighs 150 pounds must be between 5′5″ and 6′3″ to fall in the normal range.

7. A person who is 67″ tall has a normal weight range of 120 pounds to 160 pounds.

9. They can build at most 370 mountain bikes per month.

11. Yes, they can build 400 cruisers and 100 mountain bikes per month. This is at the 500 bike per month limit and under the cost limitations for a month.

13. a. Let C be the total number of cruisers Bicycles Galore produces monthly and let M be the total number of mountain bikes Bicycles Galore produces monthly.

$$C + M \le 500 \quad 65C + 120M \ge 40,000$$

b. Bicycles Galore will be able to meet a demand by the board of directors for $40,000 in profit per month. Any combination of mountain bikes and cruisers in the overlapping shaded region will meet the board's demand.

c. They must make 137 mountain bikes and 363 cruisers to make $40,000 profit. If they make more mountain bikes they will make more profit.

15.

17.

19.

21.

23.

25.

27. $y \leq 2x - 3$

29. $y > -\dfrac{3}{2}x + 6$

31. $y > -\dfrac{1}{2}x + 9$

33. $y \leq -x + 1$

35. Let A be the amount in dollars Juanita invests in the account paying 4.5% interest, and let B be the amount in dollars invested in the account paying 3.75% interest.

$$A + B \leq 750,000 \quad 0.045A + 0.0375B \geq 30,000$$

37. a. Let P be the number of power bars, and let D be the number of sports drinks that need to be consumed by the athletes.

$$240P + 300D \geq 2000 \quad 30P + 70D \geq 350$$

b. If a racer carries 4 drinks, he or she must also carry 4 power bars.

39.

41.

43.   No solution

45.

47.

49.

Chapter 9 Review Exercises

1. $x = 5, x = -5$

2. $y = 61, y = -61$

3. $a = 1, a = -13$

4. $x = 11$ or $x = -49$

5. $x = 27$ or $x = -13$

6. $m = 10.5, m = 3.7$

7. No solution

8. No solution

9. $x = \dfrac{13}{2}, x = \dfrac{-7}{2}$

10. $x = \dfrac{6}{5}, x = \dfrac{-8}{5}$

11. $x = 23.5$ or $x = -26.5$

12. $y = \dfrac{32}{3}, y = -8$

13. $x = 24$ or $x = -10$

14. $x = \dfrac{7}{2}, x = -2$

15. Patsy will be 60 miles from Davenport, Iowa, after about 4.83 hours and again after about 6.68 hours.

16. Tracy will be 100 miles from Albuquerque, New Mexico, after about 26.97 hours and again after about 30.05 hours.

17. $-5 < x < 4$

18. $-8 \leq x \leq -1$

19. $x < -8$ or $x > 1$

20. $x \leq -2$ or $x \geq 1$

21. $-8.5 < x < 8.5$

22. $-3 \leq w \leq 3$

23. $x < -6.5$ or $x > 6.5$

24. $y \leq \dfrac{-2}{3}$ or $y \geq \dfrac{2}{3}$

25. $x \leq -15$ or $x \geq 9$

26. $x \leq -12$ or $x \geq 22$

27. $4 \leq x \leq 10$

28. $0.1 < w < 9.9$

29. $x < -15$ or $x > 5$

30. $t \le 0$ or $t \ge 4$

31. $x \le -6$ or $x \ge -4$

32. No solutions.

33. **a.** $f(x) < g(x)$: $-2 < x < 2$

   b. $f(x) > g(x)$: $x < -2$ or $x > 2$

34. **a.** $f(x) < g(x)$: $-4 < x < -2$

   b. $f(x) > g(x)$: $x < -4$ or $x > -2$

35. Men's heights below 64 inches or above 76 inches are considered unusual.

36. Any gestational period for women of less than 26 days or more than 299 days is considered unusual.

37. $x < -7$ or $x > -2$

38. $-10 \le x \le 10$

39. $-8 < x < -4$

40. $(-\infty, -8]$ or $[-6, \infty)$

41. $(-2, 0)$ or $(5, \infty)$

42. $\left[-\dfrac{5}{3}, \dfrac{1}{2}\right]$

43. $-8 < x < -5$

44. $0 < x < 4$

45. $x < -3$ or $x > 6$

46. $-2 < x \le 7$

47. $x < -6$ or $-5 \le x < 2$

48. $(-\infty, -8)$ or $[4, \infty)$

49. $(-\infty, -4)$ or $\left(-\dfrac{1}{2}, 6\right)$

50. $-1 < x < 9$

51. $x < -4$ or $1 < x < 6$

52.

53.

54.

55.

56.

57. No solution

58.

59.

60. Let R be regular tickets, and let S be student tickets.

$S + R \leq 12,000 \qquad 9S + 15R \geq 140,000$

61. $y \leq \dfrac{1}{3}x - 6$

62. $y > -\dfrac{1}{2}x + 6$

Chapter 9 Test

1. $w = 5, w = -5$

2. $x = 9, x = -23$

3. No solution

4. $x = 9$ or $x = -19$

5. $x = 2, x = -1$

6. $-3 < x < 9$

7. $t \geq 15, t \leq 1$

8. $\dfrac{-16}{3} < n < \dfrac{8}{3}$

9. $n > 5, n < \dfrac{-1}{3}$

10. $-9 < x < 17$

11. Black-tailed prairie dogs have a body temperature that is considered unusual if it is less than 36.172°C or more than 36.628°C.

12. $x < -5$ or $x > 2$

13. $-4 < x < 7$

14. $\left(-\infty, -\dfrac{3}{2}\right]$ or $[4, \infty)$

15. $[-4, 3)$

16. $(-\infty, -4)$ or $[1, 5)$

17. $(-\infty, -3)$ or $(0, 6)$

18. $y > -\dfrac{1}{2}x + 6$

19.

20.

21.

22. Let M be the number of hours per week Georgia needs to study for her math class, and let H be the number of hours per week Georgia needs to study for her history class.

$$M \geq 12 \quad M + H \leq 20$$

Cumulative Review for Chapters 1–9

1. $(-3a)^4$

2. $\dfrac{16}{81}$

3. 21

4. $y = \dfrac{7}{3}x + 2$

5. $n = \dfrac{3}{2}$

6. $c = \dfrac{a - b}{ab}$

7. $m = \dfrac{2(P - 3)}{n^2}$

8. a. $S = 528$. Gustavo's monthly salary is $528 if he works 48 hours.

   b. $S = 352$. Gustavo's monthly salary is $352 if he works 32 hours.

   c. $h \approx 72.73$. Gustavo must work approximately 72.73 hours if he wants to earn $800.

9. $x < \dfrac{11}{3}$

10. $x < 6.72$

11. It will cost $410 for Donna to take 20 children to see the 3-D movie.

12.

x	$y = |x - 3|$
-5	8
-3	6
-1	4
1	2
3	0
5	2
6	3
8	5
9	6

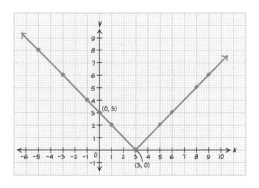

The graph is nonlinear.

13. $y = -\dfrac{2}{3}x + 4$

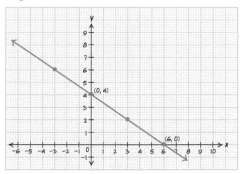

14. x-intercept: $(5, 0)$, y-intercept: $(0, -4)$

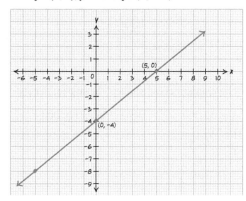

15. $y = 3x - 4$

16. $y = -\dfrac{1}{3}x + 2$

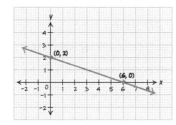

17. Slope: $\dfrac{3}{5}$, y-intercept: $(0, -2)$

18. $y = -\dfrac{1}{5}x + 5$

19. $y = -\dfrac{3}{4}x + \dfrac{13}{2}$

20. $y = \dfrac{1}{4}x - 3$

21. a. $m = \dfrac{2}{3}$ **b.** $(0, 4)$ **c.** $(-6, 0)$ **d.** $y = \dfrac{2}{3}x + 4$

22. a. $m = \dfrac{15}{4}$ **b.** $(0, -5)$ **c.** $\left(\dfrac{4}{3}, 0\right)$ **d.** $y = \dfrac{15}{4}x - 5$

23. a. Steve plans to run 11 miles in week 4.
     b. Steve plans to run 20 miles in week 10.

24. $x = -4$ $y = 2$

25. $x = -3$ $y = -8$

26. Inconsistent system. No solution.

27. $s = 105$ $w = 15$

The rate of the plane is 105 mph, and the rate of the wind is 15 mph.

28. Hamid should mix $2\dfrac{2}{3}$ liters of 6% HCl solution with $1\dfrac{1}{3}$ liters of 24% HCl solution to get 4 liters of 12% HCl solution.

29. Infinitely many solutions

30. The length of the rectangle is 8.5 centimeters, and the width is 5.5 centimeters.

31. Aivy should invest $5000 in the CD and $3000 in the bond fund to earn $325 a year in interest.

32.

33.

34. a. $-27x^{12}y^9$ **b.** $-18a^5b^5$ **c.** $-108x^9y^8$

35. a. t^4 **b.** $-\dfrac{b}{4}$ **c.** $5y$

36. $\dfrac{9x^2y^2}{100}$

37. a. $\dfrac{-2}{ab^2}$ **b.** $\dfrac{4x^4}{y^6}$ **c.** $\dfrac{y^3}{125x^3}$

38. a. 1.95×10^{-4} **b.** 5.289×10^{10}

39. a. 0.00003004 **b.** $927{,}000{,}000$

40. Three terms; degree is 3.

41. Degree of the term $5a^3b$ is 4.

Degree of the term $3a^5$ is 5.   Degree of the term $-6b$ is 1.

Degree of the term ab^2 is 3.   Degree of the polynomial is 5.

42. $-4b^2 + 7b + 6$ **43.** $4x - 11$

44. a. $2x^2 - 9x - 35$ **b.** $3y^3 - y^2 - 3y + 1$

c. $9x^2 - 24x + 16$ **d.** $33a - 26$

45. $-x + 2 - \dfrac{3}{x}$ **46.** $3x - 5$

47. $5x - 2$

48. a. $6x(x^2y - 3y + 4)$ **b.** $(5x + 2)(y + 3)$

49. $2(3a - 2)(b + 6)$

50. a. $(x - 7)(x + 2)$ **b.** $-(n - 3)(n + 6)$

c. $(5y - 1)(4y + 3)$

51. a. $-(x + 5)(x - 5)$ or $(5 - x)(5 + x)$

b. $(3y + 1)(3y - 1)$ **c.** $(3t - 2)^2$

d. Prime   **e.** $3(y + 2)(y - 2)$

52. a. Linear   **b.** Neither   **c.** Quadratic

53. a. $x = -\dfrac{2}{3}, x = 4$ **b.** $x = 0, x = -5$ **c.** $n = \pm 9$

54. 0

55. a. $c = 6$. The cost is $6 per person if 10 parents agree to help pay for the plaque.

b. $c = 4$. The lowest possible cost per parent is $4.

56. a. $x = \dfrac{7}{2}$ is excluded   **b.** $t = -3, t = \dfrac{4}{3}$ are excluded

c. $y = -\dfrac{5}{2}, y = \dfrac{1}{3}$ are excluded

57. a. $\dfrac{-6}{x}$ **b.** $\dfrac{1}{n + 1}$ **c.** $\dfrac{1}{t + 2}$

58. a. $T = 3.75$. The two office specialists working together can complete the job in 3.75 hours, or 3 hours and 45 minutes.

   b. $T \approx 3.43$. The two office specialists working together can complete the job in about 3.43 hours, or 3 hours and 26 minutes.

59. a. $\dfrac{5n + 7}{2n^2 + 17n + 35}$ simplified   **b.** $\dfrac{4x + 1}{x + 7}$ **c.** -4

60. a. $\dfrac{-2}{5}$ **b.** $\dfrac{-5}{4y}$

   c. $\dfrac{x - 3}{x + 5}$ **d.** $\dfrac{(y + 3)(y - 1)}{(y - 4)(y + 6)}$

61. The price for a 1-pound jar of barbeque sauce is $0.39 per ounce.

62. The car's speed is 3080 feet per minute.

63. a. $\dfrac{-4}{3}$ **b.** $\dfrac{-14}{3xy}$

   c. $\dfrac{(t + 2)(t - 1)}{(t - 4)(t + 3)}$ **d.** $\dfrac{(a + 3)(a - 4)}{(a - 2)^2}$

64. a. $\dfrac{-y}{18x}$ **b.** $\dfrac{1}{2b + 10}$ or $\dfrac{1}{2(b + 5)}$

65. a. 6   **b.** $6t$

   c. $\dfrac{8}{(y - 2)(y + 3)}$ **d.** $\dfrac{4x - 7}{(x - 1)(x + 5)}$

66. a. $10x^2y$ **b.** $(b - 1)(b - 2)$

   c. $4h(h - 3)$ **d.** $(a - 5)(a - 3)(a + 4)$

67. a. $\dfrac{3x + 12}{(x - 1)(x + 4)}, \dfrac{-2x^2 + 2x}{(x - 1)(x + 4)}$

   b. $\dfrac{5k^2 - 25k}{(k + 6)(k - 6)(k - 5)}, \dfrac{8k + 48}{(k + 6)(k - 6)(k - 5)}$

68. a. $\dfrac{17}{2y}$ **b.** $\dfrac{y^2 - 9y + 2}{(y - 4)(y - 1)}$

69. a. $\dfrac{5}{3}$ **b.** $\dfrac{-2x + 3y}{4x + y}$

70. a. $x = 3$ **b.** No solution   **c.** $k = 0, k = 3$

71. a. $C = 14$. The average cost per person is $14 if 25 people attend the retirement lunch.

   b. $n = 50$. There must be 50 people who attend the lunch for the average cost per person to be $12.

72. a. $a = 1$ **b.** $b = 8$ **c.** $x = 9, x = -2$

73. Kenzo's work rate is $\dfrac{1}{3}$ per hour.

74. It will take 2.4 hours, or 2 hours and 24 minutes, to copy the announcements using both machines.

75. $\dfrac{1}{5}$ **76.** $\dfrac{25 \text{ miles}}{1 \text{ gallon}}$

77. 36 ounces of coffee beans for $31.00; the unit rate is $0.86 per ounce.

   48 ounces of coffee beans for $25.00; the unit rate is $0.52 per ounce.

   The better buy is 48 ounces of coffee beans for $25.00.

78. The length of the wall on the blueprint will be 2.5 inches.

79. a. $n = -\dfrac{2}{5}$ **b.** $x = -4$ **c.** $t = 9$

80. $d = 50t; d = 375$ when $t = 7.5$

81. a. $W = 10.5t$ **b.** $W = 336$

   The amount of weekly paycheck is $336 for 32 hours of work.

82. $y = \dfrac{-3}{x}; y = \dfrac{-3}{2}$ when $x = 2$

83. a. $s = \dfrac{200}{t}$ **b.** $s = 33\dfrac{1}{3}$

   The speed is $33\dfrac{1}{3}$ mph, or approximately 33.33 mph, for 6 hours of driving.

84. a. $f(-4) = 33$ **b.** $f(-1) = 3$

85. a. Let P be the population of the United States in millions, and let t be the years since 2000.

     $P = 2.7t + 282.1$

   b. The population of the United States will be 314.5 million in 2012.

   c. Domain: [0, 13]; range: [282.1, 317.2]

   d. Vertical intercept: (0, 282.1). The population of the United States was about 282.1 million in 2000.

   e. (15.9, 325). The United States population will reach 325 million in about 2016. This is beyond the domain of the model, so it may be model breakdown.

86. a. Let $R(t)$ be the total revenue (in billions of dollars) for Cisco Systems, Inc., and let t represent the years since 2000.

     $R(t) = 4.9t + 0.3$

   b. Vertical intercept: (0, 0.3). The total revenue for Cisco Systems, Inc. in 2000 was about 300 million.

   c. Domain: [3, 10] (due to the economic downturn) Range: [15, 49.3]

   d. The model predicts Cisco Systems' revenue to be $49.3 billion in 2010.

   e. The model predicts Cisco Systems' revenue to be $64 billion in 2013. This is beyond the domain of the model, so it may be model breakdown.

   f. The slope is 4.9, which means that Cisco Systems' revenue is increasing at a rate of $4.9 billion per year.

87. Domain: $\mathbb{R}$

88. Domain: $\mathbb{R}, x \neq -1, x \neq \dfrac{3}{2}$

89. On the sixth day of the month, a person sleeps 7 hours.

90. a. $P(14) = 58$. 58 people out of 100 remain on the diet plan 14 days after starting the diet.

   b. $m = -3$. The number of people remaining on the diet plan decreases by 3 per day.

91. a. $f(3) = -18$ **b.** $x = 11$

   c. Domain: All real numbers; Range: All real numbers

92. a. $h(32) = -9$ **b.** $x = 15$

   c. Domain: All real numbers; Range: All real numbers

93. a. $g(10) = 7$

   b. Domain: All real numbers; Range: $\{7\}$

94. a. $f(6) = 8$ **b.** $x = -6$

   c. Domain: All real numbers; Range: All real numbers

95. a. $f(x) + g(x) = 5x + 3$

   b. $f(x) - g(x) = -x - 11$

   c. $f(x)g(x) = 6x^2 + 2x - 28$

96. a. $f(x) + g(x) = x^2 + x + 8$

   b. $f(x) - g(x) = -x^2 + x - 2$

   c. $f(x)g(x) = x^3 + 3x^2 + 5x + 15$

97. $(f \circ g)(x) = 2x^2 - 2$

98. $(f \circ g)(x) = 9x^2 + 15x + 6$

99. $t \geq 16.25$. The percentage of Canadian TV subscribers who use satellite services will be greater than those who use cable services after 2016.

100. $x < 4$

101. $x \leq 3$

102. Sandra must have $2750 or more per week in sales to earn at least $565 per week.

103. $x = 10$ or $x = -14$

104. $a = 24$ or $a = -8$

105. No solution.

106. $r = -\dfrac{1}{3}$ or $r = -3$

107. $-5 < x < 9$

108. $-9 \leq x \leq 6$

109. $x \leq -10$ or $x \geq 2$

110. $x < \dfrac{2}{3}$ or $x > 4$

111. $(-\infty, 2)$ or $(5, \infty)$

112. $[-5, 8)$

113. $-9 \leq x \leq 1$

114. $-7 < x < -2$ or $x \geq 3$

115.

116.

CHAPTER 10
Section 10.1

1. 5

3. 8

5. $\dfrac{4}{3}$

7. $\dfrac{10}{7}$

9. $\dfrac{1}{4}$

11. -7

13. $-\dfrac{5}{8}$

15. Not real

17. Not real

19. $\sqrt{15} \approx 3.87$

21. $\sqrt{51} \approx 7.14$

23. $\sqrt{7} \approx 2.65$

25. Not real

27. 6

29. 1

31. 2

33. Not real

35. Not real

37. $\sqrt{13}$

39. a. $t \approx 1.77$. It will take the ball approximately 1.77 seconds to fall 50 feet.

   b. $t \approx 2.24$. It will take the ball approximately 2.24 seconds to fall 80 feet.

41. a. The variable s represents the speed of the car in miles per hour, and d represents the length in feet of the skid mark left by the car.

   b. $s \approx 51.61$. The speed of the car was approximately 51.61 mph when the length of the skid mark was 200 feet.

   c. $s \approx 43.95$. The speed of the car was approximately 43.95 mph when the length of the skid mark was 145 feet.

43. a. $t \approx 0.71$. It takes the ball approximately 0.71 second to fall 8 feet.

45. $P = 15$. Eamond will earn $15 in profit from selling 50 wristbands.

47. $x \approx 1.39$. The length of the side of the cube is about 1.39 inches.

49. $d = 9$. A person can see a distance of 9 miles if the person is 36 feet above the surface of the earth.

51. $d \approx 8.06$ **53.** $d \approx 10.20$ **55.** $d \approx 7.81$

57. $d \approx 17.26$ **59.** x **61.** a^3

63. $4x$ **65.** $-x^{10}$ **67.** $-a$

69. $-2y^3$ **71.** $5x^{11}$ **73.** $\dfrac{x^2}{7}$

75. $\dfrac{y^5}{6}$ **77.** 2 **79.** 1

81. -2 **83.** -5 **85.** 2

87. 1 **89.** 4 **91.** 10

93. $\dfrac{1}{7}$ **95.** y^4 **97.** a

99. -4 **101.** -5 **103.** -2

105. Not real   **107.** ab^4 **109.** $7z$

111. $\dfrac{x^2}{9}$ **113.** 2 **115.** Not real

117. 10 **119.** -1

Section **10.2**

1. $x^{\frac{1}{2}}$ **3.** $c^{\frac{3}{2}}$ **5.** $t^{\frac{2}{3}}$

7. $(5xy)^{\frac{1}{2}}$ **9.** $4^{\frac{1}{7}}m^{\frac{3}{7}}n^{\frac{6}{7}}p^{\frac{2}{7}}$ **11.** $\sqrt[3]{r}$

13. $\sqrt[3]{n^2}$ **15.** $\sqrt[3]{xy}$ **17.** $\sqrt[5]{rs^2}$

19. $\sqrt{xy^3z}$ **21.** 3 **23.** 10

25. -4 **27.** $\dfrac{1}{5}$ **29.** $3\sqrt{2}$

31. $5\sqrt{5}$ **33.** $4\sqrt{5}$ **35.** $5\sqrt{3}$

37. $\sqrt{34}$ **39.** $2\sqrt{37}$

41. a. $5\sqrt{2}$ **b.** $\sqrt{50} \approx 7.07$

43. a. $2\sqrt{3}$ **b.** $\sqrt{12} \approx 3.46$

45. a. $2\sqrt{7}$ **b.** $\sqrt{28} \approx 5.29$

47. a. $3\sqrt{6}$ **b.** $\sqrt{54} \approx 7.35$

49. $b^4\sqrt{b}$ **51.** a^2 **53.** $x^7\sqrt{x}$

55. y **57.** $4x^3$ **59.** $8a\sqrt{a}$

61. $7a^2$ **63.** $3a^2\sqrt{5}$ **65.** $2x\sqrt{10x}$

67. $5b^5\sqrt{3b}$ **69.** $2xy^2$ **71.** $6xyz^2\sqrt[3]{18y^2z^2}$

73. $2np\sqrt[4]{60m^3p}$ **75.** $-2cd^2$ **77.** $2mn^2$

79. $-2\sqrt{5}$ **81.** $12\sqrt{3}$ **83.** $2\sqrt{3} + 3\sqrt{2}$

85. $2\sqrt{x} - 7\sqrt{2}$ **87.** $-\sqrt{a}$ **89.** $6b + 3a\sqrt{b}$

91. $-32 + x\sqrt{3} - \sqrt{3}$

93. $6\sqrt{2}$ **95.** $14\sqrt{3}$ **97.** $3 + 2\sqrt{7}$

99. $9\sqrt{2}$ **101.** $8\sqrt{5} + 11\sqrt{2}$

103. a. $7x - 5x$ **b.** $2x$

105. a. $-4a^2 - 4a^2$ **b.** $-8a^2$

107. a. $-4 + 2x\sqrt{x} + 5x\sqrt{x}$ **b.** $-4 + 7x\sqrt{x}$

109. $6\sqrt[3]{a}$

111. $12\sqrt{2x} + 4\sqrt[3]{2x}$

113. $-4ab^2\sqrt[5]{2c^3}$ **115.** $23xy^2\sqrt[4]{x}$

117. $-3\sqrt[3]{7xy} + 3\sqrt[5]{7xy}$

Section **10.3**

1. 6 **3.** 6 **5.** $2\sqrt{11}$

7. $4\sqrt{5}$ **9.** 12 **11.** $5\sqrt{6}$

13. $3x\sqrt{2}$ **15.** $2a^2\sqrt{10}$ **17.** $6x^2$

19. $10x^2\sqrt{x}$ **21.** $2a^4\sqrt{15a}$ **23.** $4x^8\sqrt{5x}$

25. 17 **27.** $6x$ **29.** xyz

31. $21y$ **33.** $14a^3$ **35.** $14a\sqrt{6a}$

37. $2x$ **39.** $35m^3n^6\sqrt[4]{mn}$ **41.** $14x^3y\sqrt[3]{20y^2}$

43. $36x^4y^6\sqrt[5]{686x^2}$ **45.** $A = 12$ **47.** $A = \dfrac{3}{2}$

49. $2 - 5\sqrt{2}$ **51.** $3\sqrt{2} - \sqrt{15}$ **53.** $\sqrt{2x} - 2\sqrt{2}$

55. $-12\sqrt{2} + 2\sqrt{5}$ **57.** $x + \sqrt{11x}$

59. $6 - 2\sqrt{3} + 3\sqrt{6} - 3\sqrt{2}$ **61.** $20 + 6\sqrt{7}$

63. $x - \sqrt{5x} + \sqrt{3x} - \sqrt{15}$ **65.** -1

67. $9 - x$ **69.** $19 + 8\sqrt{3}$

71. $a^2 + 2a\sqrt{11} + 11$ **73.** $4 - 4\sqrt{y} + y$

75. $x^2 - 2x\sqrt{5} + 5$ **77.** 5 **79.** 6

81. $3x$ **83.** $\dfrac{1}{3}$ **85.** $\dfrac{x}{4}$

87. $\dfrac{4\sqrt{3}}{3}$ **89.** $-5\sqrt{3}$ **91.** $\dfrac{\sqrt{5x}}{3x}$

93. $\dfrac{\sqrt{2a}}{5a}$ **95.** $4 - 2\sqrt{3}$

97. $\dfrac{7\sqrt{7} - 7\sqrt{3}}{4}$ **99.** $\dfrac{-12 + 4\sqrt{x}}{x - 9}$

101. $\dfrac{-2\sqrt{7} + 20}{93}$

103. The length of the rectangle is $3\sqrt{6}$.

105. The width of the rectangle is 4.

107. $\dfrac{\sqrt[3]{245x^2y}}{7xy}$ **109.** $\dfrac{\sqrt[3]{36xy^2}}{14xy}$

111. $\dfrac{\sqrt[4]{10a^2b^3}}{2ab^2}$ **113.** $\dfrac{4\sqrt[4]{36y^2z^2}}{3yz}$

Section **10.4**

1. a.

A radical function seems appropriate here because the scatterplot increases rapidly and curves slightly.

b.

The graph fits the data well and seems to follow the pattern.

c. The cost to produce 550,000 heaters is approximately $8.57 million.

d. The cost to produce 1,500,000 heaters is approximately $12.07 million.

e. Domain: [0, 15], range: [3.2, 12.07]

3. a. The graph fits the data well and seems to follow the pattern.

b. A basilisk lizard with body mass of 50 grams will have a leg length of ≈0.061 meter.

c. A basilisk lizard with body mass of 100 grams will have a leg length of ≈0.077 meter.

d. A basilisk lizard with leg length of 0.1 meter will have a body mass of ≈222.6 grams.

5. a. The airspeed of a butterfly with a thoracic mass of 0.05 gram is 2.92 meters per second.

b. The airspeed of a butterfly with a thoracic mass of 0.12 gram is 4.93 meters per second.

c. Range: [0.28, 12.95]

7. a. $f(81) = 22.5$ **b.** $f(25) = 12.5$

9. a. $f(45) \approx 12.847$ **b.** $f(32) = 12$

11. a. $f(28) = 6$ **b.** $f(113) = 11$

13. a. $f(50) \approx 6.325$ **b.** $f(59) = 7$

15. a. $f(-60) \approx -1.694$ **b.** $f(-2207) = -3$

17. a. $f(5) \approx 3.344$ **b.** $f(27.473) \approx 12$

19. a. $f(5) = 3$ **b.** $f(-3) = 1$

21. a. $f(4) = 2$ **b.** $f(-7.5) = -1.5$

23. a. This is an odd root.   **b.** Domain: $(-\infty, \infty)$
   c. Range: $(-\infty, \infty)$

25. a. This is an even root.   **b.** Domain: $[-4, \infty)$
   c. Range: $[0, \infty)$

27. a. This is an even root.   **b.** Domain: $(-\infty, -5]$
   c. Range: $[0, \infty)$

29. a. This is an odd root.   **b.** Domain: $(-\infty, \infty)$
   c. Range: $(-\infty, \infty)$

31. a. Even   **b.** Domain: $(-\infty, -2]$
   c. Range: $(-\infty, 0]$

33. Domain: All real numbers, range: All real numbers

35. Domain: $[0, \infty)$, range: $[0, \infty)$

37. Domain: All real numbers, range: All real numbers

39. Domain: $[0, \infty)$, range: $[0, \infty)$

41. Domain: $[-12, \infty)$, range: $[0, \infty)$

43. Domain: $[-7, \infty)$, range: $[0, \infty)$

45. Domain: All real numbers, range: All real numbers

47. Domain: $[-2, \infty)$, range: $[0, \infty)$

49. Domain: $[23, \infty)$, range: $[0, \infty)$

51. Domain: $(-\infty, 3]$, range: $[0, \infty)$

53. Domain: $(-\infty, -10]$, range: $[0, \infty)$

55. Domain: All real numbers, range: All real numbers

57. Domain: $\left[-\dfrac{5}{3}, \infty\right)$, range: $[0, \infty)$

59. Domain: $\left(-\infty, \dfrac{9}{4}\right]$, range: $[0, \infty)$

61. $f(x) = \sqrt{x + 7}$

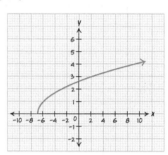

63. $g(x) = \sqrt{x - 8}$

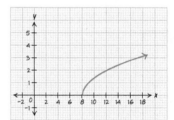

65. $f(x) = -\sqrt{x + 3}$

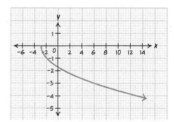

67. $f(x) = -\sqrt{x - 6}$

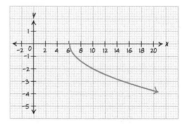

69. $f(x) = \sqrt[3]{x} + 2$

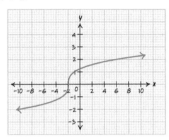

71. $h(x) = \sqrt[3]{x} - 11$

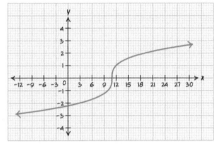

73. $f(x) = \sqrt{9 - x}$

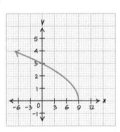

75. $g(x) = -\sqrt{x - 3}$

77. $h(x) = \sqrt[5]{2x}$

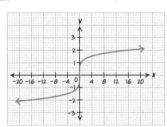

79. $g(x) = 2\sqrt{x} + 3$

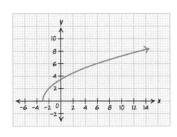

Section **10.5**

1. $x = 16$ is a solution. **3.** $x = 81$ is not a solution.

5. $x = 26$ is not a solution. **7.** $x = 4$ is a solution.

9. Maria's work is not correct. She concludes that $\sqrt{-9} = -3$, but this is not correct because a negative number under the radical sign $\left(\sqrt{-9}\,\right)$ is not a real number and cannot be equal to a real number (-3).

11. Marilyn's work is correct.

13. Jaydy's work is not correct. She concludes that $-\sqrt{-1} = 1$, but this is not correct because the square root of a negative number is not a real number.

15. $a = 16$ **17.** No solution **19.** $x = 37$

21. $y = 0$ **23.** $a = 225$

25. No solution **27.** $y = 8$

29. a. $h = 52.02$. The ball was dropped from a height of 52.02 meters.

b. $h = 364.5$. The ball was dropped from a height of 364.5 meters.

31. a. $d = 67.5$. The length of the skid mark was 67.5 feet.

b. $d \approx 45.63$. The length of the skid mark was approximately 45.63 feet.

33. $x = 27$. Andrew must sell 27 wristbands to make a profit of $20.

35. $A \approx 127{,}551.02$. The irrigation system covers an area of approximately 127,551.02 square feet.

37. $x = 14$ **39.** No solution **41.** $z = 3$

43. $a = -13$

45. No solution

47. Mackenzie's work is not correct. She did not isolate the radical before squaring. She then simplified $(2\sqrt{x})^2$ incorrectly (correctly simplified, this would be $4x$, not $2x$).

49. Andrew's work is not correct. He did not isolate the radical before squaring. He then simplified $(\sqrt{x} + 1)^2$ incorrectly (correctly simplified, this would be $x + 2\sqrt{x} + 1$, not $x + 1$). The equation would be easier to solve correctly if the radical were isolated first.

51. Victor's work is not correct. If he had checked the solution, this would have revealed that $x = 36$ is not a solution to the equation. There is no solution for the equation $\sqrt{x} = -6$.

53. Margaret's work is incorrect. She did not square the left side correctly, since $(\sqrt{-x})^2 = -x$. The correct answer is $x = -81$.

55. Rio did not use the distance formula correctly. The differences between the x- and y-coordinates squared should be added under the radical sign. The distance formula does not use a quotient.

57. Ethan found the differences between the x and y of the ordered pairs $(y_1 - x_1$ and $y_2 - x_2)$ rather than correctly finding the difference between the x-coordinates and y-coordinates $(x_2 - x_1$ and $y_2 - y_1)$.

59. $x = 2, x = -1$ **61.** $x = \dfrac{3}{2}, x = -1$ **63.** $x = 4$

65. No solution   **67.** No solution   **69.** $x = 4$

71. The period of a pendulum of length 3 feet is 1.92 seconds.

73. For a period of 1 second, the pendulum needs to be about 0.81 foot (9.7 inches) in length.

75. a. Jim Bob's can make 26.552 hundred thousand space heaters with a budget of $15 million.
   b. Jim Bob's can make 14.767 hundred thousand space heaters with a budget of $12 million.

77. a. The body mass of a mammal with a body length of 1 meter is 27.8 kg.
   b. The body mass of a mammal with a body length of 2.4 meters is 384.7 kg.

79. The average distance from the sun to Uranus is approximately 19.2 AU.

81. It takes Pluto approximately 248.3 years to orbit the sun.

83. $x = 16$

85. $w = 2$ **87.** $x = 4$ **89.** $x = \dfrac{2}{3}$

91. No solution.   **93.** $x = -1, x = 3$

95. $x = 105.5$ **97.** $x = 5$ **99.** $x = 24.6$

101. $x = 32$ **103.** Radical   **105.** Rational

107. Linear   **109.** Quadratic

111. a. Equation   **b.** $x = 19$

113. a. Equation   **b.** $x = -6, x = -2$

115. a. Expression   **b.** $11n^2 + 4n - 35$

117. a. Equation   **b.** $x = 13$

Section **10.6**

1. $8i$ **3.** $9i$ **5.** -6

7. $2i\sqrt{5} \approx 4.472i$ **9.** $10i\sqrt{2} \approx 14.142i$

11. $12 - 10i$ **13.** $8i$ **15.** $3 + 4i$

17. $\approx 4.098i$ **19.** $-12 - 12i\sqrt{7} \approx -12 - 31.749i$

21. Real part = 2   Imaginary part = 5

23. Real part = 2.3   Imaginary part = -4.9

25. Real part = 3   Imaginary part = 0

27. Real part = 0   Imaginary part = 7

29. $8 + 9i$ **31.** $7.9 - 1.7i$ **33.** $3 - 4i$

35. $-5 + 7i$ **37.** $-4 - 3i$ **39.** $6.5 - 9.2i$

41. 5 **43.** $-13 + 26i$ **45.** $-14 - 22i$

47. $60.75 - 54i$ **49.** $-60 + 32i$ **51.** 58

53. $13 + 84i$ **55.** $4 + 3i$ **57.** $\dfrac{7}{2} - 2i$

59. $\dfrac{37}{72} - \dfrac{1}{3}i \approx 0.514 - 0.333i$

---

61. $\dfrac{16}{13} - \dfrac{11}{13}i$ **63.** $\dfrac{17}{29} + \dfrac{1}{29}i$

65. $-\dfrac{29}{85} + \dfrac{82}{85}i$ **67.** $\dfrac{1082}{221} + \dfrac{197}{221}i$

69. $x = \pm 3i$ **71.** $y = \pm i\sqrt{7}$

73. $x = 8 \pm \dfrac{2\sqrt{6}}{3}i \approx 8 + 1.633i$

75. $x = \pm i\sqrt{10}$

77. $x = 0, x = 1, x = -\dfrac{7}{5}$

79. $x = \pm i\sqrt{4}$

Chapter 10 Review Exercises

1. -6 **2.** -10 **3.** Not real

4. Not real   **5.** 3 **6.** 5

7. -4 **8.** -1

9. a. $t \approx 2.26$. The ball will fall 25 meters in approximately 2.26 seconds.
   b. $t \approx 1.56$. The ball will fall 12 meters in approximately 1.56 seconds.

10. a. $t \approx 2.56$. The ball will fall 32 meters in approximately 2.56 seconds.
   b. $t \approx 1.36$. The ball will fall 9 meters in approximately 1.36 seconds.

11. $d \approx 7.07$ **12.** $d \approx 3.61$ **13.** 4

14. 2 **15.** Not real   **16.** $\sqrt{10}$

17. y^5 **18.** y^3 **19.** $5x^2$

20. $6x^3$ **21.** x^3y **22.** xy^2

23. $2ab^2c^6$

24. a. $\sqrt[4]{xy^3}$ **b.** $\sqrt{3a}$

25. a. $4^{\frac{1}{5}}x^{\frac{2}{3}}$ **b.** $7^{\frac{1}{2}}a^{\frac{1}{2}}b^{\frac{1}{2}}$

26. $5\sqrt{3}$ **27.** $3\sqrt{6}$ **28.** $x^3\sqrt{x}$

29. $2y\sqrt{y}$ **30.** $2x\sqrt{5x}$ **31.** $2x^4\sqrt{6x}$

32. $12xy^2$ **33.** $30m^3n^5\sqrt{5n}$ **34.** $4c^5d^4\sqrt{55c}$

35. $-2xy^2\sqrt[3]{y}$ **36.** $4xy\sqrt[3]{y^2}$ **37.** $b^2\sqrt[4]{56a^2b^2}$

38. $n^2\sqrt[4]{25m^3n^3}$ **39.** $ac\sqrt[5]{-40a^2b^3}$ **40.** $3\sqrt{3} \approx 5.20$

41. $3\sqrt{5} \approx 6.71$ **42.** $10\sqrt{2} \approx 14.14$ **43.** $5\sqrt{10} \approx 15.81$

44. $6\sqrt{3x}$ **45.** $11\sqrt{6y}$ **46.** $4 + 2x\sqrt{x}$

47. $17y - 5y\sqrt{y}$ **48.** $12\sqrt{3a} + 7\sqrt[3]{3a}$

49. $-2a\sqrt[3]{b^2}$ **50.** $21ac^2\sqrt[5]{2a^2b^3}$ **51.** $3\sqrt{2}$

52. $4y$ **53.** $2x^2\sqrt{6x}$ **54.** $7a$

55. $3b^3$ **56.** $3ab\sqrt[3]{2b}$ **57.** $18x^3y^5z^2\sqrt[3]{10x^2}$

58. $5 + 5\sqrt{2}$ **59.** $-28\sqrt{a} - 7\sqrt{7}$

60. $3 + 3\sqrt{6} - \sqrt{2} - 2\sqrt{3}$

61. 10 **62.** $3 - \sqrt{5}$ **63.** $9 + \sqrt{3}$

64. $-5 + \sqrt{x}$ **65.** 4 **66.** $3x$

67. $\dfrac{5\sqrt{7}}{7}$ **68.** $\dfrac{-3\sqrt{5}}{5}$ **69.** $\dfrac{5\sqrt[3]{4xy^2}}{2y}$

70. $\dfrac{12 + 4\sqrt{2}}{7}$ **71.** $\dfrac{3 - 3\sqrt{5}}{4}$

72. a. $P(3) \approx 13.76$. In the third month of the year, Big Jim's Mart had a profit of about $13.76 thousand.

   b. $P(8) \approx 15.96$. In August, Big Jim's Mart had a profit of about $15.96 thousand.

73. $W(4) \approx 51.39$. A four-year-old alpaca weighs about 51.39 kilograms.

74. Domain: $x \geq 0$, range: $y \leq 0$

75. Domain: $x \geq 0$, range: $y \geq 0$

76. Domain: $x \geq \dfrac{7}{2}$, range: $y \geq 0$

77. Domain: $x \leq 7$, range: $y \geq 0$

78. Domain: All real numbers, range: All real numbers

79. Domain: $x \geq 0$, range: $y \geq 0$

80. Domain: $x \geq 0$, range: $y \leq 0$

81. Domain: All real numbers, range: All real numbers

82. Domain: $x \geq 5$, range: $y \leq 0$

83. Domain: $x \leq 18$, range: $y \leq 0$

84.

85.

86.

87.

88.

89.

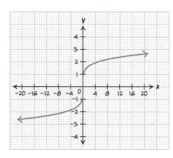

90. Yes, $x = 4$ is a solution to the radical equation.

91. No, $x = 2$ is not a solution to the radical equation.

92. $a = -8$ **93.** $x = -22$

94. $x = 5$ **95.** $x = 7$

96. No solution **97.** No solution

98. $x = 20$ **99.** $x = 13.5$ **100.** $x = 2.8$

101. $x = 120$. Nelson needs to sell 120 baskets of blueberries to make a profit of $12.00.

102. $h = 576$. The rock falls 576 feet in 6 seconds.

103. Big Jim's Mart will have a profit of about $17,000 in the eleventh month of the year.

104. A 5-year-old alpaca will weigh about 60 kilograms.

105. $5i$ **106.** $4i\sqrt{2}$

107. $7i$ **108.** $\left(6 + 5\sqrt{2}\right) + \left(-2\sqrt{10} + 3\sqrt{5}\right)i$

109. $7 + 10i$ **110.** $5.9 - 2.4i$ **111.** $1 + 4i$

112. $2.9 + 7.1i$ **113.** $34 - 13i$ **114.** $-23 + 52i$

115. 13 **116.** $4 + \dfrac{7}{3}i$ **117.** $1.4 - 0.8i$

118. $\dfrac{14}{13} - \dfrac{21}{13}i$ **119.** $-\dfrac{13}{25} + \dfrac{41}{25}i$ **120.** $-\dfrac{19}{25} - \dfrac{42}{25}i$

121. $0.777 + 0.008i$

Chapter 10 Test

1. -9 2. -3 3. $-6a^4$

4. a^4b 5. $d \approx 9.90$ 6. 5

7. $\dfrac{x}{3}$ 8. $2\sqrt{15}$ 9. 4.90

10. $2b^2\sqrt{7b}$ 11. $5ab\sqrt{a}$ 12. $-2np^2\sqrt[5]{m^3n^2}$

13. $-3 + 6\sqrt{3}$ 14. $14\sqrt{2}$ 15. $x\sqrt{6}$

16. $4\sqrt{3}$ 17. $5x^2\sqrt{2x}$ 18. $4 + 2\sqrt{10}$

19. $-58 + 2\sqrt{5}$ 20. 23 21. 5

22. $\dfrac{-\sqrt{6}}{2}$ 23. $\dfrac{5\sqrt[3]{9m^2n}}{3n}$ 24. $10 - 5\sqrt{3}$

25. $a = 484$ 26. No solution

27. $x = -5, x = 3$ 28. $x = 23$ 29. $x = 59$

30. $v(20) \approx 344.1$. The speed of sound in air is about 344.1 meters per second when the temperature is 20°C.

31. $T(h) \approx 90$. When $h \approx 137174.2$, add 1500 to allow time to pull the cord. The plane would have to be at an altitude of about 138,674 feet. This is not reasonable, so it is not possible for the daredevil to free-fall for 1.5 minutes.

32. Domain: $x \geq -7$, range: $(-\infty, 0]$

33. Domain: All real numbers, range: All real numbers

34.

35.

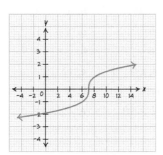

36. $4.1 - 1.4i$ 37. $1 + 18i$ 38. $31 - 29i$

39. $-25.875 - 19.875i$

40. $\dfrac{32}{41} - \dfrac{40}{41}i$ 41. $\dfrac{4}{85} + \dfrac{33}{85}i$

CHAPTER 11

Section 11.1

1. This function is a quadratic function.

3. This function is a linear function.

5. This function is a quadratic function.

7. Other.

9. This function is a quadratic function.

11. This function is a quadratic function.

13. This function is a quadratic function.

15. **a.** $(-5, 1)$ **b.** $x < -5$ **c.** $x > -5$
    d. $(-7.5, 0)(-2.5, 0)$ **e.** $(0, -3)$

17. **a.** $(4, 25)$ **b.** $x < 4$ **c.** $x > 4$
    d. $(-1, 0)(9, 0)$ **e.** $(0, 9)$ **f.** 21

19. **a.** $(-1, 4)$ **b.** $x > -1$ **c.** $x < -1$
    d. None.   **e.** $(0, 5)$ **f.** 9.5
    g. $x = 3$ and $x = -5$

21. Horizontal intercepts: $(-4, 0), (3, 0)$
    Vertical intercept: $(0, 6)$

23. Horizontal intercepts: $(-10, 0), (15, 0)$
    Vertical intercept: $(0, -15)$

25. **a.** D = Average number of days above 70°F in San Diego, California, during month m.
    m = Month of the year (i.e., $m = 1$ represents January)

   b. A quadratic would fit best. The data look like a downward facing parabola.

   c. The vertex is at about $(8, 31)$ and is a maximum point. Thus, August has the greatest number of days on average above 70°F in San Diego, California.

   d. Using the shape of the distribution, there would be about 7 days above 70°F in San Diego, California, during the month of April.

27. **a.**   **b.**

   c. This model fits the data reasonably well; the point at the top is low for a vertex, but otherwise the data are shaped like a quadratic.

   d. The vertex for the model is at about $(4, 11{,}238)$ and is a maximum point for this function.

   e. This vertex represents that in 1994, the number of cable television systems in the United States reached a maximum of 11,238.

29. **a.**

b. The vertex of this parabola is at about (5, 128.5), which means that the tennis ball will reach its highest point in the air at 128.5 meters after about 5 seconds.

c. $H(2) = 81.4$. About 2 seconds after being hit, the tennis ball will reach a height of 81.4 meters.

d. According to the graph, the tennis ball will hit the ground at about 10.224 seconds.

31. a. According to the graph, the revenue from selling T-shirts for $10 each would be about $1000.

b. According to the graph, the maximum monthly revenue would be about $1100.

c. The bookstore should charge $15 for each T-shirt to maximize the monthly revenue.

d. The revenue may go down after the vertex in this situation because people are less likely to purchase these T-shirts for more than $15 each, according to this graph.

33. A quadratic model would best fit these data. The vertex is $(-5, 8)$, which is a maximum point.

35. A quadratic model would best fit these data. The vertex is $(5, -5)$, which is a minimum point.

37. A linear model would best fit these data.

39. A linear model would best fit these data.

41.

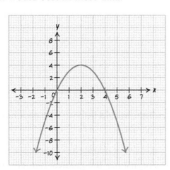

a. There are two horizontal intercepts.

b. There is one vertical intercept.

43.

a. There are two horizontal intercepts.

b. There is one vertical intercept.

45. The vertex has to touch the *x*-axis.

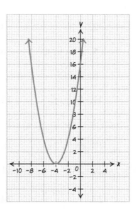

47. a. Above the horizontal axis

b. Below the *x*-axis

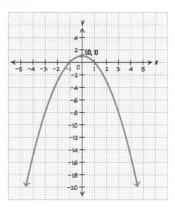

Section **11.2**

1. h; positive.   **3.** k; negative.

5. $|a| > 1$ **7.** a; positive.

9. $h = 0, k = 0$

11. a. $(-2.5, -3)$ **b.** $x = -2.5$ **c.** $(-5.5, 4)$

13. a. $(5.5, -6)$ **b.** $x = 5.5$ **c.** $(2, 5)$

15. a. $(-4, -8)$ **b.** $x = -4$ **c.** Positive.

     d. $h = -4, k = -8$ **e.** $(2, 15)$

17. a. $(2, 10)$ **b.** $x = 2$ **c.** Negative.

     d. $h = 2, k = 10$ **e.** $(5, -6)$

19.

21.

23.

25.

27.

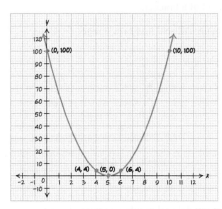

29. a. $P(90) = 6796.55$, so in 1990, the poverty threshold was about \$6,796.55 for individuals under 65 years old in the United States.

b. $P(80) = 4024.55$, so in 1980, the poverty threshold was about \$4,024.55 for individuals under 65 years old in the United States.

c.

d. According to this model, the poverty threshold for individuals under 65 years old in the United States reached a minimum of about \$1406 in 1957, which seems to make sense.

e. According to the graph, the poverty threshold for individuals under 65 years old in the United States was \$3000 in 1975 and 1939; 1939 shows model breakdown.

f. Range: [1406, 6796.55]

31. a.

b. In 1996, households and nonprofit organizations invested about \$2453 billion in time and savings accounts.

c. In about 1993, these time and savings accounts were at their lowest levels with about \$2300 billion invested.

d. According to the graph, households and nonprofit organizations invested \$3000 billion in about 1987 and again in 1999.

e. Range: [2300, 6125]

33. a. $h(2) = 192$, which means that 2 seconds after being dropped from the roof of a building, the object dropped will be at a height of about 192 feet.

b.

c. According to the graph, the object will hit the ground about 4 seconds after being dropped from the roof of the building.

d. Domain: [0, 4]; range: [0, 256]

35. a. $P(100) = 2.74$, so the monthly profit made from selling round-trip airline tickets from New York City to Orlando, Florida, when the tickets are sold for $100 each is $2.74 million.

b. Selling round-trip airline tickets from New York City to Orlando, Florida, for $120 each will produce a maximum profit of $2.75 million.

c.

d. According to the graph, the company will have a monthly profit of about $2 million when selling round-trip airline tickets from New York City to Orlando, Florida, for $295 each and −$50; −$50 is model breakdown.

e. Domain: [60, 300]; range: [1.95, 2.75]

37. a. $E(4) = 7.784$, so the epidemic threshold for the fourth week of 2006 was 7.784%

b.

c. According to the graph, in the 23rd week of 2006, there was not a flu epidemic; the epidemic threshold was about 7%.

d. The vertex for this model is (10, 8), which means that in week 10 of 2006, the epidemic threshold reached a maximum of 8%.

e. Domain: [1, 26]; range: [6.5, 8]

39. Domain: All real numbers; range: $(-\infty, 15]$

41. Domain: All real numbers; range: $[-58, \infty)$

43. Domain: All real numbers; range: $[0, \infty)$

45. Domain: All real numbers; range: $(-\infty, 4]$

47. Domain: All real numbers; range: $y \geq -9$

The domain should be all real numbers. The range is using a "greater than" sign, but it should use a "greater than or equal to" sign.

49. Domain: $(-\infty, \infty)$; range: $(-\infty, 7]$

The domain is correct, but the range is assuming that the parabola is facing upward and there is a parenthesis on the 7 instead of a bracket.

51. Domain: All real numbers; range: $[-4, \infty)$

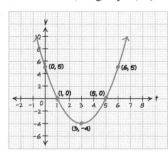

53. Domain: All real numbers; range: $[0, \infty)$

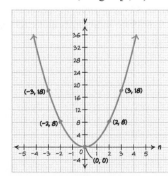

55. Domain: All real numbers; range: $[2, \infty)$

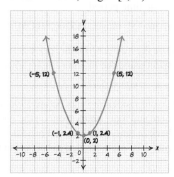

57. Domain: All real numbers; range: $(-\infty, 0]$

59. Domain: All real numbers; range: $[2, \infty)$

61. Domain: All real numbers; range: $[-8, \infty)$

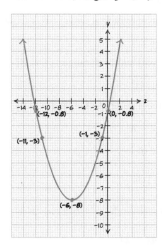

63. Domain: All real numbers; range: $(-\infty, -15]$

65. Domain: All real numbers; range: $(-\infty, 25]$

67. Domain: All real numbers; range: $[-2500, \infty)$

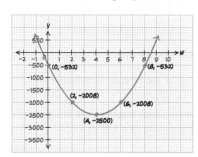

69. a. Vertex: $(0, 100)$

    b. The parabola is narrow.

    c. The parabola faces upward.

    d. X Min: -10 X Max: 10

        Y Min: 0   Y Max: 600

71. a. Vertex: $(-30, -50)$

    b. The parabola is neither wide nor narrow.

    c. The parabola faces upward.

    d. X Min: -45 X Max: -10

        Y Min: -60 Y Max: 70

73. a. Vertex: $(-20, 50)$

    b. The parabola is wide.

    c. The parabola faces upward.

    d. X Min: -100 X Max: 60

        Y Min: 45   Y Max: 60

75. a. Vertex: (1000, 1000)

   b. The parabola is wide.

   c. The parabola faces upward.

   d. X Min: 0   X Max: 2000

   Y Min: 900   Y Max: 1500

77. a. Vertex: (−25,000, −10,000)

   b. The parabola is narrow.

   c. The parabola faces downward.

   d. X Min: −25010   X Max: −24990

   Y Min: −11000   Y Max: −9900

Section **11.3**

1. $f(x) = 2.0(x + 5)^2 - 15$

3. $f(x) = 0.4(x - 4)^2 + 3.2$

5. $f(x) = 2(x + 1.5)^2 - 20$

7. $f(x) = 2.7(x - 5)^2 - 8$

9. $f(x) = -2(x - 7)^2 + 15$

11. $f(x) = 4(x + 2)^2 - 10$

13. Change k to shift the graph up.

15. Change h to shift the graph right.

17. Change a to make the graph wider.

19. Change both h and k to shift the graph left and up.

21. a. Let $R(p)$ be the revenue in dollars from selling gloves at a price of p dollars. $R(p) = -(p - 20)^2 + 500$

   b. The total revenue reaches a maximum of $500 from selling the gloves for $20 a pair.

   c. This model predicts the revenue will be about $496 if the gloves sell for $22 a pair.

   d. Domain: [6, 35]; range: [275, 500]

23. a. Let $T(m)$ be the average monthly low temperatures (in degrees Fahrenheit) in Anchorage, Alaska, during month m (i.e., $m = 1$ represents January). $T(m) = -2.56(m - 7)^2 + 51$

   b. The highest average low temperature for Anchorage, Alaska, is about 51°F in July.

   c. This model predicts the average low temperature in March to be 10°F.

   d. Domain: [3, 11]; range: [10, 51]

25. a. Let $F(t)$ be the number of Hispanic families in thousands in the United States below the poverty level t years since 1990.

$$F(t) = 46(t - 9.5)^2 + 1520$$

   b. In 2005, there were approximately 2,911,500 Hispanic families in the United States under the poverty level.

   c. In about 1999 or 2000, the number of Hispanic families in the United States under the poverty level reached a

minimum of about 1,520,000. This is probably true only for this close time period.

   d. Domain: [6, 15]; range: [1520, 2911.5]

27. a. Let $H(t)$ be the number of hours per year the average person spent using the Internet t years since 1990.

$$H(t) = 5.7(t - 5)^2 + 5$$

   b. If you use this model for years before 1995, the model shows more and more hours spent on the Internet as you go back in time. This is model breakdown because the Internet was just beginning to take off in the early 1990s.

   c. Domain: [5, 12]; range: [5, 284]

   d. $H(11) = 210.2$. In 2001, the average person spent 210 hours using the Internet.

   e. According to this model, people spent 365 hours per year on the Internet in 2003.

29. a. Let $H(d)$ be the height of the baseball (in feet) from the ground, and let d be the horizontal distance of the ball (in feet) from home plate.

$$H(d) = -0.0026(d - 230)^2 + 140$$

   b. Domain: [0, 400]; range: [2.46, 140]

   c. This vertex of this model is (230, 140), which means that at a distance of 230 feet after being hit, the baseball will be at a maximum height of about 140 feet from the ground.

   d. $H(450) = 14.16$, If the center wall of the stadium is 450 feet from home plate and is 10 feet tall, the ball will make it over the wall.

31. $y = -4(x + 5)^2 + 8$

   Domain: All real numbers; range: $(-\infty, 8]$

33. $y = (x - 5)^2 - 4$

   Domain: All real numbers; range: $[-4, \infty)$

35. $y = 12(x + 55)^2 - 9000$

   Domain: All real numbers; range: $[-9000, \infty)$

37. $y = -(x - 6)^2 + 14$

   Domain: All real numbers; range: $(-\infty, 14]$

39. $y = 3.2x - 15$

   Domain: All real numbers; range: All real numbers

41. $y = -1.5x^2 + 8$

   Domain: All real numbers; range: $(-\infty, 8]$

43. $y = -0.4(x + 5)^2$

   Domain: All real numbers; range: $(-\infty, 0]$

45. $f(x) = x^2 + x - 6$

47. $f(x) = -x^2 + 9$

49. $f(x) = -2x^2 + 8$

51. $f(x) = \dfrac{10}{9}(x + 2)^2 + 5$

53. $f(x) = x^2 + 4x - 21$

55. $f(x) = x^2 - 6x + 8$

57. $f(x) = 3x^2 - 14x + 8$

or $f(x) = x^2 - \dfrac{14}{3}x + \dfrac{8}{3}$

59. $f(x) = 5x^2 - 30x + 40$

61. $f(x) = -3x^2 - 5.25x + 1.5$

63. $f(x) = -4x^2 + \dfrac{50}{3}x + 6$

Section 11.4

1. $x = 10$ $x = -10$ **3.** $x = 9$ $x = -9$

5. $x = 13$ $x = -13$ **7.** $x = \pm 8$

9. $a = \pm 13$ **11.** $a = \pm 5$

13. $x = \pm 7$ **15.** $r = \pm 5$

17. $t = \pm 5$ **19.** $x = \pm 4$

21. $b = \pm 4$ **23.** $x = 12$ $x = -2$

25. $x = 3$ $x = -17$ **27.** $x = 21.6$ $x = -7.6$

29. $x \approx 4.268$ $x \approx 7.732$ **31.** $x \approx 0.690$ $x \approx -8.690$

33. The correct answers are $x = 2$, $x = -10$. When applying the square root property, the student did not include the negative square root, so one answer was missed.

35. a. $t \approx 1.58$. It will take approximately 1.58 seconds for the ball to fall to a height of 20 feet.

b. $t \approx 1.94$. It will take approximately 1.94 seconds for the ball to hit the ground.

37. a. $t \approx 1.75$. It will take approximately 1.75 seconds for the rock to fall to a height of 10 meters.

b. $t \approx 2.26$. It will take approximately 2.26 seconds for the rock to hit the ground.

39. $r \approx 977.21$. The radius of the circular region is approximately 977.21 feet.

41. $s = 15$. The length of each side of the room is 15 feet.

43. a. In 1998, 27.2 million cassette singles were shipped by major recording media manufacturers.

b. In about 1989 and 1997, about 50 million cassette singles were shipped by major recording media manufacturers.

c. Vertex = (13, 85.6). In 1993, the number of cassette singles shipped by major recording media manufacturers reached a maximum of 85.6 million.

d. Anytime before about 1988 is probably model breakdown, and anytime after 1999 will also be model breakdown because the model gives a negative number of cassette singles being shipped.

45. a. In 2000, personal households and nonprofit organizations invested about $3133 billion in time and savings accounts.

b. According to this model, personal households and nonprofit organizations invested about $7500 billion in time and savings deposits in the years 1976 and 2010. 1976 might be model breakdown.

c. Vertex: (3, 2300). In about 1993, personal households and nonprofit organizations invested about $2300 billion in time and savings deposits. This was the minimum amount invested around this time.

47. a. Let $P(t)$ be the poverty threshold (in dollars) for a family of four in t years since 1900.

$$P(t) = 17(t - 67)^2 + 2920$$

b. The poverty threshold for a family of four in 1990 was about $11,913.

c. Domain: [60, 95]; range: [2920, 16,248]

d. The poverty threshold for a family of four was $5000 in about 1956 and 1978; 1956 would be model breakdown.

49. a. After 5 minutes, there would be about 1125 gallons of water remaining in the tank.

b. After about 10 minutes, there would be only 500 gallons of water remaining in the tank.

c. After about 18 minutes, there would be only 20 gallons of water remaining in the tank.

51. $x = \pm 3i$ **53.** $t = \pm 4i$

55. $x = 8 \pm \dfrac{2\sqrt{6}}{3}i \approx 8 + 1.633i$

57. A 6.1% interest rate would turn a deposit of $800 into $900 in 2 years.

59. A 3.68% interest rate would turn a deposit of $2000 into $2150 in 2 years.

61. $b \approx 4.58$ **63.** $a = 15$

65. $c \approx 4.24$ **67.** $c = 10$

69. a. $b = 12.5$. The height of the roof is 12.5 feet.

b. $c \approx 19.53$. The common rafter length is approximately 19.53 feet.

71. a. $b = 12.75$. The height of the roof is 12.75 feet.

b. $c = 21.25$. The common rafter length is 21.25 feet.

73. $c = 20$. The diagonal of the room is 20 feet.

75. $c = 500$. The diagonal of the warehouse is 500 feet.

$A = 120,000$. The area of the warehouse is 120,000 square feet.

77. The guy wire is approximately 2236.068 feet long.

79. Abida should put the base of the ladder 15 feet away from the house.

Section 11.5

1. $a = 1$ $b = -5$ $c = 21$

3. $a = -1$ $b = 12$ $c = -16$

5. $a = 1$ $b = -6$ $c = 12$

7. $a = -4$ $b = -3$ $c = 10$

9. a. 4   **b.** 16

11. a. -7 **b.** 49

13. a. 2.5 **b.** 6.25

15. $x = -3, x = -7$ **17.** $x = 4 \pm \sqrt{2}; x \approx 5.41, x \approx 2.59$

19. $y = 11 \pm \sqrt{10}; y \approx 14.16, y \approx 7.84$

21. $a = 8 \pm \sqrt{3}; a \approx 6.27, a \approx 9.73$

23. $x = 9, x = -7$

25. Austin did not add $\left(\dfrac{1}{2}b\right)^2$ to the right side of the equation.

$$x^2 + 2x = 3$$
$$x^2 + 2x + (1)^2 = 3 + (1)^2$$
$$(x + 1)^2 = 4$$
$$x + 1 = \pm 2$$
$$x = 1, -3$$

27. Diego did not include both positive and negative possibilities as solutions to $\sqrt{16}$.

$$x^2 - 4x = 12$$
$$x^2 - 4x + 4 = 12 + 4$$
$$(x - 2)^2 = 16$$
$$x - 2 = \pm 4$$
$$x = 6, -2$$

29. $x = 1 \quad x = -7$

31. $x \approx 16.185 \quad x \approx -0.185$

33. $x = -2 \pm i\sqrt{3}$

35. $x \approx 0.352 \quad x \approx -11.352$

37. $x = 2 \quad x = 7$

39. $m = -4 \pm 2i$

41. $x = 1 \quad x = -5$

43. $x = 0 \quad x = -\dfrac{7}{5}$

45. $x = 2 \quad x = -\dfrac{10}{7}$

47. $f(x) = (x + 3)^2 - 1$

49. $g(t) = (t - 4)^2 - 36$

51. $f(x) = \left(x - \dfrac{7}{2}\right)^2 - \dfrac{9}{4}$

53. $h(x) = 3(x + 2)^2 + 12$

55. $f(t) = 2(t - 4)^2 - 44$

57. $f(x) = 4\left(x + \dfrac{5}{8}\right)^2 - \dfrac{345}{16}$

59. $g(x) = 0.5(x + 7)^2 - 54.5$

61. $f(x) = 0.2(x - 17.5)^2 - 71.25$

63. $c(p) = \dfrac{2}{7}\left(p - \dfrac{35}{4}\right)^2 - \dfrac{1249}{56}$

65. Domain: All real numbers; range: $[-16, \infty)$

67. Domain: All real numbers; Range: $[-5, \infty)$

69. Domain: All real numbers; range: $[10, \infty)$

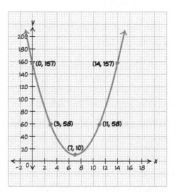

71. Domain: All real numbers; range: $(-\infty, 18]$

73. Domain: All real numbers; range: $(-\infty, 32]$

75. Domain: All real numbers; range: $[-12, \infty)$

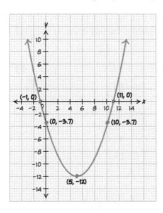

77. Domain: All real numbers; range: $[0.2, \infty)$

79. Domain: All real numbers; range: $[-16, \infty)$

81. Domain: All real numbers; range: $[-1, \infty)$

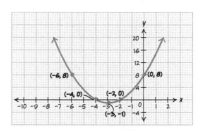

83. Domain: All real numbers; range: $[-36, \infty)$

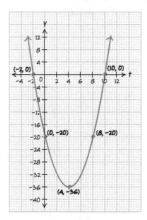

85. Domain: All real numbers; range: $[-2.25, \infty)$

87. Domain: All real numbers; range: $[12, \infty)$

89. Domain: All real numbers; range: $[-44, \infty)$

91. Domain: All real numbers; range: $[-21.5625, \infty)$

93. Domain: All real numbers; range: $[-54.5, \infty)$

Section **11.6**

1. $x = -5, x = -3$

3. $x = 5, x = 2$

5. $a = -1 \pm 2\sqrt{2}$; $a \approx 1.83, a \approx -3.83$

7. $x = \dfrac{7 \pm \sqrt{3}}{2}$; $x \approx 4.37, x \approx 2.63$

9. $x = \dfrac{1 \pm \sqrt{5}}{3}$; $x \approx 1.08, x \approx -0.41$

11. $x = -4, x = 1$

13. $x = -0.5, x = 5$

15. $x \approx -1.07, x \approx 2.82$

17. $a = \dfrac{5}{3}, a = -\dfrac{1}{5}$

19. $y = \dfrac{-6 \pm \sqrt{65}}{5}$; $y \approx 0.41, y \approx -2.81$

21. Liliana did not put the equation in the form $ax^2 + bx + c = 0$ and improperly identified the values for a, b, and c.

$$x^2 + 2x + 1 = 0$$
$$a = 1 \qquad b = 2 \qquad c = 1$$
$$x = \frac{-(2) \pm \sqrt{(2)^2 - 4(1)(1)}}{2(1)}$$
$$x = \frac{-(2) \pm \sqrt{0}}{2}$$
$$x = -1$$

23. Cassandra did not take the opposite of b for the first step in using the formula. The opposite of -5 is 5.

$$3x^2 - 5x - 12 = 0$$
$$a = 3 \qquad b = -5 \qquad c = -12$$
$$x = \frac{-(-5) \pm \sqrt{(-5)^2 - 4(3)(-12)}}{2(3)}$$
$$x = \frac{5 \pm \sqrt{169}}{6}$$
$$x = \frac{5 \pm 13}{6}$$
$$x = 3, x = -\frac{4}{3}$$

25. a. $5000 = -2x^2 + 250x$

b. $x = 25, x = 100$

c. The photographer must sell at least 25 copies of his photographs to make a profit of $5000.00.

27. $x \approx 7.75, x \approx 32.25$

The Web designer must work at least 7.75 hours to make a revenue of $500.00.

29. a. *When* is a reference to time t.

b. The value of the height h is 0 when the rocket hits the ground.

$$0 = -16t^2 + 160t + 5$$

c. The equation in part b is quadratic.

d. $t \approx -0.04, t \approx 8.79$

e. The negative solution $t \approx -0.04$ does not make sense for this problem, but $t \approx 8.79$ does make sense. The rocket will hit the ground approximately 8.79 seconds after launch.

31. a. $t \approx 1.28$. The rock will fall to a height of 52 meters in approximately 1.28 seconds.

b. $t \approx 3.50$. The rock will hit the ground in approximately 3.50 seconds.

33. a. $L(55) = 22.63$. In 1955, about 22.63 thousand tons of lead were used in paint in the United States.

b. In about 1965, 5500 tons of lead were used in paints in the United States. 1984 would be considered model breakdown.

c. In 1945, about 51 thousand tons of lead were used in paints in the United States. 2005 would be model breakdown.

35. a. The current in the wire after 0.5 second would be about 3.75 amperes.

b. After about 3 seconds, the current would reach 20 amperes.

c. After about 5 seconds, the current would reach 60 amperes.

37. a. The marginal cost of producing the 201st pair of shoes would be $27.

b. For the marginal cost to be $20 per pair of shoes, you would be producing the 163rd pair of shoes.

39. a. The marginal cost of producing the 401st bike would be $158.

b. For the marginal cost to be $700 per bike, you would be producing the 1073rd bike.

41. a. One second after launch, the rocket was 186 feet high.

b. The rocket first reached 450 feet 2.9 seconds into the flight.

c. The rocket will first reach a height of 600 feet about 4.95 seconds into the flight.

d. The rocket never reached a height of 700 feet. The rocket reached a maximum of 627 feet.

43. a. In 2000, an average person spent 141 hours on the Internet.

b. In 1999, an average person spent 100 hours on the Internet. 1989 would be model breakdown.

c. In 2004, an average person spent about 1 hour per day on the Internet. 1984 would be model breakdown.

45. $x = -\dfrac{5}{4} \pm \dfrac{\sqrt{39}}{4}i \approx -1.25 + 1.561i$

47. $x = 0, x = 1, x = -\dfrac{7}{5}$

49. $x = 0, x = 7 \pm 4i$

51. $x = 7 \pm \dfrac{\sqrt{2}}{2}i$

53. $a = 3, a = -5$

55. $t \approx -1.67, t \approx 1.67$

57. $x = 0, x = 5$

59. $x = 0, x \approx 0.55$

61. $x = 18.4$

63. $x+ = 0, x = -\dfrac{3}{5}$

65. $x = 13, x = 5$

67. $x = 2, x = 0.5$

69. $w \approx 5.93, w \approx 2.07$

71. $f \approx 3.22, f \approx -4.62$

73. $d = -7, d = 5$

75. $b = -4, b = 7$

77. $s = -9 \pm 3i$

79. $d = -12, d = -22$

81. $f \approx 14.46, f \approx -10.46$

83. $p \approx -3.95, p \approx 2.28$

85. $\dfrac{-2}{3} \pm \dfrac{2i\sqrt{14}}{3}$

87. $x = 8 \pm i\sqrt{6}$

89. $x = 12, x = 0, x = -7$

91. $x = 1$

93. $d \approx -6.43$

95. $x \approx 10.05, x \approx 20.05$

97. $x \approx 6.62, x \approx -3.62$

99. $(3, 10), (-4, 10)$

101. No real solution.

103. $(-5, -1)$

105. $(-3, -25)$

107. $(-4, 12), (3, 12)$

109. $\approx (-3.71, 0.295), (2.71, 6.71)$

111. $(-0.41, -10.07), (2.41, 4.07)$

113. No real solution.

115. $(-4, 19), (1.71, 8.39)$

117. $(2.5, 7.25), (3, 8)$

119. $(-2.54, -1.04), (1.21, -0.72)$

121. $(-3, -29)$

123. No real solution.

125. No real solution.

127. $(-1.41, 0.17), (1.41, 5.83)$

Section 11.7

1. $y = -2x^2 - 6x - 7$: C, downward, y-int: $(0, -7)$.

$y = -0.5x^2 - x + 7$: A, downward, y-int: $(0, 7)$.

$y = x^2 + 4x + 4$: B, upward, y-int: $(0, 4)$.

$y = x^2 - 5x - 6$: None, upward, y-int: $(0, -6)$.

3. $y = -2(x - 3)^2 - 9$: None, downward.

$y = 2(x - 3)^2 - 9$: A, upward, vertex: $(3, -9)$.

$y = 2(x + 4)^2 + 1$: C, upward, vertex: $(-4, 1)$.

$y = 2(x + 4)^2 - 9$: B, upward, vertex: $(-4, -9)$.

5. Vertex: $(-3, -1)$

Vertical intercept: $(0, 8)$

Horizontal intercepts: $(-4, 0), (-2, 0)$

7. Vertex: $(3, -12)$

Vertical intercept: $(0, 15)$

Horizontal intercepts: $(1, 0), (5, 0)$

9. Vertex: $(8, -20)$

Vertical intercept: $(0, 236)$

Horizontal intercepts: $(5.764, 0), (10.236, 0)$

11. Vertex: $(-1.2, 2.8)$

Vertical intercept: $(0, 10)$

Horizontal intercepts: None

13. Vertex: $(2, -2)$

Vertical intercept: $(0, 4)$

Horizontal intercepts: $(0.845, 0), (3.155, 0)$

15. a. The cost to produce 30 uniforms would be about $2975.

   b. The vertex is $(50, 2875)$, which means the minimum cost would be $2875, producing 50 uniforms.

   c. According to the model, the school can never produce uniforms for $1600, which would be model breakdown.

17. a. The revenue from selling 5 thousand digital cameras would be $375 thousand.

   b. The company must sell 10 thousand cameras or 20 thousand cameras to generate revenue of $600,000.

   c. The company must sell 15 thousand cameras to maximize its revenue.

19. a. According to this model, the annual net sales for Home Depot in 1995 were about $14,471 million.

   b. Home Depot's net sales were $30,000 million in about 1998.

   c. The vertex is $(-0.728, 2118.9)$, which means that in 1989 Home Depot's net sales were at a low point of $2118.90 million.

21. a. According to this model, the net income for Quiksilver in 1999 was about $30.4 million.

   b. According to this model, Quiksilver's net income reached $18 million in 1997 and again in 2004.

   c. The vertex is $(10.77, 35.08)$, which means that in about 2001, Quiksilver reached a maximum net sales of $35.08 million.

23. a. The ball is at a height of 4 feet when it is hit.

   b. The ball reached a height of 20 feet about 0.5 second and again 2 seconds after being hit.

   c. The ball reached its maximum height 1.25 seconds after being hit.

   d. The ball reached a maximum height of 29 feet.

   e. If the ball does not get caught, the ball will hit the ground 2.596 seconds after being hit.

25. a. The ball is at a height of 4.2 feet when it is hit.

   b. The ball reached a height of 40 feet at 0.744 second and again 3.0055 seconds after being hit.

   c. The ball's maximum height is 60.45 feet.

   d. If the ball does not get caught, the ball will hit the ground 3.819 seconds after being hit.

27. a. $H(6) = 58.4$. In June, the average high temperature in Melbourne, Australia, is 58.4°F.

   b. The vertex is $(7.22, 57.056)$, which means that in July, the average high temperature in Melbourne, Australia, reaches its minimum of 57.056°F.

   c. During September and May, the average temperature of Melbourne, Australia, is about 60°F.

29. Domain: All real numbers; range: $[-16, \infty)$

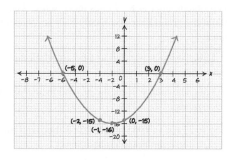

31. Domain: All real numbers; range: $(-\infty, 6.25]$

33. Domain: All real numbers; range: $[-264.5, \infty)$

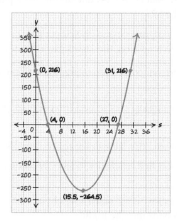

35. Domain: All real numbers; range: $[5, \infty)$

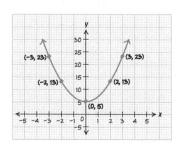

37. Domain: All real numbers; range: $(-\infty, -3]$

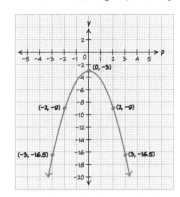

39. Domain: All real numbers; range: $(-\infty, -5]$

41. Domain: All real numbers; range: $(-\infty, 2.8125]$

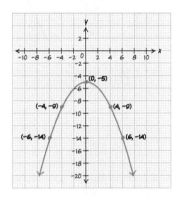

43. Domain: All real numbers; range: $[-52.9, \infty)$

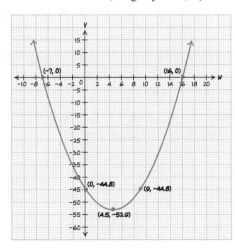

45. Domain: All real numbers; range: $[-3.1, \infty)$

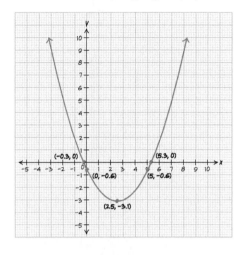

47. Domain: All real numbers; range: $(-\infty, 86.8]$

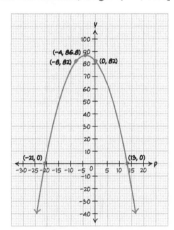

49. Domain: All real numbers; range: $(-\infty, 17]$

51.

53.

55.

57.

59.

61.

63.

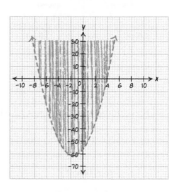

65. $y < x^2 + x - 12$ **67.** $y \geq -0.5(x + 5)(x + 1)$

Chapter 11 Review Exercises

1. a. Vertex $= (-1, 9)$ **b.** $x < -1$

  c. $x > -1$ **d.** $(-4, 0), (2, 0)$ **e.** $(0, 8)$

2. a. $x = -1$

  b. a would be negative, since the graph faces downward.

  c. $h = -1, \quad k = 9$ **d.** $f(1) = 5$ **e.** $x = -5.5, x = 3.5$

3. a. $x = 1$

  b. a would be positive, since the graph faces upward.

  c. $h = 1, k = -4$ **d.** $f(-1.5) = 2.25$

  e. $x = -1.6, x = 3.6$

4. a. Vertex: $(1, -4)$ **b.** $x > 1$ **c.** $x < 1$

  d. $(-1, 0), (3, 0)$ **e.** $(0, -3)$

5. a. $P(8) = 637.87$. In 1998, the population of North Dakota was approximately 638 thousand.

b.

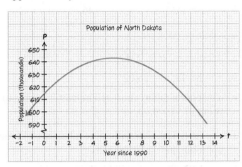

c. Vertex = (5.6, 643). In about 1996, the population of North Dakota reached a maximum of about 643 thousand people.

d. The population of North Dakota was about 640,000 in about 1994 and about 1998.

e. Range: $606.55 \leq P(t) \leq 643$

6. a. There were approximately 17.9 thousand murders in the United States in 1996.

b. Vertex: (2.5, 23). In about 1993, the most murders occurred in the United States at 23 thousand.

c. In 1997 and 1988, there were about 14,500 murders in the United States.

d. Range: [10.295, 23]

7. $h(x) = (x + 3)^2 - 16$
Domain: $(-\infty, \infty)$; range: $[-16, \infty)$

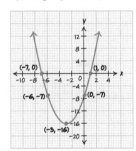

8. $f(x) = 1.25(x - 4)^2 - 20$
Domain: $(-\infty, \infty)$; range: $[4, \infty)$

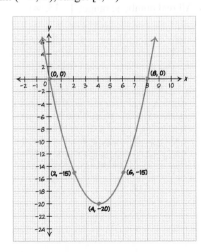

9. $g(x) = -\dfrac{1}{4}(x - 8)^2 + 9$
Domain: $(-\infty, \infty)$; range: $(-\infty, 9]$

10. $h(x) = -2(x + 4.5)^2 + 12.5$
Domain: $(-\infty, \infty)$; range: $(-\infty, 12.5]$

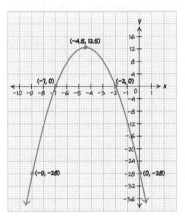

11. $g(x) = -0.5(x + 7)^2 - 3$
Domain: $(-\infty, \infty)$; range: $(-\infty, -3]$

12. $f(x) = 3(x - 8)^2 + 4$
Domain: $(-\infty, \infty)$; range: $[4, \infty)$

13. a. Let $J(t)$ be the number of juveniles arrested for possession of drugs t years since 1990.

$$J(t) = -3095(t - 7)^2 + 124,683$$

b. Domain: [1, 11]; range [13,263, 124,683]

c. In 2000, there were approximately 96,828 juveniles arrested for drug possession.

d. The juvenile arrests were down to 50,000 again in about 2002.

14. a. Let $R(t)$ be the obligations of the U.S. Department of Commerce for research and development in millions of dollars t years since 1990. $R(t) = 17(t - 8.1)^2 + 982$

b. Domain: [4, 12]; range: [982, 1267.77]

c. $R(8) = 982.17$. In 1998, the research and development obligations of the U.S. Department of Commerce were approximately $982 million.

d. The research and development obligations for the U.S. Department of Commerce reached $1.5 billion in about 1993 and in 2004.

15. a. In 1995, the median sales price of a new home in the western United States was $142,310.

b. In 2003, the median sales price of a new home in the western United States reached $250,000.

c. Vertex: (2.72, 136.73). In about 2003, the median sales price of a new home in the western United States reached a low of $136,730.

16. a. In 2004, the median asking price of houses in Memphis, Tennessee, was $158,360.

b. In 2005 and again in 2009, the median asking price of houses in Memphis, Tennessee, reached $165,000.

c. Vertex: (6.95, 170.84). In about 2007, the median asking price of houses in Memphis, Tennessee, reached a high of $170,840.

17. $t = \pm 13$

18. $m = \pm 7$

19. $m = \pm 4i$

20. $x = -4, x = -10$

21. $x \approx 11.66, x \approx 0.34$

22. $a = 7 \pm i\sqrt{3}$

23. $g = 9 \pm 2i$

24. $c \approx -3.76, x \approx -8.24$

25. $p \approx 4.87, p \approx 3.13$

26. $b \approx 13.27$

27. $a \approx 9.80$

28. $x \approx -27.11, x \approx 1.11$

29. $x = 13, x = -1$

30. $x = 6, x = -11$

31. $x \approx 0.75 \pm 2.11i$

32. $f(x) = (x + 4)^2 - 5$

33. $g(x) = -6\left(x - \dfrac{5}{3}\right)^2 - \dfrac{4}{3}$

34. $y = (x + 1)^2 - 9$

35. $y = -3(x + 1)^2 + 12$

36. $x = -2, x = 6$

37. $t = -9, t = \dfrac{7}{2}$

38. $x = -3 \pm 3i$

39. $x \approx 2.19, x \approx -5.19$

40. $x \approx 2.10, x \approx -1.32$

41. $n = \dfrac{57}{13}, n = -3$

42. $x \approx -0.28, x \approx -2.39$

43. $a \approx -3.87, a \approx +3.87$

44. $x = -2 \pm \dfrac{\sqrt{3}}{3}i$

45. $b = -2 \pm i\sqrt{5}$

46. $t = 0, t = 3 \pm 2i$

47. $h = 0, h = -4 \pm 7i$

48. a. $4500 = -2x^2 + 225x$

b. $x \approx 86.48, x \approx 26.02$

c. The photographer must sell at least 27 prints to make a profit of $4500.00.

49. a. $t \approx 1.01$. The rock will fall to a height of 13 meters in approximately 1.01 seconds.

b. $t \approx 1.92$. The rock will hit the ground in approximately 1.92 seconds.

50. Domain: All real numbers; range: $(-\infty, 2.5]$

51. Domain: All real numbers; range: $[7, \infty)$

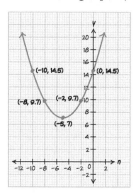

52. Domain: All real numbers; range: $[-15, \infty)$

53. Domain: All real numbers; range: $(-\infty, 28]$

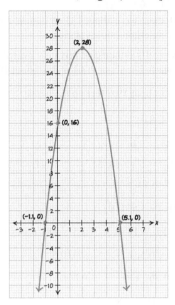

54. $(-3, -24), (4, 11)$ **55.** $(-2, 11), (6, -21)$

56. $(1, 13), (4.5, 118)$ **57.** $(-1.46, -12.32), (5.46, 22.32)$

58. $(3, 9), (5, 9)$

59. a. The largest possible rectangular area is 1250 ft².

   b. The largest possible area requires a length of 50 feet and a width of 25 feet.

60. $y < 2x^2 + 24x - 10$

61. $y \geq 0.5x^2 - 4x - 6$

62. $y \leq 2.5(x - 4)^2 - 18$

63. $y > -0.8(x + 1)^2 - 3$

64. $(-4, 3), (2, 6)$

65. $(-4, 0), (2, 9)$

Chapter 11 Test

1. a. $V(8) \approx 1578$. In 2008, there were approximately 1578 thousand violent crimes in the United States.

   b.

   c. Vertex = $(4, 1370)$. In 2004, the number of violent crimes in the United States was at a minimum of 1370 thousand.

   d. According to this graph, there were 1.5 million violent crimes in 2001 and again in 2007.

2. $(-6, 4)$, and $(4, 8)$ **3.** $x = -\dfrac{7}{3}, x = 4$

4. $x = \dfrac{7}{4}, x = \dfrac{5}{2}$

5. a. Let $O(t)$ be the total outlays in billions of dollars for national defense and veterans benefits by the United States t years since 1990. $O(t) = 1.9(t - 6)^2 + 308$

b. Domain: [1, 11]; range: [308, 355.5]

c. In 1998, the total outlays for national defense and veterans benefits by the United States were about $315.6 billion.

d. Total outlays for national defense and veterans benefits by the United States reached half a trillion dollars in about 2006.

6. a. Let $R(t)$ be the revenue for the U.S. commercial space industry from the satellite manufacturing in billions of dollars t years since 1990.

$$R(t) = -1.225(t - 8)^2 + 11.8$$

b. Domain: [6,10]; range: [6.9, 11.8]. In this case, we did not go back from the data because it resulted in a very small revenue in 1995, and that seemed like model breakdown.

c. $R(10) = 6.9$. In 2000, the revenue from satellite manufacturing was about $6.9 billion.

d. Vertex = (8, 11.8). In 1998, the revenue from satellite manufacturing reached a maximum of $11.8 billion.

7. Domain: All real numbers; range: $(-\infty, 3.5]$

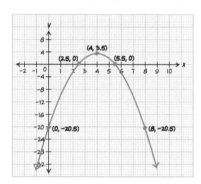

8. Domain: All real numbers; range: $[10, \infty)$

9. Domain: All real numbers; range: $(-\infty, -17]$

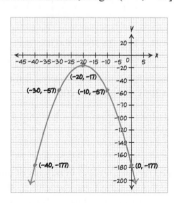

10. $(1, -2)$ and $\left(-\dfrac{11}{9}, -\dfrac{982}{81}\right)$

11. a. In 2000, there were about 1230.8 thousand privately owned single-unit houses started.

b. There were 1000 thousand privately owned single-unit houses started in about 2001 and in about 1996.

12. The ladder is about 19.6 feet up the house.

13. $(-7, 4), (-4, 8)$

14. a. $(-3, -4)$ **b.** $x > -3$ **c.** $x < -3$
   d. $x = -3$ **e.** $(0, 5)$ **f.** $(-5, 0), (-1, 0)$
   g. $f(x) = x^2 + 6x + 5$

15. $(-8.449, 0), (-3.551, 0)$

16. $x = 3, x = 15$ **17.** $x = \pm 2.5$ **18.** $b \approx 10.39$

19. $x = -5 + i\sqrt{0.5}, x = -5 - i\sqrt{0.5}$

20. $x \approx -1 + 0.86i, x \approx -1 - 0.86i$

21. $f(x) = 3(x + 4)^2 - 78$

22.

Cumulative Review for Chapters 1–11

1. $m = 4$ **2.** $t = 1, t = 10$

3. $x = 9, x = 5$ **4.** $a = \dfrac{74}{3}$

5. $x = 0, x = \dfrac{8}{3}$ **6.** $m = \dfrac{108}{17} \approx 6.35, m = -5$

7. $c = 12$ **8.** $n = 0, n = -18, n = 12$

9. $x = -1, x = 5$ **10.** $h \approx -8.68$

11. $c = -\dfrac{41}{3}$ **12.** $w = 3$

13. $x = -22$ **14.** $x = 5$

15. $m = \dfrac{n + 5}{4n}$ **16.** $b = \dfrac{\frac{5}{2}(c - 7a)}{a^2} = \dfrac{5c}{2a^2} - \dfrac{35}{2a}$

17. $x = 5, y = 4$ **18.** $(-5, -22)$ and $(2, -1)$

19. Inconsistent system; no solution.

20. $m = 1, n = -1$

21. $(2.13, 2.08)$ and $(-2.04, -11.60)$

22. Consistent system with dependent lines; infinite number of solutions.

23. $y = \dfrac{9}{2}x - 10$ **24.** $y = -\dfrac{1}{8}x + 6$

25. $y = -0.4x + 8.8$

26. $\dfrac{-1}{m + 5}$ **27.** $\dfrac{4}{a + 4}$ **28.** $\dfrac{3a + 4}{4a - 7}$

29. $x^3 y$ **30.** $5\sqrt{3}$ **31.** $2x\sqrt{5x}$

32. a. Let $C(n)$ be the cost to produce custom printed tote bags, and let n be the number of bags.

$$C(n) = 3.55n + 50$$

  b. 200 bags will cost $760.

  c. Slope $= 3.55$. The cost to produce custom printed tote bags is increased by $3.55 per bag.

33. a. Let $P(t)$ be the population of Pittsburgh, Pennsylvania, in millions t years since 2000.

$$P(t) = -0.012t + 2.434$$

  b. Domain: $[-2, 12]$; range: $[2.29, 2.458]$

  c. The population of Pittsburgh, Pennsylvania, will be about 2.29 million in 2012.

  d. The slope is -0.012. The population of Pittsburgh, Pennsylvania, is decreasing by 12,000 people per year.

  e. In 2015, the population of Pittsburgh, Pennsylvania, will be 2.25 million.

34. a. Let $R(p)$ be the revenue from selling four-person tents (in dollars) if they are priced at p dollars each.

$$R(p) = -0.989(p - 70)^2 + 3250$$

  b. The vertex is $(70, 3250)$. When the price is $70 per four-person tent, the revenue generated is at a maximum of $3250.

  c. When the price is $60 per four-person tent, the revenue generated is $3151.10.

  d. Domain: $[20, 100]$; range: $[777.5, 3250]$

35. a. Let $E(t)$ be the net summer electricity capacity in the United States (in millions of kilowatts) t years since 2000.

$$E(t) = 12t + 915$$

  b. Domain: $[-2, 12]$; range: $[891, 1059]$

  c. In 2015, the net summer electricity capacity in the United States will be about 1095 million kilowatts.

  d. The slope is 12. The net summer electricity capacity in the United States is increasing by 12 million kilowatts per year.

  e. The vertical intercept is $(0, 915)$, which means in the year 2000, the net summer electricity capacity in the United States was 915 million kilowatts.

36. $\dfrac{x + 3}{x - 2}$ **37.** $-\dfrac{h - 4}{h + 2}$

38. $\dfrac{6}{(n + 4)(n + 7)}$ **39.** $\dfrac{v + 7}{v - 8}$

40. $\dfrac{-4h + 41}{(h - 5)(h + 2)}$ **41.** $\dfrac{3x^2 + 6x - 11}{(x - 7)(x + 2)(x + 3)}$

42. $4 + 2x\sqrt{x}$ **43.** $17y - 5y\sqrt{y}$

44. $2x\sqrt{10}$ **45.** $4 - 8\sqrt{3}$ **46.** $3x$

47.

48.

49.

50.

51.

52.

53.

54.

55. $\dfrac{5\sqrt{7}}{7}$ **56.** $\dfrac{12 + 4\sqrt{2}}{7}$

57. a. $-5x + 26$ **b.** $14x^2 + 20x - 144$ **c.** $14x - 28$

58. a. $-2x^2 - 2x + 5$ **b.** $6x^3 + 7x^2 - 47x + 36$
c. $6x^2 + 15x - 31$ **d.** $18x^2 - 33x + 3$

59. a. 20.6 **b.** -104
c. 1.4 **d.** -6.72

60. a. -12 **b.** 90
c. 32 **d.** -2

61. a. $f(21) = -23$ **b.** $x = -6.5$
c. Domain: All real numbers; range: All real numbers

62. a. $g(9) = 20$
b. Domain: All real numbers; range: {20}

63. a. $h(-8) = -12$ **b.** $x = 13.75$
c. Domain: All real numbers; range: All real numbers

64. During the first 8 minutes of a jogathon, the eighth-grader has run 3.5 laps.

65. a. $(0, 9)$ **b.** $(15, 0)$ **c.** $m = -\dfrac{3}{5}$
d. $y = -\dfrac{3}{5}x + 9$

66. a. $f(8) = 4$ **b.** $x = -4$
c. Domain: All real numbers; range: All real numbers

67. a. $m = -\dfrac{2}{9}$ **b.** $(0, 2)$ **c.** $(9, 0)$
d. $y = \dfrac{-2}{9}x + 2$

68. Domain: All real numbers except $x = -6$ and $x = 4$

69. Domain: $x \le 3$

70. a. Let x be the amount in dollars Greg is investing at 3%, and let y be the amount in dollars Greg is investing at 2.5%.

$$x + y = 900{,}000$$
$$0.03x + 0.025y = 25{,}800$$

b. \$240,000 should be invested at 2.5%, and \$660,000 should be invested at 3%.

71. They need to mix 80 pounds of the \$11.99 per pound mild roast coffee with 120 pounds of the \$8.99 per pound bold roast coffee to make 200 pounds of a \$10.19 per pound blend.

72. Deeva needs to make at least \$2750 per week in sales to earn at least \$410 per week.

73. There are four terms. $24x^3y$: variable term, coefficient 24
$-7x^2y^2$: variable term, coefficient -7
$12y^3$: variable term, coefficient 12
-10: constant term

74. There are four terms. $-6x^5$: variable term, coefficient -6
$4x^2$: variable term, coefficient 4
$-2x$: variable term, coefficient -2
4: constant term

75. $24x^3y$ has degree 4.
$-7x^2y^2$ has degree 4.
$12y^3$ has degree 3.
-10 has degree 0.
The degree of the polynomial is 4.

76. $-6x^5$ has degree 5.
$4x^2$ has degree 2.
$-2x$ has degree 1.
4 has degree 0.
The degree of the polynomial is 5.

77. Polynomial

78. Not a polynomial. The variable y has a negative exponent.

79. $b + 7 + \dfrac{33}{b - 4}$

80. $2t + 5$

81. $x < -2$

82. $x \geq -2$

83. $3 < x < 21$

84. $-2 \leq x \leq \dfrac{16}{3}$

85. $x \leq 6$ or $x \geq 12$

86. $x < -3$ or $x > 11$

87. $y1 < y2$ for $x < 8$ **88.** $m = -5$ or $m = 10$

89. $a = 7$ or $a = 11$

90.

91.

92. $b \approx 13.27$ **93.** $a \approx 9.80$

94. $\dfrac{81m^{16}n^{20}}{625}$ **95.** $-40x^4y^9$

96. $\dfrac{3g^2h^4}{2}$ **97.** $-\dfrac{7x^3y^6}{10}$

98. $-\dfrac{3b^4}{2a}$ **99.** $\dfrac{6m^2n^2}{5}$

100. a. $S(6) = 65.56$. In 2006, Sweden's GDP per employed person was \$65,560.

   b. Sweden's GDP per employed person will be greater than that of the Netherlands after 2008.

101. a. In 2007, there were about 8780 loans to African American owned small businesses.

   b. Let $T(t)$ be the total number of loans (in thousands) given to African American and Hispanic American owned small businesses t years past 2000. $T(t) = 2.59t + 2.27$

   c. There will be about 28,170 loans given to African American and Hispanic American owned small businesses in 2010.

102. $(a + 3)(a + 8)$ **103.** $3n(n - 7)(n - 2)$

104. $(2x - 5y)(8x - 7)$ **105.** $(5k + 7)(5k - 7)$

106. $(4t + 3)(3t - 7)$ **107.** $5(z - 2)(z^2 + 2z + 4)$

108. a. The population of this city will be about 78 thousand in 2015.

   b. There will be about 4700 burglaries in this city in 2015.

   c. Let $K(t)$ be the number of burglaries in hundreds in this city t years since 2000. $K(t) = 1.2t + 29$

   d. In 2020, there will be about 5300 burglaries in this city.

109. $f(x) = (x + 5)^2 - 39$

110. a. $I(d) = \dfrac{36{,}000}{d^2}$

   b. The illumination of this light at a distance of 40 feet from the source is 22.5 foot-candles.

   c. An illumination of 50 foot-candles occurs at a distance of approximately 26.8 feet from the source.

111. $11 + i$ **112.** $-10 + 5i$

113. $21 + i$ **114.** $3 - 4i$

115. $\dfrac{7}{2} - \dfrac{1}{2}i$ **116.** $m = \pm 7i$

117. $y = 9, y = -7$

118. $x = 3 \pm 4i$

119. $x = 1 + i, x = 1 - i$

120. $(5x^8)^{\frac{1}{2}}$

121. $\sqrt[3]{(16m^5)^2}$ or $\sqrt[3]{256m^{10}}$

CHAPTER 12
Section 12.1

1. This function is an exponential function because the variable is in the exponent.

3. This function is an exponential function because the variable is in the exponent.

5. This function is a quadratic function because the degree of the polynomial is 2.

7. This function is a quadratic function because the degree of the polynomial is 2.

9. Other, because there is a variable in the numerator and in the denominator.

11. Let $L(h)$ be the number of *Lactobacillus acidophilus* bacteria present after h hours have passed.

   a. $L(h) = 30(2)^h$

   b. After 12 hours, there are 122,880 bacteria present.

   c. After 24 hours, there are 503,316,480 bacteria present.

   d. After just 15 hours, there are about 1 million bacteria present.

13. Let $E(h)$ be the number of *E. coli* bacteria present after h hours have passed.

 a. $E(h) = 3(2)^{2h}$

 b. After 5 hours, there are approximately 3072 bacteria present.

 c. After about 9.17 hours, there are 1 million bacteria present.

15. Let $S(n)$ be the number of *Streptococcus lactis* bacteria present after n 26-minute time intervals have passed.

 a. $S(n) = 8(2)^n$

 b. $S(15) = 262,144$. After 6.5 hours, there are 262,144 bacteria present.

17. Let $B(h)$ be the number of bacteria present after h hours have passed.

 a. $B(h) = 8(3)^{2h}$

 b. After 10 hours, there are approximately 2.7894×10^{10} bacteria present.

19. Let $T(h)$ be the number of *Treponema pallidum* bacteria present after h hours have passed.

 a. $T(h) = 12(2)^{\frac{h}{33}}$

 b. $T(168) = 409$. After 1 week, there are approximately 409 bacteria present.

21. Let $F(n)$ be the number of square meters burnt after n 6-minute time intervals have passed.

 a. $F(n) = 2^{n+1}$ or $F(n) = 2(2)^n$

 b. After $\frac{1}{2}$ hour, there are 64 square meters burnt.

23. Let $H(t)$ be the number of Hispanic centenarians in the year t years since 1990.

 a. $H(t) = 2072(2)^{\frac{t}{7.5}}$

 b. In 2050, there will be approximately 530,432 Hispanic centenarians in the United States.

25. Let $I(t)$ be the population of India (in millions) in the year t years since 1971.

 a. $I(t) = 560(2)^{\frac{t}{33}}$

 b. In 2015, there will be approximately 1411 million people in India.

 c. Midway through the year 2031, there will be approximately 2 billion people in India.

27. Internet search: approximately 65 years.

29. a. $50,000

 b. Your opinion.

 c. Let $S(w)$ be salary option 2 (in dollars) for week w of the job: $S(w) = 0.01(2)^{w-1}$

 d. The total salary from option 2 for 25 weeks of work is $335,544.31.

 e. Option 2 is the better deal for 25 weeks of work.

 f. Option 1 offers $40,000 for 20 weeks of work, and option 2 offers $10,485.75 for 20 weeks of work. Therefore, option 1 is the better deal for 20 weeks of work.

31. Let $P(t)$ be the percentage of lead-210 left in a body t years after a person has died.

 a. $P(t) = 100\left(\frac{1}{2}\right)^{\frac{t}{22}}$

 b. Approximately 60 years after death, there will be about 15.10% of lead-210 left in the body.

 c. Approximately 95 years after death, there will be about 5% of lead-210 left in the body.

33. Let $P(d)$ be the percentage of radon-222 left after d days.

 a. $P(d) = 100\left(\frac{1}{2}\right)^{\frac{d}{3.825}}$

 b. After approximately 30 days, there will be about 0.44% of radon-222 left.

 c. After approximately 16.5 days, there will be about 5% of radon-222 left.

35. a. The graph is decreasing.

 b. This is an example of exponential decay.

 c. $f(10) = 22$

 d. $x = 6$ for $f(x) = 40$

 e. $f(0) = 100$

37. a. The graph is increasing.

 b. This is an example of exponential growth.

 c. $h(5) = 20$

 d. $x = 15$ for $h(x) = 100$

 e. $h(0) = 10$

39. a. The graph is decreasing.

 b. This is an example of exponential decay.

 c. $g(7.5) = 20$

 d. $x = 4$ for $g(x) = 30$

 e. $g(0) = 60$

41. $f(x) = 25(4)^x$

43. $f(x) = -35(7)^x$

45. $f(x) = 2000(0.2)^x$

47. $f(x) = 32(1.5)^x$

49. $f(x) = 6400(0.125)^x$

51. The base $b = 3$, and the coefficient $a = 5$.

53. The base $b = \frac{1}{5}$, and the coefficient $a = 200$.

55. The base $b = 2$, and the coefficient $a = -4$.

57. Let $E(h)$ be the number of *E. coli* bacteria present after h hours have passed: $E(h) = 3(2)^{2h}$.

 a. The base $b = 2$.

 b. The coefficient $a = 3$.

 c. The coefficient $a = 3$ represents the number of *E. coli* bacteria present at time $t = 0$ (at the start).

59. Let $M(h)$ be the number of *Treponema pallidum* bacteria present after h hours have passed: $T(h) = 12(2)^{\frac{h}{33}}$

 a. The base $b = 2$.

 b. The coefficient $a = 12$.

 c. The coefficient $a = 12$ represents the number of *Treponema pallidum* bacteria present at time $t = 0$ (at the start).

61. $f(x) = 3(4)^{\frac{x}{5}}$

63. $f(x) = -7(3)^{\frac{x}{10}}$

65. $f(x) = 1701\left(\frac{1}{3}\right)^{\frac{x}{6}}$

67. $f(x) = 80(4)^{x-2}$

69. $f(x) = 2(6)^{x-5}$

71. $f(x) = 3584(0.25)^{x-4}$

73. The function is increasing because the base is greater than 1.

75. The function is decreasing because the base is less than 1.

77. The function is increasing because the base is greater than 1.

79. The function is decreasing because the base is less than 1.

Section 12.2

1. Exponential equation.

3. Power equation.

5. Power equation.

7. Exponential equation.

9. Power equation.

11. $x = 3$ **13.** $c = 5$ **15.** $t = -2$

17. $x = -4$ **19.** $d = 5$ **21.** $w = 2$

23. $x = 4$ **25.** $x = -4$ **27.** $x = -5$

29. $x = 3$ **31.** $x = 0$ **33.** $m = 0$

35. $t = 0$

37. $x = -2$. Tom evaluated $\frac{1}{16}$ as 4^2 instead of $\frac{1}{16} = 4^{-2}$. So he missed the negative sign in the exponent.

39. a. There are 25,600 *Lactobacillus acidophilus* bacteria present after 8 hours have passed.

b. There are 800 *Lactobacillus acidophilus* bacteria present after 3 hours have passed.

41. a. After 8 hours have passed, 32,805 people have heard the rumor.

b. It takes 4 hours for the rumor to have spread to 405 people.

43. $x = 3$ **45.** $c = 3$ **47.** $c = 3$

49. $t = 2$ **51.** $m = 2$ **53.** $x = 2$

55. $x = 4$ **57.** $x = 4$ **59.** $w = 3$

61. $x = 2$ **63.** $x = \pm 5$ **65.** $w = \pm 5$

67. $x = -6$

69. Warrick forgot to put the $\pm$ symbol on the final answer. Both positive 6 and negative 6 are correct answers.

$$x = \pm 6 \text{ is the correct answer.}$$

71. Frank divided 216 by 3 instead of raising 216 to the power $\frac{1}{3}$.

$$r = 6 \text{ is the correct answer.}$$

73. a. An NBA basketball with radius 12 cm has a volume of about 7238.2 cm³.

b. An International Basketball Federation basketball with a volume of 8011cm³ has a radius of about 12.4 cm.

75. The length of the side is 4.5 in.

77. $x = 2$ **79.** $x \approx \pm 2.6$ **81.** $c \approx \pm 1.2$

83. $x = 5$ **85.** $b = \pm 6$

87. Exponential $k = 4$ **89.** Power $r \approx 1.6$

91. Exponential $x = 3$ **93.** Power $g = 2$

95. Power $h \approx \pm 2.2$ **97.** Exponential $x = 3$

99. Power $x = \pm 3$ **101.** Exponential $x = 7$

Section 12.3

1. a. a is positive because the graph is above the x-axis.

b. $b > 1$ because we have exponential growth with $a > 0$.

c. The graph is increasing.

d. Domain: All real numbers $(-\infty, \infty)$

e. Range: $(0, \infty)$

3. a. a is positive because the graph is above the x-axis.

b. $b < 1$ because we have exponential decay with $a > 0$.

c. The graph is decreasing.

d. Domain: All real numbers

e. Range: $(0, \infty)$

5. a. a is negative because the graph is below the x-axis.

b. $b < 1$ because we have exponential growth with $a < 0$.

c. The graph is increasing.

d. Domain: All real numbers $(-\infty, \infty)$

e. Range: $(-\infty, 0)$

7. a. a is negative because the graph is below the x-axis.

b. $b > 1$ because we have exponential decay with $a < 0$.

c. The graph is decreasing.

d. Domain: All real numbers

e. Range: $(-\infty, 0)$

9. a. a is negative because the graph is below the x-axis.

b. $b > 1$ because we have exponential decay with $a < 0$.

c. The graph is decreasing.

d. Domain: All real numbers $(-\infty, \infty)$

e. Range: $(-\infty, 0)$

11. $f(x) = 7(2)^x$

$a = 7$, so the y-intercept is $(0, 7)$.

$b = 2$, $b > 1$, and $a > 0$, so the graph is increasing.

Domain: $(-\infty, \infty)$, range: $(0, \infty)$

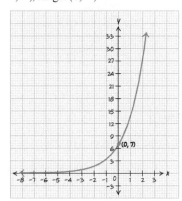

13. $g(x) = 3(1.2)^x$

$a = 3$, so the y-intercept is $(0, 3)$.

$b = 1.2$, $b > 1$, and $a > 0$, so the graph is increasing.

Domain: $(-\infty, \infty)$, range: $(0, \infty)$

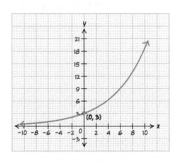

15. $h(x) = 12(1.4)^x$

$a = 12$, so the y-intercept is $(0, 12)$.

$b = 1.4$, $b > 1$, and $a > 0$, so the graph is increasing.

Domain: $(-\infty, \infty)$, range: $(0, \infty)$

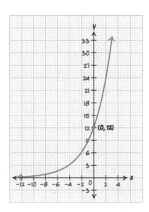

17. $p(t) = 140\left(\dfrac{1}{2}\right)^t$

$a = 140$, so the y-intercept is $(0, 140)$.

$b = \dfrac{1}{2}$, $b < 1$, and $a > 0$, so the graph is decreasing.

Domain: $(-\infty, \infty)$, range: $(0, \infty)$

19. $f(x) = 250\left(\dfrac{1}{4}\right)^x$

$a = 250$, so the y-intercept is $(0, 250)$.

$b = \dfrac{1}{4}$, $b < 1$, and $a > 0$, so the graph is decreasing.

Domain: $(-\infty, \infty)$, range: $(0, \infty)$

21. a.

Number of E. Coli Bacteria in a Sample

b. The B-intercept is $(0, 4)$. At the start, there were 4 *E. coli* bacteria present in the sample.

23. a.

Number of Radium-203 Atoms Remaining in a Sample

b. The N-intercept is $(0, 5000)$. At the start, there were 5000 radium-203 atoms present in the sample.

25. $f(x) = -2(1.4)^x$

$a = -2$, so the y-intercept is $(0, -2)$.

$b = 1.4$, $b > 1$, and $a < 0$, so the graph is decreasing.

Domain: $(-\infty, \infty)$, range: $(-\infty, 0)$

33. $h(t) = -0.4(1.5)^t$

$a = -0.4$, so the vertical intercept is $(0, -0.4)$.

$b = 1.5$, $b > 1$, and $a < 0$, so the graph is decreasing.

Domain: $(-\infty, \infty)$, range: $(-\infty, 0)$

27. $g(t) = -3(0.7)^t$

$a = -3$, so the vertical intercept is $(0, -3)$.

$b = 0.7$, $b < 1$, and $a < 0$, so the graph is increasing.

Domain: $(-\infty, \infty)$, range: $(-\infty, 0)$

35. $c(n) = 550\left(\dfrac{3}{4}\right)^n$

$a = 550$, so the vertical intercept is $(0, 550)$.

$b = \dfrac{3}{4}$, $b < 1$, and $a > 0$, so the graph is decreasing.

Domain: $(-\infty, \infty)$, range: $(0, \infty)$

29. $h(m) = 0.5(2.5)^m$

$a = 0.5$, so the vertical intercept is $(0, 0.5)$.

$b = 2.5$, $b > 1$, and $a > 0$, so the graph is increasing.

Domain: $(-\infty, \infty)$, range: $(0, \infty)$

37. $f(x) = -500\left(\dfrac{1}{5}\right)^x$

$a = -500$, so the vertical intercept is $(0, -500)$.

$b = \dfrac{1}{5}$, $b < 1$, and $a < 0$, so the graph is increasing.

Domain: $(-\infty, \infty)$, range: $(-\infty, 0)$

31. $j(w) = -0.5(4)^w$

$a = -0.5$, so the vertical intercept is $(0, -0.5)$.

$b = 4$, $b > 1$, and $a < 0$, so the graph is decreasing.

Domain: $(-\infty, \infty)$, range: $(-\infty, 0)$

39. $f(x) = -700(0.95)^x$

$a = -700$, so the vertical intercept is $(0, -700)$.

$b = 0.95$, $b < 1$, and $a < 0$, so the graph is increasing.

Domain: $(-\infty, \infty)$, range: $(-\infty, 0)$

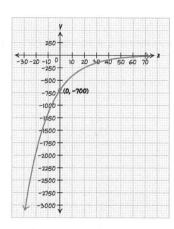

41. The student wrote that the domain started at zero and the range started at 7.

Domain: $(-\infty, \infty)$, range: $(0, \infty)$

43. The student wrote the domain correctly, but the range should be from zero to infinity.

Domain: $(-\infty, \infty)$, range: $(0, \infty)$

45. a. $y = 10$ **b.** Domain: $(-\infty, \infty)$
   c. Range: $(10, \infty)$

47. a. $y = -5$ **b.** Domain: $(-\infty, \infty)$
   c. Range: $(-\infty, -5)$

49. a. $y = 3$ **b.** Domain: $(-\infty, \infty)$ **c.** Range: $(3, \infty)$

51. a. $y = 0$ **b.** Domain: $(-\infty, \infty)$ **c.** Range: $(0, \infty)$

53. a. $y = -6$ **b.** Domain: $(-\infty, \infty)$ **c.** Range: $(-\infty, -6)$

55. Horizontal asymptote: $y = 30$

Domain: $(-\infty, \infty)$, range: $(30, \infty)$

57. Horizontal asymptote: $y = 3$

Domain: $(-\infty, \infty)$, range: $(3, \infty)$

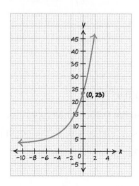

59. Horizontal asymptote: $y = -12$

Domain: $(-\infty, \infty)$, range: $(-\infty, -12)$

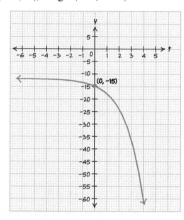

61. Horizontal asymptote: $y = -50$

Domain: $(-\infty, \infty)$, range: $(-\infty, -50)$

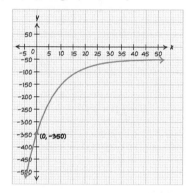

63. Horizontal asymptote: $y = 25$

Domain: $(-\infty, \infty)$, range: $(25, \infty)$

65. Domain: $(-\infty, \infty)$, range: $(-\infty, \infty)$

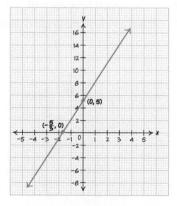

67. Domain: $(-\infty, \infty)$, range: $[3, \infty)$

69. Domain: $(-\infty, \infty)$, range: $(0, \infty)$

71. Domain: $(-\infty, \infty)$, range: $(-\infty, \infty)$

73. Domain: $(-\infty, \infty)$, range: $[-75, \infty)$

Section 12.4

1. $f(x) = 25(1.5)^x$

3. $f(x) = 900(0.9)^x$

5. b, because the function is increasing too rapidly.

7. a, because the y-intercept is too low.

9. Adjust $a = 3.5$. The new equation is $f(x) = 3.5(1.2)^x$.

11. Adjust $a = 78$. The new equation is $f(x) = 78(0.45)^x$.

13. Adjust $b = 1.3$. The new equation is $f(x) = 8(1.3)^x$.

15. Adjust $b = 0.5$. The new equation is $f(x) = 120(0.5)^x$.

17. Adjust $a = 5$ and $b = 1.2$. The new equation is
$f(x) = 5(1.2)^x$.

19. a. Let $I(t)$ be the number of Internet hosts (in millions) in the year t years since 1990. Then $I(t) = 0.184(1.92)^t$.

   b. In 1997, there were approximately 17.7 million Internet hosts.

   c. Domain: $[0, 8]$, range: $[0.18, 33.98]$

   d. Partway through the year 1998, the number of Internet hosts reached 35 million.

21. a. Let $N(t)$ be the number of nuclear warheads in the U.S. arsenal in the year t years since 1940. Then $N(t) = 0.78(1.70)^t$.

   b. In 1970, there were approximately 157 nuclear warheads stockpiled in the U.S. arsenal.

   c. Domain: $[5, 20]$, range: $[11, 31{,}701]$

   d. By the end of 1960, the number of stockpiled nuclear warheads in the U.S. arsenal surpassed 50,000.

23. a. Let $V(t)$ be the volume of water left in the cylinder t seconds after the start of the experiment. Then $V(t) = 15.86(0.994)^t$.

   b. Six minutes after the start of the experiment, approximately 1.82 liters of water remain in the cylinder.

   c. Domain: $[0, 500]$, range: $[0.78, 15.86]$

   d. It took approximately 459 seconds for there to be only 1 liter of water remaining in the cylinder.

25. a. Let $R(d)$ be the river gage height, in feet above normal, d days after the rainfall event. Then $R(d) = 14(0.553)^d$.

   b. Ten days after the rainfall event, the gage height will read 0.037 foot above normal.

   c. Domain: $[0, 12]$, range: $[0.01, 14]$

27. $f(x) = 4(1.32)^x$
Domain: $(-\infty, \infty)$, range: $(0, \infty)$

29. $f(x) = 94(0.63)^x$
Domain: $(-\infty, \infty)$, range: $(0, \infty)$

31. $f(x) = 4.2(1.27)^x$
Domain: $(-\infty, \infty)$, range: $(0, \infty)$

33. $f(x) = 462(0.54)^t$
Domain: $(-\infty, \infty)$, range: $(0, \infty)$

35. The data plot shows an increasing curve with positive values, so we know that $a > 0$ and $b > 1$. The student's model, therefore, is incorrect. The student miscalculated the value of b by multiplying both sides of $3.58 \approx b^7$ by $\frac{1}{7}$ instead of raising each side of the equation to the $\frac{1}{7}$ th power. As a result, the value of a is incorrect as well.

37. $f(x) = -17(1.22)^x$
Domain: $(-\infty, \infty)$, range: $(-\infty, 0)$

39. $f(x) = -56(0.45)^x$
Domain: $(-\infty, \infty)$, range: $(-\infty, 0)$

41. $f(x) = -247(1.24)^x$
Domain: $(-\infty, \infty)$, range: $(-\infty, 0)$

43. $f(x) = -178(0.63)^x$
Domain: $(-\infty, \infty)$, range: $(-\infty, 0)$

45. Exponential: Text messaging continues to grow rapidly.

47. Exponential: Music downloads continue to grow rapidly.

49. Linear: Steady growth of New Hampshire's population.

51. a. Let $V(m)$ be the number of visitors to MySpace.com (in millions) m months after the site started. Then $V(m) = 0.15(1.21)^m$.

b. Domain: $[9, 36]$, range: $[0.8, 143.3]$

c. MySpace.com reached 50 million visitors after about 30 months.

53. a. Let $P(t)$ be the population of Georgia (in millions) in the year t years since 2000. Then $P(t) = 0.195t + 8.13$.

b. Domain: $[0, 15]$, range: $[8.13, 11.06]$

c. The population of Georgia will reach 11 million in the year 2014.

55. $f(x) = 3(x + 4)^2 - 10$

57. $f(x) = 79.9(0.70)^x$

59. $f(x) = 0.2x + 0.3$

Section 12.5

1. 3% growth

3. 25% growth

5. 250% growth

7. 5% decay

9. 64% decay

11. a. In 1990, the population of white-tailed deer was approximately 2.57 million.

b. The population of white-tailed deer grows at a rate of 8% per year.

c. This population might stop growing at the rate of 8% per year because of limited food or space.

13. a. In 2015, the population of the Virgin Islands will be approximately 108.14 thousand.

b. The population of the Virgin Islands is decreasing at a rate of 0.061% per year.

15. Let $P(t)$ be the population after t years have passed. Then $P(t) = 40(1.03)^t$.

17. Let $P(t)$ be the population after t years have passed. Then $P(t) = 200(0.98)^t$.

19. a. Let $H(t)$ be the population of humpback whales t years after 1981. Then $H(t) = 350(1.14)^t$.

b. Domain: $[-2, 15]$, range: $[269, 2498]$

c. In 1990, the humpback whale population was approximately 1138.

21. a. Let $D(t)$ be the population of Denmark (in millions) t years after 2008. Then $D(t) = 5.5(1.00295)^t$.

b. In 2020, the population of Denmark will be approximately 5.70 million.

23. Compound interest formula: $A = P\left(1 + \dfrac{r}{n}\right)^{nt}$

25. Compound interest formula: $A = P\left(1 + \dfrac{r}{n}\right)^{nt}$

27. Compound interest formula: $A = P\left(1 + \dfrac{r}{n}\right)^{nt}$

29. Continuously compounding interest formula: $A = Pe^{rt}$

31. The missing variable is A.
$A = ?$
$P = 20,000$
$r = 0.03$
$n = 365$
$t = 5$

33. The missing variable is t.
$A = 8000$
$P = 4000$
$r = 0.0275$
$n = 12$
$t = ?$

35. The missing variable is r.
$A = 1000$
$P = 500$
$r = ?$
$n = 365$
$t = 10$

37. \$16,470.09

39. \$16,486.65

41. \$1,928,712.77

43. \$1,928,699.39

45. \$400,639.19

47. \$405,520.00

49. The second option, with an interest rate of 3.95% compounded continuously, will have the larger balance after 5 years.

Chapter 12 Review Exercises

1. a. Let $P(t)$ be the population of Africa (in millions) in the year t years since 1996. Then $P(t) = 731.5(2)^{\frac{t}{28}}$.

b. In 2005, the population of Africa was approximately 914.06 million.

2. a. Let $F(d)$ be the number of people with flu symptoms after d days. Then $F(d) = (3)^d$.

b. After 2 weeks, approximately 4,782,969 people have flu symptoms. This is possibly model breakdown.

3. a. Let $P(d)$ be the percentage of polonium-210 left in a sample after d days. Then $P(d) = 100\left(\dfrac{1}{2}\right)^{\frac{d}{138}}$.

b. After 300 days, there will be about 22.16% of the polonium-210 sample left.

4. a. Let $P(t)$ be the percentage of thorium-228 left in a sample after t years. Then $P(t) = 100\left(\dfrac{1}{2}\right)^{\frac{t}{1.9}}$.

b. After 50 years, there will be about 0.00000197% of the polonium-210 sample left. This amount approaches 0%.

5. $f(x) = 5000(0.8)^x$

6. $f(x) = 0.2(7.6)^x$

7. $x = 3$ **8.** $x = 5$ **9.** $x = 4$

10. $x = 7$ **11.** $x = 3.5$ **12.** $x = \pm 5$

13. $x = 6$ **14.** $x = \pm 6$ **15.** $x = -5$

16. $x = -4$ **17.** $x = -3$ **18.** $x = -5$

19. a. a is positive because the y-intercept is above the origin.

  b. b is greater than 1, because $a > 0$ and the function is increasing.

  c. Increasing.

  d. Domain: $(-\infty, \infty)$, range: $(0, \infty)$

20. a. a is negative because the y-intercept is below the origin.

  b. b is greater than 1, because $a < 0$ and the function is decreasing.

  c. Decreasing.

  d. Domain: $(-\infty, \infty)$, range: $(-\infty, 0)$

21. a. $a > c$, because the y-intercept for $f(x)$ is greater than the y-intercept of $g(x)$.

  b. $b < d$, because $f(x)$ is increasing at a slower rate than $g(x)$.

22. a. Decreasing.

  b. This is an example of exponential decay.

  c. $f(20) = 5$

  d. $x = 10$

  e. $(0, 20)$

23. a. Increasing, because $b > 1$ and $a > 0$.

  b. This is an example of exponential growth.

  c. $(0, 2)$

24. Since $a > 0$ and $b > 1$, the function is increasing.

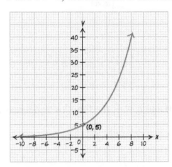

25. Since $a < 0$ and $b < 1$, the function is increasing.

26. Since $a > 0$ and $b < 1$, the function is decreasing.

27. Since $a < 0$ and $b < 1$, the function is increasing.

28. Since $a > 0$ and $b < 1$, the function is decreasing.

29. Since $a < 0$ and $b > 1$, the function is decreasing.

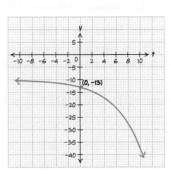

30. Domain: $(-\infty, \infty)$, range: $(0, \infty)$

31. Domain: $(-\infty, \infty)$, range: $(-\infty, 0)$

32. Domain: $(-\infty, \infty)$, range: $(20, \infty)$

33. Domain: $(-\infty, \infty)$, range: $(-\infty, -10)$

34. a. Let $W(t)$ be the number of nonstrategic warheads in the U.S. arsenal in the year t years since 1950. Then $W(t) = 52.3(1.74)^t$.

    b. Domain: [0, 11], range: [52, 23,150]

    c. The model predicts that there were approximately 212,198 nonstrategic warheads in the U.S. arsenal in the year 1965. This could be model breakdown.

35. a. Let $C(s)$ be the number of counts from a Geiger counter from the decay of barium-137 after s seconds. Then $C(s) = 3098(0.996)^s$.

    b. After 10 minutes, the Geiger counter ticks off about 280 counts per minute.

    c. Domain: [0, 1800], range: [2, 3098]

36. a. In 2005, the population of Franklin's gulls was approximately 551.89 thousand.

    b. The population of Franklin's gulls decays at a rate of 5.95% per year.

    c. This population might stop declining at the rate of 5.95% per year because of environmental intervention.

37. a. Let $E(t)$ be the population of the European Union (in millions) t years after 2008. Then $E(t) = 491(1.0012)^t$.

    b. In 2020, the population of the European Union will be approximately 498.12 million.

38. The amount of money in the account after 10 years is $12,735.78.

39. The amount of money in the account after 25 years is $837,289.75.

40. The amount of money in the account after 15 years is $91,102.95.

Chapter 12 Test

1. a. Let $B(h)$ be the number of bacteria present (in millions) h hours after 12 noon have passed. Then $B(h) = 5(2)^h$.

    b. By 6:00 P.M. there are 320 million bacteria on the bathroom door handle.

    c. $B(h) = 5(2)^{4h}$

2. a. Let $P(t)$ be the percentage of thallium-210 left in a sample after m minutes. Then $P(m) = 100\left(\dfrac{1}{2}\right)^{\frac{m}{1.32}}$.

    b. After 15 minutes, there is 0.038% of the thallium-210 sample left, which means that there is approximately 0% left.

3. The investment will be worth $1521.03 after 12 years.

4. The investment will be worth $326,646.80 after 35 years.

5. a. a is negative because the graph is below the x-axis.

    b. $b < 1$ because we have exponential growth with $a < 0$.

    c. Domain: $(-\infty, \infty)$, range: $(-\infty, 0)$

6. a. The graph is increasing.

    b. $f(1) = -4$

    c. $x = -2$

    d. $(0, -8)$.

7. a. Let $C(t)$ be the number of CD singles shipped (in millions) in the mid-1990s in the year t years since 1990. Then $C(t) = 1.56(1.71)^t$.

    b. Domain: [0, 10], range: [1.56, 333.49]

    c. $C(10) = 1.56(1.71)^{10} \approx 333.49$. In 2000, there were approximately 333.49 million CD singles shipped.

8. a. Let $P(t)$ be the number of professionals in developing countries (in millions) in the year t years since 2009. Then $P(t) = 4(1.065)^t$.

    b. By the year 2013, there will be approximately 5.15 million professionals in developing countries.

9. Since $a < 0$ and $b > 1$, the function is decreasing. Domain: $(-\infty, \infty)$, range: $(-\infty, 0)$

10. Since $a > 0$ and $b < 1$, the function is decreasing. Domain: $(-\infty, \infty)$, range: $(0, \infty)$

11. Since $a > 0$ and $b < 1$, the function is decreasing. Domain: $(-\infty, \infty)$, range: $(50, \infty)$

12. Since $a < 0$ and $b < 1$, the function is increasing. Domain: $(-\infty, \infty)$, range: $(-\infty, -20)$

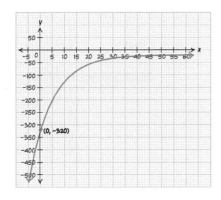

13. $x = 5$ **14.** $x = 3$ **15.** $x = 4$

16. $x = 6$ **17.** $x = -4$ **18.** $x = \pm 3$

19. $x = \pm 5.2$

CHAPTER 13
Section 13.1

1. This is a one-to-one function.

3. This is a one-to-one function.

5. This is not a one-to-one function.

7. This is a one-to-one function.

9. This is not a one-to-one function.

11. $f(x) = \dfrac{1}{2}x + 3$ is a one-to-one function.

13. $h(x) = 2.5x^2 + 3x - 9$ is not a one-to-one function.

15. $f(x) = 2x^3 + 4$ is a one-to-one function.

17. $f(x) = 4x^3 + 2x^2 - 5x - 4$ is not a one-to-one function.

19. $f(x) = 2x^4$ is not a one-to-one function.

21. $g(x) = 3(1.2)^x$ is a one-to-one function.

23. $f(x) = 100(0.4)^x + 20$ is a one-to-one function.

25. $f(x) = 20$ is not a one-to-one function.

27. **a.** $t(N) = -0.003N + 15.23$

    b. Domain: $[1019, 5125.7]$, range: $[-1, 12]$

    c. In 1999, there were about 2000 homicides of 15 to 19-year-olds in the United States.

29. **a.** Range: $-2500 \le P \le 25,000$

    b. $b(P) = 0.18P + 454.55$

    c. There is a \$3000 profit from selling 1000 books.

    d. You would need to sell 1355 books to make a \$5000 profit.

    e. Domain: $-2500 \le P \le 25,000$, range: $0 \le b \le 5000$

31. **a.** $t(P) = 0.389P - 97.191$

    b. The U.S. population reached 260 million in about 1994.

    c. For the inverse function $t(P) = 0.389P - 97.191$, the input variable P represents the U.S. population in millions, and the output variable t represents the number of years since 1990.

33. **a.** $c(M) = 0.667M - 6666.667$

    b. They would have to sell about 20,014 CDs for "Math Dude" to earn \$40,000.

    c. Domain: $25,000 \le M \le 85,000$, range: $10,000 \le c \le 50,000$

35. $f^{-1}(x) = \dfrac{1}{3}x - \dfrac{5}{3}$ 37. $g^{-1}(t) = -\dfrac{1}{4}t + 2$

39. $h^{-1}(x) = \dfrac{3}{2}x + \dfrac{27}{2}$ 41. $f^{-1}(x) = 5x - 3$

43. $h^{-1}(x) = 2.5x + 4$ 45. $P^{-1}(t) = -0.4t - 3$

47. Yes, they are inverses.   49. Yes, they are inverses.

51. No, they are not inverses.

53.

55.

57.

59.

61. a.

61. b.

63. a.

63. b.

65. a.

65. b.

67. a.

67. b.

69. a.

69. b.

71. a.

71. b.

73.

75.

77.

79. Yes, it is a function. Yes, it has an inverse. It passes the vertical line test, so it is a function, and it passes the horizontal line test, so it must have an inverse.

81. No, it is not a function. This is a vertical line, and it will not pass the vertical line test.

Section **13.2**

1. The base is 5.

3. The base is 10.

5. The base is e.

7. 3   **9.** 3   **11.** 8

13. 3   **15.** -1 **17.** -1

19. -2 **21.** -2 **23.** 0

25. 4   **27.** 3   **29.** 1

31. 1   **33.** 2.097   **35.** 2.439

37. 3.807   **39.** 4.787

41. a. $\dfrac{\log 40}{\log 3} \approx 3.358$ **b.** $\dfrac{\ln 40}{\ln 3} \approx 3.358$

43. a. $\dfrac{\log 63}{\log 5} \approx 2.574$ **b.** $\dfrac{\ln 63}{\ln 5} \approx 2.574$

45. 1.654   **47.** -1.080

49. 2.338   **51.** -0.572

53. 4.227   **55.** $10^3 = 1000$

57. $10^{-2} = 0.01$ **59.** $2^3 = 8$

61. $3^4 = 81$ **63.** $e^5 = e^5$

65. $3^{-2} = \dfrac{1}{9}$

67. $5^{-2} = \dfrac{1}{25}$ **69.** $\log_2 1024 = 10$

71. $\log_5 625 = 4$ **73.** $\log_{25} 5 = 0.5$

75. $\log 100{,}000 = 5$ **77.** $\log_{\frac{1}{5}}\left(\dfrac{1}{625}\right) = 4$

79. $\log_{\frac{1}{2}}\left(\dfrac{1}{8}\right) = 3$ **81.** $\log_3 729 = 2x$

83. $f^{-1}(x) = \dfrac{\log x}{\log 7}$ **85.** $h^{-1}(c) = \log c$

87. $m^{-1}(r) = \dfrac{\log r}{\log 5}$ **89.** $f^{-1}(x) = 3^x$

91. $g^{-1}(x) = e^x$ **93.** $f^{-1}(x) = \dfrac{\log\left(\frac{x}{3}\right)}{\log 4}$

95. $h^{-1}(x) = \dfrac{\log(2x)}{\log 9}$ **97.** $x = 1000$

99. $t = e^2 \approx 7.389$ **101.** $w \approx 13.967$

103. $m = 4$ **105.** $x \approx 1.644$

107. $t \approx \dfrac{25}{2} = 12.5$ **109.** $x \approx 18.199$

Section 13.3

1. a. $f(50) = 2$ **b.** $x = 125$

3. a. $h(250) = 4$ **b.** $x = 20$

5. a. $g(40) = -3$ **b.** $x = 13$

7. a. $h(3) = -11$ **b.** $x = 5$

9. The base is greater than 1, because the graph is increasing.

11. The base is less than 1, because the graph is decreasing.

13.

15.

17.

19.

21.

23.

25.

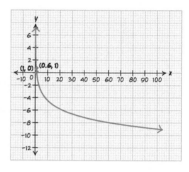

27. Domain: $(0, \infty)$, range: $(-\infty, \infty)$

29. Domain: $(0, \infty)$, range: $(-\infty, \infty)$

31. Domain: $(0, \infty)$, range: $(-\infty, \infty)$

33. Domain: $(0, \infty)$, range: $(-\infty, \infty)$

35. Domain: $(0, \infty)$, range: $(-\infty, \infty)$

37. Domain: $(0, \infty)$, range: $(-\infty, \infty)$

39. $f^{-1}(x) = \dfrac{1}{2}x - 6$

41. $f^{-1}(x) = \dfrac{\log x}{\log 4}$

43. $g^{-1}(x) = 9^x$

45.

47.

49.

51.

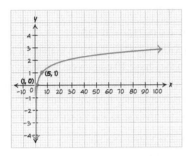

53. 2.477	**55.** 3.091	**57.** 4.005
59. 4.744	**61.** −0.446	**63.** $x = 512$

65. $x = 10,000,000$ **67.** $x = \dfrac{1}{16}$

Section **13.4**

1. $\log 5 + \log x$

3. $\ln x + \ln y$

5. $\ln 4 + \ln a + 3 \ln b$

7. $\ln 2 + 2 \ln h + 3 \ln k$

9. $\log_3\left(\dfrac{1}{2}\right) + \log_3 a + 2 \log_3 b + 3 \log_3 c$

11. $\log x - \log y$

13. $\log 12 - \log m$

15. $\log 2 + 2 \log x - \log y$

17. $\ln 3 + 4 \ln x + 3 \ln y - \ln z$

19. $\dfrac{1}{2} \log 5 + \dfrac{1}{2} \log x$

21. $\dfrac{1}{2} \ln 7 + \dfrac{1}{2} \ln a + \dfrac{1}{2} \ln b$

23. $\dfrac{1}{2} \log_9 2 + \log_9 w + \dfrac{3}{2} \log_9 z$

25. $\dfrac{2}{5} \ln m + \dfrac{3}{5} \ln p$

27. $\dfrac{1}{2} \log_{15} 3 + 2 \log_{15} x + \dfrac{3}{2} \log_{15} y - 5 \log_{15} z$

29. $\ln (xy)$ **31.** $\log (a^2 b^3)$ **33.** $\ln\left(\dfrac{x}{y}\right)$

35. $\log(5x^2 yz^3)$ **37.** $\log_3\left(\dfrac{ab^2}{c^5}\right)$

39. $\log_5(7\sqrt{xy})$ **41.** $\ln\left(\dfrac{\sqrt{7ab^3}}{c^4}\right)$

43. $\ln\left(\dfrac{16,807a^2 b^4}{c^3 d^2}\right)$ **45.** $\log_3\left(\dfrac{a^2 b^2}{243c^3}\right)$

47. $\log_5(7x^3 y^3)$ **49.** $\log\left(\dfrac{\sqrt{15xy^5}}{z^4}\right)$

51. $\log(x^2 + 4x - 12)$ **53.** $\ln(x^2 - 10x + 21)$

55. There is no expansion for the expression $\log(x + 5)$. We can expand when there is multiplication or division inside the logarithm, not for addition or subtraction inside the logarithm.

57. The student incorrectly multiplied two separate log functions instead of multiplying just inside one log function. The expression $\log x + \log y$ comes together as $\log(xy)$.

59. $\log_b 32 = 7$	**61.** $\log_b 8 = 1$
63. $\log_b 15 = -6$	**65.** $\log_b 50,000 = 10$

67. $\log_b 0.25 = 6$

Section **13.5**

1. $w \approx 4.395$	**3.** $x \approx 3.679$	**5.** $x \approx -0.410$
7. $x \approx 2.227$	**9.** $x \approx -6.221$	

11. a. Let $C(t)$ be the number of hours the Cray C90 has been used per academic year t years since 1980. Then $C(t) = 0.311(2.057)^t$.

   b. Domain: $[7, 20]$, range: $[48.5, 572,066]$

   c. The Cray C90 was in use approximately 65,727 hours in the 1997 academic school year. The Cray C90 computer had 16 processors, and could run more than one computing job at a time. Typically, several jobs were running simultaneously, which is why the number of hours used per year is so high.

   d. The Cray C90 was in use approximately 500,000 hours in the academic school year of 2000.

13. $x = 8$	**15.** $x \approx -6.208$	**17.** $x \approx 9.002$
19. $x \approx 2.319$	**21.** $x = 7$	**23.** $t = 6$
25. $h \approx 11.000$	**27.** $m \approx 7.600$	**29.** $n = 3$

31. The world population will reach 10 billion midway through the year 2023 (48.7 years after 1975).

33. The white-tailed deer population reached 5 million late in the year 1998 (18.7 years past 1980).

35. a. South Africa's population will be down to 40 million by the year 2026 (18.1 years past 2008).

   b. South Africa's population will be down to 21.9 million by the year 2146 (138.3 years past 2008) if the trend continues.

37. $x = 2$	**39.** $m \approx -2.926$	**41.** $x = \pm 2$
43. $x \approx \pm 2.449$	**45.** $t = 12$	**47.** $x \approx 2.268$

49. To double their money in 8 years, they would need to invest at 8.67% compounded daily.

51. To double your money in 12 years, you would need to invest at 5.78% compounded continuously.

53. To double your money in 7 years, you would need to invest at 9.94% compounded monthly.

55. It takes approximately 9.9 years to double your money at 7% compounded monthly.

57. It takes approximately 7.7 years to double your money at 9% compounded continuously.

59. It takes approximately 54.9 years to triple your money at 2% compounded daily.

61. It takes approximately 43.9 years to triple your money at 2.5% compounded continuously.

63. $f^{-1}(x) = \dfrac{\log\left(\frac{x}{5}\right)}{\log(3)}$

65 $h^{-1}(x) = \dfrac{\ln\left(\frac{x}{-2.4}\right)}{\ln 4.7}$

67. $g^{-1}(x) = \ln\left(\dfrac{x}{-3.4}\right)$

69. $n \approx 1.088, n \approx -1.838$

71. $d \approx 2.091$

73. $x \approx 10.514$

75. $n \approx 5.236, n \approx 0.764$

77. $(3.098, 75.145)$

79. $(-4.130, -12.566)$

81. $(7.214, 8.013)$ and $(1.859, 54.111)$

Section **13.6**

1. $x = 10,000$

3. $x \approx 148.413$

5. $x = 16$

7. $x = 19.6$

9. $x \approx 4.1297$

11. An earthquake that has an intensity of 2000 cm has a magnitude of about 7.3.

13. An earthquake that has an intensity of 500,000 cm has a magnitude of about 9.7.

15. The intensity of this 8.0 magnitude earthquake was 10,000 cm.

17. The intensity of this 6.6 magnitude earthquake was 398.11 cm.

19. Scope mouthwash with a hydrogen ion concentration of 1.0×10^{-7} M has a pH of 7.

21. Car battery acid with a pH of 1 has a hydrogen ion concentration of 1.0×10^{-1} M.

23. Oven cleaner with a pH of 14 has a hydrogen ion concentration of 1.0×10^{-14} M.

25. Blood plasma with a pH level between 7.35 and 7.45 has a hydrogen ion concentration between 3.55×10^{-8} M and 4.47×10^{-8} M.

27. The chain saw with an intensity of 10^{-1} watt/m² have a decibel level of 110 dB.

29. Raindrops with an intensity of 10^{-8} watt/m² have a decibel level of 40 dB.

31. A jackhammer with a decibel level of 120 dB has an intensity of 1 watt/m².

33. $x = 50$

35. $h = -8192$

37. $t \approx 0.045$

39. $r \approx 3.389$

41. $p \approx -0.342$

43. $x \approx 14.434$

45. $x \approx 4.405$

47. Matt made the base 10 on the second step when it should have been e.

49. Frank added 3 and 5 on the second step when he should have subtracted 5 from both sides of the equation.

51. $t \approx 6.325$

53. $x \approx 6.347$

55. $x = -13.5, x = -5.5$

57. $x = 1$

59. $x \approx 6.249, x \approx -7.916$

61. $x \approx 0.0003$

63. $x = 3$

65. $x = -2.5, x = 1$

67. $t = 0, t = -5, t = -1$

69. $d \approx 0.667$

Chapter 13 Review Exercises

1. $f^{-1}(x) = \dfrac{5}{7}x + 5$

2. $g^{-1}(t) = -\dfrac{1}{2}t + 3$

3. $h^{-1}(x) = \dfrac{\log x}{\log 5}$

4. $f^{-1}(x) = \dfrac{\log\left(\frac{x}{3.5}\right)}{\log 6}$

5. $g^{-1}(x) = \ln\left(\dfrac{x}{2}\right)$

6. $f^{-1}(x) = 5^x$

7. $h^{-1}(t) = 0.2^t$

8. a. $e(D) = 0.0025D - 0.125$

  b. The AEM Toy Company can manufacture 4050 dolls when they have 10 employees working.

  c. The AEM Toy Company must have 3 employees working on a particular day to manufacture 1000 dolls.

  d. Domain: $2050 \leq D \leq 12,050$, range: $5 \leq e \leq 30$

9. a. $d(P) = 0.222P + 66.667$

  b. The AEM Toy Company must sell 2731 dolls to make a $12,000 profit.

  d. Domain: $1950 \leq P \leq 17,700$, range: $500 \leq d \leq 4000$

10. This function is a one-to-one function.

11. This function is not a one-to-one function.

12. $\log_4 64 = 3$

13. $\log_3 1 = 0$

14. $\log_8 8^5 = 5$

15. $\log_2\left(\dfrac{1}{8}\right) = -3$

16. $f(x) = \log_{2.5}(x)$

17. $f(x) = \log_{0.4}(x)$

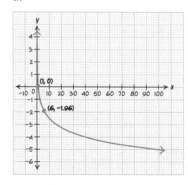

18. Domain: $(0, \infty)$, range: $(-\infty, \infty)$

19. Domain: $(0, \infty)$, range: $(-\infty, \infty)$

20. $\log 7 + \log x + \log y$ **21.** $\log_5 3 + 3 \log_5 a + 4 \log_5 b$

22. $\ln 2 + 3 \ln x + 4 \ln y$ **23.** $\dfrac{1}{5} \log_7 3 + \dfrac{3}{5} \log_7 x + \dfrac{1}{5} \log_7 y$

24. $\dfrac{1}{2} \log_3 5 + \dfrac{1}{2} \log_3 a + \log_3 b + \dfrac{3}{2} \log_3 c$

25. $\log 3 + 3 \log x + 5 \log y - 4 \log z$

26. $\log 4 + 5 \log a + \log b - 3 \log c$

27. $\log(4x^3 y^2 z)$ **28.** $\log\left(\dfrac{2x^4 y^5}{z^2}\right)$

29. $\log_3\left(\dfrac{ab^3}{c^2}\right)$ **30.** $\ln\left(\dfrac{7x^2}{y^5 z^2}\right)$

31. $\log(x^2 - 5x - 14)$

32. a. In 2005, the population of Franklin's gulls was approximately 551.89 thousand.

　b. According to the model, the population of Franklin's gulls reached 500,000 midway through the year 2006.

　c. This population might stop declining at this rate, owing to environmental intervention.

33. It takes approximately 11.6 years to double your money at 6% compounded monthly.

34. It takes approximately 8.2 years to double your money at 8.5% compounded continuously.

35. $w \approx 1.822$ **36.** $t = -5$ **37.** $x \approx 2.656$

38. $x \approx -0.021$ **39.** $x \approx 1.841$ **40.** $x = -2$

41. $x \approx 0.466$ **42.** $x \approx \pm 1.414$

43. The intensity of this 5.7 magnitude earthquake was 50.12 cm.

44. Cranberry juice, with a hydrogen ion concentration of 3.7×10^{-3} M, has a pH of 2.4.

45. Shampoo, with a pH of 5.6, has a hydrogen ion concentration of 2.5×10^{-6} M.

46. $x = 0.0001$ **47.** $t = 32{,}768$ **48.** $x = 9998$

49. $t \approx 0.003$ **50.** $x \approx 17.678$ **51.** $x \approx 7.266$

52. $x = -3$ **53.** $x \approx 3.976$

Chapter 13 Test

1. It takes approximately 19.8 years to double your money at 3.5% compounded monthly.

2. The intensity of this 7.0 magnitude earthquake was 1000 cm.

3. $x = -0.375$ **4.** $x \approx 11.462$

5. $x \approx 2.524$ **6.** $x \approx 0.413$

7. No, the graph is not one-to-one because it does not pass the horizontal line test.

8. $\log(16a^{17} b^{15})$ **9.** $\log\left(\dfrac{5xy^3}{z^4}\right)$

10. $\ln 4 + 3 \ln a + \ln b + 4 \ln c$

11. $\log 3 + \log x + 5 \log y - \dfrac{1}{2} \log z$

12.

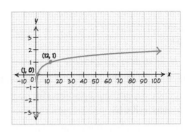

13. Domain: $(0, \infty)$, range: $(-\infty, \infty)$

14. a. Let $C(t)$ be the number of CD singles shipped (in millions) in the year t years since 1990. Then $C(t) = 1.56(1.71)^t$.

　b. Domain: $[0, 10]$, range: $[1.56, 333.49]$

　c. In 2000, there were approximately 333.49 million CD singles shipped.

　d. In 1992, there were approximately 5 million CD singles shipped.

15. $f^{-1}(x) = \dfrac{1}{5}x - \dfrac{2}{5}$ **16.** $g^{-1}(x) = 15^x$

17. $f^{-1}(x) = \dfrac{\log x}{\log 5}$ **18.** $h^{-1}(x) = \dfrac{\log\left(\frac{x}{2}\right)}{\log 7}$

19. A solution with a pH of 2.58 has a hydrogen ion concentration of 2.63×10^{-3} M.

20. $\log_3 200 \approx 4.8227$

Cumulative Review for Chapters 1–13

1. $x = \dfrac{\ln\left(\frac{16}{3}\right)}{\ln(4.2)} \approx 1.166$ **2.** $x = 6$

3. $t = 1, t = 9$ **4.** $c = \dfrac{e^5 + 7}{2}$ **5.** $b = -1$

6. $n \approx 0.984, n \approx -1.544$ **7.** $h = 0, h = -2 \pm 2\sqrt{3}$

8. $x = \dfrac{\frac{\ln 45}{\ln 2} + 7}{3} \approx 4.164$ **9.** $g \approx -4.046$

10. $x = \dfrac{-1 \pm \sqrt{57}}{2}$ **11.** $x = \dfrac{5 + \sqrt{481}}{2} \approx 13.466$

12. $x = -5 + \ln 89$ **13.** $b = 13, b = -27$

14. $t = 9, t = 3$ **15.** $x = 4$ **16.** $x = \pm 2$

17. $x = 2$ **18.** $b = -9$

19. $x = 32$ **20.** $z = 25$

21. $x = 2 + i, x = 2 - i$

22. $x = \dfrac{2}{5} + \dfrac{3}{5}i, x = \dfrac{2}{5} - \dfrac{3}{5}i$

23. $(7, 15)$ **24.** $(3.2, 4.2)$

25. Infinite number of solutions.

26. $(-6, 18)$ and $(4, 48)$ **27.** $(3, 6)$ and $\left(\dfrac{1}{3}, -\dfrac{98}{9}\right)$

28. No real solution.

29. Let $P(t)$ be the gross profit for UTstarcom, Inc. (in millions) t years since 1990.

　a. $P(t) = 0.48(1.74)^t$

　b. Domain: $[4, 15]$, range: $[4.4, 1947.5]$

　c. In 2005, the gross profit for UTstarcom, Inc reached $2 billion.

30. Let $C(t)$ be the number of cocaine-related emergency department episodes (for people over the age of 35) t years since 1990.

   a. $C(t) = 7336.3t + 23,245.7$

   b. In the year 2003, the number of cocaine-related emergency department episodes (for people over the age of 35) was 118,618.

   c. In 2006, the number of cocaine-related emergency department episodes (for people over the age of 35) reached 140,000.

   d. The slope is 7336.3. The number of cocaine-related emergency department episodes (for people over the age of 35) increases by 7336.3 cases each year.

   e. Domain: $[-1, 15]$, range: $[15,909, 133,290]$

31. a. $f(9) = 29$ **b.** $f\left(\dfrac{5}{4}\right) = -2$

   c. Domain: $(-\infty, \infty)$, range: $(-\infty, \infty)$

32. Exponential: $(-\infty, \infty)$

33. Radical: $\left[\dfrac{4}{5}, \infty\right)$

34. Polynomial: $(-\infty, \infty)$

35. Logarithmic: $(-7, \infty)$

36. Rational: $\mathbb{R}, x \neq 2, -5$

37. a. $f(x) + g(x) = 1.5x + 9.5$

   b. $f(g(x)) = -7x + 23.25$

   c. $f(x)g(x) = -7x^2 + 11.25x + 22$

38. a. $f(3) - g(3) = 12$ **b.** $f(g(5)) = -123$

   c. $f(4)g(4) = -21$

39. a. $f(x) - g(x) = 3x^2 + 9x - 9$

   b. $f(g(x)) = 48x^2 - 148x + 110$

   c. $f(x)g(x) = 12x^3 - x^2 - 43x + 14$

40. a. $f(5) - g(5) = -101$ **b.** $f(g(2)) = -1173$

   c. $f(3)g(3) = -414$

41. $L(V(t))$ is the amount of litter in tons left in Yellowstone National Park in year t.

42. a. In 1995, 20.5% of the U.S. triathlon members were women.

   b. In the year 2017, the percentage of U.S. triathlon members that are women will be greater than that of men.

43. $x > \dfrac{8}{3}$ **44.** $x \geq 3.2$

45. $x < 2$ or $x > 12$ **46.** $-\dfrac{13}{3} \leq x \leq 1$

47. $(-3, 1]$ **48.** $(-\infty, -8] \cup [7, \infty)$

49. a. Slope: $m = -\dfrac{5}{2}$ **b.** x-intercept: $(2, 0)$

   c. y-intercept: $(0, 5)$ **d.** $y = -\dfrac{5}{2}x + 5$

50. $y = \dfrac{2}{3}x - 12$ **51.** $y < \dfrac{2}{3}x - 9$

52. Let $P(t)$ be the population of Detroit, Michigan, in thousands t years since 2000.

   a. $P(t) = -31t + 4673$

   b. In 2015, the population of Detroit, Michigan, will be about 4208 thousand.

   c. The slope is -31. The population of Detroit, Michigan, is decreasing by 31 thousand each year.

53. Sarah needs $13\frac{1}{3}$ ml of 15% HCl solution and $16\frac{2}{3}$ ml of 60% HCl solution to make 30 ml of 40% HCl solution.

54. Let $W(t)$ be the number of women triathletes in the United States t years since 1990.

   a. $W(t) = 106.5t^2 + 1100$

   b. Domain: $[0, 20]$, range: $[1100, 43,700]$

   c. In 2005, there were 25,063 women triathletes in the United States.

   d. The vertex is $(0, 1100)$. In 1990, there were 1100 women triathletes in the United States. This was the lowest number during this time.

   e. In 2009, there were about 40,000 women triathletes in the United States.

55.

56.

57.

58.

59.

60.

61.

62.

63.

64.

65.

66.

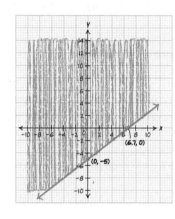

67. $11d - 6$

68. $14x^2 + 19x - 40$

69. $2x^2 - 5x + 8$

70. $9t^2 - 24t + 16$

71. $14p^2 - p - 24$

72. $\dfrac{1}{x + 4}$

73. $5x\sqrt{x} - 31$

74. $-14y^3 + 48y^2 + 21y$

75. $\ln\left(\dfrac{x^2(x - 1)}{x + 3}\right)$

76. $\log_2(256) = 8$

77. $10^4 = 10{,}000$

78. $2 + 3i$

79. $7 - 3i$

80. $5 - 5i$

81. $\dfrac{9}{5} - \dfrac{7}{5}i$

82. $\dfrac{3a - 1}{(a - 3)(a + 1)}$

83. $-48x^2$

84. $\dfrac{x + 2}{5}$

85. $6x^3$

86. $25t^2 - 30t + 9$

87. $x \approx 18.14$ cm

88.

89. $(2x + 3)(x - 7)$

90. $(5r + 8t)(5r - 8t)$

91. $7g(3g - 8)(2g + 5)$

92. $(t + 7)(t^2 - 7t + 49)$

93. $(2x - 3)^2$

94. Second-degree polynomial

95. $f(x) = 3(x + 4)^2 - 58$

96. a. The average price for baseball tickets in 2010 is $28.00.

b. The vertex is $(-10.7, 5.67)$. In 1979, the average price for baseball tickets was $5.67. This was a minimum for this model.

c. In 2017, the average price for baseball tickets will be $40.77.

97. Let $T(m)$ be the number of thorium-233 atoms after m minutes.

a. $T(m) = 5000\left(\dfrac{1}{2}\right)^{\frac{m}{22}}$

b. After about 51 minutes, there will be only 1000 of the thorium-233 atoms left.

c. By the end of the experiment, there will be only 17 of the thorium-233 atoms left.

98. $f^{-1}(x) = \dfrac{1}{3}x - 4$

99. $g^{-1}(x) = \dfrac{\log\left(\frac{x}{4}\right)}{\log 3}$

100. $H^+ = 1 \times 10^{-6}$ M

101. Let $P(t)$ be the Muslim population in Israel (in millions) t years since 2008.

a. $P(t) = 1.24(1.028)^t$

b. The Muslim population in Israel in 2012 will be 1.38 million.

c. The Muslim population in Israel will reach 2 million by the year 2025.

102. $60m^6n^5$

103. $\dfrac{81g^{12}}{h^{16}}$

104. 8

105. $\dfrac{12x^2z^7}{5y^7}$

106. $\dfrac{16a}{5b^{13}}$

107. $\dfrac{3m}{2n^2}$

108. $a > 0$. The graph is above the x-axis.

109. $b > 1$. The graph is increasing and $a > 0$.

110. Domain: $(-\infty, \infty)$, range: $(0, \infty)$

111. $a > 0$. The graph is facing upward.

112. $(h, k) = (-1, -2)$: (h, k) is the vertex of the parabola.

113. $f(2.5) = 18$

114. $f(2) = 12$

$f(-4) = 12$

115. Domain: $(-\infty, \infty)$, range: $[-2, \infty)$

116. $m > 0$. The graph is increasing.

117. $b = -1$. The y-intercept is $(0, -1)$.

118. $m = \dfrac{2}{3}$

119. $f(3) = 1$

120. Domain: $(-\infty, \infty)$, range: $(-\infty, \infty)$

CHAPTER 14

Section 14.1

1. Opens up, vertex $(-4, -57)$, axis of symmetry $x = -4$

3. Opens right, vertex $(-19, -2)$, axis of symmetry $y = -2$

5. Opens left, vertex $(4, 0)$, axis of symmetry $y = 0$

7. Opens down, vertex $(12.5, 28.25)$, axis of symmetry $x = 12.5$

9. Opens right, vertex $(0, 0)$, axis of symmetry $y = 0$

11. $x = y^2 + 10y + 21$

13. $x = -2y^2 + 15y + 8$

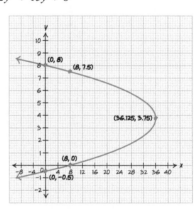

15. $x = \frac{1}{2}(y - 4)^2 + 5$

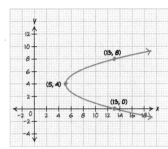

17. $x = (y + 2)^2 - 6$

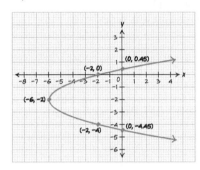

19. $x = -2(y + 5)^2 + 4$

21. $x = \frac{y^2}{36}$

23. $y = \frac{1}{15}x^2$

25. $28x = y^2$

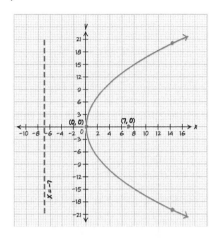

27. $y = \frac{x^2}{4}$ **29.** $x = \frac{y^2}{24}$ **31.** $x = -\frac{y^2}{40}$

33. The receiver should be $1\frac{1}{8}$ ft above the center of the satellite along the axis of symmetry.

35. The arch that is 40 feet from the center of the bridge is 42 feet high.

37. The cables that are 1000 feet from the center of the bridge are 192 feet high.

39. $x^2 + y^2 = 36$

41. $(x - 4)^2 + (y - 9)^2 = 16$

43. $(x + 2)^2 + (y - 3)^2 = 144$

45. $(x + 1)^2 + (y + 4)^2 = 0.25$

47. $x^2 + y^2 = 9$; center $= (0, 0)$, radius $= 3$.

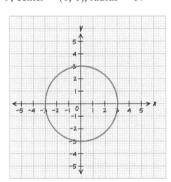

49. $(x - 5)^2 + (y - 4)^2 = 25$; center $= (5, 4)$, radius $= 5$.

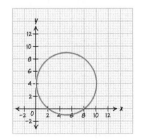

51. $(x + 4)^2 + (y + 1)^2 = 1$; center $= (-4, -1)$, radius $= 1$.

53. $(x - 8)^2 + (y + 2)^2 = 36$; center $= (8, -2)$, radius $= 6$.

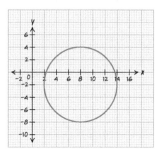

55. $(x + 1)^2 + (y - 3)^2 = 1$; center $= (-1, 3)$, radius $= 1$.

57. $(x + 3)^2 + (y - 6)^2 = 36$; center $= (-3, 6)$, radius $= 6$.

59. $\left(x + \dfrac{1}{2}\right)^2 + \left(y - \dfrac{1}{2}\right)^2 = 9$; center $= \left(-\dfrac{1}{2}, \dfrac{1}{2}\right)$, radius $= 3$.

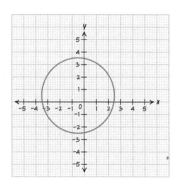

61. $x^2 + (y - 2)^2 = 4$

63. $(x + 4)^2 + (y - 2)^2 = 9$

65. $(x - 10)^2 + (y - 10)^2 = 25$

67. $x^2 + y^2 = 9$
This is a circle with center $= (0, 0)$ and radius $= 3$.

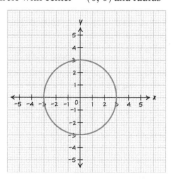

69. $y = x^2 - 4x - 12$
This is a parabola with vertex $= (2, -16)$.

71. $x = y^2 + 8y + 15$
This is a parabola with vertex $= (-1, -4)$.

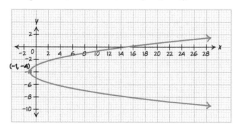

73. $x^2 + (y - 3)^2 = 49$
This is a circle with center $= (0, 3)$ and radius $= 7$.

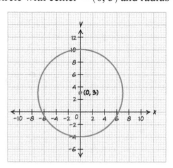

75. $x = \dfrac{1}{32}y^2$
This is a parabola with vertex $= (0, 0)$.

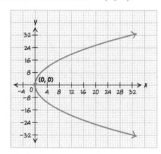

Section **14.2**

1. $\dfrac{x^2}{4} + \dfrac{y^2}{16} = 1$

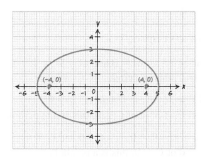

3. $\dfrac{x^2}{25} + \dfrac{y^2}{9} = 1$

5. $x^2 + \dfrac{y^2}{9} = 1$

7. $\dfrac{x^2}{10} + \dfrac{y^2}{49} = 1$

9. $\dfrac{x^2}{9} + \dfrac{y^2}{4} = 1$

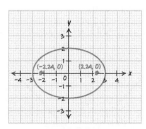

11. $\dfrac{x^2}{36} + y^2 = 1$

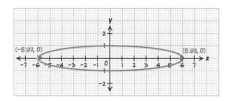

13. $\dfrac{x^2}{9} + \dfrac{y^2}{20} = 1$

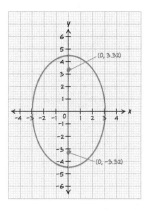

15. $\dfrac{x^2}{64} + \dfrac{y^2}{16} = 1$

Foci: $(-6.93, 0)$ and $(6.93, 0)$.

17. $\dfrac{x^2}{4} + \dfrac{y^2}{9} = 1$

Foci: $(0, -2.24)$ and $(0, 2.24)$.

19. $\dfrac{x^2}{225} + \dfrac{y^2}{100} = 1$

Foci: $(-11.18, 0)$ and $(11.18, 0)$.

21. $\dfrac{x^2}{13{,}479{,}912.25} + \dfrac{y^2}{12{,}649{,}080} = 1$

23. $\dfrac{x^2}{784{,}996} + \dfrac{y^2}{782{,}880} = 1$. Aphelion ≈ 932 million miles.

25. Width: 135 cm, depth: 30.75 cm.

27. Let w be half the width of the arch, and let h be the height of the arch.

$$\dfrac{w^2}{3600} + \dfrac{h^2}{1225} = 1$$

29. $\dfrac{x^2}{4} - \dfrac{y^2}{9} = 1$

Vertices $= (2, 0), (-2, 0)$

Foci $= \left(\sqrt{13}, 0\right), \left(-\sqrt{13}, 0\right) \approx (3.6, 0), (-3.6, 0)$

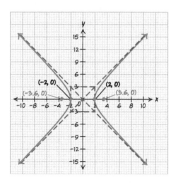

31. $\dfrac{y^2}{36} - \dfrac{x^2}{4} = 1$

Vertices $= (0, 6), (0, -6)$

Foci $= \left(0, \sqrt{40}\right), \left(0, -\sqrt{40}\right) \approx (0, 6.3), (0, -6.3)$

33. $\dfrac{x^2}{25} - y^2 = 1$

Vertices $= (5, 0), (-5, 0)$

Foci $= \left(\sqrt{26}, 0\right), \left(-\sqrt{26}, 0\right) \approx (5.1, 0), (-5.1, 0)$

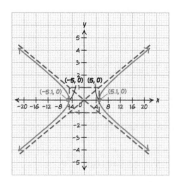

35. $\dfrac{y^2}{9} - x^2 = 1$

Vertices $= (0, 3), (0, -3)$

Foci $= \left(0, \sqrt{10}\right), \left(0, -\sqrt{10}\right) \approx (0, 3.2), (0, -3.2)$

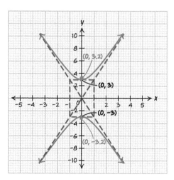

37. $\dfrac{x^2}{16} - \dfrac{y^2}{9} = 1$

Foci $= (5, 0), (-5, 0)$

39. $\dfrac{y^2}{4} - \dfrac{x^2}{1} = 1$

Foci $= \left(0, \sqrt{5}\right), \left(0, -\sqrt{5}\right)$

41. $3x^2 + 3y^2 = 27$ $\qquad A = 3$ and $C = 3$

Since $A = C$, this is a circle.

43. $4x^2 - 9y^2 = 36$ $\qquad A = 4$ and $C = -9$

Since $A \neq C$, $A < 0$, or $C < 0$, this is a hyperbola.

45. $6y^2 + 2y + x - 9 = 0$ $\qquad A = 0$ and $C = 6$

Since $A = 0$ or $C = 0$, this is a parabola.

47. $64x^2 + 36y^2 = 576$ $\qquad A = 64$ and $C = 36$

Since $A \neq C$, $A > 0$, and $C > 0$, this is an ellipse.

49. Ellipse; $\dfrac{x^2}{16} + \dfrac{y^2}{36} = 1$

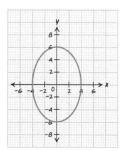

51. Hyperbola; $\dfrac{x^2}{49} - \dfrac{y^2}{100} = 1$

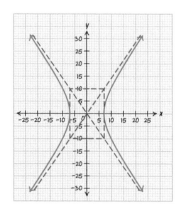

53. Ellipse; $\dfrac{x^2}{2} + \dfrac{y^2}{4} = 1$

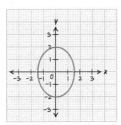

55. Circle; $x^2 + y^2 = \dfrac{1}{4}$

57. Circle; $(x + 1.5)^2 + (y - 2.5)^2 = 11$

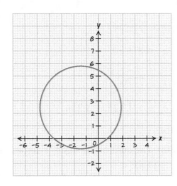

Section **14.3**

1. $a_1 = 4,\ a_2 = 10,\ a_3 = 16,\ a_4 = 22$

3. $f(1) = 2,\ f(2) = 8,\ f(3) = 18,\ f(4) = 32$

5. $a_1 = -4,\ a_2 = 4,\ a_3 = -4,\ a_4 = 4,\ a_5 = -4$

7. $-17,\ -11,\ 7,\ 61,\ 223.$

9. $\dfrac{1}{2}, \dfrac{8}{9}, \dfrac{6}{5}, \dfrac{16}{11}, \dfrac{5}{3}$ **11.** $\dfrac{1}{4}, \dfrac{1}{16}, \dfrac{1}{64}, \dfrac{1}{256}, \dfrac{1}{1024}$

13. $-1, \dfrac{1}{4}, -\dfrac{1}{9}, \dfrac{1}{16}, -\dfrac{1}{25}$

15. $n = 20$ **17.** $n = 14$ **19.** $n = 11$

21. $n = 12$ **23.** $n = 162$

25. $a_n = 4n - 5$

27. $a_n = 4 + (n - 1)6$

29. $f(n) = 3^n - 20$

31. $a_n = 4n(-1)^n$

33. $a_n = \dfrac{4n}{n + 7}$

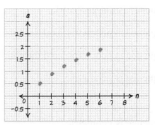

35. Arithmetic, common difference $d = 4$.

37. Arithmetic, common difference $d = 2.35$.

39. Not arithmetic.

41. Arithmetic, common difference $d = -3.45$.

43. Arithmetic, common difference $d = -\dfrac{1}{2}$.

45. Arithmetic, common difference $d = 6$.

$$a_n = -2 + 6n$$

47. Arithmetic, common difference $d = 1.25$.

$$a_n = 2.75 + 1.25n$$

49. Not arithmetic.

51. Arithmetic, common difference $d = -\dfrac{2}{3}$.

$$a_n = \dfrac{14}{3} - \dfrac{2}{3}n$$

53. a. $a_n = 35,100 + 900n$

 b. Your salary will be $45,900 in the 12th year of employment.

 c. In your 28th year of employment, your salary will be $60,300.

55. a. $a_n = 52,500 - 4500n$

 b. The car will be worth $3000 in the 11th year.

 c. In the 7th year, the car will be worth $21,000.

57. a. $a_n = 9 + n$

 b. You will save $41 during the 32nd week.

 c. During week 52, you will save $61.

59. a. It costs $415 to produce 100 candy bars.

 b. One thousand candy bars can be produced for a cost of $550.

 c. Common difference $d = 0.15$. The cost of production increases by $0.15 per candy bar produced.

61. a. $a_n = n$

 b. There are 10 cups in the 10th row.

63. $a_n = -2n + 17$

65. $a_n = 3.5n + 3.5$

67. $a_n = 4.75n + 9.25$

69. $a_n = 0.2n - 37.2$

Section **14.4**

1. Yes, the sequence is geometric, and the common ratio is 1.5.

3. Yes, the sequence is geometric, and the common ratio is $\dfrac{1}{3}$.

5. No, the sequence is not geometric.

7. Yes, the sequence is geometric, and the common ratio is 2.

9. Yes, the sequence is geometric, and the common ratio is -3.

11. Yes, the sequence is geometric.

$$a_n = 3(2)^{n-1}$$

13. Yes, the sequence is geometric.

$$a_n = 2(-4)^{n-1}$$

15. Yes, the sequence is geometric.

$$a_n = 625(0.2)^{n-1}$$

17. No, the sequence is not geometric.

19. Yes, the sequence is geometric.

$$a_n = -4(0.5)^{n-1}$$

21. a. $a_n = 56,000(1.015)^{n-1}$

 b. $a_7 = 61,232.82$. Your salary will be $61,232.82 in the 7th year of employment.

 c. During your 25th year of employment, you will earn a salary of $80,052.

23. a. $a_n = 8\left(\dfrac{1}{2}\right)^{n-1}$

 b. $a_3 = 2$. The ball bounces to a height of 2 ft after the 3rd bounce.

25. a. $a_n = 5(2)^{n-1}$

 b. $a_7 = 320$. On day 7, there were 320 people with the flu.

27. a. $a_n = 21,000(0.93)^{n-1}$

 b. A four-year-old Honda Civic hybrid is worth $16,891.50.

29. a. $a_n = 10\left(\dfrac{1}{2}\right)^{\frac{n}{2}}$

 b. After six hours, there is 1.25 mg of morphine left in the patient.

31. $a_n = 2(5)^{n-1}$ **33.** $a_n = 16,384\left(\dfrac{1}{4}\right)^{n-1}$

35. $a_n = 3(-2)^{n-1}$ **37.** $a_n = 256\left(-\dfrac{1}{2}\right)^{n-1}$

39. Geometric, $a_n = 11(2)^{n-1}$

41. Arithmetic, $a_n = 8 + 6n$

43. Geometric, $a_n = 7776\left(\dfrac{1}{2}\right)^{n-1}$

45. Arithmetic, $a_n = -41.25 + 3.25n$

47. a. $a_n = 180n$

 b. $a_{10} = 1800$. The sum of the interior angles of a 12-sided polygon is 1800°.

49. a. $a_n = 200,000 - 8000n$

 b. The machine will be worth $120,000 when it is 10 years old.

51. a. $a_n = 10 + 5n$

 b. You should be jogging 35 minutes during the 5th week after surgery.

Section **14.5**

1. a. $20.5 + 156 + 198 + 162 + 125 + 248 + 244$
 $+ 209 + 165 + 262 + 214 + 60.6 + 176 + 172$
 $+ 161 + 237 + 83 + 182 + 164 + 203 + 14.4$

 b. The 2009 Giro d' Italia professional bike race was 3456.5 km in length.

3. $\displaystyle\sum_{n=1}^{5}(2n + 7) = (2(1) + 7) + (2(2) + 7) + (2(3) + 7)$

$$+ (2(4) + 7) + (2(5) + 7) = 65$$

5. $\displaystyle\sum_{n=1}^{4}(4^n) = 4 + 4^2 + 4^3 + 4^4 = 340$

7. $\displaystyle\sum_{n=1}^{6}(5n(-1)^n) = (5(-1)) + (10(-1)^2) + (15(-1)^3)$

$$+ (20(-1)^4) + (25(-1)^5)$$

$$+ (30(-1)^6) = 15$$

9. $\sum_{n=1}^{5}\left(\dfrac{1}{n}\right) = 1 + \dfrac{1}{2} + \dfrac{1}{3} + \dfrac{1}{4} + \dfrac{1}{5} = \dfrac{137}{60}$

11. $\sum_{n=1}^{8}(n^2 + 5n) = (1 + 5) + (2^2 + 10) + (3^2 + 15)$
$$+ (4^2 + 20) + (5^2 + 25) + (6^2 + 30)$$
$$+ (7^2 + 35) + (8^2 + 40) = 384$$

13. $\sum_{n=1}^{8}(3(-2)^n) = (3(-2)) + (3(-2)^2) + (3(-2)^3) + (3(-2)^4)$
$$+ (3(-2)^5) + (3(-2)^6) + (3(-2)^7)$$
$$+ (3(-2)^8) = 510$$

15. a. $a_n = 41,200 + 800n$

   b. Your salary will be $53,200 in the 15th year of employment.

   c. You will have earned a total of $714,000 over a 15-year period of employment.

17. a. $a_n = 6 + 2n$

   b. You will save $22 during the 8th week.

   c. You will have saved a total of $858 during the first 26 weeks.

19. a. $a_n = 14 + n$

   b. A total of 246 blocks are needed to build a wall with 12 rows.

21. $S_{30} = 1890$ **23.** $S_{15} = 825$

25. $S_{40} = -7460$ **27.** $S_{52} = 3629.6$

29. $S_{27} = 234$

31. a. $a_n = 42,000(1.02)^{n-1}$

   b. Your salary will be $55,418.11 during the 15th year of employment.

   c. You will have earned a total of $726,323.51 over a 15-year career.

33. a. $a_n = 10(1.10)^{n-1}$

   b. You will save $19.49 during the 8th week.

   c. You will have saved a total of $1091.82 during the first 26 weeks

35. a. $a_n = 3(2)^{n-1}$

   b. There are 48 people diagnosed with the flu on the 5th day.

   c. There were 49,149 people diagnosed with the flu during the first two weeks.

37. $S_9 = 29,523$ **39.** $S_6 = 274,512$

41. $S_{11} = -621,937,812$ **43.** $S_{12} \approx 449.999$

45. $S_{10} \approx -666.597$

47. Geometric.   **49.** Geometric.

   $S_{10} = 10,230$ $S_6 = 1,092$

51. Arithmetic.   **53.** Geometric.

   $S_{23} = 2,783$ $S_{12} \approx 7,389.524$

55. Arithmetic.

   $S_{10} = 272.5$

Chapter 14 Review Exercises

1. $x = y^2 + 6y - 16$

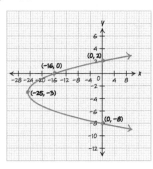

2. $y = 2x^2 - 24x - 30$

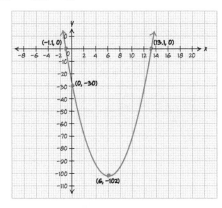

3. $x = -1.5(y + 2)^2 + 6$

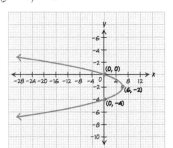

4. $x = -\dfrac{1}{2}y^2 - 3y - 8$

5. $x = \dfrac{y^2}{48}$

6. $y = \dfrac{x^2}{-20}$

7. $x = \dfrac{y^2}{-8}$

8. $y = \dfrac{x^2}{14}$

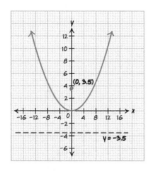

9. $(x - 2)^2 + (y - 8)^2 = 9$

10. $(x - 5)^2 + (y + 2)^2 = 6.25$

11. $x^2 + y^2 = 16$; center $= (0, 0)$, radius $= 4$.

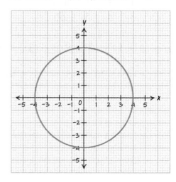

12. $(x - 5)^2 + (y - 2)^2 = 4$; center $= (5, 2)$, radius $= 2$.

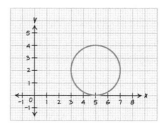

13. $(x + 4)^2 + (y - 6)^2 = 1$; center $= (-4, 6)$, radius $= 1$.

14. $(x + 3)^2 + (y + 7)^2 = 0.25$; center $= (-3, -7)$, radius $= 0.5$.

15. $(x + 6)^2 + (y - 5)^2 = 100$; center $= (-6, 5)$, radius $= 10$.

16. $(x - 4)^2 + (y + 2)^2 = 25$; center $= (4, -2)$, radius $= 5$.

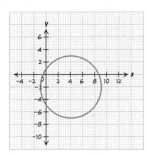

17. $(x - 2)^2 + (y - 6)^2 = 16$ **18.** $(x + 4)^2 + (y - 2)^2 = 36$

19. $x = \dfrac{y^2}{20}$ **20.** $y = \dfrac{x^2}{-12}$

21. $\dfrac{x^2}{16} + \dfrac{y^2}{25} = 1$

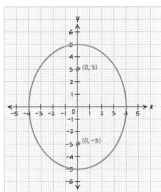

22. $\dfrac{x^2}{0.25} + \dfrac{y^2}{1} = 1$

23. $\dfrac{x^2}{4} + \dfrac{y^2}{100} = 1$

24. $\dfrac{x^2}{4} + \dfrac{y^2}{20} = 1$

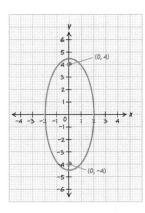

25. $\dfrac{x^2}{16} - \dfrac{y^2}{25} = 1$

Vertices $= (4, 0), (-4, 0)$

Foci $= \left(\sqrt{41}, 0\right), \left(-\sqrt{41}, 0\right) \approx (6.4, 0), (-6.4, 0)$

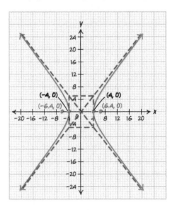

26. $\dfrac{y^2}{100} - \dfrac{x^2}{4} = 1$

Vertices $= (0, 10), (0, -10)$

Foci $= \left(0, \sqrt{104}\right), \left(0, -\sqrt{104}\right) \approx (0, 10.2), (0, -10.2)$

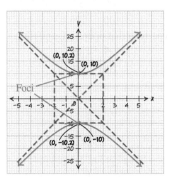

27. $\dfrac{x^2}{16} - y^2 = 1$

Vertices $= (4, 0), (-4, 0)$

Foci $= \left(\sqrt{17}, 0\right), \left(-\sqrt{17}, 0\right) \approx (4.1, 0), (-4.1, 0)$

28. $\dfrac{y^2}{25} - \dfrac{x^2}{9} = 1$

Vertices $= (0, 5), (0, -5)$

Foci $= \left(0, \sqrt{34}\right), \left(0, -\sqrt{34}\right) \approx (0, 5.8), (0, -5.8)$

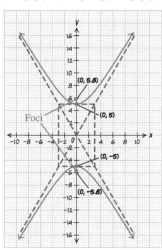

29. This is an ellipse. $\dfrac{x^2}{100} + \dfrac{y^2}{225} = 1$

30. This is an ellipse. $\dfrac{x^2}{400} + \dfrac{y^2}{25} = 1$

31. This is a hyperbola that opens up and down.

$$\dfrac{y^2}{100} - \dfrac{x^2}{225} = 1$$

32. This is a hyperbola that opens left and right.

$$\dfrac{x^2}{100} - \dfrac{y^2}{64} = 1$$

33. Ellipse; $\dfrac{x^2}{9} + y^2 = 1$

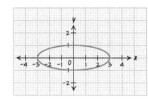

34. Circle; $(x - 9)^2 + (y - 6)^2 = 9$

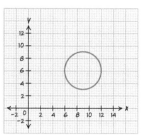

35. Hyperbola; $\dfrac{y^2}{25} - x^2 = 1$

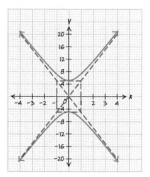

36. Parabola; $x = \dfrac{2}{3}y^2 - 2y + 7$

37. Circle; $(x + 3)^2 + y^2 = 9$

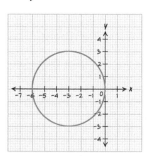

38. Hyperbola; $\dfrac{x^2}{36} - \dfrac{y^2}{9} = 1$

39. Parabola; $y = 0.5x^2 + 4x - 6$

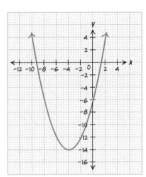

40. Ellipse; $\dfrac{x^2}{49} + y^2 = 1$

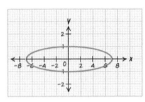

41. $-13, -6, 1, 8, 15;$ $a_n = 7n - 20$

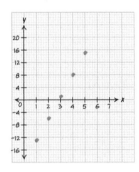

42. $6, 9, 13.5, 20.25, 30.375;$ $a_n = 4(1.5)^n$

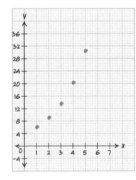

43. $-\dfrac{1}{8}, \dfrac{1}{16}, -\dfrac{1}{24}, \dfrac{1}{32}, -\dfrac{1}{40};$ $a_n = \dfrac{(-1)^n}{8n}$

44. $0.22, 0.4, 0.55, 0.67, 0.77;$ $a_n = \dfrac{2n}{n + 8}$

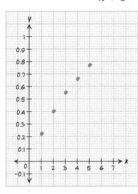

45. $n = 15$ **46.** $n = 9$

47. $n = 22$ **48.** $n = 66$

49. Arithmetic, common difference $d = -3$.

$$a_n = 85 - 3n$$

50. Arithmetic, common difference $d = 2.5$.

$$a_n = -6.5 + 2.5n$$

51. Not arithmetic.

52. Arithmetic, common difference $d = -\dfrac{5}{2}$.

$$a_n = \dfrac{17}{2} - \dfrac{5}{2}n$$

53. a. $a_n = 3800 + 200n$

   b. In 2015, the attendance on Easter Sunday at North Coast Church will be 6800.

   c. The attendance on Easter Sunday at North Coast Church was 6000 in the year 2011.

54. a. $a_n = 29{,}500 - 2500n$

   b. The car will be worth \$14,500 in the sixth year.

   c. The car will be 11 years old when it is worth \$2000.

55. $a_n = 6.5n + 33.5$ **56.** $a_n = -8n + 20$

57. Geometric, $a_n = 3(4)^{n-1}$

58. Geometric, $a_n = 36\left(\dfrac{1}{3}\right)^{n-1}$

59. Geometric, $a_n = 0.5(-2)^{n-1}$

60. Not geometric.

61. a. $a_n = 4000(1.02)^n$

   b. $a_8 = 4686.64$. After eight years, the product will cost \$4686.64.

62. a. $a_n = 42{,}000(1.0125)^{n-1}$

   b. During your fifth year of employment, your salary will be \$44,139.70.

   c. During your 16th year of employment, your salary will be \$50,603.

63. $a_n = 32(1.5)^{n-1}$ **64.** $a_n = 81\left(\dfrac{1}{3}\right)^{n-1}$

65. $\displaystyle\sum_{n=1}^{7} (4n - 20) = (4(1) - 20) + (4(2) - 20) + (4(3) - 20)$
$$+ (4(4) - 20) + (4(5) - 20)$$
$$+ (4(6) - 20) + (4(7) - 20)$$
$$= -28$$

66. $\displaystyle\sum_{n=1}^{6} (5(-2)^n) = (5(-2)) + (5(-2)^2) + (5(-2)^3)$
$$+(5(-2)^4) + (5(-2)^5) + (5(-2)^6)$$
$$= 210$$

67. **a.** $a_n = 37,100 + 900n$

  b. Your salary will be $50,600 in the 15th year of employment.

  c. You will have earned a total of $664,500 over a 15-year period of employment.

68. **a.** $a_n = 2 + 3n$

  b. On the 5th day, you will pick 17 apricots.

  c. You will pick a total of 343 ripe apricots during the first two weeks.

69. During a 15-year career, you will have earned a total of $688,226.05.

70. **a.** $a_n = 10,000(1.2)^{n-1}$

  b. During the seven-day event, 129,159 people attended the car show.

71. $S_{14} = 518$ **72.** $S_{23} = 6267.5$

73. $S_{11} = 10,106.52459$ **74.** $S_{20} = -15.99998$

Chapter 14 Test

1. $(x + 7)^2 + (y - 4)^2 = 64$

2. Focus $= (9, 0)$, directrix : $x = -9$.

3. $\dfrac{x^2}{100} - \dfrac{y^2}{36} = 1$

This is a hyperbola in standard form.

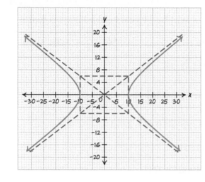

4. $x = -y^2 + 12$

This is a parabola.

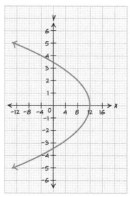

5. $\dfrac{x^2}{4} + \dfrac{y^2}{49} = 1$

This is an ellipse.

6. $(x - 3)^2 + (y - 7)^2 = 81$

This is a circle in standard form.

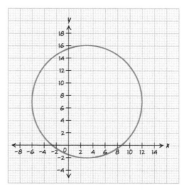

7. $x = \dfrac{y^2}{-8}$ **8.** $\dfrac{x^2}{4} + \dfrac{y^2}{36} = 1$

9. An arithmetic sequence has a common difference; therefore, the difference between successive terms is constant. A geometric sequence has a common ratio; therefore, the ratio between successive terms is constant.

10. $-12, 36, -108, 324, -972.$

11. $2, 3, \dfrac{18}{5}, 4, \dfrac{30}{7}$ **12.** $n = 23$ **13.** $n = 316$

14. Geometric, $a_n = 250\left(\dfrac{1}{5}\right)^{n-1}$

15. Arithmetic, $a_n = 31.5 - 7.5n$

16. **a.** $a_n = 2 + 3n$

  b. By the third week, you should be stretching your injured knee for 11 minutes at one time.

c. In the tenth week, you will be stretching your injured knee for half an hour at one time.

17. a. $a_n = 60{,}000(1.025)^{n-1}$

b. Your salary will be $95,919.01 in the 20th year.

c. You will have earned a total of $1,532,679.46 in salary over a 20-year career.

18. $\sum_{n=1}^{6} (2n^2) = 2 + 2(2)^2 + 2(3)^2 + 2(4)^2 + 2(5)^2 + 2(6)^2 = 182$

19. $S_{15} = 7110$ **20.** $S_{12} = 38{,}453.56699$

Cumulative Review for Chapters 1–14

1. $a = 6$

2. $t = 3, t = -9$

3. $x = \dfrac{23}{2}$

4. $m = \dfrac{31}{3}$

5. $h = 14$

6. $n = 3$

7. $x = \dfrac{e^4 + 5}{2} \approx 29.799$

8. $b = -\dfrac{11}{2}, b = 5$

9. $h = 8, h = -\dfrac{24}{5}$

10. $x = -1$

11. $t = 4$

12. $n = 9$

13. $g = 4.5, g = -5.25$

14. $a = -\dfrac{33}{7}$

15. $x \approx 0.996$

16. $x = \dfrac{41}{2}$

17. $m = -\dfrac{236}{3}$

18. $r = 0, r = -8, r = 5$

19. $h = \dfrac{1}{3}, h = -\dfrac{5}{3}$

20. $x = -2$

21. $t \approx \pm 3.98$

22. No solution.

23. $(0.5, 4)$

24. $\left(-\dfrac{3}{8}, \dfrac{125}{16}\right)$ and $(2, 9)$

25. $\left(-\dfrac{7}{3}, -\dfrac{71}{9}\right)$ and $(5, -25)$

26. Rosemary should use 8 ml of 5% saline solution and 12 ml of 10% saline solution to make the 20 ml of 8% saline solution she needs for the science lab.

27. Let $P(n)$ be the profit in dollars from manufacturing and selling n custom MP3 players.

a. $P(n) = \dfrac{-1}{250}(n - 1200)^2 + 4800$

b. Domain: $[150, 2000]$, range: $[390, 4800]$.

c. The profit from manufacturing and selling 1000 custom MP3 players is $4640.

d. Vertex: $(1200, 4800)$. The profit from manufacturing and selling 1200 custom MP3 players is $4800. This is the maximum profit.

28. Let $R(t)$ be the primary revenue for the Wikimedia Foundation (in millions of dollars) t years since 2000.

a. $R(t) = 0.003(2.62)^t$

b. Domain: $[2, 10]$, range: $[0.021, 45.723]$

c. The primary revenue for the Wikimedia Foundation was approximately $45.7 million in 2010.

d. According to this model, the Wikimedia Foundation reached $50 million in annual primary revenue in the year 2010.

29. Let $N(t)$ be the total circulation of U.S. Sunday newspapers (in millions) t years since 2000.

a. $N(t) = -2.05t + 65.55$

b. In 2010, the total circulation of U.S. Sunday newspapers was 45.05 million.

c. The model predicts that the total circulation of U.S. Sunday newspapers will be only 25 million by the year 2020.

d. Slope $= -2.05$. Each year, the total U.S. Sunday newspaper circulation decreases by 2.05 million.

e. Domain: $[-5, 20]$, range: $[24.55, 75.8]$.

30. Domain: All real numbers except for -9 and 2.

31. Domain: Set of all real numbers

32. Domain: Set of all real numbers

33.

34. $a > -7$

35. $n \geq \dfrac{79}{3}$

36. $h \leq \dfrac{1}{2}$ or $h \geq 4$

37. All real numbers.

38. $x \leq 0.9$ or $x \geq 1.9$

39. $x \leq -3$ or $x > 7$

40. $x < -2.5$ or $x > 4$

41. a. In 2008, there were 398.7 thousand apprenticeship training registrations for all major trade groups in Canada.

b. $(5.1, 165.98)$. In 1995, there were 165.98 thousand apprenticeship training registrations for all major trade groups in Canada. This is the least number of registrations during this time.

c. In 1985 and again in 2005, there were 300 thousand apprenticeship training registrations for all major trade groups in Canada.

42. Let $B(h)$ be the number of bacteria present after h hours.

a. $B(h) = 2000(2)^{3h}$

b. After approximately 3 hours, there will be 1 million bacteria.

c. There will 65,536,000 bacteria present after 5 hours.

43. $f^{-1}(x) = \dfrac{3}{2}x + 12$

44. $g^{-1}(x) = \dfrac{\log\left(\frac{x}{4}\right)}{\log(3)}$

45. a. $f(3) = 2.5$

   b. Domain: $(-\infty, \infty)$, range: $\{2.5\}$.

46. a. $f(x) + g(x) = 5.4x - 4.3$

   b. $f(g(x)) = 6.8x - 1.6$

   c. $f(x)g(x) = 6.8x^2 - 18.4x - 18.9$

47. a. $f(2) - g(2) = 10.5$

   b. $(f \circ g)(7) = -69.25$

   c. $f(2)g(2) = 161.5$

48. a. $f(x) + g(x) = 3x^2 + 7x - 10$

   b. $f(g(x)) = 27x^2 - 60x + 26$

   c. $f(x)g(x) = 9x^3 - 34x + 24$

49. The intensity of this earthquake is 316.228 cm.

50. $y = -\dfrac{7}{3}x - \dfrac{29}{3}$ **51.** $y > \dfrac{3}{5}x - 6$

52. $y = \dfrac{1}{4}x - 6$

53. $y = -3x^2 - 24x + 2$

54. $y = -1.5(2.5)^x$

55. $y = \sqrt{x + 17}$

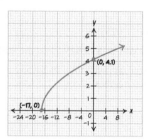

56. $y = \dfrac{1}{3}(x + 4)^2 - 10$

57. $5x - 30y = 180$

58. $y = 800(0.2)^x$

59. $y = \log_9 x$

60. $y = \sqrt[3]{x} + 9$

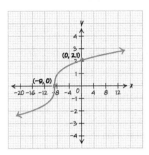

61. $y = 3(1.6)^x + 20$

62. $y < x^2 - 5x - 14$

63. $y \geq 2x + 3$

64. $5x - 6y < 6$

65. $y \geq -3(x - 1)^2 + 8$

66. a. Let $P(t)$ be the population of Syria in millions t years since 2010.

$$P(t) = 22.5\,(1.00913)^t$$

b. The population of Syria in 2015 will be about 23.5 million.

67. $\ln\left(\dfrac{20xy^3}{3z}\right)$

68. $\log_7 16{,}807 = 5$

69. a. Let P be the profit in millions of dollars, and let t be the time in seconds that it takes to produce a product.

$$P = \dfrac{14.4}{t}$$

b. The profit is $1.44 million if it takes 10 seconds to produce each product.

70. $22\sqrt{3a} - 10\sqrt{a}$

71. $9m^3 + 11m^2 - 2m + 9$

72. $\dfrac{(x - 4)(x + 2)}{(x - 3)}$

73. $3x^2 - 3x + 4$

74. $30x^2 - 43x - 8$

75. $4x^2 - 27x + 42$

76. $-14 + 12\sqrt{3w} + 6w$

77. $4a^2 + 27a + 35$

78. $25x^2 - 60x + 36$

79. $\dfrac{(3h - 4)(h + 7)}{(h - 2)(h + 2)}$

80. $\dfrac{5m^2 + 39m - 12}{(m + 7)(m - 3)}$

81. a. There will be 5260 graduating students at this college in 2012.

b. In 2012, 50% of the graduating students at this college will attend graduation ceremonies.

c. There will be 2630 graduating students attending graduation ceremonies at this college in 2012.

d. Let $A(t)$ be the number of graduating students attending graduation ceremonies at this college t years since 2000. $A(t) = 2924 + 31.3t - 4.65t^2$.

e. There will be approximately 2347 graduating students attending graduation ceremonies at this college in 2015.

82. $(2x + 7)(x - 4)$ **83.** $5(2a + 3b)(2a - 3b)$

84. $(h + 5)(h^2 - 5h + 25)$ **85.** $3m(7m + 2)(m - 8)$

86. $5(3x - 8)(4x - 7)$ **87.** Degree 3.

88. $f(x) = 4(x - 6)^2 - 18$

89. a. The profit for Beach Shack Rentals one year after it opened was $16.89 thousand.

    b. After approximately 38 months, the profit for Beach Shack Rentals will be $25,000.

90. $\dfrac{x^2}{2y^3}$ **91.** $\dfrac{-48a^5}{b^7c^5}$

92. $\dfrac{-1}{64m^6n^{24}}$ **93.** Domain: $x > -3$

94. Domain: $x \le 5$

95. Domain: Set of all real numbers

96. $x \approx 10.25$ **97.** $x = -6$

98. Domain: $(-\infty, 10]$; range: $[0, \infty)$

99. The value of "a" is negative. The y-intercept is below the x-axis.

100. The value of "b" is less than 1. This is an increasing function with $a < 0$.

101. Domain: $(-\infty, \infty)$, range: $(-\infty, 0)$

102. The value of a is positive because the parabola opens upward.

103. The vertex of the parabola is $(-2, -16)$. Therefore $h = -2$ and $k = -16$.

104. $f(-4) = -12$

105. $x = -6$ and $x = 2$ when $f(x) = 0$.

106. Domain: $(-\infty, \infty)$, range: $[-16, \infty)$

107. The value of m is positive because the slope of the line is positive.

108. $b = -3$ **109.** $m = \dfrac{2}{5}$

110. $x = -5$ when $f(x) = -5$.

111. Domain: $(-\infty, \infty)$, range: $(-\infty, \infty)$

112. $6a^2b^3c$ **113.** $3xy\sqrt[3]{2y^2}$

114. $\dfrac{\sqrt{14ab}}{2b}$ **115.** $12 + 6\sqrt{3} + 2\sqrt{5} + \sqrt{15}$

116. $9 - 3i$ **117.** $-4 + 8i$

118. 97 **119.** $94 - 2i$ **120.** $\dfrac{5}{4} - \dfrac{3}{2}i$

121. $\dfrac{46}{29} + \dfrac{28}{29}i$ **122.** $\dfrac{6}{5} - \dfrac{8}{5}i$

123. $x = -2 \pm 5i$ **124.** $x = -6 \pm 2i, x = 0$

125. $x = \pm i\sqrt{70}$ **126.** $x = 6 \pm 2i$

127. $(x - 3)^2 + (y + 9)^2 = 144$

128. Focus $= (-11, 0)$, directrix: $x = 11$

129. Hyperbola. $\dfrac{x^2}{144} - \dfrac{y^2}{64} = 1$

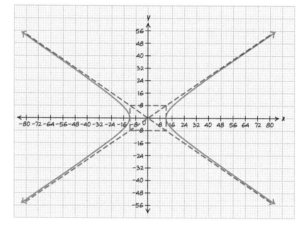

130. Ellipse. $\dfrac{x^2}{4} + \dfrac{y^2}{121} = 1$

131. Parabola. $x = -y^2 - 2y + 10$

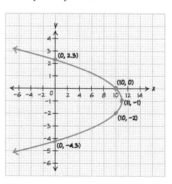

132. Circle. $(x + 8)^2 + (y - 3)^2 = 36$

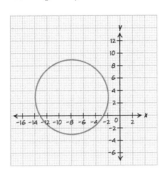

133. $y^2 = -24x$

134. $\dfrac{x^2}{144} + \dfrac{y^2}{25} = 1$

135. $a_n = 23 + 11n$

136. $-10, 20, -40, 80, -160$

137. $-\dfrac{3}{2}, -\dfrac{24}{11}, -\dfrac{18}{7}, -\dfrac{48}{17}, -3$

138. $n = 84$

139. $n = 44$

140. Arithmetic, $a_n = 51 - 3n$

141. Geometric, $a_n = 96(4)^{n-1}$

142. a. $a_n = 54,175 + 825n$
  b. Your salary will be \$62,425 in the 10th year of employment.
  c. You will have earned a total of \$587,125 over a 10-year period of employment.

143. a. $a_n = 55,000(1.015)^{n-1}$
  b. Your salary will be \$62,886.45 in the 10th year of employment.
  c. You will have earned a total of \$588,649.69 over a 10-year period of employment.

144. $\displaystyle\sum_{n=1}^{6}(2n^3) = 2 + 2(2)^3 + 2(3)^3 + 2(4)^3 + 2(5)^3 + 2(6)^3 = 882$

145. $S_{15} = 495$

146. $S_{12} \approx 28,987.51066$

APPENDIX A

1. a. The point $(x, y, z) = (0, 5, 1)$ is not a solution of the system.
  b. The point $(x, y, z) = (0, 5, -3)$ is not a solution of the system.

3. a. The point $(x, y, z) = (-5, 0, 1)$ is not a solution of the system.
  b. The point $(x, y, z) = (10, 0, -3)$ is a solution of the system.

5. a. $x = 16, y = 1, z = 0$ is not a solution of the system.
  b. $x = 0, y = 7, z = -8$ is a solution of the system.

7. $(x, y, z) = (4, 0, 1)$

9. $(x, y, z) = (-2, 2, 3)$

11. $(x, y, z) = (1, -1, 2)$

13. $(x, y, z) = (1, -2, 3)$

15. a. This is a 2×2 matrix.
  b. -1 is in the $(1, 2)$ position.

17. a. This is a 2×3 matrix.
  b. -2 is in the $(1, 3)$ position.

19. a. This is a 4×3 matrix.
  b. -3 is in the $(4, 1)$ position.

21. $\begin{bmatrix} 2 & -1 & -5 \\ 4 & 6 & -1 \end{bmatrix}$

23. $\begin{bmatrix} 1 & -1 & 0 \\ -3 & 4 & -1 \end{bmatrix}$

25. $\begin{bmatrix} -2 & 3 & -1 & 0 \\ 1 & 1 & -1 & 5 \\ 1 & -1 & 1 & 2 \end{bmatrix}$

27. $\begin{bmatrix} -1 & 1 & 1 & 3 \\ 0 & 3 & -2 & 1 \\ -1 & 0 & 2 & 0 \end{bmatrix}$

29. $(x, y) = \left(\dfrac{7}{3}, -2\right)$

31. $(x, y) = (-2, -5)$

33. $(x, y, z) = \left(\dfrac{9}{2}, \dfrac{5}{2}, -2\right)$

35. $(x, y, z) = \left(\dfrac{23}{4}, -\dfrac{1}{2}, -5\right)$

37. $\begin{bmatrix} 1 & -1 & -5 \\ 0 & -1 & -3 \end{bmatrix}$

39. $\begin{bmatrix} 4 & 3 & 7 \\ 0 & 8 & 17 \end{bmatrix}$

41. $\begin{bmatrix} 1 & 1 & 1 & 2 \\ 0 & 1 & 0 & -1 \\ 0 & 0 & 2 & 4 \end{bmatrix}$

43. $\begin{bmatrix} -12 & 0 & -8 & -36 \\ 0 & -6 & 4 & 24 \\ 0 & 0 & 1 & 3 \end{bmatrix}$

45. $(x, y) = (-2, 5)$

47. $(x, y) = (-3, 6)$

49. $(x, y, z) = (3, 0, -1)$

51. $(x, y, z) = (-1, 0, -3)$

53. $(x, y, z) = (4, 6, -1)$

55. $f(x) = -x^2 + 4x - 1$

57. $f(x) = x^2 + 5x + 4$

59. $f(x) = 2x^2 + 5x - 3$

61. $f(x) = -3x^2 + 10x + 8$

Index